For
reference

Not for return

W9-CAE-513

Financial Aid for Veterans, Military Personnel, and Their Families 2012 - 2014

RSP FINANCIAL AID DIRECTORIES OF INTEREST TO VETERANS, MILITARY PERSONNEL & THEIR FAMILIES

College Student's Guide to Merit and Other No-Need Funding
Selected as one of the "Outstanding Titles of the Year" by *Choice,* this directory describes 1,300 no-need funding opportunities for college students. 490 pages. ISBN 1588412121. $32.50, plus $7 shipping.

Directory of Financial Aids for Women
There are 1,400+ funding programs set aside for women described in this biennial directory, which has been called "the cream of the crop" by *School Library Journal* and the "best available reference source" by *Guide to Reference.* 552 pages. ISBN 1588412164. $45, plus $7 shipping.

Financial Aid for African Americans
Nearly 1,300 funding opportunities open to African American college students, professionals, and postdoctorates are described in this award-winning directory. 490 pages. ISBN 1588412172. $42.50, plus $7 shipping.

Financial Aid for Asian Americans
This is the source to use if you are looking for funding for Asian Americans, from college-bound high school seniors to professionals and postdoctorates; more than 900 sources of free money are described here. 350 pages. ISBN 1588412180. $40, plus $7 shipping.

Financial Aid for Hispanic Americans
The 1,100 biggest and best sources of free money available to undergraduates, graduates students, professionals, and postdoctorates of Mexican, Puerto Rican, Central American, or other Latin American heritage are described here. 446 pages. ISBN 1588412199. $42.50, plus $7 shipping.

Financial Aid for Native Americans
Detailed information is provided on nearly 1,400 funding opportunities open to American Indians, Native Alaskans, and Native Pacific Islanders for college, graduate school, or professional activities. 506 pages. ISBN 1588412202. $45, plus $7 shipping.

Financial Aid for Research and Creative Activities Abroad
Described here are more than 1,000 scholarships, fellowships, grants, etc. available to support research, professional, or creative activities abroad. 422 pages. ISBN 1588412067. $45, plus $7 shipping.

Financial Aid for Study and Training Abroad
This directory, which the reviewers call "invaluable," describes nearly 1,000 financial aid opportunities available to support study abroad. 362 pages. ISBN 1588412059. $40, plus $7 shipping.

Financial Aid for the Disabled and Their Families
Named one of the "Best Reference Books of the Year" by *Library Journal,* this directory describes in detail 1,200+ funding opportunities. 530 pages. ISBN 158841227X. $40, plus $7 shipping.

Financial Aid for Veterans, Military Personnel, and Their Families
According to *Reference Book Review,* this directory (with its 1,428 entries) is "the most comprehensive guide available on the subject." 488 pages. ISBN 1588412261. $40, plus $7 shipping.

High School Senior's Guide to Merit and Other No-Need Funding
Here's your guide to 1,100 funding programs that *never* look at income level when making awards to college-bound high school seniors. 416 pages. ISBN 1588412105. $29.95, plus $7 shipping.

How to Pay for Your Degree in Nursing
You'll find 900 scholarships, fellowships, loans, grants, and awards here that can be used for study, research, professional, or other nursing activities. 250 pages. ISBN 1588412075. $30, plus $7 shipping.

Kaplan Scholarships
Given 5 stars (highest rating) on Amazon.com, this directory identifies 3,000 of the best scholarships and other sources of "free" money for beginning and continuing undergraduate students. 576 pages. ISBN 1419553089. $22.50, plus $7 shipping.

Money for Christian College Students
This is the only directory to describe 850 funding opportunities available to support Christian students working on an undergraduate or graduate degree. 264 pages. ISBN 1588412253. $30, plus $7 shipping.

Money for Graduate Students in the Social & Behavioral Sciences
Looking for money to pay for a graduate degree in the social/behavioral sciences? Here are 1,100 funding programs for you. 316 pages. ISBN 1588412016. $42.50, plus $7 shipping.

Financial Aid for Veterans, Military Personnel, and Their Families 2012 - 2014

Thirteenth Edition

Gail A. Schlachter
R. David Weber

A Listing of Scholarships, Fellowships, Grants-in-Aid, and Other Sources of Free Money Available Primarily or Exclusively to Veterans, Military Personnel, and Their Family Members, Plus a Set of Six Indexes (Program Title, Sponsoring Organization, Residency, Tenability, Subject, and Deadline Date)

Reference Service Press
El Dorado Hills, California

ISBN 10: 1588412261
ISBN 13: 9781588412263
ISSN: 0896-7792

10 9 8 7 6 5 4 3 2 1

Reference Service Press (RSP) began in 1977 with a single financial aid publication *(Directory of Financial Aids for Women)* and now specializes in the development of financial aid resources in multiple formats, including books, print-on-demand reports, eBooks, and online sources. Long recognized as a leader in the field, RSP has been called, by the *Simba Report on Directory Publishing,* "a true success in the world of independent directory publishers." Both Kaplan Educational Centers and Military.com have hailed RSP as "the leading authority on scholarships."

Reference Service Press
El Dorado Hills Business Park
5000 Windplay Drive, Suite 4
El Dorado Hills, CA 95762-9319
(916) 939-9620
Fax: (916) 939-9626
E-mail: info@rspfunding.com
Visit our web site: www.rspfunding.com

Previously issued as **Financial Aid for Veterans, Military Personnel, and Their Dependents**
Manufactured in the United States of America

Price: $40.00, plus $7 shipping.

ACADEMIC INSTITUTIONS, LIBRARIES, ORGANIZATIONS, AND OTHER QUANTITY BUYERS:
Discounts on this book are available for bulk purchases. Write or call for information on our discount programs.

Contents

Introduction

WHY THIS DIRECTORY IS NEEDED

More than one third of America's population today has either direct or indirect ties to the armed services. This includes more than 25 million veterans, 3 million active-duty military personnel, and millions of their family members (spouses, parents, children, grandchildren, and other descendants).

Over the years, a number of organizations have attempted to reward the members of these groups in a variety of ways. In 1944, Congress established the Veterans Administration (now called the Department of Veterans Affairs) to develop programs for the benefit of the men and women who served in previous wars. Today, the DVA provides a wide variety of funding opportunities to veterans and their families. Many state governments have also established or expanded programs that complement federal benefits. In addition, voluntary and other private organizations (most notably the American Legion) have raised millions of dollars to provide financial aid to their members, other veterans or military personnel, or their family members. Similarly, to recruit, retain, and reward their personnel (especially since the advent of the all-volunteer military), the armed services have developed wide-ranging benefits for members and those who are related to them. In all, billions of dollars a year are now set aside in the form of publicly- and privately-funded scholarships, fellowships, grants-in-aid, and other sources of financial aid for veterans, military personnel, and their family members.

While numerous print and online listings have been prepared to identify and describe general financial aid opportunities (those open to all segments of society), none of those resources have ever covered more than a small portion of the programs available primarily or exclusively for veterans, military personnel, or their family members. That's why Gail A. Schlachter and R. David Weber biennially issue *Financial Aid for Veterans, Military Personnel, and Their Families,* which identifies billions of dollars set aside for individuals with ties to the military to support study, research, creative activities, travel, career development, emergencies, and much more.

WHAT'S UNIQUE ABOUT THE DIRECTORY?

Financial Aid for Veterans, Military Personnel, and Their Families is the first and only publication to provide comprehensive information on the more than 1,400 programs aimed specifically at those with ties to the military. The listings in the 2012-2014 edition of this book cover every major field of study, are sponsored by more than 550 different private and public agencies and organizations, and are open to all levels of applicants—from high school students, to college students, to professionals and others. By using this biennially-issued directory, the one out of three Americans eligible for military-related benefits (and the counselors, advisers, and librarians who are there to serve them) can easily identify the vast array of available funding programs. And, not only does *Financial Aid for Veterans, Military Personnel, and Their Families* provide the most comprehensive coverage of available funding, it also displays the most informative program descriptions (on the average, more than twice the detail found in any other listing).

In addition to this extensive and focused coverage, the directory offers several other unique features. First of all, hundreds of funding opportunities listed here have never been covered in any other source. So, even if you have checked elsewhere, you will want to look at *Financial Aid for Veterans, Military Personnel, and Their Families* for additional leads. Further, all the funding described here is substantial; every program offers at least $1,000, and many award $20,000 or more or pay all college expenses. And, here's another plus: all of the funding programs in this edition of the directory offer "free" money;

not one of the programs will ever require you to pay anything back (provided, of course, that you meet the program requirements).

Unlike other funding directories, which generally follow a straight alphabetical arrangement, *Financial Aid for Veterans, Military Personnel, and Their Families* groups entries by both type of program (e.g., scholarships, grants-in-aid) and recipient groups (veterans, military personnel, and their family members)—thus making it easy to pinpoint appropriate programs. The same convenience is offered in the indexes, where the entries are also subdivided by program type and recipient group. With this arrangement, users with one set of characteristics (e.g., veterans) will be able to find all programs set aside specifically for them—and not be distracted or have to waste time sorting through descriptions of programs intended for members of the other groups.

In fact, everything about the directory has been designed to make your search for funding as easy as possible. You can identify programs not only by recipient group, but by program title, sponsoring organizations, where you live, where you want to spend the money, specific subject areas, and even deadline date (so fundseekers working within specific time constraints can locate programs that are still open). Plus, you'll find all the information you need to decide if a program is a match for you: purpose, eligibility requirements, financial data, duration, special features, limitations, number awarded, and application deadline. You even get fax numbers, toll-free numbers, e-mail addresses, and web site locations (when available), along with complete contact information, to make your requests for applications proceed smoothly.

The unique value of *Financial Aid for Veterans, Military Personnel, and Their Families* has been consistently praised by the reviewers. *Reference Book Review* wrote, "This is the most comprehensive guide available on the subject of financial aid for those with ties to the military." The directory was "enthusiastically reviewed" by *American Reference Books Annual* (which judged it to be "exceptionally useful"), was called "comprehensive" and "authoritative" by *Midwest Book Review,* and was pronounced "easy to use" by *College & Research Library News.* In the view of *Booklist,* "This book fills a noteworthy gap" and libraries across the country "should make this well-conceived and useful information source a part of their reference collection." Perhaps Military.com summed it up best: "the definitive source."

WHAT'S EXCLUDED?

While this book is intended to be the most comprehensive source of information on funding available to veterans, military personnel, and their family members, there are some programs we've specifically excluded from the directory:

- *Awards open equally to all segments of the population.* Only funding opportunities set aside specifically for those with ties to the military are covered here.

- *Programs administered by individual academic institutions solely for their own students.* The directory identifies "portable" programs—ones that can be used at any number of schools. Financial aid administered by individual schools specifically for their own students is not covered. Write directly to the schools you are considering to get information on their offerings.

- *Service or nonmonetary programs for veterans, military personnel, and their family members.* To obtain information about service programs' benefits (e.g., job counseling, medical and dental care, treatment for alcohol or drug dependency) or nonmonetary benefits (such as burial flags, presidential certificates, or complimentary licenses for hunting and fishing), check with your state veteran's agency, your local DVA office, or the most recent annual edition of the DVA's *Federal Benefits for Veterans and Dependents.*

- *Indirect aid programs,* where funds go to military-related agencies rather than directly to veterans, military personnel, or their family members. To obtain that information, check with your state veteran's agency or your local DVA office.

SAMPLE ENTRY

(1) **[43]**

(2) **GOOGLE-SVA Scholarship**

(3) Student Veterans of America
P.O. Box 77673
Washington, DC 20013
(703) 642-5360   Toll-free: (888) 668-1656
Fax: (703) 642-2054
E-mail: SVA@studentveterans.org
Web: www.studentveterans.org/?page=Programs

(4) **Summary** To provide funding to veterans working on a bachelor's or graduate degree in a computer-related field.

(5) **Eligibility** This program is open to sophomores, juniors, seniors, and graduate students at U.S. colleges and universities who are veterans (must possess a DD-214) and were honorably discharged or are still in good standing with their branch of service. Applicants must be working full time on a degree in computer science, computer engineering, or a closely-related technical field (e.g., software engineering, electrical engineering (with a heavy computer science course load), information systems, information technology, applied networking, or system administration). Along with their application, they must submit a 1,000-word personal statement that covers their reasons for applying for this scholarship, their reasons for choosing their major, their professional objectives as they relate to their degree, their role as a leader in their community and/or chapter, and any additional community service initiatives in which they have been involved. Financial need is not considered in the selection process..

(6) **Financial data** The stipend is $10,000.

(7) **Duration** 1 year.

(8) **Additional information** This program is sponsored by Google.

(9) **Number awarded** 8 each year.

(10) **Deadline** March of each year.

DEFINITION

(1) **Entry number:** Consecutive number that is given to each entry and used to identify the entry in the index.

(2) **Program title:** Title of scholarship, fellowship, grant-in-aid, or other source of free money described in the directory.

(3) **Sponsoring organization:** Name, address, telephone number, toll-free number, fax number, e-mail address, and/or web site (when information was supplied) for the organization sponsoring the program.

(4) **Summary:** Identifies the major program requirements; read the rest of the entry for additional detail.

(5) **Eligibility:** Describes qualifications required of applicants, application procedures, and selection process.

(6) **Financial data:** Financial details of the program, including fixed sum, average amount, or range of funds offered, expenses for which funds may and may not be applied, and cash-related benefits supplied (e.g., room and board).

(7) **Duration:** Period for which support is provided; renewal prospects.

(8) **Additional information:** Any unusual (generally nonmonetary) benefits, restrictions, or requirements associated with the program.

(9) **Number awarded:** Total number of recipients each year or other specified period.

(10) **Deadline:** The month by which applications must be submitted.

- *Money for study or research outside the United States.* Since there are comprehensive and up-to-date directories that describe the funding available for study and research abroad (particularly Reference Service Press's biennial *Financial Aid for Study and Training Abroad* and *Financial Aid for Research and Creative Activities Abroad),* only programs that support study, research, or other activities in the United States are covered here.

- *Restrictive geographic coverage.* In general, programs are excluded if they are open only to residents of a narrow geographic area (anything below the state level). To get information on these geographically restrictive programs, contact Reference Service Press directly or use *RSP FundingFinder,* Reference Service Press's subscription-based online funding database.

- *Programs offering limited financial support.* Comprehensive coverage is provided in this directory only for programs that can substantively impact the financial situation of veterans, military personnel, and their family members. Scholarships, fellowships, and grants-in-aid must pay at least $1,000 a year or they are not included here. Also excluded are programs that offer military personnel the opportunity to pursue college training but do not provide any financial support beyond their current salary. For information on these more limited programs, contact Reference Service Press directly or use *RSP FundingFinder.*

- *Money that must be repaid.* Only "free money" is identified here. If a program requires repayment or charges interest, it's not listed. Now you can find out about billions of dollars in aid and know (if you meet the program requirements) that not one dollar of that will ever need to be repaid.

WHAT'S UPDATED?

The preparation of each new edition of *Financial Aid for Veterans, Military Personnel, and Their Families* involves extensive updating and revision. To insure that the information included in the directory is both reliable and current, the editors at Reference Service Press 1) reviewed and updated all relevant programs covered in the previous edition of the directory, 2) collected information on all programs open to veterans, military personnel, and their families that were added to Reference Service Press' funding database since the last edition of the directory, and then 3) searched extensively for new program leads in a variety of sources, including printed directories, news reports, journals, newsletters, house organs, annual reports, and sites on the Internet. We only include program descriptions that are written directly from information supplied by the sponsoring organization in print or online (no information is ever taken from secondary sources). When that information could not be found, we sent up to four collection letters (followed by up to three telephone or email inquiries, if necessary) to those sponsors. Despite our best efforts, however, some sponsoring organizations still failed to respond and, as a result, their programs are not included in this edition of the directory.

The 2012-2014 edition of the directory completely revises and updates the earlier biennial edition. Programs that have ceased operations have been dropped. Profiles of continuing programs have been rewritten to reflect operations in 2012-2014; nearly 80% of these programs reported substantive changes in their locations, requirements (particularly application deadline), or benefits since 2010. In addition, more than 450 new entries have been added to the program section of the directory. The resulting listing presents the 1,400+ biggest and best sources of free money available to those with ties to the military, including scholarships, fellowships, and grants-in-aid.

HOW THE DIRECTORY IS ORGANIZED

Financial Aid for Veterans, Military Personnel, and Their Families is divided into two separate sections: 1) a descriptive list of financial aid programs designed primarily or exclusively for veterans, military personnel, and their family members; and 2) a set of six indexes to help you find the funding you need.

Funding Available to Veterans, Military Personnel, and Their Families. The first section of the directory describes 1,428 financial aid programs set aside primarily or exclusively for those with ties to the military. Entries in this section are grouped into the following three categories to guide readers in their search for a specific kind of financial assistance:

- **Scholarships:** Programs that support studies at the undergraduate level in the United States. Money is available to entering or continuing students in any type of public or private postsecondary institution, ranging from technical schools and community colleges to major universities in the United States.

- **Fellowships:** Programs that support study, research, projects, or other activities for entering or continuing graduate students as well as professionals and postdoctorates in the United States.

- **Grants-in-Aid:** Programs that provide financial assistance for property and income tax liabilities, travel, emergency situations, service in dangerous military zones, burial costs, loan repayment, etc.

Each of these three categories is further divided into three recipient groupings: veterans, military personnel, and their family members (children, spouses, parents, grandchildren, other relatives, etc.). Within these subdivisions, entries are arranged by program title. Programs that supply more than one type of assistance or assistance to more than one specific group are listed in all relevant subsections. For example, both undergraduate *and* graduate family members may apply for the Chan-Padgett Special Forces Memorial Scholarship, so that program is described in the "Families" section of both the Scholarship *and* Fellowship chapters.

Each program entry in the directory has been designed to provide a concise profile that includes information (when available) on program title, organization address, telephone numbers (including toll-free and fax numbers), e-mail addresses and web site, purpose, eligibility, money awarded, duration, special features, limitations, number of awards, and application deadline (see the sample entry on page 7).

The information reported for each of the programs in this section was gathered from research conducted through the first half of 2012. While the listing is intended to cover as comprehensively as possible the biggest and best sources of free money available to veterans, military personnel, and their families, some sponsoring organizations did not post information online or respond to our research inquiries and, consequently, are not included in this edition of the directory.

Indexes. To help you find the aid you need, we have constructed six indexes; these will let you access the listings by program title, sponsoring organization, residency, tenability, subject focus, and deadline date. These indexes use a word-by-word alphabetical arrangement. Note: numbers in the index refer to entry numbers, not to page numbers in the book.

Program Title Index. If you know the name of a particular funding program and want to find out where it is covered in the directory, use the Program Title Index. To assist you in your search, every program is listed by all its known names, former names, and abbreviations. Since one program can be listed in more than one subsection (e.g., a program providing assistance to veterans at both the undergraduate and graduate levels is listed in two subsections), each entry number in the index has been coded to indicate program type (e.g., S = Scholarships) and the intended recipient group (e.g., V = Veterans). By using this coding system, readers can turn directly to the programs that match their financial needs and eligibility characteristics.

Sponsoring Organization Index. This index provides an alphabetical listing of the 550 agencies that offer funding to veterans, military personnel, and their families. As in the Program Title Index, entry numbers have been coded to indicate both program type and recipient group.

Residency Index. Some programs listed in this book are restricted to veterans, military personnel, or their families in a particular state or region. Others are open to those with ties to the military wherever they live. This index helps you identify programs available only to residents in your area as well as programs that have no residency requirements. Further, to assist you in your search, we've also indicated the program types and recipient groups eligible for the funding offered to residents in each of the areas listed in the index.

Tenability Index. This index identifies the geographic locations where the funding described in the directory may be used. Index entries (city, county, state, region) are arranged alphabetically and subdivided by program type and recipient group. Use this index when you or your family members are looking for money to support research, study, or other activities in a particular geographic area.

Subject Index. This index allows the reader to use more than 250 subject headings to identify the subject focus of each of the financial aid opportunities designed primarily or exclusively for veterans, military personnel, and their families listed in the first section of the directory. Extensive "see" and "see also" references are provided to aid in the search for appropriate funding.

Calendar Index. Since most financial aid programs have specific deadline dates, some may have closed by the time you begin to look for funding. You can use the Calendar Index to determine which programs are still open. This index is arranged by recipient group and divided by program type (e.g., scholarships, grants-in-aid) and month during which the deadline falls. Filing dates can and quite often do vary from year to year; consequently, this index should be used only as a guide for deadlines beyond 2014.

HOW TO USE THE DIRECTORY

Here are some tips to help you get the most out of the funding opportunities listed in this edition of *Financial Aid for Veterans, Military Personnel, and Their Families.*

To Locate Programs Offering a Particular Type of Assistance. If you are looking for programs offering a particular type of funding (e.g., a scholarship for undergraduate courses, a grant-in-aid for emergency situations), turn to the appropriate category in the first section (scholarships, fellowships, or grants-in-aid) and read through all the entries in the subsection that applies (i.e., veterans, military personnel, or family members). Since programs with multiple purposes are listed in every appropriate location, each of the three target population subsections functions as a self-contained entity. In fact, you can browse through any of the sections or subsections in the directory without first consulting an index.

To Find Information on a Particular Financial Aid Program. If you know the name of a particular financial aid program, the type of assistance offered by the program (e.g., fellowship, grant-in-aid) and the intended recipients (veterans, military personnel, or family members), then go directly to the appropriate category in the first section of the directory, where you will find the program profiles arranged alphabetically by title. But be careful: program titles can be misleading. The Air Force Health Professions Scholarship Program is available only to graduate students and therefore is listed under Fellowships not Scholarships. The Anne M. Gannett Award for Veterans is actually a scholarship, as is the Massachusetts Public Service Grant Program. Consequently, if you are looking for a specific program and do not find it in the subsection you have checked, be sure to refer to the Program Title Index to see if it is covered elsewhere in the directory. To save time, always check the Program Title Index first if you know the name of a specific award but are not sure under which subsection it would be listed.

To Locate Programs Sponsored by a Particular Organization. The Sponsoring Organization Index makes it easy to determine groups that provide financial assistance to veterans, military personnel, and their families, or to identify specific financial aid programs offered by a particular organization. Each entry number in the index is coded to identify program type and recipient group, so that you can quickly target appropriate entries.

To Browse Quickly Through the Listings. Turn to the type of funding and recipient sections that interest you and read the "Summary" paragraph in each entry. In seconds, you'll know if this is an opportunity that might apply to you. If it is, read the rest of the information in the entry to make sure you meet all of the program requirements before writing or going online for an application form. Please, save your time and energy. Don't apply if you don't qualify!

To Locate Programs Open to Residents of or Tenable in a Particular Area. The Residency Index identifies financial aid programs open to veterans, military personnel, or their family members who reside in a particular state, region, or country. The Tenability Index shows where the money can be spent. In both indexes, "see" and "see also" references are used liberally, to help you find the funding that's right for you, and index entries for a particular geographic area are divided by both program type and recipient group. When using these indexes, always check the listings under the term "United States," since the programs indexed there have no geographic restrictions and can be used in any area.

To Locate Financial Aid Programs for Veterans, Military Personnel, and Their Families in a Particular Subject Area. Turn to the Subject Index first if you are interested in identifying financial aid programs for veterans, military personnel, or their family members that focus on a particular subject area. To help you structure your search, the type of funding indexed (scholarships, fellowships, grants-in-aid) and the recipient group (veterans, military personnel, family members) are clearly identified. Extensive cross-references are provided.

To Locate Financial Aid Programs for Veterans, Military Personnel, or Their Families by Deadline Date. If you are working with specific time constraints and want to weed out the financial aid programs whose filing dates you won't be able to meet, turn first to the Calendar Index and check the program references listed under the recipient group, program type, and month. Note: not all sponsoring organizations supplied deadline information; those programs are listed under the "Deadline not specified" entries in the index. To identify every relevant financial aid program, regardless of filing dates, read through all the entries in each of the program categories (scholarships, fellowships. grants-in-aid) and recipient subsections (veterans, military personnel, family members) that apply.

To Locate Financial Aid Programs Open to All Segments of the Population. Only programs available to individuals with ties to the military are listed in this publication. However, there are thousands of other programs that are open equally to all segments of the population. To identify these programs, talk to your local librarian, check with your financial aid office on campus, look at the list of RSP print resources on the page opposite the title page in this directory, or see if your library subscribes to Reference Service Press' interactive online funding database; for more information on that resource, go online to: www.rspfunding.com/esubscriptions.html.

PLANS TO UPDATE THE DIRECTORY

This volume, covering 2012-2014, is the thirteenth biennial edition of *Financial Aid for Veterans, Military Personnel, and Their Families.* The next edition will cover the years 2014-2016 and will be released in the first half of 2014.

OTHER RELATED PUBLICATIONS

In addition to *Financial Aid for Veterans, Military Personnel, and Their Families,* Reference Service Press publishes several other titles dealing with fundseeking, including the biennially-issued *Directory of Financial Aids for Women* and *College Student's Guide to Merit and Other No-Need Funding.* For more information on these and other related publications, you can 1) write to Reference Service Press' Marketing Department at 5000 Windplay Drive, Suite 4, El Dorado Hills, CA 95762; 2) call us at (916) 939-9620; 3) send us an e-mail message at info@rspfunding.com; 4) fax us at (916) 939-9626; or 5) visit us on the web: www.rspfunding.com.

ACKNOWLEDGEMENTS

A debt of gratitude is owed all the organizations that contributed information to this edition of *Financial Aid for Veterans, Military Personnel, and Their Families.* Their generous cooperation has helped to make this publication a current and comprehensive survey of awards.

ABOUT THE AUTHORS

Dr. Gail A. Schlachter has worked for more than three decades as a library manager, a library educator, and an administrator of library-related publishing companies. Among the reference books to her credit are the biennially-issued *Money for Graduate Students in the Physical & Earth Sciences* and two award-winning bibliographic guides: *Minorities and Women: A Guide to Reference Literature in the Social Sciences* (which was chosen as an "Outstanding Reference Title of the Year" by *Choice*) and *Reference Sources in Library and Information Services* (which won the first Knowledge Industry Publications "Award for Library Literature"). She was the reference book review editor for *RQ* (now *Reference and User Services Quarterly*) for 10 years, is a past president of the American Library Association's Reference and User Services Association (RUSA, formerly RASD), is serving her fifth elected term on the American Library Association's governing council, and is a former editor-in-chief of *Reference and User Services Quarterly*. In recognition of her outstanding contributions to reference service, Dr. Schlachter was named the "Outstanding Alumna" by the University of Wisconsin School of Library and Information Studies and has been awarded both the Isadore Gilbert Mudge Citation and the Louis Shores/Oryx Press Award.

Dr. R. David Weber taught history and economics at Los Angeles Harbor College (in Wilmington, California) for many years and continues to teach history as an emeritus professor. During his years of full-time teaching there, and at East Los Angeles College, he directed the Honors Program and was frequently selected as the "Teacher of the Year." Dr. Weber is the author of a number of critically-acclaimed reference works, including *Dissertations in Urban History* and the three-volume *Energy Information Guide*. With Gail Schlachter, he is the author of Reference Service Press's award-winning *Financial Aid for Hispanic Americans* and a number of other financial aid titles, including *How to Pay for Your Law Degree* and *Financial Aid for the Disabled and Their Families*, which was chosen as one of the "Best Reference Books of the Year" by *Library Journal*.

Financial Aid Programs for Veterans, Military Personnel and Their Families

Scholarships ●

Fellowships ●

Grants-in-Aid ●

Scholarships

Veterans ●

Military Personnel ●

Family Members ●

Described here are 833 funding programs available to veterans, military personnel, and their family members who are or will be entering or continuing students in public or private postsecondary institutions, ranging from technical schools and community colleges to major universities in the United States. All of this is "free" money. Not one dollar will need to be repaid (provided, of course, that recipients meet all program requirements). Of these listings, 142 are available to veterans, 237 to military personnel, and 454 to their family members (spouses, children, grandchildren, parents, and other relatives). If you are looking for a particular program and don't find it in this section, be sure to check the Program Title Index to see if it is covered elsewhere in the directory.

Veterans

[1]
10TH MOUNTAIN DIVISION (LIGHT INFANTRY) SCHOLARSHIPS

Northern New York Community Foundation, Inc.
120 Washington Street, Suite 400
Watertown, NY 13601
(315) 782-7110   Fax: (315) 782-0047
E-mail: info@nnycf.org
Web: www.nnycf.org/scholarships.asp?mm=6

Summary To provide money for college to current and former members of the 10th Mountain Division and their dependents.

Eligibility This program is open to current and former members of the 10th Mountain Division and their dependents (children and spouses). Applicants must be high school seniors applying for the freshmen year or traditional or non-traditional students enrolled as full-time undergraduates in any year of college or technical school. Along with their application, they must submit a 150-word essay on the character traits that have contributed the most to their success, how they have contributed to their success, and how each will contribute to their vision of a successful life. High school juniors who will graduate early because they are in an advanced placement program may also apply. Interviews are required. Selection is based on academics, personal data, and need.

Financial data The stipend is $5,000.

Duration 1 year.

Number awarded Varies each year; recently, 8 of these scholarships were awarded.

Deadline March of each year.

[2]
11TH ARMORED CAVALRY VETERANS OF VIETNAM AND CAMBODIA SCHOLARSHIP

11th Armored Cavalry Veterans of Vietnam and
 Cambodia
Attn: National Headquarters
P.O. Box 956
Coffeyville, TX 76034-0956
Web: www.11thcavnam.com/scholar.html

Summary To provide financial assistance for college to members of the 11th Armored Cavalry Veterans of Vietnam and Cambodia (11ACVVC) and to their children.

Eligibility This program is open to 1) current members of the 11ACVVC; 2) children and stepchildren of current members of the 11ACVVC; 3) children whose legal guardian is a current member of the 11ACVVC; 4) children of 11th Armored Cavalry troopers who were killed in action, died of wounds, or died as a result of service in Vietnam or Cambodia; and 5) children and stepchildren of 11th Armored Cavalry Regiment veterans who served in Vietnam or Cambodia but are not members of the 11ACVVC. There is no age limit. Applicants must be enrolled or planning to enroll as an undergraduate student. Along with their application, they must submit brief essays on 1) the field of study they plan to enter and why; and 2) why they would be a worthy recipient of this scholarship. Selection is based on those essays (15 points),

completeness and legibility of the application (7 points), and grades (8 points); financial need is not considered.

Financial data The stipend is $3,000; funds are paid directly to the recipient's school, in 2 equal installments.

Duration 1 year; nonrenewable.

Additional information This program began in 1997. Recipients must use the awarded money within 44 months.

Number awarded Up to 24 each year. Since the program was established, it has awarded a total of 268 scholarships, with a value of $842,000, including the $5,000 Colonel Charles L. Schmidt Leadership Scholarship.

Deadline May of each year.

[3]
82ND AIRBORNE DIVISION ASSOCIATION AWARDS

82nd Airborne Division Association
Attn: Educational Fund Treasurer
P.O. Box 65089
Fayetteville, NC 28306-5089
(281) 346-2546   E-mail: 82dassnedfund@earthlink.net
Web: www.82ndassociation.org/Scholarships.html

Summary To provide money for college to members of the 82d Airborne Division Association and their dependent children.

Eligibility Eligible to apply for this award are 1) dependent children of 82nd Airborne Division Association voting members; 2) dependent children of 82nd Airborne servicemen killed in combat; 3) dependent children of deceased Life or All American members of the 82nd Airborne Division Association; and 4) former active-duty 82nd Airborne Division troopers who are association members, are within 2 years of honorable discharge, and served no more than 2 enlistments. Applicants must be enrolled in an accredited university or college. Selection is based on academics and need.

Financial data The stipend is $1,500 per year. Funds are paid to the recipient's college or university.

Duration 1 semester (the second in a school year); recipients may reapply for up to 3 additional annual awards.

Additional information In years when a suitable candidate applies, 1 of these awards is designated the General Mathew B. Ridgeway Scholarship. Membership in the association is open to anyone who ever served in the 82nd Airborne Division, anyone who is currently serving on active duty in jump status, and anyone who has ever served in any of the uniformed services on either jump or glider status and was honorably discharged.

Number awarded Varies each year; recently, $128,250 in scholarships was awarded.

Deadline October of each year.

[4]
AAPA VETERAN'S CAUCUS SCHOLARSHIPS

American Academy of Physician Assistants-Veterans
 Caucus
Attn: Veterans Caucus
P.O. Box 362
Danville, PA 17821-0362
(570) 271-0292   Fax: (570) 271-5850
E-mail: admin@veteranscaucus.org
Web: www.veteranscaucus.org

Summary To provide funding to veterans of any of the uniformed services studying to become physician assistants.

Eligibility This program is open to U.S. citizens who are currently enrolled in a physician assistant program. The program must be approved by the Commission on Accreditation of Allied Health Education. Applicants must be honorably discharged members of 1 of the 7 uniformed services of the United States. Selection is based on military honors and awards received, civic and college honors and awards received, professional memberships and activities, and GPA. An electronic copy of the applicant's DD Form 214 must accompany the application.

Financial data The stipend is $2,000.

Duration 1 year.

Additional information This program includes the following named scholarships: the Donna Jones Moritsugu Memorial Scholarship, the SSGT Craig Ivory Memorial Scholarships, the American Legion Post 40 (Danville, Pennsylvania) Scholarship, the Tim and Jackie Egan Scholarship, the Ken Gartzke Scholarship, the Bruce Cunningham Scholarship, and the Vicki Lianne Moritsugu Memorial Scholarship.

Number awarded Varies each year.

Deadline February of each year.

[5]
ADRIENNE ALIX SCHOLARSHIP
American Legion Auxiliary
Department of New Hampshire
State House Annex
25 Capitol Street, Room 432
Concord, NH 03301-6312
(603) 271-2212   Toll Free: (800) 778-3816
Fax: (603) 271-5352
E-mail: nhalasec@amlegion.state.nh.us
Web: www.nhlegion.org

Summary To provide financial assistance to New Hampshire residents, including those recently discharged from the military, who wish to refresh or upgrade their skills.

Eligibility This program is open to New Hampshire residents and to members of a unit of the American Legion Auxiliary, Department of New Hampshire, who have been members for at least 3 consecutive years. Applicants must be 1) reentering the workforce or upgrading skills; 2) displaced from the workforce; or 3) recently discharged honorably from the military. They must be interested in taking a refresher course or advancing their knowledge or techniques needed in today's workforce at a school in any state. Along with their application, they must submit a 500-word essay explaining their career goals and objectives.

Financial data The stipend is $1,000.

Duration 1 year.

Number awarded 1 each year.

Deadline April of each year.

[6]
AFCEA DISABLED WAR VETERANS SCHOLARSHIPS
Armed Forces Communications and Electronics Association
Attn: AFCEA Educational Foundation
4400 Fair Lakes Court
Fairfax, VA 22033-3899
(703) 631-6138   Toll Free: (800) 336-4583, ext. 6138
Fax: (703) 631-4693   E-mail: scholarshipsinfo@afcea.org
Web: www.afcea.org/education/scholarships/military

Summary To provide financial assistance to disabled military personnel and veterans who are majoring in specified scientific fields in college.

Eligibility This program is open to active-duty service personnel and honorably discharged U.S. military veterans, Reservists, and National Guard members who are disabled because of wounds received during service in Enduring Freedom (Afghanistan) or Iraqi Freedom operations. Applicants must be enrolled full or part time at an accredited 2- or 4-year college or university or in a distance learning or online degree program. They must be working toward a degree in engineering (aerospace, computer, electrical, or systems), computer science, computer engineering technology, computer network systems, computer information systems, electronics engineering technology, mathematics, physics, information systems management, information systems security, technology management, or other field directly related to the support of U.S. intelligence or national security enterprises. Selection is based on academics, leadership, and need.

Financial data The stipend is $2,500.

Duration 1 year.

Number awarded 2 each year: 1 for spring and 1 for fall.

Deadline March of each year for fall; November of each year for spring. Armed Forces Communications and Electronics Association Disabled War Veterans Scholarships.

[7]
ALASKA NATIONAL GUARD STATE TUITION REIMBURSEMENT PROGRAM
Alaska National Guard
Attn: Education Services Officer
P.O. Box 5800
Fort Richardson, AK 99505-5800
(907) 428-6477   Fax: (907) 428-6929
E-mail: ngmneducation@ng.army.mil
Web: www.akguard.com

Summary To provide financial assistance to current and former members of the Alaska National Guard who wish to work on a bachelor's or master's degree in the state.

Eligibility This program is open to members of the Alaska National Guard (Air and Army) and Naval Militia who have a rating of E-1 through O-5, including warrant officers, and are attending a university program in Alaska. Eligibility extends to members who 1) have satisfactorily completed their service contract and who served honorably in federal active service or federally-funded state active service after September 11, 2001; or 2) have been separated or discharged from the Guard because of a service-connected injury, disease, or disability. First priority is given to undergraduates; if funding is available, students working on a second bachelor's degree or a master's degree may be supported. Non-prior servicemembers must complete Initial Active Duty for Training (IADT); prior servicemembers are eligible immediately.

Financial data Recipients are entitled to reimbursement equivalent to 100% of the cost of tuition and fees at the University of Alaska, to a maximum of $7,500 per fiscal year.

Duration 1 semester; may be renewed for a total of 144 semester credits.

Number awarded Varies each year.

Deadline Applications may be submitted at any time, but they must be received at least 90 days after the last official day of the class or term.

[8]
AMERICAN AIRLINES VETERAN'S INITIATIVE SCHOLARSHIP

Women in Aviation, International
Attn: Scholarships
Morningstar Airport
3647 State Route 503 South
West Alexandria, OH 45381-9354
(937) 839-4647   Fax: (937) 839-4645
E-mail: scholarships@wai.org
Web: www.wai.org/education/scholarships.cfm

Summary To provide funding to veterans who are members of Women in Aviation, International (WAI) and interested in attending college, flight school, or other institution.

Eligibility This program is open to veterans of the U.S. military who are WAI members and interested in studying aviation or aeronautics at an accredited college, flight school, or other institution of higher education. Along with their application, they must submit 2 letters of recommendation, a 500-word essay on their aviation history and goals, a resume, copies of all aviation licenses and medical certificates, and the last 3 pages of their pilot logbook (if applicable). Selection is based on achievements, attitude toward self and others, commitment to success, dedication to career, financial need, motivation, reliability, responsibility, and teamwork.

Financial data The stipend is $5,000. Funds are paid directly to the college, flight school, or other institution.

Duration 1 year.

Additional information WAI is a nonprofit professional organization dedicated to encouraging women to consider an aviation career and to providing educational outreach activities and networking resources to women active in the industry. This program began in 2011 by American Airlines.

Number awarded 1 each year.

Deadline November of each year.

[9]
AMERICAN LEGION AUXILIARY SCHOLARSHIP FOR NON-TRADITIONAL STUDENTS

American Legion Auxiliary
8945 North Meridian Street
Indianapolis, IN 46260
(317) 569-4500   Fax: (317) 569-4502
E-mail: alahq@alaforveterans.org
Web: www.alaforveterans.org

Summary To provide financial assistance for college to nontraditional students affiliated with the American Legion.

Eligibility This program is open to members of the American Legion, American Legion Auxiliary, or Sons of the American Legion who have paid dues for the 2 preceding years and the calendar year in which application is being made. Applicants must be nontraditional students who are either 1) returning to school after some period of time during which their formal education was interrupted, or 2) just beginning their education at a later point in life. Selection is based equally on scholastic standing and academics, character and leadership, goals, and need.

Financial data The stipend is $1,000, paid directly to the recipient's school.

Duration 1 year.

Additional information Applications are available from the president of the candidate's own unit or from the secretary or education chair of the department.

Number awarded 5 each year: 1 in each division of the American Legion Auxiliary.

Deadline Applications must be submitted to the unit president by February of each year.

[10]
AMERICAN SYSTEMS HBCU SCHOLARSHIPS

Armed Forces Communications and Electronics
  Association
Attn: AFCEA Educational Foundation
4400 Fair Lakes Court
Fairfax, VA 22033-3899
(703) 631-6138   Toll Free: (800) 336-4583, ext. 6138
Fax: (703) 631-4693   E-mail: scholarshipsinfo@afcea.org
Web: www.afcea.org

Summary To provide funding to students, especially enlisted personnel and veterans, who are majoring in fields of science, technology, engineering, or mathematics (STEM) at an Historically Black College or University (HBCU).

Eligibility This program is open to sophomores and juniors enrolled full time at an accredited 2- or 4-year HBCU or in a distance learning or online degree program affiliated with those institutions. They must be working toward a bachelor's degree in such STEM fields as engineering (aerospace, computer, electrical, or systems), computer science, computer engineering technology, computer information systems, mathematics, physics, information systems management, or other field directly related to the support of U.S. intelligence or homeland security enterprises. Special consideration is given to military enlisted personnel and veterans.

Financial data The stipend is $5,000.

Duration 1 year; may be renewed.

Additional information This program began in 2010 with support from American Systems.

Number awarded At least 2 each year.

Deadline April of each year.

[11]
AMVETS NATIONAL SCHOLARSHIPS FOR VETERANS

AMVETS National Headquarters
Attn: Scholarships
4647 Forbes Boulevard
Lanham, MD 20706-3807
(301) 459-9600   Toll Free: (877) 7-AMVETS, ext. 3043
Fax: (301) 459-7924   E-mail: amvets@amvets.org
Web: www.amvets.org/programs/scholarships.html

Summary To provide money for college or graduate school to certain veterans who are members of AMVETS.

Eligibility This program is open to AMVETS members who are veterans and U.S. citizens. Applicants must be interested in working full time on an undergraduate degree, graduate degree, or certification from an accredited technical/trade school. They must have exhausted all other government aid. Selection is based on financial need, academic promise, military duty and awards, volunteer activities, community services, jobs held during the past 4 years, and an essay of 50 to 100 words on "What a Higher Education Means to Me."

Financial data The stipend is $1,000 per year.

Duration Up to 4 years.

Additional information Requests for applications must be accompanied by a self-addressed stamped envelope.

Number awarded 3 each year.

Deadline April of each year.

[12]
ANCA SCHOLARSHIPS

Army Nurse Corps Association
Attn: Education Committee
P.O. Box 39235
San Antonio, TX 78218-1235
(210) 650-3534   Fax: (210) 650-3494
E-mail: education@e-anca.org
Web: e-anca.org/ANCAEduc.htm

Summary To provide financial assistance to students who have a connection to the Army and are interested in working on an undergraduate or graduate degree in nursing.

Eligibility This program is open to U.S. citizens attending colleges or universities that have accredited programs offering associate, bachelor's, master's, or doctoral degrees in nursing. Applicants must be 1) nursing or anesthesia students who plan to enter a component of the U.S. Army and are not participating in a program funded by a component of the U.S. Army; 2) nursing or anesthesia students who have previously served in a component of the U.S. Army; 3) Army Nurse Corps officers enrolled in an undergraduate or graduate nursing program not funded by a component of the U.S. Army; 4) enlisted soldiers in a component of the U.S. Army who are working on a baccalaureate degree in nursing not funded by a component of the U.S. Army; or 5) nursing or anesthesia students whose parent(s), spouse, and/or children are serving or have served in a component of the U.S. Army. Along with their application, they must submit a personal statement on their professional career objectives, reasons for applying for this scholarship, financial need, special considerations, personal and academic interests, and why they are preparing for a nursing career.

Financial data The stipend is $3,000. Funds are sent directly to the recipient's school.

Duration 1 year.

Additional information Although the sponsoring organization is open to officers of the Army Nurse Corps, it does not have an official affiliation with the Army. Therefore, students who receive these scholarships do not incur any military service obligation.

Number awarded 1 or more each year.

Deadline March of each year.

[13]
ANDREW J. ZABIEREK MEMORIAL SCHOLARSHIPS

Andrew J. Zabierek Foundation
P.O. Box 533
Chelmsford, MA 01824
(978) 726-2913   E-mail: info@ajzfoundation.org
Web: www.ajzfoundation.org

Summary To provide financial assistance to veterans from New England who are working on an undergraduate degree.

Eligibility This program is open to residents of the New England states who are honorably discharged veterans. Applicants must be working on a postsecondary or technical degree at a college or university in any state. Along with their application, they must submit a 500-word personal reflection essay on how their service has impacted them personally, how they will continue to serve their community and country in the future, and their educational and professional goals after they complete their education. Financial need is considered in the selection process.

Financial data The stipend is $1,500.

Duration 1 year.

Additional information This program was established in 2004 to honor Lance Corporal Andrew J. Zabierek, who was killed in action in Al Anbar provide of Iraq.

Number awarded 1 or 2 each year.

Deadline May of each year.

[14]
ANNE M. GANNETT AWARD FOR VETERANS

National Federation of Music Clubs
1646 Smith Valley Road
Greenwood, IN 46142
(317) 882-4003   Fax: (317) 882-4019
E-mail: info@nfmc-music.org
Web: nfmc-music.org

Summary To provide financial assistance for undergraduate education to members of the National Federation of Music Clubs (NFMC) whose careers have been delayed or interrupted as a result of their service in the U.S. armed forces.

Eligibility This program is open to undergraduate students who are majoring in music and whose musical careers were interrupted by military service. Applicants must be student members of the federation and U.S. citizens. Along with their application, they must submit an essay on their reason for wanting this award and their future plans. Financial need is not considered in the selection process.

Financial data The stipend is $1,500.

Duration 1 year.

Additional information The application fee is $20.

Number awarded 1 each odd-numbered year.

Deadline May of each odd-numbered year.

[15]
ARMY AVIATION ASSOCIATION OF AMERICA SCHOLARSHIPS

Army Aviation Association of America Scholarship
  Foundation
Attn: AAAA Scholarship Foundation
755 Main Street, Suite 4D
Monroe, CT 06468-2830
(203) 268-2450   Fax: (203) 268-5870
E-mail: aaaa@quad-a.org
Web: www.quad-a.org

Summary To provide financial aid for undergraduate or graduate study to members of the Army Aviation Association of America and their relatives.

Eligibility This program is open to association members (or deceased members) and their spouses, unmarried siblings, unmarried children, and unmarried grandchildren. Applicants must be enrolled or accepted for enrollment as an undergraduate or graduate student at an accredited college or university. Graduate students must include a 250-word essay on their life experiences, work history, and aspirations. Some scholarships are specifically reserved for enlisted, warrant officer, company grade, and Department of the Army civilian members. Selection is based on academic merit and personal achievement.

Financial data Stipends range up to $3,000 per year.

Duration Scholarships may be for 1, 2, or 4 years.

Number awarded Varies each year; recently, $309,500 in scholarships was awarded to 209 students. Since the program began in 1963, the foundation has awarded more than $4.1 million to nearly 2,500 qualified applicants.

Deadline April of each year.

[16]
ASSE FOUNDATION MILITARY SERVICE SCHOLARSHIP

American Society of Safety Engineers
Attn: ASSE Foundation
1800 East Oakton Street
Des Plaines, IL 60018
(847) 768-3435   Fax: (847) 768-3434
E-mail: agabanski@asse.org
Web: www.asse.org

Summary To provide financial assistance to upper-division and graduate student members of the American Society of Safety Engineers (ASSE), especially those who have served in the military.

Eligibility This program is open to ASSE student members who are working on an undergraduate or graduate degree in occupational safety, health, and environment or a closely-related field (e.g., industrial or environmental engineering, environmental science, industrial hygiene, occupational health nursing). Priority is given to students who have served in the military. Applicants must be full-time students who have completed at least 60 semester hours with a GPA of 3.0 or higher as undergraduates or at least 9 semester hours with a GPA of 3.5 or higher as graduate students. Along with their application, they must submit 2 essays of 300 words or less: 1) why they are seeking a degree in occupational safety and health or a closely-related field, a brief description of their current activities, and how those relate to their career goals and objectives; and 2) why they should be awarded this

scholarship (including career goals and financial need). U.S. citizenship is not required.

Financial data The stipend is $1,000 per year.

Duration 1 year; recipients may reapply.

Number awarded 1 each year.

Deadline November of each year.

[17]
AUSA/JOSEPH P. AND HELEN T. CRIBBINS SCHOLARSHIP

Association of the United States Army
Attn: Executive Assistant
2425 Wilson Boulevard
Arlington, VA 22201
(703) 841-4300, ext. 2652
Toll Free: (800) 336-4570, ext. 2652
E-mail: ausa-info@ausa.org
Web: www.ausa.org

Summary To provide financial assistance to active-duty and honorably-discharged soldiers interested in studying engineering in college.

Eligibility This program is open to 1) soldiers currently serving in the active Army, Army Reserve, or Army National Guard of any rank; and 2) honorably-discharged soldiers from any component of the total Army. Applicants must have been accepted at an accredited college or university to work on a degree in engineering or a related field (e.g., computer science, biotechnology). Along with their application, they must submit a 1-page autobiography, 2 letters of recommendation, and a transcript of high school or college grades (depending on which they are currently attending). Selection is based on academic merit and personal achievement. Financial need is not normally a selection criterion but in some cases of extreme need it may be used as a factor; the lack of financial need, however, is never a cause for nonselection.

Financial data The stipend is $2,000; funds are sent directly to the recipient's college or university.

Duration 1 year.

Number awarded 1 or more each year.

Deadline June of each year.

[18]
BETTER CHANCE SCHOLARSHIP

Associates of Vietnam Veterans of America
Attn: Scholarship Program
8719 Colesville Road, Suite 100
Silver Spring, MD 20910
(301) 585-4000   Toll Free: (800) VVA-1316
Fax: (301) 585-0519
Web: www.avva.org/scholarship.html

Summary To provide money for college to members of Vietnam Veterans of America (VVA) and Associates of Vietnam Veterans of America (AVVA), their families, and the families of Vietnam veterans killed or missing in action.

Eligibility This program is open to members of VVA and AVVA; their spouses, children, and grandchildren; and the spouses, children, and grandchildren of Vietnam veterans killed in action (KIA) or missing in action (MIA). Especially encouraged to apply are average students who are not eligible for academic scholarships but who can demonstrate financial need. Applicants must submit essays on their goals, work experience, and community service.

Financial data Stipends are $1,000, $750, or $500.
Duration 1 year.
Additional information This program began in 1998.
Number awarded Normally 3 each year: 1 at $1,000, 1 at $750, and 1 at $500.
Deadline June of each year.

[19]
BOSTON POST SAME SCHOLARSHIPS

Society of American Military Engineers-Boston Post
c/o William Naughton, Scholarship Committee Chair
Kleinfelder
215 First Street, Suite 320
Cambridge, MA 01742
(617) 497-7800   E-mail: bnaughton@kleinfelder.com
Web: www.sameboston.org/index.cfm?ac=scholarships

Summary To provide funding to residents of New England (especially those with ties to the military) who are majoring in a program related to construction in any state.

Eligibility This program is open to residents of New England who are currently enrolled in an accepted engineering or architecture program, preferably in civil engineering, environmental engineering, architecture, or other construction-related program, at a college or university in any state. Applicants must have completed at least 1 academic year and have at least 1 year remaining. They must be nominated by their institution. Along with their application, they must submit a resume describing their academic and career objectives, extracurricular and community activities, work experience, and special interests or hobbies; transcripts; documentation of financial need; and a personal letter describing their qualifications and needs. An interview is required. Selection is based on academic achievement, financial need, extracurricular and community activities, the letter, and the interview. Preference is given to applicants who are enrolled in ROTC (preferably not a recipient of an ROTC scholarship), have current or prior service in the U.S. armed forces, are interested in the U.S. Public Health Service, and/or are interested in other public service with federal, state, or local government. U.S. citizenship is required.

Financial data The stipend is $2,000 per year.
Duration 1 year.
Number awarded Approximately 25 each year.
Deadline February of each year.

[20]
BUICK ACHIEVERS SCHOLARSHIP PROGRAM

Scholarship America
Attn: Scholarship Management Services
One Scholarship Way
P.O. Box 297
St. Peter, MN 56082
(507) 931-1682   Toll Free: (866) 243-4644
Fax: (507) 931-9168
E-mail: buickachievers@scholarshipamerica.org
Web: www.buickachievers.com

Summary To provide financial assistance to students (particularly veterans and their dependents) who are entering college for the first time and planning to major in specified fields related to engineering, design, or business.

Eligibility This program is open to high school seniors and graduates who are planning to enroll full time at an accredited 4-year college or university as first-time freshmen. Applicants must be planning to major in accounting, business administration, engineering (chemical, controls, electrical, environmental, industrial, manufacturing, mechanical, plastic/polymers, or engineering technology), design (graphic, industrial, product, or transportation), ergonomics, finance, industrial hygiene, labor and industrial relations, management (logistics, manufacturing, operations, or supply chain), marketing, mathematics, occupational health and safety, or statistics. U.S. citizenship or permanent resident status is required. Selection is based on academic achievement, financial need, participation and leadership in community and school activities, work experience, educational and career goals, and other unusual circumstances. Special consideration is given to first-generation college students, women, minorities, military veterans, and dependents of military personnel.

Financial data Stipends are $25,000 or $2,000 per year.
Duration 1 year; renewable up to 3 more years (or 4 years if entering a 5-year engineering program).
Additional information This program is funded by the General Motors Foundation.
Number awarded 1,100 each year: 100 at $25,000 and 1,000 at $2,000.
Deadline March of each year.

[21]
CALIFORNIA FEE WAIVER PROGRAM FOR RECIPIENTS OF THE MEDAL OF HONOR AND THEIR CHILDREN

California Department of Veterans Affairs
Attn: Division of Veterans Services
1227 O Street, Room 101
P.O. Box 942895
Sacramento, CA 94295
(916) 653-2573   Toll Free: (877) 741-8532
Fax: (916) 653-2563   TDD: (800) 324-5966
Web: www.cdva.ca.gov/VetServices/Education.aspx

Summary To provide money for college to veterans in California who received the Medal of Honor and their children.

Eligibility This program is open to recipients of the Medal of Honor and their children younger than 27 years of age reside in California. Applicants must be attending or planning to attend a community college or a university in the California State University or the University of California system.

Financial data Full-time college students receive a waiver of tuition and registration fees at any publicly-supported community or state college or university in California.
Duration 1 year; may be renewed.
Number awarded Varies each year.
Deadline Deadline not specified.

[22]
CALIFORNIA LEGION AUXILIARY PAST PRESIDENTS' PARLEY NURSING SCHOLARSHIPS

American Legion Auxiliary
Department of California
Veterans War Memorial Building
401 Van Ness Avenue, Room 113
San Francisco, CA 94102-4586
(415) 861-5092   Fax: (415) 861-8365
E-mail: calegionaux@calegionaux.org
Web: www.calegionaux.org/scholarships.htm

Summary To provide funding to California residents who are current military personnel, veterans, or members of their families and interested in studying nursing in the state.
Eligibility This program is open to California residents who are currently serving on active military duty, veterans who served during wartime, or the spouse, widow(er), or child of such a veteran. Applicants must be entering or continuing students of nursing at an accredited institution of higher learning in California. Selection is based on the application (25%), scholarship (25%), character and leadership (25%), and financial need (25%).
Financial data Stipends range up to $2,000.
Duration 1 year.
Number awarded Varies each year.
Deadline March of each year.

[23]
CALIFORNIA LEGION AUXILIARY SCHOLARSHIPS FOR CONTINUING AND/OR REENTRY STUDENTS

American Legion Auxiliary
Department of California
Veterans War Memorial Building
401 Van Ness Avenue, Room 113
San Francisco, CA 94102-4586
(415) 861-5092　　　　　　Fax: (415) 861-8365
E-mail: calegionaux@calegionaux.org
Web: www.calegionaux.org/scholarships.htm

Summary To provide funding to California residents who are active-duty military personnel, veterans, or children of veterans and require assistance to continue their education.
Eligibility This program is open to California residents who are 1) active-duty military personnel; 2) veterans of World War I, World War II, Korea, Vietnam, Grenada/Lebanon, Panama, or Desert Shield/Desert Storm; and 3) children of veterans who served during those periods of war. Applicants must be continuing or reentry students at a college, university, or business/trade school in California. Selection is based on the application (25%), scholarship (25%), character and leadership (25%), and financial need (25%).
Financial data The stipend is $1,000 or $500.
Duration 1 year.
Additional information This program includes 1 scholarship designated as the Mel Foronda Memorial Scholarship.
Number awarded 5 each year: 3 at $1,000 and 2 at $500.
Deadline March of each year.

[24]
CAPTAIN SEAN P. GRIMES PHYSICIAN ASSISTANT EDUCATIONAL SCHOLARSHIP AWARD

Society of Army Physician Assistants
c/o Harold Slusher
6762 Candlewood Drive
P.O. Box 07490
Fort Myers, FL 33919
(239) 482-2162　　　　　　Fax: (239) 482-2162
E-mail: hal.shusher@juno.com
Web: www.sapa.org/SeanScholarshipPage.htm

Summary To provide funding to current and former Army personnel interested in training as a physician assistant.
Eligibility This program is open to Army veterans, Army active-duty soldiers, Army National Guard soldiers, and Army Reservists. Soldiers may be of any enlisted or officer rank from E-5 through O-4. Applicants may be seeking initial training as a physician assistant or current physician assistants working on a baccalaureate, master's, or doctoral degree. They must have a GPA of 2.5 or higher. Candidates for initial training must be enrolled in an ARC-PA approved program. Other candidates must be enrolled at an accredited college or university. Financial need is considered.
Financial data The stipend is $6,000.
Duration 1 year.
Additional information This program began in 2006.
Number awarded 1 each year.
Deadline January of each year.

[25]
CAREER COLLEGE ASSOCIATION'S IMAGINE AMERICA MILITARY AWARD PROGRAM

Career College Association
Attn: Imagine America Foundation
1101 Connecticut Avenue, N.W., Suite 901
Washington, DC 20036
(202) 336-6719　　　　　　Fax: (202) 408-8102
E-mail: scholarships@imagine-america.org
Web: www.imagine-america.org/grantsformilitary

Summary To provide funding to veterans and military personnel interested in attending a participating career college.
Eligibility This program is open to active-duty, reservist, honorably-discharged, and retired veterans of a U.S. military service branch. Applicants must be interested in attending 1 of more than 300 participating career colleges. They must be able to demonstrate the likelihood of enrolling and successfully completing postsecondary education. All applications are submitted online to the college where the student wishes to enroll. Selection is based on the likelihood of successfully completing postsecondary education and financial need.
Financial data The stipend is $1,000. Funds must be used for payment of tuition at a participating career college.
Duration 1 year.
Additional information The Imagine America Foundation (originally known as the Career College Foundation) established this program in 2004.
Number awarded Varies each year.
Deadline June of each year.

[26]
COLORADO LEGION AUXILIARY PAST PRESIDENT'S PARLEY NURSE'S SCHOLARSHIP

American Legion Auxiliary
Department of Colorado
7465 East First Avenue, Suite D
Denver, CO 80230
(303) 367-5388　　　　　　Fax: (303) 367-5388
E-mail: dept-sec@alacolorado.com
Web: www.alacolorado.com/index_files/Forms.htm

Summary To provide funding to wartime veterans and their descendants in Colorado who are interested in attending school in the state to prepare for a career in nursing.
Eligibility This program is open to 1) daughters, sons, spouses, granddaughters, and great-granddaughters of veterans, and 2) veterans who served in the armed forces during eligibility dates for membership in the American Legion.

Applicants must be Colorado residents who have been accepted by an accredited school of nursing in the state. Along with their application, they must submit a 500-word essay on the topic, "Americanism." Selection is based on that essay (25%), scholastic ability (25%), financial need (25%), references (13%), and dedication to chosen field (12%).

Financial data Stipends range from $500 to $1,000.

Duration 1 year; nonrenewable.

Number awarded Varies each year, depending on the availability of funds.

Deadline April of each year.

[27]
CONNECTICUT TUITION WAIVER FOR VETERANS

Connecticut Office of Financial and Academic Affairs for Higher Education
Attn: Student Financial Aid
61 Woodland Street
Hartford, CT 06105-2326
(860) 947-1855   Toll Free: (800) 842-0229 (within CT)
Fax: (860) 947-1311   E-mail: sfa@ctdhe.org
Web: www.ctohe.org/SFA/default.htm

Summary To provide money for college or graduate school to certain Connecticut veterans and military personnel or their dependents.

Eligibility This program is open to 1) honorably-discharged Connecticut veterans who served at least 90 days during specified periods of wartime; 2) active members of the Connecticut Army and Air National Guard; 3) Connecticut residents who are a dependent child or surviving spouse of a member of the armed forces killed in action on or after September 11, 2001 who was also a Connecticut resident; and 4) Connecticut residents who are dependent children of a person officially declared missing in action or a prisoner of war while serving in the armed forces after January 1, 1960. Applicants must be attending or planning to attend a public college or university in the state.

Financial data The program provides a waiver of 100% of tuition for students working on an undergraduate or graduate degree at the University of Connecticut, 100% of tuition for general fund courses at campuses of Connecticut State University, 50% of tuition for extension and summer courses at campuses of Connecticut State University, 100% of tuition at all Connecticut community colleges, and 50% or fees at Charter Oak State College.

Duration Up to 4 years.

Additional information This is an entitlement program; applications are available from the respective college financial aid offices.

Number awarded Varies each year.

Deadline Deadline not specified.

[28]
DALLAS AND DONNA LIPSCOMB SCHOLARSHIP

American Academy of Physician Assistants-Veterans Caucus
Attn: Veterans Caucus
P.O. Box 362
Danville, PA 17821-0362
(570) 271-0292   Fax: (570) 271-5850
E-mail: admin@veteranscaucus.org
Web: www.veteranscaucus.org

Summary To provide financial assistance to veterans (either single parents or from the Air Force) who are studying to become physician assistants.

Eligibility This program is open to U.S. citizens who are currently enrolled in a physician assistant program. The program must be approved by the Commission on Accreditation of Allied Health Education. Applicants must be honorably discharged members of the armed forces who is a single parent; if no single parent applies, the award is presented to a veteran of the U.S. Air Force. Selection is based on military honors and awards received, civic and college honors and awards received, professional memberships and activities, and GPA. An electronic copy of the applicant's DD Form 214 must accompany the application.

Financial data The stipend is $2,000.

Duration 1 year.

Number awarded 1 each year.

Deadline February of each year.

[29]
DARLENE HOOLEY SCHOLARSHIP FOR OREGON VETERANS

Oregon Student Access Commission
Attn: Grants and Scholarships Division
1500 Valley River Drive, Suite 100
Eugene, OR 97401-2146
(541) 687-7395   Toll Free: (800) 452-8807, ext. 7395
Fax: (541) 687-7414   TDD: (800) 735-2900
E-mail: awardinfo@osac.state.or.us
Web: www.oregonstudentaid.gov/scholarships.aspx

Summary To provide financial assistance to veterans in Oregon who served during the Global War on Terror and are interested in working on an undergraduate or graduate degree at a college in the state.

Eligibility This program is open to Oregon veterans who served during the Global War on Terror; there is no minimum length of service requirement. Preference is given to members of active-duty Reserves and the National Guard who were deployed to an overseas conflict. Applicants must be enrolled or planning to enroll at least half time as an undergraduate or graduate student at a college or university in Oregon. Financial need is considered in the selection process.

Financial data Stipends for scholarships offered by the Oregon Student Access Commission (OSAC) range from $200 to $10,000 but recently averaged $2,300.

Duration 1 year; recipients may reapply.

Additional information This program is administered by OSAC with funds from the Oregon Community Foundation.

Number awarded Varies each year.

Deadline February of each year.

[30]
DATATEL ANGELFIRE SCHOLARSHIP

Datatel Scholars Foundation
4375 Fair Lakes Court
Fairfax, VA 22033
(703) 968-9000, ext. 4549   Toll Free: (800) 486-4332
Fax: (703) 968-4625   E-mail: scholars@datatel.com
Web: www.datatelscholars.org

Summary To provide funding to graduating high school seniors, college students, and graduate students who will be studying at a Datatel client school and are veterans, veterans' dependents, or refugees from southeast Asia.

Eligibility This program is open to 1) veterans who served in the Asian theater (Vietnam, Cambodia, or Laos) between 1964 and 1975; 2) their spouses and children; 3) refugees from Vietnam, Cambodia, or Laos; and 4) veterans who served in Operation Desert Storm, Operation Enduring Freedom, and/or Operation Iraqi Freedom. Applicants must attend a Datatel client college or university during the upcoming school year as a full- or part-time undergraduate or graduate student. They must first apply to their institution, which selects 2 semifinalists and forwards their applications to the sponsor. Along with their application, they must include a 1,000-word personal statement that discusses how the conflict has affected them personally, summarizes how the conflict has impacted their educational goals, and describes how being awarded this scholarship will help them achieve their goals. Selection is based on the quality of the personal statement (60%) and academic merit (40%).

Financial data The stipend is $1,700. Funds are paid directly to the institution.

Duration 1 year.

Additional information Datatel, Inc. produces advanced information technology solutions for higher education. It has more than 750 client sites in the United States and Canada. This scholarship was created to commemorate those who lost their lives in Vietnam or Iraq and is named after a memorial administered by the Disabled American Veterans Association in Angelfire, New Mexico.

Number awarded 10 each year.

Deadline Students must submit online applications to their institution or organization by January of each year.

[31]
DKF VETERANS ASSISTANCE FOUNDATION SCHOLARSHIPS

DKF Veterans Assistance Foundation
P.O. Box 7166
San Carlos, CA 94070
(650) 595-3896   E-mail: admin@dkfveterans.com
Web: www.dkfveterans.com

Summary To provide financial assistance for college in any state to California residents who are veterans of Operation Enduring Freedom (OEF) in Afghanistan or Operation Iraqi Freedom (OIF) or the dependents of deceased or disabled veterans of those actions.

Eligibility This program is open to 1) veterans of the U.S. armed forces (including the Coast Guard) who served in support of OEF or OIF within the central command area of responsibility; and 2) dependents of those veterans who were killed in action or incurred disabilities rated as 75% or more. Applicants must be residents of California enrolled or planning to enroll full time at a college, university, community college, or trade institution in any state. Along with their application, they must submit a cover letter introducing themselves and their educational goals.

Financial data The stipend is $5,000 per year for students at universities and state colleges or $1,500 per year for students at community colleges and trade institutions.

Duration 1 year; may be renewed up to 3 additional years, provided the recipient maintains a GPA of 3.0 or higher.

Additional information This foundation began in 2005.

Number awarded A limited number are awarded.

Deadline Deadline not specified.

[32]
DR. AURELIO M. CACCOMO FAMILY FOUNDATION MEMORIAL SCHOLARSHIP

AMVETS National Headquarters
Attn: Scholarships
4647 Forbes Boulevard
Lanham, MD 20706-3807
(301) 459-9600   Toll Free: (877) 7-AMVETS, ext. 3043
Fax: (301) 459-7924   E-mail: amvets@amvets.org
Web: www.amvets.org/programs_scholarships.html

Summary To provide financial assistance for college to veterans and members of the National Guard and Reserves who are members of AMVETS.

Eligibility This program is open to AMVETS members who are veterans or currently serving in the National Guard or Reserves. Applicants must be interested in working full or part time on an undergraduate degree or certification from an accredited technical/trade school. They must have exhausted all other government aid. U.S. citizenship is required. Selection is based on financial need, academic promise, military duty and awards, volunteer activities, community services, jobs held during the past 4 years, and an essay of 50 to 100 words on "This award will help me achieve my career/vocational goal, which is..."

Financial data The stipend is $3,000.

Duration 1 year; nonrenewable.

Additional information Requests for applications must be accompanied by a self-addressed stamped envelope.

Number awarded 2 each year.

Deadline April of each year.

[33]
EDUCATION FOUNDATION FOR THE COLORADO NATIONAL GUARD GRANTS

National Guard Association of Colorado
Attn: Education Foundation, Inc.
P.O. Box 440889
Aurora, CO 80044-0889
(303) 909-6369   Fax: (720) 535-5925
E-mail: BernieRogoff@comcast.net
Web: efcong.org/Grants

Summary To provide financial assistance to members of the Colorado National Guard and their families who are interested in attending college or graduate school in any state.

Eligibility This program is open to current and retired members of the Colorado National Guard and their dependent unmarried children and spouses. Applicants must be enrolled or planning to enroll full or part time at a college, university, trade school, business school, or graduate school in any state. Along with their application, they must submit an essay, up to 2 pages in length, on their desire to continue their education, what motivates them, their financial need, their commitment to academic excellence, and their current situation. Selection is based on academic achievement, community involvement, and financial need.

Financial data Stipends are at least $1,000 per year.

Duration 1 year; may be renewed.

Number awarded Varies each year; recently, 38 of these grants, with a total value of $50,000, were awarded.

Deadline   July of each year for fall semester; January of each year for spring semester.

[34]
EDWARD T. CONROY MEMORIAL SCHOLARSHIP PROGRAM

Maryland Higher Education Commission
Attn: Office of Student Financial Assistance
6 North Liberty Street, Ground Suite
Baltimore, MD 21201
(410) 767-3300   Toll Free: (800) 974-0203
Fax: (410) 332-0250   TDD: (800) 735-2258
E-mail: osfamail@mhec.state.md.us
Web: www.mhec.state.md.us/financialAid/descriptions.asp

Summary   To provide money for college or graduate school in Maryland to children and spouses of victims of the September 11, 2001 terrorist attacks and specified categories of veterans, public safety employees, and their children or spouses.

Eligibility   This program is open to entering and continuing undergraduate and graduate students in the following categories: 1) children and surviving spouses of victims of the September 11, 2001 terrorist attacks who died in the World Trade Center in New York City, in the Pentagon in Virginia, or on United Airlines Flight 93 in Pennsylvania; 2) veterans who have, as a direct result of military service, a disability of 25% or greater and have exhausted or are no longer eligible for federal veterans' educational benefits; 3) children of armed forces members whose death or 100% disability was directly caused by military service; 4) POW/MIA veterans of the Vietnam Conflict and their children; 5) state or local public safety officers or volunteers who became 100% disabled in the line of duty; and 6) children and unremarried surviving spouses of state or local public safety employees or volunteers who died or became 100% disabled in the line of duty. The parent, spouse, veteran, POW, or public safety officer or volunteer must have been a resident of Maryland at the time of death or when declared disabled. Financial need is not considered.

Financial data   The amount of the award is equal to tuition and fees at a Maryland postsecondary institution, to a maximum of $19,000 for children and spouses of the September 11 terrorist attacks or $9,000 for all other recipients.

Duration   Up to 5 years of full-time or 8 years of part-time study.

Additional information   Recipients must enroll at a 2- or 4-year Maryland college or university as a full-time or part-time degree-seeking undergraduate or graduate student or attend a private career school.

Number awarded   Varies each year.

Deadline   July of each year.

[35]
E.E. MIXON SECOND DRAGOON FOUNDATION SCHOLARSHIPS

E.E. Mixon Second Dragoon Foundation
c/o Scott C. Pierce
217 Painted Fall Way
Cary, NC 27513
(203) 979-7083   E-mail: scott@2nddragoons.org
Web: 2nddragoons.org/index/?q=node/15

Summary   To provide financial assistance for college to former members of the U.S. Army's Second Cavalry Regiment and the children of current and former members.

Eligibility   This program is open to former members of the Second Cavalry Regiment and the children of current or former members. Members of other Army units and their children may also be considered, especially if they have a previous connection with the Second Cavalry Regiment or other U.S. Cavalry Regiments. Applicants must submit a 500-word essay on 1 of the following topics: 1) how our military presence in Europe contributed to the end of the Cold War; 2) the role of the non-commissioned officer corps in the U.S. military; 3) what America means to them; or 4) their strategy for the way forward in Afghanistan. They must be attending or planning to attend a college or university. Selection is based on the essay and a statement of their educational goals, projected or current field of study, and personal or family affiliation with a cavalry unit.

Financial data   Stipends range from $250 to $1,000 per year. Funds are deposited directly into the recipient's college tuition account.

Duration   1 semester; may be renewed.

Number awarded   Varies each year; recently, 3 of these scholarships were awarded.

Deadline   July of each year.

[36]
EXEMPTION FOR TEXAS VETERANS

Texas Higher Education Coordinating Board
Attn: Grants and Special Programs
1200 East Anderson Lane
P.O. Box 12788
Austin, TX 78711-2788
(512) 427-6340   Toll Free: (800) 242-3062
Fax: (512) 427-6420   E-mail: grantinfo@thecb.state.tx.us
Web: www.collegeforalltexans.com

Summary   To exempt Texas veterans from payment of tuition for undergraduate or graduate study at public universities in the state.

Eligibility   Eligible are veterans who currently reside in Texas and were legal residents of the state when they entered the U.S. armed forces and served for at least 181 days of active military duty, excluding basic training, during specified periods of wartime. Applicants must have received an honorable discharge or separation or a general discharge under honorable conditions. They must be enrolled at a public college or university in Texas and all their other federal veterans education benefits (not including Pell and SEOG grants) may not exceed the value of this exemption.

Financial data   Veterans who are eligible for this benefit are entitled to free tuition and fees at state-supported colleges and universities in Texas.

Duration   Exemptions may be claimed up to 150 credit hours, including undergraduate and graduate study.

Additional information   This program was established under provisions of the Hazlewood Act, and is also referred to as Hazlewood Exemption for Texas Veterans.

Number awarded   Varies each year; recently, 8,885 of these awards were granted.

Deadline   Deadline not specified.

[37]
FIRST SERGEANT DOUGLAS AND CHARLOTTE DEHORSE SCHOLARSHIP

Catching the Dream
8200 Mountain Road, N.E., Suite 203
Albuquerque, NM 87110-7835
(505) 262-2351   Fax: (505) 262-0534
E-mail: NScholarsh@aol.com
Web: www.catchingthedream.org

Summary   To provide financial assistance to American Indians who have ties to the military and are working on an undergraduate or graduate degree.

Eligibility   This program is open to American Indians who 1) have completed 1 year of an Army, Navy, or Air Force Junior Reserve Officer Training (JROTC) program; 2) are enrolled in an Army, Navy, or Air Force Reserve Officer Training (ROTC) program; or 3) are a veteran of the U.S. Army, Navy, Air Force, Marines, Merchant Marine, or Coast Guard. Applicants must be enrolled in college or graduate school. They must submit an application, personal essay, high school transcripts, and letters of recommendation.

Financial data   A stipend is awarded (amount not specified).

Duration   1 year.

Additional information   This program began in 2007.

Number awarded   1 or more each year.

Deadline   April of each year for fall semester or quarter; September of each year for spring semester or winter quarter.

[38]
FORCE RECON ASSOCIATION SCHOLARSHIPS

Force Recon Association
P.O. Box 425
Rowe, MA 01367
E-mail: commchief@forcerecon.com
Web: www.forcerecon.com

Summary   To provide money for college to members of the Force Recon Association and their dependents.

Eligibility   This program is open to members of the Force Recon Association and family members of a relative who served both in the U.S. Marine Corps and was or is assigned to a Force Reconnaissance Company. The relative must be either an active or deceased member of the Force Recon Association. Family members include wives and widows, sons and daughters (including adopted and stepchildren), grandchildren, and great-grandchildren. Applicants may be pursuing scholastic, vocational, or technical education. Along with their application, they must submit a personal statement on why they desire this scholarship, their proposed course of study, their progress in their current course of study, and their long-range career goals. Selection is based on academic achievement, letters of recommendation, demonstrated character, and the written statements.

Financial data   A stipend is awarded (amount not specified).

Duration   1 year; may be renewed.

Number awarded   1 or more each year.

Deadline   Applications must be received at least 2 weeks prior to the annual meeting of the Force Recon Association.

[39]
FRA NON-MEMBER SCHOLARSHIPS

Fleet Reserve Association
Attn: FRA Education Foundation
125 North West Street
Alexandria, VA 22314-2754
(703) 683-1400   Toll Free: (800) FRA-1924
Fax: (703) 549-6610   E-mail: scholars@fra.org
Web: www.fra.org

Summary   To provide financial assistance for college or graduate school to current or former sea service personnel and their families.

Eligibility   This program is open to 1) active-duty, Reserve, honorably-discharged veterans, and retired members of the U.S. Navy, Marine Corps, and Coast Guard; and 2) their spouses, children, and grandchildren. Applicants must be enrolled as full-time undergraduate or graduate students but they are not required to be members of the sponsoring organization. Along with their application, they must submit an essay on why they want to go to college and what they intend to accomplish with their degree. Selection is based on academic record, financial need, extracurricular activities, leadership skills, and participation in community activities. U.S. citizenship is required.

Financial data   A stipend is awarded (amount not specified).

Duration   1 year; may be renewed.

Number awarded   1 or more each year.

Deadline   April of each year.

[40]
FRA SCHOLARSHIPS

Fleet Reserve Association
Attn: FRA Education Foundation
125 North West Street
Alexandria, VA 22314-2754
(703) 683-1400   Toll Free: (800) FRA-1924
Fax: (703) 549-6610   E-mail: scholars@fra.org
Web: www.fra.org

Summary   To provide financial assistance for college or graduate school to members of the Fleet Reserve Association (FRA) and their families.

Eligibility   This program is open to members of the FRA and the dependent children, grandchildren, and spouses of living or deceased members. Applicants must be enrolled as full-time undergraduate or graduate students. Along with their application, they must submit an essay on why they want to go to college and what they intend to accomplish with their degree. Selection is based on academic record, financial need, extracurricular activities, leadership skills, and participation in community activities. U.S. citizenship is required.

Financial data   The stipend is $5,000 per year.

Duration   1 year; may be renewed.

Additional information   Membership in the FRA is restricted to active-duty, retired, and reserve members of the Navy, Marines, and Coast Guard.

Number awarded   6 each year.

Deadline   April of each year.

[41]
GENERAL EMMETT PAIGE SCHOLARSHIPS

Armed Forces Communications and Electronics
Association
Attn: AFCEA Educational Foundation
4400 Fair Lakes Court
Fairfax, VA 22033-3899
(703) 631-6138   Toll Free: (800) 336-4583, ext. 6138
Fax: (703) 631-4693 E-mail: scholarshipsinfo@afcea.org
Web: www.afcea.org/education/scholarships/military

Summary To provide financial assistance to veterans, military personnel, and their family members who are majoring in specified scientific fields in college.

Eligibility This program is open to veterans, persons on active duty in the uniformed military services, and their spouses or dependents who are currently enrolled full time in an accredited 4-year college or university in the United States. Graduating high school seniors are not eligible, but veterans entering college as freshmen may apply. Spouses or dependents must be sophomores or juniors. Applicants must be U.S. citizens, be of good moral character, have demonstrated academic excellence, be motivated to complete a college education, and be working toward a degree in engineering (aerospace, computer, electrical, or systems), computer engineering technology, electronics engineering technology, computer network systems, mathematics, physics, information systems security, information systems management, technology management, computer science, or other field directly related to the support of U.S. intelligence enterprises or national security. They must have a GPA of 3.0 or higher. Along with their application, they must provide a copy of Discharge Form DD214, Certificate of Service, or facsimile of their current Department of Defense or Coast Guard Identification Card. Financial need is not considered.

Financial data The stipend is $2,500 per year.

Duration 1 year; may be renewed.

Number awarded Varies each year; recently, 5 of these scholarships were awarded.

Deadline April of each year.

[42]
GEORGE L. PATT SCHOLARSHIP

Illinois Association of Realtors
Attn: Illinois Real Estate Educational Foundation
522 South Fifth Street
P.O. Box 2607
Springfield, IL 62708
Toll Free: (866) 854-REEF   Fax: (217) 241-9935
E-mail: lclayton@iar.org
Web: www.ilreef.org/Scholarships.htm

Summary To provide financial assistance to veterans in Illinois who are preparing for a career in real estate at a college or university in the state.

Eligibility This program is open to U.S. veterans in Illinois who are either 1) working on an undergraduate college or university degree in the field of real estate; or 2) studying real estate administration to establish themselves as an association executive in a realtor organization. Applicants must be Illinois residents studying at a school in the state. Along with their application, they must submit a 1,000-word statement of their general activities and intellectual interests, employment (if any), contemplated line of study, and career they expect to

follow. Selection is based on the applicant's record of military service, record of academic achievement, course of study and career goals, references and recommendations, and financial need. Finalists are interviewed.

Financial data The stipend is $1,000.

Duration 1 year.

Number awarded 1 each year.

Deadline March of each year.

[43]
GOOGLE-SVA SCHOLARSHIP

Student Veterans of America
P.O. Box 77673
Washington, DC 20013
E-mail: SVA@studentveterans.org
Web: www.studentveterans.org/?page=Programs

Summary To provide funding to veterans working on a bachelor's or graduate degree in a computer-related field.

Eligibility This program is open to sophomores, juniors, seniors, and graduate students at U.S. colleges and universities who are veterans (must possess a DD-214) and were honorably discharged or are still in good standing with their branch of service. Applicants must be working full time on a degree in computer science, computer engineering, or a closely-related technical field (e.g., software engineering, electrical engineering (with a heavy computer science course load), information systems, information technology, applied networking, system administration). Along with their application, they must submit a 1,000-word personal statement that covers their reasons for applying for this scholarship, their reasons for choosing their major, their professional objectives as they relate to their degree, their role as a leader in their community and/or chapter, and any additional community service initiatives in which they have been involved. Financial need is not considered in the selection process.

Financial data The stipend is $10,000.

Duration 1 year.

Additional information This program is sponsored by Google.

Number awarded 8 each year.

Deadline March of each year.

[44]
GROGAN MEMORIAL SCHOLARSHIP

American Academy of Physician Assistants-Veterans
Caucus
Attn: Veterans Caucus
P.O. Box 362
Danville, PA 17821-0362
(570) 271-0292   Fax: (570) 271-5850
E-mail: admin@veteranscaucus.org
Web: www.veteranscaucus.org

Summary To provide funding to veterans and their dependents studying to become physician assistants.

Eligibility This program is open to U.S. citizens who are currently enrolled in a physician assistant program. The program must be approved by the Commission on Accreditation of Allied Health Education. Applicants must be honorably discharged members of any branch of the military or the dependents of those members. Selection is based on military honors and awards received, civic and college honors and awards received, professional memberships and activities, and GPA. An electronic copy of the applicant's DD Form 214 must accompany the application.

Financial data The stipend is $2,000.

Duration 1 year.

Number awarded 1 each year.

Deadline February of each year.

[45]
HENRY J. REILLY MEMORIAL SCHOLARSHIP FOR COLLEGE SOPHOMORES AND JUNIORS

Reserve Officers Association of the United States
Attn: Scholarship Program
One Constitution Avenue, N.E.
Washington, DC 20002-5618
(202) 646-7719   Toll Free: (800) 809-9448, ext. 719
Fax: (202) 547-1641   E-mail: scholarship@roa.org
Web: www.roa.org

Summary To provide financial assistance to members of the Reserve Officers Association (ROA) and their children or grandchildren who are completing the sophomore or junior year of college.

Eligibility Applicants for this scholarship must be active or associate members of the association or their children or grandchildren (under the age of 26). Children, age 21 or under, of deceased members who were active and paid up at the time of their death are also eligible. Spouses are not eligible, unless they are members of the association. ROTC members do not qualify as sponsors. Applicants must provide evidence of full-time enrollment at a regionally-accredited 4-year college or university, demonstrate leadership qualities, have earned a GPA of 3.3 or higher in high school and 3.0 or higher in college, have scored at least 1875 on the SAT or 55 on the English/math ACT, and (if appropriate) have registered for the draft. Community college students who are transferring to a 4-year college and university are also eligible. They must submit an application and a 500-word essay on career goals.

Financial data The stipend is $1,000 per year.

Duration 1 year; may be renewed.

Number awarded The sponsor awards a total of 30 scholarships each year.

Deadline May of each year.

[46]
HOWARD R. HARPER SCHOLARSHIPS

Enlisted Association of the National Guard of Iowa
c/o Jerald D. Hansen, Secretary
1409 East Coolbaugh Street
Red Oak, IA 51566
(712) 623-2804
Web: www.eangi.users01.com/index-4.html

Summary To provide funding to members of the Enlisted Association of the National Guard of Iowa (EANGI) and their dependents who are interested in attending college.

Eligibility This program is open to EANGI members and their spouses and children. Applicants must be attending or accepted at a VA-approved college or vocational/technical school (which may be in any state). Along with their application, they must submit a copy of their transcript, a letter with specific facts as to their desire to continue their education and why financial assistance is required, 3 letters of recommendation, and 1 academic reference.

Financial data The stipend is $1,500.

Duration 1 year.

Additional information Membership in EANGI is open to enlisted members of the Iowa Army or Air National Guard, active component members assigned to the Iowa Army or Air National Guard, and retired or honorably-discharged Iowa Army or Air National Guard enlisted personnel.

Number awarded 5 each year.

Deadline January of each year.

[47]
IDAHO LEGION AUXILIARY NURSES SCHOLARSHIP

American Legion Auxiliary
Department of Idaho
905 Warren Street
Boise, ID 83706-3825
(208) 342-7066   E-mail: idalegionaux@msn.com
Web: idahoala.org/scholarships.aspx

Summary To provide financial assistance to Idaho veterans and their descendants who are interested in studying nursing at a school in any state.

Eligibility This program is open to student nurses who are veterans or the children or grandchildren of veterans and are residents of Idaho. Applicants must be attending or planning to attend a school of nursing in any state. They may be traditional or nontraditional students between 17 and 35 years of age. Selection is based on need, academics, and deportment.

Financial data The stipend is $1,000.

Duration 1 year.

Number awarded 1 each year.

Deadline May of each year.

[48]
ILLINOIS AMERICAN LEGION AUXILIARY PAST PRESIDENTS PARLEY NURSES SCHOLARSHIP

American Legion Auxiliary
Department of Illinois
2720 East Lincoln Street
P.O. Box 1426
Bloomington, IL 61702-1426
(309) 663-9366   Fax: (309) 663-5827
E-mail: karen.boughan@ilala.org
Web: www.ilala.org/scholar.html

Summary To provide financial assistance to Illinois veterans and their descendants who are attending college in any state to prepare for a career as a nurse.

Eligibility This program is open to veterans who served during designated periods of wartime and their children, grandchildren, and great-grandchildren. Applicants must be currently enrolled at a college or university in any state and studying nursing. They must be residents of Illinois or members of the American Legion Family, Department of Illinois. Selection is based on commitment (25%), character (25%), academic rating (20%), and need (30%).

Financial data The stipend is $1,000.

Duration 1 year.

Additional information Applications may be obtained only from a local unit of the American Legion Auxiliary.

Number awarded 1 or more each year.

Deadline April of each year.

[49]
ILLINOIS NATIONAL GUARD GRANT PROGRAM

Illinois Student Assistance Commission
Attn: Scholarship and Grant Services
1755 Lake Cook Road
Deerfield, IL 60015-5209
(847) 948-8550   Toll Free: (800) 899-ISAC
Fax: (847) 831-8549   TDD: (800) 526-0844
E-mail: isac.studentservices@isac.illinois.gov
Web: www.collegeillinois.org

Summary To provide financial assistance to current or former members of the Illinois National Guard who are interested in attending college or graduate school in the state.

Eligibility This program is open to members of the Illinois National Guard who are 1) currently active or 2) have been active for at least 5 consecutive years, have been called to federal active duty for at least 6 months, and are within 12 months after their discharge date. Applicants must also be enrolled at an Illinois public 2- or 4-year college or university and have served at least 1 full year in the Guard.

Financial data Recipients are eligible for payment of tuition and some fees for either undergraduate or graduate study at an Illinois state-supported college or university.

Duration This assistance extends for 8 semesters or 12 quarters (or the equivalent in part-time study).

Number awarded Varies each year.

Deadline September of each year for the academic year; February of each year for spring semester, winter quarter, or spring quarter; June of each year for summer term.

[50]
ILLINOIS VETERAN GRANT PROGRAM

Illinois Student Assistance Commission
Attn: Scholarship and Grant Services
1755 Lake Cook Road
Deerfield, IL 60015-5209
(847) 948-8550   Toll Free: (800) 899-ISAC
Fax: (847) 831-8549   TDD: (800) 526-0844
E-mail: isac.studentservices@isac.illinois.gov
Web: www.collegeillinois.org

Summary To provide financial assistance to Illinois veterans who are interested in attending college or graduate school in the state.

Eligibility This program is open to Illinois residents who served in the U.S. armed forces (including members of the Reserves and the Illinois National Guard) for at least 1 year on active duty and have been honorably discharged. The 1-year service requirement does not apply to veterans who 1) served in a foreign country in a time of hostilities in that country, 2) were medically discharged for service-related reasons, or 3) were discharged prior to August 11, 1967. Applicants must have been Illinois residents for at least 6 months before entering service and they must have returned to Illinois within 6 months after separation from service. Current members of the Reserve Officer Training Corps are not eligible.

Financial data This program pays tuition and certain fees at Illinois public colleges, universities, and community colleges.

Duration This scholarship may be used for the equivalent of up to 4 years of full-time enrollment, provided the recipient maintains the minimum GPA required by their school.

Additional information This is an entitlement program; once eligibility has been established, no further applications are necessary.

Number awarded Varies each year.

Deadline Applications may be submitted at any time.

[51]
IVY DIVISION ASSOCIATION ANNUAL SCHOLARSHIP

National 4th Infantry (IVY) Division Association
c/o Don Kelby, Executive Director
P.O. Box 1914
St. Peters, MO 63376-0035
(314) 606-1969   E-mail: 4thidaed@swbell.net
Web: www.4thinfantry.org/content/scholarships-donations

Summary To provide money for college to members of the National 4th Infantry (IVY) Division Association and their families.

Eligibility This program is open to association members in good standing and all blood relatives of active association members in good standing. Recipients are chosen by lottery.

Financial data The stipend is $1,000.

Duration 1 year; may be renewed.

Additional information The trust fund from which these scholarships are awarded was created by the officers and enlisted men of the 4th Infantry Division as a living memorial to the men of the division who died in Vietnam. Originally, it was only open to children of members of the division who died in the line of duty in Vietnam between August 1, 1966 and December 31, 1977. When all those eligible had completed college, it adopted its current requirements.

Number awarded 1 or more each year.

Deadline June of each year.

[52]
JACK E. BARGER, SR. MEMORIAL NURSING SCHOLARSHIPS

Pennsylvania State Nurses Association
Attn: Nursing Foundation of Pennsylvania
2578 Interstate Drive, Suite 101
Harrisburg, PA 17110
(717) 692-0542   Toll Free: (888) 707-PSNA
Fax: (717) 692-4540   E-mail: nfp@panurses.org
Web: www.panurses.org/2008/section.cfm?SID=21&ID=4

Summary To provide financial assistance to veterans, military personnel, and their dependents who are studying nursing in Pennsylvania.

Eligibility This program is open to veterans, active-duty military personnel, and the children and spouses of veterans and active-duty military personnel. Applicants must be residents of Pennsylvania and currently enrolled in an undergraduate professional school of nursing in the state. Recipients are selected by lottery from among the qualified applicants.

Financial data The stipend is $1,000.

Duration 1 year.

Additional information This program is sponsored by the Department of Pennsylvania Veterans of Foreign Wars (VFW). Recipients must attend the VFW Convention to accept the scholarship; travel, meals, and overnight expenses are paid by the VFW.

Number awarded 6 each year.

Deadline   April of each year.

[53]
JEREMIAH TENHET US ARMY MILITARY INTELLIGENCE SCHOLARSHIP

American Academy of Physician Assistants-Veterans
  Caucus
Attn: Veterans Caucus
P.O. Box 362
Danville, PA 17821-0362
(570) 271-0292   Fax: (570) 271-5850
E-mail: admin@veteranscaucus.org
Web: www.veteranscaucus.org

Summary   To provide financial assistance to Army veterans who served in Afghanistan and their dependents who are studying to become physician assistants.

Eligibility   This program is open to U.S. citizens who are currently enrolled in a physician assistant program. The program must be approved by the Commission on Accreditation of Allied Health Education. Applicants must be honorably discharged members of the United States Army who served in Afghanistan or the dependents of those members. Selection is based on military honors and awards received, civic and college honors and awards received, professional memberships and activities, and GPA. An electronic copy of the applicant's DD Form 214 must accompany the application.

Financial data   The stipend is $2,000.

Duration   1 year.

Number awarded   1 each year.

Deadline   February of each year.

[54]
JOHN KEYS KENTUCKY SONS OF THE AMERICAN LEGION SCHOLARSHIP

Sons of the American Legion
Detachment of Kentucky
Independence Squadron 275
P.O. Box 18791
Erlanger, KY 41018-0791
E-mail: SAL275@fuse.net
Web: moonbrothers275.org/indexSALhtml

Summary   To provide money for college to members of Kentucky squadrons of the Sons of the American Legion and to veterans who are residents of Kentucky.

Eligibility   This program is open to 1) members of the Sons of the American Legion who belong to a squadron in Kentucky, and 2) honorably-discharged veterans of the U.S. armed forces who are residents of Kentucky (regardless of length or period of service). Applicants must be enrolled (and have completed some course work) at a postsecondary institution in any state. Along with their application, they must submit a letter explaining their background, career objectives, current educational program, and financial need.

Financial data   The stipend varies, depending on the availability of funds; recently, they averaged $1,000. Awards are made directly to the recipient's institution.

Duration   1 year.

Additional information   This program began in 1988.

Number awarded   1 or 2 each year; since the program began, it has awarded more than 60 scholarships.

Deadline   March of each year.

[55]
JOSEPH A. MCALINDEN DIVERS' SCHOLARSHIP

Navy-Marine Corps Relief Society
Attn: Education Division
875 North Randolph Street, Suite 225
Arlington, VA 22203-1757
(703) 696-4960   Fax: (703) 696-0144
E-mail: education@nmcrs.org
Web: www.nmcrs.org/education.html

Summary   To provide financial assistance to current and former Navy and Marine Corps divers and their families who are interested in working on an undergraduate degree in a field related to ocean agriculture.

Eligibility   This program is open to Navy and Marine Corps active-duty and retired divers (includes Reservists serving on active duty for more than 90 days), their children under 23 years of age, and their spouses. Applicants must be working full time on their first undergraduate degree in oceanography, ocean agriculture, aquaculture, or a related field; they may also be engaged in advanced diver training, certification, or recertification. Financial need is considered.

Financial data   The stipend ranges from $500 to $3,000, depending on the need of the recipient.

Duration   1 year.

Number awarded   1 or more each year.

Deadline   Applications may be submitted at any time.

[56]
KAISER PERMANENTE COLORADO DIVERSITY SCHOLARSHIP PROGRAM

Kaiser Permanente
Attn: Physician Recruitment Services
10350 East Dakota Avenue
Denver, CO 80231-1314
(303) 344-7299   Toll Free: (866) 239-1677
Fax: (303) 344-7818
E-mail: co-diversitydevelopment@kp.org
Web: scholarselect.com

Summary   To provide funding to veterans and other Colorado residents who come from diverse backgrounds and are interested in working on an undergraduate or graduate degree in a health care field at a public college in the state.

Eligibility   This program is open to all residents of Colorado, including those who identify as 1 or more of the following: African American, Asian Pacific, Latino, lesbian, gay, bisexual, transgender, intersex, Native American, U.S. veteran, and/or a person with a disability. Applicants must be enrolled or planning to enroll full time at a publicly-funded college, university, or technical school in Colorado as 1) a graduating high school senior with a GPA of 2.7 or higher; 2) a GED recipient with a GED score of 520 or higher; 3) an undergraduate student; or 4) a graduate or doctoral student. They must be preparing for a career in health care (e.g., athletic training, audiology, cardiovascular perfusion technology, clinical medical assisting, cytotechnology, dental assisting, dental hygiene, diagnostic medicine, dietetics, emergency medical technology, medicine, nursing, occupational therapy, pharmacy, phlebotomy, physical therapy, physician assistant, radiology, respiratory therapy, social work, sports medicine, surgical technology). Along with their application, they must submit 300-word essays on 1) a brief story from their childhood and the aspects of their experience that will contribute to their become a good health care provided; 2) what giving back to the community means to them and their experiences in community involvement that demonstrate their commitment to health care; and 3) what they consider the most pressing issue in health care today. Selection is based on academic achievement, character qualities, community outreach and volunteering, and financial need. U.S. citizenship is required.

Financial data Stipends range from $1,400 to $2,600.

Duration 1 year.

Number awarded Varies each year; recently, 17 of these scholarships were awarded.

Deadline February of each year.

[57]
KANSAS MILITARY SERVICE SCHOLARSHIPS

Kansas Board of Regents
Attn: Student Financial Assistance
1000 S.W. Jackson Street, Suite 520
Topeka, KS 66612-1368
(785) 296-3518   Fax: (785) 296-0983
E-mail: dlindeman@ksbor.org
Web: www.kansasregents.org/scholarships_and_grants

Summary To provide money for college to residents of Kansas who have served or are still serving in the military.

Eligibility This program is open to students who graduated from high school in Kansas or received a GED credential and have been a resident of the state for at least 2 years. Applicants must have served in the U.S. armed forces in Iraq or Afghanistan, or in international waters or on foreign soil in support of military operations in Iraq or Afghanistan, for at least 90 days after September 11, 2001 or for less than 90 days because of injuries received during such service. They must still be in military service or have received an honorable discharge with orders that indicate they served after September 11, 2001 in Operations Enduring Freedom, Nobel Eagle, and/or Iraqi Freedom. Qualified veterans and military personnel may enroll at a public postsecondary institution in Kansas, including area vocational schools, area vocational/technical schools, community colleges, the municipal university, state educational institutions, or technical colleges. Priority is given to applicants who can demonstrate financial need.

Financial data Qualifying students are permitted to enroll at an approved Kansas institution without payment of tuition or fees. If they receive any federal military tuition assistance, that money must be applied first, and they are eligible only for the remaining balance in scholarship assistance.

Duration 1 year; renewable for up to 10 semesters, as long as the recipient remains in good academic standing.

Additional information This program began in 2007.

Number awarded Varies each year.

Deadline April of each year.

[58]
KANSAS TUITION WAIVER FOR PRISONERS OF WAR

Kansas Board of Regents
Attn: Student Financial Assistance
1000 S.W. Jackson Street, Suite 520
Topeka, KS 66612-1368
(785) 296-3518   Fax: (785) 296-0983
E-mail: dlindeman@ksbor.org
Web: www.kansasregents.org/scholarships_and_grants

Summary To provide financial assistance for college to residents of Kansas who have been a prisoner of war.

Eligibility This program is open to current residents of Kansas who entered active service in the U.S. armed forces as a resident of the state. Applicants must have been declared a prisoner of war after January 1, 1960 while serving in the armed forces. They must be enrolled or planning to enroll at a public educational institution in Kansas, including area vocational/technical schools and colleges, community colleges, the state universities, and Washburn University.

Financial data Qualifying students are permitted to enroll at an approved Kansas institution without payment of tuition or fees. They are responsible for other costs, such as books, room, and board.

Duration 1 year; may be renewed for a total of 10 semesters of undergraduate study.

Additional information This program began in 2005.

Number awarded Varies each year.

Deadline Deadline not specified.

[59]
LANCASTER SCHOLARSHIP

Susquehanna Foundation for the Blind
244 North Queen Street
Lancaster, PA 17603
(717) 291-5951
Web: www.sabvi.org/Grants%20and%20Scholarships

Summary To provide funding to Pennsylvania residents who are legally blind veterans and interested in working on a undergraduate or graduate degree at a college in any state.

Eligibility This program is open to veterans who are residents of Pennsylvania and legally blind. Applicants must be attending or planning to attend an institution of higher education at any level in any state. Along with their application, they must submit a brief description of their career goal. Financial need is considered in the selection process.

Financial data The stipend is $1,000 per year.

Duration 1 year; may be renewed up to 3 additional years.

Number awarded 1 or more each year.

Deadline January of each year.

[60]
LANGEA TONY LOPEZ SCHOLARSHIP

Louisiana National Guard Enlisted Association
c/o MSG Chad J. Anderson
Gillis Long Center
5445 Point Clair Road
Carville, LA 70721
(225) 319-4846   Fax: (225) 319-4880
E-mail: chad.j.anderson1@us.army.mil
Web: langea.org/templates/benefits/scholarship

Summary To provide funding to members of the Louisiana National Guard Enlisted Association (LANGEA) and their dependents who plan to attend college in any state.

Eligibility This program is open to members of the association, their spouses and unmarried dependent children, and the unremarried spouses and unmarried dependent children of deceased members who were in good standing at the time of their death. The qualifying LANGEA members must have at least 1 year remaining on their enlistment following completion of the school year for which the application is submitted or have served 20 years of more in the Louisiana National Guard. Applicants must be enrolled or planning to enroll full time at an accredited college, university, trade school, or business school in any state. Graduate students are not eligible. Selection is based on academic achievement, character, leadership, and financial need.

Financial data The stipend is $2,000.

Duration 1 year; nonrenewable.

Number awarded 3 each year.

Deadline February of each year.

[61]
LDRSHIP AWARDS

Career College Association
Attn: Imagine America Foundation
1101 Connecticut Avenue, N.W., Suite 901
Washington, DC 20036
(202) 336-6743   Fax: (202) 408-8102
E-mail: ldrship@career.org
Web: www.imagine-america.org/ldrship

Summary To provide financial assistance to veterans and military personnel who are attending a career college that is a member of the Career College Association.

Eligibility This program is open to active-duty, reservist, honorably-discharged, and retired veterans of a U.S. military service branch. Applicants must have completed at least 1 term at 1 of the 300 participating career colleges. They must have maintained a GPA of 3.5 or higher and an attendance record of at least 95%. They must submit an application, a recommendation from a faculty member or administrator at their college, and their current college transcript.

Financial data The stipend is $2,500. Funds must be used for payment of tuition at a participating career college.

Duration 1 year.

Additional information The Imagine America Foundation (previously the Career College Foundation) began this program in 2004. It stands for Loyalty, Duty, Respect, Selfless Service, Honor, Integrity and Personal Courage.

Number awarded Varies each year; recently, 10 of these scholarships were granted.

Deadline April of each year.

[62]
LILLIAN CAMPBELL MEDICAL SCHOLARSHIP

Wisconsin Veterans of Foreign Wars
P.O. Box 6128
Monona, WI 53716-0128
(608) 221-5276   Fax: (608) 221-5277
E-mail: wivfw@att.net
Web: vfwofwi.com/?w=wisconsin

Summary To provide financial assistance to students working on a degree in a medical field in Wisconsin who served in the military or are related to a person who did.

Eligibility This program is open to students who have completed at least 1 year of study in Wisconsin in a program in nursing, pharmacy, physician assistant, medical or surgical technology, physical or occupational therapy, dental assisting, radiology, or other related medical profession. Applicants or a member of their immediate family (parent, sibling, child, spouse, or grandparent) must have served in the military. They must have a high school diploma or GED but may be of any age. Along with their application, they must submit a 200-word essay on why they are studying this medical profession. Financial need is considered in the selection process.

Financial data The stipend is $1,000.

Duration 1 year.

Number awarded 1 or more each year.

Deadline April of each year.

[63]
LT. COL. DAVID H. GWINN SCHOLARSHIP

American Academy of Physician Assistants-Veterans Caucus
Attn: Veterans Caucus
P.O. Box 362
Danville, PA 17821-0362
(570) 271-0292   Fax: (570) 271-5850
E-mail: admin@veteranscaucus.org
Web: www.veteranscaucus.org

Summary To provide financial assistance to Air Force veterans who are studying to become physician assistants.

Eligibility This program is open to U.S. citizens who are currently enrolled in a physician assistant program. The program must be approved by the Commission on Accreditation of Allied Health Education. Applicants must be honorably discharged members of the United States Air Force. Selection is based on military honors and awards received, civic and college honors and awards received, professional memberships and activities, and GPA. An electronic copy of the applicant's DD Form 214 must accompany the application.

Financial data The stipend is $2,000.

Duration 1 year.

Number awarded 1 each year.

Deadline February of each year.

[64]
LUCILLE PARRISH WARD VETERAN'S AWARD

National Federation of Music Clubs
1646 Smith Valley Road
Greenwood, IN 46142
(317) 882-4003   Fax: (317) 882-4019
E-mail: info@nfmc-music.org
Web: nfmc-music.org

Summary To provide financial assistance to undergraduate student members of the National Federation of Music Clubs (NFMC) whose careers have been delayed or interrupted as a result of their service in the U.S. armed forces.

Eligibility This program is open to undergraduate students who are majoring in music and whose musical careers were interrupted by service in the armed forces. Veterans who served overseas receive preference. Student membership in the federation and U.S. citizenship are required. Applicants must submit a 30-minute performance/audition CD. Selection is based on worthiness, character, background, musical talent, potential ability, and financial need.

Financial data The stipend is $2,250.

Duration 1 year; may be renewed if the recipient maintains a GPA of 3.0 or higher.

Additional information The entry fee is $20.

Number awarded 1 each year.

Deadline May of each year.

[65]
MAINE VIETNAM VETERANS SCHOLARSHIP FUND

Maine Community Foundation
Attn: Program Director
245 Main Street
Ellsworth, ME 04605
(207) 667-9735   Toll Free: (877) 700-6800
Fax: (207) 667-0447   E-mail: info@mainecf.org
Web: www.mainecf.org/statewidescholars.aspx

Summary To provide financial assistance for college or graduate school to Vietnam veterans or the dependents of Vietnam or other veterans in Maine.

Eligibility This program is open to residents of Maine who are Vietnam veterans or the descendants of veterans who served in the Vietnam Theater. As a second priority, children of veterans from other time periods are also considered. Graduating high school seniors, nontraditional students, undergraduates, and graduate students are eligible to apply. Selection is based on financial need, extracurricular activities, work experience, academic achievement, and a personal statement of career goals and how the applicant's educational plans relate to them.

Financial data The stipend is $1,000 per year.

Duration 1 year.

Additional information This program began in 1985. There is a $3 processing fee.

Number awarded 3 to 6 each year.

Deadline April of each year.

[66]
MAJOR GENERAL DUANE L. "DUKE" CORNING MEMORIAL SCHOLARSHIP

South Dakota National Guard Enlisted Association
c/o Jody Smith
2823 West Main Street
Rapid City, SD 57702-8170
(605) 737-6224   E-mail: jody.smith2@us.army.mil
Web: www.sdngea.com/scholarship.html

Summary To provide financial assistance to current and retired members of the South Dakota National Guard Enlisted Association (SDNGEA), the National Guard Association of South Dakota (NGASD), and their dependents who are interested in attending college in any state.

Eligibility This program is open to current and retired members of the SDNGEA and the NGASD and the dependents of current and retired members of those associations. Applicants must be graduating high school seniors or full-time undergraduate students at a college or university in any state. They must submit a 300-page autobiography that includes their experiences to date and their hopes and plans for the future. Selection is based on the essay; awards, honors, and offices in high school, college, or trade school; GPA and ACT/SAT scores; letters of recommendation; and extracurricular and community activities and honors.

Financial data The stipend is $1,000.

Duration 1 year; nonrenewable.

Number awarded 1 each year.

Deadline March of each year.

[67]
MARIA C. JACKSON/GENERAL GEORGE A. WHITE SCHOLARSHIP

Oregon Student Access Commission
Attn: Grants and Scholarships Division
1500 Valley River Drive, Suite 100
Eugene, OR 97401-2146
(541) 687-7395   Toll Free: (800) 452-8807, ext. 7395
Fax: (541) 687-7414   TDD: (800) 735-2900
E-mail: awardinfo@osac.state.or.us
Web: www.oregonstudentaid.gov/scholarships.aspx

Summary To provide financial assistance to veterans and children of veterans and military personnel in Oregon who are interested in attending college or graduate school in the state.

Eligibility This program is open to residents of Oregon who served, or whose parents are serving or have served, in the U.S. armed forces. Applicants or their parents must have resided in Oregon at the time of enlistment. They must be enrolled or planning to enroll at a college or graduate school in the state. College and university undergraduates must have a GPA of 3.75 or higher, but there is no minimum GPA requirement for graduate students or those attending a technical school. Selection is based on academics and need.

Financial data Stipends for scholarships offered by the Oregon Student Access Commission (OSAC) range from $200 to $10,000 but recently averaged $2,300.

Number awarded Varies each year.

Deadline February of each year.

[68]
MARINE CORPS LEAGUE SCHOLARSHIPS

Marine Corps League
Attn: National Executive Director
P.O. Box 3070
Merrifield, VA 22116-3070
(703) 207-9588   Toll Free: (800) MCL-1775
Fax: (703) 207-0047   E-mail: mcl@mcleague.org
Web: www.mcleague.org

Summary To provide college aid to students whose parents served in the Marines and to members of the Marine Corps League or Marine Corps League Auxiliary.

Eligibility This program is open to 1) children of Marines who lost their lives in the line of duty; 2) spouses, children, grandchildren, great-grandchildren, and stepchildren of active Marine Corps League and/or Auxiliary members; and 3) members of the Marine Corps League and/or Marine Corps League Auxiliary who are honorably discharged and in need of rehabilitation training not provided by government programs. Applicants must be seeking further education and training as a full-time student and be recommended by the commandant of an active chartered detachment of the Marine Corps League or the president of an active chartered unit of the Auxiliary. Financial need is not considered.

Financial data A stipend is awarded (amount not specified). Funds are paid directly to the recipient.

Duration 1 year; may be renewed up to 3 additional years (all renewals must complete an application and attach a transcript from the college or university).

Number awarded Varies, depending upon the amount of funds available each year.

Deadline June of each year.

[69]
MARINES' MEMORIAL ASSOCIATION SCHOLARSHIP FUND

Marines' Memorial Association
c/o Marines Memorial Club and Hotel
609 Sutter Street
San Francisco, CA 94102
(415) 673-6672   Fax: (415) 441-3649
E-mail: member@marineclub.com
Web: www.marineclub.com/membership/scholarship.php

Summary To provide money for college to members of the Marines' Memorial Association and their descendants.

Eligibility This program is open to active members of the association and their children and grandchildren. Applicants must be enrolled or planning to enroll in an undergraduate degree program at a college or university. Selection is based on academic merit, activities, and financial need.

Financial data Stipends are $5,000 or $2,500.

Duration 1 year.

Additional information Membership in the association is open to veterans of the Marines, Army, Navy, Air Force, or Coast Guard and to personnel currently serving in a branch of the armed forces. This program includes a number of named scholarships, including the Colonel Jack Barnes Scholarship, the Colonel Richard Hallock Scholarship, the Sergeants Henry and Jeanne Rose Scholarship, and the Evelyn Bukovac Hamilton Health Care Scholarship.

Number awarded 10 at $5,000 and 12 at $2,500.

Deadline April of each year.

[70]
MARYLAND SCHOLARSHIPS FOR VETERANS OF THE AFGHANISTAN AND IRAQ CONFLICTS

Maryland Higher Education Commission
Attn: Office of Student Financial Assistance
6 North Liberty Street, Ground Suite
Baltimore, MD 21201
(410) 767-3300   Toll Free: (800) 974-0203
Fax: (410) 332-0250   TDD: (800) 735-2258
E-mail: osfamail@mhec.state.md.us
Web: www.mhec.state.md.us/financialAid/descriptions.asp

Summary To provide financial assistance for college to residents of Maryland who have served in the armed forces in Afghanistan or Iraq and their children and spouses.

Eligibility This program is open to Maryland residents who are 1) a veteran who served at least 60 days in Afghanistan on or after October 24, 2001 or in Iraq on or after March 19, 2003; 2) an active-duty member of the armed forces who served at least 60 days in Afghanistan or Iraq on or after those dates; 3) a member of a Reserve component of the armed forces or the Maryland National Guard who was activated as a result of the Afghanistan or Iraq conflicts and served at least 60 days; and 4) the children and spouses of such veterans, active-duty armed forces personnel, or members of Reserve forces or Maryland National Guard. Applicants must be enrolled or accepted for enrollment in a regular undergraduate program at an eligible Maryland institution. In the selection process, veterans are given priority over dependent children and spouses.

Financial data The stipend is equal to 50% of the annual tuition, mandatory fees, and room and board of a resident undergraduate at a 4-year public institution within the University System of Maryland, currently capped at $9,430 per year. The total amount of all state awards may not exceed the cost of attendance as determined by the school's financial aid office or $19,000, whichever is less.

Duration 1 year; may be renewed for an additional 4 years of full-time study or 7 years of part-time study, provided the recipient remains enrolled in an eligible program with a GPA of 2.5 or higher.

Additional information This program is scheduled to expire in 2016.

Number awarded Varies each year.

Deadline February of each year.

[71]
MASSACHUSETTS VETERANS TUITION WAIVER PROGRAM

Massachusetts Office of Student Financial Assistance
454 Broadway, Suite 200
Revere, MA 02151
(617) 391-6070   Fax: (617) 727-0667
E-mail: osfa@osfa.mass.edu
Web: www.osfa.mass.edu

Summary To provide financial assistance for college to Massachusetts residents who are veterans.

Eligibility Applicants for these scholarships must have been permanent legal residents of Massachusetts for at least 1 year and veterans who served actively during the Spanish-American War, World War I, World War II, Korea, Vietnam, the Lebanese peace keeping force, the Grenada rescue mission, the Panamanian intervention force, the Persian Gulf, or Operation Restore Hope in Somalia. They may not be in default on any federal student loan.

Financial data Eligible veterans are exempt from any tuition payments for an undergraduate degree or certificate program at public colleges or universities in Massachusetts.

Duration Up to 4 academic years (130 semester hours).

Additional information Recipients may enroll either part or full time in a Massachusetts publicly-supported institution.

Number awarded Varies each year.

Deadline Deadline not specified.

[72]
MCIA/JOHN J. GUENTHER MERIT SCHOLARSHIP

Marine Corps Intelligence Association, Inc.
Attn: Marine Corps Intelligence Educational Foundation
P.O. Box 1028
Quantico, VA 22134-1028
E-mail: scholarship@mcia-inc.org
Web: www.mcia-inc.org/7.html

Summary To provide financial assistance for college to members of the Marine Corps Intelligence Association (MCIA) and their dependent children.

Eligibility This program is open to current MCIA members, their dependent children, and their survivors. Applicants must be attending or planning to attend an accredited 4-year college or university as a full-time student. They must submit a 300-word essay on a risk that has led to a significant change in their personal or intellectual life, the most challenging obstacles they have had to overcome and what they learned from the experience, and where they envision themselves in 10 years. Selection is based on the essay, academic achievement, extracurricular activities, and work experience. Financial need is not considered.

Financial data   The stipend is $2,000.

Duration   1 year.

Additional information   Membership in the MCIA is open to Marine Corps intelligence personnel, including active duty, Reserve, and retired.

Number awarded   At least 1 each year.

Deadline   July of each year.

[73]
MG EUGENE C. RENZI, USA (RET.)/MANTECH INTERNATIONAL CORPORATION TEACHER'S SCHOLARSHIP

Armed Forces Communications and Electronics
  Association
Attn: AFCEA Educational Foundation
4400 Fair Lakes Court
Fairfax, VA 22033-3899
(703) 631-6138   Toll Free: (800) 336-4583, ext. 6138
Fax: (703) 631-4693   E-mail: scholarshipsinfo@afcea.org
Web: www.afcea.org

Summary   To provide financial assistance to undergraduate and graduate students (especially veterans) who are preparing for a career as a teacher of science and mathematics.

Eligibility   This program is open to full-time sophomores, juniors, seniors, and graduate students at accredited colleges and universities in the United States. Applicants must be U.S. citizens preparing for a career as a teacher of science, mathematics, or information technology at a middle or secondary school. They must have a GPA of 3.0 or higher. In the selection process, first consideration is given to wounded or disabled veterans, then to honorably discharged veterans. Financial need is not considered.

Financial data   The stipend is $2,500.

Duration   1 year.

Additional information   This program was established in 2008 with support from ManTech International Corporation.

Number awarded   1 each year.

Deadline   March of each year.

[74]
MICA SCHOLARSHIPS

Military Intelligence Corps Association
Attn: Scholarship Committee
P.O. Box 13020
Fort Huachuca, AZ 85670-3020
(520) 227-3894   E-mail: execdir@micorps.org
Web: www.micastore.com/Scholarships.html

Summary   To provide financial assistance for college to members of the Military Intelligence Corps Association (MICA) and their immediate family.

Eligibility   This program is open to active-duty, Reserve, National Guard, and retired military intelligence soldiers who are MICA members and to their immediate family (spouses, children, or other relatives living with and supported by the MICA member). Applicants must be attending or accepted for attendance at an accredited college, university, vocational school, or technical institution. Along with their application, they must submit a 1-page essay on their reasons for applying for the scholarship, including their educational plans,

ambitions, goals, and personal attributes or experiences they feel will enable them to reach their goals. Financial need is not considered in the selection process.

Financial data   Stipend amounts vary depending on the availability of funds and the number of qualified applicants, but recently were $5,000. Funds are to be used for tuition, books, and classroom fees; support is not provided for housing, board, travel, or administrative purposes.

Duration   1 year; recipients may reapply.

Number awarded   Varies each year; recently, 4 of these scholarships were awarded.

Deadline   May of each year.

[75]
MIKE NASH MEMORIAL SCHOLARSHIP FUND

Vietnam Veterans of America
Attn: Mike Nash Scholarship Program
8719 Colesville Road, Suite 100
Silver Spring, MD 20910-3919
(301) 585-4000   Toll Free: (800) VVA-1316
Fax: (301) 585-0519   E-mail: finance@vva.org
Web: www.vva.org/scholarship.html

Summary   To provide financial assistance for college to members of Vietnam Veterans of America (VVA), their families, and the families of other Vietnam veterans.

Eligibility   This program is open to 1) members of VVA; 2) the spouses, children, stepchildren, and grandchildren of VVA members; and 3) the spouses, children, stepchildren, and grandchildren of MIA, KIA, or deceased Vietnam veterans. Applicants must be enrolled or planning to enroll at least half time at an accredited college, university, or technical institution. Along with their application, they must submit high school or college transcripts; SAT, ACT, or other recognized test scores; a statement of current educational goals and objectives; a 500-word essay on "What a Veteran Means to Me;" and documentation of financial need.

Financial data   The stipend is $1,500 per year.

Duration   1 year; renewable up to 3 additional years.

Additional information   This program began in 1991 and given its current name in 1997.

Number awarded   Varies each year; recently, 9 of these scholarships were awarded.

Deadline   May of each year.

[76]
MILDRED R. KNOLES SCHOLARSHIPS

American Legion Auxiliary
Department of Illinois
2720 East Lincoln Street
P.O. Box 1426
Bloomington, IL 61702-1426
(309) 663-9366   Fax: (309) 663-5827
E-mail: karen.boughan@ilala.org
Web: www.ilala.org/scholar.html

Summary   To provide funding to Illinois veterans and their descendants who are attending college in any state.

Eligibility   This program is open to veterans who served during designated periods of wartime and their children, grandchildren, and great-grandchildren. Applicants must be currently enrolled at a college or university in any state and studying any field except nursing. They must be residents of Illinois or members of the American Legion Family, Department of Illinois. Along with their application, they must submit a 1,000-word essay on "What My Education Will Do for Me." Selection is based on that essay (25%) character and leadership (25%), scholarship (25%), and financial need (25%).

Financial data The stipend is $1,000.

Duration 1 year.

Additional information Applications may be obtained only from a local unit of the American Legion Auxiliary.

Number awarded Varies each year.

Deadline March of each year.

[77]
MINNESOTA G.I. BILL PROGRAM

Minnesota Office of Higher Education
Attn: Manager of State Financial Aid Programs
1450 Energy Park Drive, Suite 350
St. Paul, MN 55108-5227
(651) 642-0567   Toll Free: (800) 657-3866
Fax: (651) 642-0675   TDD: (800) 627-3529
E-mail: Ginny.Dodds@state.mn.us
Web: www.ohe.state.mn.us/mPg.cfm?pageID=891

Summary To provide financial assistance for college or graduate school in the state to residents of Minnesota who served in the military after September 11, 2001 and the families of deceased or disabled military personnel.

Eligibility This program is open to residents of Minnesota enrolled at colleges and universities in the state as undergraduate or graduate students. Applicants must be 1) a veteran who is serving or has served honorably in a branch of the U.S. armed forces at any time on or after September 11, 2001; 2) a non-veteran who has served honorably for a total of 5 years or more cumulatively as a member of the Minnesota National Guard or other active or Reserve component of the U.S. armed forces, and any part of that service occurred on or after September 11, 2001; or 3) a surviving child or spouse of a person who has served in the military at any time on or after September 11, 2001 and who has died or has a total and permanent disability as a result of that military service. Financial need is considered in the selection process.

Financial data The stipend is $1,000 per semester for full-time study or $500 per semester for part-time study. The maximum award is $3,000 per fiscal year or $10,000 per lifetime.

Duration 1 year; may be renewed, provided the recipient continues to make satisfactory academic progress.

Additional information This program was established by the Minnesota Legislature in 2007.

Number awarded Varies each year.

Deadline Deadline not specified.

[78]
MISSOURI AMERICAN LEGION COMMANDER'S SCHOLARSHIPS

American Legion
Department of Missouri
3341 American Avenue
P.O. Box 179
Jefferson City, MO 65102-0179
(573) 893-2353   Toll Free: (800) 846-9023
Fax: (573) 893-2980   E-mail: info@missourilegion.org
Web: www.missourilegion.org/default_016.htm

Summary To provide financial assistance to veterans in Missouri who are interested in attending college in the state.

Eligibility This program is open to residents of Missouri who served at least 90 days in the U.S. armed forces and received an honorable discharge. Applicants must be enrolled or planning to enroll full time at an accredited vocational/technical school, college, or university in Missouri.

Financial data The stipend is $1,000.

Duration 1 year.

Number awarded 2 each year.

Deadline April of each year.

[79]
MONTANA HONORABLY DISCHARGED VETERAN WAIVER

Office of the Commissioner of Higher Education
Attn: Montana University System
State Scholarship Coordinator
2500 Broadway
P.O. Box 203201
Helena, MT 59620-3201
(406) 444-0638   Toll Free: (800) 537-7508
Fax: (406) 444-1469   E-mail: snewlun@montana.edu
Web: www.mus.edu

Summary To provide financial assistance for undergraduate or graduate studies to selected Montana veterans.

Eligibility This program is open to honorably-discharged veterans who served with the U.S. armed forces and who are residents of Montana. Only veterans who at some time qualified for U.S. Department of Veterans Affairs (VA) educational benefits, but who are no longer eligible or have exhausted their benefits, are entitled to this waiver. Veterans who served any time prior to May 8, 1975 are eligible to work on undergraduate or graduate degrees. Veterans whose service began after May 7, 1975 are eligible only to work on their first undergraduate degree. They must have received an Armed Forces Expeditionary Medal for service in Lebanon, Grenada, or Panama; served in a combat theater in the Persian Gulf between August 2, 1990 and April 11, 1991 and received the Southwest Asia Service Medal; were awarded the Kosovo Campaign Medal; or served in a combat theater in Afghanistan or Iraq after September 11, 2001 and received the Global War on Terrorism Expeditionary Medal, the Afghanistan Campaign Medal, or the Iraq Campaign Medal. Financial need must be demonstrated.

Financial data Veterans eligible for this benefit are entitled to attend any unit of the Montana University System without payment of registration or incidental fees.

Duration Students are eligible for continued fee waiver as long as they make academic progress as full-time students.

Number awarded Varies each year.

Deadline Deadline not specified.

[80]
MONTGOMERY GI BILL (ACTIVE DUTY)

Department of Veterans Affairs
Attn: Veterans Benefits Administration
810 Vermont Avenue, N.W.
Washington, DC 20420
(202) 418-4343   Toll Free: (888) GI-BILL1
Web: www.gibill.va.gov

Summary To provide financial assistance for college, graduate school, and other types of postsecondary schools to new enlistees in any of the armed forces after they have completed their service obligation.

Eligibility This program is open to veterans who received an honorable discharge and have a high school diploma, a GED, or, in some cases, up to 12 hours of college credit; veterans who already have a bachelor's degree are eligible to work on a master's degree or higher. Applicants must also meet the requirements of 1 of the following categories: 1) entered active duty for the first time after June 30, 1985, had military pay reduced by $100 per month for the first 12 months, and continuously served for 3 years, or 2 years if that was their original enlistment, or 2 years if they entered Selected Reserve within a year of leaving active duty and served 4 years (the 2 by 4 program); 2) entered active duty before January 1, 1977, had remaining entitlement under the Vietnam Era GI Bill on December 31, 1989, served at least 1 day between October 19, 1984 and June 30, 1985, and stayed on active duty through June 30, 1988 (or June 30, 1987 if they entered Selected Reserve within 1 year of leaving active duty and served 4 years); 3) on active duty on September 30, 1990 and separated involuntarily after February 2, 1991, involuntarily separated on or after November 30, 1993, or voluntarily separated under either the Voluntary Separation Incentive (VSI) or Special Separation Benefit (SSB) program, and before separation had military pay reduced by $1,200; or 4) on active duty on October 9, 1996, had money remaining in an account from the Veterans Educational Assistance Program (VEAP), elected Montgomery GI Bill (MGIB) by October 9, 1997, and paid $1,200. Certain National Guard members may also qualify under category 4 if they served on full-time active duty between July 1, 1985 and November 28, 1989, elected MGIB between October 9, 1996 and July 8, 1997, and paid $1,200. Following completion of their service obligation, participants may enroll in colleges or universities for associate, bachelor, or graduate degrees; in courses leading to a certificate or diploma from business, technical, or vocational schools; for apprenticeships or on-the-job training programs; in correspondence courses; in flight training; for preparatory courses necessary for admission to a college or graduate school; for licensing and certification tests approved for veterans; or in state-approved teacher certification programs. Veterans who wish to enroll in certain high-cost technology programs (life science, physical science, engineering, mathematics, engineering and science technology, computer specialties, and engineering, science, and computer management) may be eligible for an accelerated payment.

Financial data For veterans in categories 1, 3, and 4 who served on active duty for 3 years or more, the current monthly stipend for college or university work is $1,473 for full-time study. For enlistees whose initial active-duty obligation was less than 3 years, the current monthly stipend for college or university work is $1,196. For veterans in category 2 with remaining eligibility, the current monthly stipend for institutional study full time is $1,661 for no dependents, $1,697 with 1 dependent, $1,728 with 2 dependents, and $16 for each additional dependent. Lower rates apply for less than full-time study, apprenticeships and on-the-job training, cooperative education, correspondence courses, and flight training.

Duration 36 months; active-duty servicemembers must utilize the funds within 10 years of leaving the armed services; Reservists may draw on their funds while still serving.

Additional information This was the basic VA education program, referred to as Chapter 30, until the passage of the Post-9/11 GI Bill in 2009. Veterans who have remaining benefits available from this program may utilize those or transfer them to the new program.

Number awarded Varies each year.

Deadline Deadline not specified.

[81]
MOPH SCHOLARSHIP PROGRAM

Military Order of the Purple Heart
Attn: Scholarships
5413-B Backlick Road
Springfield, VA 22151-3960
(703) 642-5360   Toll Free: (888) 668-1656
Fax: (703) 642-2054
E-mail: scholarship@purpleheart.org
Web: www.purpleheart.org/Scholarships/Default.aspx

Summary To provide financial assistance for college or graduate school to members of the Military Order of the Purple Heart (MOPH) and their families.

Eligibility This program is open to 1) members of the MOPH; 2) direct descendants (children, stepchildren, adopted children, grandchildren, and great-grandchildren) of veterans who are MOPH members or who were members at the time of death; 3) direct descendants of veterans killed in action or who died of wounds but did not have the opportunity to join the order; and 4) spouses and widows of MOPH members, veterans killed in action, and veterans who died of wounds. Applicants must be graduating seniors or graduates of an accredited high school who are enrolled or accepted for enrollment in a full-time program of study in a college, university, or trade school. They must have a GPA of 2.75 or higher. U.S. citizenship is required. Along with their application, they must submit an essay of 200 to 300 words on a topic that changes annually but recently was, "The Price of Freedom." Financial need is not considered in the selection process.

Financial data The stipend is $3,000 per year.

Duration 1 year; may be renewed up to 2 additional years.

Additional information Membership in MOPH is open to all veterans who received a Purple Heart Medal and were discharged under conditions other than dishonorable. A processing fee of $15 is required.

Number awarded Varies each year; recently, 83 of these scholarships were awarded.

Deadline February of each year.

[82]
NARRAGANSETT BAY POST SAME SCHOLARSHIP

Society of American Military Engineers-Narragansett Bay
    Post
Attn: Scholarship Committee
15 Mohegan Avenue
New London, CT 06320
(860) 444-8312   Fax: (860) 444-8219
E-mail: Gregory.j.carabine@uscg.mil
Web: posts.same.org/Narragansett/scholarship.htm

Summary To provide financial assistance to residents of New England, particularly those with ties to the military, who are interested in working on a bachelor's degree in construction-related fields at colleges in any state.

Eligibility This program is open to residents of New England (preferably Connecticut, Massachusetts, and Rhode Island) who are graduating high school seniors or students currently enrolled at a college or university in any state. Applicants must be interested in working on a bachelor's degree in an accredited engineering or architectural program, preferably in civil engineering, environmental engineering, architecture, or other construction-related program. Preference is given to students who 1) are dependents of or sponsored by a member of the Narragansett Bay Post of the Society of American Military Engineers (SAME); 2) are enrolled in ROTC (preferably not a recipient of an ROTC scholarship); and 3) have prior U.S. military service and/or public service. Along with their application, they must submit a 500-word essay about themselves, their achievements, or their situation. Selection is based on that essay, grades and class rank, school or community honors, extracurricular activities, leadership, volunteer activities, and completeness and quality of the application. U.S. citizenship is required.

Financial data   The stipend is $1,000.

Duration   1 year.

Number awarded   1 each year.

Deadline   May of each year.

[83]
NATIONAL GUARD ASSOCIATION OF CALIFORNIA SCHOLARSHIPS

National Guard Association of California
Attn: Executive Director
3336 Bradshaw Road, Suite 230
Sacramento, CA 95827-2615
(916) 362-3411   Toll Free: (800) 647-0018
Fax: (916) 362-3707
Web: ngac.org

Summary   To provide funding to members or former members of the National Guard in California and their dependents interested in attending college in any state.

Eligibility   This program is open to 1) dependents of service members of the California National Guard who have died, have been wounded, are currently serving, or have served in the Global War on Terrorism; 2) medically or honorably discharged California National Guard veterans who served in Operation Enduring Freedom (OEF) or Operation Iraqi Freedom (OIF); 3) California National Guard service members who are currently serving or have served in the Global War on Terrorism; or 4) dependents of retired California National Guard service members who are life members of the National Guard Association of California. Applicants must be attending or planning to attend a college, university, or trade school in any state. Along with their application, they must submit a 500-word essay on the greatest challenge they have faced and how it has impacted them. Selection is based on that essay; unweighted GPA; extracurricular activities, honors, and/or awards; recommendations; and (if case of a tie) SAT or ACT scores.

Financial data   Stipends range from $250 to $1,000. Funds are paid directly to the recipient.

Duration   1 year.

Number awarded   Varies each year; recently, 19 of these scholarships were awarded.

Deadline   May of each year.

[84]
NATIONAL GUARD ASSOCIATION OF MARYLAND SCHOLARSHIPS

National Guard Association of Maryland
Attn: Scholarship Committee
P.O. Box 16675
Baltimore, MD 21221-0675
(410) 557-2606   Toll Free: (800) 844-1394
Fax: (410) 893-7529 E-mail: executivedirector@ngam.net
Web: www.ngam.net/benefits/scholarships.html

Summary   To provide funding to current and former members of the Maryland National Guard and their dependents who are interested in attending college in any state.

Eligibility   This program is open to active and retired members of the Maryland National Guard and their spouses and children. Applicants must be enrolled or planning to enroll in an accredited college, university, or vocational/technical school in any state on either a part-time or full-time basis. They must submit a resume in which they outline their academic background, activities in which they have participated, and honors they have received; 3 letters of recommendation; the name of the college; and information on financial need.

Financial data   The stipend is $1,000. Funds are paid directly to the recipient's university for tuition, fees, and books.

Duration   1 year; recipients may reapply.

Number awarded   Varies each year; recently, 17 of these scholarships were awarded.

Deadline   March of each year.

[85]
NATIONAL GUARD ASSOCIATION OF NEW HAMPSHIRE SCHOLARSHIPS

National Guard Association of New Hampshire
Attn: Scholarship Committee
P.O. Box 22031
Portsmouth, NH 03802-2031
(603) 540-9608   E-mail: info@nganh.org
Web: www.nganh.org

Summary   To provide money to members of the National Guard Association of New Hampshire and their dependents who are interested in attending college.

Eligibility   This program is open to current members of the National Guard Association of New Hampshire (officer, enlisted, or retired) and their dependents. Applicants must be attending or planning to attend an accredited college or university in any state. Along with their application, they must submit a 1-page essay on a topic that changes annually; recently, they were asked to give their thoughts on whether or not United States efforts to support and stabilize democratic governments in Afghanistan and Iraq will lead to greater stability in the Southwest Asian region.

Financial data   The stipend is $1,000.

Duration   1 year.

Number awarded   1 each year.

Deadline   April of each year.

[86]
NATIONAL GUARD ASSOCIATION OF SOUTH CAROLINA SCHOLARSHIPS

National Guard Association of South Carolina
Attn: NGASC Scholarship Foundation
132 Pickens Street
Columbia, SC 29205
(803) 254-8456   Toll Free: (800) 822-3235
Fax: (803) 254-3869   E-mail: nginfo@ngasc.org
Web: www.ngasc.org/?page_id=11

Summary   To provide funding to current and former South Carolina National Guard members and their dependents who are interested in attending college or graduate school.

Eligibility   This program is open to undergraduate students who are 1) current, retired, or deceased members of the South Carolina National Guard; 2) their dependents; and 3) members of the National Guard Association of South Carolina (NGASC). Graduate students are also eligible if they are members of the South Carolina National Guard. Applicants must be attending or interested in attending a college or university in any state as a full-time student. Several of the scholarships include additional restrictions on school or academic major; some are granted only for academic excellence, but most are based on both academics and financial need.

Financial data   The stipend is $1,500 or $1,000.

Duration   1 year; may be renewed up to 3 additional years.

Number awarded   Varies each year; recently, 42 of these scholarships were awarded: 1 at $1,500 and 41 at $1,000.

Deadline   January of each year.

[87]
NATIONAL GUARD ASSOCIATION OF TENNESSEE SCHOLARSHIP PROGRAM

National Guard Association of Tennessee
Attn: Scholarship Committee
4332 Kenilwood Drive
Nashville, TN 37204-4401
(615) 833-9100   Toll Free: (888) 642-8448 (within TN)
Fax: (615) 833-9173   E-mail: larry@ngatn.org
Web: www.ngatn.org

Summary   To provide financial assistance for college to members or dependents of members of the National Guard Association of Tennessee (NGATN).

Eligibility   This program is open to active Tennessee National Guard members and to active annual or life members of the NGATN. If no active Guard or association member qualifies, the scholarships may be awarded to the child of a Guard or association member, including life members who have retired or are deceased. All applicants must be high school seniors or graduates who meet entrance or continuation requirements at a Tennessee college or university. Selection is based on leadership in school and civic activities, motivation for continued higher education, academic achievement in high school and/or college, and financial need.

Financial data   The stipends are $1,500.

Duration   1 year.

Number awarded   6 each year: 1 to an active National Guard member; 2 to current association members or their dependents; 2 to active National Guard members or their dependents; and 1 to a current Guard member who was mobilized for Operations Desert Storm, Noble Eagle, Enduring Freedom, or Iraqi Freedom.

Deadline   June of each year.

[88]
NATIONAL GUARD ASSOCIATION OF TEXAS SCHOLARSHIP PROGRAM

National Guard Association of Texas
Attn: NGAT Educational Foundation
3706 Crawford Avenue
Austin, TX 78731-6803
(512) 454-7300   Toll Free: (800) 252-NGAT
Fax: (512) 467-6803   E-mail: rlindner@ngat.org
Web: www.ngat.org

Summary   To provide funding to members and dependents of members of the National Guard Association of Texas who are interested in attending college or graduate school.

Eligibility   This program is open to annual and life members of the association and their spouses and children (associate members and their dependents are not eligible). Applicants may be high school seniors, undergraduate students, or graduate students, either enrolled or planning to enroll at an institution of higher education in any state. Along with their application, they must submit an essay on their desire to continue their education. Selection is based on scholarship, citizenship, and leadership.

Financial data   Stipends range from $500 to $5,000.

Duration   1 year (nonrenewable).

Additional information   This program includes 1 scholarship sponsored by USAA Insurance Corporation.

Number awarded   Varies each year; recently, 13 of these scholarships were awarded: 1 at $5,000, 3 at $2,500, 1 at $2,000, 3 at $1,250, 4 at $1,000, and 1 at $500.

Deadline   February of each year.

[89]
NAUS SCHOLARSHIP PROGRAM

National Association for Uniformed Services
Attn: Scholarship Committee
5535 Hempstead Way
Springfield, VA 22151
(703) 750-1342   Toll Free: (800) 842-3451, ext. 1803
Fax: (703) 354-4380   E-mail: scholarship@naus.org
Web: www.naus.org

Summary   To provide financial assistance for college to members of the National Association for Uniformed Services (NAUS) and their families.

Eligibility   This program is open to NAUS members, their spouses, and their children. Applicants must be high school seniors or undergraduates enrolled full or part time in a degree- or certificate-granting program. High school seniors must have a GPA of 3.0 or higher and undergraduates must have a GPA of 2.5 or higher. Along with their application, they must submit statements, up to 100 words each, on 1) their reasons for enrolling in a postsecondary education program; and 2) a list of academic achievements, personal achievements, extracurricular activities, and any community service performed in the past 2 years. Financial need is not considered in the selection process.

Financial data   The stipend is $2,000.

Duration   1 year.

Additional information   Membership in NAUS is open to members of the armed forces, veterans, retirees, their spouses, and their widow(er)s.

Number awarded 5 each year.
Deadline April of each year.

[90]
NCPOA/BART LONGO MEMORIAL SCHOLARSHIPS

National Chief Petty Officers' Association
c/o Marjorie Hays, Treasurer
1014 Ronald Drive
Corpus Christi, TX 78412-3548
Web: www.goatlocker.org/ncpoa/scholarship.htm

Summary To provide financial assistance for college or graduate school to members of the National Chief Petty Officers' Association (NCPOA) and their families.

Eligibility This program is open to members of the NCPOA and the children, stepchildren, and grandchildren of living or deceased members. Applicants may be high school seniors or graduates entering a college or university or students currently enrolled full time as undergraduate or graduate students. Selection is based on academic achievement and participation in extracurricular activities; need is not considered.

Financial data The stipend is $1,000.

Duration 1 year.

Additional information Membership in the NCPOA is limited to men and women who served or are serving as Chief Petty Officers in the U.S. Navy, U.S. Coast Guard, or their Reserve components for at least 30 days.

Number awarded 2 each year: 1 to a high school senior or graduate and 1 to an undergraduate or graduate student.

Deadline May of each year.

[91]
NEW MEXICO VIETNAM VETERAN SCHOLARSHIPS

New Mexico Department of Veterans' Services
Attn: Benefits Division
407 Galisteo Street, Room 142
P.O. Box 2324
Santa Fe, NM 87504-2324
(505) 827-6374   Toll Free: (866) 433-VETS
Fax: (505) 827-6372   E-mail: alan.martinez@state.nm.us
Web: www.dvs.state.nm.us/benefits.html

Summary To provide funding to Vietnam veterans in New Mexico who are interested in working on an undergraduate or master's degree at a public college in the state.

Eligibility This program is open to Vietnam veterans who have been residents of New Mexico for at least 10 years. Applicants must have been honorably discharged and have been awarded the Vietnam Service Medal or the Vietnam Campaign Medal. They must be planning to attend a state-supported college, university, or community college in New Mexico to work on an undergraduate or master's degree. Awards are granted on a first-come, first-served basis.

Financial data The scholarships provide full payment of tuition and purchase of required books at any state-funded postsecondary institution in New Mexico.

Duration 1 year.

Deadline Deadline not specified.

[92]
NEW YORK STATE MILITARY SERVICE RECOGNITION SCHOLARSHIPS

New York State Higher Education Services Corporation
Attn: Student Information
99 Washington Avenue
Albany, NY 12255
(518) 473-1574   Toll Free: (888) NYS-HESC
Fax: (518) 473-3749   TDD: (800) 445-5234
E-mail: webmail@hesc.com
Web: www.hesc.com

Summary To provide funding to disabled veterans and the family members of deceased or disabled veterans who are residents of New York and interested in attending college in the state.

Eligibility This program is open to New York residents who served in the armed forces of the United States or state organized militia at any time on or after August 2, 1990 and became severely and permanently disabled as a result of injury or illness suffered or incurred in a combat theater or combat zone or during military training operations in preparation for duty in a combat theater or combat zone of operations. Also eligible are the children, spouses, or financial dependents of members of the armed forces of the United States or state organized militia who at any time after August 2, 1990 1) died, became severely and permanently disabled as a result of injury or illness suffered or incurred, or are classified as missing in action in a combat theater or combat zone of operations; 2) died as a result of injuries incurred in those designated areas; or 3) died or became severely and permanently disabled as a result of injury or illness suffered or incurred during military training operations in preparation for duty in a combat theater or combat zone of operations. Applicants must be attending or accepted at an approved program of study as full-time undergraduates at a public college or university or private institution in New York.

Financial data At public colleges and universities, this program provides payment of actual tuition and mandatory educational fees; actual room and board charged to students living on campus or an allowance for room and board for commuter students; and allowances for books, supplies, and transportation. At private institutions, the award is equal to the amount charged at the State University of New York (SUNY) for 4-year tuition and average mandatory fees (or the student's actual tuition and fees, whichever is less) plus allowances for room, board, books, supplies, and transportation.

Duration This program is available for 4 years of full-time undergraduate study (or 5 years in an approved 5-year bachelor's degree program).

Number awarded Varies each year.

Deadline April of each year.

[93]
NEW YORK VETERANS TUITION AWARDS

New York State Higher Education Services Corporation
Attn: Student Information
99 Washington Avenue
Albany, NY 12255
(518) 473-1574   Toll Free: (888) NYS-HESC
Fax: (518) 473-3749   TDD: (800) 445-5234
E-mail: webmail@hesc.com
Web: www.hesc.com

Summary   To provide tuition assistance to eligible veterans enrolled in a college or graduate school in New York.

Eligibility   This program is open to veterans who served in the U.S. armed forces in 1) Indochina between February 28, 1961 and May 7, 1975; 2) hostilities that occurred after February 28, 1961 as evidenced by receipt of an Armed Forces Expeditionary Medal, Navy Expeditionary Medal, or Marine Corps Expeditionary Medal; 3) the Persian Gulf on or after August 2, 1990; or 4) Afghanistan on or after September 11, 2001. Applicants must have been discharged from the service under honorable conditions, must be a New York resident, must be a U.S. citizen or eligible noncitizen, must be enrolled full or part time at an undergraduate or graduate degree-granting institution in New York or in an approved vocational training program in the state, must be charged at least $200 tuition per year, and must apply for a New York Tuition Assistance Program (TAP) award.

Financial data   For full-time study, the maximum stipend is tuition or $5,295, whichever is less. For part-time study, the stipend is based on the number of credits certified and the student's actual part-time tuition.

Duration   For undergraduate study, up to 8 semesters, or up to 10 semesters for a program requiring 5 years for completion; for graduate study, up to 6 semesters; for vocational programs, up to 4 semesters. Award limits are based on full-time study or equivalent part-time study.

Additional information   If a TAP award is also received, the combined academic year award cannot exceed tuition costs. If it does, the TAP award will be reduced accordingly.

Number awarded   Varies each year.

Deadline   April of each year.

[94]
NHA ACTIVE DUTY SCHOLARSHIPS

Naval Helicopter Association
Attn: Scholarship Fund
P.O. Box 180578
Coronado, CA 92178-0578
(619) 435-7139   Fax: (619) 435-7354
Web: nhascholarshipfund.org/scholarships-available.html

Summary   To provide money for college or graduate school to active-duty and former personnel who are working or have worked in rotary wing activities of the sea services.

Eligibility   This program is open to active-duty or former Navy, Marine Corps, or Coast Guard rotary wing aviators, aircrewmen, or support personnel. Applicants must be working on or planning to work on an undergraduate or graduate degree in any field. Along with their application, they must submit a personal statement on their academic and career aspirations. Selection is based on that statement, academic proficiency, scholastic achievements and awards, extracurricular activities, employment history, and recommendations.

Financial data   Stipends are approximately $2,000.

Duration   1 year.

Number awarded   4 each year: 2 to undergraduates and 2 to graduate students.

Deadline   February of each year.

[95]
NONRESIDENT TUITION WAIVERS FOR VETERANS AND THEIR DEPENDENTS WHO MOVE TO TEXAS

Texas Higher Education Coordinating Board
Attn: Grants and Special Programs
1200 East Anderson Lane
P.O. Box 12788
Austin, TX 78711-2788
(512) 427-6340   Toll Free: (800) 242-3062
Fax: (512) 427-6420   E-mail: grantinfo@thecb.state.tx.us
Web: www.collegeforalltexans.com

Summary   To exempt veterans who move to Texas and their dependents from the payment of nonresident tuition at public institutions of higher education in the state.

Eligibility   Eligible for these waivers are former members of the U.S. armed forces and commissioned officers of the Public Health Service who are retired or have been honorably discharged, their spouses, and dependent children. Applicants must have moved to Texas upon separation from the service and be attending or planning to attend a public college or university in the state. They must have indicated their intent to become a Texas resident by registering to vote and doing 1 of the following: owning real property in Texas, registering an automobile in Texas, or executing a will indicating that they are a resident of the state.

Financial data   Although persons eligible under this program are still classified as nonresidents, they are entitled to pay the resident tuition at Texas institutions of higher education on an immediate basis.

Duration   1 year.

Number awarded   Varies each year.

Deadline   Deadline not specified.

[96]
NORTH CAROLINA NATIONAL GUARD ASSOCIATION SCHOLARSHIPS

North Carolina National Guard Association
Attn: Educational Foundation, Inc.
7410 Chapel Hill Road
Raleigh, NC 27607-5047
(919) 851-3390   Toll Free: (800) 821-6159 (within NC)
Fax: (919) 859-4990
E-mail: peggyncngaef@bellsouth.net
Web: ncnga.org

Summary   To provide financial assistance to members and dependents of members of the North Carolina National Guard Association who plan to attend college in any state.

Eligibility   This program is open to active and associate members of the association as well as the spouses, children, grandchildren, and legal dependents of active, associate, or deceased members. Applicants must be high school seniors, high school graduates, or students currently enrolled at a college or university in any state. Selection is based on financial need, academic achievement, citizenship, leadership, and other application information. The most outstanding applicants receive scholarships provided by the SECU Foundation. Applicants who meet specified additional requirements qualify for various memorial and special scholarships.

Financial data   Stipends are $10,000 or $5,000 for the SECU Foundation Scholarships, $1,000 for memorial and special scholarships, $1,000 for citizenship awards, $800 for general scholarships, or $400 for community college scholarships.

Duration 1 year; may be renewed.

Additional information This program, which began in 1968, includes a number of named memorial and special scholarships. Other scholarships are funded by the SECU Foundation of the State Employees' Credit Union and the USAA Insurance Corporation. The association also funds the Academic Excellence Leadership Award ($1,000) for outstanding applicants and the Special Population Scholarship ($1,000) for applicants with disabilities.

Number awarded Varies each year; recently, 37 of these scholarships were awarded: 2 SECU Foundation Scholarships (1 at $10,000 and 1 at $5,000), 18 memorial and special scholarships at $1,000, 2 citizenship awards are $1,000, 10 general scholarships at $800, and 5 community college scholarships at $400.

Deadline January of each year for high school graduates and college students; February for high school seniors.

[97]
NORTH CAROLINA VIETNAM VETERANS SCHOLARSHIP PROGRAM

North Carolina Vietnam Veterans, Inc.
c/o Bud Gross, Treasurer
601 Compton Road
Raleigh, NC 27609
(919) 787-7228   E-mail: info@ncvvi.org
Web: www.ncvvi.org

Summary To provide financial assistance to North Carolina residents who are Vietnam veterans or the dependents of veterans and interested in attending college in any state.

Eligibility This program is open to current residents of Chatham, Durham, Franklin, Granville, Harnett, Johnston, Nash, or Wake counties in North Carolina who are either a Vietnam veteran or the veteran's spouse, child, foster child, adopted child, or grandchild. Families of members of North Carolina Vietnam Veterans, Inc. (NCVVI) who live in any county of the state are also eligible. Applicants must be attending or planning to attend a college, university, community college, or trade school in any state. They must submit a copy of the Department of Defense Form DD214 to document Vietnam service; a birth certificate and/or marriage license (as needed); a personal statement about themselves, including work experience, anticipated career, and goals; a list of current activities and awards; and an essay of 600 to 900 words on a topic that changes annually; recently, the topic was "Why was the transition from Vietnam to the United States a major problem for many veterans and still lingers to this date?"

Financial data Stipends range from $500 to $1,500. Funds are paid on a reimbursement basis (presentation of paid receipts for tuition, fees, and/or books).

Duration 1 year.

Additional information This program includes the Mike Hooks Memorial Scholarship.

Number awarded 1 or more each year.

Deadline February of each year.

[98]
OHIO LEGION AUXILIARY DEPARTMENT PRESIDENT'S SCHOLARSHIP

American Legion Auxiliary
Department of Ohio
1100 Brandywine Boulevard, Suite D
P.O. Box 2760
Zanesville, OH 43702-2760
(740) 452-8245   Fax: (740) 452-2620
E-mail: ala_katie@rrohio.com
Web: www.alaohio.org/Scholarships

Summary To provide funding to veterans and their descendants in Ohio who are interested in attending college.

Eligibility This program is open to honorably-discharged veterans and the children, grandchildren, and great-grandchildren of living, deceased, or disabled honorably-discharged veterans who served during designated periods of wartime. Applicants must be residents of Ohio, seniors at an accredited high school, planning to enter a college in any state, and sponsored by an American Legion Auxiliary Unit. Along with their application, they must submit an original article (up to 500 words) written by the applicant on a topic that changes annually. Recently, students were asked to write on "Education and the American Dream." Selection is based on character, Americanism, leadership, scholarship, and need.

Financial data Stipends are $1,500 or $1,000. Funds are paid to the recipient's school.

Duration 1 year.

Number awarded 1 at $1,500 and 1 at $1,000.

Deadline February of each year.

[99]
OHIO LEGION SCHOLARSHIPS

American Legion
Department of Ohio
60 Big Run Road
P.O. Box 8007
Delaware, OH 43015
(740) 362-7478   Fax: (740) 362-1429
E-mail: legion@ohiolegion.com
Web: www.ohiolegion.com/scholarships/info.htm

Summary To provide financial assistance to residents of Ohio who are members of the American Legion, their families, or dependents of deceased military personnel and interested in attending college in any state.

Eligibility This program is open to residents of Ohio who are Legionnaires, direct descendants of living or deceased Legionnaires, or surviving spouses or children of deceased U.S. military personnel who died on active duty or of injuries received on active duty. Applicants must be attending or planning to attend colleges, universities, or other approved postsecondary schools in any state with a vocational objective. Selection is based on academic achievement as measured by course grades, scholastic test scores, difficulty of curriculum, participation in outside activities, and the judging committee's general impression.

Financial data Stipends are $2,500 or $1,500.

Duration 1 year.

Number awarded Varies each year; recently, 9 of these scholarships were awarded: 1 at $2,500 and 8 at $1,500.

Deadline April of each year.

[100]
OKLAHOMA TUITION WAIVER FOR PRISONERS OF WAR, PERSONS MISSING IN ACTION, AND DEPENDENTS

Oklahoma State Regents for Higher Education
Attn: Director of Scholarship and Grant Programs
655 Research Parkway, Suite 200
P.O. Box 108850
Oklahoma City, OK 73101-8850
(405) 225-9239   Toll Free: (800) 858-1840
Fax: (405) 225-9230   E-mail: studentinfo@osrhe.edu
Web: www.okcollegestart.org

Summary To provide financial assistance for college to Oklahoma residents (or their dependents) who were declared prisoners of war or missing in action.

Eligibility Applicants for this assistance must be veterans who were declared prisoners of war or missing in action after January 1, 1960 and were residents of Oklahoma at the time of entrance into the armed forces or when declared POW/MIA. Dependent children of those veterans are also eligible as long as they are under 24 years of age. Selection is based on financial need, academic aptitude and achievement, student activity participation, academic level, and academic discipline or field of study.

Financial data Eligible applicants are entitled to receive free tuition at any Oklahoma state-supported postsecondary educational, technical, or vocational school.

Duration Assistance continues for 5 years or until receipt of a bachelor's degree, whichever occurs first.

Additional information This assistance is not available to persons eligible to receive federal benefits.

Number awarded Varies each year.

Deadline Deadline not specified.

[101]
ONGEA SCHOLARSHIP PROGRAM

Ohio National Guard Enlisted Association
Attn: Scholarship Chair
1299 Virginia Avenue
Columbus, OH 43212
(740) 574-5932   Toll Free: (800) 642-6642
Fax: (614) 486-2216   E-mail: ongea@juno.com
Web: www.ongea.org/12.html

Summary To provide financial assistance to members of the Ohio National Guard Enlisted Association (ONGEA) and children of members of the ONGEA Auxiliary who are interested in attending college in any state.

Eligibility This program is open to 1) children of ONGEA and ONGEA Auxiliary members (ONGEA member spouses must be Auxiliary members in order for a child to be eligible); 2) unmarried dependent children of deceased ONGEA and ONGEA Auxiliary members who were in good standing the time of their death; and 3) ONGEA members (if married, the spouse must also be a member of the Auxiliary). Applicants must be enrolling as full-time undergraduate students at a college, university, trade school, or business school in any state. Selection is based on academic record, character, leadership, and financial need.

Financial data Stipends are $1,000 or $500. After verification of enrollment is provided, checks are sent to the recipient and made out to the recipient's school.

Duration 1 year; nonrenewable.

Additional information This program is sponsored jointly by ONGEA, the ONGEA Auxiliary, USAA Insurance Corporation, and the First Cleveland Cavalry Association.

Number awarded 5 to 10 each year, depending upon the availability of funds.

Deadline March of each year.

[102]
OREGON EDUCATIONAL AID FOR VETERANS

Oregon Department of Veterans' Affairs
Attn: Educational Aid Program
700 Summer Street N.E., Suite 150
Salem, OR 97301-1285
(503) 373-2085   Toll Free: (800) 828-8801 (within OR)
Fax: (503) 373-2362   TDD: (503) 373-2217
E-mail: orvetsbenefits@odva.state.or.us
Web: www.oregon.gov

Summary To provide financial assistance for college to certain Oregon veterans.

Eligibility This program is open to veterans who served on active duty in the U.S. armed forces for not less than 90 days during the Korean War or subsequent to June 30, 1958. Applicants must be residents of Oregon released from military service under honorable conditions. They must be enrolled or planning to enroll in classroom instruction, home study courses, or vocational training from an accredited educational institution. U.S. citizenship is required.

Financial data Full-time students receive up to $150 per month and part-time students up to $100 per month.

Duration Benefits are paid for as many months as the veteran spent in active service, up to a maximum of 36 months. One month of entitlement will be charged for each month paid, regardless of the amount paid.

Additional information Educational Aid will not be paid if the veteran is receiving federal GI training benefits for that course. School officials are required to certify the amount that the student paid for tuition, lab fees, books, and supplies; payments for each month or portion of a month are made only if the actual cost of the course is equal to or greater than the payment amount.

Number awarded Varies each year.

Deadline Applications must be submitted at the time of enrollment.

[103]
PARALYZED VETERANS OF AMERICA EDUCATIONAL SCHOLARSHIP PROGRAM

Paralyzed Veterans of America
Attn: Education and Training Foundation
801 18th Street, N.W.
Washington, DC 20006-3517
(202) 416-7651   Toll Free: (800) 424-8200, ext. 776
Fax: (202) 416-7641   TDD: (800) 795-HEAR
E-mail: christih@pva.org
Web: www.pva.org

Summary To provide money for college to members of the Paralyzed Veterans of America and their families.

Eligibility This program is open to association members, spouses of members, and unmarried dependent children of members under 24 years of age. Applicants must be attending or planning to attend an accredited U.S. college or university. They must be U.S. citizens. Along with their application, they must submit a personal statement explaining why they wish to further their education, short- and long-term academic goals, how this will meet their career objectives, and how it will affect the PVA membership. Selection is based on that statement, academic records, letters of recommendation, and extracurricular and community activities.

Financial data Stipends are $1,000 for full-time students or $500 for part-time students.

Duration 1 year.

Additional information This program began in 1986.

Number awarded Varies each year; recently 14 full-time and 3 part-time students received these scholarships. Since this program was established, it has awarded more than $300,000 in scholarships.

Deadline May of each year.

[104]
PAT TILLMAN MILITARY SCHOLARS PROGRAM

Pat Tillman Foundation
2121 South Mill Avenue, Suite 214
Tempe, AZ 85282
(480) 621-4074   Fax: (480) 621-4075
E-mail: scholarships@pattillmanfoundation.org
Web: www.pattillmanfoundation.org/tillman-military-scholars

Summary To provide financial assistance to veterans, active servicemembers, and their spouses who are interested in working on an undergraduate or graduate degree.

Eligibility This program is open to veterans and active servicemembers of all branches of the armed forces from both the pre- and post-September 11 era and their spouses; children are not eligible. Applicants must be enrolled or planning to enroll full time at a 4-year public or private college or university to work on an undergraduate, graduate, or postgraduate degree. Current and former servicemembers must submit 400-word essays on 1) their motivation and decision to serve in the U.S. military and how that decision and experience has changed their life and ambitions; and 2) their educational and career goals, how they will incorporate their military service experience into those goals, and how they intend to continue their service to others and the community. Spouses must submit 400-word essays on 1) their previous service to others and the community; and 2) their educational and career goals, how they will incorporate their service experiences and the impact of their spouse's military service into those goals, and how they intend to continue their service to others and the community. Selection is based on those essays, educational and career ambitions, record of military service, record of personal achievement, demonstration of service to others in the community, desire to continue such service, and leadership potential.

Financial data The stipend depends on the need of the recipient and the availability of funds.

Duration 1 year; may be renewed, provided the recipient maintains a GPA of 3.0 or higher, remains enrolled full time, and participates in civic action or community service.

Additional information This program began in 2009.

Number awarded Varies each year; recently, 60 students received a total of $916,000 through this program.

Deadline March of each year.

[105]
PETER CONNACHER MEMORIAL SCHOLARSHIPS

Oregon Student Access Commission
Attn: Grants and Scholarships Division
1500 Valley River Drive, Suite 100
Eugene, OR 97401-2146
(541) 687-7395   Toll Free: (800) 452-8807, ext. 7395
Fax: (541) 687-7414   TDD: (800) 735-2900
E-mail: awardinfo@osac.state.or.us
Web: www.oregonstudentaid.gov/scholarships.aspx

Summary To provide money for college or graduate school to ex-prisoners of war and their descendants.

Eligibility Applicants must be U.S. citizens who 1) were military or civilian prisoners of war; or 2) are the descendants of ex-prisoners of war. They must be full-time undergraduate or graduate students. A copy of the ex-prisoner of war's discharge papers from the U.S. armed forces must accompany the application. In addition, written proof of POW status must be submitted, along with a statement of the relationship between the applicant and the ex-prisoner of war (father, grandfather, etc.). Selection is based on academic record and financial need. Preference is given to Oregon residents or their dependents.

Financial data Stipends for scholarships offered by the Oregon Student Access Commission (OSAC) range from $200 to $10,000 but recently averaged $2,300.

Duration 1 year; may be renewed for up to 3 additional years for undergraduate students or 2 additional years for graduate students. Renewal is dependent on evidence of continued financial need and satisfactory academic progress.

Additional information This program is administered by the OSAC with funds provided by the Oregon Community Foundation. Funds are also provided by the Columbia River Chapter of American Ex-prisoners of War, Inc.

Number awarded Varies each year; recently, 4 of these scholarships were awarded.

Deadline February of each year.

[106]
POST-9/11 GI BILL

Department of Veterans Affairs
Attn: Veterans Benefits Administration
810 Vermont Avenue, N.W.
Washington, DC 20420
(202) 418-4343   Toll Free: (888) GI-BILL1
Web: www.gibill.va.gov/benefits/post_911_gibill/index.html

Summary To provide funding to veterans or military personnel who entered service on or after September 11, 2001.

Eligibility This program is open to current and former military personnel who 1) served on active duty for at least 90 aggregate days after September 11, 2001; or 2) were discharged with a service-connected disability after 30 days. Applicants must be planning to enroll in an educational program, including work on an undergraduate or graduate degree, vocational/technical training, on-the-job training, flight training, correspondence training, licensing and national testing programs, and tutorial assistance.

Financial data Participants working on an undergraduate or graduate degree at public institutions in their state receive full payment of tuition and fees. For participants who attend private institutions in most states, tuition and fee reimbursement is capped at $17,500 per academic year; the reimbursement rate is higher at private schools in Arizona, Michigan, New Hampshire, New York, Pennsylvania, South Carolina, and Texas. Benefits for other types of training programs depend on the amount for which the veteran qualified under prior educational programs. Veterans also receive a monthly housing allowance based on the national average Basic Allowance for Housing (BAH) for an E-5 with dependents (currently $673.50) or $1,347 per month at schools in foreign countries); an annual book allowance of $1,000; and (for participants who live in a rural county remote from an educational institution) a rural benefit payment of $500 per year.

Duration Most participants receive up to 36 months of entitlement under this program. Benefits are payable for up to 15 years following release from active duty.

Additional information This program, referred to as Chapter 33, began in 2009 as a replacement for previous educational programs for veterans and military personnel (e.g., Montgomery GI Bill, REAP). Current participants in those programs may be able to transfer benefits from those programs to this new plan. To qualify for 100% of Post 9/11-GI Bill benefits, transferees must have at least 36 months of active-duty service. Transferees with less service are entitled to smaller percentages of benefits, ranging down to 40% for those with only 90 days of service.

Number awarded Varies each year; since the program began, it has awarded nearly $4 billion in benefits to more than 295,000 veterans.

Deadline Deadline not specified.

[107]
RANGER MEMORIAL SCHOLARSHIPS

National Ranger Memorial Foundation
Attn: Executive Secretary
P.O. Box 53369
Fort Benning, GA 31995
(706) 687-0906   E-mail: rangermemorial@gmail.com
Web: rangermemorial.com/scholarship_application.aspx

Summary To provide money for college to current and former U.S. Army Rangers and their descendants.

Eligibility This program is open to Rangers from any era and their descendants; awards are limited to descendants of Rangers who served during the World War II era for Ranger Battalions Association of WWII scholarships. Applicants must be graduating high school seniors or students currently enrolled at an accredited 2- or 4-year educational or technical institution. They must have a GPA of 3.0 or higher. Along with their application, they must submit information on their leadership activities, future goals and how they plan to attain those, and honors and awards received to date. Financial need is not considered in the selection process.

Financial data The stipend is $1,000.

Duration 1 year.

Additional information The National Ranger Memorial Foundation began awarding scholarships in 1999. The Ranger Battalions Association of WWII became a partner in 2007 and offered additional scholarships to descendants of World War II era Rangers.

Number awarded 49 each year: 45 offered by the National Ranger Memorial Foundation and 4 by the Ranger Battalions Association of WWII.

Deadline May of each year.

[108]
RHODE ISLAND EDUCATIONAL BENEFITS FOR DISABLED AMERICAN VETERANS

Division of Veterans Affairs
480 Metacom Avenue
Bristol, RI 02809-0689
(401) 254-8350   Fax: (401) 254-2320
TDD: (401) 254-1345   E-mail: devangelista@dhs.ri.gov
Web: www.dhs.ri.gov

Summary To provide assistance to disabled veterans in Rhode Island who wish to pursue higher education at a public institution in the state.

Eligibility This program is open to permanent residents of Rhode Island who have been verified by the Department of Veterans Affairs (DVA) as having a disability of at least 10% resulting from military service.

Financial data Eligible veterans are entitled to take courses at any public institution of higher education in Rhode Island without the payment of tuition, exclusive of other fees and charges.

Number awarded Varies each year.

Deadline Deadline not specified.

[109]
ROSAMOND P. HAEBERLE MEMORIAL SCHOLARSHIP

Daughters of the American Revolution-Michigan State Society
c/o Toni Barger, Memorial Scholarship Committee
130 Lake Region Circle
Winter Haven, FL 33881-9535
(863) 326-1687   E-mail: tonibarger@aol.com
Web: www.michigandar.org/scholarships.htm

Summary To provide funding to Michigan veterans and military personnel interested in attending college in the state.

Eligibility This program is open to residents of Michigan who have served on active duty in the U.S. armed forces (including Reserves and National Guard) for at least 6 continuous months and are either currently serving in the armed forces or have received a separation from active duty under honorable conditions. Applicants must be currently accepted to and/or enrolled at a 2- or 4-year accredited college, university, or technical/trade school in Michigan. They must be enrolled at least half time and have a cumulative high school or undergraduate GPA of 2.5 or higher. Along with their application, they must submit a 1-page essay on what serving their country has meant to them and how it has influenced their future goals and priorities. Selection is based on academic performance, extracurricular activities, community service, potential to succeed in an academic environment, financial need, and military service record.

Financial data The stipend is $1,500.

Duration 1 year.

Additional information This program began in 2007.

Number awarded 1 each year.

Deadline March of each year.

[110]
RSF MEMORIAL SCHOLARSHIP

Missouri Society of Professional Engineers
Attn: MSPE Educational Foundation
200 East McCarty Street, Suite 200
Jefferson City, MO 65101-3113
(573) 636-4861   Toll Free: (888) 666-4861
Fax: (573) 636-5475   E-mail: marladay@mspe.org
Web: www.mspe.org/edfoundation.html

Summary To provide funding to military personnel and veterans who are residents of any state and currently studying engineering at selected universities in Missouri.

Eligibility This program is open to military personnel (including active, National Guard, Reserves, ROTC cadets, and veterans) who are U.S. citizens and residents of any state. Applicants must be sophomores or juniors currently enrolled in or planning to transfer to an engineering program at 1 of the following institutions in Missouri: University of Missouri, College of Engineering, Columbia; University of Missouri, School of Engineering, Kansas City; Missouri University of Science and Technology, School of Engineering, Rolla; Missouri University of Science and Technology, School of Materials, Energy, and Earth Resources, Rolla; University of Missouri St. Louis/Washington University Joint Undergraduate Engineering Program; Southeast Missouri State University, Engineering Physics Program, Cape Girardeau; St. Louis University, Parks College of Engineering and Aviation, St. Louis; and Washington University, School of Engineering and Applied Sciences, St. Louis. Along with their application, they must submit a 1,000-word essay on their interest in engineering, their major area of study and area of specialization, the occupation they propose to pursue after graduation, their long-term goals, and how they hope to achieve those. Selection is based on the essay (10 points), academic achievement (5 points), extracurricular college or community activities (5 points), work experience (10 points), recommendations (10 points), and financial need (10 points).

Financial data The stipend is $1,500.
Duration 1 year.
Number awarded 1 each year.
Deadline December of each year.

[111]
RUBY LORRAINE PAUL SCHOLARSHIP FUND

American Legion Auxiliary
Department of Nebraska
P.O. Box 5227
Lincoln, NE 68505-0227
(402) 466-1808   Fax: (402) 466-0182
E-mail: neaux@windstream.net
Web: www.nebraskalegionaux.net

Summary To provide funding to students in Nebraska who have a connection to the American Legion and plan to attend college in any state and study any field except nursing.

Eligibility Applicants must have been residents of Nebraska for at least 3 years and either 1) have been a member for at least 2 years of the American Legion, American Legion Auxiliary, or Sons of the American Legion, or 2) be the child, grandchild, or great-grandchild of an American Legion or American Legion Auxiliary member who has been a member for at least 2 years. They must be high school seniors or graduates who maintained a GPA of 3.0 or higher during the last 2 semesters of high school and have been accepted at an accredited college or university in any state to study any field except nursing. Along with their application, they must submit a brief essay describing their chosen field and how this scholarship will help them achieve their goals. Financial need is considered in the selection process.

Financial data A stipend is awarded (amount not specified).
Duration 1 year.
Number awarded 1 each year.
Deadline February of each year.

[112]
RUBY PAUL CAMPAIGN FUND SCHOLARSHIP

American Legion Auxiliary
Department of Nebraska
P.O. Box 5227
Lincoln, NE 68505-0227
(402) 466-1808   Fax: (402) 466-0182
E-mail: neaux@windstream.net
Web: www.nebraskalegionaux.net

Summary To provide financial assistance to students in Nebraska who have a connection to the American Legion and plan to attend college in any state.

Eligibility Applicants must have been residents of Nebraska for at least 3 years and either 1) have been a member for at least 2 years of the American Legion, American Legion Auxiliary, or Sons of the American Legion, or 2) be the child, grandchild, or great-grandchild of an American Legion or American Legion Auxiliary member who has been a member for at least 2 years. They must be high school seniors or graduates who maintained a GPA of 3.0 or higher during the last 2 semesters of high school and have been accepted at an accredited college or university in any state. Along with their application, they must submit a brief essay describing their chosen field and how this scholarship will help them achieve their goals. Financial need is considered.

Financial data A stipend is awarded (amount not specified).
Duration 1 year.
Number awarded 1 each year.
Deadline February of each year.

[113]
SCHNEIDER-EMANUEL AMERICAN LEGION SCHOLARSHIPS

American Legion
Department of Wisconsin
2930 American Legion Drive
P.O. Box 388
Portage, WI 53901-0388
(608) 745-1090   Fax: (608) 745-0179
E-mail: info@wilegion.org
Web: www.wilegion.org

Summary To provide financial assistance to members of the American Legion in Wisconsin and their children or grandchildren who plan to attend college in any state.

Eligibility This program is open to seniors and graduates from accredited Wisconsin high schools. Applicants must be at least 1 of the following 1) a child whose father, mother, or legal guardian is a member of the Department of Wisconsin of the American Legion, American Legion Auxiliary, or Sons of the American Legion; 2) a grandchild whose grandfather, grandmother, or legal guardian is a member of the Department of Wisconsin of the American Legion, American Legion Auxiliary, or Sons of the American Legion; 3) a member of the Sons of the American Legion, American Legion Auxiliary, or Junior American Legion Auxiliary; or 4) a veteran and an American Legion member in Wisconsin. Applicants must have participated in Legion and Auxiliary youth programs. They must be planning to attend a college or university in any state to work on a baccalaureate degree. Selection is based on moral character; scholastic excellence (GPA of 3.0 or higher); participation and accomplishment in American Legion affiliated activities; and personality, leadership, and participation in general extracurricular activities.

Financial data The stipend is $1,000.

Duration 1 year.

Additional information This program began in 1968.

Number awarded 3 each year.

Deadline February of each year.

[114]
SCHUYLER S. PYLE SCHOLARSHIP

Fleet Reserve Association
Attn: FRA Education Foundation
125 North West Street
Alexandria, VA 22314-2754
(703) 683-1400   Toll Free: (800) FRA-1924
Fax: (703) 549-6610   E-mail: scholars@fra.org
Web: www.fra.org

Summary To provide financial assistance for college or graduate school to members of the Fleet Reserve Association (FRA) and their families.

Eligibility This program is open to members of the FRA and the dependent children, grandchildren, and spouses of living or deceased members. Applicants must be enrolled as full-time undergraduate or graduate students. Along with their application, they must submit an essay on why they want to go to college and what they intend to accomplish with their degree. Selection is based on academic record, financial need, extracurricular activities, leadership skills, and participation in community activities. U.S. citizenship is required.

Financial data The stipend is $5,000 per year.

Duration 1 year; may be renewed.

Additional information Membership in the FRA is restricted to active-duty, retired, and Reserve members of the Navy, Marine Corps, and Coast Guard.

Number awarded 1 each year.

Deadline April of each year.

[115]
SCOTT DOMINGUEZ-CRATERS OF THE MOON CHAPTER SCHOLARSHIP

American Society of Safety Engineers
Attn: ASSE Foundation
1800 East Oakton Street
Des Plaines, IL 60018
(847) 768-3435   Fax: (847) 768-3434
E-mail: agabanski@asse.org
Web: www.asse.org

Summary To provide financial assistance to undergraduate and graduate student members of the American Society

of Safety Engineers (ASSE), particularly those with ties to the military, who are from designated western states.

Eligibility This program is open to ASSE members who are working on an undergraduate or graduate degree in occupational safety, health, and environment or a closely-related field (e.g., industrial or environmental engineering, environmental science, industrial hygiene, occupational health nursing). First priority is given to residents within the service area of Craters of the Moon Chapter in Idaho; second priority is given to residents of other states in ASSE Region II (Arizona, Colorado, Montana, Nevada, New Mexico, Utah, and Wyoming). Special consideration is also given to 1) employees of a sponsoring organization or their dependents; 2) students who are serving their country through active duty in the armed forces or are honorably discharged; 3) former members of the Boy Scouts, Girl Scouts, FFA, or 4-H; 4) recipients of awards from service organizations; and 5) students who have provided volunteer service to an ASSE chapter in a leadership role. Undergraduates must have completed at least 60 semester hours with a GPA of 3.0 or higher. Graduate students must have completed at least 9 semester hours with a GPA of 3.5 or higher and have had a GPA of 3.0 or higher as an undergraduate. Full-time students must be ASSE student members; part-time students must be ASSE general or professional members. Along with their application, they must submit 2 essays of 300 words or less: 1) why they are seeking a degree in occupational safety and health or a closely-related field, a brief description of their current activities, and how those relate to their career goals and objectives; and 2) why they should be awarded this scholarship (including career goals and financial need). U.S. citizenship is not required.

Financial data The stipend is $1,000 per year.

Duration 1 year; recipients may reapply.

Additional information This program is sponsored by the ASSE Craters of the Moon Chapter.

Number awarded 1 each year.

Deadline November of each year.

[116]
SERGEANT MAJOR DOUGLAS R. DRUM MEMORIAL SCHOLARSHIP

American Military Retirees Association, Inc.
Attn: Scholarship Committee
5436 Peru Street, Suite 1
Plattsburgh, NY 12901
(518) 563-9479   Toll Free: (800) 424-2969
Fax: (518) 324-5204   E-mail: info@amra1973.org
Web: www.amra1973.org/Scholarship

Summary To provide financial assistance for college to members of the American Military Retirees Association (AMRA) and their dependents.

Eligibility This program is open to current members of AMRA and their dependents, children, and grandchildren. Applicants must be attending or planning to attend an accredited college or university. Along with their application, they must submit a 750-word essay on why they deserve this scholarship. Selection is based on academics, leadership, character, citizenship, and community service.

Financial data Stipends are $5,000, $2,500, or $1,000.

Duration 1 year.

Additional information Membership in AMRA is open to all retired members of the armed forces, regardless of rank.

Number awarded Varies each year; recently, 24 of these scholarships were awarded: 12 to incoming freshmen (1 at $5,000, 1 at $2,500, and 10 at $1,000) and 12 to returning college students (1 at $5,000, 1 at $2,500, and 10 at $1,000).

Deadline February of each year.

[117]
SOCIETY OF ARMY PHYSICIAN ASSISTANTS SCHOLARSHIP

American Academy of Physician Assistants-Veterans
  Caucus
Attn: Veterans Caucus
P.O. Box 362
Danville, PA 17821-0362
(570) 271-0292   Fax: (570) 271-5850
E-mail: admin@veteranscaucus.org
Web: www.veteranscaucus.org

Summary To provide financial assistance to Army veterans who are studying to become physician assistants.

Eligibility This program is open to U.S. citizens who are currently enrolled in a physician assistant program. The program must be approved by the Commission on Accreditation of Allied Health Education. Applicants must be honorably discharged members of the United States Army. Selection is based on military honors and awards received, civic and college honors and awards received, professional memberships and activities, and GPA. An electronic copy of the applicant's DD Form 214 must accompany the application.

Financial data The stipend is $2,000.

Duration 1 year.

Number awarded 1 each year.

Deadline February of each year.

[118]
SOCIETY OF SPONSORS OF THE UNITED STATES NAVY CENTENNIAL SCHOLARSHIP

Navy-Marine Corps Relief Society
Attn: Education Division
875 North Randolph Street, Suite 225
Arlington, VA 22203-1757
(703) 696-4960   Fax: (703) 696-0144
E-mail: education@nmcrs.org
Web: www.nmcrs.org/education.html

Summary To provide funding to Navy and Marine Corps veterans who were wounded in combat in Iraq or Afghanistan and are interested in becoming a teacher.

Eligibility This program is open to Navy and Marine Corps veterans who were injured in combat in Operations Enduring Freedom, Iraqi Freedom, or New Dawn. Applicants must be enrolled full time in an undergraduate program leading to a bachelor's degree and teacher licensure. They must have a GPA of 2.5 or higher. Along with their application, they must submit a 1-page essay describing the factors in their background and military experience that convinced them to prepare for a career in education and the special qualities they will bring to the classroom that will have a positive impact on the youth of America. Financial need is not considered.

Financial data The stipend is $3,000 per year. Funds are paid directly to the student.

Duration 1 year; recipients may reapply.

Additional information The Society of Sponsors of the United States Navy, an organization of women who serve as sponsors of ships, established this program in 2008 to honor the centennial of its founding.

Number awarded Up to 5 each year.

Deadline Applications may be submitted at any time.

[119]
SOUTH DAKOTA REDUCED TUITION FOR VETERANS

South Dakota Board of Regents
Attn: Scholarship Committee
306 East Capitol Avenue, Suite 200
Pierre, SD 57501-2545
(605) 773-3455   Fax: (605) 773-2422
E-mail: info@sdbor.edu
Web: www.sdbor.edu/students/redtuit_Veterans.htm

Summary To provide free tuition at South Dakota public colleges and universities to certain veterans.

Eligibility This program is open to current residents of South Dakota who have been discharged from the military forces of the United States under honorable conditions. Applicants must meet 1 of the following criteria: 1) served on active duty at any time between August 2, 1990 and March 3, 1991; 2) received an Armed Forces Expeditionary Medal, Southwest Asia Service Medal, or other U.S. campaign or service medal for participation in combat operations against hostile forces outside the boundaries of the United States: or 3) have a service-connected disability rating of at least 10%. They may not be eligible for any other educational assistance from the U.S. government. Qualifying veterans must apply for this benefit within 20 years after the date proclaimed for the cessation of hostilities or within 6 years from and after the date of their discharge from military service, whichever is later. They must be attending or planning to attend a South Dakota state-supported institution of higher education or state-supported technical or vocational school.

Financial data Eligible veterans receive a waiver of tuition. The waiver applies only to tuition, not fees.

Duration Eligible veterans are entitled to receive 1 month of tuition waiver for each month of qualifying service, from a minimum of 1 year to a maximum of 4 years.

Number awarded Varies each year.

Deadline Deadline not specified.

[120]
STUDENT VETERANS OF AMERICA-ILLINOIS PATRIOT EDUCATION FUND

Student Veterans of America
P.O. Box 77673
Washington, DC 20013
E-mail: SVA@studentveterans.org
Web: www.studentveterans.org/?page=Programs

Summary To provide financial assistance to veterans from Illinois who are working on a bachelor's or graduate degree at a college or university in the state.

Eligibility This program is open to student veterans who are working on an undergraduate or graduate degree at a college or university in Illinois. Applicants must have a strong Illinois connection (e.g., lived in the state prior to service). Selection is based on academic achievement, participation in

Student Veterans of America (SVA), community involvement, and a personal essay.

Financial data The stipend is $1,000.

Duration 1 year.

Additional information These program, first awarded in 2012, is supported by the Illinois Patriot Education Fund (IPEF).

Number awarded Varies each year; recently 7 of these scholarships were awarded.

Deadline January of each year.

[121]
TAILHOOK EDUCATIONAL FOUNDATION SCHOLARSHIPS

Tailhook Educational Foundation
9696 Businesspark Avenue
P.O. Box 26626
San Diego, CA 92196-0626
(858) 689-9223   Toll Free: (800) 322-4665
E-mail: tag@tailhook.net
Web: www.tailhook.org/Foundation.html

Summary To provide financial assistance for college to personnel associated with naval aviation and their children.

Eligibility This program is open to 1) the children (natural, step, and adopted) of current or former U.S. Navy or Marine Corps personnel who served as an aviator, flight officer, or air crewman, or 2) personnel and children of personnel who are serving or have served on board a U.S. Navy aircraft carrier as a member of the ship's company or air wing. Applicants must be enrolled or accepted for enrollment at an accredited college or university. Selection is based on educational and extracurricular achievements, merit, and citizenship.

Financial data Stipend range from $1,500 to $15,000.

Duration 1 to 2 years.

Number awarded Varies each year; recently, 71 of these scholarships were awarded.

Deadline March of each year.

[122]
TENNESSEE FALLEN HEROES MEMORIAL SCHOLARSHIP

Tennessee Marine Family
Attn: Scholarship Coordinator
P.O. Box 291021
Nashville, TN 37229-1021
E-mail: scholarship@tnmarinefamily.org
Web: www.tnmarinefamily.org/scholarship.html

Summary To provide financial assistance to veterans and other residents of Tennessee who are attending or planning to attend college in the state.

Eligibility This program is open to residents of Tennessee who are graduating high school seniors, honorably discharged from military service, or currently attending a college or trade school. Applicants must be enrolled or planning to enroll full time at an accredited college, university, or trade school in Tennessee. Along with their application, they must submit an essay of 500 to 1,000 words on the meaning of the phrase, "Support Our Troops." Selection is based on academic achievement, community and extracurricular involvement, leadership positions held, and awards and recognition.

Financial data The stipend is $1,000.

Duration 1 year.

Additional information This program was established in 2007 to show support for members of the U.S. armed forces killed in combat. Applicants are not required, however, to have a relationship to those deceased military personnel.

Number awarded Varies each year; recently, 3 of these scholarships were awarded.

Deadline April of each year.

[123]
TENNESSEE HELPING HEROES GRANTS

Tennessee Student Assistance Corporation
Parkway Towers
404 James Robertson Parkway, Suite 1510
Nashville, TN 37243-0820
(615) 741-1346   Toll Free: (800) 342-1663
Fax: (615) 741-6101   E-mail: TSAC.Aidinfo@tn.gov
Web: www.tn.gov/collegepays/mon_college/hh_grant.htm

Summary To provide funding to veterans and current Reservists or National Guard members who are residents of Tennessee and enrolled at a college or university in the state.

Eligibility This program is open to residents of Tennessee who are veterans honorably discharged from the U.S. armed forces and former or current members of a Reserve or Tennessee National Guard unit who were called into active military service. Applicants must have been awarded, on or after September 11, 2001, the Iraq Campaign Medal, the Afghanistan Campaign Medal, or the Global War on Terrorism Expeditionary Medal. They must be enrolled at least half time at an eligible college or university in Tennessee and receive no final failing grade in any course. No academic standard or financial need requirements apply.

Financial data Grants are $1,000 per semester for full-time study or $500 per semester for part-time study. Funds are awarded after completion of each semester of work.

Duration Grants are awarded until completion of the equivalent of 8 full semesters of work, completion of a baccalaureate degree, or the eighth anniversary of honorable discharge from military service, whichever comes first.

Additional information This program was added as a component of the Tennessee Education Lottery Scholarship Program in 2005.

Number awarded Varies each year; recently, 503 students received $680,000 in scholarships.

Deadline August of each year for fall enrollment, January of each year for spring, or April of each year for summer.

[124]
U.S. ARMY WOMEN'S FOUNDATION LEGACY SCHOLARSHIPS

U.S. Army Women's Foundation
Attn: Scholarship Committee
P.O. Box 5030
Fort Lee, VA 23801-0030
(804) 734-3078   E-mail: info@awfdn.org
Web: www.awfdn.org/programs/legacyscholarships.shtml

Summary To provide money for college to women who are serving or have served in the Army and their children.

Eligibility This program is open to 1) women who have served or are serving honorably in the U.S. Army, U.S. Army Reserve, or Army National Guard; and 2) children of women who served honorably in the U.S. Army, U.S. Army Reserve, or Army National Guard. Applicants must be 1) upper-division students at an accredited college or university and have a GPA of 3.0 or higher; or 2) high school graduates or GED recipients enrolled at a community college and have a GPA of 2.5 or higher. Along with their application, they must submit a 2-page essay on why they should be considered for this scholarship, their future plans as related to their program of study, and information about their community service, activities, and work experience. Selection is based on merit, academic potential, community service, and financial need.

Financial data The stipend is $2,500 for college and university students or $1,000 for community college students.

Duration 1 year.

Number awarded 5 to 10 each year.

Deadline January of each year.

[125]
UTAH TUITION WAIVER FOR PURPLE HEART RECIPIENTS

Utah Department of Veteran's Affairs
Attn: Director
550 Foothill Boulevard, Room 202
Salt Lake City, UT 84108
(801) 326-2372   Toll Free: (800) 894-9497 (within UT)
Fax: (801) 326-2369   E-mail: veterans@utah.gov
Web: veterans.utah.gov/homepage/stateBenefits/index.html

Summary To provide a tuition waiver to veterans in Utah who received a Purple Heart award and are interested in working on an undergraduate or graduate degree at a public institution in the state.

Eligibility This program is open to residents of Utah who received a Purple Heart award as a result of military service. Applicants must be working on an undergraduate or master's degree at a public college or university in the state.

Financial data Tuition at the rate for residents of the state is waived for qualified veterans.

Duration Tuition is waived until completion of a bachelor's or master's degree.

Number awarded Varies each year.

Deadline Deadline not specified.

[126]
VA MORTGAGE CENTER.COM MILITARY EDUCATION SCHOLARSHIP PROGRAM

VA Mortgage Center.com
2101 Chapel Plaza Court, Suite 107
Columbia, MO 65203
(573) 876-2729   Toll Free: (800) 405-6682
E-mail: jbuerck@vamc.com
Web: www.vamortgagecenter.com/scholarships.html

Summary To provide financial assistance for college to students who have a tie to the military.

Eligibility This program is open to 1) current and prospective ROTC program students; 2) active-duty military personnel with plans to attend college; 3) honorably-discharged veterans of the U.S. military; and 4) children of veterans or active-duty military. Applicants must be attending or planning to attend college as a full-time student. Selection is based primarily on an essay.

Financial data The stipend is $1,000.

Duration 1 year.

Additional information This program began in 2007.

Number awarded 10 each year: 5 each term.

Deadline April or October of each year.

[127]
VAA/ANGEA SCHOLARSHIP

Virginia Army/Air National Guard Enlisted Association
Attn: SMSgt Lori W. Flinn Scholarship Chair
15249 Fountain Road
Ashland, VA 23005
(804) 519-6491   E-mail: Scholarship@vaaangea.org
Web: www.vaaangea.org

Summary To provide financial assistance to members of the Virginia Army/Air National Guard Enlisted Association (VaA/ANGEA) and their families who are interested in attending college in any state.

Eligibility This program is open to 1) enlisted soldiers or enlisted airmen currently serving as a member of the Virginia National Guard (VNG) who are also a member of the VaA/ANGEA; 2) retired enlisted soldiers or retired enlisted airmen of the VNG who are also a member of the VaA/ANGEA; 3) spouses of current enlisted soldiers or enlisted airmen of the VNG who are also a member of the VaA/ANGEA; 4) spouses of retired enlisted soldiers or retired enlisted airmen of the VNG who are also a member of the VaA/ANGEA; and 5) dependents of current or retired enlisted soldiers or airmen of the VNG (a copy of the dependency decree may be required) who are also a member of the VaA/ANGEA. Applicants must submit a copy of their school transcript (high school or college), a letter with specific facts about their desire to continue their education and their need for assistance, 3 letters of recommendation, a letter of academic reference, and a photocopy of their VaA/ANGEA membership card. Selection is based on academics (15 points), personal statement (15 points), letters of recommendation (16 points), school involvement (15 points), community involvement (15 points), responsibility (15 points), and financial need (9 points).

Financial data Generally, stipends are $1,000 or $500.

Duration 1 year; recipients may reapply.

Number awarded Generally, 2 scholarships at $1,000 and 4 scholarships at $500 are awarded each year.

Deadline March of each year.

[128]
VADM SAMUEL L. GRAVELY, JR., USN (RET.) MEMORIAL SCHOLARSHIPS

Armed Forces Communications and Electronics Association
Attn: AFCEA Educational Foundation
4400 Fair Lakes Court
Fairfax, VA 22033-3899
(703) 631-6138   Toll Free: (800) 336-4583, ext. 6138
Fax: (703) 631-4693   E-mail: scholarshipsinfo@afcea.org
Web: www.afcea.org

Summary To provide funding to students (particularly those who are veterans or current military personnel) majoring in specified scientific fields at an Historically Black College or University (HBCU).

Eligibility This program is open to sophomores and juniors enrolled full or part time at an accredited 2- or 4-year HBCU or in a distance learning or online degree program affiliated with those institutions. They must be working toward a bachelor's degree in engineering (aerospace, computer, electrical, or systems), computer science, computer engineering technology, computer information systems, mathematics, physics, information systems management, or other field directly related to the support of U.S. intelligence or homeland security enterprises. Special consideration is given to military enlisted personnel and veterans.

Financial data The stipend is $5,000.

Duration 1 year; may be renewed.

Additional information This program was established in 2009 with support from American Systems.

Number awarded At least 2 each year.

Deadline April of each year.

[129]
VETERANS EDUCATIONAL ASSISTANCE PROGRAM (VEAP)

Department of Veterans Affairs
Attn: Veterans Benefits Administration
810 Vermont Avenue, N.W.
Washington, DC 20420
(202) 418-4343   Toll Free: (888) GI-BILL1
Web: www.gibill.va.gov/benefits/other_programs/veap.html

Summary To provide financial assistance for college or graduate school to veterans who first entered active duty between January 1, 1977 and June 30, 1985.

Eligibility Veterans who served and military servicemembers currently serving are eligible if they 1) entered active duty between January 1, 1977 and June 30, 1985; 2) were released under conditions other than dishonorable or continue on active duty; 3) served for a continuous period of 181 days or more (or were discharged earlier for a service-connected disability); and 4) have satisfactorily contributed to the program. No individuals on active duty could enroll in this program after March 31, 1987. Veterans who enlisted for the first time after September 7, 1980 or entered active duty as an officer or enlistee after October 16, 1981 must have completed 24 continuous months of active duty. Benefits are available for the pursuit of an associate, bachelor, or graduate degree at a college or university; a certificate or diploma from a business, technical, or vocational school; apprenticeship or on-the-job training programs; cooperative courses; correspondence school courses; tutorial assistance; remedial, refresher, and deficiency training; flight training; study abroad programs leading to a college degree; nontraditional training away from school; and work-study for students enrolled at least three-quarter time.

Financial data Participants contribute to the program, through monthly deductions from their military pay, from $25 to $100 monthly, up to a maximum of $2,700. They may also, while on active duty, make a lump sum contribution to the training fund. When the participant elects to use the benefits for an approved course of education or training, the Department of Veterans Affairs (VA) will match the contribution at the rate of $2 for every $1 made by the participant.

Duration Participants receive monthly payments for the number of months they contributed or for 36 months, whichever is less. The amount of the payments is determined by dividing the number of months benefits will be paid into the participant's training fund total. Participants have 10 years from the date of last discharge or release from active duty within which to use these benefits.

Additional information A participant may leave this program at the end of any 12-consecutive-month period of participation and those who do so may have their contributions refunded.

Number awarded Varies each year.

Deadline Applications may be submitted at any time.

[130]
VETERANS OF ENDURING FREEDOM (AFGHANISTAN) AND IRAQI FREEDOM SCHOLARSHIP

Armed Forces Communications and Electronics Association
Attn: AFCEA Educational Foundation
4400 Fair Lakes Court
Fairfax, VA 22033-3899
(703) 631-6138   Toll Free: (800) 336-4583, ext. 6138
Fax: (703) 631-4693 E-mail: scholarshipsinfo@afcea.org
Web: www.afcea.org

Summary To provide financial assistance to veterans and military personnel who served in Afghanistan or Iraq and are working on an undergraduate degree in fields related to the support of U.S. intelligence enterprises.

Eligibility This program is open to active-duty and honorably discharged U.S. military members (including Reservists and National Guard personnel) who served in Enduring Freedom (Afghanistan) or Iraqi Freedom operations. Applicants must be enrolled at a 2- or 4-year institution in the United States and working on an undergraduate degree in computer engineering technology, computer information systems, computer network systems, computer science, electronics engineering technology, engineering (aerospace, computer, electrical, or systems), information systems management, information systems security, mathematics, physics, technology management, or other field directly related to the support of U.S. intelligence enterprises or national security. Along with their application, they must submit an essay that includes a brief synopsis of relevant work experience (including military assignments), a brief statement of career goals after graduation, and an explanation of how their academic and career goals will contribute to the areas related to communications, intelligence and/or information systems, and the mission of the Armed Forces Communications and Electronics Association (AFCEA). Financial need is also considered.

Financial data The stipend is $2,500.

Duration 1 year.

Additional information This program began in 2005 with funding from the Northern Virginia Chapter of AFCEA.

Number awarded 12 each year: 6 for the fall semester and 6 for the spring semester.

Deadline March of each year for fall semester; October of each year for spring semester.

[131]
VETERANS OF THE VIETNAM WAR NATIONAL SCHOLARSHIP PROGRAM

Veterans of the Vietnam War, Inc.
Attn: Assistance in Education Program
805 South Township Boulevard
Pittston, PA 18640-3327
(570) 603-9740   Fax: (570) 603-9741
Web: www.vvnw.org

Summary To provide money for college to members of Veterans of the Vietnam War (VVnW) and their families.

Eligibility This program is open to members of the VVnW in good standing for at least 1 year and their spouses, children, adopted children, foster children, and other immediate descendants. Applicants must be enrolled in or accepted to a program of postsecondary education. Selection is based on a random drawing; financial need and merit are not considered.

Financial data The stipend is $1,000. Funds are paid directly to the recipient.

Duration 1 year.

Number awarded 1 or more each year, depending on the availability of funds.

Deadline October of each year.

[132]
VII CORPS DESERT STORM VETERANS ASSOCIATION SCHOLARSHIP

VII Corps Desert Storm Veterans Association
Attn: Scholarship Committee
Army Historical Foundation
2425 Wilson Boulevard
Arlington, VA 22201
(703) 978-6867   E-mail: viicorpsdsva@aol.com
Web: www.desertstormvets.org/Scholarship.html

Summary To provide financial assistance for college to students who served, or are the spouses or other family members of individuals who served, with VII Corps in Operations Desert Shield, Desert Storm, or related activities.

Eligibility Applicants must have served, or be a family member of those who served, with VII Corps in Operations Desert Shield/Desert Storm, Provide Comfort, or 1 of the support base activities. Scholarships are limited to students entering or enrolled in accredited technical institutions (trade or specialty), 2-year colleges, and 4-year colleges or universities. Awards will not be made to individuals receiving military academy appointments or full 4-year scholarships. Letters of recommendation and a transcript are required. Selection is not based solely on academic standing; consideration is also given to extracurricular activities and other self-development skills and abilities obtained through on-the-job training or correspondence courses. Priority is given to survivors of VII Corps soldiers who died during Operations Desert Shield/Desert Storm or Provide Comfort, veterans who are also members of the VII Corps Desert Storm Veterans Association, and family members of veterans who are also members of the VII Corps Desert Storm Veterans Association.

Financial data The stipend ranges from $1,000 to $5,000 per year. Funds are paid to the recipients upon proof of admission or registration at an accredited academic institution.

Duration 1 year; recipients may reapply.

Additional information This program began in 1998.

Number awarded Approximately 3 each year.

Deadline January of each year.

[133]
VOCATIONAL REHABILITATION AND EMPLOYMENT VETSUCCESS PROGRAM

Department of Veterans Affairs
Attn: Veterans Benefits Administration
Vocational Rehabilitation and Employment Service
810 Vermont Avenue, N.W.
Washington, DC 20420
(202) 418-4343   Toll Free: (800) 827-1000
Web: www.vba.va.gov/bin/vre/index.htm

Summary To provide funding to veterans with service-connected disabilities who need assistance to find employment or, if seriously disabled, to live independently.

Eligibility This program is open to veterans who have a service-connected disability of at least 10% or a memorandum rating of 20% or more from the Department of Veterans Affairs (VA). They must qualify for services provided by the VA VetSuccess that include assistance finding and keeping a job, including the use of special employer incentives and job accommodations; on-the-job training, apprenticeships, and non-paid work experiences; postsecondary training at a college, vocational, technical, or business school; supportive rehabilitation services such as case management, counseling, and medical referrals; independent living services for veterans unable to work due to the severity of their disabilities.

Financial data While in training and for 2 months after, eligible disabled veterans may receive subsistence allowances in addition to their disability compensation or retirement pay. Generally, the current full-time monthly rate is $566.97 with no dependents, $703.28 with 1 dependent, $828.76 with 2 dependents, and $60.41 for each additional dependent; proportional rates apply for less than full-time training.

Duration Veterans remain eligible for these services up to 12 years from either the date of separation from active military service or the date the veteran was first notified by VA of a service-connected disability rating (whichever came later).

Number awarded Varies each year.

Deadline Applications are accepted at any time.

[134]
WEST VIRGINIA VETERAN'S RE-EDUCATION SCHOLARSHIP PROGRAM

West Virginia Department of Veteran's Assistance
Attn: Scholarship Program
1321 Plaza East, Suite 109
Charleston, WV 25301-1400
(304) 558-3661   Toll Free: (866) WV4-VETS (within WV)
Fax: (304) 558-3662 E-mail: Angela.S.Meadows@wv.gov
Web: www.veterans.wv.gov

Summary To provide financial assistance to veterans in West Virginia who wish to return to college after completing their military service.

Eligibility This program is open to residents of West Virginia who have been honorably discharged after at least 181 consecutive days of military service; Reservists with active duty for training only are not eligible. Applicants must be eligible for federal Pell grants or be unemployed and have exhausted all federal educational benefits from the Department of Veterans Affairs (VA). They must be attending or planning to attend a college or university in West Virginia and apply through their institution.

Financial data The stipend is $500 per term for full-time students or $250 per term for part-time students. The maximum award per calendar year is $1,500.
Duration 1 year; may be renewed upon reapplication if the student maintains a cumulative GPA of at least 2.0.
Number awarded Varies each year.
Deadline July of each year for the fall semester; November of each year for the spring semester.

[135]
WILMA D. HOYAL/MAXINE CHILTON SCHOLARSHIPS

American Legion Auxiliary
Department of Arizona
4701 North 19th Avenue, Suite 100
Phoenix, AZ 85015-3727
(602) 241-1080   Fax: (602) 604-9640
E-mail: secretary@aladeptaz.org
Web: aladeptaz.org/Scholarships.html

Summary To provide financial assistance to veterans, the dependents of veterans, and other students who are majoring in selected subjects at Arizona public universities.
Eligibility This program is open to second-year or upper-division full-time students majoring in political science, public programs, or special education at public universities in Arizona (the University of Arizona, Northern Arizona University, or Arizona State University). Applicants must have been Arizona residents for at least 1 year. They must have a GPA of 3.0 or higher. U.S. citizenship is required. Honorably-discharged veterans and immediate family members of veterans receive preference. Selection is based on scholarship (25%), financial need (40%), character (20%), and leadership (15%).
Financial data The stipend is $1,000.
Duration 1 year; renewable.
Number awarded 1 to each of the 3 universities.
Deadline May of each year.

[136]
WISCONSIN G.I. BILL TUITION REMISSION PROGRAM

Wisconsin Department of Veterans Affairs
201 West Washington Avenue
P.O. Box 7843
Madison, WI 53707-7843
(608) 266-1311   Toll Free: (800) WIS-VETS
Fax: (608) 267-0403   E-mail: WDVAInfo@dva.state.wi.us
Web: www.dva.state.wi.us/Ben_education.asp

Summary To provide financial assistance for college or graduate school to Wisconsin veterans and their dependents.
Eligibility This program is open to current residents of Wisconsin who 1) were residents of the state when they entered or reentered active duty in the U.S. armed forces, or 2) have moved to the state and have been residents for any consecutive 12-month period after entry or reentry into service. Applicants must have served on active duty for at least 2 continuous years or for at least 90 days during specified wartime periods. Also eligible are 1) qualifying children and unremarried surviving spouses of Wisconsin veterans who died in the line of duty or as the direct result of a service-connected disability; and 2) children and spouses of Wisconsin veterans who have a service-connected disability rated by the U.S. Department of Veterans Affairs as 30% or greater. Children

must be between 17 and 25 years of age (regardless of the date of the veteran's death or initial disability rating) and be a Wisconsin resident for tuition purposes. Spouses remain eligible for 10 years following the date of the veteran's death or initial disability rating; they must be Wisconsin residents for tuition purposes but they may enroll full or part time. Students may attend any institution, center, or school within the University of Wisconsin (UW) System or the Wisconsin Technical College System (WCTS). There are no income limits, delimiting periods following military service during which the benefit must be used, or limits on the level of study (e.g., vocational, undergraduate, professional, or graduate).
Financial data Veterans who qualify as a Wisconsin resident for tuition purposes are eligible for a remission of 100% of standard academic fees and segregated fees at a UW campus or 100% of program and material fees at a WCTS institution. Veterans who qualify as a Wisconsin veteran for purposes of this program but for other reasons fail to meet the definition of a Wisconsin resident for tuition purposes at the UW system are eligible for a remission of 100% of non-resident fees. Spouses and children of deceased or disabled veterans are entitled to a remission of 100% of tuition and fees at a UW or WCTS institution.
Duration Up to 8 semesters or 128 credits, whichever is greater.
Additional information This program was established in 2005 as a replacement for Wisconsin Tuition and Fee Reimbursement Grants.
Number awarded Varies each year.
Deadline Applications must be submitted within 14 days from the office start of the academic term: in October for fall, March for spring, or June for summer.

[137]
WISCONSIN JOB RETRAINING GRANTS

Wisconsin Department of Veterans Affairs
201 West Washington Avenue
P.O. Box 7843
Madison, WI 53707-7843
(608) 266-1311   Toll Free: (800) WIS-VETS
Fax: (608) 267-0403   E-mail: WDVAInfo@dva.state.wi.us
Web: www.dva.state.wi.us/Ben_retraininggrants.asp

Summary To provide funds to recently unemployed Wisconsin veterans or their families who need financial assistance while being retrained for employment.
Eligibility This program is open to current residents of Wisconsin who 1) were residents of the state when they entered or reentered active duty in the U.S. armed forces, or 2) have moved to the state and have been residents for any consecutive 12-month period after entry or reentry into service. Applicants must have served on active duty for at least 2 continuous years or for at least 90 days during specified wartime periods. Unremarried spouses and minor or dependent children of deceased veterans who would have been eligible for the grant if they were living today may also be eligible. The applicant must, within the year prior to the date of application, have become unemployed (involuntarily laid off or discharged, not due to willful misconduct) or underemployed (experienced an involuntary reduction of income). Underemployed applicants must have current annual income from employment that does not exceed federal poverty guidelines (currently $14,521 for a family of 1, rising to $50,557 for a

family of 8). All applicants must be retraining at accredited schools in Wisconsin or in a structured on-the-job program. Course work toward a college degree does not qualify. Training does not have to be full time, but the program must be completed within 2 years and must reasonably be expected to lead to employment.

Financial data The maximum grant is $3,000 per year; the actual amount varies, depending upon the amount of the applicant's unmet need. In addition to books, fees, and tuition, the funds may be used for living expenses.

Duration 1 year; may be renewed 1 additional year.

Number awarded Varies each year.

Deadline Applications may be submitted at any time.

[138]
WISCONSIN VETERANS EDUCATION (VETED) REIMBURSEMENT GRANTS

Wisconsin Department of Veterans Affairs
201 West Washington Avenue
P.O. Box 7843
Madison, WI 53707-7843
(608) 266-1311   Toll Free: (800) WIS-VETS
Fax: (608) 267-0403   E-mail: WDVAInfo@dva.state.wi.us
Web: www.dva.state.wi.us/Ben_VetEd.asp

Summary To provide financial assistance for undergraduate education to Wisconsin veterans.

Eligibility This program is open to current residents of Wisconsin who 1) were residents of the state when they entered or reentered active duty in the U.S. armed forces, or 2) have moved to the state and have been residents for any consecutive 12-month period after entry or reentry into service. Applicants must have served on active duty for at least 2 continuous years or for at least 90 days during specified wartime periods. They must be working full or part time on a degree, certificate of graduation, or course completion at an eligible campus of the University of Wisconsin, technical college, or approved private institution of higher education in Wisconsin or Minnesota. Their household income must be below $50,000 plus $1,000 for each dependent in excess of 2 dependents. Veterans seeking reimbursement through this program must first apply for Wisconsin G.I. Bill benefits. To qualify for reimbursement, they must achieve at least a 2.0 GPA or an average grade of "C" in the semester for which reimbursement is requested. Veterans may use this program up to 10 years after leaving active duty. Once a veteran reaches the 10-year delimiting date, he or she may "bank" up to 60 unused credits for part-time study.

Financial data Eligible veterans are entitled to reimbursement of 100% of the costs of tuition and fees not covered by other grants, scholarships, or remissions, to a maximum of the UW-Madison rate for the same number of credits.

Duration The amount of reimbursement depends on the time the veteran served on active duty: 30 credits or 2 semesters for 90 to 180 days of active service, 60 credits or 4 semesters for 181 to 730 days of active service, or 120 credits or 8 semesters for 731 days or more of active service.

Additional information This program was established in 2005 as a replacement for the former Wisconsin Part-Time Study Grants. Reimbursement is not provided to students for payment amounts for which they are eligible under other programs, including the Wisconsin G.I. Bill.

Number awarded Varies each year.

Deadline Applications must be received within 60 days of the start of the course, semester, or term.

[139]
WOMEN MARINES ASSOCIATION SCHOLARSHIP PROGRAM

Women Marines Association
P.O. Box 377
Oaks, PA 19456-0377
Toll Free: (888) 525-1943
E-mail: scholarship@womenmarines.org
Web: www.womenmarines.org/scholarships.aspx

Summary To provide money for college or graduate school to students with ties to the military who are sponsored by members of the Women Marines Association (WMA).

Eligibility Applicants must be sponsored by a WMA member and fall into 1 of the following categories: 1) have served or are serving in the U.S. Marine Corps, regular or Reserve; 2) are a direct descendant by blood or legal adoption or a stepchild of a Marine on active duty or who has served honorably in the U.S. Marine Corps, regular or Reserve; 3) are a sibling or a descendant of a sibling by blood or legal adoption or a stepchild of a Marine on active duty or who has served honorably in the U.S. Marine Corps, regular or Reserve; or 4) have completed 2 years in a Marine Corps JROTC program. WMA members may sponsor an unlimited number of applicants per year. High school seniors must submit transcripts (GPA of 3.0 or higher) and SAT or ACT scores. Undergraduate and graduate students must have a GPA of 3.0 or higher.

Financial data The stipend is $1,500 per year.

Duration 1 year; may be renewed 1 additional year.

Additional information This program includes the following named scholarships: the WMA Memorial Scholarships, the Lily H. Gridley Memorial Scholarship, the Ethyl and Armin Wiebke Memorial Scholarship, the Maj. Megan Malia McClung Memorial Scholarship, the Agnes Sopcak Memorial Scholarship, the Virginia Guveyan Memorial Scholarship, and the LaRue A. Ditmore Music Scholarships. Applicants must know a WMA member to serve as their sponsor; the WMA will not supply listings of the names or addresses of chapters or individual members.

Number awarded Varies each year.

Deadline January of each year.

[140]
WYOMING OVERSEAS COMBAT VETERAN TUITION BENEFIT

Wyoming Veterans Commission
Attn: Executive Director
5410 Bishop Boulevard
Cheyenne, WY 82009
(307) 777-8151   Toll Free: (800) 833-5987
Fax: (307) 777-8150   E-mail: larry.barttelbort@wyo.gov
Web: sites.google.com

Summary To provide funding to Wyoming veterans who served in overseas combat anytime except during the Vietnam era and are interested in attending college in the state.

Eligibility This program is open to Wyoming veterans who served anytime except during the Vietnam era and were residents of Wyoming for at least 1 year before entering military service. Applicants must have received an honorable discharge and have been awarded the armed forces expeditionary medal or other authorized service or campaign medal indicating service to the United States in an armed conflict in a foreign country. They must enroll at the University of Wyoming or a community college in the state within 10 years following completion of military service.

Financial data Qualifying veterans are eligible for free resident tuition at the University of Wyoming or at any of the state's community colleges.

Duration Up to 10 semesters.

Additional information Applications may be obtained from the institution the applicant is planning to attend.

Number awarded Varies each year.

Deadline Applications may be submitted at any time, but they should be received 2 or 3 weeks before the beginning of the semester.

[141]
WYOMING VIETNAM VETERAN TUITION BENEFIT

Wyoming Veterans Commission
Attn: Executive Director
5410 Bishop Boulevard
Cheyenne, WY 82009
(307) 777-8151   Toll Free: (800) 833-5987
Fax: (307) 777-8150   E-mail: larry.barttelbort@wyo.gov
Web: sites.google.com

Summary To provide financial assistance to Wyoming veterans who served during the Vietnam era and are interested in attending college in the state.

Eligibility This program is open to Wyoming veterans who 1) served on active duty with the U.S. armed forces between August 5, 1964 and May 7, 1975; 2) received a Vietnam service medal between those dates; 3) received an honorable discharge; 4) have lived in Wyoming for at least 1 year; and 5) have exhausted their veterans' benefits entitlement or for some other reason are no longer eligible for U.S. Department of Veterans Affairs benefits. Applicants must be attending or planning to attend the University of Wyoming or a community college in the state.

Financial data Qualifying veterans are eligible for free resident tuition at the University of Wyoming or at any of the state's community colleges.

Duration Up to 10 semesters.

Additional information Applications may be obtained from the institution the applicant is planning to attend.

Number awarded Varies each year.

Deadline Applications may be submitted at any time, but they should be received 2 or 3 weeks before the beginning of the semester.

[142]
YELLOW RIBBON PROGRAM OF THE POST-9/11 GI BILL

Department of Veterans Affairs
Attn: Veterans Benefits Administration
810 Vermont Avenue, N.W.
Washington, DC 20420
(202) 418-4343   Toll Free: (888) GI-BILL1
Web: www.gibill.va.gov

Summary To provide financial assistance to veterans and their dependents who qualify for the Post-9/11 GI Bill and wish to attend a high cost private or out-of-state college or graduate school.

Eligibility Maximum Post-9/11 GI Bill benefits are available to veterans who 1) served on active duty for at least 36 aggregate months after September 11, 2001; or 2) were honorably discharged for a service-connected disability and served at least 30 continuous days after September 11, 2001. Military personnel currently on active duty and their spouses may qualify for Post-9/11 GI Bill benefits but are not eligible for the Yellow Ribbon Program. This program is available to veterans who qualify for those benefits at the 100% rate, the children of those veterans to whom they wish to transfer their benefits, and the children and spouses of active-duty personnel who qualify for benefits at the 100% rate to whom they wish to transfer those benefits. Applicants must be working on or planning to work on an undergraduate or graduate degree at a private or out-of-state public institution that charges tuition in excess of the $17,500 cap imposed by the Post-9/11 GI Bill and that has agreed with the Department of Veterans Affairs (VA) to participate in this program.

Financial data Colleges and universities that charge more than $17,500 per academic year in tuition and fees (or a higher amount at schools in Arizona, Michigan, New Hampshire, New York, Pennsylvania, South Carolina, and Texas) agree to waive tuition (up to 50%) for qualifying veterans and dependents. The amount that the college or university waives is matched by VA.

Duration Most participants receive up to 36 months of entitlement under this program. Benefits are payable for up to 15 years following release from active duty.

Number awarded Varies each year.

Deadline Deadline not specified.

Military Personnel

[143]
10TH MOUNTAIN DIVISION (LIGHT INFANTRY) SCHOLARSHIPS

Northern New York Community Foundation, Inc.
120 Washington Street, Suite 400
Watertown, NY 13601
(315) 782-7110   Fax: (315) 782-0047
E-mail: info@nnycf.org
Web: www.nnycf.org/scholarships.asp?mm=6

Summary To provide money for college to current and former members of the 10th Mountain Division and their dependents.

Eligibility This program is open to current and former members of the 10th Mountain Division and their dependents (children and spouses). Applicants must be high school seniors applying for the freshmen year or traditional or non-traditional students enrolled as full-time undergraduates in any year of college or technical school. Along with their application, they must submit a 150-word essay on the character traits that have contributed the most to their success, how they have contributed to their success, and how each will contribute to their vision of a successful life. High school juniors who will graduate early because they are in an advanced placement program may also apply. Interviews are required. Selection is based on academics, personal data, and need.

Financial data The stipend is $5,000.

Duration 1 year.

Number awarded Varies each year; recently, 8 of these scholarships were awarded.

Deadline March of each year.

[144]
AFCEA DISABLED WAR VETERANS SCHOLARSHIPS

Armed Forces Communications and Electronics
Association
Attn: AFCEA Educational Foundation
4400 Fair Lakes Court
Fairfax, VA 22033-3899
(703) 631-6138   Toll Free: (800) 336-4583, ext. 6138
Fax: (703) 631-4693 E-mail: scholarshipsinfo@afcea.org
Web: www.afcea.org/education/scholarships/military

Summary To provide financial assistance to disabled military personnel and veterans who are majoring in specified scientific fields in college.

Eligibility This program is open to active-duty service personnel and honorably discharged U.S. military veterans, Reservists, and National Guard members who are disabled because of wounds received during service in Enduring Freedom (Afghanistan) or Iraqi Freedom operations. Applicants must be enrolled full or part time at an accredited 2- or 4-year college or university or in a distance learning or online degree program. They must be working toward a degree in engineering (aerospace, computer, electrical, or systems), computer science, computer engineering technology, computer network systems, computer information systems, electronics engineering technology, mathematics, physics, information systems management, information systems security, technology management, or other field directly related to the support of U.S. intelligence or national security enterprises. Selection is based on academics, leadership, and need.

Financial data The stipend is $2,500.

Duration 1 year.

Number awarded 2 each year: 1 for spring and 1 for fall.

Deadline March of each year for fall; November of each year for spring. Armed Forces Communications and Electronics Association Disabled War Veterans Scholarships.

[145]
AFCEA ROTC SCHOLARSHIPS

Armed Forces Communications and Electronics
Association
Attn: AFCEA Educational Foundation
4400 Fair Lakes Court
Fairfax, VA 22033-3899
(703) 631-6138   Toll Free: (800) 336-4583, ext. 6138
Fax: (703) 631-4693 E-mail: scholarshipsinfo@afcea.org
Web: www.afcea.org/education/scholarships/rotc/rotc1.asp

Summary To provide financial assistance to ROTC cadets who are majoring in fields related to communications and electronics.

Eligibility This program is open to ROTC cadets majoring in electronics, engineering (aerospace, chemical, computer, electrical, or systems), mathematics, computer science, physics, science or mathematics education, technology management, foreign languages, global security and intelligence studies, security and intelligence, international studies, or

other fields directly related to the support of U.S. national security enterprises. Applicants must be nominated by their ROTC professor, be entering their junior or senior year, be U.S. citizens, be of good moral character, have demonstrated academic excellence, be motivated to complete a college education and serve as officers in the U.S. armed forces, and be able to demonstrate financial need.

Financial data The stipend is $2,000.

Duration 1 year; may be renewed.

Number awarded 24 each year, divided equally among Army, Navy/Marine Corps, and Air Force ROTC programs; for each service, 4 are awarded to rising juniors and 4 to rising seniors.

Deadline February of each year.

[146]
AIR FORCE PROFESSIONAL OFFICER COURSE EARLY RELEASE PROGRAM

U.S. Air Force
Attn: Headquarters AFROTC/RRUE
Enlisted Commissioning Section
551 East Maxwell Boulevard
Maxwell AFB, AL 36112-5917
(334) 953-2091   Toll Free: (866) 4-AFROTC
Fax: (334) 953-6167   E-mail: enlisted@afrotc.com
Web: afrotc.com/scholarships/enlisted-scholarships

Summary To allow selected enlisted Air Force personnel to earn a baccalaureate degree by providing financial assistance for full-time college study as an ROTC cadet.

Eligibility Eligible to participate in this program are enlisted members of the Air Force under the age of 30 (or otherwise able to be commissioned before becoming 35 years of age) who have completed at least 1 year on continuous active duty, have served on station for at least 1 year, and have no more than 2 years remaining to complete their initial baccalaureate degree. Scholarship applicants must be younger than 31 years of age when they graduate and earn their commission. All applicants must have been accepted at a college or university offering the AFROTC 4-year program and must have a cumulative college GPA of 2.5 or higher. Their Air Force Officer Qualifying Test (AFOQT) scores must be at least 15 on the verbal and 10 on the quantitative. Applicants who have not completed 24 units of college work must have an ACT composite score of 24 or higher or an SAT combined critical reading and mathematics score of 1100 or higher. U.S. citizenship is required. Recently, priority was given to students in the following technical majors: architecture, chemistry, computer science, engineering (especially aeronautical, aerospace, architectural, astronautical, civil, computer, electrical, environmental, and mechanical), mathematics, meteorology/atmospheric sciences, operations research, and physics.

Financial data Participants receive a stipend of $250 to $500 per month and an allowance of $900 per year for books. No other scholarship funding is provided.

Duration 2 years (no more and no less).

Additional information Upon completing their degree, selectees are commissioned as officers in the Air Force with a 4-year service obligation. Recipients must attend a school with annual tuition and fees less than $15,000 per year. They are not allowed to pay the difference to attend a higher cost school.

Number awarded Varies each year.

Deadline October of each year.

[147]
AIR FORCE RESERVE TUITION ASSISTANCE

U.S. Air Force Reserve
Attn: Air Reserve Personnel Center
Directorate of Personnel Services
6760 East Irvington Place
Denver, CO 80280-4000
(303) 676-7037   Toll Free: (800) 525-0102
Fax: (478) 327-2215
E-mail: arpc.contactcenter@arpc.denver.af.mil
Web: www.arpc.afrc.af.mil

Summary To provide financial assistance for college or graduate school to members of the Air Force Reserve.

Eligibility This program is open to Air Force Reserve members interested in working on an undergraduate or graduate degree either through distance learning or on-campus courses from an accredited postsecondary institution. Applicants must be actively participating (for pay and points) and in good standing (not have a UIF, not placed on a control roster, not pending or issued an Article 15, and/or not pending court martial). They must submit a degree plan specifying all classes for which they are seeking assistance. Enlisted students must have retainability that extends beyond the last course approved for assistance or they must extend or re-enlist; commissioned officers must have a mandatory separation date of not less than 24 months of service commitment starting at the end of the last course completed.

Financial data Undergraduates receive 100% of tuition, to a maximum of $250 per semester hour or $4,500 per year; graduate students receive 75% of tuition, to a maximum of $250 per semester hour or $4,500 per year.

Duration 1 year; may be renewed.

Number awarded Varies each year.

Deadline Applications may be submitted at any time.

[148]
AIR FORCE ROTC BIOMEDICAL SCIENCES CORPS

U.S. Air Force
Attn: Headquarters AFROTC/RRUC
551 East Maxwell Boulevard
Maxwell AFB, AL 36112-5917
(334) 953-2091   Toll Free: (866) 4-AFROTC
Fax: (334) 953-6167   E-mail: afrotc1@maxwell.af.mil
Web: afrotc.com

Summary To provide financial assistance to students who are interested in joining Air Force ROTC in college and preparing for a career as a physical therapist, optometrist, or pharmacist.

Eligibility This program is open to U.S. citizens who are freshmen or sophomores in college and interested in a career as a physical therapist, optometrist, or pharmacist. Applicants must have a GPA of 2.0 or higher and meet all other academic and physical requirements for participation in AFROTC. At the time of their Air Force commissioning, they may be no more than 31 years of age. They must agree to serve for at least 4 years as nonline active-duty Air Force officers following graduation from college.

Financial data Awards are type 2 AFROTC scholarships that provide for payment of tuition and fees, to a maximum of $18,000 per year, plus an annual book allowance of $900. All recipients are also awarded a tax-free subsistence allowance for 10 months of each year that is $350 per month during their sophomore year, $450 during their junior year, and $500 during their senior year.

Duration 2 or 3 years, provided the recipient maintains a GPA of 2.0 or higher.

Additional information Recipients must also complete 4 years of aerospace studies courses at 1 of the 144 colleges and universities that have an Air Force ROTC unit on campus or 1 of the 984 colleges that have cross-enrollment agreements with those institutions. They must also attend a 4-week summer training camp at an Air Force base, usually between their sophomore and junior years. Following completion of their bachelor's degree, scholarship recipients earn a commission as a second lieutenant in the Air Force and serve at least 4 years.

Deadline June of each year.

[149]
AIR FORCE ROTC HIGH SCHOOL SCHOLARSHIPS

U.S. Air Force
Attn: Headquarters AFROTC/RRUC
551 East Maxwell Boulevard
Maxwell AFB, AL 36112-6106
(334) 953-2091   Toll Free: (866) 4-AFROTC
Fax: (334) 953-6167   E-mail: afrotc1@maxwell.af.mil
Web: afrotc.com/scholarships/high-school

Summary To provide financial assistance to high school seniors or graduates who are interested in joining Air Force ROTC in college and are willing to serve as Air Force officers following completion of their bachelor's degree.

Eligibility This program is open to high school seniors who are U.S. citizens at least 17 years of age and have been accepted at a college or university with an Air Force ROTC unit on campus or a college with a cross-enrollment agreement with such a college. Applicants must have a cumulative GPA of 3.0 or higher and an ACT composite score of 24 or higher or an SAT score of 1100 or higher (mathematics and critical reading portion only). They must agree to serve for at least 4 years as active-duty Air Force officers following graduation from college. Recently, scholarships were offered to students planning to major (in order or priority) in 1) the science and technical fields of architecture, chemistry, computer science, engineering (aeronautical, aerospace, astronautical, architectural, civil, computer, electrical, environmental, or mechanical), mathematics, meteorology and atmospheric sciences, nuclear physics, operations research, or physics; 2) foreign languages (Chinese, Dutch, French, German, Japanese, Italian, Korean, Spanish American, Polish, Persian-Farsi, Brazilian, Spanish-Castilian, Russian, Tagalog, Turkish, Vietnamese, southeast Asian languages, or Slavic languages); 3) all other fields.

Financial data Type 1 scholarships provide payment of full tuition and most laboratory fees, as well as $900 per year for books. Type 2 scholarships pay the same benefits except tuition is capped at $18,000 per year; students who attend an institution where tuition exceeds $18,000 must pay the difference. Type 7 scholarships pay full tuition and most laboratory fees, but students must attend a public college or university where they qualify for the in-state tuition rate or a college or university where the tuition is less than the in-state rate; they may not attend an institution with higher tuition and pay the difference. Approximately 5% of scholarship offers are for Type 1, approximately 20% are for Type 2, and approximately 75% are for Type 7. All recipients are also awarded a tax-free subsistence allowance for 10 months of each year that is $300 per month as a freshman, $350 per month as a sophomore, $450 per month as a junior, and $500 per month as a senior.

Duration 4 years.

Additional information While scholarship recipients can major in any subject, they must enroll in 4 years of aerospace studies courses at 1 of the 144 colleges and universities that have an Air Force ROTC unit on campus; students may also attend 1,025 other colleges that have cross-enrollment agreements with the institutions that have an Air Force ROTC unit on campus. Recipients must attend a 4-week summer training camp at an Air Force base, usually between their sophomore and junior years. Most cadets incur a 4-year active-duty commitment.

Number awarded Approximately 2,000 each year.

Deadline November of each year.

[150]
AIR FORCE ROTC NURSING SCHOLARSHIPS

U.S. Air Force
Attn: Headquarters AFROTC/RRUC
551 East Maxwell Boulevard
Maxwell AFB, AL 36112-5917
(334) 953-2091   Toll Free: (866) 4-AFROTC
Fax: (334) 953-6167   E-mail: afrotc1@maxwell.af.mil
Web: afrotc.com/admissions/professional-programs/nursing

Summary To provide financial assistance to college students who are interested in a career as a nurse, are interested in joining Air Force ROTC, and are willing to serve as Air Force officers following completion of their bachelor's degree.

Eligibility This program is open to U.S. citizens who are freshmen or sophomores in college and interested in a career as a nurse. Applicants must have a cumulative GPA of 2.5 or higher at the end of their freshman year and meet all other academic and physical requirements for participation in AFROTC. They must be interested in working on a nursing degree from an accredited program. At the time of Air Force commissioning, they may be no more than 31 years of age. They must be able to pass the Air Force Officer Qualifying Test (AFOQT) and the Air Force ROTC Physical Fitness Test.

Financial data Awards are type 1 AFROTC scholarships that provide for full payment of tuition and fees plus an annual book allowance of $900. All recipients are also awarded a tax-free subsistence allowance for 10 months of each year that is $350 per month during their sophomore year, $450 during their junior year, and $500 during their senior year.

Duration 2 or 3 years, provided the recipient maintains a GPA of 2.5 or higher.

Additional information Recipients must also complete 4 years of aerospace studies courses at 1 of the 144 colleges and universities that have an Air Force ROTC unit on campus or 1 of the 984 colleges that have cross-enrollment agreements with those institutions. They must also attend a 4-week summer training camp at an Air Force base, usually between their sophomore and junior years. Following completion of their bachelor's degree, scholarship recipients earn a com-

mission as a second lieutenant in the Air Force and serve at least 4 years.

Deadline June of each year.

[151]
AIR FORCE ROTC PROFESSIONAL OFFICER CORPS INCENTIVE

U.S. Air Force
Attn: Headquarters AFROTC/RRUC
551 East Maxwell Boulevard
Maxwell AFB, AL 36112-5917
(334) 953-2091   Toll Free: (866) 4-AFROTC
Fax: (334) 953-6167   E-mail: afrotc1@maxwell.af.mil
Web: afrotc.com/learn-about/programs-and-scholarships

Summary To provide financial assistance for undergraduate and graduate studies to individuals who have completed 2 years of college and who are willing to join Air Force ROTC and serve as Air Force officers following completion of their degree.

Eligibility Applicants must be U.S. citizens who have completed 2 years of the general military course at a college or university with an Air Force ROTC unit on campus or a college with a cross-enrollment agreement with such a college. They must be full-time students, have a GPA of 2.0 or higher both cumulatively and for the prior term, be enrolled in both Aerospace Studies class and Leadership Laboratory, pass the Air Force Officer Qualifying Test, meet Air Force physical fitness and weight requirements, and be able to be commissioned before they become 31 years of age. They must agree to serve for at least 4 years as active-duty Air Force officers following graduation from college with either a bachelor's or graduate degree.

Financial data This scholarship provides a monthly subsistence allowance of $450 as a junior or $500 as a senior.

Duration Until completion of a graduate degree.

Additional information Scholarship recipients must complete 4 years of aerospace studies courses at 1 of the 144 colleges and universities that have an Air Force ROTC unit on campus; students may also attend 984 other colleges that have cross-enrollment agreements with the institutions that have an Air Force ROTC unit on campus. Recipients must also attend a 4-week summer training camp at an Air Force base between their junior and senior year.

Number awarded Varies each year.

Deadline Deadline not specified.

[152]
AIR FORCE SERVICES CLUB MEMBERSHIP SCHOLARSHIP PROGRAM

Air Force Services Agency
Attn: HQ AFSVA/SVOFT
10100 Reunion Place, Suite 501
San Antonio, TX 78216-4138
(210) 395-7787
E-mail: web.clubs-operations@randolph.af.mil
Web: www.afclubs.net/CN_Scholarship.htm

Summary To recognize and reward, with academic scholarships, Air Force Club members and their families who submit outstanding essays.

Eligibility This program is open to Air Force Club members and their spouses, children, and stepchildren who have been accepted by or are enrolled at an accredited college or university. Grandchildren are eligible if they are the dependent of a club member. Applicants may be undergraduate or graduate students enrolled full or part time. They must submit an essay of up to 500 words on a topic that changes annually; a recent topic was "My Contribution to the Air Force." Applicants must also include a 1-page summary of their long-term career and life goals and previous accomplishments, including civic, athletic, and academic awards.

Financial data Awards are $1,000 scholarships.

Duration The competition is held annually.

Additional information This competition, first held in 1997, is sponsored by Chase Bank and the Coca-Cola Company.

Number awarded 25 each year.

Deadline Entries must be submitted to the member's base services commander or division chief by June of each year.

[153]
AIR FORCE TUITION ASSISTANCE PROGRAM

U.S. Air Force
Attn: Air Force Personnel Center
Headquarters USAF/DPPAT
550 C Street West, Suite 10
Randolph AFB, TX 78150-4712
Fax: (210) 565-2328
Web: www.airforce.com

Summary To provide financial assistance for college or graduate school to active-duty Air Force personnel.

Eligibility Eligible to apply for this program are active-duty Air Force personnel who have completed 2 years of their service obligation.

Financial data Air Force personnel chosen for participation in this program continue to receive their regular Air Force pay. The Air Force will pay 100% of the tuition costs in an approved program, to a maximum of $4,500 per year or $250 per semester hour, whichever is less.

Duration Up to 4 years.

Additional information Applications and further information about this program are available from counselors at the education centers on Air Force bases. Most Air Force personnel who receive tuition assistance participate in the Community College of the Air Force; there, participants earn a 2-year associate degree by combining on-the-job technical training or attendance at Air Force schools with enrollment in college courses at a civilian institution during off-duty hours. In addition, each Air Force base offers at least 4 subject areas in which selected Air Force personnel can receive tuition assistance for study leading to a bachelor's degree, and 2 disciplines in which they can pursue graduate study.

Number awarded Varies each year.

Deadline Deadline not specified.

[154]
AIRMAN SCHOLARSHIP AND COMMISSIONING PROGRAM

U.S. Air Force
Attn: Headquarters AFROTC/RRUE
Enlisted Commissioning Section
551 East Maxwell Boulevard
Maxwell AFB, AL 36112-6106
(334) 953-2091   Toll Free: (866) 4-AFROTC
Fax: (334) 953-6167   E-mail: enlisted@afrotc.com
Web: afrotc.com/scholarships/enlisted-scholarships

Summary To allow selected enlisted Air Force personnel to separate from the Air Force and earn a bachelor's degree in approved majors by providing financial assistance for full-time college study, especially in designated fields.

Eligibility This program is open to active-duty enlisted members of the Air Force who have completed at least 1 year of continuous active duty and at least 1 year on station. Applicants normally must have completed at least 24 semester hours of graded college credit with a cumulative college GPA of 2.5 or higher. If they have not completed 24 hours of graded college credit, they must have an ACT score of 24 or higher or an SAT combined critical reading and mathematics score of 1100 or higher. They must also have scores on the Air Force Officer Qualifying Test (AFOQT) of 15 or more on the verbal scale and 10 or more on the quantitative scale and be able to pass the Air Force ROTC Physical Fitness Test. Applicants must have been accepted at a college or university (including cross-town schools) offering the AFROTC 4-year program. When they complete the program and receive their commission, they may not be 31 years of age or older. U.S. citizenship is required. Recently, priority was given to students in the following technical majors: architecture, chemistry, computer science, engineering (especially aeronautical, aerospace, architectural, astronautical, civil, computer, electrical, environmental, and mechanical), mathematics, meteorology/atmospheric sciences, operations research, and physics.

Financial data Awards are type 2 AFROTC scholarships that provide for payment of tuition and fees, to a maximum of $18,000 per year, plus an annual book allowance of $900. All recipients are also awarded a tax-free subsistence allowance of $350 to $500 per month.

Duration 2 to 4 years, until completion of a bachelor's degree.

Additional information Selectees separate from the active-duty Air Force, join an AFROTC detachment, and become full-time students. Upon completing their degree, they are commissioned as officers and returned to active duty in the Air Force with a service obligation of 4 years of active duty and 4 years of Reserves. Further information is available from base education service officers or an Air Force ROTC unit.

Number awarded Varies each year.

Deadline October of each year.

[155]
ALABAMA NATIONAL GUARD EDUCATIONAL ASSISTANCE PROGRAM

Alabama Commission on Higher Education
Attn: Grants Coordinator
100 North Union Street
P.O. Box 302000
Montgomery, AL 36130-2000
(334) 242-2273   Fax: (334) 242-0268
E-mail: cheryl.newton@ache.alabama.gov
Web: www.ache.alabama.gov/StudentAsst/Programs.htm

Summary To provide financial assistance to members of the Alabama National Guard interested in attending college or graduate school in the state.

Eligibility This program is open to Alabama residents who are enrolled in an associate, baccalaureate, master's, or doctoral program at a public college, university, community college, technical college, or junior college in the state; are making satisfactory academic progress as determined by the eligible institution; and are members in good standing of the Alabama National Guard who have completed basic training and advanced individual training. Applicants may be receiving federal veterans benefits, but they must show a cost less aid amount of at least $25.

Financial data Scholarships cover tuition, educational fees, books, and supplies, up to a maximum of $1,000 per year. All Alabama Student Grant program proceeds for which the student is eligible are deducted from this award.

Duration Up to 12 years after the date of the first grant payment to the student through this program.

Number awarded Varies each year; awards are determined on a first-in, first-out basis as long as funds are available.

Deadline July of each year.

[156]
ALASKA NATIONAL GUARD STATE TUITION REIMBURSEMENT PROGRAM

Alaska National Guard
Attn: Education Services Officer
P.O. Box 5800
Fort Richardson, AK 99505-5800
(907) 428-6477   Fax: (907) 428-6929
E-mail: ngmneducation@ng.army.mil
Web: www.akguard.com

Summary To provide financial assistance to current and former members of the Alaska National Guard who wish to work on a bachelor's or master's degree in the state.

Eligibility This program is open to members of the Alaska National Guard (Air and Army) and Naval Militia who have a rating of E-1 through O-5, including warrant officers, and are attending a university program in Alaska. Eligibility extends to members who 1) have satisfactorily completed their service contract and who served honorably in federal active service or federally-funded state active service after September 11, 2001; or 2) have been separated or discharged from the Guard because of a service-connected injury, disease, or disability. First priority is given to undergraduates; if funding is available, students working on a second bachelor's degree or a master's degree may be supported. Non-prior servicemembers must complete Initial Active Duty for Training (IADT); prior servicemembers are eligible immediately.

Financial data Recipients are entitled to reimbursement equivalent to 100% of the cost of tuition and fees at the University of Alaska, to a maximum of $7,500 per fiscal year.

Duration 1 semester; may be renewed for a total of 144 semester credits.

Number awarded Varies each year.

Deadline Applications may be submitted at any time, but they must be received at least 90 days after the last official day of the class or term.

[157]
AMEDD ENLISTED COMMISSIONING PROGRAM (AECP)

U.S. Army
Attn: Recruiting Command, RCHS-SVD-AECP
1307 Third Avenue
Fort Knox, KY 40121-2726
(502) 626-0381   Toll Free: (800) 223-3735, ext. 60381
Fax: (502) 626-0952   E-mail: aecp@usarec.army.mil
Web: www.goarmy.com

Summary To provide financial assistance to enlisted Army personnel who are interested in completing a bachelor's degree in nursing and becoming a commissioned officer.

Eligibility This program is open to enlisted Army personnel of grade E-4 or above in the active component, Reserves, or National Guard who have at least 3 but no more than 16 years of active federal service. Applicants must be interested in enrolling full time at an accredited school of nursing to work on a bachelor's degree and becoming a licensed registered nurse. They must be U.S. citizens, have a GPA of 2.5 or higher, have SAT scores of at least 450 in critical reading and 450 in mathematics, have an enrollment GT score of 110 or higher, be able to complete a bachelor's degree in nursing within 24 calendar months, be between 21 and 42 years of age, be eligible to become a commissioned officer in the active component following licensure, and agree to fulfill a 3-year additional service obligation.

Financial data The stipend is $9,000 per year for tuition and $1,000 for books. Participants are not allowed to attend a school whose tuition exceeds $9,000. They continue to draw their regular pay and allowances while attending nursing school.

Duration Participants must be able to complete all degree requirements in 24 consecutive months or less.

Number awarded Up to 100 each year.

Deadline January of each year.

[158]
AMERICAN SYSTEMS HBCU SCHOLARSHIPS

Armed Forces Communications and Electronics
   Association
Attn: AFCEA Educational Foundation
4400 Fair Lakes Court
Fairfax, VA 22033-3899
(703) 631-6138   Toll Free: (800) 336-4583, ext. 6138
Fax: (703) 631-4693 E-mail: scholarshipsinfo@afcea.org
Web: www.afcea.org

Summary To provide funding to students, especially enlisted personnel and veterans, who are majoring in fields of science, technology, engineering, or mathematics (STEM) at an Historically Black College or University (HBCU).

Eligibility This program is open to sophomores and juniors enrolled full time at an accredited 2- or 4-year HBCU or in a distance learning or online degree program affiliated with those institutions. They must be working toward a bachelor's degree in such STEM fields as engineering (aerospace, computer, electrical, or systems), computer science, computer engineering technology, computer information systems, mathematics, physics, information systems management, or other field directly related to the support of U.S. intelligence or homeland security enterprises. Special consideration is given to military enlisted personnel and veterans.

Financial data The stipend is $5,000.

Duration 1 year; may be renewed.

Additional information This program began in 2010 with support from American Systems.

Number awarded At least 2 each year.

Deadline April of each year.

[159]
ANCA SCHOLARSHIPS

Army Nurse Corps Association
Attn: Education Committee
P.O. Box 39235
San Antonio, TX 78218-1235
(210) 650-3534   Fax: (210) 650-3494
E-mail: education@e-anca.org
Web: e-anca.org/ANCAEduc.htm

Summary To provide financial assistance to students who have a connection to the Army and are interested in working on an undergraduate or graduate degree in nursing.

Eligibility This program is open to U.S. citizens attending colleges or universities that have accredited programs offering associate, bachelor's, master's, or doctoral degrees in nursing. Applicants must be 1) nursing or anesthesia students who plan to enter a component of the U.S. Army and are not participating in a program funded by a component of the U.S. Army; 2) nursing or anesthesia students who have previously served in a component of the U.S. Army; 3) Army Nurse Corps officers enrolled in an undergraduate or graduate nursing program not funded by a component of the U.S. Army; 4) enlisted soldiers in a component of the U.S. Army who are working on a baccalaureate degree in nursing not funded by a component of the U.S. Army; or 5) nursing or anesthesia students whose parent(s), spouse, and/or children are serving or have served in a component of the U.S. Army. Along with their application, they must submit a personal statement on their professional career objectives, reasons for applying for this scholarship, financial need, special considerations, personal and academic interests, and why they are preparing for a nursing career.

Financial data The stipend is $3,000. Funds are sent directly to the recipient's school.

Duration 1 year.

Additional information Although the sponsoring organization is open to officers of the Army Nurse Corps, it does not have an official affiliation with the Army. Therefore, students who receive these scholarships do not incur any military service obligation.

Number awarded 1 or more each year.

Deadline March of each year.

[160]
ARIZONA NATIONAL GUARD STATE EDUCATION REIMBURSEMENT PROGRAM

Arizona Army National Guard
Soldier Support Center
Attn: Education Services Officer
5636 East McDowell Road
Phoenix, AZ 85008-3495
(602) 267-2885   Fax: (602) 267-2912
E-mail: azsoldiersupportcenter@us.army.mil
Web: www.azguard.gov

Summary To provide financial assistance for college to members of the Arizona Army or Air National Guard.

Eligibility This program is open to members of the Arizona Army and Air National Guard who have completed Advanced Infantry Training (AIT) or Officer Basic Course (OBC). Applicants must have attended annual training or equivalent training and may not have any AWOLs. They must be working on a college degree or certification at an Arizona institution.

Financial data Recipients are reimbursed for the actual cost of completed education, to a maximum of $250 per credit hour, $2,296 per semester, or $6,500 per state fiscal year.

Duration 1 year; may be renewed if the recipient maintains satisfactory drill performance.

Number awarded Varies each year.

Deadline Applications for reimbursement must be submitted no later than 15 calendar days after the start of school.

[161]
ARKANSAS NATIONAL GUARD TUITION INCENTIVE PROGRAM

Arkansas National Guard
Attn: Education Services Officer
DCSPER-ED
Camp Robinson
North Little Rock, AR 72199-9600
(501) 212-4021   Fax: (501) 212-4039
E-mail: Education@ar.ngb.army.mil
Web: www.arguard.org/Education/ta.html

Summary To provide financial assistance for college to members of the Arkansas National Guard.

Eligibility This program is open to members of the Arkansas National Guard who have 10 years or less of service. Applicants must have a sufficient score on the standard military entrance examination to be rated as Category IIIA or higher (i.e., AFQT score of at least 50 or equivalent). They must be enrolled or accepted for enrollment in an undergraduate program at a participating college or university in Arkansas. Non-prior service applicants must enlist in the Arkansas National Guard for at least 6 year; enlisted members must reenlist or extend for at least 3 years; warrant and commissioned officers must commit to at least 2 years of service.

Financial data The stipend is $2,500 per semester for fall or spring semester or $1,250 for summer term; the maximum award in a fiscal year is $5,000.

Duration 1 semester; may be renewed if the recipient maintains a GPA of 2.0 or higher.

Number awarded Varies each year.

Deadline August of each year for fall semester; December of each year for spring semester; May of each year for first summer term; June of each year for second summer term.

[162]
ARMY AVIATION ASSOCIATION OF AMERICA SCHOLARSHIPS

Army Aviation Association of America Scholarship
  Foundation
Attn: AAAA Scholarship Foundation
755 Main Street, Suite 4D
Monroe, CT 06468-2830
(203) 268-2450   Fax: (203) 268-5870
E-mail: aaaa@quad-a.org
Web: www.quad-a.org

Summary To provide financial aid for undergraduate or graduate study to members of the Army Aviation Association of America and their relatives.

Eligibility This program is open to association members (or deceased members) and their spouses, unmarried siblings, unmarried children, and unmarried grandchildren. Applicants must be enrolled or accepted for enrollment as an undergraduate or graduate student at an accredited college or university. Graduate students must include a 250-word essay on their life experiences, work history, and aspirations. Some scholarships are specifically reserved for enlisted, warrant officer, company grade, and Department of the Army civilian members. Selection is based on academic merit and personal achievement.

Financial data Stipends range up to $3,000 per year.

Duration Scholarships may be for 1, 2, or 4 years.

Number awarded Varies each year; recently, $309,500 in scholarships was awarded to 209 students. Since the program began in 1963, the foundation has awarded more than $4.1 million to nearly 2,500 qualified applicants.

Deadline April of each year.

[163]
ARMY NATIONAL GUARD TUITION ASSISTANCE

U.S. Army National Guard
c/o DANTES
6490 Saufley Field Road
Pensacola, FL 32509-5243
(850) 452-1085   Fax: (850) 452-1161
E-mail: tahelp@voled.doded.mil
Web: www.nationalguard.com/benefits/money-for-college

Summary To provide financial assistance for college or graduate school to members of the Army National Guard in each state.

Eligibility This program is open to members of the Army National Guard in every state who are interested in attending a college, community college, or university within the state. Applicants must have sufficient time to complete the course before their Expiration Time of Service (ETS) date. They must be interested in working on a high school diploma or equivalent (GED), certificate, associate degree, bachelor's degree, master's degree, or first professional degree, including those in architecture, Certified Public Accountant (C.P.A.), podiatry, dentistry (D.D.S. or D.M.D.), medicine (M.D.), optometry, osteopathic medicine, pharmacy (Pharm.D.), or theology (M.Div. or M.H.L.). Commissioned officers must agree to remain in the Guard for at least 4 years following completion of the course for which assistance is provided, unless they are involuntarily separated from the service.

Financial data Assistance provides up to 100% of tuition (to a maximum of $250 per semester hour or $4,500 per person per fiscal year).

Duration Participants in Officer Candidate School (OCS), Warrant Officer Candidate School (WOCS), and ROTC Simultaneous Membership Program (SMP) may enroll in up to 15 semester hours per year until completion of a baccalaureate degree. Warrant Officers are funded to complete an associate degree.

Additional information Tuition assistance may be used along with federal Pell Grants but not with Montgomery GI Bill benefits. State tuition assistance programs can be used concurrently with this program, but not to exceed 100% of tuition costs.

Number awarded Varies each year; recently, more than 22,000 Guard members received tuition assistance.

Deadline Deadline not specified.

[164]
ARMY RESERVE TUITION ASSISTANCE

U.S. Army Reserve
Attn: Director, USAR Education
ARPC-PS
1 Reserve Way
St. Louis, MO 63132-5200
Toll Free: (800) 452-0201
Web: www.goarmy.com/reserve/benefits/education.html

Summary To provide financial assistance for college or graduate school to specified members of the U.S. Army Reserve (USAR).

Eligibility This program is open to USAR soldiers in the following categories: TPU, JRU, IMA, ROTC Simultaneous Membership Program Cadets (non-scholarship holders), and Chaplain Candidates. Members of the Active Guard Reserve (AGR) are covered by Regular Army tuition assistance and are not eligible for this program. Soldiers who have been flagged for weight control or because of the results of their Army Physical Fitness Test (APFT) are still eligible, but soldiers who have been flagged for adverse actions cannot receive this assistance. Applicants must be working on their first credential at the diploma, certificate associate, baccalaureate, or graduate level. Commissioned officers must agree to participate actively for 4 years in the Selected Reserve from the date of completion of the course for which tuition assistance is provided. Enlisted soldiers must certify that sufficient time remains within their Time In Service (TIS) to complete the course before their Expiration Term of Service (ETS).

Financial data Assistance is provided at the rate of $250 per credit hour, to a maximum of $4,500 per fiscal year.

Duration 1 year; may be renewed.

Number awarded Varies each year.

Deadline Applications may be submitted at any time.

[165]
ARMY ROTC 4-YEAR SCHOLARSHIPS

U.S. Army
ROTC Cadet Command
Attn: Scholarship Branch
204 1st Cavalry Regiment Road, Building 1002
Fort Knox, KY 40121
(502) 624-7371   Toll Free: (888) 550-ARMY
Fax: (502) 624-6937   E-mail: train2lead@usacc.army.mil
Web: www.rotc.usaac.army.mil/scholarships.aspx

Summary   To provide financial assistance to high school seniors or graduates who are interested in enrolling in Army ROTC in college.

Eligibility   Applicants for this program must 1) be U.S. citizens; 2) be between 17 and 26 years of age; 3) score at least 920 on the combined mathematics and critical reading SAT or 19 on the ACT; 4) have a high school GPA of 2.5 or higher; and 5) meet medical and other regulatory requirements. Current college or university students may apply if their school considers them beginning freshmen with 4 academic years remaining for a bachelor's degree.

Financial data   This scholarship provides financial assistance of up to $20,000 per year for college tuition and educational fees or for room and board, whichever the student selects. In addition, a flat rate of $1,200 per year is provided for the purchase of textbooks, classroom supplies, and equipment. Recipients are also awarded a stipend for up to 10 months of each year that is $300 per month during their freshman year, $350 per month during their sophomore year, $450 per month during their junior year, and $500 per month during their senior year.

Duration   4 years, until completion of a baccalaureate degree.

Additional information   Scholarship recipients participate in the Army ROTC program as part of their college curriculum by enrolling in 4 years of military science classes and attending a 6-week summer camp between the junior and senior years. Following graduation, they receive a commission as a Regular Army, Army Reserve, or Army National Guard officer. Scholarship winners must serve in the Army for 8 years, including 4 years of full-time service and 4 years in the Individual Ready Reserve (IRR). They may elect to serve part time in the Army Reserve or Army National Guard while pursuing a civilian career.

Number awarded   Approximately 1,500 each year.

Deadline   January of each year.

[166]
ARMY ROTC COLLEGE SCHOLARSHIP PROGRAM

U.S. Army
ROTC Cadet Command
Attn: Scholarship Branch
204 1st Cavalry Regiment Road, Building 1002
Fort Knox, KY 40121
(502) 624-7371   Toll Free: (888) 550-ARMY
Fax: (502) 624-6937   E-mail: train2lead@usacc.army.mil
Web: www.rotc.usaac.army.mil/scholarships.aspx

Summary   To provide financial assistance to students who are or will be enrolled in Army ROTC.

Eligibility   This program is open to U.S. citizens between 17 and 26 years of age who have already completed 1 or 2 years in a college or university with an Army ROTC unit on campus or in a college with a cross-enrollment agreement with a college with an Army ROTC unit on campus. Applicants must have 2 or 3 years remaining for their bachelor's degree (or 4 years of a 5-year bachelor's program) and must be able to complete that degree before their 31st birthday. They must have a high school GPA of 2.5 or higher and scores of at least 920 on the combined mathematics and critical reading SAT or 19 on the ACT.

Financial data   These scholarships provide financial assistance for college tuition and educational fees, up to an annual amount of $20,000. In addition, a flat rate of $1,200 is provided for the purchase of textbooks, classroom supplies, and equipment. Recipients are also awarded a stipend for up to 10 months of each year that is $350 per month during their sophomore year, $450 per month during their junior year, and $500 per month during their senior year.

Duration   2 or 3 years, until the recipient completes the bachelor's degree.

Additional information   Applications must be made through professors of military science at 1 of the schools hosting the Army ROTC program. Preference is given to students who have already enrolled as non-scholarship students in military science classes at 1 of the more than 270 institutions with an Army ROTC unit on campus, at 1 of the 75 college extension centers, or at 1 of the more than 1,000 colleges with cross-enrollment or extension agreements with 1 of the colleges with an Army ROTC unit. Scholarship winners must serve full time in the Army for 4 years. They may elect to serve part time in the Army Reserve or Army National Guard while pursuing a civilian career.

Number awarded   Varies each year; a recent allocation provided for 700 4-year scholarships, 1,800 3-year scholarships, and 2,800 2-year scholarships.

Deadline   December of each year.

[167]
ARMY ROTC NURSE PROGRAM

U.S. Army
ROTC Cadet Command
Attn: Scholarship Branch
204 1st Cavalry Regiment Road, Building 1002
Fort Knox, KY 40121
(502) 624-7371   Toll Free: (888) 550-ARMY
Fax: (502) 624-6937   E-mail: train2lead@usacc.army.mil
Web: www.rotc.usaac.army.mil/scholarships.aspx

Summary   To provide financial assistance to high school seniors or graduates who are interested in enrolling in Army ROTC and majoring in nursing in college.

Eligibility   Applicants for the Army Reserve Officers' Training Corps (ROTC) Nurse program must 1) be U.S. citizens; 2) be at least 17 years of age by October of the year in which they are seeking a scholarship; 3) be no more than 27 years of age when they graduate from college after 4 years; 4) score at least 1050 on the combined mathematics and critical reading SAT or 21 on the ACT; 5) have a high school GPA of 3.0 or higher; and 6) meet medical and other regulatory requirements. This program is open to ROTC scholarship applicants who wish to enroll in a nursing program at 1 of approximately 100 designated partner colleges and universities and become Army nurses after graduation.

Financial data   This scholarship provides financial assistance toward college tuition and educational fees up to an annual amount of $17,000. In addition, a flat rate of $1,000 is provided for the purchase of textbooks, classroom supplies, and equipment. Recipients are also awarded a stipend for up to 10 months of each year that is $300 per month during their freshman year, $350 per month during their sophomore year, $450 per month during their junior year, and $500 per month during their senior year.

Duration 4 years, until completion of a baccalaureate degree. A limited number of 2-year and 3-year scholarships are also available to students who are already attending an accredited B.S.N. program on a campus affiliated with ROTC.

Additional information This program was established in 1996 to ensure that ROTC cadets seeking nursing careers would be admitted to the upper-level division of a baccalaureate program. The 56 partnership nursing schools affiliated with Army ROTC have agreed to guarantee upper-level admission to students who maintain an established GPA during their first 2 years. During the summer, recipients have the opportunity to participate in the Nurse Summer Training Program, a paid 3- to 4-week clinical elective at an Army hospital in the United States, Germany, or Korea. Following completion of their baccalaureate degree, participants become commissioned officers in the Army Nurse Corps. Scholarship winners must serve in the military for 8 years. That service obligation may be fulfilled 1) by serving on active duty for 4 years followed by service in the Army National Guard (ARNG), the United States Army Reserve (USAR), or the Inactive Ready Reserve (IRR) for the remainder of the 8 years; or 2) by serving 8 years in an ARNG or USAR troop program unit that includes a 3- to 6-month active-duty period for initial training.

Number awarded A limited number each year.

Deadline November of each year.

[168]
ARMY SPECIALIZED TRAINING ASSISTANCE PROGRAM (STRAP)

U.S. Army
Human Resources Command, Health Services Division
Attn: AHRC-OPH-AN
1500 Spearhead Division Avenue
Fort Knox, KY 40122-5408
Toll Free: (888) ARMY-HRC
E-mail: askhrc@conus.army.mil
Web: www.goarmy.com/amedd/education.html

Summary To provide funding to members of the United States Army Reserve (USAR) or Army National Guard (ARNG) who are engaged in additional training in designated health care fields that are considered critical for wartime medical needs.

Eligibility This program is open to members of the USAR or ARNG who are currently 1) medical residents (in orthopedic surgery, family practice, emergency medicine, general surgery, obstetrics/gynecology, or internal medicine); 2) dental residents (in oral surgery, prosthodontics, or comprehensive dentistry); 3) nursing students working on a master's degree in critical care or nurse anesthesia; or 4) associate degree or diploma nurses working on a bachelor's degree. Applicants must agree to a service obligation of 1 year for every 6 months of support received.

Financial data This program pays a stipend of $2,088 per month.

Additional information During their obligated period of service, participants must attend Extended Combat Training (ECT) at least 12 days each year and complete the Officer Basic Leadership Course (OBLC) within the first year.

Number awarded Varies each year.

Deadline Applications may be submitted at any time.

[169]
ARMY TUITION ASSISTANCE BENEFITS

U.S. Army
Human Resources Command
AHRC-PDE-EI
Attn: Education Incentives and Counseling Branch
1500 Spearhead Division Avenue
Fort Knox, KY 40122-5408
Toll Free: (888) ARMY-HRC
E-mail: askhrc@conus.army.mil
Web: www.goarmyed.com

Summary To provide financial assistance to Army personnel interested in working on an undergraduate or graduate degree.

Eligibility This program is open to active-duty Army personnel, including members of the Army National Guard and Army Reserve on active duty. Applicants must first visit an education counselor to declare an educational goal and establish an educational plan. They may enroll in up to 15 semester hours of academic courses.

Financial data Those selected for participation in this program receive their regular Army pay and 100% of tuition at the postsecondary educational institution of their choice, but capped at $4,500 per year or $250 per semester hour, whichever is less.

Duration Until completion of a bachelor's or graduate degree.

Additional information This program is part of the Army Continuing Education System (ACES). Further information is available from counselors at the education centers at all Army installations with a troop strength of 750 or more.

Number awarded Varies each year.

Deadline Deadline not specified.

[170]
ASMC MEMBERS' CONTINUING EDUCATION PROGRAM AWARD

American Society of Military Comptrollers
Attn: National Awards Committee
415 North Alfred Street
Alexandria, VA 22314
(703) 549-0360   Toll Free: (800) 462-5637
Fax: (703) 549-3181   E-mail: lloyd@asmconline.org
Web: awards.asmconline.org

Summary To provide financial assistance for continuing education to members of the American Society of Military Comptrollers (ASMC).

Eligibility Applicants for this assistance must have been members of the society for at least 2 full years and must have been active in the local chapter at some level (e.g., board member, committee chair or member, volunteer for chapter events), They must be enrolled or planning to enroll at an academic institution in a field of study directly related to military comptrollership, including business administration, economics, public administration, accounting, or finance. Selection is based on individual merit.

Financial data Stipends are $3,000 or $1,500.

Duration 1 year.

Additional information The ASMC is open to all financial management professionals employed by the U.S. Department of Defense and Coast Guard, both civilian and military. The applicant whose service to the society is judged the most exceptional is designated the Dick Vincent Scholarship winner.

Number awarded 11 each year: 1 at $3,000 (the Dick Vincent Scholarship) and 10 at $1,500.

Deadline March of each year.

[171]
ASSOCIATION OF OLD CROWS ENLISTED TUITION GRANTS

Association of Old Crows
Attn: AOC Educational Foundation
1000 North Payne Street
Alexandria, VA 22314-1652
(703) 549-1600   Fax: (703) 549-2589
Web: www.crows.org/aef/scholarship-a-grants.html

Summary To provide financial assistance to military enlisted personnel who are pursuing off-duty college-level education programs in fields related to electronics.

Eligibility This program is open to military enlisted personnel (rank of E-4 and above) who are utilizing the tuition assistance programs of the armed services to study physics, engineering, or other field related to electronic warfare or information superiority during their off-duty hours. Selection is based on academic excellence and financial need.

Financial data Support is provided to supplement the funding available through the tuition assistance programs.

Duration 1 semester; may be renewed.

Additional information Funding is provided by local chapters of this organization, which was founded by World War II veterans who had engaged in electronic warfare to disrupt enemy communications and radars. The program was code-named "Raven" and its operators became known as Old Crows. For information on a chapter in your area, contact the AOC Educational Foundation.

Number awarded Varies each year; recently, a total of $160,000 per year was available for this program.

Deadline Deadline not specified.

[172]
AUSA/JOSEPH P. AND HELEN T. CRIBBINS SCHOLARSHIP

Association of the United States Army
Attn: Executive Assistant
2425 Wilson Boulevard
Arlington, VA 22201
(703) 841-4300, ext. 2652
Toll Free: (800) 336-4570, ext. 2652
E-mail: ausa-info@ausa.org
Web: www.ausa.org

Summary To provide financial assistance to active-duty and honorably-discharged soldiers interested in studying engineering in college.

Eligibility This program is open to 1) soldiers currently serving in the active Army, Army Reserve, or Army National Guard of any rank; and 2) honorably-discharged soldiers from any component of the total Army. Applicants must have been accepted at an accredited college or university to work on a degree in engineering or a related field (e.g., computer science, biotechnology). Along with their application, they must submit a 1-page autobiography, 2 letters of recommendation, and a transcript of high school or college grades (depending on which they are currently attending). Selection is based on academic merit and personal achievement. Financial need is not normally a selection criterion but in some cases of extreme need it may be used as a factor; the lack of financial need, however, is never a cause for nonselection.

Financial data The stipend is $2,000; funds are sent directly to the recipient's college or university.

Duration 1 year.

Number awarded 1 or more each year.

Deadline June of each year.

[173]
BG BENJAMIN B. TALLEY SCHOLARSHIP

Society of American Military Engineers-Anchorage Post
Attn: BG B.B. Talley Scholarship Endowment Fund
P.O. Box 6409
Anchorage, AK 99506-6409
(907) 244-8063   E-mail: cturletes@gci.net
Web: www.sameanchorage.org/h_about/scholinfo.html

Summary To provide financial assistance to student members of the Society of American Military Engineers (SAME) from Alaska who are working on a bachelor's or master's degree in designated fields of engineering or the natural sciences.

Eligibility This program is open to members of the Anchorage Post of SAME who are residents of Alaska, attending college in Alaska, an active-duty military member stationed in Alaska, or a dependent of an active-duty military member stationed in Alaska. Applicants must be 1) sophomores, juniors, or seniors majoring in engineering, architecture, construction or project management, natural sciences, physical sciences, applied sciences, or mathematics at an accredited college or university; or 2) students working on a master's degree in those fields. They must have a GPA of 2.5 or higher. U.S. citizenship is required. Along with their application, they must submit an essay of 250 to 500 words on their career goals. Selection is based on that essay, academic achievement, participation in school and community activities, and work/family activities; financial need is not considered.

Financial data Stipends range up to $3,000.

Duration 1 year.

Additional information This program began in 1997.

Number awarded Varies each year; at least 1 scholarship is reserved for a master's degree students.

Deadline December of each year.

[174]
BOSTON POST SAME SCHOLARSHIPS

Society of American Military Engineers-Boston Post
c/o William Naughton, Scholarship Committee Chair
Kleinfelder
215 First Street, Suite 320
Cambridge, MA 01742
(617) 497-7800   E-mail: bnaughton@kleinfelder.com
Web: www.sameboston.org/index.cfm?ac=scholarships

Summary To provide funding to residents of New England (especially those with ties to the military) who are majoring in a program related to construction in any state.

Eligibility This program is open to residents of New England who are currently enrolled in an accepted engineering or architecture program, preferably in civil engineering, environmental engineering, architecture, or other construction-related program, at a college or university in any state. Applicants must have completed at least 1 academic year and have at least 1 year remaining. They must be nominated by their institution. Along with their application, they must submit a resume describing their academic and career objectives, extracurricular and community activities, work experience, and special interests or hobbies; transcripts; documentation of financial need; and a personal letter describing their qualifications and needs. An interview is required. Selection is based on academic achievement, financial need, extracurricular and community activities, the letter, and the interview. Preference is given to applicants who are enrolled in ROTC (preferably not a recipient of an ROTC scholarship), have current or prior service in the U.S. armed forces, are interested in the U.S. Public Health Service, and/or are interested in other public service with federal, state, or local government. U.S. citizenship is required.

Financial data The stipend is $2,000 per year.

Duration 1 year.

Number awarded Approximately 25 each year.

Deadline February of each year.

[175]
BRIGADIER GENERAL ROSCOE C. CARTWRIGHT AWARDS

The ROCKS, Inc.
c/o WSC Associates, LLP
7700 Old Branch Avenue, Suite A202
Clinton, MD 20735
(301) 856-9319   Toll Free: (877) 762-5732
Fax: (301) 856-5220   E-mail: therocks@aol.com
Web: www.rocksinc.org

Summary To provide financial assistance to students enrolled in ROTC programs at Historically Black Colleges and Universities (HBCUs).

Eligibility This program is open to Army and Air Force Cadets and Navy Midshipmen at HBCUs. Applicants must be planning to enter military service as officers following graduation from college. They must submit a letter of recommendation from their Professor of Military Science evaluating their appearance, attitude, character, dedication, initiative, integrity, judgment, leadership potential, and written and oral communication ability. Financial need is not considered in the selection process.

Financial data The stipend is $1,200.

Duration 1 year.

Additional information This program began in 1974.

Number awarded Varies each year.

Deadline February of each year.

[176]
CALIFORNIA ENLISTED ASSOCIATION OF THE NATIONAL GUARD OF THE UNITED STATES SCHOLARSHIP PROGRAM

California Enlisted Association of the National Guard of the United States
c/o CSM Harry Courtney, President
P.O. Box 323
Seaside, CA 93955
(831) 242-7733   E-mail: hjc47@aol.com
Web: www.caleangus.org/Membership.html

Summary To provide financial assistance to enlisted members of the California National Guard who are interested in obtaining additional education.

Eligibility This program is open to members of the California Army and Air National Guards who have completed at least 1 year of military service. The program supports 2 categories of applicants: Category A for those who hold a military rank of E-3 to E-6 and Category B for those who hold a military rank of E-7 to E-9. Applicants must be enrolled in an educational program whose goal is an associate or bachelor's degree or certification in a subject matter that will enhance their ability to support the unit's mission and goals. Along with their application, they must submit a personal statement that discusses how they plan to apply their educational accomplishments to their civilian and military professional and career goals; a current transcript, and a letter of endorsement from their commanding officer. Awards are granted first to Category A applicants; if funding is sufficient, applicants in Category B are considered.

Financial data A stipend is awarded (amount not specified).

Duration 1 year; may be renewed for 1 additional year.

Number awarded Varies each year.

Deadline August of each year.

[177]
CALIFORNIA LEGION AUXILIARY PAST PRESIDENTS' PARLEY NURSING SCHOLARSHIPS

American Legion Auxiliary
Department of California
Veterans War Memorial Building
401 Van Ness Avenue, Room 113
San Francisco, CA 94102-4586
(415) 861-5092   Fax: (415) 861-8365
E-mail: calegionaux@calegionaux.org
Web: www.calegionaux.org/scholarships.htm

Summary To provide funding to California residents who are current military personnel, veterans, or members of their families and interested in studying nursing in the state.

Eligibility This program is open to California residents who are currently serving on active military duty, veterans who served during wartime, or the spouse, widow(er), or child of such a veteran. Applicants must be entering or continuing students of nursing at an accredited institution of higher learning in California. Selection is based on the application (25%), scholarship (25%), character and leadership (25%), and financial need (25%).

Financial data Stipends range up to $2,000.

Duration 1 year.

Number awarded Varies each year.

Deadline March of each year.

[178]
CALIFORNIA LEGION AUXILIARY SCHOLARSHIPS FOR CONTINUING AND/OR REENTRY STUDENTS

American Legion Auxiliary
Department of California
Veterans War Memorial Building
401 Van Ness Avenue, Room 113
San Francisco, CA 94102-4586
(415) 861-5092   Fax: (415) 861-8365
E-mail: calegionaux@calegionaux.org
Web: www.calegionaux.org/scholarships.htm

Summary To provide funding to California residents who are active-duty military personnel, veterans, or children of veterans and require assistance to continue their education.

Eligibility This program is open to California residents who are 1) active-duty military personnel; 2) veterans of World War I, World War II, Korea, Vietnam, Grenada/Lebanon, Panama, or Desert Shield/Desert Storm; and 3) children of veterans who served during those periods of war. Applicants must be continuing or reentry students at a college, university, or business/trade school in California. Selection is based on the application (25%), scholarship (25%), character and leadership (25%), and financial need (25%).

Financial data The stipend is $1,000 or $500.

Duration 1 year.

Additional information This program includes 1 scholarship designated as the Mel Foronda Memorial Scholarship.

Number awarded 5 each year: 3 at $1,000 and 2 at $500.

Deadline March of each year.

[179]
CALIFORNIA NATIONAL GUARD EDUCATION ASSISTANCE AWARD PROGRAM

Office of the Adjutant General
Joint Force Headquarters
Attn: Katrina Beck
9800 Goethe Road, Box 37
Sacramento, CA 95826
(916) 854-4255   Fax: (916) 854-3739
E-mail: Katrina.beck2@us.army.mil
Web: www.calguard.ca.gov/education/Pages/default.aspx

Summary To provide financial assistance to members of the California National Guard who are interested in attending college or graduate school in the state.

Eligibility This program is open to residents of California who have served at least 2 years as active members of the California National Guard, the State Military Reserve, or the Naval Militia. Applicants must be planning to attend a college, university, community college, or vocational/technical institute in the state to obtain a certificate, degree (associate, bachelor's, master's, or doctoral) or diploma that they do not currently hold. They must agree to remain an active member of the Guard, Reserve, or Militia as long as they participate in the program.

Financial data The maximum stipends are equal to those provided by Cal Grants A and B; recently, those were $12,192 at branches of the University of California, $9,708 at nonpub-

lic institutions, $5,472 at branches of the California State University system, or $1,551 at community colleges. Graduate students receive an additional stipend of $500 for books and supplies.

Duration 1 year; may be renewed, provided the recipient maintains a GPA of 2.0 or higher.

Additional information This program operates in partnership with the California Student Aid Commission.

Number awarded Up to 1,000 each year.

Deadline The priority deadline for new applications is June of each year.

[180]
CAPTAIN SEAN P. GRIMES PHYSICIAN ASSISTANT EDUCATIONAL SCHOLARSHIP AWARD

Society of Army Physician Assistants
c/o Harold Slusher
6762 Candlewood Drive
P.O. Box 07490
Fort Myers, FL 33919
(239) 482-2162   Fax: (239) 482-2162
E-mail: hal.shusher@juno.com
Web: www.sapa.org/SeanScholarshipPage.htm

Summary To provide funding to current and former Army personnel interested in training as a physician assistant.

Eligibility This program is open to Army veterans, Army active-duty soldiers, Army National Guard soldiers, and Army Reservists. Soldiers may be of any enlisted or officer rank from E-5 through O-4. Applicants may be seeking initial training as a physician assistant or current physician assistants working on a baccalaureate, master's, or doctoral degree. They must have a GPA of 2.5 or higher. Candidates for initial training must be enrolled in an ARC-PA approved program. Other candidates must be enrolled at an accredited college or university. Financial need is considered.

Financial data The stipend is $6,000.

Duration 1 year.

Additional information This program began in 2006.

Number awarded 1 each year.

Deadline January of each year.

[181]
CAREER COLLEGE ASSOCIATION'S IMAGINE AMERICA MILITARY AWARD PROGRAM

Career College Association
Attn: Imagine America Foundation
1101 Connecticut Avenue, N.W., Suite 901
Washington, DC 20036
(202) 336-6719   Fax: (202) 408-8102
E-mail: scholarships@imagine-america.org
Web: www.imagine-america.org/grantsformilitary

Summary To provide funding to veterans and military personnel interested in attending a participating career college.

Eligibility This program is open to active-duty, reservist, honorably-discharged, and retired veterans of a U.S. military service branch. Applicants must be interested in attending 1 of more than 300 participating career colleges. They must be able to demonstrate the likelihood of enrolling and successfully completing postsecondary education. All applications are submitted online to the college where the student wishes to enroll. Selection is based on the likelihood of successfully completing postsecondary education and financial need.

Financial data The stipend is $1,000. Funds must be used for payment of tuition at a participating career college.
Duration 1 year.
Additional information The Imagine America Foundation (originally known as the Career College Foundation) established this program in 2004.
Number awarded Varies each year.
Deadline June of each year.

[182]
CIVIL ENGINEER CORPS OPTION OF THE SEAMAN TO ADMIRAL-21 PROGRAM

U.S. Navy
Attn: Commander, Naval Service Training Command
250 Dallas Street, Suite A
Pensacola, FL 32508-5268
(850) 452-9433   Fax: (850) 452-2486
E-mail: PNSC_STA21@navy.mil
Web: www.sta-21.navy.mil

Summary To allow outstanding enlisted Navy personnel to complete a bachelor's degree and receive a commission in the Civil Engineer Corps (CEC).
Eligibility This program is open to U.S. citizens who are currently serving on active duty in the Navy as enlisted personnel in any rating. Applicants must have completed at least 4 years of active duty, of which at least 3 years were in an other than formal training environment. They must be high school graduates (or GED recipients) who are able to complete requirements for a professional Accreditation Board for Engineering and Technology (ABET) engineering degree or National Architectural Accrediting Board (NAAB) architectural degree within 36 months or less. Preferred specialties are civil, electrical, mechanical, or ocean engineering. When applicants complete their degree requirements, they must be younger than 42 years of age. Within the past 3 years, they must have taken the SAT (and achieved scores of at least 500 on the mathematics section and 500 on the critical reading section) or the ACT (and achieved a score of 41 or higher, including at least 21 on the mathematics portion and 20 on the English portion).
Financial data Awardees continue to receive their regular Navy pay and allowances while they attend college on a full-time basis. They also receive reimbursement for tuition, fees, and books up to $10,000 per year. If base housing is available, they are eligible to live there. Participants are not eligible to receive benefits under the Navy's Tuition Assistance Program (TA), the Montgomery GI Bill (MGIB), the Navy College Fund, or the Veterans Educational Assistance Program (VEAP).
Duration Selectees are supported for up to 36 months of full-time, year-round study or completion of a bachelor's degree, as long as they maintain a GPA of 3.0 or higher.
Additional information This program was established in 2001 as a replacement for the Civil Engineer Corps Enlisted Commissioning Program (CECECP). Upon acceptance into the program, selectees attend the Naval Science Institute (NSI) in Newport, Rhode Island for an 8-week program in the fundamental core concepts of being a naval officer (navigation, engineering, weapons, military history and justice, etc.). They then enter a college or university with an NROTC unit that is designated for the CEC to work full time on a bachelor's degree. They become members of and drill with the

NROTC unit. When they complete their degree, they are commissioned as ensigns in the United States Naval Reserve and assigned to initial training as an officer in the CEC. After commissioning, 5 years of active service are required.
Number awarded Varies each year.
Deadline June of each year.

[183]
COAST GUARD COLLEGE STUDENT PRE-COMMISSIONING INITIATIVE

U.S. Coast Guard
Attn: Recruiting Command
2300 Wilson Boulevard, Suite 500
Arlington, VA 22201
(703) 235-1775   Toll Free: (877) NOW-USCG
Fax: (703) 235-1881
E-mail: Margaret.A.Jackson@uscg.mil
Web: www.gocoastguard.com

Summary To provide financial assistance to college students at minority or other designated institutions who are willing to serve in the Coast Guard following graduation.
Eligibility This program is open to students entering their junior or senior year at a college or university designated as an Historically Black College or University (HBCU), Hispanic Serving Institution (HSI), Tribal College or University (TCU), or the University of Guam, the University of Hawaii (at Manoa, Hilo, or West Oahu), Argosy University (Hawaii), or the Institute of American Indian and Alaska Native Culture (Santa Fe, New Mexico). Applicants must be U.S. citizens; have a GPA of 2.5 or higher; have scores of 1100 or higher on the critical reading and mathematics SAT, 23 or higher on the ACT, 4AQR/4PFAR on the ASTB, or 109 or higher on the SVAB GT; be between 19 and 27 years of age; and meet all physical requirements for a Coast Guard commission. They must agree to attend the Coast Guard Officer Candidate School following graduation and serve on active duty as an officer for at least 3 years.
Financial data Those selected to participate receive full payment of tuition, books, and fees; monthly housing and food allowances; medical and life insurance; special training in leadership, management, law enforcement, navigation, and marine science; 30 days of paid vacation per year; and a monthly salary of up to $2,200.
Duration Up to 2 years.
Number awarded Varies each year.
Deadline January of each year.

[184]
COAST GUARD RESERVE USAA SCHOLARSHIP

U.S. Coast Guard
Attn: CG-131
2100 Second Street, S.W., Stop 7801
Washington, DC 20593-7801
(202) 475-5477   E-mail: george.m.rubesha@uscg.mil
Web: www.uscg.mil/RESERVE/docs/pay_benefits/usaa.asp

Summary To provide financial assistance for college or graduate school to members of the Coast Guard Reserves and their dependents.
Eligibility This program is open to Coast Guard enlisted reservists (SELRES or IRR) and their dependents who are registered in the Defense Enrollment Eligibility Reporting System (DEERS). Applicants must be enrolled or accepted

for enrollment at 1) an accredited institution in a program leading to an associate, bachelor's, master's, or doctoral degree; or 2) a 2- or 4-year course of study at an accredited technical or vocational training school. Along with their application, they must submit a 1-page essay on how the participation of themselves, their spouse, or their parent in the Coast Guard Reserve has contributed to their success.

Financial data The stipend is $1,000.

Duration 1 year.

Additional information This program is sponsored by the United States Automobile Association (USAA) Insurance Corporation.

Number awarded 6 each year.

Deadline June of each year.

[185]
COAST GUARD TUITION ASSISTANCE PROGRAM

U.S. Coast Guard Institute
Attn: Commanding Officer
5900 S.W. 64th Street, Room 233
Oklahoma City, OK 73169-6990
(405) 954-1360   Fax: (405) 954-7245
E-mail: CGI-PF-Tuition_Assistance@uscg.mil
Web: www.uscg.mil

Summary To provide financial assistance to members and employees of the Coast Guard who are interested in pursuing additional education during their off-duty hours.

Eligibility This program is open to Coast Guard members who are interested in pursuing additional education at the high school, vocational/technical, undergraduate, graduate, or professional level. Civilian employees with at least 90 days of Coast Guard service and Selected Reservists are also eligible. Enlisted members must have at least 12 months remaining on their active-duty contracts or Selected Reserve obligation after completion of the course. Active-duty officers must agree to fulfill a 2-year service obligation following completion of the course; officers of the selected reserve must agree to fulfill a 4-year service obligation following completion of the course. Civilian employees must agree to retain employment with the Coast Guard for 1 month for each completed course credit hour. For military personnel, the command education services officer (ESO) must certify that the course of instruction is Coast Guard mission or career related. The supervisor of civilian employees must certify that the education is career related. All courses must be related to the mission of the Coast Guard or the individual's career or professional development.

Financial data Active-duty, Reserve, and civilian Coast Guard members receive full payment of all expenses for completion of a high school degree or equivalent. For college courses (vocational/technical, undergraduate, and graduate), 100% of the cost of tuition is reimbursed, to a maximum of $250 per semester hour or $4,500 per fiscal year.

Duration Until completion of a bachelor's or graduate degree.

Additional information Graduate students must earn a grade of "B" or higher to receive reimbursement; undergraduates must earn a grade of "D" or higher.

Number awarded Varies each year; recently, more than 10,000 Coast Guard active-duty members, Reservists, and civilian employees received tuition assistance worth approximately $14.5 million.

Deadline Applications may be submitted at any time.

[186]
COLORADO NATIONAL GUARD STATE TUITION ASSISTANCE

Department of Military and Veterans Affairs
Attn: CODAG-TA
6848 South Revere Parkway
Centennial, CO 80112-6703
(720) 250-1550   Fax: (720) 250-1559
E-mail: tuition@dmva.state.co.us
Web: www.dmva.state.co.us/page/ta

Summary To provide financial assistance for college or graduate school to members of the Colorado National Guard.

Eligibility This program is open to members of the Colorado National Guard who have completed at least 6 months of military service and are currently in drilling status. Applicants must be enrolled or planning to enroll at a public institution of higher education in Colorado to work on an associate, bachelor's, or master's degree.

Financial data This program provides payment of up to 100% of the in-state tuition at public institutions in Colorado.

Duration 1 semester; may be renewed as long as the recipient remains an active member of the Guard and maintains a GPA of 2.0 or higher. Assistance is limited to a total of 132 semester hours.

Additional information Recipients must serve 1 year in the Guard for each semester or quarter of assistance received.

Number awarded Varies each year.

Deadline June of each year for the fall semester; November of each year for the spring semester; April of each year for the summer term.

[187]
CONGRESSMAN DAVID L. HOBSON CIVIL ENGINEERING SCHOLARSHIP

Army Engineer Association
Attn: Executive Director
P.O. Box 30260
Alexandria, VA 22310-8260
(703) 428-7084   Fax: (703) 428-6043
E-mail: xd@armyengineer.com
Web: www.armyengineer.com/scholarships.htm

Summary To provide financial assistance to members of the Army Engineer Association (AEA) and their families interested in studying civil engineering in college.

Eligibility This program is open to AEA members and their families who are U.S. citizens. Applicants must be enrolled full time at an accredited college or university and working on a bachelor's degree in civil engineering. Along with their application, they must submit a 600-word essay that lists their academic and professional goals, extracurricular activities, and military service (if applicable). Selection is based on that essay, scholastic aptitude, and letters of recommendation.

Financial data The stipend is $3,000.

Duration 1 year; nonrenewable.

Additional information This program is sponsored by the engineering firm, Trimble.

Number awarded 4 each year.

Deadline July of each year.

[188]
CONNECTICUT NATIONAL GUARD EDUCATIONAL ASSISTANCE PROGRAM
Connecticut National Guard
Attn: Education Service Officer
360 Broad Street
Hartford, CT 06105-3795
(860) 524-4816
Web: states.ng.mil

Summary To provide financial assistance for college to members of the Connecticut National Guard.

Eligibility This program is open to active members of the Connecticut National Guard who are interested in working on an undergraduate degree at any branch of the University of Connecticut, any of the 4 state universities, or any of the 13 community/technical colleges in Connecticut. Applicants must have been residents of the state and a satisfactory Guard participant for at least 12 months.

Financial data The program provides a full waiver of tuition at state colleges or universities in Connecticut.

Duration 1 year; may be renewed.

Number awarded Varies each year.

Deadline Deadline not specified.

[189]
CONNECTICUT NATIONAL GUARD FOUNDATION SCHOLARSHIPS
Connecticut National Guard Foundation, Inc.
Attn: Scholarship Committee
360 Broad Street
Hartford, CT 06105-3795
(860) 241-1550   Fax: (860) 293-2929
E-mail: scholarship.committee@ctngfoundation.org
Web: www.ctngfoundation.org/Scholarship.asp

Summary To provide money for college to members of the Connecticut National Guard and their families.

Eligibility This program is open to members of the Connecticut Army National Guard and Organized Militia, their children, and their spouses. Applicants must be enrolled or planning to enroll in an accredited college or technical program. Along with their application, they must submit a letter of recommendation, a list of extracurricular activities, high school or college transcripts, and a 200-word statement on their educational and future goals. Selection is based on achievement and citizenship.

Financial data Stipends are $2,000 or $1,000.

Duration 1 year.

Number awarded 5 at $2,000 and 5 at $1,000.

Deadline March of each year.

[190]
CONNECTICUT TUITION WAIVER FOR VETERANS
Connecticut Office of Financial and Academic Affairs for Higher Education
Attn: Student Financial Aid
61 Woodland Street
Hartford, CT 06105-2326
(860) 947-1855   Toll Free: (800) 842-0229 (within CT)
Fax: (860) 947-1311   E-mail: sfa@ctdhe.org
Web: www.ctohe.org/SFA/default.htm

Summary To provide money for college or graduate school to certain Connecticut veterans and military personnel or their dependents.

Eligibility This program is open to 1) honorably-discharged Connecticut veterans who served at least 90 days during specified periods of wartime; 2) active members of the Connecticut Army and Air National Guard; 3) Connecticut residents who are a dependent child or surviving spouse of a member of the armed forces killed in action on or after September 11, 2001 who was also a Connecticut resident; and 4) Connecticut residents who are dependent children of a person officially declared missing in action or a prisoner of war while serving in the armed forces after January 1, 1960. Applicants must be attending or planning to attend a public college or university in the state.

Financial data The program provides a waiver of 100% of tuition for students working on an undergraduate or graduate degree at the University of Connecticut, 100% of tuition for general fund courses at campuses of Connecticut State University, 50% of tuition for extension and summer courses at campuses of Connecticut State University, 100% of tuition at all Connecticut community colleges, and 50% or fees at Charter Oak State College.

Duration Up to 4 years.

Additional information This is an entitlement program; applications are available from the respective college financial aid offices.

Number awarded Varies each year.

Deadline Deadline not specified.

[191]
CSM ROBERT W. ELKEY AWARD
Army Engineer Association
Attn: Executive Director
P.O. Box 30260
Alexandria, VA 22310-8260
(703) 428-7084   Fax: (703) 428-6043
E-mail: xd@armyengineer.com
Web: www.armyengineer.com/scholarships.htm

Summary To provide financial assistance for college or graduate school to enlisted members of the Army Engineer Association (AEA).

Eligibility This program is open to AEA members serving in an active, Reserve, or National Guard component Army Engineer unit, school, or organization within the Corps of Engineers of the United States Army. Applicants must be enlisted personnel (PVT, PFC, SPC, CPL, SGT, or SSG). They must be working on or planning to work on an associate, bachelor's, or master's degree at an accredited college or university. Selection is based primarily on financial need, although potential for academic success and standards of conduct as supported by personal references are also considered.

Financial data The stipend is $1,000.

Duration 1 year.

Number awarded 3 each year.

Deadline June of each year.

[192]
CSM VINCENT BALDASSARI MEMORIAL SCHOLARSHIPS

Enlisted Association National Guard of New Jersey
Attn: Scholarship Chair
3650 Saylors Pond Road
Fort Dix, NJ 08640
(609) 562-0260   Fax: (609) 562-0283
Web: www.eang-nj.org/scholarships.html

Summary To provide financial assistance to New Jersey National Guard members and their children who are interested in attending college in any state.

Eligibility This program is open to 1) children of New Jersey National Guard members who are also members of the Enlisted Association National Guard of New Jersey, and 2) drilling Guard members who are also members of the Association. Applicants must be attending or planning to attend a college or university in any state. Along with their application, they must submit 1) information on their church, school, and community activities; 2) a list of honors they have received; 3) letters of recommendation; 4) transcripts; and 5) a letter with specific facts about their desire to continue their education and specifying their career goals. Financial need is not considered in the selection process.

Financial data The stipend is $1,000.

Duration 1 year.

Number awarded Varies each year; recently, 5 of these scholarships were awarded.

Deadline May of each year.

[193]
CSM VIRGIL R. WILLIAMS SCHOLARSHIP PROGRAM

Enlisted Association of the National Guard of the United
    States
3133 Mount Vernon Avenue
Alexandria, VA 22305-2640
(703) 519-3846   Toll Free: (800) 234-EANG
Fax: (703) 519-3849   E-mail: eangus@eangus.org
Web: www.eangus.org/resources/scholarships_grants.aspx

Summary To provide financial assistance to National Guard members and their dependents who are members of the Enlisted Association of the National Guard of the United States (EANGUS) and entering or continuing in college.

Eligibility This program is open to high school seniors and current college students who are enrolled or planning to enroll as full-time undergraduate students. They must be 1) National Guard members who belong to EANGUS; 2) unmarried sons and daughters of EANGUS members; 3) spouses of EANGUS members; or 4) unremarried spouses and unmarried dependent children of deceased EANGUS members who were in good standing at the time of their death. Honorary, associate, or corporate membership alone does not qualify. Applicants must submit a copy of their school transcript, 3 letters of recommendation, a letter of academic reference (from their principal, dean, or counselor), a photocopy of the qualifying state and/or national membership card (parent's, spouse's or applicant's), and a personal letter with specific facts as to their desire to continue their education and why financial assistance is necessary. Application packets must be submitted to the state EANGUS association; acceptable packets are then sent to the national offices for judging.

Selection is based on academic achievement, character, leadership, and financial need.

Financial data The stipend is $2,000.

Duration 1 year; nonrenewable.

Additional information Recent sponsors of this program included USAA Insurance Corporation, GEICO Insurance, the Armed Forces Benefit Association, and the Armed Forces Insurance Company.

Number awarded Varies each year; recently, 10 of these scholarships were awarded.

Deadline Applications must first be verified by the state office and then submitted by June to the national office.

[194]
DEDICATED ARMY NATIONAL GUARD SCHOLARSHIPS

U.S. Army National Guard
c/o DANTES
6490 Saufley Field Road
Pensacola, FL 32509-5243
(850) 452-1085   Fax: (850) 452-1161
Web: www.nationalguard.com

Summary To provide financial assistance to college and graduate students who are interested in enrolling in Army ROTC and serving in the Army National Guard following graduation.

Eligibility This program is open to full-time students entering their sophomore or junior year of college with a GPA of 2.5 or higher. High school seniors are also eligible if they plan to attend a military junior college (MJC), have a GPA of 2.5 or higher, and have scores of at least 19 on the ACT or 920 on the combined mathematics and critical reading SAT. Graduate students may also be eligible if they have only 2 years remaining for completion of their degree. Students who have been awarded an ROTC campus-based scholarship may apply to convert to this program during their freshman year. Applicants must meet all medical and moral character requirements for enrollment in Army ROTC. They must be willing to enroll in the Simultaneous Membership Program (SMP) of an ROTC unit on their campus; the SMP requires simultaneous membership in Army ROTC and the Army National Guard.

Financial data Participants receive full reimbursement of tuition, a grant of $1,200 per year for books, plus an ROTC stipend for 10 months of the year at $350 per month during their sophomore year, $450 per month during their junior year, and $500 per month during their senior year. As a member of the Army National Guard, they also receive weekend drill pay at the pay grade of E-5 during their junior year or E-6 during their senior year.

Duration 2 or 3 years for college students; 2 years for high school seniors entering an MJC.

Additional information After graduation, participants serve 3 to 6 months on active duty in the Officer Basic Course (OBC). Following completion of OBC, they are released from active duty and are obligated to serve 8 years in the Army National Guard.

Number awarded Approximately 600 each year.

Deadline Deadline not specified.

[195]
DELAWARE NATIONAL GUARD EDUCATION ASSISTANCE PROGRAM

Delaware National Guard
Attn: Education Services Officer
State Tuition Reimbursement Program
First Regiment Road
Wilmington, DE 19808-2191
(302) 326-7012   Fax: (302) 326-7029
Web: www.delawarenationalguard.com

Summary To provide financial assistance to members of the Delaware National Guard who plan to attend college in the state.

Eligibility This program is open to active members of the Delaware National Guard who are interested in working on an associate or bachelor's degree at a school in Delaware. Applicants must have made satisfactory progress in their assigned military career field, may not have missed more than 6 periods of scheduled unit training assembly periods in the preceding 12 months, and must have avoided all adverse personnel actions. They must earn a grade of 2.0 or higher in all courses to qualify for tuition reimbursement.

Financial data Participants receive reimbursement of 100% of the tuition at state-supported colleges and universities in Delaware, to a maximum of $1,236 per semester at Delaware Technical and Community college, $4,270 per semester at the University of Delaware, or $3,240.50 per semester at Delaware State University. Students who attend a Delaware private college are reimbursed up to $243 per credit hour. If total funding appropriated by the legislature is insufficient for all qualified applicants, the available funds are distributed among recipients according to a maximum allowable fair percentage formula. Recipients must complete 6 years of satisfactory membership in the Delaware National Guard (before, during, and after participation in the program) or repay the funds received.

Duration 1 semester; may be renewed. Guard members are eligible for this assistance only for 10 years after the date on which they begin the first course for which reimbursement was granted.

Number awarded Varies each year; recently, a total of $490,000 was available for this program.

Deadline September of each year for fall semester; January of each year for winter semester; March of each year for spring semester; June of each year for summer semester.

[196]
DISTRICT OF COLUMBIA NATIONAL GUARD TUITION ASSISTANCE

District of Columbia National Guard
Attn: Education Services Office
2001 East Capitol Street, S.E.
Washington, DC 20003-1719
(202) 685-9825   Fax: (202) 685-9815
E-mail: joanne.thweatt@dc.ngb.army.mil
Web: states.ng.mil/sites/DC/education/Pages/tuition.aspx

Summary To provide financial assistance for college or graduate school (in selected fields) to current members of the District of Columbia National Guard.

Eligibility This program is open to traditional, technician, and AGR members of the District of Columbia Air and Army National Guard. Applicants must have a high school diploma

or equivalency and currently be working on an associate, bachelor's, or master's degree at an accredited postsecondary education institution. In some instances, support may also be available for an M.D., D.O., P.A., or J.D. degree.

Financial data Army National Guard members are eligible for up to $4,500 per year in federal tuition assistance; they may supplement that with up to $1,500 per year in District tuition assistance. Air National Guard members do not have access to federal tuition assistance, so they may receive up to $6,000 in District tuition assistance. Funds must be used to pay for tuition, fees, and/or books.

Duration 1 semester; recipients may reapply.

Number awarded Varies each year.

Deadline July of each year for the fall session, October of each year for the spring session, or April of each year for the summer session.

[197]
DIVISION COMMANDER'S HIP POCKET SCHOLARSHIPS

U.S. Army
ROTC Cadet Command
Attn: Scholarship Branch
204 1st Cavalry Regiment Road, Building 1002
Fort Knox, KY 40121
(502) 624-7371   Toll Free: (888) 550-ARMY
Fax: (502) 624-6937   E-mail: train2lead@usacc.army.mil
Web: www.rotc.usaac.army.mil/scholarships.aspx

Summary To enable soldiers who are nominated by their Division Commanding General to obtain an early discharge from the Army and return to college to participate in the Army Reserve Officers' Training Corps (ROTC).

Eligibility Enlisted soldiers who have served at least 2 but less than 10 years on active duty are eligible for this program. They must be nominated by their Division Commanding General to obtain an early discharge in order to enroll in a baccalaureate degree program. Nominees must have a cumulative high school or college GPA of 2.5 or higher, a score of at least 21 on the ACT or 1100 on the combined mathematics and critical reading SAT, a General Technical (GT) score of 110 or higher, and a recent (within the past 6 months) Army Physical Fitness Test (APFT) score of 180 or higher (including 60 points in each event). They may not have a spouse who is also in the military or dependent children under 18 years of age (those requirements may be waived). At the time they graduate and are commissioned, they must be under 31 years of age. Selection is made by the Division Commanding General; no additional review is made by Cadet Command Headquarters.

Financial data Scholarship winners receive full payment of tuition, a grant of $1,200 per year for books and supplies, a monthly stipend of up to $500 per month (depending on academic status) for 10 months per year, and pay for attending the 6-week Leader Development and Assessment Course (LDAC) during the summer between the junior and senior year of college.

Duration 2, 3, or 4 years.

Additional information Recipients who had previously qualified for benefits from the Army College Fund and/or the Montgomery GI Bill are still entitled to receive those in addition to any benefits from this program. Upon graduation from college, scholarship winners are commissioned as second lieutenants and are required to serve in the military for 8 years. That obligation may be fulfilled by serving 4 years on active duty followed by 4 years in the Inactive Ready Reserve (IRR).

Number awarded Varies each year; recently, 117 of these scholarships were awarded.

Deadline March of each year.

[198]
DR. AURELIO M. CACCOMO FAMILY FOUNDATION MEMORIAL SCHOLARSHIP

AMVETS National Headquarters
Attn: Scholarships
4647 Forbes Boulevard
Lanham, MD 20706-3807
(301) 459-9600   Toll Free: (877) 7-AMVETS, ext. 3043
Fax: (301) 459-7924   E-mail: amvets@amvets.org
Web: www.amvets.org/programs_scholarships.html

Summary To provide financial assistance for college to veterans and members of the National Guard and Reserves who are members of AMVETS.

Eligibility This program is open to AMVETS members who are veterans or currently serving in the National Guard or Reserves. Applicants must be interested in working full or part time on an undergraduate degree or certification from an accredited technical/trade school. They must have exhausted all other government aid. U.S. citizenship is required. Selection is based on financial need, academic promise, military duty and awards, volunteer activities, community services, jobs held during the past 4 years, and an essay of 50 to 100 words on "This award will help me achieve my career/vocational goal, which is..."

Financial data The stipend is $3,000.

Duration 1 year; nonrenewable.

Additional information Requests for applications must be accompanied by a self-addressed stamped envelope.

Number awarded 2 each year.

Deadline April of each year.

[199]
DR. JON L. BOYES, VICE ADMIRAL, USN (RET.) MEMORIAL SCHOLARSHIP

Armed Forces Communications and Electronics
  Association
Attn: AFCEA Educational Foundation
4400 Fair Lakes Court
Fairfax, VA 22033-3899
(703) 631-6138   Toll Free: (800) 336-4583, ext. 6138
Fax: (703) 631-4693 E-mail: scholarshipsinfo@afcea.org
Web: www.afcea.org

Summary To provide financial assistance to Navy ROTC midshipmen who are majoring in electrical engineering.

Eligibility This program is open to Navy ROTC midshipmen enrolled full time at an accredited degree-granting 4-year college or university in the United States. Applicants must be sophomores or juniors at the time of application and have a GPA of 3.0 or higher with a major in electrical engineering. Their application must be endorsed by the professor of naval science at their institution. Selection is based on demonstrated dedication, superior performance, and potential to serve as an officer in the United States Navy. Financial need is not considered in the selection process.

Financial data The stipend is $3,000.

Duration 1 year.

Number awarded 1 each year.

Deadline February of each year.

[200]
EANGGA SCHOLARSHIP

Enlisted Association of the National Guard of Georgia
Attn: Executive Director
P.O. Box 602
Ellenwood, GA 30294
(678) 644-9245   E-mail: csmharber@comcast.net
Web: www.eangga.com

Summary To provide financial assistance to members of the Enlisted Association of the National Guard of Georgia (EANGGA) and their families who are interested in attending college in any state.

Eligibility This program is open to EANGGA who have been in good standing for at least 1 year and to their children and spouses. Applicants must be enrolled or planning to enroll at a college or university in any state. Selection is based primarily on an essay, up to 7 pages in length, on a patriotic theme (e.g., heritage of the U.S. flag, history of the National Guard or a National Guard unit, acts of heroism by American patriots, our Constitution or Bill of Rights, civil liberties and other issues in a democratic state).

Financial data A stipend is awarded (amount not specified).

Duration 1 year.

Number awarded 2 each year.

Deadline April of each year.

[201]
EANGTN SCHOLARSHIP PROGRAM

Enlisted Association of the National Guard of Tennessee
Attn: Scholarship Committee
4332 Kenilwood Drive, Suite B
Nashville, TN 37204-4401
(615) 781-2000   Fax: (615) 833-9173
E-mail: betty@eangtn.org
Web: www.eangtn.org/Scholarships.htm

Summary To provide financial assistance to members of the Enlisted Association of the National Guard of Tennessee (EANGTN) and to their dependents who are interested in attending college in any state.

Eligibility This program is open to students who are members of both the Tennessee National Guard and EANGTN or the dependent son, daughter, or spouse of a member in good standing. Children must be unmarried, unless they are also a member of the National Guard. Applicants must be entering or continuing at a college or university in any state. Along with their application, they must submit a transcript, a letter with specific facts as to their desire to continue their education and why financial assistance is required, 3 letters of recommendation, and a letter of academic reference.

Financial data The stipend is $1,000. Funds are paid to the recipient's school once enrollment is confirmed.

Duration 1 year.

Additional information In 1985, the National Guard Association of Tennessee (NGAT) agreed that the EANGTN would fund the scholarships of both associations. Additional funding is also provided by USAA Insurance Corporation.

Number awarded 6 each year.

Deadline January of each year.

[202]
EANGUT SCHOLARSHIP

Enlisted Association of the National Guard of Utah
Attn: Scholarship Committee
17800 South Camp Williams Road
Riverton, UT 84065-4999
(801) 699-1680 E-mail: Derek.dimond1@us.army.mil
Web: www.eangut.org

Summary To provide financial assistance to National Guard members who are active members of the Enlisted Association National Guard of Utah (EANGUT) and their families entering or continuing in college in the state.

Eligibility This program is open to members of EANGUT, their spouses, their children, and the spouses and unmarried dependent children of deceased members. Applicants must be attending or planning to attend a college, university, or vocational/technical school in Utah. EANGUT members must have at least 1 year remaining on their enlistment or have completed 20 or more years of service. Along with their application, they must submit a brief statement on their desire to continue their education and why financial assistance is requested. Selection is based on academic achievement, citizenship, and financial need.

Financial data The stipend is $1,000, including $500 contributed by EANGUT and $500 by USAA Insurance Corporation.

Duration 1 year.

Number awarded 1 or more each year.

Deadline July of each year.

[203]
EDUCATION FOUNDATION FOR THE COLORADO NATIONAL GUARD GRANTS

National Guard Association of Colorado
Attn: Education Foundation, Inc.
P.O. Box 440889
Aurora, CO 80044-0889
(303) 909-6369 Fax: (720) 535-5925
E-mail: BernieRogoff@comcast.net
Web: efcong.org/Grants

Summary To provide financial assistance to members of the Colorado National Guard and their families who are interested in attending college or graduate school in any state.

Eligibility This program is open to current and retired members of the Colorado National Guard and their dependent unmarried children and spouses. Applicants must be enrolled or planning to enroll full or part time at a college, university, trade school, business school, or graduate school in any state. Along with their application, they must submit an essay, up to 2 pages in length, on their desire to continue their education, what motivates them, their financial need, their commitment to academic excellence, and their current situation. Selection is based on academic achievement, community involvement, and financial need.

Financial data Stipends are at least $1,000 per year.

Duration 1 year; may be renewed.

Number awarded Varies each year; recently, 38 of these grants, with a total value of $50,000, were awarded.

Deadline July of each year for fall semester; January of each year for spring semester.

[204]
EXPLOSIVE ORDNANCE DISPOSAL OPTION OF THE SEAMAN TO ADMIRAL-21 PROGRAM

U.S. Navy
Attn: Commander, Naval Service Training Command
250 Dallas Street, Suite A
Pensacola, FL 32508-5268
(850) 452-9433 Fax: (850) 452-2486
E-mail: PNSC_STA21@navy.mil
Web: www.sta-21.navy.mil

Summary To allow outstanding enlisted Navy personnel to complete a bachelor's degree and receive a commission as an explosive ordnance disposal (EOD) officer.

Eligibility This program is open to U.S. citizens who are currently serving on active duty in the U.S. Navy or Naval Reserve, including Full Time Support (FTS), Selected Reserves (SELRES), and Navy Reservists on active duty, except for those on active duty for training (ACDUTRA). Applicants must have 1 of the following NECs: 5332, 5333, 5334, 5335, 5336, 5337, 5342, 5343 and 8493 or 8494. They must be high school graduates (or GED recipients) who are able to complete requirements for a baccalaureate degree in 36 months or less. When they complete their degree requirements, they must be younger than 29 years of age. That age limitation may be adjusted upward for active service on a month-for-month basis up to 24 months, and waivers are considered for enlisted personnel who possess particularly exceptional qualifications if they can complete their degree prior to their 35th birthday. Within the past 3 years, they must have taken the SAT (and achieved scores of at least 500 on the mathematics section and 500 on the critical reading section) or the ACT (and achieved a score of 41 or higher, including at least 21 on the mathematics portion and 20 on the English portion). They must also meet physical regulations that include qualification for diving duty and/or combat swimmer. Preference is given to applicants who plan to major in a technical field (e.g., chemistry, computer science, engineering, mathematics, oceanography, operations analysis, physical sciences, or physics).

Financial data Awardees continue to receive their regular Navy pay and allowances while they attend college on a full-time basis. They also receive reimbursement for tuition, fees, and books up to $10,000 per year. If base housing is available, they are eligible to live there. Participants are not eligible to receive benefits under the Navy's Tuition Assistance Program (TA), the Montgomery GI Bill (MGIB), the Navy College Fund, or the Veterans Educational Assistance Program (VEAP).

Duration Selectees are supported for up to 36 months of full-time, year-round study or completion of a bachelor's degree, as long as they maintain a GPA of 2.5 or higher.

Additional information This program was established in 2001 as a replacement for the Seaman to Admiral Program (established in 1994), the Enlisted Commissioning Program, and other specialized programs for sailors to earn a commission. Upon acceptance into the program, selectees attend the Naval Science Institute (NSI) in Newport, Rhode Island for an

8-week program in the fundamental core concepts of being a naval officer (navigation, engineering, weapons, military history and justice, etc.). They then enter a college or university with an NROTC unit or affiliation to work full time on a bachelor's degree. They become members of and drill with the NROTC unit. When they complete their degree, they are commissioned as ensigns in the United States Naval Reserve and assigned to initial training as an EOD officer. After commissioning, 5 years of active service are required.

Number awarded Varies each year.

Deadline June of each year.

[205]
FCDA SCHOLARSHIPS

First Cavalry Division Association
Attn: Foundation
302 North Main Street
Copperas Cove, TX 76522-1703
(254) 547-6537 Fax: (254) 547-8853
E-mail: firstcav@1cda.org
Web: www.1cda.org/Foundation_Overview.htm

Summary To provide financial assistance for undergraduate education to soldiers currently or formerly assigned to the First Cavalry Division and their families.

Eligibility This program is open to children of soldiers who died or have been declared totally and permanently disabled from injuries incurred while serving with the First Cavalry Division during any armed conflict; children of soldiers who died while serving in the First Cavalry Division during peacetime; and active-duty soldiers currently assigned or attached to the First Cavalry Division and their spouses and children.

Financial data The stipend is $1,200 per year. The checks are made out jointly to the student and the school and may be used for whatever the student needs, including tuition, books, and clothing.

Duration 1 year; may be renewed up to 3 additional years.

Additional information Requests for applications must be accompanied by a self-addressed stamped envelope.

Number awarded Varies each year; since the program was established, it has awarded more than $783,800 to 468 children of disabled and deceased Cavalry members and more than $212,900 to 300 current members of the Division and their families.

Deadline June of each year.

[206]
FIRST SERGEANT DOUGLAS AND CHARLOTTE DEHORSE SCHOLARSHIP

Catching the Dream
8200 Mountain Road, N.E., Suite 203
Albuquerque, NM 87110-7835
(505) 262-2351 Fax: (505) 262-0534
E-mail: NScholarsh@aol.com
Web: www.catchingthedream.org

Summary To provide financial assistance to American Indians who have ties to the military and are working on an undergraduate or graduate degree.

Eligibility This program is open to American Indians who 1) have completed 1 year of an Army, Navy, or Air Force Junior Reserve Officer Training (JROTC) program; 2) are enrolled in an Army, Navy, or Air Force Reserve Officer Training (ROTC) program; or 3) are a veteran of the U.S. Army,

Navy, Air Force, Marines, Merchant Marine, or Coast Guard. Applicants must be enrolled in college or graduate school. They must submit an application, personal essay, high school transcripts, and letters of recommendation.

Financial data A stipend is awarded (amount not specified).

Duration 1 year.

Additional information This program began in 2007.

Number awarded 1 or more each year.

Deadline April of each year for fall semester or quarter; September of each year for spring semester or winter quarter.

[207]
FLORIDA NATIONAL GUARD EDUCATIONAL DOLLARS FOR DUTY (EDD) PROGRAM

Department of Military Affairs
Attn: Education Services Officer
82 Marine Street
St. Augustine, FL 32084-5039
(904) 823-0417 Toll Free: (800) 342-6528
Web: dma.myflorida.com

Summary To provide financial assistance for college graduate school to members of the Florida National Guard.

Eligibility This program is open to current members of the Florida National Guard. Applicants must be attending or planning to attend a college or university in Florida to work on an undergraduate or master's degree. College preparatory and vocational/technical programs also qualify. Guard members who already have a master's degree are not eligible.

Financial data The program provides for payment of 100% of tuition and fees at a public college or university or an equivalent amount at a private institution.

Duration 1 year; may be renewed.

Number awarded Varies each year; recently, approximately 765 Florida National Guard members utilized this program.

Deadline Deadline not specified.

[208]
FORCE RECON ASSOCIATION SCHOLARSHIPS

Force Recon Association
P.O. Box 425
Rowe, MA 01367
E-mail: commchief@forcerecon.com
Web: www.forcerecon.com

Summary To provide money for college to members of the Force Recon Association and their dependents.

Eligibility This program is open to members of the Force Recon Association and family members of a relative who served both in the U.S. Marine Corps and was or is assigned to a Force Reconnaissance Company. The relative must be either an active or deceased member of the Force Recon Association. Family members include wives and widows, sons and daughters (including adopted and stepchildren), grandchildren, and great-grandchildren. Applicants may be pursuing scholastic, vocational, or technical education. Along with their application, they must submit a personal statement on why they desire this scholarship, their proposed course of study, their progress in their current course of study, and their long-range career goals. Selection is based on academic achievement, letters of recommendation, demonstrated character, and the written statements.

Financial data A stipend is awarded (amount not specified).

Duration 1 year; may be renewed.

Number awarded 1 or more each year.

Deadline Applications must be received at least 2 weeks prior to the annual meeting of the Force Recon Association.

[209]
FRA NON-MEMBER SCHOLARSHIPS

Fleet Reserve Association
Attn: FRA Education Foundation
125 North West Street
Alexandria, VA 22314-2754
(703) 683-1400   Toll Free: (800) FRA-1924
Fax: (703) 549-6610   E-mail: scholars@fra.org
Web: www.fra.org

Summary To provide financial assistance for college or graduate school to current or former sea service personnel and their families.

Eligibility This program is open to 1) active-duty, Reserve, honorably-discharged veterans, and retired members of the U.S. Navy, Marine Corps, and Coast Guard; and 2) their spouses, children, and grandchildren. Applicants must be enrolled as full-time undergraduate or graduate students but they are not required to be members of the sponsoring organization. Along with their application, they must submit an essay on why they want to go to college and what they intend to accomplish with their degree. Selection is based on academic record, financial need, extracurricular activities, leadership skills, and participation in community activities. U.S. citizenship is required.

Financial data A stipend is awarded (amount not specified).

Duration 1 year; may be renewed.

Number awarded 1 or more each year.

Deadline April of each year.

[210]
FRA SCHOLARSHIPS

Fleet Reserve Association
Attn: FRA Education Foundation
125 North West Street
Alexandria, VA 22314-2754
(703) 683-1400   Toll Free: (800) FRA-1924
Fax: (703) 549-6610   E-mail: scholars@fra.org
Web: www.fra.org

Summary To provide financial assistance for college or graduate school to members of the Fleet Reserve Association (FRA) and their families.

Eligibility This program is open to members of the FRA and the dependent children, grandchildren, and spouses of living or deceased members. Applicants must be enrolled as full-time undergraduate or graduate students. Along with their application, they must submit an essay on why they want to go to college and what they intend to accomplish with their degree. Selection is based on academic record, financial need, extracurricular activities, leadership skills, and participation in community activities. U.S. citizenship is required.

Financial data The stipend is $5,000 per year.

Duration 1 year; may be renewed.

Additional information Membership in the FRA is restricted to active-duty, retired, and reserve members of the Navy, Marines, and Coast Guard.

Number awarded 6 each year.

Deadline April of each year.

[211]
FREDERICK C. BRANCH MARINE CORPS
LEADERSHIP SCHOLARSHIPS

U.S. Navy
Attn: Naval Education and Training Command
NSTC OD2
250 Dallas Street, Suite A
Pensacola, FL 32508-5268
(850) 452-4941, ext. 29395
Toll Free: (800) NAV-ROTC, ext. 29395
Fax: (850) 452-2486
E-mail: pnsc_nrotc.scholarship@navy.mil
Web: www.nrotc.navy.mil/hist_black.aspx

Summary To provide financial assistance to students at specified Historically Black Colleges or Universities (HBCUs) who are interested in joining Navy ROTC to prepare for service as an officer in the U.S. Marine Corps.

Eligibility This program is open to students attending or planning to attend 1 of 17 specified HBCUs with a Navy ROTC unit on campus. Applicants may either apply through their local Marine recruiter for a 4-year scholarship or be nominated by the professor of naval science at their institution and meet academic requirements set by each school for 2- or 3-year scholarships. They must be U.S. citizens between 17 and 23 years of age who are willing to serve for 4 years as active-duty Marine Corps officers following graduation from college. They must not have reached their 27th birthday by the time of college graduation and commissioning; applicants who have prior active-duty military service may be eligible for age adjustments for the amount of time equal to their prior service, up to a maximum of 36 months. The qualifying scores are 1000 composite on the SAT or 22 composite on the ACT. Current enlisted and former military personnel are also eligible if they will complete the program by the age of 30.

Financial data These scholarships provide payment of full tuition and required educational fees, as well as a specified amount for textbooks, supplies, and equipment. The program also provides a stipend for 10 months of the year that is $250 per month as a freshman, $300 per month as a sophomore, $350 per month as a junior, and $400 per month as a senior.

Duration Scholarships are available for 2-, 3-, or 4-year terms.

Additional information Recipients must complete 4 years of study in naval science classes as students at 1 of the following HBCUs: Allen University, Clark Atlanta University, Dillard University, Florida A&M University, Hampton University, Howard University, Huston-Tillotson University, Morehouse College, Norfolk State University, Prairie View A&M University, Savannah State University, Southern University and A&M College, Spelman College, Tennessee State University, Texas Southern University, Tuskegee University, or Xavier University. After completing the program, all participants are commissioned as second lieutenants in the Marine Corps Reserve with an 8-year service obligation, including 4 years of active duty. Current military personnel who are accepted into this program are released from active duty and are not eligible for active-duty pay and allowances, medical benefits, or other active-duty entitlements.

Number awarded Varies each year.

Deadline January of each year for students applying for a 4-year scholarship through their local Marine recruiter; July of each year if applying for a 2- or 3-year scholarship through the Navy ROTC unit at their institution.

[212]
GENERAL EMMETT PAIGE SCHOLARSHIPS

Armed Forces Communications and Electronics
  Association
Attn: AFCEA Educational Foundation
4400 Fair Lakes Court
Fairfax, VA 22033-3899
(703) 631-6138   Toll Free: (800) 336-4583, ext. 6138
Fax: (703) 631-4693 E-mail: scholarshipsinfo@afcea.org
Web: www.afcea.org/education/scholarships/military

Summary To provide financial assistance to veterans, military personnel, and their family members who are majoring in specified scientific fields in college.

Eligibility This program is open to veterans, persons on active duty in the uniformed military services, and their spouses or dependents who are currently enrolled full time in an accredited 4-year college or university in the United States. Graduating high school seniors are not eligible, but veterans entering college as freshmen may apply. Spouses or dependents must be sophomores or juniors. Applicants must be U.S. citizens, be of good moral character, have demonstrated academic excellence, be motivated to complete a college education, and be working toward a degree in engineering (aerospace, computer, electrical, or systems), computer engineering technology, electronics engineering technology, computer network systems, mathematics, physics, information systems security, information systems management, technology management, computer science, or other field directly related to the support of U.S. intelligence enterprises or national security. They must have a GPA of 3.0 or higher. Along with their application, they must provide a copy of Discharge Form DD214, Certificate of Service, or facsimile of their current Department of Defense or Coast Guard Identification Card. Financial need is not considered.

Financial data The stipend is $2,500 per year.

Duration 1 year; may be renewed.

Number awarded Varies each year; recently, 5 of these scholarships were awarded.

Deadline April of each year.

[213]
GEORGIA'S HERO SCHOLARSHIP PROGRAM

Georgia Student Finance Commission
Attn: Scholarships and Grants Division
2082 East Exchange Place, Suite 200
Tucker, GA 30084-5305
(770) 724-9000   Toll Free: (800) 505-GSFC
Fax: (770) 724-9089   E-mail: gacollege411@gsfc.org
Web: www.gacollege411.org

Summary To provide financial assistance for college to members of the National Guard or Reserves in Georgia and their children and spouses.

Eligibility This program is open to Georgia residents who are active members of the Georgia National Guard or U.S. Military Reserves, were deployed outside the United States for active-duty service on or after February 1, 2003 to a location designated as a combat zone, and served in that combat zone for at least 181 consecutive days. Also eligible are 1) the children, younger than 25 years of age, of Guard and Reserve members who completed at least 1 term of service (of 181 days each) overseas on or after February 1, 2003; 2) the children, younger than 25 years of age, of Guard and Reserve members who were killed or totally disabled during service overseas on or after February 1, 2003, regardless of their length of service; and 3) the spouses of Guard and Reserve members who were killed in a combat zone, died as a result of injuries, or became 100% disabled as a result of injuries received in a combat zone during service overseas on or after February 1, 2003, regardless of their length of service. Applicants must be interested in attending a unit of the University System of Georgia, a unit of the Georgia Department of Technical and Adult Education, or an eligible private college or university in Georgia.

Financial data The stipend for full-time study is $2,000 per academic year, not to exceed $8,000 during an entire program of study. The stipend for part-time study is prorated appropriately.

Duration 1 year; may be renewed (if satisfactory progress is maintained) for up to 3 additional years.

Additional information This program, which stands for Helping Educate Reservists and their Offspring, began in 2005.

Number awarded Varies each year.

Deadline June of each year.

[214]
GETCHELL AND ROTC SCHOLARSHIPS

Daedalian Foundation
Attn: Scholarship Committee
55 Main Circle (Building 676)
P.O. Box 249
Randolph AFB, TX 78148-0249
(210) 945-2113   Fax: (210) 945-2112
E-mail: kristi@daedalians.org
Web: www.daedalians.org/foundation/scholarships.htm

Summary To provide financial assistance to ROTC students who wish to become military pilots.

Eligibility This program is open to students who are currently enrolled in an ROTC program at their college or university. Applicants must be interested in preparing for a career as a military pilot. They must apply through their ROTC detachment. Selection is based on intention to pursue a career as a military pilot, demonstrated moral character and patriotism, scholastic and military standing and aptitude, and physical condition and aptitude for flight. Financial need may also be considered.

Financial data The stipend is $2,000.

Duration 1 year.

Number awarded 19 each year: 5 designated as Getchell Scholarships, 8 for Air Force ROTC cadets, 3 for Army ROTC cadets, and 3 for Navy/Marine ROTC midshipmen.

Deadline November of each year.

[215]
GLADYS MCPARTLAND SCHOLARSHIPS

United States Marine Corps Combat Correspondents
  Association
Attn: Executive Director
110 Fox Court
Wildwood, FL 34785
(352) 748-4698   E-mail: usmccca@cfl.rr.com
Web: www.usmccca.org/archives/4941

Summary To provide financial assistance to members of the U.S. Marine Corps Combat Correspondents Association (USMCCCA) or their dependents and Marines in designated occupational fields who are interested in studying any field in college.

Eligibility This program is open to 1) members of USMCCCA, their dependents, and their spouses; and 2) active-duty Marines in Occupational Fields 4300 and 4600 and their dependents who are USMCCCA members or will agree to become members if awarded a scholarship. Applicants must be enrolled or planning to enroll in an undergraduate program in any field. Along with their application, they must submit 500-word essays on 1) their noteworthy achievements and long-range goals; and 2) the United States I want to see in 15 years and my role in the transformation. Financial need is not considered in the selection process.

Financial data Stipends range up to $3,000; funds are disbursed directly to the recipient's institution to be used exclusively for tuition, books, and/or fees.

Duration 1 year.

Number awarded 1 or more each year.

Deadline May of each year.

[216]
GREEN TO GOLD NON-SCHOLARSHIP PROGRAM

U.S. Army
ROTC Cadet Command
Attn: Scholarship Branch
204 1st Cavalry Regiment Road, Building 1002
Fort Knox, KY 40121
(502) 624-7371   Toll Free: (888) 550-ARMY
Fax: (502) 624-6937   E-mail: train2lead@usacc.army.mil
Web: www.goarmy.com

Summary To provide financial assistance to soldiers who wish to obtain an early discharge from the Army and return to college to participate in the Army Reserve Officers' Training Corps (ROTC).

Eligibility This program is open to enlisted soldiers who have served at least 2 years on active duty and have also completed at least 2 years of college with a GPA of 2.0 or higher. Applicants must be under 30 years of age when they graduate (waivers up to 32 years of age are available). They apply for this program to obtain an early discharge from active duty in order to enroll in a baccalaureate degree program.

Financial data Cadets receive a stipend for 10 months of the year that is $450 per month during their junior year and $500 per month during their senior year, as well as pay for attending the 6-week Leader Development and Assessment Course (LDAC) during the summer between their junior and senior year of college.

Duration 2 years.

Additional information Cadets who had previously qualified for benefits from the Army College Fund and/or the Mont-

gomery GI Bill are still entitled to receive those in addition to any benefits from this program. Cadets are also entitled to participate in the Simultaneous Membership Program and serve with pay in a drilling unit of the Army Reserve or Army National Guard. Upon graduation from college, cadets are commissioned as second lieutenants and are required to serve in the military for 8 years. That obligation may be fulfilled by serving 3 years on active duty and 5 years in the Inactive Ready Reserve (IRR).

Number awarded Varies each year.

Deadline March or September of each year.

[217]
GREEN TO GOLD SCHOLARSHIP PROGRAM

U.S. Army
ROTC Cadet Command
Attn: Scholarship Branch
204 1st Cavalry Regiment Road, Building 1002
Fort Knox, KY 40121
(502) 624-7371   Toll Free: (888) 550-ARMY
Fax: (502) 624-6937   E-mail: train2lead@usacc.army.mil
Web: www.goarmy.com

Summary To provide scholarships and other payments to soldiers who wish to obtain an early discharge from the Army and return to college to participate in the Army Reserve Officers' Training Corps (ROTC).

Eligibility This program is open to enlisted soldiers who have served at least 2 years on active duty plus 3 months of active duty for each month of specialized training. Applicants must have a cumulative high school or college GPA of 2.5 or higher, a General Technical (GT) score of 110 or higher, and a recent (within the past 6 months) Army Physical Fitness Test (APFT) score of 180 or higher (including 60 points in each event). They may have no more than 3 dependents including a spouse (that requirement may be waived) and must be under 31 years of age when they graduate and are commissioned. They must have been accepted at a college or university offering Army ROTC. U.S. citizenship is required.

Financial data Scholarship winners receive up to $20,000 per year as support for tuition and fees or for room and board, whichever the recipient selects; additional support up to $1,200 per year for textbooks, supplies, and equipment; a stipend for 10 months of the year that is $350 per month during their sophomore year, $450 per month during their junior year, and $500 per month during their senior year; and pay for attending the 6-week Leader Development and Assessment Course (LDAC) during the summer between the junior and senior year of college.

Duration Scholarships are for 2, 3, or 4 years; soldiers without prior college credit or whose colleges accept them as academic freshmen are eligible for 4-year scholarships; soldiers with 1 year of college completed are eligible for 3-year scholarships; soldiers with 2 years of college completed are eligible for 2-year scholarships.

Additional information Recipients who had previously qualified for benefits from the Army College Fund and/or the Montgomery GI Bill are still entitled to receive those in addition to any benefits from this program. Upon graduation from college, scholarship winners are commissioned as second lieutenants and are required to serve in the military for 8 years. That obligation may be fulfilled by serving 4 years on active duty followed by 4 years in the Inactive Ready Reserve (IRR).

Number awarded   Varies each year.

Deadline   March or September of each year.

[218]
GUARANTEED RESERVE FORCES DUTY SCHOLARSHIPS

U.S. Army National Guard
c/o DANTES
6490 Saufley Field Road
Pensacola, FL 32509-5243
(850) 452-1085   Fax: (850) 452-1161
Web: www.nationalguard.com

Summary   To provide financial assistance to college and graduate students who are willing to enroll in Army ROTC and serve in a Reserve component of the Army following graduation.

Eligibility   This program is open to full-time students entering their junior year of college who have a GPA of 2.5 or higher and scores of 920 on the SAT or 19 on the ACT. Applicants must meet all other medical and moral character requirements for enrollment in Army ROTC and be able to complete the basic course requirements or basic training. They must be willing to enroll in the Simultaneous Membership Program (SMP) of an ROTC unit on their campus; the SMP requires simultaneous membership in Army ROTC and either the Army National Guard or Army Reserve.

Financial data   Participants receive full reimbursement of tuition, a grant of $1,200 per year for books, plus an ROTC stipend for 10 months of the year at $450 per month during their junior year and $500 per month during their senior year. As a member of the Army National Guard or Army Reserve, they also receive weekend drill pay at the pay grade of E-5 during their junior year or E-6 during their senior year.

Duration   2 years.

Additional information   After graduation, participants serve 3 to 6 months on active duty in the Officer Basic Course (OBC). Following completion of OBC, they are released from active duty and are obligated to serve 8 years in the Army National Guard or Army Reserve.

Number awarded   Approximately 400 each year.

Deadline   Deadline not specified.

[219]
HENRY J. REILLY MEMORIAL SCHOLARSHIP FOR COLLEGE SOPHOMORES AND JUNIORS

Reserve Officers Association of the United States
Attn: Scholarship Program
One Constitution Avenue, N.E.
Washington, DC 20002-5618
(202) 646-7719   Toll Free: (800) 809-9448, ext. 719
Fax: (202) 547-1641   E-mail: scholarship@roa.org
Web: www.roa.org

Summary   To provide financial assistance to members of the Reserve Officers Association (ROA) and their children or grandchildren who are completing the sophomore or junior year of college.

Eligibility   Applicants for this scholarship must be active or associate members of the association or their children or grandchildren (under the age of 26). Children, age 21 or under, of deceased members who were active and paid up at the time of their death are also eligible. Spouses are not eligible, unless they are members of the association. ROTC members do not qualify as sponsors. Applicants must provide evidence of full-time enrollment at a regionally-accredited 4-year college or university, demonstrate leadership qualities, have earned a GPA of 3.3 or higher in high school and 3.0 or higher in college, have scored at least 1875 on the SAT or 55 on the English/math ACT, and (if appropriate) have registered for the draft. Community college students who are transferring to a 4-year college and university are also eligible. They must submit an application and a 500-word essay on career goals.

Financial data   The stipend is $1,000 per year.

Duration   1 year; may be renewed.

Number awarded   The sponsor awards a total of 30 scholarships each year.

Deadline   May of each year.

[220]
HISTORICALLY BLACK COLLEGE SCHOLARSHIPS

U.S. Navy
Attn: Naval Education and Training Command
NSTC OD2
250 Dallas Street, Suite A
Pensacola, FL 32508-5268
(850) 452-4941, ext. 29395
Toll Free: (800) NAV-ROTC, ext. 29395
Fax: (850) 452-2486
E-mail: pnsc_nrotc.scholarship@navy.mil
Web: www.nrotc.navy.mil/hist_black.aspx

Summary   To provide financial assistance to students at specified Historically Black Colleges or Universities (HBCUs) who are interested in joining Navy ROTC to prepare for service as an officer in the U.S. Navy.

Eligibility   This program is open to students attending or planning to attend 1 of 17 specified HBCUs with a Navy ROTC unit on campus. Applicants must be nominated by the professor of naval science at their institution and meet academic requirements set by each school. They must be U.S. citizens between 17 and 23 years of age who are willing to serve for 4 years as active-duty Navy officers following graduation from college. They must not have reached their 27th birthday by the time of college graduation and commissioning; applicants who have prior active-duty military service may be eligible for age adjustments for the amount of time equal to their prior service, up to a maximum of 36 months. The qualifying scores are 530 critical reading and 520 mathematics on the SAT or 22 on English and 21 on mathematics on the ACT. Current enlisted and former military personnel are also eligible if they will complete the program by the age of 30.

Financial data   These scholarships provide payment of full tuition and required educational fees, as well as a specified amount for textbooks, supplies, and equipment. The program also provides a stipend for 10 months of the year that is $250 per month as a freshman, $300 per month as a sophomore, $350 per month as a junior, and $400 per month as a senior.

Duration   Up to 4 years.

Additional information   Recipients must complete 4 years of study in naval science classes as students at 1 of the following HBCUs: Allen University, Clark Atlanta University, Dillard University, Florida A&M University, Hampton University, Howard University, Huston-Tillotson University, Morehouse College, Norfolk State University, Prairie View A&M University, Savannah State University, Southern University and A&M College, Spelman College, Tennessee State University, Texas Southern University, Tuskegee University, or Xavier University. After completing the program, all participants are commissioned as ensigns in the Naval Reserve with an 8-year service obligation, including 4 years of active duty. Current military personnel who are accepted into this program are released from active duty and are not eligible for active-duty pay and allowances, medical benefits, or other active-duty entitlements.

Number awarded Varies each year.

Deadline January of each year.

[221]
HNGEA SCHOLARSHIP

Hawaii National Guard Enlisted Association
c/o Larnette H. Doi, Scholarship Committee Chair
360 Mamala Bay Drive
Hickam AFB, HI 9683-5517
E-mail: larnette.doi@hickam.af.mil
Web: www.hngea.net/Scholarship%20Webpage.htm

Summary To provide financial assistance for college to members of the Hawaii National Guard Enlisted Association (HNGEA) and their dependents.

Eligibility This program is open to HNGEA members and their dependent spouses and children. Applicants must be attending or interested in attending a college or university in Hawaii as an undergraduate student. They must have a GPA of at least 2.5 for the current semester and 2.0 overall. Along with their application, they must submit a letter describing their educational goals and need for the scholarship. Selection is based on that letter (10 points), academic achievement (50 points), participation in the organization (10 points), and financial need (30 points).

Financial data Stipends range from $500 to $2,000.

Duration 1 year.

Number awarded Varies each year.

Deadline June of each year.

[222]
HONOLULU POST SAME SCHOLARSHIPS

Society of American Military Engineers-Honolulu Post
P.O. Box 201445
Honolulu, HI 96820
Web: www.samehonolulu.org

Summary To provide financial assistance to residents of Hawaii, particularly those with ties to the military, who are interested in attending college in any state to work on an undergraduate or graduate degree in engineering or architecture.

Eligibility This program is open to residents of Hawaii who are graduating high school seniors or current undergraduates enrolled or planning to enroll full time at an accredited college or university in any state. Applicants must be planning to work on an undergraduate or graduate degree in engineering or architecture. They must be U.S. citizens and have a GPA of 3.0 or higher. Military affiliation or experience (i.e., ROTC, member or dependent of a member of the Society of Military Engineers (SAME), military dependent, Junior ROTC) is not required but is given preference. Along with their application, they must submit a transcript; a resume of work experience,

academic activities, and extracurricular accomplishments; and a 1-page essay on how their engineering or architecture degree will impact our nation.

Financial data The stipend is $2,500.

Duration 1 year.

Number awarded Varies each year; recently, 6 of these scholarships were awarded.

Deadline March of each year.

[223]
HOWARD R. HARPER SCHOLARSHIPS

Enlisted Association of the National Guard of Iowa
c/o Jerald D. Hansen, Secretary
1409 East Coolbaugh Street
Red Oak, IA 51566
(712) 623-2804
Web: www.eangi.users01.com/index-4.html

Summary To provide funding to members of the Enlisted Association of the National Guard of Iowa (EANGI) and their dependents who are interested in attending college.

Eligibility This program is open to EANGI members and their spouses and children. Applicants must be attending or accepted at a VA-approved college or vocational/technical school (which may be in any state). Along with their application, they must submit a copy of their transcript, a letter with specific facts as to their desire to continue their education and why financial assistance is required, 3 letters of recommendation, and 1 academic reference.

Financial data The stipend is $1,500.

Duration 1 year.

Additional information Membership in EANGI is open to enlisted members of the Iowa Army or Air National Guard, active component members assigned to the Iowa Army or Air National Guard, and retired or honorably-discharged Iowa Army or Air National Guard enlisted personnel.

Number awarded 5 each year.

Deadline January of each year.

[224]
HUMAN RESOURCES OPTION OF THE SEAMAN TO ADMIRAL-21 PROGRAM

U.S. Navy
Attn: Commander, Naval Service Training Command
250 Dallas Street, Suite A
Pensacola, FL 32508-5268
(850) 452-9433   Fax: (850) 452-2486
E-mail: PNSC_STA21@navy.mil
Web: www.sta-21.navy.mil

Summary To allow outstanding enlisted Navy personnel to complete a bachelor's degree and receive a commission as a human resources officer.

Eligibility This program is open to U.S. citizens who are currently serving on active duty in the U.S. Navy or Naval Reserve, including Full Time Support (FTS), Selected Reserves (SELRES), and Navy Reservists on active duty, except for those on active duty for training (ACDUTRA). Applicants must be high school graduates (or GED recipients) who are able to complete requirements for a baccalaureate degree in 36 months or less. They must be planning to work on a degree in human resources/personnel, financial management, manpower systems analysis, operations analysis, business administration, education/training management, or a related field. When they complete their degree require-ments, they must be younger than 29 years of age. Within the past 3 years, they must have taken the SAT (and achieved scores of at least 500 on the mathematics section and 500 on the critical reading section) or the ACT (and achieved a score of 41 or higher, including at least 21 on the mathematics por-tion and 20 on the English portion).

Financial data   Awardees continue to receive their regular Navy pay and allowances while they attend college on a full-time basis. They also receive reimbursement for tuition, fees, and books up to $10,000 per year. If base housing is avail-able, they are eligible to live there. Participants are not eligible to receive benefits under the Navy's Tuition Assistance Pro-gram (TA), the Montgomery GI Bill (MGIB), the Navy College Fund, or the Veterans Educational Assistance Program (VEAP).

Duration   Selectees are supported for up to 36 months of full-time, year-round study or completion of a bachelor's degree, as long as they maintain a GPA of 2.5 or higher.

Additional information   Upon acceptance into the pro-gram, selectees attend the Naval Science Institute (NSI) in Newport, Rhode Island for an 8-week program in the funda-mental core concepts of being a naval officer (navigation, engineering, weapons, military history and justice, etc.). They then enter a college or university with an NROTC unit or affil-iation to work full time on a bachelor's degree. They become members of and drill with the NROTC unit. When they com-plete their degree, they are commissioned as ensigns in the United States Naval Reserve and assigned to initial training as a human resources officer. After commissioning, 5 years of active service are required.

Number awarded   Varies each year.

Deadline   June of each year.

[225]
ILLINOIS NATIONAL GUARD GRANT PROGRAM

Illinois Student Assistance Commission
Attn: Scholarship and Grant Services
1755 Lake Cook Road
Deerfield, IL 60015-5209
(847) 948-8550   Toll Free: (800) 899-ISAC
Fax: (847) 831-8549   TDD: (800) 526-0844
E-mail: isac.studentservices@isac.illinois.gov
Web: www.collegeillinois.org

Summary   To provide financial assistance to current or for-mer members of the Illinois National Guard who are inter-ested in attending college or graduate school in the state.

Eligibility   This program is open to members of the Illinois National Guard who are 1) currently active or 2) have been active for at least 5 consecutive years, have been called to federal active duty for at least 6 months, and are within 12 months after their discharge date. Applicants must also be enrolled at an Illinois public 2- or 4-year college or university and have served at least 1 full year in the Guard.

Financial data   Recipients are eligible for payment of tuition and some fees for either undergraduate or graduate study at an Illinois state-supported college or university.

Duration   This assistance extends for 8 semesters or 12 quarters (or the equivalent in part-time study).

Number awarded   Varies each year.

Deadline   September of each year for the academic year; February of each year for spring semester, winter quarter, or spring quarter; June of each year for summer term.

[226]
INDIANA NATIONAL GUARD SUPPLEMENTAL GRANT PROGRAM

State Student Assistance Commission of Indiana
Attn: Grants and Scholarships
W462 Indiana Government Center South
402 West Washington Street
Indianapolis, IN 46204
(317) 232-2355   Toll Free: (888) 528-4719 (within IN)
Fax: (317) 232-3260   E-mail: grants@ssaci.in.gov
Web: www.in.gov/ssaci/2339.htm

Summary   To provide financial assistance to members of the Indiana National Guard who are interested in attending designated colleges in the state.

Eligibility   This program is open to members of the Indiana Air and Army National Guard who are in active drilling status and have not been AWOL at any time during the preceding 12 months. Applicants must be high school graduates seeking their first associate or bachelor's degree. Allowances may be made for students who earned a GED certificate or were home schooled, but only on a case-by-case basis following a written appeal. As part of the application process, students must file the Free Application for Federal Student Aid (FAFSA). If they qualify as dependent students based on FAFSA data, their parents must be residents of Indiana; if the FAFSA standards define them as independent students, they must be Indiana residents.

Financial data   The award provides payment of 100% of the tuition costs at state-funded colleges and universities in Indiana. No funding is provided for books, room, or board.

Duration   1 year; may be renewed.

Additional information   This assistance may be used only at the following state funded colleges and universities: Ball State University, Indiana State University, Indiana University (all campuses), Indiana University/Purdue University-India-napolis, Indiana University/Purdue University-Fort Wayne, Indiana University/Purdue University-Columbus, Ivy Tech Community College (all campuses), Purdue University (all campuses, University of Southern Indiana, Vincennes Uni-versity, and Western Governors University-Indiana.

Number awarded   Varies each year.

Deadline   March of each year.

[227]
IOWA NATIONAL GUARD EDUCATIONAL ASSISTANCE PROGRAM

Iowa National Guard
Joint Forces Headquarters Iowa
Attn: NGIA-PER-ESO
7105 N.W. 70th Avenue
Johnston, IA 50131-1824
(515) 252-4517   Toll Free: (800) 294-6607, ext. 4517
Fax: (515) 252-4025   E-mail: educationia@ng.army.mil
Web: www.iowanationalguard.com

Summary   To provide financial assistance to members of the Iowa National Guard who wish to attend college.

Eligibility   This program is open to residents of Iowa who are members of an Iowa Army or Air National Guard unit.

Applicants must have satisfactorily completed Initial Entry Training (Basic Training and Advanced Individual Training), have maintained satisfactory performance of duty (including attending a minimum 90% of scheduled drill dates and scheduled annual training in the preceding 12 months), have maintained satisfactory academic progress as determined by their academic institution, and have not completed their baccalaureate degree. They may be seeking to attend a state-supported university, community college, or participating private accredited institution of postsecondary education located in Iowa.

Financial data Awards provide payment of at least 50% of the tuition rate at Iowa Board of Regents schools or 50% of the tuition rate at the institution attended by the National Guard member, whichever is less. Recently, available funding permitted payment of 90% of the Regents rate, or a maximum of $2,888 per semester for full-time enrollment. Funds may be used for any educational expense, including tuition, room, board, supplies, books, fees, and other associated costs.

Duration 1 year; may be renewed.

Additional information This program began in 1999.

Number awarded Varies each year, depending on the availability of funds. Assistance is provided on a first-come, first-served basis.

Deadline September of each year for fall term or January of each year for spring term.

[228]
JACK E. BARGER, SR. MEMORIAL NURSING SCHOLARSHIPS

Pennsylvania State Nurses Association
Attn: Nursing Foundation of Pennsylvania
2578 Interstate Drive, Suite 101
Harrisburg, PA 17110
(717) 692-0542   Toll Free: (888) 707-PSNA
Fax: (717) 692-4540   E-mail: nfp@panurses.org
Web: www.panurses.org/2008/section.cfm?SID=21&ID=4

Summary To provide financial assistance to veterans, military personnel, and their dependents who are studying nursing in Pennsylvania.

Eligibility This program is open to veterans, active-duty military personnel, and the children and spouses of veterans and active-duty military personnel. Applicants must be residents of Pennsylvania and currently enrolled in an undergraduate professional school of nursing in the state. Recipients are selected by lottery from among the qualified applicants.

Financial data The stipend is $1,000.

Duration 1 year.

Additional information This program is sponsored by the Department of Pennsylvania Veterans of Foreign Wars (VFW). Recipients must attend the VFW Convention to accept the scholarship; travel, meals, and overnight expenses are paid by the VFW.

Number awarded 6 each year.

Deadline April of each year.

[229]
JOE KING SCHOLARSHIPS

Council of College and Military Educators
c/o Cynthia Bruce, Scholarship Committee Chair
American Council on Education, Military Evaluations
One Dupont Circle, Suite 250
Washington, DC 20036
(202) 939-9432   E-mail: cynthia_bruce@ace.nche.edu
Web: www.ccmeonline.org/scholarships.aspx

Summary To provide financial assistance to members of the armed services who are interested in working on an undergraduate or master's degree.

Eligibility This program is open to members of the uniformed services, including active, Guard, and Reserves, who have completed basic military training or officer candidate school. Applicants must be currently enrolled full time at an accredited institution that is a member of the Council of College and Military Educators (CCME) and working on an associate, bachelor's, or master's degree. Undergraduates must have a GPA of 2.0 or higher and graduate students must have a GPA of 3.0 or higher. Along with their application, they must submit an essay of up to 300 words on how their academic goals and qualifications support the mission of CCME. Financial need is not considered in the selection process.

Financial data The stipend is $1,000.

Duration 1 year.

Number awarded 5 each year.

Deadline October of each year.

[230]
JOHN AND ALICE EGAN MULTI-YEAR MENTORING SCHOLARSHIP PROGRAM

Daedalian Foundation
Attn: Scholarship Committee
55 Main Circle (Building 676)
P.O. Box 249
Randolph AFB, TX 78148-0249
(210) 945-2113   Fax: (210) 945-2112
E-mail: kristi@daedalians.org
Web: www.daedalians.org/foundation/scholarships.htm

Summary To provide financial assistance to college students who are participating in a ROTC program and wish to become military pilots.

Eligibility This program is open to students who have completed at least the freshman year at an accredited 4-year college or university and have a GPA of 3.0 or higher. Applicants must be participating in an ROTC program and be medically qualified for flight training. They must plan to apply for and be awarded a military pilot training allocation at the appropriate juncture in their ROTC program. Selection is based on intention to prepare for a career as a military pilot, demonstrated moral character and patriotism, scholastic and military standing and aptitude, and physical condition and aptitude for flight. Financial need may also be considered.

Financial data The stipend is $2,500 per year, including $500 provided by a local Flight of the organization and $2,000 as a matching award provided by the foundation.

Duration 1 year; may be renewed up to 2 or 3 additional years, provided the recipient maintains a GPA of 3.0 or higher and is enrolled in an undergraduate program.

Additional information This program began in 2003. It includes a mentoring component.

Number awarded Up to 11 each year.

Deadline July of each year.

[231]
JOHN CORNELIUS/MAX ENGLISH MEMORIAL SCHOLARSHIP AWARD

Marine Corps Tankers Association
c/o Buster Diggs, Scholarship Chair
1829 Ballentine Drive
Alpine, CA 91901
E-mail: Tigertanker2003@yahoo.com
Web: www.usmarinetankers.org/scholarship-program

Summary To provide financial assistance for college or graduate school to children and grandchildren of members of the Marine Corps Tankers Association and to Marine and Navy personnel currently serving in tank units.

Eligibility This program is open to high school seniors and graduates who are children, grandchildren, or under the guardianship of an active, Reserve, retired, or honorably discharged Marine who served in a tank unit. Marine or Navy Corpsmen currently assigned to tank units are also eligible. Applicants must be enrolled or planning to enroll full time at a college or graduate school. Their parent or grandparent must be a member of the Marine Corps Tankers Association or, if not a member, must join if the application is accepted. Along with their application, they must submit an essay on their educational goals, future aspirations, and concern for the future of our society and for the peoples of the world. Selection is based on that essay, academic record, school activities, leadership potential, and community service.

Financial data The stipend is at least $2,000 per year.

Duration 1 year; recipients may reapply.

Number awarded 8 to 12 each year.

Deadline March of each year.

[232]
JOSEPH A. MCALINDEN DIVERS' SCHOLARSHIP

Navy-Marine Corps Relief Society
Attn: Education Division
875 North Randolph Street, Suite 225
Arlington, VA 22203-1757
(703) 696-4960   Fax: (703) 696-0144
E-mail: education@nmcrs.org
Web: www.nmcrs.org/education.html

Summary To provide financial assistance to current and former Navy and Marine Corps divers and their families who are interested in working on an undergraduate degree in a field related to ocean agriculture.

Eligibility This program is open to Navy and Marine Corps active-duty and retired divers (includes Reservists serving on active duty for more than 90 days), their children under 23 years of age, and their spouses. Applicants must be working full time on their first undergraduate degree in oceanography, ocean agriculture, aquaculture, or a related field; they may also be engaged in advanced diver training, certification, or recertification. Financial need is considered.

Financial data The stipend ranges from $500 to $3,000, depending on the need of the recipient.

Duration 1 year.

Number awarded 1 or more each year.

Deadline Applications may be submitted at any time.

[233]
KANSAS ARMY NATIONAL GUARD SCHOLARSHIP

Kansas Army National Guard
Attn: Recruiting and Retention Command Headquarters
1710 S.W. Topeka Boulevard
Topeka, KS 66612
(785) 806-2121   E-mail: sharon.watson3@us.army.mil
Web: www.kansasarmynationalguard.com/benefits.shtml

Summary To provide financial assistance to Army ROTC students in Kansas.

Eligibility This program is open to non-scholarship Army ROTC students planning to enroll full time at a state university in Kansas. Applicants must be U.S. citizens and residents of Kansas eligible for in-state tuition. They must have an ACT score of 19 or higher, be able to meet medical and physical fitness requirements for military service, and be able to complete all requirements for a college degree and a commission while they are younger than 30 years of age (may be extended to 40 years of age upon petition). Selection is based on scholastic potential and achievement, participation in extracurricular activities, demonstrated leadership, interest in service with the Kansas Army National Guard, and an interview.

Financial data This program provides free tuition at the participating schools (where there are Army ROTC programs). Beginning with their fifth semester in the program, recipients also are given a stipend of $200 per month. Recipients must agree to become a commissioned officer and serve at least 8 years in the military after completing ROTC and graduating from college. That service includes at least 4 years in the Kansas Army National Guard, 2 years with a Reserve component unit, and 2 years in the Individual Ready Reserves (IRR). If they fail to graduate or fulfill the military service obligation, they must either repay all funds received or serve 4 years as an enlisted member of the Kansas Army National Guard.

Duration 4 years, or until the recipient completes the baccalaureate degree.

Number awarded 40 each year.

Deadline January of each year.

[234]
KANSAS MILITARY SERVICE SCHOLARSHIPS

Kansas Board of Regents
Attn: Student Financial Assistance
1000 S.W. Jackson Street, Suite 520
Topeka, KS 66612-1368
(785) 296-3518   Fax: (785) 296-0983
E-mail: dlindeman@ksbor.org
Web: www.kansasregents.org/scholarships_and_grants

Summary To provide money for college to residents of Kansas who have served or are still serving in the military.

Eligibility This program is open to students who graduated from high school in Kansas or received a GED credential and have been a resident of the state for at least 2 years. Applicants must have served in the U.S. armed forces in Iraq or Afghanistan, or in international waters or on foreign soil in support of military operations in Iraq or Afghanistan, for at least 90 days after September 11, 2001 or for less than 90 days because of injuries received during such service. They must still be in military service or have received an honorable discharge with orders that indicate they served after September 11, 2001 in Operations Enduring Freedom, Nobel Eagle, and/or Iraqi Freedom. Qualified veterans and military personnel may enroll at a public postsecondary institution in Kansas, including area vocational schools, area vocational/technical schools, community colleges, the municipal university, state educational institutions, or technical colleges. Priority is given to applicants who can demonstrate financial need.

Financial data Qualifying students are permitted to enroll at an approved Kansas institution without payment of tuition or fees. If they receive any federal military tuition assistance, that money must be applied first, and they are eligible only for the remaining balance in scholarship assistance.

Duration 1 year; renewable for up to 10 semesters, as long as the recipient remains in good academic standing.

Additional information This program began in 2007.

Number awarded Varies each year.

Deadline April of each year.

[235]
KANSAS NATIONAL GUARD EDUCATIONAL ASSISTANCE

Kansas Board of Regents
Attn: Student Financial Assistance
1000 S.W. Jackson Street, Suite 520
Topeka, KS 66612-1368
(785) 296-3518   Fax: (785) 296-0983
E-mail: dlindeman@ksbor.org
Web: www.kansasregents.org/scholarships_and_grants

Summary To provide financial assistance to members of the Kansas National Guard who wish to take additional college courses.

Eligibility This program is open to members of the Kansas National Guard (Air or Army) who are interested in working on a vocational, associate, or bachelor's degree. Applicants must be newly enlisted or reenlisted Guard member with no more than 15 years of service. They must agree to complete their current service obligation plus 3 months of additional service for each semester of assistance received.

Financial data The program reimburses up to 100% of tuition and fees at public and designated private institutions in Kansas.

Duration 1 semester; may be renewed.

Number awarded Varies each year; recently, approximately 300 of these awards were granted each semester.

Deadline September of each year for fall semester; February of each year for spring semester.

[236]
KENTUCKIANA POST SAME SCHOLARSHIP

Society of American Military Engineers-Kentuckiana Post
c/o Erin Hall, Scholarship Committee Co-Chair
Messer Construction Company
11001 Plantside Drive
Louisville, KY 40299
(502) 261-9775   E-mail: ehall@messer.com
Web: posts.same.org/kentuckiana

Summary To provide financial assistance to students in Indiana and Kentucky, particularly those with ties to the military, who are interested in majoring in engineering in college.

Eligibility This program is open to students who fall into 1 of the following categories: a dependent of a current Society of American Military Engineers (SAME) Kentuckiana Post

member; an employee or dependent of an employee of a Kentuckiana Post sustaining member firm; an employee or dependent of an employee of the Louisville District Corps of Engineers; a current student member of the Kentuckiana Post; a student whose permanent home address is within the Kentuckiana Post's geographic boundary (Kentucky and Indiana) and who is enrolled in an ROTC program or military academy; or an individual on active duty or the dependent of an individual on active duty who is assigned to an installation within the Kentuckiana Post's geographic boundary. Applicants must be U.S. citizens accepted at an undergraduate ABET-accredited engineering program; undergraduates enrolled in engineering technology programs are not eligible. Along with their application, they must submit an essay of 300 to 500 words on a topic that changes annually; recently, applicants were invited to write on how winning this scholarship would promote a promising future for their engineering career and how they might envision that career supporting the mission of SAME. Financial need is not considered in the selection process.

Financial data The stipend is $4,000 per year.

Duration 1 year; may be renewed 1 additional year.

Additional information Recipients are required to attend the scholarship luncheon ceremony in Louisville in May.

Number awarded Up to 5 each year.

Deadline March of each year.

[237]
KENTUCKY NATIONAL GUARD TUITION AWARD PROGRAM

Kentucky Higher Education Assistance Authority
Attn: Student Aid Branch
100 Airport Road
P.O. Box 798
Frankfort, KY 40602-0798
(502) 696-7392   Toll Free: (800) 928-8926, ext. 7392
Fax: (502) 696-7373   TDD: (800) 855-2880
E-mail: studentaid@kheaa.com
Web: www.kheaa.com/website/kheaa/military_ky?main=7

Summary To provide financial assistance for college or graduate school to members of the Kentucky National Guard.

Eligibility This program is open to active enlisted members of the Kentucky National Guard who are interested in working full or part time on an undergraduate or graduate degree. Applicants must have maintained standards of satisfactory membership in the Guard, including passing the most recent physical fitness test, meeting the height-weight standard, meeting attendance standards, having no unsatisfactory performance or absence-without-leave records, and having no other restrictions on their personnel file. Preference is given to applicants working on their first undergraduate degree.

Financial data The program provides payment of full tuition and fees at any state-supported university, community college, or vocational or technical school in Kentucky.

Duration 1 semester; may be renewed.

Number awarded Varies each year.

Deadline March of each year for summer or fall terms; September of each year for spring term.

[238]
LANGEA TONY LOPEZ SCHOLARSHIP

Louisiana National Guard Enlisted Association
c/o MSG Chad J. Anderson
Gillis Long Center
5445 Point Clair Road
Carville, LA 70721
(225) 319-4846   Fax: (225) 319-4880
E-mail: chad.j.anderson1@us.army.mil
Web: langea.org/templates/benefits/scholarship

Summary   To provide funding to members of the Louisiana National Guard Enlisted Association (LANGEA) and their dependents who plan to attend college in any state.

Eligibility   This program is open to members of the association, their spouses and unmarried dependent children, and the unremarried spouses and unmarried dependent children of deceased members who were in good standing at the time of their death. The qualifying LANGEA members must have at least 1 year remaining on their enlistment following completion of the school year for which the application is submitted or have served 20 years of more in the Louisiana National Guard. Applicants must be enrolled or planning to enroll full time at an accredited college, university, trade school, or business school in any state. Graduate students are not eligible. Selection is based on academic achievement, character, leadership, and financial need.

Financial data   The stipend is $2,000.

Duration   1 year; nonrenewable.

Number awarded   3 each year.

Deadline   February of each year.

[239]
LARRY STRICKLAND LEADERSHIP AWARD AND SCHOLARSHIP

Association of the United States Army
Attn: Strickland Memorial Scholarship Fund
2425 Wilson Boulevard
Arlington, VA 22201
(703) 841-4300, ext. 2693
Toll Free: (800) 336-4570, ext. 2693
E-mail: jspencer@ausa.org
Web: www.ausa.org

Summary   To recognize and reward, with funding for additional education, Army noncommissioned officers who demonstrate outstanding leadership.

Eligibility   This award is presented to a noncommissioned officer who best exemplifies "the Army's vision and influences others in shaping future leaders." Candidates must also be interested in obtaining additional education.

Financial data   The award consists of a plaque and $4,000 to assist in covering educational costs that Army tuition assistance does not pay, such as instructional fees, laboratory fees, and books.

Duration   The award is presented annually.

Additional information   This award was established in 2003 to honor SGM Larry L. Strickland, who was killed in the Pentagon on September 11, 2001.

Number awarded   3 each year.

Deadline   Deadline not specified.

[240]
LDRSHIP AWARDS

Career College Association
Attn: Imagine America Foundation
1101 Connecticut Avenue, N.W., Suite 901
Washington, DC 20036
(202) 336-6743   Fax: (202) 408-8102
E-mail: ldrship@career.org
Web: www.imagine-america.org/ldrship

Summary   To provide financial assistance to veterans and military personnel who are attending a career college that is a member of the Career College Association.

Eligibility   This program is open to active-duty, reservist, honorably-discharged, and retired veterans of a U.S. military service branch. Applicants must have completed at least 1 term at 1 of the 300 participating career colleges. They must have maintained a GPA of 3.5 or higher and an attendance record of at least 95%. They must submit an application, a recommendation from a faculty member or administrator at their college, and their current college transcript.

Financial data   The stipend is $2,500. Funds must be used for payment of tuition at a participating career college.

Duration   1 year.

Additional information   The Imagine America Foundation (previously the Career College Foundation) began this program in 2004. It stands for Loyalty, Duty, Respect, Selfless Service, Honor, Integrity and Personal Courage.

Number awarded   Varies each year; recently, 10 of these scholarships were granted.

Deadline   April of each year.

[241]
LOUIS J. SCHOBER MEMORIAL SCHOLARSHIP

Society of American Military Engineers-Louisiana Post
c/o Anthony Goodgion, Education Committee Chair
Linfield, Hunter & Junius, Inc.
3608 18th Street, Suite 200
Metairie, LA 70002
(504) 833-5300   Fax: (504) 833-5350
E-mail: agoodgion@lhjunius.com
Web: posts.same.org/louisiana/YoungMembers.htm

Summary   To provide financial assistance to engineering students at universities in Louisiana (particularly those with ties to the military) and to children of members of the Louisiana Post of the Society of American Military Engineers (SAME) at schools in any state.

Eligibility   This program is open to students currently working on an undergraduate degree in engineering. Applicants must be either 1) enrolled at a college or university in Louisiana, or 2) the children of a member of the SAME Louisiana Post (who may be studying at a college or university in any state). Graduate students are not eligible; high school seniors may be considered if no suitable college students apply. Selection is based primarily on academic record and demonstration of leadership characteristics; other factors considered are participation in SAME posts and activities, enrollment in an ROTC program, former or current military service, and participation in school and community activities.

Financial data   The stipend is $2,000.

Duration   1 year; nonrenewable.

Number awarded   1 or more each year.

Deadline   May of each year.

[242]
LOUISIANA NATIONAL GUARD STATE TUITION EXEMPTION PROGRAM

Louisiana National Guard
Attn: Education Services Office
Military Development (DMP-XD)
Jackson Barracks
New Orleans, LA 70146-0330
(504) 278-8304   Toll Free: (800) 899-6355
Web: geauxguard.com/resources/education

Summary To provide financial assistance to members of the Louisiana National Guard who are interested in attending college in the state.

Eligibility This program is open to active drilling members of the Louisiana Army National Guard or Air National Guard. Guard members are ineligible if they have been disqualified by their unit commander for any adverse action, have already obtained a bachelor's degree, are placed on academic probation or suspension, test positive on a drug/alcohol test or declare themselves as a self-referral, are separated or transfer to the Inactive National Guard, or have 9 or more AWOLs. Applicants must have been accepted for admission or be enrolled in a Louisiana public institution of higher learning, either part time or full time.

Financial data Recipients are exempt from all tuition charges at Louisiana state-funded colleges, universities, or community colleges.

Duration The exemption may be claimed for 5 separate academic years or until the receipt of a bachelor's degree, whichever occurs first.

Additional information The state legislature established this program in 1974.

Number awarded Varies each year.

Deadline Deadline not specified.

[243]
LTG AND MRS. JOSEPH M. HEISER SCHOLARSHIP

U.S. Army Ordnance Corps Association
Attn: Heiser Scholarship
P.O. Box 377
Aberdeen Proving Ground, MD 21005-0377
(410) 272-8540   Fax: (410) 272-8425
Web: www.usaocaweb.org/scholarships.htm

Summary To provide money for college to soldiers serving in the U.S. Army Ordnance Corps and members of the U.S. Army Ordnance Corps Association (OCA) and their families.

Eligibility This program is open to Ordnance soldiers (active and reserve), OCA members, and immediate family of OCA members. Applicants must be entering or attending a college or university to work on an associate or baccalaureate degree. Along with their application, they must submit 1) an essay of 1,000 to 1,500 words on the missions, heritage, or history of the U.S. Army Ordnance Corps; and 2) an essay of 300 to 500 words on their educational and career goals. Selection is based on the essays, scholastic aptitude, and grades.

Financial data The stipend is $1,000.

Duration 1 year.

Number awarded Varies each year; recently, 9 of these scholarships were awarded.

Deadline June of each year.

[244]
MAINE NATIONAL GUARD EDUCATION ASSISTANCE PROGRAM

Maine National Guard
Attn: Education
Camp Keyes
Augusta, ME 04333-0033
(207) 626-4370   Toll Free: (800) 462-3101 (within ME)
Fax: (207) 626-4509
Web: www.me.ngb.army.mil

Summary To provide financial assistance for undergraduate or graduate study to members of the Maine National Guard.

Eligibility This program is open to active members of the Maine National Guard who are interested in working on an undergraduate or graduate degree or certificate at a college or university within the state. Applicants must be Maine residents who have successfully completed basic training or received a commission. They may not have any unsatisfactory record of participation in the Guard. First priority is given to Guard members who do not have a baccalaureate degree and are working on a degree; second priority is given to members without a graduate degree who are working on a degree, teacher certification, principal certification, or superintendent certification; third priority is for all others.

Financial data This program provides payment of up to 100% of tuition and fees at a Maine accredited public post-secondary institution. Recipients may also attend a private college or university in Maine, but the benefit is capped at the tuition rates at the University of Maine.

Duration 1 semester; may be renewed for a total of 150 credit hours, as long as the recipient maintains satisfactory participation in the Guard and an academic GPA of 2.0 or higher.

Number awarded Varies each year.

Deadline October of each year for college terms beginning from January through April; February of each year for college terms beginning from May through July; June of each year for college terms beginning in August or September.

[245]
MAJOR GENERAL DUANE L. "DUKE" CORNING MEMORIAL SCHOLARSHIP

South Dakota National Guard Enlisted Association
c/o Jody Smith
2823 West Main Street
Rapid City, SD 57702-8170
(605) 737-6224   E-mail: jody.smith2@us.army.mil
Web: www.sdngea.com/scholarship.html

Summary To provide financial assistance to current and retired members of the South Dakota National Guard Enlisted Association (SDNGEA), the National Guard Association of South Dakota (NGASD), and their dependents who are interested in attending college in any state.

Eligibility This program is open to current and retired members of the SDNGEA and the NGASD and the dependents of current and retired members of those associations. Applicants must be graduating high school seniors or full-time undergraduate students at a college or university in any state. They must submit a 300-page autobiography that includes their experiences to date and their hopes and plans for the future. Selection is based on the essay; awards, honors, and offices in high school, college, or trade school; GPA and ACT/SAT scores; letters of recommendation; and extracurricular and community activities and honors.

Financial data The stipend is $1,000.

Duration 1 year; nonrenewable.

Number awarded 1 each year.

Deadline March of each year.

[246]
MARINE CORPS TUITION ASSISTANCE PROGRAM

U.S. Marine Corps
Attn: Lifelong Learning Center
3098 Range Road
Quantico, VA 22134-5028
(703) 784-9550   E-mail: vernon.taylor@usmc.mil
Web: www.usmc-mccs.org/education/mta.cfm

Summary To provide financial assistance for undergraduate or graduate study to Marine Corps personnel.

Eligibility Eligible for assistance under this program are active-duty Marines who wish to take college courses for academic credit during off-duty time. Funding is available for vocational/technical, undergraduate, graduate, undergraduate development, independent study, and distance learning programs. Commissioned officers must agree to remain on active duty for 2 years after the completion of any funded courses. All students must successfully complete their courses with a satisfactory grade.

Financial data Those selected for participation in this program receive their regular Marine Corps pay and 100% of tuition at the postsecondary educational institution of their choice, but capped at $4,500 per year or $250 per semester hour, whichever is less.

Duration Until completion of a bachelor's or graduate degree.

Number awarded Varies each year; in recent years, approximately 20,000 Marines availed themselves of this funding.

Deadline Deadline not specified.

[247]
MARINES' MEMORIAL ASSOCIATION SCHOLARSHIP FUND

Marines' Memorial Association
c/o Marines Memorial Club and Hotel
609 Sutter Street
San Francisco, CA 94102
(415) 673-6672   Fax: (415) 441-3649
E-mail: member@marineclub.com
Web: www.marineclub.com/membership/scholarship.php

Summary To provide money for college to members of the Marines' Memorial Association and their descendants.

Eligibility This program is open to active members of the association and their children and grandchildren. Applicants must be enrolled or planning to enroll in an undergraduate degree program at a college or university. Selection is based on academic merit, activities, and financial need.

Financial data Stipends are $5,000 or $2,500.

Duration 1 year.

Additional information Membership in the association is open to veterans of the Marines, Army, Navy, Air Force, or Coast Guard and to personnel currently serving in a branch of

the armed forces. This program includes a number of named scholarships, including the Colonel Jack Barnes Scholarship, the Colonel Richard Hallock Scholarship, the Sergeants Henry and Jeanne Rose Scholarship, and the Evelyn Bukovac Hamilton Health Care Scholarship.

Number awarded 10 at $5,000 and 12 at $2,500.

Deadline April of each year.

[248]
MARYLAND NATIONAL GUARD STATE TUITION ASSISTANCE

Maryland National Guard
Attn: Education Services Office
Fifth Regiment Armory
29th Division Street, Room D24
Baltimore, MD 21201-2288
(410) 576-6093   Toll Free: (800) 492-2526
Fax: (410) 576-6082
E-mail: mdng_education@md.ngb.army.mil
Web: www.goarmyed.com

Summary To provide partial tuition reimbursement to members of the Maryland National Guard working on an undergraduate or graduate degree at a college in the state.

Eligibility This program is open to members of the Maryland National Guard who have at least 24 months of service remaining in the Guard from the start of the course date. Priority is given to junior enlisted personnel (grades E-1 through E-6). Applicants must be attending or planning to attend a state-supported college or university or a designated private institution in Maryland to work on an undergraduate or graduate degree. They must agree to remain a member of the Guard for at least 2 years for receipt of a bachelor's or lower degree or for 4 years for receipt of a master's or higher degree.

Financial data Eligible Guard members receive an amount equal to 50% of their college/university tuition and related course fees, to a maximum of $5,000 per fiscal year.

Duration 1 semester; recipients may reapply.

Additional information Individuals must apply for reimbursement within 45 days after their course is completed. They must have earned at least a grade of "C" in the course to qualify for reimbursement.

Number awarded Varies each year.

Deadline Deadline not specified.

[249]
MARYLAND NATIONAL GUARD STATE TUITION WAIVER

Maryland National Guard
Attn: Education Services Office
Fifth Regiment Armory
29th Division Street, Room D24
Baltimore, MD 21201-2288
(410) 576-6093   Toll Free: (800) 492-2526
Fax: (410) 576-6082
E-mail: mdng_education@md.ngb.army.mil
Web: www.goarmyed.com

Summary To waive tuition for members of the Maryland National Guard at colleges and universities in the state.

Eligibility All state-supported colleges and universities and 2 private universities in Maryland have developed a tuition waiver program for members of the National Guard who are taking graduate or undergraduate courses.

Financial data The amount of the waiver ranges from 25% to 50%. Most 4-year colleges waive 50% of tuition for up to 6 credits per semester.

Duration 1 semester; recipients may reapply.

Additional information Some schools also limit the number of credits for which a Guard member can receive waivers during any semester.

Number awarded Varies each year.

Deadline Deadline not specified.

[250]
MARYLAND SCHOLARSHIPS FOR VETERANS OF THE AFGHANISTAN AND IRAQ CONFLICTS

Maryland Higher Education Commission
Attn: Office of Student Financial Assistance
6 North Liberty Street, Ground Suite
Baltimore, MD 21201
(410) 767-3300   Toll Free: (800) 974-0203
Fax: (410) 332-0250   TDD: (800) 735-2258
E-mail: osfamail@mhec.state.md.us
Web: www.mhec.state.md.us/financialAid/descriptions.asp

Summary To provide financial assistance for college to residents of Maryland who have served in the armed forces in Afghanistan or Iraq and their children and spouses.

Eligibility This program is open to Maryland residents who are 1) a veteran who served at least 60 days in Afghanistan on or after October 24, 2001 or in Iraq on or after March 19, 2003; 2) an active-duty member of the armed forces who served at least 60 days in Afghanistan or Iraq on or after those dates; 3) a member of a Reserve component of the armed forces or the Maryland National Guard who was activated as a result of the Afghanistan or Iraq conflicts and served at least 60 days; and 4) the children and spouses of such veterans, active-duty armed forces personnel, or members of Reserve forces or Maryland National Guard. Applicants must be enrolled or accepted for enrollment in a regular undergraduate program at an eligible Maryland institution. In the selection process, veterans are given priority over dependent children and spouses.

Financial data The stipend is equal to 50% of the annual tuition, mandatory fees, and room and board of a resident undergraduate at a 4-year public institution within the University System of Maryland, currently capped at $9,430 per year. The total amount of all state awards may not exceed the cost of attendance as determined by the school's financial aid office or $19,000, whichever is less.

Duration 1 year; may be renewed for an additional 4 years of full-time study or 7 years of part-time study, provided the recipient remains enrolled in an eligible program with a GPA of 2.5 or higher.

Additional information This program is scheduled to expire in 2016.

Number awarded Varies each year.

Deadline February of each year.

[251]
MASSACHUSETTS ARMED FORCES TUITION WAIVER PROGRAM

Massachusetts Office of Student Financial Assistance
454 Broadway, Suite 200
Revere, MA 02151
(617) 391-6070   Fax: (617) 727-0667
E-mail: osfa@osfa.mass.edu
Web: www.osfa.mass.edu

Summary To waive tuition at Massachusetts public colleges and universities for members of the armed forces.

Eligibility Applicants for this assistance must have been permanent legal residents of Massachusetts for at least 1 year and stationed in Massachusetts as members of the Army, Navy, Marine Corps, Air Force, or Coast Guard. They may not be in default on any federal student loan. They must enroll in at least 3 undergraduate credits per semester.

Financial data Eligible military personnel are exempt from any tuition payments toward an undergraduate degree or certificate program at public colleges or universities in Massachusetts.

Duration Up to 4 academic years, for a total of 130 semester hours.

Additional information Recipients may enroll either part or full time in a Massachusetts publicly-supported institution.

Number awarded Varies each year.

Deadline April of each year.

[252]
MASSACHUSETTS NATIONAL GUARD EDUCATIONAL ASSISTANCE PROGRAM

Massachusetts National Guard
Attn: Education Services Office
50 Maple Street
Milford, MA 01757-3604
(508) 233-6590   Toll Free: (888) 301-3103, ext. 6753
Fax: (508) 233-6781   E-mail: ma-education@ng.army.mil
Web: states.ng.mil

Summary To provide financial assistance to members of the Massachusetts National Guard interested in working on an undergraduate or graduate degree at a college in the state.

Eligibility This program is open to actively participating members of the Army or Air National Guard in Massachusetts. Applicants must have less than 9 AWOLs (Absence Without Leave) at all times and must not ETS (Expiration of Term of Service) during the period enrolled. They must be accepted for admission or enrolled at 1 of 28 Massachusetts public colleges, universities, or community colleges and working on an associate, bachelor's, master's, or doctoral degree. The institution must have a vacancy after all tuition-paying students and all students who are enrolled under any scholarship or tuition waiver provisions have enrolled.

Financial data Eligible Guard members are exempt from any tuition payments at colleges or universities operated by the Commonwealth of Massachusetts and funded by the Massachusetts Board of Higher Education.

Duration Up to a total of 130 semester hours.

Additional information Recipients may enroll either part or full time in a Massachusetts state-supported institution. This program, commonly referred to as the 100% Tuition

Waiver Program, is funded through the Massachusetts Board of Higher Education.

Number awarded   Varies each year.

Deadline   Deadline not specified.

[253]
MATCHING SCHOLARSHIP PROGRAM

Daedalian Foundation
Attn: Scholarship Committee
55 Main Circle, Building 676
P.O. Box 249
Randolph AFB, TX 78148-0249
(210) 945-2113   Fax: (210) 945-2112
E-mail: kristi@daedalians.org
Web: www.daedalians.org/foundation/scholarships.htm

Summary   To provide financial assistance to ROTC and other college students who wish to become military pilots.

Eligibility   Eligible are students who are attending or have been accepted at an accredited 4-year college or university and have demonstrated the desire and potential to become a commissioned military pilot. Usually, students in ROTC units of all services apply to local chapters (Flights) of Daedalian; if the Flight awards a scholarship, the application is forwarded to the Daedalian Foundation for 1 of these matching scholarships. College students not part of a ROTC program are eligible to apply directly to the Foundation if their undergraduate goals and performance are consistent with Daedalian criteria. Selection is based on intention to pursue a career as a military pilot, demonstrated moral character and patriotism, scholastic and military standing and aptitude, and physical condition and aptitude for flight. Financial need may also be considered. Additional eligibility criteria may be set by a Flight Scholarship Selection Board.

Financial data   The amount awarded varies but is intended to serve as matching funds for the Flight scholarship. Generally, the maximum awarded is $2,000.

Number awarded   Up to 99 each year.

Deadline   Students who are members of Daedalian Flights must submit their applications by November of each year; students who apply directly to the Daedalian Foundation must submit their applications by July of each year.

[254]
MCIA/JOHN J. GUENTHER MERIT SCHOLARSHIP

Marine Corps Intelligence Association, Inc.
Attn: Marine Corps Intelligence Educational Foundation
P.O. Box 1028
Quantico, VA 22134-1028
E-mail: scholarship@mcia-inc.org
Web: www.mcia-inc.org/7.html

Summary   To provide financial assistance for college to members of the Marine Corps Intelligence Association (MCIA) and their dependent children.

Eligibility   This program is open to current MCIA members, their dependent children, and their survivors. Applicants must be attending or planning to attend an accredited 4-year college or university as a full-time student. They must submit a 300-word essay on a risk that has led to a significant change in their personal or intellectual life, the most challenging obstacles they have had to overcome and what they learned from the experience, and where they envision themselves in 10 years. Selection is based on the essay, academic achieve-

ment, extracurricular activities, and work experience. Financial need is not considered.

Financial data   The stipend is $2,000.

Duration   1 year.

Additional information   Membership in the MCIA is open to Marine Corps intelligence personnel, including active duty, Reserve, and retired.

Number awarded   At least 1 each year.

Deadline   July of each year.

[255]
MEDAL OF HONOR AFCEA ROTC SCHOLARSHIPS

Armed Forces Communications and Electronics
   Association
Attn: AFCEA Educational Foundation
4400 Fair Lakes Court
Fairfax, VA 22033-3899
(703) 631-6138   Toll Free: (800) 336-4583, ext. 6138
Fax: (703) 631-4693   E-mail: scholarshipsinfo@afcea.org
Web: www.afcea.org

Summary   To provide financial assistance to ROTC cadets who demonstrate outstanding leadership performance and potential.

Eligibility   This program is open to ROTC cadets enrolled full time at an accredited degree-granting 4-year college or university in the United States. Applicants must be sophomores or juniors at the time of application and have a GPA of 3.0 or higher with a major in an academic discipline. They must be U.S. citizens. Selection is based on demonstrated leadership performance and potential and strong commitment to serve in the U.S. armed forces.

Financial data   The stipend is $5,000.

Duration   1 year.

Additional information   This program, established in 2005, is sponsored by the Congressional Medal of Honor Foundation in partnership with the Armed Forces Communications and Electronics Association (AFCEA) Educational Foundation.

Number awarded   4 each year: 1 each for Army, Navy, Marine Corps, and Air Force ROTC students.

Deadline   February of each year.

[256]
MEDICAL CORPS OPTION OF THE SEAMAN TO ADMIRAL-21 PROGRAM

U.S. Navy
Attn: Commander, Naval Service Training Command
250 Dallas Street, Suite A
Pensacola, FL 32508-5268
(850) 452-9433   Fax: (850) 452-2486
E-mail: PNSC_STA21@navy.mil
Web: www.sta-21.navy.mil

Summary   To allow outstanding enlisted Navy personnel to complete a bachelor's degree, be accepted to medical school, earn an M.D. or D.O. degree, and be commissioned in the Navy Medical Corps.

Eligibility   This program is open to U.S. citizens who are currently serving on active duty in the U.S. Navy or Naval Reserve, including Full Time Support (FTS), Selected Reserves (SELRES), and Navy Reservists on active duty, except for those on active duty for training (ACDUTRA). Applicants must be high school graduates (or GED recipients) who are able to 1) complete requirements for a baccalaureate degree within 36 months; 2) complete a medical degree through the Uniformed Services University of Health Services (USUHS) or the Health Professions Scholarship Program (HPSP); and 3) complete 20 years of active commissioned service as a physician by age 62. Within the past 3 years, they must have taken the SAT (and achieved scores of at least 500 on the mathematics section and 500 on the critical reading section) or the ACT (and achieved a score of 41 or higher, including at least 21 on the mathematics portion and 20 on the English portion).

Financial data Awardees continue to receive their regular Navy pay and allowances while they attend college on a full-time basis. They also receive reimbursement for tuition, fees, and books up to $10,000 per year. If base housing is available, they are eligible to live there. Participants are not eligible to receive benefits under the Navy's Tuition Assistance Program (TA), the Montgomery GI Bill (MGIB), the Navy College Fund, or the Veterans Educational Assistance Program (VEAP).

Duration Selectees are supported for up to 36 months of full-time, year-round study or completion of a bachelor's degree, as long as they maintain a GPA of 3.0 or higher. They are then supported until completion of a medical degree.

Additional information Upon acceptance into the program, selectees attend the Naval Science Institute (NSI) in Newport, Rhode Island for an 8-week program in the fundamental core concepts of being a naval officer (navigation, engineering, weapons, military history and justice, etc.). They then enter an NROTC affiliated college or university with a pre-medical program that confers an accredited B.S. degree to pursue full-time study. They become members of and drill with the NROTC unit. After they complete their bachelor's degree, they are commissioned as an ensign in the Naval Reserve. They must apply to and be accepted at medical school, either the USUSH or a civilian medical school through the HPSP. Following completion of medical school, they are promoted to lieutenant and assigned to active duty in the Medical Corps. Selectees incur a service obligation of 5 years for their baccalaureate degree support plus whatever obligation they incur for medical degree support (usually 7 years if they attend USUSH or 4 years if they attend a civilian institution through HPSP).

Number awarded Varies each year.

Deadline June of each year.

[257]
MEDICAL SERVICE CORPS INSERVICE PROCUREMENT PROGRAM (MSC-IPP)

U.S. Navy
Attn: Navy Medicine Professional Development Center
Code O3C
8901 Wisconsin Avenue, 16th Floor, Tower 1
Bethesda, MD 20889-5611
(301) 319-4520   Fax: (301) 295-1783
E-mail: mscipp@nmetc.med.navy.mil
Web: www.med.navy.mil

Summary To provide funding to Navy and Marine enlisted personnel who wish to earn an undergraduate or graduate degree in selected health care specialties while continuing to receive their regular pay and allowances.

Eligibility This program is open to enlisted personnel who are serving on active duty in any rating in pay grade E-5 through E-9 of the U.S. Navy, U.S. Marine Corps, or the Marine Corps Reserve serving on active duty (including Full Time Support of the Reserve). Applicants must be interested in working on a degree to become commissioned in the following medical specialties: environmental health, health care administration, industrial hygiene, occupational therapy, pharmacy, physician assistant, radiation health, or social work. If they plan to work on a graduate degree, they must have scores of at least 1000 on the GRE or 500 on the GMAT; if they plan to work on a bachelor's or physician assistant degree, they must have scores of at least 1000 on the SAT (including 460 on the mathematics portion) or 42 on the ACT (21 on the English portion, 21 on the mathematics portion). They must be U.S. citizens who can be commissioned before they reach their 42nd birthday.

Financial data Participants receive payment of tuition, mandatory fees, a book allowance, and full pay and allowances for their enlisted pay grade. They are eligible for advancement while in college.

Duration 24 to 48 months of full-time, year-round study, until completion of a relevant degree.

Additional information Following graduation, participants are commissioned in the Medical Service Corps and attend Officer Indoctrination School. They incur an 8-year military service obligation, including at least 3 years served on active duty.

Number awarded Varies each year; recently, 36 of these positions were available: 2 in environmental health, 14 in health care administration, 1 in occupational therapy, 1 in pharmacy, 15 in physician assistant, 2 in radiation health, and 1 in social work.

Deadline August of each year.

[258]
MG LEIF J. SVERDRUP AWARD

Army Engineer Association
Attn: Executive Director
P.O. Box 30260
Alexandria, VA 22310-8260
(703) 428-7084   Fax: (703) 428-6043
E-mail: xd@armyengineer.com
Web: www.armyengineer.com/scholarships.htm

Summary To provide financial assistance for college or graduate school to officers who are members of the Army Engineer Association (AEA).

Eligibility This program is open to AEA members serving in an active, Reserve, or National Guard component Army Engineer unit, school, or organization within the Corps of Engineers of the United States Army. Applicants must be commissioned officers (2LT, 1LT, or CPT) or warrant officers (WO1 or WO2). They must be working on or planning to work on an associate, bachelor's, or master's degree at an accredited college or university. Selection is based primarily on financial need, although potential for academic success and standards of conduct as supported by personal references are also considered.

Financial data The stipend is $1,000.

Duration 1 year.

Number awarded 1 or 2 each year.

Deadline June of each year.

[259]
MICA SCHOLARSHIPS

Military Intelligence Corps Association
Attn: Scholarship Committee
P.O. Box 13020
Fort Huachuca, AZ 85670-3020
(520) 227-3894   E-mail: execdir@micorps.org
Web: www.micastore.com/Scholarships.html

Summary To provide financial assistance for college to members of the Military Intelligence Corps Association (MICA) and their immediate family.

Eligibility This program is open to active-duty, Reserve, National Guard, and retired military intelligence soldiers who are MICA members and to their immediate family (spouses, children, or other relatives living with and supported by the MICA member). Applicants must be attending or accepted for attendance at an accredited college, university, vocational school, or technical institution. Along with their application, they must submit a 1-page essay on their reasons for applying for the scholarship, including their educational plans, ambitions, goals, and personal attributes or experiences they feel will enable them to reach their goals. Financial need is not considered in the selection process.

Financial data Stipend amounts vary depending on the availability of funds and the number of qualified applicants, but recently were $5,000. Funds are to be used for tuition, books, and classroom fees; support is not provided for housing, board, travel, or administrative purposes.

Duration 1 year; recipients may reapply.

Number awarded Varies each year; recently, 4 of these scholarships were awarded.

Deadline May of each year.

[260]
MICHAEL WILSON SCHOLARSHIPS

Air Force Association
Attn: Scholarship Manager
1501 Lee Highway
Arlington, VA 22209-1198
(703) 247-5800, ext. 4807
Toll Free: (800) 727-3337, ext. 4807
Fax: (703) 247-5853   E-mail: lcross@afa.org
Web: www.afa.org/MichaelWilson

Summary To provide financial assistance to Air Force ROTC cadets who are entering their junior or senior year of college.

Eligibility This program is open to Air Force ROTC cadets entering their junior or senior year as full-time students with a GPA of 2.8 or higher. Applicants must be enrolled in the Professional Air Force ROTC Officer Course program and attending both the Aerospace Studies class and the Leadership Laboratory each semester. Along with their application, they must submit essays of 500 words each on the following topics: 1) how their choice of a major or career will support the mission of the Air Force; 2) what single issue affecting the military would they bring to the attention of the President if they had the opportunity to speak with him; and 3) who or what inspired them to make the choice to become a leader in the Air Force and why.

Financial data The stipend is $15,000.

Duration 1 year.

Number awarded 2 each year.

Deadline Deadline not specified.

[261]
MICHIGAN NATIONAL GUARD UNIVERSITY AND COLLEGE TUITION GRANTS

Department of Military and Veterans Affairs
Attn: State Education Office
2500 South Washington Avenue
Lansing, MI 48913-5101
(517) 481-7646   Toll Free: (800) 292-1386
E-mail: serpmich@michigan.gov
Web: www.michigan.gov

Summary To provide financial assistance to members of the Michigan National Guard who are enrolled at designated universities in the state.

Eligibility This program is open to all members of the Michigan National Guard who are in good standing with their unit and have completed basic training. Applicants must be enrolled full time at 1 of the following institutions: Baker College, Cleary University, Cornerstone University, Davenport University, Eastern Michigan University, Ferris State University, Kalamazoo Valley Community College, Kirtland Community College, Lake Superior State University, Lansing Community College, Lawrence Tech University, Mid Michigan Community College, Miller College, Northern Michigan University, Oakland University, Olivet College, Rochester College, Siena Heights University, Spring Arbor University, University of Detroit Mercy, University of Phoenix, Walsh College, or Western Michigan University.

Financial data The amount of the grant varies at each participating institution.

Duration 1 semester; may be renewed for a total of 4 years.

Additional information These grants are in addition to funds received through the Michigan National Guard State Education Reimbursement Program.

Number awarded Varies each year.

Deadline Deadline not specified.

[262]
MILITARY NONRESIDENT TUITION WAIVER FOR MEMBERS, SPOUSES OR CHILDREN ASSIGNED TO DUTY IN TEXAS

Texas Higher Education Coordinating Board
Attn: Grants and Special Programs
1200 East Anderson Lane
P.O. Box 12788
Austin, TX 78711-2788
(512) 427-6340   Toll Free: (800) 242-3062
Fax: (512) 427-6420 E-mail: grantinfo@thecb.state.tx.us
Web: www.collegeforalltexans.com

Summary To exempt military personnel stationed in Texas and their dependents from the payment of nonresident tuition at public institutions of higher education in the state.

Eligibility Eligible for these waivers are members of the U.S. armed forces and commissioned officers of the Public Health Service from states other than Texas, their spouses, and dependent children. Applicants must be assigned to Texas and attending or planning to attend a public college or university in the state.

Financial data Although persons eligible under this program are classified as nonresidents, they are entitled to pay the resident tuition at Texas institutions of higher education, regardless of their length of residence in Texas.

Duration 1 year; may be renewed.

Number awarded Varies each year.

Deadline Deadline not specified.

[263]
MILITARY NONRESIDENT TUITION WAIVER FOR MEMBERS, SPOUSES OR CHILDREN WHO REMAIN CONTINUOUSLY ENROLLED IN HIGHER EDUCATION IN TEXAS

Texas Higher Education Coordinating Board
Attn: Grants and Special Programs
1200 East Anderson Lane
P.O. Box 12788
Austin, TX 78711-2788
(512) 427-6340　　　　　Toll Free: (800) 242-3062
Fax: (512) 427-6420　E-mail: grantinfo@thecb.state.tx.us
Web: www.collegeforalltexans.com

Summary To waive nonresident tuition at Texas public colleges and universities for members of the armed forces and their families who are no longer in the military.

Eligibility Eligible for these waivers are members of the U.S. armed forces, commissioned officers of the Public Health Service (PHS), their spouses, and their children. Applicants must have previously been eligible to pay tuition at the resident rate while enrolled in a degree or certificate program at a Texas public college or university because they were a member, spouse, or child of a member of the armed forces or PHS. This waiver is available after the servicemember, spouse, or parent is no longer a member of the armed forces or a commissioned officer of the PHS. The student must remain continuously enrolled in the same degree or certificate program in subsequent terms or semesters.

Financial data The student's eligibility to pay tuition and fees at the rate provided for Texas students does not terminate because the member, spouse, or parent is no longer in the service.

Duration 1 year.

Additional information This program became effective in September 2003.

Number awarded Varies each year.

Deadline Deadline not specified.

[264]
MINNESOTA G.I. BILL PROGRAM

Minnesota Office of Higher Education
Attn: Manager of State Financial Aid Programs
1450 Energy Park Drive, Suite 350
St. Paul, MN 55108-5227
(651) 642-0567　　　　　Toll Free: (800) 657-3866
Fax: (651) 642-0675　　　　TDD: (800) 627-3529
E-mail: Ginny.Dodds@state.mn.us
Web: www.ohe.state.mn.us/mPg.cfm?pageID=891

Summary To provide financial assistance for college or graduate school in the state to residents of Minnesota who served in the military after September 11, 2001 and the families of deceased or disabled military personnel.

Eligibility This program is open to residents of Minnesota enrolled at colleges and universities in the state as undergraduate or graduate students. Applicants must be 1) a veteran who is serving or has served honorably in a branch of

the U.S. armed forces at any time on or after September 11, 2001; 2) a non-veteran who has served honorably for a total of 5 years or more cumulatively as a member of the Minnesota National Guard or other active or Reserve component of the U.S. armed forces, and any part of that service occurred on or after September 11, 2001; or 3) a surviving child or spouse of a person who has served in the military at any time on or after September 11, 2001 and who has died or has a total and permanent disability as a result of that military service. Financial need is considered in the selection process.

Financial data The stipend is $1,000 per semester for full-time study or $500 per semester for part-time study. The maximum award is $3,000 per fiscal year or $10,000 per lifetime.

Duration 1 year; may be renewed, provided the recipient continues to make satisfactory academic progress.

Additional information This program was established by the Minnesota Legislature in 2007.

Number awarded Varies each year.

Deadline Deadline not specified.

[265]
MINNESOTA NATIONAL GUARD STATE TUITION REIMBURSEMENT

Department of Military Affairs
Attn: Education Services Officer
JFMN-J1-ARED
20 West 12th Street
St. Paul, MN 55155-2098
(651) 282-4589　　　　　Toll Free: (800) 657-3848
Fax: (651) 282-4694 E-mail: ngmneducation@ng.army.mil
Web: www.minnesotanationalguard.org

Summary To provide financial assistance for college or graduate school to members of the Minnesota National Guard.

Eligibility Eligible for this program are members of the Minnesota Army or Air National Guard in grades E-1 through O-5 (including warrant officers) who are enrolled as undergraduate or graduate students at colleges or universities in Minnesota. Reimbursement is provided only for undergraduate courses completed with a grade of "C" or better or for graduate courses completed with a grade of "B" or better. Guard members who served on federal active status or federally-funded state active service after September 11, 2001 are eligible for this assistance for up to 2 years after completion of their service contract (or up to 8 years if they were separated or discharged because of a service-connected injury, disease, or disability).

Financial data The maximum reimbursement rate is 100% of the undergraduate tuition rate at the University of Minnesota Twin Cities campus, with a maximum benefit of $10,000 per fiscal year.

Duration 1 semester, to a maximum of 18 credits per semester; may be renewed until completion of an associate, bachelor's, master's, or doctoral degree or 144 semester credits, whichever comes first.

Number awarded Varies each year.

Deadline Deadline not specified.

[266]
MISSISSIPPI NATIONAL GUARD STATE EDUCATIONAL ASSISTANCE PROGRAM

Mississippi Military Department
Attn: Education Services and Incentives Office
JFH-MS-J1-ED
1410 Riverside Drive
P.O. Box 5027
Jackson, MS 39296-5027
(601) 313-6248   Fax: (601) 313-6151
E-mail: msedu@ng.army.mil
Web: ms.ng.mil

Summary To provide financial assistance to members of the Mississippi National Guard who are interested in attending college in the state.

Eligibility This program is open to members of the Mississippi Army or Air National Guard who have completed basic training and are in good standing. Applicants must be registered to vote in Mississippi and be enrolled or accepted for enrollment at an accredited college or university (public or private) in the state. They may not currently be receiving federal tuition assistance.

Financial data Stipends cover the actual cost of tuition, to a maximum of $4,500 per year or $250 per semester hour.

Duration 1 year; may be renewed until the Guard member earns a bachelor's degree, as long as the member maintains a minimum GPA of 2.0. The full benefit must be utilized within a 10-year period.

Number awarded Varies each year.

Deadline Applications must be submitted not later than 2 weeks after the start date of the semester.

[267]
MISSOURI NATIONAL GUARD STATE TUITION ASSISTANCE PROGRAM

Office of the Adjutant General
Attn: NGMO-PER-INC (State TA)
2302 Militia Drive
Jefferson City, MO 65101-1203
(573) 638-9500, ext. 7023   Toll Free: (888) 526-MONG
Fax: (573) 638-9620   E-mail: ngmo.stateta@ng.army.mil
Web: www.moguard.com

Summary To provide financial assistance for college to members of the Missouri National Guard.

Eligibility This program is open to members of the Missouri National Guard who are participating satisfactorily in required training. Applicants must be enrolled or accepted for enrollment as a full-time or part-time undergraduate at an approved public or private institution of higher learning. If they have already completed some college courses, they must have earned a GPA of 2.5 or higher. As recently structured, priority is given to personnel in the following order: 1) officers who do not have a bachelor's degree, regardless of their length of service; 2) non-prior service enlistees accessed to fill a valid unit vacancy; 3) prior service transfers access to fill a valid unit vacancy; and 4) prior service beyond first term with less than 10 years total military service.

Financial data The program provide 100% tuition assistance for Guard members with 10 years or less of service and 50% tuition for those with more than 10 and less than 17 years of service. Tuition is paid at the rate of $261.60 per

semester hour and may not exceed 39 hours per state fiscal year.

Duration Support is provided for 10 semesters, 150 credit hours, or completion of a bachelor's degree, whichever comes first. Recipients must maintain a GPA of 2.5 or higher.

Additional information This program began in 1998.

Number awarded Varies each year, depending on the availability of funds.

Deadline Applications must be submitted before the start date of class for standard 16-week semesters or within 30 days after the start date for classes shorter than the standard 16-weeks.

[268]
MONTANA NATIONAL GUARD SCHOLARSHIPS

Montana National Guard
Attn: Education Service Officer
P.O. Box 4789
Fort Harrison, MT 59636-4789
(406) 324-3237   E-mail: Julie.benson1@us.army.mil
Web: www.montanaguard.com/hro/html/educationpg2.cfm

Summary To provide financial assistance for college to members of the Montana National Guard.

Eligibility This program is open to members of the Montana National Guard who are enrolled or accepted for enrollment at a college, university, vocational/technical college, or other VA-approved training program in the state. Applicants must be in pay grades E-1 through E-7, W-1 through W-3, or O-1 through O-2; have completed Initial Active Duty for Training; have a high school diploma or GED; be eligible for Montgomery GI Bill Selected Reserve Benefits or be under a 6-year obligation to the Montana National Guard; and not have completed more than 16 years of military service. Funds are awarded on a first-come, first-served basis until exhausted.

Financial data Stipends are $1,500 per semester for study at a college or university or $400 per semester at a community college.

Duration 1 year; may be renewed.

Number awarded Varies each year.

Deadline Deadline not specified.

[269]
MONTGOMERY GI BILL (SELECTED RESERVE)

Department of Veterans Affairs
Attn: Veterans Benefits Administration
810 Vermont Avenue, N.W.
Washington, DC 20420
(202) 418-4343   Toll Free: (888) GI-BILL1
Web: www.gibill.va.gov

Summary To provide financial assistance for college or graduate school to members of the Reserves or National Guard.

Eligibility Eligible to apply are members of the Reserve elements of the Army, Navy, Air Force, Marine Corps, and Coast Guard, as well as the Army National Guard and the Air National Guard. To be eligible, a Reservist must 1) have a 6-year obligation to serve in the Selected Reserves signed after June 30, 1985 (or, if an officer, to agree to serve 6 years in addition to the original obligation); 2) complete Initial Active Duty for Training (IADT); 3) meet the requirements for a high school diploma or equivalent certificate before completing IADT; and 4) remain in good standing in a drilling Selected

Reserve unit. Reservists who enlisted after June 30, 1985 can receive benefits for undergraduate degrees, graduate training, or technical courses leading to certificates at colleges and universities. Reservists whose 6-year commitment began after September 30, 1990 may also use these benefits for a certificate or diploma from business, technical, or vocational schools; cooperative training; apprenticeship or on-the-job training; correspondence courses; independent study programs; tutorial assistance; remedial, deficiency, or refresher training; flight training; or state-approved alternative teacher certification programs.

Financial data The current monthly rate is $345 for full-time study, $258 for three-quarter time study, $171 for half-time study, or $86.25 for less than half-time study. For apprenticeship and on-the-job training, the monthly stipend is $258.75 for the first 6 months, $189.75 for the second 6 months, and $120.75 for the remainder of the program. Other rates apply for cooperative education, correspondence courses, and flight training.

Duration Up to 36 months for full-time study, 48 months for three-quarter study, 72 months for half-time study, or 144 months for less than half-time study. Benefits end 10 years from the date the Reservist became eligible for the program.

Additional information This program is frequently referred to as Chapter 1606 (formerly Chapter 106).

Number awarded Varies each year.

Deadline Applications may be submitted at any time.

[270]
MSG LYNN H. STEINMAN MEMORIAL SCHOLARSHIP

Enlisted Association National Guard of New Jersey
Attn: Scholarship Chair
3650 Saylors Pond Road
Fort Dix, NJ 08640
(609) 562-0260　　　　　　　　　Fax: (609) 562-0283
Web: www.eang-nj.org/scholarships.html

Summary To provide financial assistance to New Jersey National Guard members interested in attending college in any state.

Eligibility This program is open to drilling members of the New Jersey National Guard. Membership in the Enlisted Association National Guard of New Jersey (EANGNJ) is not required. Applicants must be attending or planning to attend a college or university in any state. Along with their application, they must submit 1) information on their church, school, and community activities; 2) a list of honors they have received; 3) letters of recommendation; 4) transcripts; and 5) a letter with specific facts about their desire to continue their education and specifying their career goals. Financial need is not considered in the selection process.

Financial data The stipend is $1,000.

Duration 1 year.

Additional information This program is administered by EANGNJ and funded by USAA Insurance Corporation.

Number awarded 1 each year.

Deadline May of each year.

[271]
NARRAGANSETT BAY POST SAME SCHOLARSHIP

Society of American Military Engineers-Narragansett Bay Post
Attn: Scholarship Committee
15 Mohegan Avenue
New London, CT 06320
(860) 444-8312　　　　　　　　　Fax: (860) 444-8219
E-mail: Gregory.j.carabine@uscg.mil
Web: posts.same.org/Narragansett/scholarship.htm

Summary To provide financial assistance to residents of New England, particularly those with ties to the military, who are interested in working on a bachelor's degree in construction-related fields at colleges in any state.

Eligibility This program is open to residents of New England (preferably Connecticut, Massachusetts, and Rhode Island) who are graduating high school seniors or students currently enrolled at a college or university in any state. Applicants must be interested in working on a bachelor's degree in an accredited engineering or architectural program, preferably in civil engineering, environmental engineering, architecture, or other construction-related program. Preference is given to students who 1) are dependents of or sponsored by a member of the Narragansett Bay Post of the Society of American Military Engineers (SAME); 2) are enrolled in ROTC (preferably not a recipient of an ROTC scholarship); and 3) have prior U.S. military service and/or public service. Along with their application, they must submit a 500-word essay about themselves, their achievements, or their situation. Selection is based on that essay, grades and class rank, school or community honors, extracurricular activities, leadership, volunteer activities, and completeness and quality of the application. U.S. citizenship is required.

Financial data The stipend is $1,000.

Duration 1 year.

Number awarded 1 each year.

Deadline May of each year.

[272]
NATIONAL GUARD ASSOCIATION OF ARIZONA SCHOLARSHIPS

National Guard Association of Arizona
Attn: Scholarship Committee
5640 East McDowell Road
Phoenix, AZ 85008
(602) 275-8305　　　　　　　　　Fax: (602) 275-9254
E-mail: ngaofaz@aol.com
Web: www.ngaaz.org/scholarship.html

Summary To provide financial assistance to students at colleges and universities in Arizona who have a connection to the National Guard and the National Guard Association of Arizona (NGAAZ).

Eligibility This program is open to full-time students at colleges, universities, and community colleges in Arizona. Applicants must be a member of 1 of the following categories: 1) a current enlisted member of the Arizona National Guard; 2) a current officer member of the Arizona National Guard who is also a member of the NGAAZ; or 3) children or spouses of NGAAZ members. Applicants must submit 2 letters of recommendation and verification of good standing from the first commander in the chain of command of the Arizona National Guard. Selection is based on GPA (25%), community service

(15%), letters of recommendation (15%), knowledge of National Guard philosophy (15%), and financial need (30%).
Financial data The stipend is $1,500.
Duration 1 year; nonrenewable.
Number awarded 3 each year: 1 to each category of applicant.
Deadline April of each year.

[273]
NATIONAL GUARD ASSOCIATION OF CALIFORNIA SCHOLARSHIPS

National Guard Association of California
Attn: Executive Director
3336 Bradshaw Road, Suite 230
Sacramento, CA 95827-2615
(916) 362-3411   Toll Free: (800) 647-0018
Fax: (916) 362-3707
Web: ngac.org
Summary To provide funding to members or former members of the National Guard in California and their dependents interested in attending college in any state.
Eligibility This program is open to 1) dependents of service members of the California National Guard who have died, have been wounded, are currently serving, or have served in the Global War on Terrorism; 2) medically or honorably discharged California National Guard veterans who served in Operation Enduring Freedom (OEF) or Operation Iraqi Freedom (OIF); 3) California National Guard service members who are currently serving or have served in the Global War on Terrorism; or 4) dependents of retired California National Guard service members who are life members of the National Guard Association of California. Applicants must be attending or planning to attend a college, university, or trade school in any state. Along with their application, they must submit a 500-word essay on the greatest challenge they have faced and how it has impacted them. Selection is based on that essay; unweighted GPA; extracurricular activities, honors, and/or awards; recommendations; and (if case of a tie) SAT or ACT scores.
Financial data Stipends range from $250 to $1,000. Funds are paid directly to the recipient.
Duration 1 year.
Number awarded Varies each year; recently, 19 of these scholarships were awarded.
Deadline May of each year.

[274]
NATIONAL GUARD ASSOCIATION OF CONNECTICUT SCHOLARSHIP PROGRAM

National Guard Association of Connecticut
Attn: Scholarship Committee
360 Broad Street
Hartford, CT 06105-3795
(860) 247-5000   Fax: (860) 247-5000
E-mail: ngact_scholarship@ngact.org
Web: www.ngact.org/scholarships.htm
Summary To provide financial assistance to members and the family of members of the National Guard Association of Connecticut (NGACT) who are interested in attending college in any state.
Eligibility This program is open to 1) NGACT members; 2) unmarried children and grandchildren of NGACT members;

3) spouses of NGACT members; and 4) unremarried spouses and unmarried dependent children and grandchildren of deceased NGACT members who were members in good standing at the time of their death. Applicants must be attending or planning to attend, on a part- or full-time basis, a college, university, trade school, or business school in any state. Graduate students are not eligible to apply. Along with their application, they must submit: an official transcript, a letter on their desire to continue their education and why financial assistance is required, 2 letters of recommendation, and 1 letter of academic reference. Selection is based on academic record, character, leadership, and need.
Financial data A stipend is awarded (amount not specified). Funds are sent to the recipient but are made payable to the recipient's choice of school. To receive the awards, proof of enrollment must be presented.
Duration 1 year.
Number awarded Varies each year.
Deadline February of each year.

[275]
NATIONAL GUARD ASSOCIATION OF FLORIDA AND ENLISTED NATIONAL GUARD ASSOCIATION OF FLORIDA SCHOLARSHIP PROGRAM

National Guard Association of Florida
Attn: Scholarship Committee
P.O. Box 3446
St. Augustine, FL 32085-3446
(904) 823-0628   Fax: (904) 839-2068
E-mail: ngafl1903@floridaguard.org
Web: www.floridaguard.org/florida-guard-scholarships.html
Summary To provide financial assistance to members of the Florida National Guard and their families who are also members of either the National Guard Association of Florida (NGOA-FL) or the Enlisted National Guard Association of Florida (ENGAF) and interested in attending college in the state.
Eligibility This program is open to active members of the Florida National Guard (enlisted, officer, and warrant officer), their spouses, and children, but preference is given to Guard members. Applicants must be residents of Florida attending or planning to attend an accredited college, university, or vocational/technical school in the state. They must also be a member, spouse of a member, or child of a member of their respective association. Selection is based on academic achievement, civic and moral leadership, character, and financial need.
Financial data Scholarships are $1,000 for full-time students or $500 for part-time students; funds are paid directly to the recipient's institution.
Duration 1 year; may be renewed.
Additional information This program is jointly sponsored by the respective associations.
Number awarded 15 each year.
Deadline June of each year.

[276]
NATIONAL GUARD ASSOCIATION OF INDIANA EDUCATIONAL GRANTS

National Guard Association of Indiana
Attn: Educational Grant Committee
2002 South Holt Road, Building 9
Indianapolis, IN 46241-4839
(317) 247-3196   Toll Free: (800) 219-2173
Fax: (317) 247-3575   E-mail: membership@ngai.net
Web: www.ngai.net/membership

Summary To provide financial assistance to members of the National Guard Association of Indiana (NGAI) and their dependents who plan to attend college in any state.

Eligibility This program is open to NGAI members who are currently serving in the Indiana National Guard and their dependents. Children and widow(er)s of former Guard members killed or permanently disabled while on duty with the Indiana National Guard are also eligible. Applicants must be attending or planning to attend a college or university in any state. Along with their application, they must submit 2 letters of recommendation, a copy of high school or college transcripts, SAT or ACT scores (if taken), a letter of acceptance from a college or university (if not currently attending college), and a 2-page essay on the educational program they intend to pursue and the goals they wish to attain. Selection is based on academic achievement, commitment and desire to achieve, extracurricular activities, accomplishments, goals, and financial need.

Financial data The stipend is $1,000.

Duration 1 year; recipients may reapply.

Number awarded 10 each year: 5 to military members and 5 to dependents.

Deadline March of each year.

[277]
NATIONAL GUARD ASSOCIATION OF MARYLAND SCHOLARSHIPS

National Guard Association of Maryland
Attn: Scholarship Committee
P.O. Box 16675
Baltimore, MD 21221-0675
(410) 557-2606   Toll Free: (800) 844-1394
Fax: (410) 893-7529 E-mail: executivedirector@ngam.net
Web: www.ngam.net/benefits/scholarships.html

Summary To provide funding to current and former members of the Maryland National Guard and their dependents who are interested in attending college in any state.

Eligibility This program is open to active and retired members of the Maryland National Guard and their spouses and children. Applicants must be enrolled or planning to enroll in an accredited college, university, or vocational/technical school in any state on either a part-time or full-time basis. They must submit a resume in which they outline their academic background, activities in which they have participated, and honors they have received; 3 letters of recommendation; the name of the college; and information on financial need.

Financial data The stipend is $1,000. Funds are paid directly to the recipient's university for tuition, fees, and books.

Duration 1 year; recipients may reapply.

Number awarded Varies each year; recently, 17 of these scholarships were awarded.

Deadline March of each year.

[278]
NATIONAL GUARD ASSOCIATION OF MASSACHUSETTS SCHOLARSHIPS

National Guard Association of Massachusetts
Attn: Education Services Office
50 Maple Street
Milford, MA 01757
(508) 735-6544   E-mail: contact@ngama.org
Web: www.ngama.org/scholarships

Summary To provide financial assistance to members of the Massachusetts National Guard and their dependents who are interested in attending college in any state.

Eligibility This program is open to 1) current members of the Massachusetts National Guard; 2) children and spouses of current members of the National Guard Association of Massachusetts (NGAMA); and 3) children and spouses of current members of the Massachusetts National Guard. Applicants must be enrolled in or planning to enroll in an accredited college or technical program in any state. Along with their application, they must submit a letter of recommendation, a list of extracurricular activities and other significant accomplishments, high school or college transcripts, and an essay on a topic that changes annually but relates to the National Guard.

Financial data The stipend is $1,000.

Duration 1 year.

Number awarded 4 each year: 2 to members of the Massachusetts National Guard, 1 to a dependent of an NGAMA member, and 1 to a dependent of a Massachusetts National Guard member.

Deadline March of each year.

[279]
NATIONAL GUARD ASSOCIATION OF MICHIGAN EDUCATIONAL GRANTS

National Guard Association of Michigan
Attn: Scholarships
P.O. Box 810
Cadillac, MI 49601
Toll Free: (800) 477-1644   Fax: (231) 775-7906
E-mail: NGAM@charter.net
Web: www.ngam.org/grants.php

Summary To provide financial assistance to members of the National Guard Association of Michigan who are interested in attending college in any state.

Eligibility This program is open to members of the association who are also current members of the Michigan National Guard. Applicants may be enlisted members of any rank, warrant officers through CW3, or commissioned officers through the rank of captain. They must be attending or planning to attend a college, university, or trade school in any state. Along with their application, they must submit a 100-word statement on their educational and military goals. Financial need is not considered in the selection process.

Financial data A stipend is awarded (amount not specified).

Duration 1 semester; may be renewed.

Number awarded Varies each year; recently, 6 of these grants were awarded.

Deadline June of each year for the fall term/semester; November of each year for the winter term/semester.

[280]
NATIONAL GUARD ASSOCIATION OF NEW HAMPSHIRE SCHOLARSHIPS

National Guard Association of New Hampshire
Attn: Scholarship Committee
P.O. Box 22031
Portsmouth, NH 03802-2031
(603) 540-9608   E-mail: info@nganh.org
Web: www.nganh.org

Summary To provide money to members of the National Guard Association of New Hampshire and their dependents who are interested in attending college.

Eligibility This program is open to current members of the National Guard Association of New Hampshire (officer, enlisted, or retired) and their dependents. Applicants must be attending or planning to attend an accredited college or university in any state. Along with their application, they must submit a 1-page essay on a topic that changes annually; recently, they were asked to give their thoughts on whether or not United States efforts to support and stabilize democratic governments in Afghanistan and Iraq will lead to greater stability in the Southwest Asian region.

Financial data The stipend is $1,000.

Duration 1 year.

Number awarded 1 each year.

Deadline April of each year.

[281]
NATIONAL GUARD ASSOCIATION OF NEW JERSEY SCHOLARSHIP PROGRAM

National Guard Association of New Jersey
Attn: Executive Director
P.O. Box 266
Wrightstown, NJ 08562
(973) 541-6776   Fax: (973) 541-6909
E-mail: nganj@aol.com
Web: nganj.org/about.htm

Summary To provide financial assistance to members of the National Guard Association of New Jersey (NGANJ) or their dependents who are interested in attending college or graduate school in any state.

Eligibility This program is open to 1) active members of the NGANJ currently enrolled full time at an approved community college, school of nursing, or 4-year college in any state; and 2) the spouses, children, and grandchildren of active, retired, or deceased members entering or attending a 4-year college or university in any state. Applicants must submit transcripts, information on the civic and academic activities in which they have participated, and a list of offices, honors, awards, and special recognitions they have received. Selection is based on academic accomplishment, leadership, and citizenship.

Financial data Stipends up to $1,000 are available.

Duration 1 year; nonrenewable.

Number awarded Varies each year; recently, 10 of these scholarships were awarded.

Deadline April of each year.

[282]
NATIONAL GUARD ASSOCIATION OF SOUTH CAROLINA SCHOLARSHIPS

National Guard Association of South Carolina
Attn: NGASC Scholarship Foundation
132 Pickens Street
Columbia, SC 29205
(803) 254-8456   Toll Free: (800) 822-3235
Fax: (803) 254-3869   E-mail: nginfo@ngasc.org
Web: www.ngasc.org/?page_id=11

Summary To provide funding to current and former South Carolina National Guard members and their dependents who are interested in attending college or graduate school.

Eligibility This program is open to undergraduate students who are 1) current, retired, or deceased members of the South Carolina National Guard; 2) their dependents; and 3) members of the National Guard Association of South Carolina (NGASC). Graduate students are also eligible if they are members of the South Carolina National Guard. Applicants must be attending or interested in attending a college or university in any state as a full-time student. Several of the scholarships include additional restrictions on school or academic major; some are granted only for academic excellence, but most are based on both academics and financial need.

Financial data The stipend is $1,500 or $1,000.

Duration 1 year; may be renewed up to 3 additional years.

Number awarded Varies each year; recently, 42 of these scholarships were awarded: 1 at $1,500 and 41 at $1,000.

Deadline January of each year.

[283]
NATIONAL GUARD ASSOCIATION OF TENNESSEE SCHOLARSHIP PROGRAM

National Guard Association of Tennessee
Attn: Scholarship Committee
4332 Kenilwood Drive
Nashville, TN 37204-4401
(615) 833-9100   Toll Free: (888) 642-8448 (within TN)
Fax: (615) 833-9173   E-mail: larry@ngatn.org
Web: www.ngatn.org

Summary To provide financial assistance for college to members or dependents of members of the National Guard Association of Tennessee (NGATN).

Eligibility This program is open to active Tennessee National Guard members and to active annual or life members of the NGATN. If no active Guard or association member qualifies, the scholarships may be awarded to the child of a Guard or association member, including life members who have retired or are deceased. All applicants must be high school seniors or graduates who meet entrance or continuation requirements at a Tennessee college or university. Selection is based on leadership in school and civic activities, motivation for continued higher education, academic achievement in high school and/or college, and financial need.

Financial data The stipends are $1,500.

Duration 1 year.

Number awarded 6 each year: 1 to an active National Guard member; 2 to current association members or their dependents; 2 to active National Guard members or their dependents; and 1 to a current Guard member who was mobilized for Operations Desert Storm, Noble Eagle, Enduring Freedom, or Iraqi Freedom.

Deadline June of each year.

[284]
NATIONAL GUARD ASSOCIATION OF TEXAS SCHOLARSHIP PROGRAM

National Guard Association of Texas
Attn: NGAT Educational Foundation
3706 Crawford Avenue
Austin, TX 78731-6803
(512) 454-7300   Toll Free: (800) 252-NGAT
Fax: (512) 467-6803   E-mail: rlindner@ngat.org
Web: www.ngat.org

Summary To provide funding to members and dependents of members of the National Guard Association of Texas who are interested in attending college or graduate school.

Eligibility This program is open to annual and life members of the association and their spouses and children (associate members and their dependents are not eligible). Applicants may be high school seniors, undergraduate students, or graduate students, either enrolled or planning to enroll at an institution of higher education in any state. Along with their application, they must submit an essay on their desire to continue their education. Selection is based on scholarship, citizenship, and leadership.

Financial data Stipends range from $500 to $5,000.

Duration 1 year (nonrenewable).

Additional information This program includes 1 scholarship sponsored by USAA Insurance Corporation.

Number awarded Varies each year; recently, 13 of these scholarships were awarded: 1 at $5,000, 3 at $2,500, 1 at $2,000, 3 at $1,250, 4 at $1,000, and 1 at $500.

Deadline February of each year.

[285]
NATIONAL GUARD ASSOCIATION OF UTAH "MINUTEMAN" SCHOLARSHIPS

National Guard Association of Utah
12953 South Minuteman Drive, Room 19835
P.O. Box 435
Draper, UT 84020
(801) 631-6314   E-mail: ngautah@ngaut.org
Web: www.ngaut.org/Scholarship.php

Summary To provide financial assistance to members of the Utah National Guard and their dependents who are interested in attending college in the state.

Eligibility This program is open to members of the Utah National Guard and their dependents who are enrolled for at least 6 credit hours at a college or university in the state. Applicants must submit 1) a 150-word description of their educational and career goals; 2) a 200- to 300-word description of leadership and extracurricular activities that they may have had or currently enjoy; 3) a 300-word essay on how the military has influenced their life; 4) a 1-page cover letter or resume; and 5) 2 letters of reference.

Financial data The stipend is $1,000. Funds are sent to the recipient's school and must be used for tuition, laboratory fees, and curriculum-required books and supplies.

Duration 1 year.

Number awarded 5 each year.

Deadline March of each year.

[286]
NATIONAL GUARD ASSOCIATION OF VERMONT SCHOLARSHIPS

National Guard Association of Vermont
Attn: Capt John Geno, President
P.O. Box 694
Essex Junction, VT 05452
(802) 338-3397   E-mail: john.geno@us.army.mil
Web: www.ngavt.org/scholarInfo.shtml

Summary To provide funding to members of the Vermont National Guard (VTNG) and their children or spouses who are interested in attending college or graduate school.

Eligibility This program is open to current members of the VTNG, their spouses, and their unmarried children. Applicants must be working, or planning to work, on an associate, undergraduate, technical, or graduate degree as a full-time student at a school in any state. Along with their application, they must submit an essay on their commitment to selfless public service or their plan for pursuing it in the future. Selection is based on academic performance, overall potential for a commitment to selfless public service, and financial need.

Financial data The stipend is $1,000. Funds are sent directly to the recipient.

Duration 1 year; recipients may reapply.

Number awarded 4 each year: 3 to undergraduates and 1 to a graduate student.

Deadline May of each year.

[287]
NATIONAL GUARD OF GEORGIA SCHOLARSHIP FUND FOR COLLEGES OR UNIVERSITIES

Georgia Guard Insurance Trust
P.O. Box 889
Mableton, GA 30126
(770) 739-9651   Toll Free: (800) 229-1053
Fax: (770) 745-0673   E-mail: director@ngaga.org
Web: www.ngaga.org/scholarships.html

Summary To provide funding to members of the Georgia National Guard and their spouses, children, and grandchildren who are interested in attending college.

Eligibility This program is open to policyholders with the Georgia Guard Insurance Trust (GGIT) who are members of the National Guard Association of Georgia (NGAGA) or the Enlisted Association of the National Guard of Georgia (EANGGA); spouses, children, and grandchildren of NGAGA and EANGGA members are also eligible. Applicants must be enrolled or planning to enroll full time at a college or university in any state and have received an academic honor while in high school. Graduating high school seniors must have a combined mathematics and critical reading SAT score of at least 1000 or a GPA of 3.0 or higher. Students already enrolled at a college or university must have a cumulative GPA of 3.0 or higher. Along with their application, they must submit transcripts, a letter with personal specific facts regarding their desire to continue their education, 2 letters of recommendation, a letter of academic reference, and an agreement to retain insurance with the GGIT for at least 2 years following completion of the school year for which the scholarship is awarded. Selection is based on academics, character, and moral and personal traits.

Financial data The stipend is $3,000.

Duration 1 year.

Number awarded Recently, this sponsor awarded a total of 10 scholarships for all of its programs.
Deadline April of each year.

[288]
NATIONAL GUARD OF GEORGIA SCHOLARSHIP FUND FOR VOCATIONAL OR BUSINESS SCHOOLS

Georgia Guard Insurance Trust
P.O. Box 889
Mableton, GA 30126
(770) 739-9651   Toll Free: (800) 229-1053
Fax: (770) 745-0673   E-mail: director@ngaga.org
Web: www.ngaga.org/scholarships.html

Summary To provide financial assistance to members of the Georgia National Guard and their spouses, children, and grandchildren who are interested in attending business or vocational school in any state.

Eligibility This program is open to policyholders with the Georgia Guard Insurance Trust (GGIT) who are members of the National Guard Association of Georgia (NGAGA) or the Enlisted Association of the National Guard of Georgia (EANGGA); spouses, children, and grandchildren of NGAGA and EANGGA members are also eligible. Applicants must be interested in enrolling full time in day or evening classes at a business or vocational school in any state. They must be able to meet program-specific admission standards and institutional requirements and complete all admission procedures for admission to a degree/diploma program in regular program status. Along with their application, they must submit transcripts, a letter with personal specific facts regarding their desire to continue their education, 2 letters of recommendation, and an agreement to retain insurance with the GGIT for at least 2 years following completion of the school year for which the scholarship is awarded. Selection is based on academics, character, and moral and personal traits.

Financial data The stipend is $3,000.
Duration 1 year.
Number awarded Recently, this sponsor awarded a total of 10 scholarships for all of its programs.
Deadline April of each year.

[289]
NAUS SCHOLARSHIP PROGRAM

National Association for Uniformed Services
Attn: Scholarship Committee
5535 Hempstead Way
Springfield, VA 22151
(703) 750-1342   Toll Free: (800) 842-3451, ext. 1803
Fax: (703) 354-4380   E-mail: scholarship@naus.org
Web: www.naus.org

Summary To provide financial assistance for college to members of the National Association for Uniformed Services (NAUS) and their families.

Eligibility This program is open to NAUS members, their spouses, and their children. Applicants must be high school seniors or undergraduates enrolled full or part time in a degree- or certificate-granting program. High school seniors must have a GPA of 3.0 or higher and undergraduates must have a GPA of 2.5 or higher. Along with their application, they must submit statements, up to 100 words each, on 1) their reasons for enrolling in a postsecondary education program; and 2) a list of academic achievements, personal achieve-

ments, extracurricular activities, and any community service performed in the past 2 years. Financial need is not considered in the selection process.

Financial data The stipend is $2,000.
Duration 1 year.
Additional information Membership in NAUS is open to members of the armed forces, veterans, retirees, their spouses, and their widow(er)s.
Number awarded 5 each year.
Deadline April of each year.

[290]
NAVAL ENLISTED RESERVE ASSOCIATION SCHOLARSHIPS

Naval Enlisted Reserve Association
Attn: Scholarship Committee
6703 Farragut Avenue
Falls Church, VA 22042-2189
(703) 534-1329   Toll Free: (800) 776-9020
Fax: (703) 534-3617   E-mail: members@nera.org
Web: www.nera.org

Summary To provide financial assistance for college to members of the Naval Enlisted Reserve Association (NERA) and their families.

Eligibility This program is open to regular or associate NERA members, the spouses of regular members, and the unmarried children and grandchildren under 23 years of age of regular members. Applicants must be graduating high school seniors or undergraduates currently attending an accredited 2- or 4-year college or university as a full- or part-time student. Along with their application, they must submit a 500-word essay on either 1) their career goals and objectives for their education; or 2) why Reservists are important to America. Financial need is not considered in the selection process.

Financial data The stipend is $2,500.
Duration 1 year.
Additional information This program is funded in part by USAA Insurance Corporation.
Number awarded 4 each year.
Deadline June of each year.

[291]
NAVAL FLIGHT OFFICER OPTION OF THE SEAMAN TO ADMIRAL-21 PROGRAM

U.S. Navy
Attn: Commander, Naval Service Training Command
250 Dallas Street, Suite A
Pensacola, FL 32508-5268
(850) 452-9433   Fax: (850) 452-2486
E-mail: PNSC_STA21@navy.mil
Web: www.sta-21.navy.mil

Summary To allow outstanding enlisted Navy personnel to complete a bachelor's degree and receive a commission as a naval flight officer (NFO).

Eligibility This program is open to U.S. citizens who are currently serving on active duty in the U.S. Navy or Naval Reserve, including Full Time Support (FTS), Selected Reserves (SELRES), and Navy Reservists on active duty, except for those on active duty for training (ACDUTRA). Applicants must be high school graduates (or GED recipients) who are able to complete requirements for a baccalaureate degree in 36 months or less. When they complete their degree requirements, they must be younger than 27 years of age (may be adjusted to 31 years of age for prior active-duty service). Within the past 3 years, they must have taken the SAT (and achieved scores of at least 500 on the mathematics section and 500 on the critical reading section) or the ACT (and achieved a score of 41 or higher, including at least 21 on the mathematics portion and 20 on the English portion). They must also achieve a score of at least the following: AQR (4), FOFAR (5) on the Aviation Selection Test Battery.

Financial data Awardees continue to receive their regular Navy pay and allowances while they attend college on a full-time basis. They also receive reimbursement for tuition, fees, and books up to $10,000 per year. If base housing is available, they are eligible to live there. Participants are not eligible to receive benefits under the Navy's Tuition Assistance Program (TA), the Montgomery GI Bill (MGIB), the Navy College Fund, or the Veterans Educational Assistance Program (VEAP).

Duration Selectees are supported for up to 36 months of full-time, year-round study or completion of a bachelor's degree, as long as they maintain a GPA of 2.5 or higher.

Additional information This program was established in 2001 as a replacement for the Aviation Enlisted Commissioning Program (AECP). Upon acceptance into the program, selectees attend the Naval Science Institute (NSI) in Newport, Rhode Island for an 8-week program in the fundamental core concepts of being a naval officer (navigation, engineering, weapons, military history and justice, etc.). They then enter a college or university with an NROTC unit or affiliation to work full time on a bachelor's degree. They become members of and drill with the NROTC unit. When they complete their degree, they are commissioned as ensigns in the United States Naval Reserve and assigned to flight training. After commissioning, participants incur an active-duty obligation of 6 years after designation as a Naval Flight Officer or 6 years from the date of disenrollment from flight training.

Number awarded Varies each year.

Deadline June of each year.

[292]
NAVY ADVANCED EDUCATION VOUCHER PROGRAM

U.S. Navy
Naval Education and Training Command
Center for Personal and Professional Development
Attn: AEV Program Office
6490 Saufley Field Road
Pensacola, FL 32509-5204
(850) 452-7271   Fax: (850) 452-1272
E-mail: rick.cusimano@navy.mil
Web: www.navycollege.navy.mil/aev/aev_home.cfm

Summary To provide financial assistance to Navy enlisted personnel who are interested in earning an undergraduate or graduate degree during off-duty hours.

Eligibility This program is open to senior enlisted Navy personnel in ranks E-7 and E-8. Applicants should be transferring to, or currently on, shore duty with sufficient time ashore to complete a bachelor's or master's degree. Personnel at rank E-7 may have no more than 16 years in service

and at E-8 no more than 18 years. The area of study must be certified by the Naval Postgraduate School as Navy-relevant.

Financial data This program covers education costs (tuition, books, and fees), to a maximum of $6,700 per year or a total of $20,000 per participant for a bachelor's degree or $20,000 per year or a total of $40,000 per participant for a master's degree.

Duration Up to 36 months from the time of enrollment for a bachelor's degree; up to 24 months from the time of enrollment for a master's degree.

Additional information Recently approved majors for bachelor's degrees included human resources, construction management, information technology, emergency and disaster management, paralegal, engineering, business administration, leadership and management, nursing, strategic foreign languages, and electrical/electronic technology. Approved fields of study for master's degrees included business administration, education and training management, emergency and disaster management, engineering and technology, homeland defense and security, human resources, information technology, leadership and management, project management, and systems analysis. Recipients of this assistance incur an obligation to remain on active duty following completion of the program for a period equal to 3 times the number of months of education completed, to a maximum obligation of 36 months.

Number awarded Varies each year; recently, 20 of these vouchers were awarded: 15 for bachelor's degrees and 5 for master's degrees.

Deadline May of each year.

[293]
NAVY COLLEGE ASSISTANCE/STUDENT HEADSTART (NAVY-CASH) PROGRAM

U.S. Navy
Attn: Navy Personnel Command
5722 Integrity Drive
Millington, TN 38054-5057
(901) 874-3070   Toll Free: (888) 633-9674
Fax: (901) 874-2651
E-mail: nukeprograms@cnrc.navy.mil
Web: www.cnrc.navy.mil

Summary To provide financial assistance to high school seniors and current college students interested in attending college for a year and then entering the Navy's nuclear program.

Eligibility Applicants must be able to meet the specific requirements of the Navy's Enlisted Nuclear Field Program. They must be enrolled or accepted for enrollment at an accredited 2-year community or junior college or 4-year college or university.

Financial data While they attend school, participants are paid a regular Navy salary at a pay grade up to E-3 (starting at $1,303.50 per month).

Duration 12 months.

Additional information After 1 year of college, participants report for enlisted recruit training in the Navy's nuclear field. Further information on this program is available from a local Navy recruiter.

Number awarded Varies each year.

Deadline Deadline not specified.

[294]
NAVY NURSE CANDIDATE PROGRAM

U.S. Navy
Attn: Navy Medicine Professional Development Center
Code OH
8901 Wisconsin Avenue, Building 1, 13th Floor, Room 13132
Bethesda, MD 20889-5611
(301) 295-1217   Toll Free: (800) USA-NAVY
Fax: (301) 295-6865   E-mail: oh@med.navy.mil
Web: www.med.navy.mil

Summary To provide financial assistance for nursing education to students interested in serving in the Navy.

Eligibility This program is open to full-time students in a bachelor of science in nursing program who are U.S. citizens under 40 years of age. Prior to or during their junior year of college, applicants must enlist in the U.S. Navy Nurse Corps Reserve. Following receipt of their degree, they must be willing to serve on active duty as a nurse in the Navy.

Financial data This program pays a $10,000 initial grant upon enlistment (paid in 2 installments of $5,000 each) and a stipend of $1,000 per month. Students are responsible for paying all school expenses.

Duration Up to 24 months.

Additional information Students who receive support from this program for 1 to 12 months incur an active-duty service obligation of 4 years; students who receive support for 13 to 24 months have a service obligation of 5 years.

Number awarded Varies each year.

Deadline Deadline not specified.

[295]
NAVY NURSE CORPS NROTC SCHOLARSHIP PROGRAM

U.S. Navy
Attn: Naval Education and Training Command
NSTC OD2
250 Dallas Street, Suite A
Pensacola, FL 32508-5268
(850) 452-4941, ext. 29395
Toll Free: (800) NAV-ROTC, ext. 29395
Fax: (850) 452-2486
E-mail: pnsc_nrotc.scholarship@navy.mil
Web: www.nrotc.navy.mil/nurse.aspx

Summary To provide financial assistance to graduating high school seniors who are interested in joining Navy ROTC and majoring in nursing in college.

Eligibility Eligible to apply for these scholarships are graduating high school seniors who have been accepted at a college with a Navy ROTC unit on campus or a college with a cross-enrollment agreement with such a college. Applicants must be U.S. citizens between the ages of 17 and 23 who plan to study nursing in college and are willing to serve for 4 years as active-duty Navy officers in the Navy Nurse Corps following graduation from college. They must not have reached their 27th birthday by the time of college graduation and commissioning; applicants who have prior active-duty military service may be eligible for age adjustments for the amount of time equal to their prior service, up to a maximum of 36 months. They must have minimum SAT scores of 530 in critical reading and 520 in mathematics or minimum ACT scores of 22 in English and 21 in mathematics.

Financial data This scholarship provides payment of full tuition and required educational fees, as well as $375 per semester for textbooks, supplies, and equipment. The program also provides a stipend for 10 months of the year that is $250 per month as a freshman, $300 per month as a sophomore, $350 per month as a junior, and $400 per month as a senior.

Duration 4 years.

Number awarded Varies each year.

Deadline January of each year.

[296]
NAVY SEAL FOUNDATION SCHOLARSHIPS

Navy Seal Foundation
Attn: Chief Financial Officer
1619 D Street, Building 5326
Virginia Beach, VA 23459
(757) 363-7490   Fax: (757) 363-7491
E-mail: info@navysealfoundation.org
Web: www.navysealfoundation.org

Summary To provide financial assistance for college to Naval Special Warfare (NSW) personnel and their families.

Eligibility This program is open to active-duty Navy SEALS, Special Warfare Combat Crewmen (SWCC), and military personnel assigned to other NSW commands. Their dependent children and spouses are also eligible. Applicants must be entering or continuing full or part-time students working on an associate or bachelor's degree. Along with their application, they must submit an essay, up to 2 pages in length, on a topic that changes annually; recently, students were asked to explore benevolence in their life and describe when they were able to demonstrate it. They may also indicate any special circumstances such as financial need, single parent status, or disabilities.

Financial data Stipends are $15,000, $7,500, or $5,000 per year.

Duration 1 year; may be renewed.

Number awarded Varies each year; recently, the Navy Seal Foundation awarded 16 scholarships for all of its programs: 3 for 4 years at $15,000 per year to high school seniors and graduates, 3 for 1 year at $7,500 to high school seniors and graduates, 3 for 1 year at $15,000 to current college students, 3 for 1 year at $7,500 to current college students, and 4 for 1 year at $5,000 to spouses.

Deadline February of each year.

[297]
NAVY TUITION ASSISTANCE PROGRAM

U.S. Navy
Attn: Naval Education and Training Command
Center for Personal and Professional Development
Code N725
6490 Saufley Field Road
Pensacola, FL 32509-5241
(850) 452-7271   Toll Free: (877) 838-1659
Fax: (850) 452-1149   E-mail: ncc@navy.mil
Web: www.navycollege.navy.mil/nta.cfm

Summary To provide financial assistance for high school, vocational, undergraduate, or graduate studies to Navy personnel.

Eligibility This program is open to active-duty Navy officers and enlisted personnel, including Naval Reservists on continuous active duty, enlisted Naval Reservists ordered to active duty for 120 days or more, and Naval Reservist officers ordered to active duty for 2 years or more. Applicants must register to take courses at accredited civilian schools during off-duty time. They must be working on their first associate, bachelor's, master's, doctoral, or professional degree. Tuition assistance is provided for courses taken at accredited colleges, universities, vocational/technical schools, private schools, and through independent study/distance learning (but not for flight training).

Financial data Those selected for participation in this program receive their regular Navy pay and 100% of tuition at the postsecondary educational institution of their choice, but capped at $250 per semester hour and 12 semester hours per fiscal year (the 12-semester hour limit may be waived upon application), or a total of $4,500 per fiscal year.

Duration Until completion of a bachelor's or graduate degree.

Additional information Officers must agree to remain on active duty for at least 2 years after completion of courses funded by this program.

Number awarded Varies each year.

Deadline Deadline not specified.

[298]
NAVY-MARINE CORPS ROTC 2-YEAR SCHOLARSHIPS

U.S. Navy
Attn: Naval Education and Training Command
NSTC OD2
250 Dallas Street, Suite A
Pensacola, FL 32508-5268
(850) 452-4941, ext. 29395
Toll Free: (800) NAV-ROTC, ext. 29395
Fax: (850) 452-2486
E-mail: pnsc_nrotc.scholarship@navy.mil
Web: www.nrotc.navy.mil/scholarships.aspx

Summary To provide financial assistance to upper-division students who are interested in joining Navy ROTC in college.

Eligibility This program is open to students who have completed at least 2 years of college (or 3 years if enrolled in a 5-year program) with a GPA of 2.5 or higher overall and 2.0 or higher in calculus and physics. Preference is given to students at colleges with a Navy ROTC unit on campus or at colleges with a cross-enrollment agreement with a college with an NROTC unit. Applicants must be U.S. citizens between the ages of 17 and 21 who plan to pursue an approved course of study in college and complete their degree before they reach the age of 27. Former and current enlisted military personnel are also eligible if they will complete the program by the age of 30.

Financial data These scholarships provide payment of full tuition and required educational fees, as well as a specified amount for textbooks, supplies, and equipment. The program also provides a stipend for 10 months of the year that is $350 per month as a junior and $400 per month as a senior.

Duration 2 years, until the recipient completes the bachelor's degree.

Additional information Applications must be made through professors of naval science at 1 of the schools hosting the Navy ROTC program. Prior to final selection, applicants must attend, at Navy expense, a 6-week summer training course at the Naval Science Institute at Newport, Rhode Island. Recipients must also complete 4 years of study in naval science classes as students either at 1 of the 74 colleges with NROTC units or at 1 of the more than 100 institutions with cross-enrollment agreements (in which case they attend their home college for their regular academic courses but attend naval science classes at a nearby school with an NROTC unit). After completing the program, all participants are commissioned as ensigns in the Naval Reserve or second lieutenants in the Marine Corps Reserve with an 8-year service obligation, including 4 years of active duty.

Number awarded Approximately 800 each year.

Deadline March of each year.

[299]
NAVY-MARINE CORPS ROTC 4-YEAR SCHOLARSHIPS

U.S. Navy
Attn: Naval Education and Training Command
NSTC OD2
250 Dallas Street, Suite A
Pensacola, FL 32508-5268
(850) 452-4941, ext. 29395
Toll Free: (800) NAV-ROTC, ext. 29395
Fax: (850) 452-2486
E-mail: pnsc_nrotc.scholarship@navy.mil
Web: www.nrotc.navy.mil/scholarships.aspx

Summary To provide financial assistance to graduating high school seniors who are interested in joining Navy ROTC in college.

Eligibility This program is open to graduating high school seniors who have been accepted at a college with a Navy ROTC unit on campus or a college with a cross-enrollment agreement with such a college. Applicants must be U.S. citizens between 17 and 23 years of age who are willing to serve for 4 years as active-duty Navy officers following graduation from college. They must not have reached their 27th birthday by the time of college graduation and commissioning; applicants who have prior active-duty military service may be eligible for age adjustments for the amount of time equal to their prior service, up to a maximum of 36 months. The qualifying scores for the Navy option are 530 critical reading and 520 mathematics on the SAT or 22 on English and 21 on mathematics on the ACT; for the Marine Corps option they are 1000 composite on the SAT or 22 composite on the ACT. Eligible academic majors are classified as Tier 1 for engineering programs of Navy interest (aerospace, aeronautical, astronautical, chemical, electrical, mechanical, naval, nuclear, ocean, and systems); Tier 2 for other engineering, mathematics, and science programs (e.g., general engineering and other engineering specialties; biochemistry and other specialties within biology; chemistry; mathematics; oceanography; pharmacology and toxicology; physics; quantitative economics; physics); or Tier 3 for selected regional and cultural area studies, designated foreign languages, or other academic majors.

Financial data These scholarships provide payment of full tuition and required educational fees, as well as a specified amount for textbooks, supplies, and equipment. The program also provides a stipend for 10 months of the year that is $250 per month as a freshman, $300 per month as a sophomore, $350 per month as a junior, and $400 per month as a senior.

Duration 4 years.

Additional information Students may apply for either a Navy or Marine Corps option scholarship but not for both. Navy option applicants apply through Navy recruiting offices; Marine Corps applicants apply through Marine Corps recruiting offices. Recipients must also complete 4 years of study in naval science classes as students either at 1 of the 74 colleges, universities, and maritime institutes with NROTC units or at 1 of the approximately 100 institutions with cross-enrollment agreements (in which case they attend their home college for their regular academic courses but attend naval science classes at a nearby school with an NROTC unit). After completing the program, all participants are commissioned as ensigns in the Naval Reserve or second lieutenants in the Marine Corps Reserve with an 8-year service obligation, including 4 years of active duty. Current military personnel who are accepted into this program are released from active duty and are not eligible for active-duty pay and allowances, medical benefits, or other active-duty entitlements.

Number awarded Approximately 2,200 each year; approximately 85% of the scholarships are awarded to students with Tier 1 or 2 majors.

Deadline January of each year.

[300]
NAVY-MARINE CORPS ROTC COLLEGE PROGRAM

U.S. Navy
Attn: Naval Education and Training Command
NSTC OD2
250 Dallas Street, Suite A
Pensacola, FL 32508-5268
(850) 452-4941, ext. 29395
Toll Free: (800) NAV-ROTC, ext. 29395
Fax: (850) 452-2486
E-mail: PNSC_NROTC.scholarship@navy.mil
Web: www.nrotc.navy.mil/scholarships.aspx

Summary To provide financial assistance to lower-division students who are interested in joining Navy ROTC in college.

Eligibility Applicants must be U.S. citizens between the ages of 17 and 21 who are already enrolled as non-scholarship students in naval science courses at a college or university with a Navy ROTC program on campus. They must apply before the spring of their sophomore year. All applications must be submitted through the professors of naval science at the college or university attended.

Financial data Participants in this program receive free naval science textbooks, all required uniforms, and a stipend for 10 months of the year that is $350 per month as a junior and $400 per month as a senior.

Duration 2 or 4 years.

Additional information Following acceptance into the program, participants attend the Naval Science Institute in Newport, Rhode Island for 6 and a half weeks during the summer between their sophomore and junior year. During the summer between their junior and senior year, they participate in an additional training program, usually at sea for Navy midshipmen or at Quantico, Virginia for Marine Corps midshipmen. After graduation from college, they are commissioned ensigns in the Naval Reserve or second lieutenants in the Marine Corps Reserve with an 8-year service obligation, including 3 years of active duty.

Deadline March of each year.

[301]
NCPOA/BART LONGO MEMORIAL SCHOLARSHIPS

National Chief Petty Officers' Association
c/o Marjorie Hays, Treasurer
1014 Ronald Drive
Corpus Christi, TX 78412-3548
Web: www.goatlocker.org/ncpoa/scholarship.htm

Summary To provide financial assistance for college or graduate school to members of the National Chief Petty Officers' Association (NCPOA) and their families.

Eligibility This program is open to members of the NCPOA and the children, stepchildren, and grandchildren of living or deceased members. Applicants may be high school seniors or graduates entering a college or university or students currently enrolled full time as undergraduate or graduate students. Selection is based on academic achievement and participation in extracurricular activities; need is not considered.

Financial data The stipend is $1,000.

Duration 1 year.

Additional information Membership in the NCPOA is limited to men and women who served or are serving as Chief Petty Officers in the U.S. Navy, U.S. Coast Guard, or their Reserve components for at least 30 days.

Number awarded 2 each year: 1 to a high school senior or graduate and 1 to an undergraduate or graduate student.

Deadline May of each year.

[302]
NEBRASKA NATIONAL GUARD TUITION ASSISTANCE PROGRAM

Nebraska Military Department
Attn: Nebraska National Guard
1300 Military Road
Lincoln, NE 68508-1090
(402) 309-7210
Web: www.neguard.com/NMD/tuition/index.html

Summary To provide an opportunity for enlisted members of the Nebraska National Guard to pursue additional education.

Eligibility Eligible for this benefit are members of the Nebraska National Guard who are enrolled in a Nebraska university, college, or community college. Commissioned and warrant officers and enlisted personnel who already have a baccalaureate degree are not eligible. Guard members must apply for this assistance within 10 years of the date of initial enlistment. The credit is not available for graduate study or noncredit courses. Priority is given to Guard members who have previously received these benefits.

Financial data Students at state-supported institutions are exempted from payment of 75% of the tuition charges at their schools. Students at independent, nonprofit, accredited colleges and universities in Nebraska receive a credit equal to the amount they would receive if they attended the University of Nebraska at Lincoln. All funds are paid directly to the school.

Duration 1 year; may be renewed.

Additional information Any member of the Nebraska National Guard who receives this assistance must agree to serve in the Guard for 3 years after completion of the courses for which assistance was given.

Number awarded Up to 1,200 each year.

Deadline June of each year for academic terms beginning between July and September; September of each year for academic terms beginning between October and December; December of each year for academic terms beginning between January and March; March of each year for academic terms beginning between April and June.

[303]
NEBRASKA TUITION CREDIT FOR ACTIVE RESERVISTS

Department of Veterans' Affairs
State Office Building
301 Centennial Mall South, Sixth Floor
P.O. Box 95083
Lincoln, NE 68509-5083
(402) 471-2458   Fax: (402) 471-2491
E-mail: john.hilgert@nebraska.gov
Web: www.vets.state.ne.us/benefits.html

Summary To provide financial assistance for college to members of Nebraska units of the active Reserves.

Eligibility Nebraska residents who are enlisted members of a Nebraska-based unit of the active selected Reserve are eligible for this benefit. They must have at least 2 years remaining on their enlistment, have agreed to serve at least 3 years in the Reserves, not have completed the tenth year of total service in the U.S. armed forces (including active and Reserve time), and be working on a degree at a state-supported college or university or an equivalent level of study in a technical community college.

Financial data Reservists who meet the requirements may receive a credit for 50% of the tuition charges at any state-supported university or college in Nebraska, including any technical community college.

Duration 1 year; may be renewed until receipt of the degree or completion of the course of study.

Number awarded Varies each year; the program is limited to 200 new applications per calendar year.

Deadline Deadline not specified.

[304]
NERA MEMBER SCHOLARSHIPS

Naval Enlisted Reserve Association
Attn: Scholarship Committee
6703 Farragut Avenue
Falls Church, VA 22042-2189
(703) 534-1329   Toll Free: (800) 776-9020
Fax: (703) 534-3617   E-mail: members@nera.org
Web: www.nera.org

Summary To provide financial assistance for college to sea service enlisted Reservists who are also members of the Naval Enlisted Reserve Association (NERA).

Eligibility This program is open to drilling Reservists of the Coast Guard, Navy, and Marines who are regular members of the association. Applicants must be attending an accredited 2- or 4-year college or university as a full- or part-time student. Along with their application, they must submit a 500-word essay on either 1) their career goals and objectives for their education; or 2) why Reservists are important to America. Financial need is not considered in the selection process.

Financial data The stipend is $3,000.

Duration 1 year.

Additional information This program is funded in part by USAA Insurance Corporation.

Number awarded 2 each year.

Deadline June of each year.

[305]
NEVADA NATIONAL GUARD STATE TUITION WAIVER PROGRAM

Nevada National Guard
Attn: Education Officer
2460 Fairview Drive
Carson City, NV 89701-6807
(775) 887-7326   Fax: (775) 887-7279
Web: www.nv.ngb.army.mil/education.cfm

Summary To provide financial assistance to Nevada National Guard members who are interested in attending college or graduate school in the state.

Eligibility This program is open to active members of the Nevada National Guard who are interested in attending a public community college, 4-year college, or university in the state. Applicants must be residents of Nevada. Independent study, correspondence courses, and study at the William S. Boyd School of Law, the University of Nevada School of Medicine, and the UNLV School of Dental Medicine are not eligible.

Financial data This program provides a waiver of 100% of tuition at state-supported community colleges, colleges, or universities in Nevada.

Duration 1 year; may be renewed.

Additional information This program was established on a pilot basis in 2003 and became permanent in 2005. Recipients must attain a GPA of at least 2.0 or refund all tuition received.

Number awarded Varies each year.

Deadline Applications must be received at least 3 weeks prior to the start of classes.

[306]
NEW HAMPSHIRE NATIONAL GUARD TUITION WAIVER PROGRAM

Office of the Adjutant General
Attn: Education Office
State Military Reservation
4 Pembroke Road
Concord, NH 03301-5652
(603) 227-1550   Fax: (603) 225-1257
TDD: (800) 735-2964
E-mail: education@nharmyguard.com
Web: www.nh.ngb.army.mil/members/education

Summary To provide financial assistance to members of the New Hampshire National Guard who are interested in attending college or graduate school in the state.

Eligibility This program is open to active members of the New Hampshire National Guard who have completed advanced individual training or commissioning and have at least a 90% attendance rate at annual training and drill assemblies. Applicants may be working on any type of academic degree at public institutions in New Hampshire. They must apply for financial aid from their school, for the New Hampshire National Guard Scholarship Program, and for federal tuition assistance.

Financial data The program provides full payment of tuition.

Duration 1 year; may be renewed.

Additional information This program began in 1996.

Number awarded Varies each year, depending on availability of space.

Deadline Deadline not specified.

[307]
NEW JERSEY NATIONAL GUARD TUITION PROGRAM

New Jersey Department of Military and Veterans Affairs
Attn: New Jersey Army National Guard Education Center
3650 Saylors Pond Road
Fort Dix, NJ 08640-7600
(609) 562-0654   Toll Free: (888) 859-0352
Fax: (609) 562-0201
Web: www.state.nj.us/military/education/NJNGTP.htm

Summary To provide financial assistance for college or graduate school to New Jersey National Guard members and the surviving spouses and children of deceased members.

Eligibility This program is open to active members of the New Jersey National Guard who have completed Initial Active Duty for Training (IADT). Applicants must be New Jersey residents who have been accepted into a program of undergraduate or graduate study at any of 31 public institutions of higher education in the state. The surviving spouses and children of deceased members of the Guard who had completed IADT and were killed in the performance of their duties while a member of the Guard are also eligible if the school has classroom space available.

Financial data Tuition for up to 15 credits per semester is waived for full-time recipients in state-supported colleges or community colleges in New Jersey.

Duration 1 semester; may be renewed.

Number awarded Varies each year.

Deadline Deadline not specified.

[308]
NEW MEXICO NATIONAL GUARD TUITION SCHOLARSHIP PROGRAM

New Mexico National Guard
Attn: Education Services Officer
47 Bataan Boulevard
Santa Fe, NM 87508
(505) 474-1245   Fax: (505) 474-1243
E-mail: EducationNM@nm.ngb.army.mil
Web: https://www.nm.ngb.army.mil/education.html

Summary To provide financial assistance to members of the New Mexico National Guard who are working on an undergraduate degree at a school in the state.

Eligibility This program is open to members of the New Mexico National Guard who are working on their first degree at the undergraduate or vocational school level. Applicants must be attending a state-supported school in New Mexico.

Financial data This program provides payment of 100% of the cost of tuition, including instructional fees in lieu of tuition and laboratory shop fees that are specifically required.

Duration 1 semester; may be renewed for up to 130 semester hours of undergraduate or vocational study.

Number awarded Varies each year, depending on the availability of funds.

Deadline June of each year for fall semester; November of each year for spring semester; April of each year for summer school.

[309]
NEW YORK RECRUITMENT INCENTIVE AND RETENTION PROGRAM

New York State Division of Military and Naval Affairs
Attn: New York National Guard Education Office
NYARNG MNP-ED
1 Buffington Street, Building 25
Watervliet, NY 12189-4000
(518) 272-4051   E-mail: education@ny.ngb.army.mil
Web: dmna.ny.gov/education/education.php?page=rirp

Summary To provide financial assistance to members of the New York State Military Forces who are interested in attending college in the state.

Eligibility This program is open to members of the New York Army National Guard, New York Air National Guard, and New York Naval Militia in good military and academic standing. Applicants must have been enrolled in a degree program for a minimum of 6 credit hours per semester, have been legal residents of New York for at least 186 days prior to using the program for the first time and 186 days per year (excluding periods of active federal service), and be enrolled in their first baccalaureate degree program. They must have completed Initial Active Duty for Training (IADT), naval enlisted code (NEC) training, or a commissioning program.

Financial data The program pays for the cost of tuition (up to $4,350 or the maximum cost of the State University of New York undergraduate tuition) for credit bearing courses, or courses that are required as a prerequisite within the declared degree program.

Duration Up to 8 semesters of full-time study, or the equivalent of 4 academic years, are supported; if the undergraduate program normally requires 5 academic years of full-time study, then this program will support 10 semesters of full-time study or the equivalent of 5 academic years. For part-time (from 6 to 11 semester hours per semester) study, the program provides up to 16 semesters of support.

Additional information This program became effective in 1997.

Number awarded Varies each year.

Deadline August of each year for fall semester; December of each year for spring semester.

[310]
NHA ACTIVE DUTY SCHOLARSHIPS

Naval Helicopter Association
Attn: Scholarship Fund
P.O. Box 180578
Coronado, CA 92178-0578
(619) 435-7139   Fax: (619) 435-7354
Web: nhascholarshipfund.org/scholarships-available.html

Summary To provide money for college or graduate school to active-duty and former personnel who are working or have worked in rotary wing activities of the sea services.

Eligibility This program is open to active-duty or former Navy, Marine Corps, or Coast Guard rotary wing aviators, aircrewmen, or support personnel. Applicants must be working on or planning to work on an undergraduate or graduate degree in any field. Along with their application, they must submit a personal statement on their academic and career aspirations. Selection is based on that statement, academic proficiency, scholastic achievements and awards, extracurricular activities, employment history, and recommendations.

Financial data Stipends are approximately $2,000.

Duration 1 year.

Number awarded 4 each year: 2 to undergraduates and 2 to graduate students.

Deadline February of each year.

[311]
NORTH CAROLINA NATIONAL GUARD ASSOCIATION SCHOLARSHIPS

North Carolina National Guard Association
Attn: Educational Foundation, Inc.
7410 Chapel Hill Road
Raleigh, NC 27607-5047
(919) 851-3390   Toll Free: (800) 821-6159 (within NC)
Fax: (919) 859-4990
E-mail: peggyncngaef@bellsouth.net
Web: ncnga.org

Summary To provide financial assistance to members and dependents of members of the North Carolina National Guard Association who plan to attend college in any state.

Eligibility This program is open to active and associate members of the association as well as the spouses, children, grandchildren, and legal dependents of active, associate, or deceased members. Applicants must be high school seniors, high school graduates, or students currently enrolled at a college or university in any state. Selection is based on financial need, academic achievement, citizenship, leadership, and other application information. The most outstanding applicants receive scholarships provided by the SECU Foundation. Applicants who meet specified additional requirements qualify for various memorial and special scholarships.

Financial data Stipends are $10,000 or $5,000 for the SECU Foundation Scholarships, $1,000 for memorial and special scholarships, $1,000 for citizenship awards, $800 for general scholarships, or $400 for community college scholarships.

Duration 1 year; may be renewed.

Additional information This program, which began in 1968, includes a number of named memorial and special scholarships. Other scholarships are funded by the SECU Foundation of the State Employees' Credit Union and the USAA Insurance Corporation. The association also funds the Academic Excellence Leadership Award ($1,000) for outstanding applicants and the Special Population Scholarship ($1,000) for applicants with disabilities.

Number awarded Varies each year; recently, 37 of these scholarships were awarded: 2 SECU Foundation Scholarships (1 at $10,000 and 1 at $5,000), 18 memorial and special scholarships at $1,000, 2 citizenship awards are $1,000, 10 general scholarships at $800, and 5 community college scholarships at $400.

Deadline January of each year for high school graduates and college students; February for high school seniors.

[312]
NORTH CAROLINA NATIONAL GUARD TUITION ASSISTANCE PROGRAM

North Carolina National Guard
Attn: Education Services Office
4105 Reedy Creek Road
Raleigh, NC 27607-6410
(919) 664-6272   Toll Free: (800) 621-4136
Fax: (919) 664-6520   E-mail: nceso@ng.army.mil
Web: www.nc.ngb.army.mil

Summary To provide financial assistance to members of the North Carolina National Guard who plan to attend college or graduate school in the state.

Eligibility This program is open to active members of the North Carolina National Guard (officer, warrant officer, or enlisted) who have at least 2 years of enlistment remaining after the end of the academic period for which tuition assistance is provided. Applicants must be enrolled in an eligible business or trade school, private institution, or public college/ university in North Carolina. They may be working on a vocational, undergraduate, graduate, or doctoral degree.

Financial data The maximum stipend is based on the highest tuition and fees at the University of North Carolina at Chapel Hill; recently, that was $5,396 for undergraduates or $6,692 for graduate students.

Duration 1 year; may be renewed.

Number awarded Varies each year.

Deadline Deadline not specified.

[313]
NORTH DAKOTA NATIONAL GUARD ENLISTED ASSOCIATION SCHOLARSHIPS

North Dakota National Guard Enlisted Association
c/o MSG Joe Lovelace
4900 107th Avenue S.E.
Minot, ND 58701-9207
E-mail: joseph.m.lovelace@us.army.mil
Web: www.ndngea.org

Summary To provide financial assistance to members of the North Dakota National Guard Enlisted Association (NDNGEA) and their families who are interested in attending college in any state.

Eligibility This program is open to association members who have at least 1 year remaining on their enlistment or have completed 20 or more years in service. Also eligible are their unmarried dependent children and spouses and the unremarried spouses and unmarried dependent children of deceased NDNGEA members who were in good standing at the time of death. Applicants must be attending or planning to attend a university, college, or trade/business school in any state. Graduate students are not eligible. Selection is based on academic achievement, leadership, character, and financial need.

Financial data The stipend is $1,000. Funds are sent directly to the school in the recipient's name.

Duration 1 year.

Number awarded 1 or more each year.

Deadline November of each year.

[314]
NORTH DAKOTA NATIONAL GUARD FEE WAIVER

North Dakota University System
Attn: Director of Financial Aid
State Capitol, Tenth Floor
600 East Boulevard Avenue, Department 215
Bismarck, ND 58505-0230
(701) 328-4114   Fax: (701) 328-2961
E-mail: nathan.stratton@ndus.edu
Web: www.ndus.edu/students/military-veterans-families

Summary To waive tuition and fees for members of the National Guard at public institutions in North Dakota.

Eligibility Eligible for this benefit are members of the North Dakota National Guard who meet the limitations and rules established by the Guard. Applicants must be attending or planning to attend a public college or university in North Dakota.

Financial data Qualified members are entitled to a waiver of all tuition and fees (except fees charged to retire outstanding bonds).

Duration 1 academic year; renewable.

Number awarded Varies each year.

Deadline Deadline not specified.

[315]
NORTH DAKOTA NATIONAL GUARD TUITION ASSISTANCE PROGRAM

North Dakota National Guard
Attn: Education Services Office
P.O. Box 5511
Bismarck, ND 58506-5511
(701) 333-3064   E-mail: ngndj1esos@ng.army.mil
Web: www.ndguard.ngb.army.mil

Summary To provide financial assistance to members of the North Dakota National Guard who plan to attend college or graduate school in the state.

Eligibility This program is open to members of the North Dakota National Guard who have a record of satisfactory participation (no more than 9 unexcused absences in the past 12 months) and service remaining after completion of the class for which they are requesting assistance. Applicants must be seeking support for trade or vocational training or work on an associate, baccalaureate, or graduate degree. They must be attending or planning to attend a North Dakota higher education public institution or a participating private institution (currently, Jamestown College, University of Mary in Bismarck, MedCenter One College of Nursing, Rasmussen College, or Trinity Bible College). Full-time AGR personnel do not qualify for this program. This is an entitlement program, provided all requirements are met.

Financial data Participating colleges and universities waive 25% of tuition for eligible courses (undergraduate only), up to 25% of the tuition at the University of North Dakota. Through this program, the National Guard provides reimbursement of the remaining 75% of tuition for eligible courses (undergraduate and graduate), or up to 75% of the tuition at the University of North Dakota. The program also reimburses 100% of all regular fees, not to exceed 100% of the regular fees charged by the University of North Dakota. State reimbursements are paid directly to the student in the form of a check, based upon the number of credit hours successfully completed.

Duration Benefits are available for up to 144 semester credit hours or the completion of an undergraduate or graduate degree, provided the recipient earns a grade of "C" or higher in each undergraduate course or "B" or higher in each graduate course.

Number awarded Varies each year.

Deadline Applications should be submitted at least 30 days before the semester begins.

[316]
NUCLEAR PROPULSION OFFICER CANDIDATE (NUPOC) PROGRAM

U.S. Navy
Attn: Navy Personnel Command
5722 Integrity Drive
Millington, TN 38054-5057
(901) 874-3070   Toll Free: (888) 633-9674
Fax: (901) 874-2651
E-mail: nukeprograms@cnrc.navy.mil
Web: www.cnrc.navy.mil

Summary To provide financial assistance to college juniors and seniors who wish to serve in the Navy's nuclear propulsion training program following graduation.

Eligibility This program is open to U.S. citizens who are entering their junior or senior year of college as a full-time student. Strong technical majors (mathematics, physics, chemistry, or an engineering field) are encouraged. Applicants must have completed at least 1 year of calculus and 1 year of physics and must have earned a grade of "C" or better in all mathematics, science, and technical courses. Normally, they must be 26 years of age or younger at the expected date of commissioning, although applicants for the design and research specialty may be up to 29 years old.

Financial data Participants become Active Reserve enlisted Navy personnel and receive a salary of up to $2,500 per month; the exact amount depends on the local cost of living and other factors. A bonus of $10,000 is also paid at the time of enlistment and another $2,000 upon completion of nuclear power training.

Duration Up to 30 months, until completion of a bachelor's degree.

Additional information Following graduation, participants attend Officer Candidate School in Pensacola, Florida for 4 months and receive their commissions. They have a service obligation of 8 years (of which at least 5 years must be on active duty), beginning with 6 months at the Navy Nuclear Power Training Command in Charleston, South Carolina and 6 more months of hands-on training at a nuclear reactor facility.

Number awarded Varies each year.

Deadline Deadline not specified.

[317]
NUCLEAR (SUBMARINE AND SURFACE) OPTION OF THE SEAMAN TO ADMIRAL-21 PROGRAM

U.S. Navy
Attn: Commander, Naval Service Training Command
250 Dallas Street, Suite A
Pensacola, FL 32508-5268
(850) 452-9433   Fax: (850) 452-2486
E-mail: PNSC_STA21@navy.mil
Web: www.sta-21.navy.mil

Summary To allow outstanding enlisted Navy personnel to complete a bachelor's degree and receive a commission in the nuclear officer community.

Eligibility This program is open to U.S. citizens who are currently serving on active duty in the U.S. Navy or Naval Reserve, including Full Time Support (FTS), Selected Reserves (SELRES), and Navy Reservists on active duty, except for those on active duty for training (ACDUTRA). Only personnel currently enrolled in the Naval Nuclear Power School or Naval Nuclear Power Training Unit or assigned there as staff pickup instructors or sea returnee instructors are eligible. Applicants must be high school graduates (or GED recipients) who are able to complete requirements for a baccalaureate degree in 36 months or less. When they complete their degree requirements, they must be younger than 26 years of age. Sea returnee staff instructors must finish prior to their 31st birthday. Applicants must have taken the SAT or ACT within the past 3 years and achieved a score of 1140 or higher on the new SAT or 50 or higher on the ACT. Their proposed college major must be in a technical area. The program is open to men and women, but women are not assigned to submarines.

Financial data Awardees continue to receive their regular Navy pay and allowances while they attend college on a full-time basis. They also receive reimbursement for tuition, fees, and books up to $10,000 per year. If base housing is available, they are eligible to live there. Participants are not eligible to receive benefits under the Navy's Tuition Assistance Program (TA), the Montgomery GI Bill (MGIB), the Navy College Fund, or the Veterans Educational Assistance Program (VEAP).

Duration Selectees are supported for up to 36 months of full-time, year-round study or completion of a bachelor's degree, as long as they maintain a GPA of 3.0 or higher.

Additional information This program was established in 2001 as a replacement for the Nuclear Enlisted Commissioning Program (NECP). Upon acceptance into the program, selectees attend the Naval Science Institute (NSI) in Newport, Rhode Island for an 8-week program in the fundamental core concepts of being a naval officer (navigation, engineering, weapons, military history and justice, etc.). They then enter 1 of 18 universities with an NROTC nuclear unit (University of Arizona, Auburn University, The Citadel, University of Idaho, University of Illinois, University of Kansas, University of New Mexico, North Carolina State University, Oregon State University, Pennsylvania State University, Purdue University, Southern University and A&M College, SUNY Maritime College, University of South Carolina, University of Texas, University of Utah, University of Washington, or University of Wisconsin) to work full time on a bachelor's degree. They become members of and drill with the NROTC unit. When they complete their degree, they are commissioned as ensigns in the United States Naval Reserve and assigned to initial training for their nuclear officer community. After commissioning, participants incur an active-duty obligation of 5 years.

Number awarded Varies each year.

Deadline June of each year.

[318]
NURSE CORPS OPTION OF THE SEAMAN TO ADMIRAL-21 PROGRAM

U.S. Navy
Attn: Commander, Naval Service Training Command
250 Dallas Street, Suite A
Pensacola, FL 32508-5268
(850) 452-9433 Fax: (850) 452-2486
E-mail: PNSC_STA21@navy.mil
Web: www.sta-21.navy.mil

Summary To allow outstanding enlisted Navy personnel to complete a bachelor's degree and receive a commission in the Nurse Corps.

Eligibility This program is open to U.S. citizens who are currently serving on active duty in the U.S. Navy or Naval Reserve, including Full Time Support (FTS), Selected Reserves (SELRES), and Navy Reservists on active duty, except for those on active duty for training (ACDUTRA). Applicants must be high school graduates (or GED recipients) who are able to complete requirements for a baccalaureate degree in nursing in 36 months or less. They must have completed at least 30 semester units in undergraduate nursing prerequisite courses with a GPA of 2.5 or higher. They must be at least 18 years of age and able to complete degree requirements and be commissioned prior to age 42. Within the past 3 years, they must have taken the SAT (and achieved scores of at least 500 on the mathematics section and 500 on the critical reading section) or the ACT (and achieved a score of 41 or higher, including at least 21 on the mathematics portion and 20 on the English portion).

Financial data Awardees continue to receive their regular Navy pay and allowances while they attend college on a full-time basis. They also receive reimbursement for tuition, fees, and books up to $10,000 per year. If base housing is available, they are eligible to live there. Participants are not eligible to receive benefits under the Navy's Tuition Assistance Program (TA), the Montgomery GI Bill (MGIB), the Navy College Fund, or the Veterans Educational Assistance Program (VEAP).

Duration Selectees are supported for up to 36 months of full-time, year-round study or completion of a bachelor's degree, as long as they maintain a GPA of 2.5 or higher.

Additional information This program was established in 2001 as a replacement for the Fleet Accession to Naval Reserve Officer Training Corps (NROTC) Nurse Option. Upon acceptance into the program, selectees attend the Naval Science Institute (NSI) in Newport, Rhode Island for an 8-week program in the fundamental core concepts of being a naval officer (navigation, engineering, weapons, military history and justice, etc.). They then enter an NROTC affiliated college or university with a nursing program that confers an accredited baccalaureate degree in nursing to pursue full-time study. They become members of and drill with the NROTC unit. When they complete their bachelor's degree in nursing, they are commissioned as ensigns in the United States Naval Reserve and assigned to initial training as an officer in the Nurse Corps. After commissioning, 5 years of active service are required.

Number awarded Varies each year.

Deadline June of each year.

[319]
OCEANOGRAPHY OPTION OF THE SEAMAN TO ADMIRAL-21 PROGRAM

U.S. Navy
Attn: Commander, Naval Service Training Command
250 Dallas Street, Suite A
Pensacola, FL 32508-5268
(850) 452-9433   Fax: (850) 452-2486
E-mail: PNSC_STA21@navy.mil
Web: www.sta-21.navy.mil

Summary   To allow outstanding enlisted Navy personnel to complete a bachelor's degree and receive a commission as an oceanography officer.

Eligibility   This program is open to U.S. citizens who are currently serving on active duty in the U.S. Navy or Naval Reserve, including Full Time Support (FTS), Selected Reserves (SELRES), and Navy Reservists on active duty, except for those on active duty for training (ACDUTRA). Applicants must be at least 18 years of age and high school graduates (or GED recipients) who are able to complete requirements for a baccalaureate degree in 36 months or less. They must be planning to work on a degree in physical science, meteorology, or physical oceanography; other related fields may be considered, as long as the applicant possesses strong analytical ability and good communication skills (both oral and written). When they complete their degree requirements, they must be younger than 35 years of age. Within the past 3 years, they must have taken the SAT (and achieved scores of at least 500 on the mathematics section and 500 on the critical reading section) or the ACT (and achieved a score of 41 or higher, including at least 21 on the mathematics portion and 20 on the English portion).

Financial data   Awardees continue to receive their regular Navy pay and allowances while they attend college on a full-time basis. They also receive reimbursement for tuition, fees, and books up to $10,000 per year. If base housing is available, they are eligible to live there. Participants are not eligible to receive benefits under the Navy's Tuition Assistance Program (TA), the Montgomery GI Bill (MGIB), the Navy College Fund, or the Veterans Educational Assistance Program (VEAP).

Duration   Selectees are supported for up to 36 months of full-time, year-round study or completion of a bachelor's degree, as long as they maintain a GPA of 2.5 or higher.

Additional information   Upon acceptance into the program, selectees attend the Naval Science Institute (NSI) in Newport, Rhode Island for an 8-week program in the fundamental core concepts of being a naval officer (navigation, engineering, weapons, military history and justice, etc.). They then enter a college or university with an NROTC unit or affiliation to work full time on a bachelor's degree. They become members of and drill with the NROTC unit. When they complete their degree, they are commissioned as ensigns in the United States Naval Reserve and assigned to initial training within the oceanography community. After commissioning, 5 years of active service are required.

Number awarded   Varies each year.

Deadline   June of each year.

[320]
OHIO NATIONAL GUARD ASSOCIATION LEADERSHIP GRANTS

Ohio National Guard Association
Attn: Leadership Grant Committee
1299 Virginia Avenue
P.O. Box 8070
Columbus, OH 43201
Toll Free: (800) 642-6642
E-mail: ONGAKoper@prodigy.net
Web: ohionga.org/scholarship.html

Summary   To provide financial assistance to members of the Ohio National Guard Association (ONGA) and their families who are interested in attending college in any state.

Eligibility   This program is open to active members (either officers or warrant officers) of the ONGA and the dependents of active, life, retired, or deceased members. Applicants must be enrolled or planning to enroll at a college or university in any state. Along with their application, they must submit transcripts, SAT/ACT scores, and a 2-page essay explaining why they should be selected to receive a grant. Selection is based on grades, future plans, membership and leadership, honors and awards, need, and overall impression.

Financial data   A stipend is awarded (amount not specified).

Duration   1 year; nonrenewable.

Additional information   This program began in 1996.

Number awarded   Varies each year; recently, 5 of these grants were awarded.

Deadline   November of each year.

[321]
OHIO NATIONAL GUARD SCHOLARSHIP PROGRAM

Adjutant General's Department
Attn: ONG Scholarship Program Office
2825 West Dublin Granville Road
Columbus, OH 43235-2789
(614) 336-7032   Toll Free: (888) 400-6484
Fax: (614) 336-7318   E-mail: ongsp@ongsp.org
Web: www.ongsp.org

Summary   To provide financial assistance to members of the Ohio National Guard interested in working on a college degree.

Eligibility   This program is open to members of the Ohio Army and Air National Guard attending a 2- or 4-year public college or university in the state. Applicants must commit to and/or complete a 6-year enlistment in the Ohio Guard. New enlistees must complete basic training and obtain a military job skill.

Financial data   The program covers 100% of the tuition and general fee charges at state-assisted 2- and 4-year colleges and universities in Ohio or an equivalent sum at private and proprietary institutions.

Duration   The grant is limited to 12 quarters or 8 semesters and participants must remain enrolled as a full-time undergraduate student for that time. Enrollment in the institution of higher education must begin not later than 12 months after the completion of Initial Active Duty for Training (IADT), or date of reenlistment, or date of extension of current enlistment.

Additional information   This program began in 1999. Grant assistance is not available for an additional baccalaureate degree, for postgraduate courses, or for courses not applicable to a degree.

Number awarded Grants are limited to the annual average student load of 4,000 full-time equivalent students per term.

Deadline June for fall term; October for winter quarter or spring semester; January for spring quarter; and March for summer term.

[322]
OKLAHOMA NATIONAL GUARD TUITION WAIVER PROGRAM

Oklahoma State Regents for Higher Education
Attn: Director of Scholarship and Grant Programs
655 Research Parkway, Suite 200
P.O. Box 108850
Oklahoma City, OK 73101-8850
(405) 225-9239   Toll Free: (800) 858-1840
Fax: (405) 225-9230   E-mail: studentinfo@osrhe.edu
Web: www.okcollegestart.org

Summary To provide financial assistance to members of the Oklahoma National Guard who plan to attend college in the state.

Eligibility This program is open to current members in good standing of the Oklahoma National Guard who do not have any other baccalaureate or graduate degree. Applicants must be attending or planning to attend a state-supported college or university in Oklahoma to work on an associate or baccalaureate degree. They must have submitted a plan for completion of their degree to the Guard. Courses leading to a certification, continuing education courses, and career technology courses that are not counted towards a degree at another institution are not covered.

Financial data Under this program, all tuition is waived.

Duration 1 year; may be renewed as long as the Guard member remains in good standing both in the unit and in the college or university, to a maximum of 6 years from the date of first application.

Number awarded Varies each year.

Deadline Deadline not specified.

[323]
ONGEA SCHOLARSHIP PROGRAM

Ohio National Guard Enlisted Association
Attn: Scholarship Chair
1299 Virginia Avenue
Columbus, OH 43212
(740) 574-5932   Toll Free: (800) 642-6642
Fax: (614) 486-2216   E-mail: ongea@juno.com
Web: www.ongea.org/12.html

Summary To provide financial assistance to members of the Ohio National Guard Enlisted Association (ONGEA) and children of members of the ONGEA Auxiliary who are interested in attending college in any state.

Eligibility This program is open to 1) children of ONGEA and ONGEA Auxiliary members (ONGEA member spouses must be Auxiliary members in order for a child to be eligible); 2) unmarried dependent children of deceased ONGEA and ONGEA Auxiliary members who were in good standing the time of their death; and 3) ONGEA members (if married, the spouse must also be a member of the Auxiliary). Applicants must be enrolling as full-time undergraduate students at a

college, university, trade school, or business school in any state. Selection is based on academic record, character, leadership, and financial need.

Financial data Stipends are $1,000 or $500. After verification of enrollment is provided, checks are sent to the recipient and made out to the recipient's school.

Duration 1 year; nonrenewable.

Additional information This program is sponsored jointly by ONGEA, the ONGEA Auxiliary, USAA Insurance Corporation, and the First Cleveland Cavalry Association.

Number awarded 5 to 10 each year, depending upon the availability of funds.

Deadline March of each year.

[324]
ORNGA SCHOLARSHIPS

Oregon National Guard Association
Attn: Scholarship Committee
1776 Militia Way, S.E.
P.O. Box 14350
Salem, OR 97309-5047
(503) 584-3456   Fax: (503) 584-3052
E-mail: info@ornga.org
Web: www.ornga.org/scholar_about.htm

Summary To provide financial assistance to members of the Oregon National Guard, the Oregon National Guard Association (ORNGA), and their children and spouses who are interested in attending college in any state.

Eligibility This program is open to active members of the Oregon Army and Air National Guard, members of the ORNGA, and their children and spouses. Applicants must be high school seniors, graduates, or GED recipients and interested in working on an undergraduate degree at a college, university, or trade school in any state. The parent, spouse, or applicant must have an ETS date beyond the end of the academic year for which the scholarship is used. Selection is based on demonstrated qualities of leadership, civic action, and academic achievement.

Financial data The stipend is $1,500.

Duration 1 year.

Number awarded 10 each year.

Deadline February of each year.

[325]
PAT TILLMAN MILITARY SCHOLARS PROGRAM

Pat Tillman Foundation
2121 South Mill Avenue, Suite 214
Tempe, AZ 85282
(480) 621-4074   Fax: (480) 621-4075
E-mail: scholarships@pattillmanfoundation.org
Web: www.pattillmanfoundation.org/tillman-military-scholars

Summary To provide financial assistance to veterans, active servicemembers, and their spouses who are interested in working on an undergraduate or graduate degree.

Eligibility This program is open to veterans and active servicemembers of all branches of the armed forces from both the pre- and post-September 11 era and their spouses; children are not eligible. Applicants must be enrolled or planning to enroll full time at a 4-year public or private college or university to work on an undergraduate, graduate, or postgraduate degree. Current and former servicemembers must submit 400-word essays on 1) their motivation and decision to serve in the U.S. military and how that decision and experience has changed their life and ambitions; and 2) their educational and career goals, how they will incorporate their military service experience into those goals, and how they intend to continue their service to others and the community. Spouses must submit 400-word essays on 1) their previous service to others and the community; and 2) their educational and career goals, how they will incorporate their service experiences and the impact of their spouse's military service into those goals, and how they intend to continue their service to others and the community. Selection is based on those essays, educational and career ambitions, record of military service, record of personal achievement, demonstration of service to others in the community, desire to continue such service, and leadership potential.

Financial data The stipend depends on the need of the recipient and the availability of funds.

Duration 1 year; may be renewed, provided the recipient maintains a GPA of 3.0 or higher, remains enrolled full time, and participates in civic action or community service.

Additional information This program began in 2009.

Number awarded Varies each year; recently, 60 students received a total of $916,000 through this program.

Deadline March of each year.

[326]
PENNSYLVANIA NATIONAL GUARD EDUCATIONAL ASSISTANCE PROGRAM

Pennsylvania Higher Education Assistance Agency
Attn: Special Programs
1200 North Seventh Street
P.O. Box 8157
Harrisburg, PA 17105-8157
(717) 720-2800   Toll Free: (800) 692-7392
Fax: (717) 720-5786   TDD: (800) 654-5988
Web: www.pheaa.org

Summary To provide money for college or graduate school to Pennsylvania National Guard members.

Eligibility This program is open to active members of the Pennsylvania National Guard who are Pennsylvania residents and serving as enlisted personnel, warrant officers, or commissioned officers of any grade. Applicants must accept an obligation to serve in the Pennsylvania National Guard for a period of 6 years from the date of entry into the program. Students who do not possess a baccalaureate degree must be enrolled full or part time in an approved program of education at an approved institution of higher learning in Pennsylvania. Master's degree students are supported on a part-time basis only. Guard members receiving an ROTC scholarship of any type are not eligible.

Financial data Full-time undergraduate students receive payment of 100% of tuition at a state-owned university. Part-time students receive either actual tuition charged or two-thirds of the full-time tuition charged to a Pennsylvania resident at a state-owned university, whichever is less. Graduate students receive either half the actual tuition charged or one-third of the full-time tuition charged to a Pennsylvania resident at a state-owned university, whichever is less. Recipients who fail to fulfill the service obligation must repay all funds received within 10 years, including interest at 7%.

Duration Up to 5 years.

Additional information This program, first offered in 1997, is jointly administered by the Pennsylvania Department of Military and Veterans Affairs and the Pennsylvania Higher Education Assistance Agency. Support for summer and graduate school is available only if funding permits.

Number awarded Varies each year; recently, 1,789 members of the Pennsylvania National Guard were enrolled in this program.

Deadline April of each year for students at colleges, universities, and transferable programs at community colleges; July of each year for students at business schools, trade/technical schools, hospital schools of nursing, and nontransferable programs at community colleges.

[327]
PILOT OPTION OF THE SEAMAN TO ADMIRAL-21 PROGRAM

U.S. Navy
Attn: Commander, Naval Service Training Command
250 Dallas Street, Suite A
Pensacola, FL 32508-5268
(850) 452-9433   Fax: (850) 452-2486
E-mail: PNSC_STA21@navy.mil
Web: www.sta-21.navy.mil

Summary To allow outstanding enlisted Navy personnel to complete a bachelor's degree and receive a commission as a pilot.

Eligibility This program is open to U.S. citizens who are currently serving on active duty in the U.S. Navy or Naval Reserve, including Full Time Support (FTS), Selected Reserves (SELRES), and Navy Reservists on active duty, except for those on active duty for training (ACDUTRA). Applicants must be high school graduates (or GED recipients) who are at least 19 years of age and able to complete requirements for a baccalaureate degree in 36 months or less. When they complete their degree requirements, they must be younger than 27 years of age (may be adjusted to 29 years of age for prior active-duty service). Within the past 3 years, they must have taken the SAT (and achieved scores of at least 500 on the mathematics section and 500 on the critical reading section) or the ACT (and achieved a score of 41 or higher, including at least 21 on the mathematics portion and 20 on the English portion). They must also achieve a score of at least the following: AQR (4), PFAR (5) on the Pilot Flight Aptitude Rating (PFAR) portions of the Aviation Selection Test Battery.

Financial data Awardees continue to receive their regular Navy pay and allowances while they attend college on a full-time basis. They also receive reimbursement for tuition, fees, and books up to $10,000 per year. If base housing is available, they are eligible to live there. Participants are not eligible to receive benefits under the Navy's Tuition Assistance Program (TA), the Montgomery GI Bill (MGIB), the Navy College Fund, or the Veterans Educational Assistance Program (VEAP).

Duration Selectees are supported for up to 36 months of full-time, year-round study or completion of a bachelor's degree, as long as they maintain a GPA of 2.5 or higher.

Additional information This program was established in 2001 as a replacement for the Aviation Enlisted Commissioning Program (AECP). Upon acceptance into the program, selectees attend the Naval Science Institute (NSI) in Newport, Rhode Island for an 8-week program in the fundamental core concepts of being a naval officer (navigation, engineering, weapons, military history and justice, etc.). They then enter a college or university with an NROTC unit or affiliation to work full time on a bachelor's degree. They become members of and drill with the NROTC unit. When they complete their degree, they are commissioned as ensigns in the United States Naval Reserve and assigned to flight training. After commissioning, participants incur an active-duty obligation of 8 years after designation as a Naval Aviator or 6 years from the date of disenrollment from flight training.

Number awarded Varies each year.

Deadline June of each year.

[328]
PLATOON LEADERS CLASS MARINE CORPS TUITION ASSISTANCE PROGRAM

U.S. Marine Corps
Attn: Marine Corps Recruiting Command
3280 Russell Road
Quantico, VA 22134-5103
(703) 784-9449   Fax: (703) 784-9859
E-mail: wendelrf@mcrc.usmc.mil
Web: www.usmc.mil

Summary To provide financial assistance to members of the Marine Corps Reserves interested in working on a bachelor's or law degree.

Eligibility This program is open to members of the Marine Corps Reserves enrolled full time in a bachelor's or law (J.D. or equivalent) degree program. Applicants must be a member of the Marine Corps Platoon Leader Class (PLC) Program and have completed 6 weeks (or more) of military training required by that program. They must agree to accept a commission in the active-duty Marine Corps and serve 5 years following completion of their degree.

Financial data This program provides reimbursement of tuition, books, and required fees, up to a maximum of $5,200 per academic year. If participants are also members of the Marine Corps Reserves, they may use any Montgomery GI Bill benefits to which they are entitled.

Duration Up to 3 consecutive years, or completion of a bachelor's or law degree.

Additional information Participants who successfully obtain a bachelor's or law degree and complete officer candidate training are commissioned as second lieutenants in the Regular Marine Corps. This program began in 1999.

Number awarded Up to 1,200 each year.

Deadline December of each year.

[329]
PNGAS SCHOLARSHIP FUND

Pennsylvania National Guard Associations
Attn: Pennsylvania National Guard Scholarship Fund
Biddle Hall (Building 9-109)
Fort Indiantown Gap
Annville, PA 17003-5002
(717) 865-9631   Toll Free: (800) 997-8885
Fax: (717) 861-5560   E-mail: oswalddean@aol.com
Web: www.pngas.net

Summary To provide funding to Pennsylvania National Guard members and the children of disabled or deceased members who are interested in attending college in any state.

Eligibility This program is open to active members of the Pennsylvania Army or Air National Guard. Children of members of the Guard who died or were permanently disabled while on Guard duty are also eligible. Applicants must be entering their first year of higher education as a full-time student or presently attending a college or vocational school in any state as a full-time student. Along with their application, they must submit an essay that outlines their military and civilian plans for the future. Selection is based on that essay, academics, leadership, and contributions to citizenship.

Financial data Stipends range from $500 to $2,000.

Duration 1 year.

Additional information The sponsoring organization includes the National Guard Association of Pennsylvania (NGAP) and the Pennsylvania National Guard Enlisted Association (PNGEA). This program, which began in 1977, includes the following named scholarships: the BG Richard E. Thorn Memorial Scholarship, the Murtha Memorial Scholarship, the BG Hugh S. Niles Memorial Scholarship, the PNGEA USAA Scholarship (sponsored by USAA Insurance), and the 28th Infantry Division Scholarship.

Number awarded Varies each year; recently, 13 of these scholarships were awarded: 2 at $2,000, 1 at $1,500, 1 at $1,000, and 9 at $500.

Deadline June of each year.

[330]
POST-9/11 GI BILL

Department of Veterans Affairs
Attn: Veterans Benefits Administration
810 Vermont Avenue, N.W.
Washington, DC 20420
(202) 418-4343   Toll Free: (888) GI-BILL1
Web: www.gibill.va.gov/benefits/post_911_gibill/index.html

Summary To provide funding to veterans or military personnel who entered service on or after September 11, 2001.

Eligibility This program is open to current and former military personnel who 1) served on active duty for at least 90 aggregate days after September 11, 2001; or 2) were discharged with a service-connected disability after 30 days. Applicants must be planning to enroll in an educational program, including work on an undergraduate or graduate degree, vocational/technical training, on-the-job training, flight training, correspondence training, licensing and national testing programs, and tutorial assistance.

Financial data Participants working on an undergraduate or graduate degree at public institutions in their state receive full payment of tuition and fees. For participants who attend private institutions in most states, tuition and fee reimbursement is capped at $17,500 per academic year; the reimbursement rate is higher at private schools in Arizona, Michigan, New Hampshire, New York, Pennsylvania, South Carolina, and Texas. Benefits for other types of training programs depend on the amount for which the veteran qualified under prior educational programs. Veterans also receive a monthly housing allowance based on the national average Basic Allowance for Housing (BAH) for an E-5 with dependents (currently $673.50) or $1,347 per month at schools in foreign countries; an annual book allowance of $1,000; and (for participants who live in a rural county remote from an educational institution) a rural benefit payment of $500 per year.

Duration Most participants receive up to 36 months of entitlement under this program. Benefits are payable for up to 15 years following release from active duty.

Additional information This program, referred to as Chapter 33, began in 2009 as a replacement for previous educational programs for veterans and military personnel (e.g., Montgomery GI Bill, REAP). Current participants in those programs may be able to transfer benefits from those programs to this new plan. To qualify for 100% of Post 9/11-GI Bill benefits, transferees must have at least 36 months of active-duty service. Transferees with less service are entitled to smaller percentages of benefits, ranging down to 40% for those with only 90 days of service.

Number awarded Varies each year; since the program began, it has awarded nearly $4 billion in benefits to more than 295,000 veterans.

Deadline Deadline not specified.

[331]
RANGER MEMORIAL SCHOLARSHIPS

National Ranger Memorial Foundation
Attn: Executive Secretary
P.O. Box 53369
Fort Benning, GA 31995
(706) 687-0906   E-mail: rangermemorial@gmail.com
Web: rangermemorial.com/scholarship_application.aspx

Summary To provide money for college to current and former U.S. Army Rangers and their descendants.

Eligibility This program is open to Rangers from any era and their descendants; awards are limited to descendants of Rangers who served during the World War II era for Ranger Battalions Association of WWII scholarships. Applicants must be graduating high school seniors or students currently enrolled at an accredited 2- or 4-year educational or technical institution. They must have a GPA of 3.0 or higher. Along with their application, they must submit information on their leadership activities, future goals and how they plan to attain those, and honors and awards received to date. Financial need is not considered in the selection process.

Financial data The stipend is $1,000.

Duration 1 year.

Additional information The National Ranger Memorial Foundation began awarding scholarships in 1999. The Ranger Battalions Association of WWII became a partner in 2007 and offered additional scholarships to descendants of World War II era Rangers.

Number awarded 49 each year: 45 offered by the National Ranger Memorial Foundation and 4 by the Ranger Battalions Association of WWII.

Deadline May of each year.

[332]
REDUCED TUITION FOR SOUTH DAKOTA
NATIONAL GUARD MEMBERS

South Dakota Board of Regents
Attn: Scholarship Committee
306 East Capitol Avenue, Suite 200
Pierre, SD 57501-2545
(605) 773-3455   Fax: (605) 773-2422
E-mail: info@sdbor.edu
Web: www.sdbor.edu

Summary To provide financial assistance for college or graduate school to members of the South Dakota National Guard.

Eligibility Eligible to apply for this assistance are members of the South Dakota Army or Air National Guard who are South Dakota residents, have satisfactorily completed Initial Active Duty for Training (IADT), meet the entrance requirements at 1 of the 6 state educational institutions or 4 state vocational/technical schools, maintain sustained membership in their National Guard unit, and maintain satisfactory academic progress.

Financial data Qualifying Guard members are eligible for a 50% reduction in tuition at any state-supported postsecondary institution in South Dakota.

Duration This assistance is available for up to 128 credit hours at the undergraduate level and up to 32 credit hours at the graduate level.

Additional information Students participating in the Army Continuing Education Systems (ACES) or the Montgomery GI Bill are not authorized to use this program.

Number awarded Varies each year.

Deadline Deadline not specified.

[333]
RESERVE EDUCATIONAL ASSISTANCE PROGRAM

Department of Veterans Affairs
Attn: Veterans Benefits Administration
810 Vermont Avenue, N.W.
Washington, DC 20420
(202) 418-4343   Toll Free: (888) GI-BILL1
Web: www.gibill.va.gov/benefits/other_programs/reap.html

Summary To provide financial assistance for college or graduate school to members of the Reserves or National Guard who are called to active duty during a period of national emergency.

Eligibility This program is open to members of the Selected Reserve and Individual Ready Reserve (including Reserve elements of the Army, Navy, Air Force, Marine Corps, and Coast Guard, as well as the Army National Guard and the Air National Guard) who have served on active duty on or after September 11, 2001 for at least 90 consecutive days. Applicants must be interested in working on an undergraduate or graduate degree, vocational or technical training, on-the-job or apprenticeship training, correspondence training, or flight training.

Financial data For full-time study at a college or university, the current monthly rate is $589.20 for personnel with consecutive service of 90 days but less than 1 year, $883.80 for personnel with consecutive service of more than 1 year but less than 2 years, or $1,178.40 for those with consecutive service of 2 years or more. Reduced rates apply for part-time college or university study, apprenticeship and on-the-job training, licensing and certification training, cooperative education, correspondence courses, and flight training.

Duration Up to 36 months for full-time study. There is no fixed time for persons eligible for this program to utilize its benefits (except in the case of a member separated from the Ready Reserve for a disability, who are entitled to benefits for 10 years after the date of eligibility).

Additional information This program, established in 2005, is frequently referred to as Chapter 1607.

Number awarded Varies each year.

Deadline Applications may be submitted at any time.

[334]
RHODE ISLAND NATIONAL GUARD STATE TUITION ASSISTANCE PROGRAM

Rhode Island National Guard
Joint Force Headquarters
Attn: Education Service Officer
645 New London Avenue
Cranston, RI 02920-3097
(401) 275-4109   Fax: (401) 275-4014
E-mail: NGRIeduc@ng.army.mil
Web: states.ng.mil/sites/RI/education/default.aspx

Summary To provide financial support to members of the National Guard in Rhode Island interested in attending college or graduate school in the state.

Eligibility This program is open to active members of the Rhode Island National Guard in good standing who are currently satisfactorily participating in all unit training assemblies and annual training periods. Applicants must have at least 1 year of service remaining. They must be enrolled in or planning to enroll in an associate, bachelor's, or master's degree program at a public institution in the state.

Financial data Qualified Guard members receive payment of tuition for up to 5 courses per semester.

Duration 1 semester; may be renewed.

Additional information This program began in 1999.

Number awarded Varies each year.

Deadline Deadline not specified.

[335]
RHODE ISLAND NATIONAL GUARD STATE TUITION EXEMPTION PROGRAM

Rhode Island National Guard
Joint Force Headquarters
Attn: Education Service Officer
645 New London Avenue
Cranston, RI 02920-3097
(401) 275-4109   Fax: (401) 275-4014
E-mail: NGRIeduc@ng.army.mil
Web: states.ng.mil/sites/RI/education/default.aspx

Summary To provide financial support to members of the Rhode Island National Guard who attend public institutions in the state.

Eligibility This program is open to active members of the Rhode Island National Guard who attend all required unit training assemblies and annual training. Applicants must be residents of Rhode Island working toward an associate, bachelors, or master's degree at a designated public institution in the state. They must pass the Guard's height and weight standards, weapons qualification, and the APFT. They may not have more than 4 unexcused absences from military duty within a 12-month period or have tested positive for any illegal drug.

Financial data Qualified Guard members are entitled to tuition-free classes at public institutions in Rhode Island. The waiver does not cover books or fees.

Duration Upon enrollment, Guard members are entitled to 2 tuition-free classes per year.

Additional information This program began in 1994. The designated institutions are the University of Rhode Island,

Rhode Island College, and the Community College of Rhode Island.

Number awarded Varies each year.

Deadline Deadline not specified.

[336]
ROBERT H. CONNAL EDUCATION AWARDS

Enlisted Association of the New York National Guard, Inc.
Attn: Educational Award Chair
330 Old Niskayuna Road
Latham, NY 12110-2224
(518) 344-2670   E-mail: awards@eanyng.org
Web: www.eanyng.org/AwardsandScholarships.html

Summary To provide financial assistance to members of the Enlisted Association of the New York National Guard (EANYNG) and their families who are interested in attending college in any state.

Eligibility This program is open to EANYNG members and their spouses, children, and grandchildren. Applicants must be high school seniors or current undergraduates at a college or university in any state. The applicant or sponsor must have belonged to EANYNG for more than 1 year. Membership in EANYNG is limited to enlisted personnel in the New York Air or Army National Guard. Selection is based on academic achievement, community service, extracurricular activities, and leadership abilities.

Financial data Stipends are $1,000 or $500.

Duration 1 year; nonrenewable.

Additional information Funding for this program is provided by the production of the association's yearly journal, members' dues, and a donation from USAA Insurance Corporation.

Number awarded 7 each year: 1 statewide scholarship at $1,000 and 6 at $500 in each region of the state.

Deadline February of each year.

[337]
ROBERT W. BRUNSMAN MEMORIAL SCHOLARSHIP

International Military Community Executives' Association
Attn: Scholarship
P.O. Box 7286
Alexandria, VA 22307-0286
(571) 207-8893   Fax: (866) 369-2435
E-mail: imcea@imcea.org
Web: www.imcea.org/scholarship.html

Summary To provide financial assistance to members of the International Military Community Executives' Association (IMCEA) who are working in the field of military morale, welfare, and recreation (MWR) and currently enrolled in college or graduate school.

Eligibility This program is open to regular IMCEA members who are currently employed in the field of military MWR. Applicants must be already enrolled at a college or university, either in-class or online, and taking undergraduate or graduate courses related to MWR. Along with their application, they must submit a 2-page essay on how all MWR services (e.g., clubs, bowling, golf, child care, libraries) might work together to create synergy and enhance the mission of IMCEA. Selection is based on that essay, participation in IMCEA activities, and involvement in military MWR services.

Financial data The stipend is $1,000.

Duration 1 year.

Additional information Regular membership in IMCEA is open to Army, Air Force, Navy, Marine Corps, and Coast Guard personnel who provide MWR services at military installations and bases worldwide.

Number awarded 1 each year.

Deadline April of each year.

[338]
ROSAMOND P. HAEBERLE MEMORIAL SCHOLARSHIP

Daughters of the American Revolution-Michigan State
  Society
c/o Toni Barger, Memorial Scholarship Committee
130 Lake Region Circle
Winter Haven, FL 33881-9535
(863) 326-1687   E-mail: tonibarger@aol.com
Web: www.michigandar.org/scholarships.htm

Summary To provide funding to Michigan veterans and military personnel interested in attending college in the state.

Eligibility This program is open to residents of Michigan who have served on active duty in the U.S. armed forces (including Reserves and National Guard) for at least 6 continuous months and are either currently serving in the armed forces or have received a separation from active duty under honorable conditions. Applicants must be currently accepted to and/or enrolled at a 2- or 4-year accredited college, university, or technical/trade school in Michigan. They must be enrolled at least half time and have a cumulative high school or undergraduate GPA of 2.5 or higher. Along with their application, they must submit a 1-page essay on what serving their country has meant to them and how it has influenced their future goals and priorities. Selection is based on academic performance, extracurricular activities, community service, potential to succeed in an academic environment, financial need, and military service record.

Financial data The stipend is $1,500.

Duration 1 year.

Additional information This program began in 2007.

Number awarded 1 each year.

Deadline March of each year.

[339]
RSF MEMORIAL SCHOLARSHIP

Missouri Society of Professional Engineers
Attn: MSPE Educational Foundation
200 East McCarty Street, Suite 200
Jefferson City, MO 65101-3113
(573) 636-4861   Toll Free: (888) 666-4861
Fax: (573) 636-5475   E-mail: marladay@mspe.org
Web: www.mspe.org/edfoundation.html

Summary To provide funding to military personnel and veterans who are residents of any state and currently studying engineering at selected universities in Missouri.

Eligibility This program is open to military personnel (including active, National Guard, Reserves, ROTC cadets, and veterans) who are U.S. citizens and residents of any state. Applicants must be sophomores or juniors currently enrolled in or planning to transfer to an engineering program at 1 of the following institutions in Missouri: University of Missouri, College of Engineering, Columbia; University of Missouri, School of Engineering, Kansas City; Missouri University of Science and Technology, School of Engineering, Rolla; Missouri University of Science and Technology, School of Materials, Energy, and Earth Resources, Rolla; University of Missouri St. Louis/Washington University Joint Undergraduate Engineering Program; Southeast Missouri State University, Engineering Physics Program, Cape Girardeau; St. Louis University, Parks College of Engineering and Aviation, St. Louis; and Washington University, School of Engineering and Applied Sciences, St. Louis. Along with their application, they must submit a 1,000-word essay on their interest in engineering, their major area of study and area of specialization, the occupation they propose to pursue after graduation, their long-term goals, and how they hope to achieve those. Selection is based on the essay (10 points), academic achievement (5 points), extracurricular college or community activities (5 points), work experience (10 points), recommendations (10 points), and financial need (10 points).

Financial data The stipend is $1,500.

Duration 1 year.

Number awarded 1 each year.

Deadline December of each year.

[340]
SCHOLARSHIPS FOR OUTSTANDING AIRMEN TO ROTC (SOAR)

U.S. Air Force
Attn: Headquarters AFROTC/RRUE
Enlisted Commissioning Section
551 East Maxwell Boulevard
Maxwell AFB, AL 36112-5917
(334) 953-2091   Toll Free: (866) 4-AFROTC
Fax: (334) 953-6167   E-mail: enlisted@afrotc.com
Web: afrotc.com/scholarships/enlisted-scholarships

Summary To allow selected enlisted Air Force personnel to earn a bachelor's degree by providing financial assistance for full-time college study.

Eligibility Eligible to participate in this program are enlisted members of the Air Force who have completed from 1 to 6 years of active duty and have at least 1 year time-on-station. Candidates must be nominated by their commanding officers and be accepted at a college or university offering the AFROTC 4-year program. Airmen with 24 semester hours or more of graded college credit must have a cumulative GPA of 2.5 or higher; airmen with less than 24 semester hours must have an ACT score of 24 or higher or an SAT combined mathematics and critical reading score of 1100 or higher. All applicants must earn Air Force Officer Qualifying Test (AFOQT) scores of 15 or more on the verbal scale and 10 or more on the quantitative scale. U.S. citizenship is required. When the recipients complete the program, they may be no more than 31 years of age. All academic majors are eligible.

Financial data Selectees receive a tuition and fees scholarship of up to $18,000 per year, an annual textbook allowance of $900, and a monthly nontaxable stipend of $250 to $500.

Duration 2 to 4 years.

Additional information Upon completing their degree, selectees are commissioned as officers in the Air Force with a 4-year service obligation.

Number awarded Approximately 50 each year.

Deadline September of each year.

[341]
SCHUYLER S. PYLE SCHOLARSHIP

Fleet Reserve Association
Attn: FRA Education Foundation
125 North West Street
Alexandria, VA 22314-2754
(703) 683-1400   Toll Free: (800) FRA-1924
Fax: (703) 549-6610   E-mail: scholars@fra.org
Web: www.fra.org

Summary To provide financial assistance for college or graduate school to members of the Fleet Reserve Association (FRA) and their families.

Eligibility This program is open to members of the FRA and the dependent children, grandchildren, and spouses of living or deceased members. Applicants must be enrolled as full-time undergraduate or graduate students. Along with their application, they must submit an essay on why they want to go to college and what they intend to accomplish with their degree. Selection is based on academic record, financial need, extracurricular activities, leadership skills, and participation in community activities. U.S. citizenship is required.

Financial data The stipend is $5,000 per year.

Duration 1 year; may be renewed.

Additional information Membership in the FRA is restricted to active-duty, retired, and Reserve members of the Navy, Marine Corps, and Coast Guard.

Number awarded 1 each year.

Deadline April of each year.

[342]
SCOTT DOMINGUEZ-CRATERS OF THE MOON CHAPTER SCHOLARSHIP

American Society of Safety Engineers
Attn: ASSE Foundation
1800 East Oakton Street
Des Plaines, IL 60018
(847) 768-3435   Fax: (847) 768-3434
E-mail: agabanski@asse.org
Web: www.asse.org

Summary To provide financial assistance to undergraduate and graduate student members of the American Society of Safety Engineers (ASSE), particularly those with ties to the military, who are from designated western states.

Eligibility This program is open to ASSE members who are working on an undergraduate or graduate degree in occupational safety, health, and environment or a closely-related field (e.g., industrial or environmental engineering, environmental science, industrial hygiene, occupational health nursing). First priority is given to residents within the service area of Craters of the Moon Chapter in Idaho; second priority is given to residents of other states in ASSE Region II (Arizona, Colorado, Montana, Nevada, New Mexico, Utah, and Wyoming). Special consideration is also given to 1) employees of a sponsoring organization or their dependents; 2) students who are serving their country through active duty in the armed forces or are honorably discharged; 3) former members of the Boy Scouts, Girl Scouts, FFA, or 4-H; 4) recipients of awards from service organizations; and 5) students who have provided volunteer service to an ASSE chapter in a leadership role. Undergraduates must have completed at least 60 semester hours with a GPA of 3.0 or higher. Graduate students must have completed at least 9 semester hours

with a GPA of 3.5 or higher and have had a GPA of 3.0 or higher as an undergraduate. Full-time students must be ASSE student members; part-time students must be ASSE general or professional members. Along with their application, they must submit 2 essays of 300 words or less: 1) why they are seeking a degree in occupational safety and health or a closely-related field, a brief description of their current activities, and how those relate to their career goals and objectives; and 2) why they should be awarded this scholarship (including career goals and financial need). U.S. citizenship is not required.

Financial data The stipend is $1,000 per year.

Duration 1 year; recipients may reapply.

Additional information This program is sponsored by the ASSE Craters of the Moon Chapter.

Number awarded 1 each year.

Deadline November of each year.

[343]
SEAMAN TO ADMIRAL-21 PROGRAM

U.S. Navy
Attn: Commander, Naval Service Training Command
250 Dallas Street, Suite A
Pensacola, FL 32508-5268
(850) 452-9433   Fax: (850) 452-2486
E-mail: PNSC_STA21@navy.mil
Web: www.sta-21.navy.mil

Summary To allow outstanding enlisted Navy personnel to complete a bachelor's degree and receive a commission.

Eligibility This program is open to U.S. citizens who are currently serving on active duty in the U.S. Navy or Naval Reserve, including Full Time Support (FTS), Selected Reserves (SELRES), and Navy Reservists on active duty, except for those on active duty for training (ACDUTRA). Applicants must be high school graduates (or GED recipients) who are able to complete requirements for a baccalaureate degree in 36 months or less. When they complete their degree requirements, they must be younger than 31 years of age. Within the past 3 years, they must have taken the SAT (and achieved scores of at least 500 on the mathematics section and 500 on the critical reading section) or the ACT (and achieved a score of 41 or higher, including at least 21 on the mathematics portion and 20 on the English portion).

Financial data Awardees continue to receive their regular Navy pay and allowances while they attend college on a full-time basis. They also receive reimbursement for tuition, fees, and books up to $10,000 per year. If base housing is available, they are eligible to live there. Participants are not eligible to receive benefits under the Navy's Tuition Assistance Program (TA), the Montgomery GI Bill (MGIB), the Navy College Fund, or the Veterans Educational Assistance Program (VEAP).

Duration Selectees are supported for up to 36 months of full-time, year-round study or completion of a bachelor's degree, as long as they maintain a GPA of 2.5 or higher.

Additional information This program was established in 2001 as a replacement for the Seaman to Admiral Program (established in 1994), the Enlisted Commissioning Program, and other specialized programs for sailors to earn a commission. Upon acceptance into the program, selectees attend the Naval Science Institute (NSI) in Newport, Rhode Island for an 8-week program in the fundamental core concepts of being a naval officer (navigation, engineering, weapons, military history and justice, etc.). They then enter a college or university with an NROTC unit or affiliation to work full time on a bachelor's degree. They become members of and drill with the NROTC unit. When they complete their degree, they are commissioned as ensigns in the United States Naval Reserve and assigned to initial training for their officer community. After commissioning, 5 years of active service are required.

Number awarded Varies each year.

Deadline June of each year.

[344]
SIMULTANEOUS MEMBERSHIP PROGRAM (SMP)

U.S. Army
ROTC Cadet Command
Attn: Scholarship Branch
204 1st Cavalry Regiment Road, Building 1002
Fort Knox, KY 40121
(502) 624-7371   Toll Free: (888) 550-ARMY
Fax: (502) 624-6937   E-mail: train2lead@usacc.army.mil
Web: www.goarmy.com/rotc/enroll/enlisted.html

Summary To provide financial assistance to individuals who serve simultaneously in the Army National Guard or Army Reserve and the Army Reserve Officers' Training Corps (ROTC) while they are in college.

Eligibility Students who are members of the Army National Guard or the Army Reserve and Army ROTC at the same time are eligible for this assistance. Applicants must have completed basic training or the equivalent, have at least 4 years remaining on their current military obligation, be full-time college juniors, have a GPA of 2.0 or higher, and be U.S. citizens.

Financial data Advanced ROTC Simultaneous Membership Program (SMP) participants are paid at the rate of at least a Sergeant E-5 for their Guard or Reserve training assemblies (recently, $226 to $315 per month, depending on the number of years of service), plus an ROTC stipend for 10 months of the year at $450 per month during their junior year and $500 per month during their senior year.

Duration Up to 2 years.

Additional information Participants serve as officer trainees in their Guard or Reserve units and, under the close supervision of a commissioned officer, perform duties commensurate with those of a second lieutenant. Cadets who successfully complete the SMP program graduate with a commission as a second lieutenant. Once commissioned, they may continue to serve in their Guard or Reserve units, or they may apply for active duty in the U.S. Army.

Number awarded Varies each year.

Deadline Deadline not specified.

[345]
SOUTH CAROLINA NATIONAL GUARD COLLEGE ASSISTANCE PROGRAM

South Carolina Commission on Higher Education
Attn: Student Services
1122 Lady Street, Suite 300
Columbia, SC 29201
(803) 737-2144   Toll Free: (877) 349-7183
Fax: (803) 737-2297   E-mail: mbrown@che.sc.gov
Web: www.che.sc.gov

Summary To provide financial assistance to members of the South Carolina National Guard who are interested in attending college in the state.

Eligibility This program is open to members of the South Carolina National Guard who are in good standing and have not already received a bachelor's or graduate degree. Applicants must be admitted, enrolled, and classified as a degree-seeking full- or part-time student at an eligible institution in South Carolina. They may not be taking continuing education or graduate course work. U.S. citizenship or permanent resident status is required.

Financial data This program provides full payment of the cost of attendance, including tuition, fees, and textbooks, to a maximum of $9,000 per year for members of the Air National Guard or $4,500 for members of the Army National Guard. The cumulative total of all benefits received from this program may not exceed $18,000.

Duration Support is provided for up to 130 semester hours of study, provided the Guard member maintains satisfactory academic progress as defined by the institution.

Additional information This program is administered by the South Carolina Commission on Higher Education in consultation with the state Adjutant General. The General Assembly established this program in 2007 as a replacement for the South Carolina National Guard Student Loan Repayment Program. Enlisted personnel are required to continue their service in the National Guard during all terms of courses covered by the benefit received. Officers must continue their service with the National Guard for at least 4 years after completion of the most recent award or degree completion.

Number awarded Varies each year.

Deadline Deadline not specified.

[346]
SPECIAL DUTY OFFICER (INFORMATION WARFARE) OPTION OF THE SEAMAN TO ADMIRAL-21 PROGRAM

U.S. Navy
Attn: Commander, Naval Service Training Command
250 Dallas Street, Suite A
Pensacola, FL 32508-5268
(850) 452-9433   Fax: (850) 452-2486
E-mail: PNSC_STA21@navy.mil
Web: www.sta-21.navy.mil

Summary To allow outstanding enlisted Navy personnel to complete a bachelor's degree and receive a commission as a special duty officer (information warfare).

Eligibility This program is open to U.S. citizens who are currently serving on active duty in the U.S. Navy or Naval Reserve, including Full Time Support (FTS), Selected Reserves (SELRES), and Navy Reservists on active duty, except for those on active duty for training (ACDUTRA). Applicants must be high school graduates (or GED recipients) who are at least 18 years of age and able to complete requirements for a baccalaureate degree in 36 months or less. Sailors in all ratings are eligible, but preference is given to cryptologic technicians, intelligence specialists, and information professionals. When they complete their degree requirements, they must be younger than 35 years of age. Within the past 3 years, they must have taken the SAT (and achieved scores of at least 500 on the mathematics section and 500 on the critical reading section) or the ACT (and achieved a score of 41 or higher, including at least 21 on the mathematics portion and 20 on the English portion). They must also meet relevant medical standards. Although technical degrees are preferred, the program does not specify required majors; instead, it seeks officers who possess strong analytical ability and communication skills (both oral and written).

Financial data Awardees continue to receive their regular Navy pay and allowances while they attend college on a full-time basis. They also receive reimbursement for tuition, fees, and books up to $10,000 per year. If base housing is available, they are eligible to live there. Participants are not eligible to receive benefits under the Navy's Tuition Assistance Program (TA), the Montgomery GI Bill (MGIB), the Navy College Fund, or the Veterans Educational Assistance Program (VEAP).

Duration Selectees are supported for up to 36 months of full-time, year-round study or completion of a bachelor's degree, as long as they maintain a GPA of 2.5 or higher.

Additional information This program was established in 2001 as a replacement for the Seaman to Admiral Program (established in 1994), the Enlisted Commissioning Program, and other specialized programs for sailors to earn a commission. Upon acceptance into the program, selectees attend the Naval Science Institute (NSI) in Newport, Rhode Island for an 8-week program in the fundamental core concepts of being a naval officer (navigation, engineering, weapons, military history and justice, etc.). They then enter a college or university with an NROTC unit or affiliation to work full time on a bachelor's degree. They become members of and drill with the NROTC unit. When they complete their degree, they are commissioned as ensigns in the United States Naval Reserve and assigned to initial training as a special duty officer (information warfare); that designation was formerly special duty officer (cryptologic). After commissioning, 5 years of active service are required.

Number awarded Varies each year.

Deadline June of each year.

[347]
SPECIAL DUTY OFFICER (INTELLIGENCE) OPTION OF THE SEAMAN TO ADMIRAL-21 PROGRAM

U.S. Navy
Attn: Commander, Naval Service Training Command
250 Dallas Street, Suite A
Pensacola, FL 32508-5268
(850) 452-9433   Fax: (850) 452-2486
E-mail: PNSC_STA21@navy.mil
Web: www.sta-21.navy.mil

Summary To allow outstanding enlisted Navy personnel to complete a bachelor's degree and receive a commission as a special duty officer (intelligence).

Eligibility This program is open to U.S. citizens who are currently serving on active duty in the U.S. Navy or Naval Reserve, including Full Time Support (FTS), Selected Reserves (SELRES), and Navy Reservists on active duty, except for those on active duty for training (ACDUTRA). Applicants must be high school graduates (or GED recipients) who are at least 18 years of age and able to complete requirements for a baccalaureate degree in 36 months or less. They may currently have any rating. When they complete their degree requirements, they must be younger than 35 years of age. Within the past 3 years, they must have taken the SAT

(and achieved scores of at least 500 on the mathematics section and 500 on the critical reading section) or the ACT (and achieved a score of 41 or higher, including at least 21 on the mathematics portion and 20 on the English portion). They must also meet relevant medical standards. Although technical degrees are preferred, the program does not specify required majors; instead, it seeks officers who possess strong analytical ability and communication skills (both oral and written).

Financial data Awardees continue to receive their regular Navy pay and allowances while they attend college on a full-time basis. They also receive reimbursement for tuition, fees, and books up to $10,000 per year. If base housing is available, they are eligible to live there. Participants are not eligible to receive benefits under the Navy's Tuition Assistance Program (TA), the Montgomery GI Bill (MGIB), the Navy College Fund, or the Veterans Educational Assistance Program (VEAP).

Duration Selectees are supported for up to 36 months of full-time, year-round study or completion of a bachelor's degree, as long as they maintain a GPA of 2.5 or higher.

Additional information This program was established in 2001 as a replacement for the Seaman to Admiral Program (established in 1994), the Enlisted Commissioning Program, and other specialized programs for sailors to earn a commission. Upon acceptance into the program, selectees attend the Naval Science Institute (NSI) in Newport, Rhode Island for an 8-week program in the fundamental core concepts of being a naval officer (navigation, engineering, weapons, military history and justice, etc.). They then enter a college or university with an NROTC unit or affiliation to work full time on a bachelor's degree. They become members of and drill with the NROTC unit. When they complete their degree, they are commissioned as ensigns in the United States Naval Reserve and assigned to initial training as a special duty officer (intelligence). After commissioning, 5 years of active service are required.

Number awarded Varies each year.

Deadline June of each year.

[348]
SPECIAL WARFARE OPTION OF THE SEAMAN TO ADMIRAL-21 PROGRAM

U.S. Navy
Attn: Commander, Naval Service Training Command
250 Dallas Street, Suite A
Pensacola, FL 32508-5268
(850) 452-9433   Fax: (850) 452-2486
E-mail: PNSC_STA21@navy.mil
Web: www.sta-21.navy.mil

Summary To allow outstanding enlisted Navy personnel to complete a bachelor's degree and receive a commission as a special warfare officer.

Eligibility This program is open to U.S. citizens who are currently serving on active duty in the U.S. Navy or Naval Reserve, including Full Time Support (FTS), Selected Reserves (SELRES), and Navy Reservists on active duty, except for those on active duty for training (ACDUTRA). Only males are eligible for this option. They must be a member of the SEAL community. Applicants must be high school graduates (or GED recipients) who are able to complete requirements for a baccalaureate degree in 36 months or less. When they complete their degree requirements, they must be younger than 29 years of age. That age limitation may be adjusted upward for active service on a month-for-month basis up to 24 months, and waivers are considered for enlisted personnel who possess particularly exceptional qualifications if they can complete their degree prior to their 35th birthday. Within the past 3 years, they must have taken the SAT (and achieved scores of at least 500 on the mathematics section and 500 on the critical reading section) or the ACT (and achieved a score of 41 or higher, including at least 21 on the mathematics portion and 20 on the English portion). They must also meet physical regulations that include qualification for diving duty and/or combat swimmer. Preference is given to applicants who plan to major in a technical field (e.g., chemistry, computer science, engineering, mathematics, oceanography, operations analysis, physical sciences, or physics).

Financial data Awardees continue to receive their regular Navy pay and allowances while they attend college on a full-time basis. They also receive reimbursement for tuition, fees, and books up to $10,000 per year. If base housing is available, they are eligible to live there. Participants are not eligible to receive benefits under the Navy's Tuition Assistance Program (TA), the Montgomery GI Bill (MGIB), the Navy College Fund, or the Veterans Educational Assistance Program (VEAP).

Duration Selectees are supported for up to 36 months of full-time, year-round study or completion of a bachelor's degree, as long as they maintain a GPA of 2.5 or higher.

Additional information This program was established in 2001 as a replacement for the Seaman to Admiral Program (established in 1994), the Enlisted Commissioning Program, and other specialized programs for sailors to earn a commission. Upon acceptance into the program, selectees attend the Naval Science Institute (NSI) in Newport, Rhode Island for an 8-week program in the fundamental core concepts of being a naval officer (navigation, engineering, weapons, military history and justice, etc.). They then enter a college or university with an NROTC unit or affiliation to work full time on a bachelor's degree. They become members of and drill with the NROTC unit. When they complete their degree, they are commissioned as ensigns in the United States Naval Reserve and assigned to initial training as a special warfare officer. After commissioning, 5 years of active service are required.

Number awarded Varies each year.

Deadline June of each year.

[349]
SUPPLY CORPS OPTION OF THE SEAMAN TO ADMIRAL-21 PROGRAM

U.S. Navy
Attn: Commander, Naval Service Training Command
250 Dallas Street, Suite A
Pensacola, FL 32508-5268
(850) 452-9433   Fax: (850) 452-2486
E-mail: PNSC_STA21@navy.mil
Web: www.sta-21.navy.mil

Summary To allow outstanding enlisted Navy personnel to complete a bachelor's degree in business, engineering, or mathematics and receive a commission in the Supply Corps.

Eligibility This program is open to U.S. citizens who are currently serving on active duty in the U.S. Navy or Naval Reserve, including Full Time Support (FTS), Selected

Reserves (SELRES), and Navy Reservists on active duty, except for those on active duty for training (ACDUTRA). Applicants must be high school graduates (or GED recipients) who are able to complete requirements for a baccalaureate degree in a business, engineering, or mathematics related field in 36 months or less. When they complete their degree requirements, they must be younger than 31 years of age. Within the past 3 years, they must have taken the SAT (and achieved scores of at least 500 on the mathematics section and 500 on the critical reading section) or the ACT (and achieved a score of 41 or higher, including at least 21 on the mathematics portion and 20 on the English portion).

Financial data Awardees continue to receive their regular Navy pay and allowances while they attend college on a full-time basis. They also receive reimbursement for tuition, fees, and books up to $10,000 per year. If base housing is available, they are eligible to live there. Participants are not eligible to receive benefits under the Navy's Tuition Assistance Program (TA), the Montgomery GI Bill (MGIB), the Navy College Fund, or the Veterans Educational Assistance Program (VEAP).

Duration Selectees are supported for up to 36 months of full-time, year-round study or completion of a bachelor's degree, as long as they maintain a GPA of 2.5 or higher.

Additional information This program was established in 2001 as a replacement for the Seaman to Admiral Program (established in 1994), the Enlisted Commissioning Program, and other specialized programs for sailors to earn a commission. Upon acceptance into the program, selectees attend the Naval Science Institute (NSI) in Newport, Rhode Island for an 8-week program in the fundamental core concepts of being a naval officer (navigation, engineering, weapons, military history and justice, etc.). They then enter a college or university with an NROTC unit or affiliation to work full time on a bachelor's degree. They become members of and drill with the NROTC unit. When they complete their degree, they are commissioned as ensigns in the United States Naval Reserve and assigned to initial training as an officer in the Supply Corps. After commissioning, 5 years of active service are required.

Number awarded Varies each year.

Deadline June of each year.

[350]
SURFACE WARFARE OFFICER/ENGINEER OPTION OF THE SEAMAN TO ADMIRAL-21 PROGRAM

U.S. Navy
Attn: Commander, Naval Service Training Command
250 Dallas Street, Suite A
Pensacola, FL 32508-5268
(850) 452-9433   Fax: (850) 452-2486
E-mail: PNSC_STA21@navy.mil
Web: www.sta-21.navy.mil

Summary To allow outstanding enlisted Navy personnel to complete a bachelor's degree and receive a commission as a surface warfare officer/engineer.

Eligibility This program is open to U.S. citizens who are currently serving on active duty in the U.S. Navy or Naval Reserve, including Full Time Support (FTS), Selected Reserves (SELRES), and Navy Reservists on active duty, except for those on active duty for training (ACDUTRA). Applicants must be high school graduates (or GED recipients) who are able to complete requirements for a baccalaureate degree in 36 months or less. When they complete their degree requirements, they must be younger than 35 years of age. Within the past 3 years, they must have taken the SAT (and achieved scores of at least 500 on the mathematics section and 500 on the critical reading section) or the ACT (and achieved a score of 41 or higher, including at least 21 on the mathematics portion and 20 on the English portion). They must also pass relevant medical standards. No specific academic major is required, but applicants are encouraged to work on a technical degree in engineering or physical science.

Financial data Awardees continue to receive their regular Navy pay and allowances while they attend college on a full-time basis. They also receive reimbursement for tuition, fees, and books up to $10,000 per year. If base housing is available, they are eligible to live there. Participants are not eligible to receive benefits under the Navy's Tuition Assistance Program (TA), the Montgomery GI Bill (MGIB), the Navy College Fund, or the Veterans Educational Assistance Program (VEAP).

Duration Selectees are supported for up to 36 months of full-time, year-round study or completion of a bachelor's degree, as long as they maintain a GPA of 2.5 or higher.

Additional information Upon acceptance into the program, selectees attend the Naval Science Institute (NSI) in Newport, Rhode Island for an 8-week program in the fundamental core concepts of being a naval officer (navigation, engineering, weapons, military history and justice, etc.). They then enter a college or university with an NROTC unit or affiliation to work full time on a bachelor's degree. They become members of and drill with the NROTC unit. When they complete their degree, they are commissioned as ensigns in the United States Naval Reserve and assigned to initial training as a special duty officer (engineering duty). After commissioning, 5 years of active service are required.

Number awarded Varies each year.

Deadline June of each year.

[351]
SURFACE WARFARE OFFICER/INFORMATION PROFESSIONAL OPTION OF THE SEAMAN TO ADMIRAL-21 PROGRAM

U.S. Navy
Attn: Commander, Naval Service Training Command
250 Dallas Street, Suite A
Pensacola, FL 32508-5268
(850) 452-9433   Fax: (850) 452-2486
E-mail: PNSC_STA21@navy.mil
Web: www.sta-21.navy.mil

Summary To allow outstanding enlisted Navy personnel to complete a bachelor's degree and receive a commission as a surface warfare officer/information professional (SWO/IP).

Eligibility This program is open to U.S. citizens who are currently serving on active duty in the U.S. Navy or Naval Reserve, including Full Time Support (FTS), Selected Reserves (SELRES), and Navy Reservists on active duty, except for those on active duty for training (ACDUTRA). Applicants must be high school graduates (or GED recipients) who are able to complete requirements for a baccalaureate degree in 36 months or less. When they complete their degree requirements, they must be younger than 28 years of age. Within the past 3 years, they must have taken the SAT

(and achieved scores of at least 500 on the mathematics section and 500 on the critical reading section) or the ACT (and achieved a score of 41 or higher, including at least 21 on the mathematics portion and 20 on the English portion). They must also pass relevant medical standards. No specific academic major is required, but applicants are encouraged to work on a technical degree in computer science, computer or electrical engineering, mathematics, physics, information systems, or operations.

Financial data Awardees continue to receive their regular Navy pay and allowances while they attend college on a full-time basis. They also receive reimbursement for tuition, fees, and books up to $10,000 per year. If base housing is available, they are eligible to live there. Participants are not eligible to receive benefits under the Navy's Tuition Assistance Program (TA), the Montgomery GI Bill (MGIB), the Navy College Fund, or the Veterans Educational Assistance Program (VEAP).

Duration Selectees are supported for up to 36 months of full-time, year-round study or completion of a bachelor's degree, as long as they maintain a GPA of 2.5 or higher.

Additional information Upon acceptance into the program, selectees attend the Naval Science Institute (NSI) in Newport, Rhode Island for an 8-week program in the fundamental core concepts of being a naval officer (navigation, engineering, weapons, military history and justice, etc.). They then enter a college or university with an NROTC unit or affiliation to work full time on a bachelor's degree. They become members of and drill with the NROTC unit. When they complete their degree, they are commissioned as ensigns in the United States Naval Reserve and assigned to initial training as a special duty officer (information professional). After commissioning, 5 years of active service are required.

Number awarded Varies each year.

Deadline June of each year.

[352]
SURFACE WARFARE OFFICER/OCEANOGRAPHY OPTION OF THE SEAMAN TO ADMIRAL-21 PROGRAM

U.S. Navy
Attn: Commander, Naval Service Training Command
250 Dallas Street, Suite A
Pensacola, FL 32508-5268
(850) 452-9433   Fax: (850) 452-2486
E-mail: PNSC_STA21@navy.mil
Web: www.sta-21.navy.mil

Summary To allow outstanding enlisted Navy personnel to complete a bachelor's degree and receive a commission as a surface warfare officer/oceanography.

Eligibility This program is open to U.S. citizens who are currently serving on active duty in the U.S. Navy or Naval Reserve, including Full Time Support (FTS), Selected Reserves (SELRES), and Navy Reservists on active duty, except for those on active duty for training (ACDUTRA). Applicants must be high school graduates (or GED recipients) who are able to complete requirements for a baccalaureate degree in 36 months or less. They must be planning to work on a technical degree in chemistry, computer science, engineering, geospatial information systems, hydrography, marine science, mathematics, meteorology, oceanography, operational analysis, physical sciences, or physics. When they complete their degree requirements, they must be younger than 28 years of age. Within the past 3 years, they must have taken the SAT (and achieved scores of at least 500 on the mathematics section and 500 on the critical reading section) or the ACT (and achieved a score of 41 or higher, including at least 21 on the mathematics portion and 20 on the English portion). They must also pass relevant medical standards.

Financial data Awardees continue to receive their regular Navy pay and allowances while they attend college on a full-time basis. They also receive reimbursement for tuition, fees, and books up to $10,000 per year. If base housing is available, they are eligible to live there. Participants are not eligible to receive benefits under the Navy's Tuition Assistance Program (TA), the Montgomery GI Bill (MGIB), the Navy College Fund, or the Veterans Educational Assistance Program (VEAP).

Duration Selectees are supported for up to 36 months of full-time, year-round study or completion of a bachelor's degree, as long as they maintain a GPA of 2.5 or higher.

Additional information Upon acceptance into the program, selectees attend the Naval Science Institute (NSI) in Newport, Rhode Island for an 8-week program in the fundamental core concepts of being a naval officer (navigation, engineering, weapons, military history and justice, etc.). They then enter a college or university with an NROTC unit or affiliation to work full time on a bachelor's degree. They become members of and drill with the NROTC unit. When they complete their degree, they are commissioned as ensigns in the United States Naval Reserve and assigned to initial training as a special duty officer (oceanography). After commissioning, 5 years of active service are required.

Number awarded Varies each year.

Deadline June of each year.

[353]
SURFACE WARFARE OFFICER OPTION OF THE SEAMAN TO ADMIRAL-21 PROGRAM

U.S. Navy
Attn: Commander, Naval Service Training Command
250 Dallas Street, Suite A
Pensacola, FL 32508-5268
(850) 452-9433   Fax: (850) 452-2486
E-mail: PNSC_STA21@navy.mil
Web: www.sta-21.navy.mil

Summary To allow outstanding enlisted Navy personnel to complete a bachelor's degree and receive a commission as a surface warfare officer (SWO).

Eligibility This program is open to U.S. citizens who are currently serving on active duty in the U.S. Navy or Naval Reserve, including Full Time Support (FTS), Selected Reserves (SELRES), and Navy Reservists on active duty, except for those on active duty for training (ACDUTRA). Applicants must be high school graduates (or GED recipients) who are able to complete requirements for a baccalaureate degree in 36 months or less. When they complete their degree requirements, they must be younger than 28 years of age. Within the past 3 years, they must have taken the SAT (and achieved scores of at least 500 on the mathematics section and 500 on the critical reading section) or the ACT (and achieved a score of 41 or higher, including at least 21 on the mathematics portion and 20 on the English portion). They

must also meet relevant medical standards. Preference is given to applicants who plan to major in a technical field (e.g., chemistry, computer science, engineering, mathematics, oceanography, operations analysis, physical sciences, or physics).

Financial data Awardees continue to receive their regular Navy pay and allowances while they attend college on a full-time basis. They also receive reimbursement for tuition, fees, and books up to $10,000 per year. If base housing is available, they are eligible to live there. Participants are not eligible to receive benefits under the Navy's Tuition Assistance Program (TA), the Montgomery GI Bill (MGIB), the Navy College Fund, or the Veterans Educational Assistance Program (VEAP).

Duration Selectees are supported for up to 36 months of full-time, year-round study or completion of a bachelor's degree, as long as they maintain a GPA of 2.5 or higher.

Additional information This program was established in 2001 as a replacement for the Seaman to Admiral Program (established in 1994), the Enlisted Commissioning Program, and other specialized programs for sailors to earn a commission. Upon acceptance into the program, selectees attend the Naval Science Institute (NSI) in Newport, Rhode Island for an 8-week program in the fundamental core concepts of being a naval officer (navigation, engineering, weapons, military history and justice, etc.). They then enter a college or university with an NROTC unit or affiliation to work full time on a bachelor's degree. They become members of and drill with the NROTC unit. When they complete their degree, they are commissioned as ensigns in the United States Naval Reserve and assigned to initial training as a surface warfare officer. After commissioning, 5 years of active service are required.

Number awarded Varies each year.

Deadline June of each year.

[354]
TAILHOOK EDUCATIONAL FOUNDATION SCHOLARSHIPS

Tailhook Educational Foundation
9696 Businesspark Avenue
P.O. Box 26626
San Diego, CA 92196-0626
(858) 689-9223   Toll Free: (800) 322-4665
E-mail: tag@tailhook.net
Web: www.tailhook.org/Foundation.html

Summary To provide financial assistance for college to personnel associated with naval aviation and their children.

Eligibility This program is open to 1) the children (natural, step, and adopted) of current or former U.S. Navy or Marine Corps personnel who served as an aviator, flight officer, or air crewman, or 2) personnel and children of personnel who are serving or have served on board a U.S. Navy aircraft carrier as a member of the ship's company or air wing. Applicants must be enrolled or accepted for enrollment at an accredited college or university. Selection is based on educational and extracurricular achievements, merit, and citizenship.

Financial data Stipend range from $1,500 to $15,000.

Duration 1 to 2 years.

Number awarded Varies each year; recently, 71 of these scholarships were awarded.

Deadline March of each year.

[355]
TENNESSEE HELPING HEROES GRANTS

Tennessee Student Assistance Corporation
Parkway Towers
404 James Robertson Parkway, Suite 1510
Nashville, TN 37243-0820
(615) 741-1346   Toll Free: (800) 342-1663
Fax: (615) 741-6101   E-mail: TSAC.Aidinfo@tn.gov
Web: www.tn.gov/collegepays/mon_college/hh_grant.htm

Summary To provide funding to veterans and current Reservists or National Guard members who are residents of Tennessee and enrolled at a college or university in the state.

Eligibility This program is open to residents of Tennessee who are veterans honorably discharged from the U.S. armed forces and former or current members of a Reserve or Tennessee National Guard unit who were called into active military service. Applicants must have been awarded, on or after September 11, 2001, the Iraq Campaign Medal, the Afghanistan Campaign Medal, or the Global War on Terrorism Expeditionary Medal. They must be enrolled at least half time at an eligible college or university in Tennessee and receive no final failing grade in any course. No academic standard or financial need requirements apply.

Financial data Grants are $1,000 per semester for full-time study or $500 per semester for part-time study. Funds are awarded after completion of each semester of work.

Duration Grants are awarded until completion of the equivalent of 8 full semesters of work, completion of a baccalaureate degree, or the eighth anniversary of honorable discharge from military service, whichever comes first.

Additional information This program was added as a component of the Tennessee Education Lottery Scholarship Program in 2005.

Number awarded Varies each year; recently, 503 students received $680,000 in scholarships.

Deadline August of each year for fall enrollment, January of each year for spring, or April of each year for summer.

[356]
TEXAS ARMED SERVICES SCHOLARSHIP PROGRAM

Texas Higher Education Coordinating Board
Attn: Grants and Special Programs
1200 East Anderson Lane
P.O. Box 12788
Austin, TX 78711-2788
(512) 427-6340   Toll Free: (800) 242-3062
Fax: (512) 427-6420   E-mail: grantinfo@thecb.state.tx.us
Web: www.collegeforalltexans.com

Summary To provide funding to high school seniors in Texas who plan to participate in an ROTC program at a college in the state and then serve in the U.S. armed forces, the Texas National Guard, or the Texas Air National Guard.

Eligibility This program is open to seniors graduating from high schools in Texas who can meet any 2 of the following requirements: 1) are on track to graduate with the Distinguished Achievement Program (DAP) or International Baccalaureate (IB) Program; 2) have a high school GPA of 3.0 or higher; 3) have an SAT score of 1590 or higher or an ACT score of 23 or higher; or 4) rank in the top third of their class. Applicants must plan to attend a public or private college or university in Texas and enter into a written agreement to com-

plete 4 years of ROTC training, graduate within 5 years, and serve 4 years as a member of the Texas Army or Air Force National Guard or as a commissioned officer in the U.S. armed services. They must apply through their state senator or representative.

Financial data The current stipend is $10,000 per year. If recipients fail to fulfill their service agreement, they must repay all funds received.

Duration 1 year; may be renewed up to 3 additional years.

Additional information This program began in 2010.

Number awarded Up to 185 each year.

Deadline Legislators must submit nominations by August of each year.

[357]
TEXAS NATIONAL GUARD TUITION ASSISTANCE PROGRAM

Texas Higher Education Coordinating Board
Attn: Grants and Special Programs
1200 East Anderson Lane
P.O. Box 12788
Austin, TX 78711-2788
(512) 427-6340   Toll Free: (800) 242-3062
Fax: (512) 427-6420   E-mail: grantinfo@thecb.state.tx.us
Web: www.collegeforalltexans.com

Summary To provide financial assistance for college or graduate school to members of the Texas National Guard.

Eligibility This program is open to Texas residents who are active, drilling members of the Texas National Guard, the Texas Air Guard, or the State Guard. Applicants may be undergraduate or graduate students attending or planning to attend a public or private college or university in Texas; attendance at career colleges or universities is not supported.

Financial data Eligible Guard members receive exemption from tuition at Texas public colleges and universities. For students who attend a private, nonprofit institution, the award is based on public university tuition charges for 12 semester credit hours at the resident rate.

Duration Tuition assistance is available for up to 12 semester credit hours per semester for up to 10 semesters or 5 academic years, whichever occurs first.

Number awarded Varies each year; recently, 864 Guard members participated in this program.

Deadline June of each year for the fall semester; November of each year for the spring semester.

[358]
THE ROCKS WASHINGTON D.C. CHAPTER SCHOLARSHIPS

The ROCKS, Inc.-Washington D.C. Chapter
c/o Col. Tommy T. Osborne, Vice President, Operations
5223 Pumphrey Drive
Fairfax, VA 22032-2626
(703) 425-7402   E-mail: tosborne@madentech.com
Web: www.therocksdc.org

Summary To provide financial assistance to high school seniors and college freshmen, especially those involved in JROTC or ROTC programs, who have a connection to the Washington, D.C. chapter of The ROCKS, Inc.

Eligibility This program is open to 1) seniors graduating from high schools in the Washington, D.C. area who have been involved in a JROTC program and plan to attend college in any state; 2) residents of any state currently enrolled as freshmen at a college or university in the Washington, D.C. area and participating in an ROTC program; and 3) direct relatives (children, siblings, nieces, nephews, grandchildren) of the Washington D.C. chapter of The Rocks, Inc. who are high school seniors or college freshmen. Applicants must have a GPA of 3.0 or higher. Along with their application, they must submit a 500-word essay on why young American men and women should join the U.S. military today. Financial need is not considered in the selection process.

Financial data   The stipend is $1,000.

Duration   1 year.

Additional information   The sponsor is an organization of African American active-duty, Reserve, retired, and former commissioned officers of the U.S. armed forces.

Number awarded   5 each year.

Deadline   February of each year.

[359]
TIDEWATER CHAPTER ROTC SCHOLARSHIP PROGRAM

Armed Forces Communications and Electronics
 Association-Tidewater Chapter
Attn: Scholarship Program
P.O. Box 65337
Langley AFB, VA 23665-0337
(757) 846-0037   E-mail: makeva.flowers@yahoo.com
Web: www.afceatidewater.com

Summary   To provide financial assistance to students enrolled in ROTC who are majoring in selected areas of science and engineering.

Eligibility   This program is open to students at colleges and universities in the United States who are enrolled in at least the first year of an ROTC program. U.S. citizenship is required. Applicants must be working full time on a degree in electrical engineering, aerospace engineering, computer engineering, mathematics, computer science, electronics, telecommunications, or physics. They must be nominated by their professor of military science, naval science, or aerospace studies. Membership in AFCEA is not required. Along with their application, they must submit a 1-page essay on: "How the AFCEA Scholarship Can Benefit My Education." Selection is based on academic achievement, participation in extracurricular activities, and financial need.

Financial data   A stipend is awarded (amount not specified). Funds are sent directly to the recipient's university.

Duration   1 year.

Deadline   April of each year.

[360]
U.S. ARMY WOMEN'S FOUNDATION LEGACY SCHOLARSHIPS

U.S. Army Women's Foundation
Attn: Scholarship Committee
P.O. Box 5030
Fort Lee, VA 23801-0030
(804) 734-3078   E-mail: info@awfdn.org
Web: www.awfdn.org/programs/legacyscholarships.shtml

Summary   To provide money for college to women who are serving or have served in the Army and their children.

Eligibility   This program is open to 1) women who have served or are serving honorably in the U.S. Army, U.S. Army

Reserve, or Army National Guard; and 2) children of women who served honorably in the U.S. Army, U.S. Army Reserve, or Army National Guard. Applicants must be 1) upper-division students at an accredited college or university and have a GPA of 3.0 or higher; or 2) high school graduates or GED recipients enrolled at a community college and have a GPA of 2.5 or higher. Along with their application, they must submit a 2-page essay on why they should be considered for this scholarship, their future plans as related to their program of study, and information about their community service, activities, and work experience. Selection is based on merit, academic potential, community service, and financial need.

Financial data   The stipend is $2,500 for college and university students or $1,000 for community college students.

Duration   1 year.

Number awarded   5 to 10 each year.

Deadline   January of each year.

[361]
USFAA SCHOLARSHIPS

United States Field Artillery Association
Attn: Scholarship Committee
Building 758, McNair Avenue
P.O. Box 33027
Fort Sill, OK 73503-0027
(580) 355-4677   Toll Free: (866) 355-4677
Fax: (580) 355-8745   E-mail: amy@fieldartillery.org
Web: www.fieldartillery.org/usfaa_scholarship/index.html

Summary   To provide financial assistance for college to members of the United States Field Artillery Association (USFAA) and their immediate family.

Eligibility   This program is open to 3 categories of students: USFAA members (officer or enlisted), immediate family of enlisted members, and immediate family of officer members. Applicants must have been accepted for admission as an undergraduate at an accredited college, university, or vocational program. Along with their application, they must submit an essay explaining their educational goals and how this scholarship will help meet those goals. Financial need is also considered in the selection process. The highest-ranked applicant receives the GEN Donald R. Keith Scholarship.

Financial data   Stipends range from $1,000 to $2,500.

Duration   1 year.

Additional information   The USFAA services the field artillery branch of the military.

Number awarded   Varies each year; recently, 11 of these scholarships were awarded: 1 at $2,500 (the GEN Donald R. Keith Scholarship), 4 at $1,500, and 6 at $1,000.

Deadline   March of each year.

[362]
USMCCCA SCHOLARSHIPS

United States Marine Corps Combat Correspondents
 Association
Attn: Executive Director
110 Fox Court
Wildwood, FL 34785
(352) 748-4698   E-mail: usmccca@cfl.rr.com
Web: www.usmccca.org/archives/4941

Summary   To provide financial assistance to members of the U.S. Marine Corps Combat Correspondents Association (USMCCCA) or their dependents and Marines in designated occupational fields who are interested in studying communications in college.

Eligibility This program is open to 1) members of USMCCCA, their dependents, and their spouses; and 2) active-duty Marines in Occupational Fields 4300 and 4600 and their dependents who are USMCCCA members or will agree to become members if awarded a scholarship. Applicants must be enrolled or planning to enroll in an undergraduate program in communications. Along with their application, they must submit 500-word essays on 1) their noteworthy achievements and long-range goals; and 2) the United States I want to see in 15 years and my role in the transformation. Financial need is not considered in the selection process.

Financial data Stipends range up to $3,000; funds are disbursed directly to the recipient's institution to be used exclusively for tuition, books, and/or fees.

Duration 1 year.

Number awarded 1 or more each year.

Deadline May of each year.

[363]
UTAH NATIONAL GUARD STATE TUITION ASSISTANCE PROGRAM

Utah Army National Guard
Attn: UT-G1-ESO
12953 South Minuteman Drive
P.O. Box 1776
Draper, UT 84020-1776
(801) 523-4534   E-mail: ngut.sta@us.army.mil
Web: www.ut.ngb.army.mil/education2

Summary To provide tuition assistance for college or graduate school to currently-enrolled members of the Utah National Guard.

Eligibility This program is open to Utah residents who are MOS/AFSC qualified members of the Utah National Guard. Applicants must be seeking funding to obtain a 1) high school diploma or GED certification; 2) undergraduate, graduate, vocational, technical, or licensure certificate; 3) associate degree; 4) baccalaureate degree; or 5) master's or first professional degree, such as architecture, certified public accountant, podiatry (D.P.M.), dentistry (D.D.S. or D.M.D.), medicine (M.D.), optometry (O.D.), osteopathic medicine (D.O.), pharmacy (D.Pharm.), law (J.D.), or theology (M.Div. or M.H.L.). Enlisted personnel must have remaining obligation on their existing enlistment contract that will extend to or beyond the last date of course enrollment for these funds. Officers must have at least 4 years of Selected Reserve service remaining from the date of completion of the course for which this funding is provided.

Financial data Support is provided for 100% of the cost of tuition, to a maximum of $250 per hour or a maximum of $4,500 per year.

Duration 1 semester; recipients may renew.

Additional information Members of the Utah Air National Guard should contact the 151st MSF-DPH, 765 North 2200 West, Salt Lake City, UT 84116. Recipients of this funding may continue to receive any GI Bill funding to which they are entitled, but they may not simultaneously apply for this and federal Tuition Assistance benefits.

Number awarded Varies each year; recently, a total of $750,000 was available for this program.

Deadline March of each year for summer term; August of each year for fall term; November of each year for winter or spring term.

[364]
UTAH NATIONAL GUARD STATE TUITION WAIVER

Utah Army National Guard
Attn: UT-G1-ESO
12953 South Minuteman Drive
P.O. Box 1776
Draper, UT 84020-1776
(801) 523-4537   E-mail: utng.education@us.army.mil
Web: www.ut.ngb.army.mil/education2

Summary To waive tuition for members of the Utah National Guard at public institutions in the state.

Eligibility This program is open to Utah residents who are MOS/AFSC qualified members of the Utah National Guard. Applicants must have been accepted as a full-time student at a public college or university in the state. They may not currently be on active duty and may not already have a 4-year degree. Along with their application, they must submit a short essay describing the difference between a Strategic Reserve Force and an Operational Reserve Force.

Financial data This program provides waiver of tuition at Utah public colleges and universities.

Duration 1 semester; recipients may renew.

Additional information Members of the Utah Air National Guard should contact the 151st MSF-DPH, 765 North 2200 West, Salt Lake City, UT 84116. Recipients of these waivers may continue to receive any GI Bill funding to which they are entitled and they may utilize state Tuition Assistance or federal Tuition Assistance to pay for fees or credits not covered by this program.

Number awarded Varies each year. Each Utah public college and university is required to set aside 2.5% of its scholarship funds for members of the National Guard.

Deadline May of each year.

[365]
VA MORTGAGE CENTER.COM MILITARY EDUCATION SCHOLARSHIP PROGRAM

VA Mortgage Center.com
2101 Chapel Plaza Court, Suite 107
Columbia, MO 65203
(573) 876-2729   Toll Free: (800) 405-6682
E-mail: jbuerck@vamc.com
Web: www.vamortgagecenter.com/scholarships.html

Summary To provide financial assistance for college to students who have a tie to the military.

Eligibility This program is open to 1) current and prospective ROTC program students; 2) active-duty military personnel with plans to attend college; 3) honorably-discharged veterans of the U.S. military; and 4) children of veterans or active-duty military. Applicants must be attending or planning to attend college as a full-time student. Selection is based primarily on an essay.

Financial data The stipend is $1,000.

Duration 1 year.

Additional information This program began in 2007.

Number awarded 10 each year: 5 each term.

Deadline April or October of each year.

[366]
VAA/ANGEA SCHOLARSHIP

Virginia Army/Air National Guard Enlisted Association
Attn: SMSgt Lori W. Flinn Scholarship Chair
15249 Fountain Road
Ashland, VA 23005
(804) 519-6491   E-mail: Scholarship@vaaangea.org
Web: www.vaaangea.org

Summary To provide financial assistance to members of the Virginia Army/Air National Guard Enlisted Association (VaA/ANGEA) and their families who are interested in attending college in any state.

Eligibility This program is open to 1) enlisted soldiers or enlisted airmen currently serving as a member of the Virginia National Guard (VNG) who are also a member of the VaA/ANGEA; 2) retired enlisted soldiers or retired enlisted airmen of the VNG who are also a member of the VaA/ANGEA; 3) spouses of current enlisted soldiers or enlisted airmen of the VNG who are also a member of the VaA/ANGEA; 4) spouses of retired enlisted soldiers or retired enlisted airmen of the VNG who are also a member of the VaA/ANGEA; and 5) dependents of current or retired enlisted soldiers or airmen of the VNG (a copy of the dependency decree may be required) who are also a member of the VaA/ANGEA. Applicants must submit a copy of their school transcript (high school or college), a letter with specific facts about their desire to continue their education and their need for assistance, 3 letters of recommendation, a letter of academic reference, and a photocopy of their VaA/ANGEA membership card. Selection is based on academics (15 points), personal statement (15 points), letters of recommendation (16 points), school involvement (15 points), community involvement (15 points), responsibility (15 points), and financial need (9 points).

Financial data Generally, stipends are $1,000 or $500.

Duration 1 year; recipients may reapply.

Number awarded Generally, 2 scholarships at $1,000 and 4 scholarships at $500 are awarded each year.

Deadline March of each year.

[367]
VADM SAMUEL L. GRAVELY, JR., USN (RET.) MEMORIAL SCHOLARSHIPS

Armed Forces Communications and Electronics
  Association
Attn: AFCEA Educational Foundation
4400 Fair Lakes Court
Fairfax, VA 22033-3899
(703) 631-6138   Toll Free: (800) 336-4583, ext. 6138
Fax: (703) 631-4693   E-mail: scholarshipsinfo@afcea.org
Web: www.afcea.org

Summary To provide funding to students (particularly those who are veterans or current military personnel) majoring in specified scientific fields at an Historically Black College or University (HBCU).

Eligibility This program is open to sophomores and juniors enrolled full or part time at an accredited 2- or 4-year HBCU or in a distance learning or online degree program affiliated with those institutions. They must be working toward a bachelor's degree in engineering (aerospace, computer, electrical, or systems), computer science, computer engineering technology, computer information systems, mathematics, physics, information systems management, or other field directly

related to the support of U.S. intelligence or homeland security enterprises. Special consideration is given to military enlisted personnel and veterans.

Financial data The stipend is $5,000.

Duration 1 year; may be renewed.

Additional information This program was established in 2009 with support from American Systems.

Number awarded At least 2 each year.

Deadline April of each year.

[368]
VETERANS OF ENDURING FREEDOM (AFGHANISTAN) AND IRAQI FREEDOM SCHOLARSHIP

Armed Forces Communications and Electronics
  Association
Attn: AFCEA Educational Foundation
4400 Fair Lakes Court
Fairfax, VA 22033-3899
(703) 631-6138   Toll Free: (800) 336-4583, ext. 6138
Fax: (703) 631-4693   E-mail: scholarshipsinfo@afcea.org
Web: www.afcea.org

Summary To provide financial assistance to veterans and military personnel who served in Afghanistan or Iraq and are working on an undergraduate degree in fields related to the support of U.S. intelligence enterprises.

Eligibility This program is open to active-duty and honorably discharged U.S. military members (including Reservists and National Guard personnel) who served in Enduring Freedom (Afghanistan) or Iraqi Freedom operations. Applicants must be enrolled at a 2- or 4-year institution in the United States and working on an undergraduate degree in computer engineering technology, computer information systems, computer network systems, computer science, electronics engineering technology, engineering (aerospace, computer, electrical, or systems), information systems management, information systems security, mathematics, physics, technology management, or other field directly related to the support of U.S. intelligence enterprises or national security. Along with their application, they must submit an essay that includes a brief synopsis of relevant work experience (including military assignments), a brief statement of career goals after graduation, and an explanation of how their academic and career goals will contribute to the areas related to communications, intelligence and/or information systems, and the mission of the Armed Forces Communications and Electronics Association (AFCEA). Financial need is also considered.

Financial data The stipend is $2,500.

Duration 1 year.

Additional information This program began in 2005 with funding from the Northern Virginia Chapter of AFCEA.

Number awarded 12 each year: 6 for the fall semester and 6 for the spring semester.

Deadline March of each year for fall semester; October of each year for spring semester.

[369]
VIRGINIA NATIONAL GUARD ASSOCIATION SCHOLARSHIP

Virginia National Guard Association
Attn: Scholarship Committee
5901 Beulah Road
Sandston, VA 23150-6112
(804) 350-0175
Web: www.vnga.org/scholarship.shtml

Summary To provide financial assistance to members of the Virginia National Guard Association (VNGA) and their families who are interested in attending college in any state.

Eligibility Applicants must have been enrolled at a college or university in any state for 1 year and qualify under 1 of the following conditions: 1) an officer or warrant officer in the Virginia National Guard and a VNGA member; 2) the dependent child or spouse of an officer or warrant officer in the Virginia National Guard who is a VNGA member; 3) the dependent child or spouse of a retired officer or warrant officer who is a VNGA member; 4) the dependent child or spouse of a deceased retired officer or warrant officer, or 5) the dependent child or spouse of a Virginia National Guard officer or warrant officer who died while in the Virginia National Guard. Along with their application, they must submit a brief description of their educational and/or military objectives, a list of their leadership positions and honors, and a brief statement of their financial need.

Financial data A stipend is awarded; the amount is determined annually.

Duration 1 year; may be renewed for 2 additional years.

Additional information The association also offers a special scholarship in memory of CW4 William C. Singletary who, in rescuing 2 elderly women from drowning, gave his own life.

Number awarded Varies each year.

Deadline September of each year.

[370]
VIRGINIA NATIONAL GUARD TUITION ASSISTANCE PROGRAM

Virginia National Guard
Attn: Educational Services Officer
Fort Pickett, Building 316
Blackstone, VA 23824-6316
(434) 298-6222   Toll Free: (888) 483-2682
Fax: (434) 298-6296   E-mail: vaeducation@ng.army.mil
Web: vko.va.ngb.army.mil/VirginiaGuard

Summary To provide financial assistance to members of the Virginia National Guard who are interested in attending college or graduate school in the state.

Eligibility This program is open to active members of the Virginia National Guard who are residents of Virginia and interested in attending college or graduate school in the state. Awards are presented in the following priority order: 1) enlisted personnel who have previously received assistance through this program; 2) officers who need to complete a bachelor's degree in order to be eligible for promotion to captain; 3) warrant officers working on an associate or bachelor's degree; 4) any member working on an undergraduate degree; and 4) any member working on a graduate degree.

Financial data The program provides reimbursement of tuition at approved colleges, universities, and vocational/technical schools in Virginia, to a maximum of $2,000 per semes-

ter or $6,000 per year. Bookstore grants up to $350 per semester are also provided.

Duration 1 semester; may be renewed.

Additional information This program began in 1983. Recipients must remain in the Guard for at least 2 years after being funded.

Number awarded Varies each year.

Deadline March of each year for summer session; June of each year for fall semester; October of each year for spring semester.

[371]
WALTER BEALL SCHOLARSHIP

Walter Beall Scholarship Foundation
c/o W. Ralph Holcombe, Secretary/Treasurer
4911 Fennell Court
Suffolk, VA 23435
(757) 484-7403   Fax: (757) 686-5952
E-mail: info@walterbeallscholarship.org
Web: www.walterbeallscholarship.org

Summary To provide financial assistance to members of the Fleet Reserve Association (FRA) and their families who are interested in studying engineering, aeronautical engineering, or aviation in college.

Eligibility This program is open to FRA members who have been in good standing for at least the past 2 consecutive years and their spouses, children, and grandchildren. Students in a Reserve officer candidate program receiving aid or attending a military academy are not eligible. Applicants must be enrolled at an accredited college, university, or technical institution in the United States in a program related to general engineering, aviation, or aeronautical engineering. Selection is based on GPA, scholastic aptitude test scores, curriculum goals, interests, community activities, awards, and financial need. U.S. citizenship is required.

Financial data The amounts of the awards depend on the availability of funds and the need of the recipients; they range from $2,000 to $5,000.

Duration 1 year; recipients may reapply.

Additional information The Walter Beall Scholarship Foundation is sponsored by the Past Regional Presidents Club of the Fleet Reserve Association. Membership in the FRA is restricted to active-duty, retired, and Reserve members of the Navy, Marine Corps, and Coast Guard.

Number awarded 1 or more each year.

Deadline April of each year.

[372]
WASHINGTON NATIONAL GUARD SCHOLARSHIP PROGRAM

Washington National Guard
Attn: Education Services Office
Building 15, G1-ED
Camp Murray, WA 98430
(253) 512-8838   Toll Free: (800) 606-9843 (within WA)
Fax: (253) 512-8941 E-mail: education@wa.ngb.army.mil
Web: washingtonguard.org/edu

Summary To provide funding to members of the Washington National Guard who wish to attend college or graduate school in the state.

Eligibility This program is open to members of the Washington National Guard who have already served for at least 1 year and have at least 2 years remaining on their current contract. Applicants must have a rank between E1 and O3. They must be attending an accredited college as a resident of Washington state and must already have utilized all available federal educational benefits. Army Guard members must have completed BCT/AIT and awarded initial MOS; Air Guard members must have completed BMT/initial tech school and been awarded "3-Level" AFSC. Graduate students are eligible, but undergraduates receive preference as long as they are making satisfactory progress toward a baccalaureate degree. The minimum GPA requirement is 2.5 for undergraduates or 3.0 for graduate students.

Financial data This program provides a stipend that is based on the number of credits completed but does not exceed the amount required for tuition, books, and fees at the University of Washington. Recipients incur a service obligation of 1 additional year in the Guard for the initial scholarship award and 1 additional year for each full year of academic credit completed with this assistance. The grant serves as a loan which is forgiven if the recipient completes the contracted service time in the Washington National Guard. Failure to meet the service obligation requires the recipient to repay the loan plus 8% interest.

Duration 1 year; may be renewed.

Number awarded Varies each year. A total of $100,000 is available for this program annually; scholarships are awarded on a first-come, first-served basis as long as funds are available.

Deadline June of each year.

[373]
WEST VIRGINIA NATIONAL GUARD EDUCATIONAL ENCOURAGEMENT PROGRAM

Office of the Adjutant General
Attn: Education Officer
1703 Coonskin Drive
Charleston, WV 25311-1085
(304) 561-6306   Toll Free: (866) 986-4326
Fax: (304) 561-6307   E-mail: kathy.kidd@us.army.mil
Web: www.wv.ngb.army.mil/education/benefits/default.aspx

Summary To provide financial assistance to members of the National Guard in West Virginia who are interested in attending college or graduate school in the state.

Eligibility This program is open to active members of the West Virginia National Guard who are residents of West Virginia and interested in attending a public or private college in the state. Applicants must have maintained satisfactory participation (90% attendance) in the Guard. They must be interested in working on a vocational, associate, bachelor's, or master's degree. In some instances, support may also be available to Guard members who are interested in working on an M.D., D.O., P.A., or J.D. degree.

Financial data The program provides payment of 100% of the tuition and fees at participating colleges and universities in West Virginia, to a maximum of $6,000 per year.

Duration 1 academic year; may be renewed.

Number awarded Varies each year.

Deadline Deadline not specified.

[374]
WISCONSIN NATIONAL GUARD ENLISTED ASSOCIATION COLLEGE GRANT PROGRAM

Wisconsin National Guard Enlisted Association
Attn: Executive Director
2400 Wright Street
Madison, WI 53704
(608) 242-3112   E-mail: WNGEA@yahoo.com
Web: www.wngea.org/MAIN/PROG/prosch.htm

Summary To provide financial assistance to members of the Wisconsin National Guard Enlisted Association (WNGEA) and their spouses and children who are interested in attending college or graduate school in any state.

Eligibility This program is open to WNGEA members, the unmarried children and spouses of WNGEA members, and the unmarried children and spouses of deceased WNGEA members. WNGEA member applicants, as well as the parents or guardians of unmarried children who are applicants, must have at least 1 year remaining on their enlistment following completion of the school year for which application is submitted (or they must have 20 or more years of service). Applicants must be enrolled at a college, university, graduate school, trade school, or business school in any state. Selection is based on need, leadership, and moral character.

Financial data Stipends are $1,000 or $500 per year.

Duration 1 year; recipients may not reapply for 2 years.

Additional information This program includes 1 scholarship sponsored by the USAA Insurance Corporation.

Number awarded Varies each year; recently, 4 of these scholarships were awarded: the Raymond A. Matera Scholarship at $1,000 and 3 others at $500 each.

Deadline April of each year.

[375]
WISCONSIN NATIONAL GUARD TUITION GRANT

Wisconsin Department of Military Affairs
Attn: Education Services Office
WIAR-PA-ED
P.O. Box 8111
Madison, WI 53708-8111
(608) 242-3159   Toll Free: (800) 335-5147
Fax: (608) 242-3154   E-mail: dustin.cebula@us.army.mil
Web: dma.wi.gov/dma/dma/education.asp

Summary To provide financial assistance for college to members of the Wisconsin National Guard.

Eligibility Eligible to apply for these grants are enlisted members and warrant officers in good standing in the Wisconsin National Guard who wish to work on an undergraduate degree. Applicants may not have been flagged for unexcused absences or failing to meet Guard standards. They must be attending or planning to attend an extension division or campus of the University of Wisconsin system, a public institution of higher education under the Minnesota-Wisconsin student reciprocity agreement, a campus of the Wisconsin Technical College System, or an accredited institution of higher education located within Wisconsin.

Financial data This program offers assistance based on the undergraduate tuition rate of the University of Wisconsin at Madison (recently, that was $8,313 per year for full-time study).

Duration 8 semesters of full-time study or completion of a bachelor's degree.

Number awarded Varies each year.

Deadline Applications may be submitted at any time, but they must be received at least 30 days prior to the beginning of the course.

[376]
WOMEN MARINES ASSOCIATION SCHOLARSHIP PROGRAM

Women Marines Association
P.O. Box 377
Oaks, PA 19456-0377
Toll Free: (888) 525-1943
E-mail: scholarship@womenmarines.org
Web: www.womenmarines.org/scholarships.aspx

Summary To provide money for college or graduate school to students with ties to the military who are sponsored by members of the Women Marines Association (WMA).

Eligibility Applicants must be sponsored by a WMA member and fall into 1 of the following categories: 1) have served or are serving in the U.S. Marine Corps, regular or Reserve; 2) are a direct descendant by blood or legal adoption or a stepchild of a Marine on active duty or who has served honorably in the U.S. Marine Corps, regular or Reserve; 3) are a sibling or a descendant of a sibling by blood or legal adoption or a stepchild of a Marine on active duty or who has served honorably in the U.S. Marine Corps, regular or Reserve; or 4) have completed 2 years in a Marine Corps JROTC program. WMA members may sponsor an unlimited number of applicants per year. High school seniors must submit transcripts (GPA of 3.0 or higher) and SAT or ACT scores. Undergraduate and graduate students must have a GPA of 3.0 or higher.

Financial data The stipend is $1,500 per year.

Duration 1 year; may be renewed 1 additional year.

Additional information This program includes the following named scholarships: the WMA Memorial Scholarships, the Lily H. Gridley Memorial Scholarship, the Ethyl and Armin Wiebke Memorial Scholarship, the Maj. Megan Malia McClung Memorial Scholarship, the Agnes Sopcak Memorial Scholarship, the Virginia Guveyan Memorial Scholarship, and the LaRue A. Ditmore Music Scholarships. Applicants must know a WMA member to serve as their sponsor; the WMA will not supply listings of the names or addresses of chapters or individual members.

Number awarded Varies each year.

Deadline January of each year.

[377]
WOSL SCHOLARSHIPS FOR WOMEN

Women's Overseas Service League
Attn: Scholarship Committee
P.O. Box 124
Cedar Knolls, NJ 07927-0124
E-mail: kelsey@openix.com
Web: www.wosl.org/scholarships.htm

Summary To provide financial assistance for college to women who are committed to a military or other public service career.

Eligibility This program is open to women who are committed to a military or other public service career. Applicants must have completed at least 12 semester or 18 quarter hours of postsecondary study with a GPA of 2.5 or higher. They must be working on an academic degree (the program

may be professional or technical in nature) and must agree to enroll for at least 6 semester or 9 quarter hours of study each academic period. Along with their application, they must submit a 250-word essay on their career goals. Financial need is considered in the selection process.

Financial data Stipends range from $500 to $1,000 per year.

Duration 1 year; may be renewed 1 additional year.

Additional information The Women's Overseas Service League is a national organization of women who have served overseas in or with the armed forces.

Deadline February of each year.

[378]
WYOMING NATIONAL GUARD EDUCATIONAL ASSISTANCE PLAN

Wyoming National Guard
Attn: Education Services Officer
5410 Bishop Boulevard
Cheyenne, WY 82009
(307) 772-5939   Toll Free: (800) 832-1959, ext. 5939
Fax: (307) 772-5132   E-mail: wyomingguard@state.wy.us
Web: wyoguard.com/education/assistance

Summary To provide financial assistance to members of the Wyoming National Guard who are interested in attending college or graduate school in the state.

Eligibility This program is open to members of the Wyoming Army National Guard and the Wyoming Air National Guard who have spent at least 6 years in the Guard or are currently serving under their initial 6-year enlistment period. New enlistees who commit to serving 6 years are also eligible. Applicants may be pursuing, or planning to pursue, a degree at any level at the University of Wyoming, a Wyoming community college, or an approved technical institution in Wyoming.

Financial data The program provides full payment of tuition at eligible institutions.

Duration Guard members may continue to receive these benefits as long as they maintain a GPA of 2.0 or higher, keep up with Guard standards for drill attendance, and remain in good standing with the Guard.

Additional information The Wyoming legislature created this program in 2001. Recipients must agree to serve in the Guard for at least 2 years after they graduate or stop using the plan.

Number awarded Varies each year.

Deadline Deadline not specified.

[379]
YOUNG PATRIOT SCHOLARSHIP

Idaho Enlisted Association of the National Guard of the
  United States
c/o Steve Vinsonhaler
7054 West Saxton Drive
Boise, ID 83714-2366
(208) 407-4887   E-mail: svinsonhaler@imd.idaho.gov
Web: eangusidaho.org/Scholarships.php

Summary To provide financial assistance to members of the Idaho Enlisted Association of the National Guard of the United States and their family members who are interested in attending college in any state.

Eligibility This program is open to 1) members of the association; 2) dependent unmarried children of members; 3) spouses of members; and 4) unmarried spouses and unmarried dependent children of deceased members who were in good standing at the time of death. Association members must also be enlisted members of the Idaho National Guard with at least 1 year remaining on their enlistment or have 20 or more years of military service. Applicants must be enrolled or planning to enroll full time at a college, university, trade school, or business school in any state. Along with their application, they must submit a 2-page essay about an activity or interest that has been meaningful to them, a personal letter providing information about themselves and their families, 2 letters of recommendation, an academic letter of recommendation, and a copy of the sponsor's current membership card or number. Family income is considered in the selection process.

Financial data The stipend is $1,500.

Duration 1 year; nonrenewable.

Number awarded 1 each year.

Deadline August of each year.

Family Members

[380]
100TH INFANTRY BATTALION MEMORIAL SCHOLARSHIP FUND

Hawai'i Community Foundation
Attn: Scholarship Department
827 Fort Street Mall
Honolulu, HI 96813
(808) 537-6333   Toll Free: (888) 731-3863
Fax: (808) 521-6286
E-mail: scholarships@hcf-hawaii.org
Web: www.hawaiicommunityfoundation.org/scholarships

Summary To provide financial assistance for college or graduate school to descendants of 100th Infantry Battalion World War II veterans.

Eligibility This program is open to entering and continuing full-time undergraduate and graduate students at 2- and 4-year colleges and universities. Applicants must be a direct descendant of a World War II veteran of the 100th Infantry Battalion (which was comprised of Americans of Japanese descent). They must be able to demonstrate academic achievement (GPA of 3.5 or higher), an active record of extracurricular activities and community service, a willingness to promote the legacy of the 100th Infantry Battalion of World War II, and financial need. Along with their application, they must submit a short statement indicating their reasons for attending college, their planned course of study, their career goals, and what community service means to them. They must also submit a separate essay on the legacy of the 100th Infantry Battalion and how they will contribute to forwarding that legacy. Current residency in Hawaii is not required.

Financial data The amounts of the awards depend on the availability of funds and the need of the recipient. Recently, the average value of each of the scholarships awarded by the foundation was more than $2,000.

Duration 1 year.

Number awarded Varies each year; recently, 2 of these scholarships were awarded.

Deadline February of each year.

[381]
10TH MOUNTAIN DIVISION DESCENDANT MERIT SCHOLARSHIP

10th Mountain Division Descendants, Inc.
c/o Don Perkins, Treasurer
P.O. Box 20011
New York, NY 10017-0001
E-mail: 10thmtndesc@gmail.com
Web: www.10thmtndivdesc.org/scholarship.html

Summary To provide money for college to descendants of members of the 10th Mountain Division.

Eligibility Eligible to apply for these scholarships are the descendants of veterans who served in the 10th Mountain Division during World War II. Applicants must be entering their first year of college. Selection is based on service to the World War II 10th Mountain Division (e.g., assisting at local chapter functions, involved in activities that support the legacy of the division, assisting at memorial services to the division, visiting veterans and/or wives or widows in nursing or private homes). Financial need is not considered. Membership in 10th Mountain Division Descendants, Inc. is not required, but it is recommended that the applicant or a parent be a member.

Financial data The stipend is $1,000.

Duration 1 year.

Number awarded 1 each year.

Deadline April each year.

[382]
10TH MOUNTAIN DIVISION (LIGHT INFANTRY) SCHOLARSHIPS

Northern New York Community Foundation, Inc.
120 Washington Street, Suite 400
Watertown, NY 13601
(315) 782-7110   Fax: (315) 782-0047
E-mail: info@nnycf.org
Web: www.nnycf.org/scholarships.asp?mm=6

Summary To provide money for college to current and former members of the 10th Mountain Division and their dependents.

Eligibility This program is open to current and former members of the 10th Mountain Division and their dependents (children and spouses). Applicants must be high school seniors applying for the freshmen year or traditional or nontraditional students enrolled as full-time undergraduates in any year of college or technical school. Along with their application, they must submit a 150-word essay on the character traits that have contributed the most to their success, how they have contributed to their success, and how each will contribute to their vision of a successful life. High school juniors who will graduate early because they are in an advanced placement program may also apply. Interviews are required. Selection is based on academics, personal data, and need.

Financial data The stipend is $5,000.

Duration 1 year.

Number awarded Varies each year; recently, 8 of these scholarships were awarded.

Deadline March of each year.

[383]
11TH ARMORED CAVALRY VETERANS OF VIETNAM AND CAMBODIA SCHOLARSHIP

11th Armored Cavalry Veterans of Vietnam and Cambodia
Attn: National Headquarters
P.O. Box 956
Coffeyville, TX 76034-0956
Web: www.11thcavnam.com/scholar.html

Summary To provide financial assistance for college to members of the 11th Armored Cavalry Veterans of Vietnam and Cambodia (11ACVVC) and to their children.

Eligibility This program is open to 1) current members of the 11ACVVC; 2) children and stepchildren of current members of the 11ACVVC; 3) children whose legal guardian is a current member of the 11ACVVC; 4) children of 11th Armored Cavalry troopers who were killed in action, died of wounds, or died as a result of service in Vietnam or Cambodia; and 5) children and stepchildren of 11th Armored Cavalry Regiment veterans who served in Vietnam or Cambodia but are not members of the 11ACVVC. There is no age limit. Applicants must be enrolled or planning to enroll as an undergraduate student. Along with their application, they must submit brief essays on 1) the field of study they plan to enter and why; and 2) why they would be a worthy recipient of this scholarship. Selection is based on those essays (15 points), completeness and legibility of the application (7 points), and grades (8 points); financial need is not considered.

Financial data The stipend is $3,000; funds are paid directly to the recipient's school, in 2 equal installments.

Duration 1 year; nonrenewable.

Additional information This program began in 1997. Recipients must use the awarded money within 44 months.

Number awarded Up to 24 each year. Since the program was established, it has awarded a total of 268 scholarships, with a value of $842,000, including the $5,000 Colonel Charles L. Schmidt Leadership Scholarship.

Deadline May of each year.

[384]
82ND AIRBORNE DIVISION ASSOCIATION AWARDS

82nd Airborne Division Association
Attn: Educational Fund Treasurer
P.O. Box 65089
Fayetteville, NC 28306-5089
(281) 346-2546   E-mail: 82dassnedfund@earthlink.net
Web: www.82ndassociation.org/Scholarships.html

Summary To provide money for college to members of the 82d Airborne Division Association and their dependent children.

Eligibility Eligible to apply for this award are 1) dependent children of 82nd Airborne Division Association voting members; 2) dependent children of 82nd Airborne servicemen killed in combat; 3) dependent children of deceased Life or All American members of the 82nd Airborne Division Association; and 4) former active-duty 82nd Airborne Division troopers who are association members, are within 2 years of honorable discharge, and served no more than 2 enlistments. Applicants must be enrolled in an accredited university or college. Selection is based on academics and need.

Financial data The stipend is $1,500 per year. Funds are paid to the recipient's college or university.

Duration 1 semester (the second in a school year); recipients may reapply for up to 3 additional annual awards.

Additional information In years when a suitable candidate applies, 1 of these awards is designated the General Mathew B. Ridgeway Scholarship. Membership in the association is open to anyone who ever served in the 82nd Airborne Division, anyone who is currently serving on active duty in jump status, and anyone who has ever served in any of the uniformed services on either jump or glider status and was honorably discharged.

Number awarded Varies each year; recently, $128,250 in scholarships was awarded.

Deadline October of each year.

[385]
ADA MUCKLESTONE MEMORIAL SCHOLARSHIPS

American Legion Auxiliary
Department of Illinois
2720 East Lincoln Street
P.O. Box 1426
Bloomington, IL 61702-1426
(309) 663-9366   Fax: (309) 663-5827
E-mail: karen.boughan@ilala.org
Web: www.ilala.org/scholar.html

Summary To provide financial assistance to high school seniors in Illinois who are the descendants of veterans and planning to attend college in any state.

Eligibility This program is open to the children, grandchildren, or great-grandchildren of veterans who served during eligibility dates for membership in the American Legion. Applicants must be high school seniors or graduates who have not yet attended an institution of higher learning and are planning to attend college in any state. They must be residents of Illinois or members of the American Legion Family, Department of Illinois. Along with their application, they must submit a 1,000-word essay on "What My Education Will Do for Me." Selection is based on that essay (25%) character and leadership (25%), scholarship (25%), and financial need (25%).

Financial data The stipend is $1,000.

Duration 1 year.

Number awarded Varies each year.

Deadline March of each year.

[386]
AIR FORCE BAND OF LIBERTY MUSICAL EXCELLENCE SCHOLARSHIP

Hanscom Spouses' Club
Attn: Scholarship Committee Chair
P.O. Box 557
Bedford, MA 01730
(781) 429-2977   E-mail: scholarship@hanscomsc.org
Web: www.hanscomsc.org/HSC/HSC_Scholarship.html

Summary To provide financial assistance to high school seniors who are children of military personnel or veterans in New England, have demonstrated proficiency in music, and plan to attend college in any state.

Eligibility This program is open to dependents of active-duty, retired, and deceased members of any branch of the armed forces, including Reservists and National Guard members who were activated during the school year. Applicants must be graduating high school seniors who have a valid military identification card and reside in New England or be a dependent whose military sponsor is stationed at Hanscom Air Force Base. They must be planning to attend a 2- or 4-year college or university in any state; they are not required to major in music, but they must be able to demonstrate accomplishment in at least 1 of the following categories: brass, classical guitar, jazz, mallet percussion, piano, strings, woodwinds, or voice. Along with their application, they must submit 1) a 2-page essay on their educational goals, how their educational experience will help prepare them to pursue future goals, and how they intend to apply their education to better their community; 2) a 2-page essay specifically addressing their music background, experience, and goals; and 3) a solo recording of their playing or singing in digital format (CD, DVD, flash drive) with or without accompaniment. Selection is based on merit.

Financial data Recently, stipends of all scholarships offered by this sponsor averaged more than $2,000.

Duration 1 year; nonrenewable.

Additional information The recipient is invited to spend a day with the Air Force Band of Liberty.

Number awarded Varies each year; recently, the sponsor awarded a total of 16 high school senior scholarships.

Deadline March of each year.

[387]
AIR FORCE SERGEANTS ASSOCIATION SCHOLARSHIPS

Air Force Sergeants Association
Attn: Scholastic Coordinator
5211 Auth Road
Suitland, MD 20746
(301) 899-3500   Toll Free: (800) 638-0594
Fax: (301) 899-8136   E-mail: balsobrooks@hqafsa.org
Web: www.hqafsa.org

Summary To provide financial assistance for undergraduate education to the dependent children of Air Force enlisted personnel.

Eligibility This program is open to the unmarried children (including stepchildren and legally adopted children) of active-duty, retired, or veteran members of the U.S. Air Force, Air National Guard, or Air Force Reserves. Applicants must be attending or planning to attend an accredited academic institution. They must have an unweighted GPA of 3.5 or higher. Their parent must be a member of the Air Force Sergeants Association or its auxiliary. Along with their application, they must submit 1) a paragraph on their life objectives and what they plan to do with the education they receive; and 2) an essay on the most urgent problem facing society today. High school seniors must also submit a transcript of all high school grades and a record of their SAT or ACT scores. Selection is based on academic record, character, leadership skills, writing ability, versatility, and potential for success. Financial need is not a consideration.

Financial data Stipends range from $1,500 to $2,500 per year. Funds may be used for tuition, room and board, fees, books, supplies, and transportation.

Duration 1 year; may be renewed if the student maintains full-time enrollment.

Additional information This program began in 1968.

Number awarded Varies each year; recently, 12 of these scholarships were awarded: 4 at $2,500, 3 at $2,000, and 5 at $1,500. Since the program began, it has awarded more than 480 scholarships worth more than $650,000.

Deadline March of each year.

[388]
AIR FORCE SERVICES CLUB MEMBERSHIP SCHOLARSHIP PROGRAM

Air Force Services Agency
Attn: HQ AFSVA/SVOFT
10100 Reunion Place, Suite 501
San Antonio, TX 78216-4138
(210) 395-7787
E-mail: web.clubs-operations@randolph.af.mil
Web: www.afclubs.net/CN_Scholarship.htm

Summary To recognize and reward, with academic scholarships, Air Force Club members and their families who submit outstanding essays.

Eligibility This program is open to Air Force Club members and their spouses, children, and stepchildren who have been accepted by or are enrolled at an accredited college or university. Grandchildren are eligible if they are the dependent of a club member. Applicants may be undergraduate or graduate students enrolled full or part time. They must submit an essay of up to 500 words on a topic that changes annually; a recent topic was "My Contribution to the Air Force." Applicants must also include a 1-page summary of their long-term career and life goals and previous accomplishments, including civic, athletic, and academic awards.

Financial data Awards are $1,000 scholarships.

Duration The competition is held annually.

Additional information This competition, first held in 1997, is sponsored by Chase Bank and the Coca-Cola Company.

Number awarded 25 each year.

Deadline Entries must be submitted to the member's base services commander or division chief by June of each year.

[389]
AIR FORCE SPOUSE SCHOLARSHIPS

Air Force Association
Attn: Manager, National Aerospace Awards
1501 Lee Highway
Arlington, VA 22209-1198
(703) 247-5800, ext. 4807
Toll Free: (800) 727-3337, ext. 4807
Fax: (703) 247-5853   E-mail: lcross@afa.org
Web: www.afa.org/aef/aid/spouse.asp

Summary To provide financial assistance for undergraduate or graduate study to spouses of Air Force members.

Eligibility This program is open to spouses of active-duty Air Force, Air National Guard, or Air Force Reserve members. Spouses who are themselves military members or in ROTC are not eligible. Applicants must have a GPA of 3.5 or higher in college (or high school if entering college for the first time) and be able to provide proof of acceptance into an accredited undergraduate or graduate degree program. They must submit a 2-page essay on their academic and career goals, the motivation that led them to that decision, and how Air Force and other local community activities in which they are involved will enhance their goals. Selection is based on the essay and 2 letters of recommendation.

Financial data The stipend is $2,500; funds are sent to the recipients' schools to be used for any reasonable cost related to working on a degree.

Duration 1 year; nonrenewable.

Additional information This program began in 1995.

Number awarded Varies each year; recently, 3 of these scholarships were awarded.

Deadline April of each year.

[390]
AIRMEN MEMORIAL FOUNDATION SCHOLARSHIP PROGRAM

Air Force Sergeants Association
Attn: Scholastic Coordinator
5211 Auth Road
Suitland, MD 20746
(301) 899-3500   Toll Free: (800) 638-0594
Fax: (301) 899-8136   E-mail: balsobrooks@hqafsa.org
Web: www.hqafsa.org

Summary To provide financial assistance for college to the dependent children of enlisted Air Force personnel.

Eligibility This program is open to the unmarried children (including stepchildren and legally adopted children) of active-duty, retired, or veteran members of the U.S. Air Force, Air National Guard, or Air Force Reserves. Applicants must be attending or planning to attend an accredited academic institution. They must have an unweighted GPA of 3.5 or higher. Along with their application, they must submit 1) a paragraph on their life objectives and what they plan to do with the education they receive; and 2) an essay on the most urgent problem facing society today. High school seniors must also submit a transcript of all high school grades and a record of their SAT or ACT scores. Selection is based on academic record, character, leadership skills, writing ability, versatility, and potential for success. Financial need is not a consideration.

Financial data Stipends are $2,000, $1,500, or $1,000; funds may be used for tuition, room and board, fees, books, supplies, and transportation.

Duration 1 year; may be renewed if the recipient maintains full-time enrollment.

Additional information The Air Force Sergeants Association administers this program, which began in 1987, on behalf of the Airmen Memorial Foundation.

Number awarded Varies each year; recently, 30 of these scholarships were awarded: 18 at $2,000, 4 at $1,500, and 8 at $1,000, including 3 sponsored by the United Services Automobile Association (USAA) Insurance Corporation. Since this program began, it has awarded more than $421,000 in financial aid.

Deadline March of each year.

[391]
AL AND WILLAMARY VISTE SCHOLARSHIP PROGRAM

101st Airborne Division Association
32 Screaming Eagle Boulevard
P.O. Box 929
Fort Campbell, KY 42223-0929
(931) 431-0199   Fax: (931) 431-0195
E-mail: 101stairbornedivisionassociation@comcast.net
Web: www.screamingeagle.org/Scholarships.aspx

Summary To provide financial assistance to the spouses, children, and grandchildren of members of the 101st Airborne Division Association who are upper-division or graduate students working on a degree in science.

Eligibility This program is open to college juniors, seniors, and graduate students who maintained a GPA of 3.75 or higher during the preceding school year and whose parent, grandparent, or spouse is (or, if deceased, was) a regular or life (not associate) member of the 101st Airborne Division. Preference is given to students working on a degree in a physical science, medical science, or other scientific research field. Applicants must submit a 500-word essay on what it means to be an American and a letter on their course of study, community service, hobbies, interests, personal achievements, and how a higher education for them in their chosen field can benefit our nation. Selection is based on the letter, career objectives, academic record, and letters of recommendation.

Financial data A stipend is awarded (amount not specified).

Duration 1 year; may be renewed.

Number awarded At least 1 each year.

Deadline May of each year.

[392]
ALABAMA G.I. DEPENDENTS' SCHOLARSHIP PROGRAM

Alabama Department of Veterans Affairs
770 Washington Avenue, Suite 470
Montgomery, AL 36102-1509
(334) 242-5077   Fax: (334) 242-5102
E-mail: willie.moore@va.state.al.us
Web: www.va.state.al.us/scholarship.htm

Summary To provide educational benefits to the dependents of disabled, deceased, and other Alabama veterans.

Eligibility This program is open to children, spouses, and unremarried widow(er)s of veterans who are currently rated as 20% or more service-connected disabled or were so rated at time of death, were a former prisoner of war, have been declared missing in action, died as the result of a service-connected disability, or died while on active military duty in the line of duty. The veteran must have been a permanent civilian resident of Alabama for at least 1 year prior to entering active military service and served honorably for at least 90 days during war time (or less, in case of death or service-connected disability). Veterans who were not Alabama residents at the time of entering active military service may also qualify if they have a 100% disability and were permanent residents of Alabama for at least 5 years prior to filing the application for this program or prior to death, if deceased. Children and stepchildren must be under the age of 26, but spouses and widow(er)s may be of any age. Spouses cease to be eligible if they become divorced from the qualifying veteran. Widow(er)s cease to be eligible if they remarry.

Financial data Eligible dependents may attend any state-supported Alabama institution of higher learning or enroll in a prescribed course of study at any Alabama state-supported trade school without payment of any tuition, book fees, or laboratory charges.

Duration This is an entitlement program for 5 years of full-time undergraduate or graduate study or part-time equivalent for all qualifying children and for spouses and unremarried widow(er)s who veteran spouse is or was rated 100% disabled or meets other qualifying requirements. Spouses and unremarried widow(er)s whose veteran spouse is or was rated between 20% and 90% disabled may attend only 3 standard academic years.

Additional information Benefits for children, spouses, and unremarried widow(er)s are available in addition to federal government benefits. Assistance is not provided for noncredit courses, placement testing, GED preparation, continuing educational courses, pre-technical courses, or state board examinations.

Number awarded Varies each year.

Deadline Applications may be submitted at any time.

[393]
ALASKA FREE TUITION FOR SPOUSE OR DEPENDENT OF ARMED SERVICES MEMBER

Department of Military and Veterans Affairs
Attn: Office of Veterans Affairs
P.O. Box 5800
Fort Richardson, AK 99505-5800
(907) 428-6016   Fax: (907) 428-6019
E-mail: jerry_beale@ak-prepared.com
Web: veterans.alaska.gov/state_benefits.htm

Summary To provide financial assistance for college to dependents and spouses in Alaska of servicemembers who died or were declared prisoners of war or missing in action.

Eligibility Eligible for this benefit are the spouses and dependent children of Alaska residents who died in the line of duty, died of injuries sustained in the line of duty, or were listed by the Department of Defense as a prisoner of war or missing in action. Applicants must be in good standing at a state-supported educational institution in Alaska.

Financial data Those eligible may attend any state-supported educational institution in Alaska without payment of tuition or fees.

Duration 1 year; may be renewed.

Additional information Information is available from the financial aid office of state-supported universities in Alaska.

Number awarded Varies each year.

Deadline Deadline not specified.

[394]
ALASKA LEGION AUXILIARY SCHOLARSHIP

American Legion Auxiliary
Department of Alaska
Attn: Secretary/Treasurer
P.O. Box 670750
Chugiak, AK 99567
(907) 688-0241   Fax: (907) 688-0241
E-mail: aladepak@qci.net
Web: alaskalegionauxiliary.org/Scholarship.htm

Summary To provide financial assistance to veterans' children in Alaska who plan to attend college in any state.

Eligibility This program is open to the children of veterans who served during eligibility dates for membership in the American Legion. Applicants must be between 17 and 24 years of age, high school seniors or graduates who have not yet attended an institution of higher learning, and residents of Alaska. They must be planning to attend a college or university in any state.

Financial data The stipend is $1,500, half of which is payable each semester toward tuition, matriculation, laboratory, or similar fees.

Duration 1 year.

Number awarded 1 each year.

Deadline March of each year.

[395]
ALASKA SEA SERVICES SCHOLARSHIPS

Navy League of the United States
Attn: Scholarships
2300 Wilson Boulevard, Suite 200
Arlington, VA 22201-5424
(703) 528-1775   Toll Free: (800) 356-5760
Fax: (703) 528-2333
E-mail: scholarships@navyleague.org
Web: www.navyleague.org

Summary To provide financial assistance to spouses and dependent children of naval personnel in Alaska who are interested in attending college in any state.

Eligibility This program is open to the spouses and dependent children of personnel serving in the Navy, Marine Corps, or Coast Guard (active duty or Reserve), retired from those services, or were serving at the time of death or missing in action status. Applicants must be residents of Alaska enrolled or planning to enroll full time at an accredited 4-year college or university in any state to work on an undergraduate degree. Selection is based on academic proficiency, character, leadership ability, community involvement, and financial need.

Financial data The stipend is $1,000 per year; funds are paid directly to the academic institution for tuition, books, and fees.

Duration 1 year; may be renewed 1 additional year.

Additional information This program began in 1986 with funds originally raised as a War Bond during World War II to honor the sailors of USS Juneau.

Number awarded Up to 4 each year.

Deadline February of each year.

[396]
ALBERT M. LAPPIN SCHOLARSHIP

American Legion
Department of Kansas
1314 S.W. Topeka Boulevard
Topeka, KS 66612-1886
(785) 232-9315   Fax: (785) 232-1399
Web: www.ksamlegion.org/programs.htm

Summary To provide financial assistance to the children of members of the Kansas American Legion or American Legion Auxiliary who plan to attend college in the state.

Eligibility This program is open to high school seniors and college freshmen and sophomores who are attending or planning to attend an approved Kansas college, university, or trade school. At least 1 of their parents must be a veteran and have been a member of an American Legion post or Auxiliary in Kansas for the past 3 consecutive years. Along with their application, they must submit an essay of 250 to 500 words on "Why I Want to Go to College." Financial need is also considered in the selection process.

Financial data The stipend is $1,000.

Duration 1 year.

Number awarded 1 each year.

Deadline February of each year.

[397]
ALBERT T. MARCOUX MEMORIAL SCHOLARSHIP

American Legion
Department of New Hampshire
State House Annex
25 Capitol Street, Room 431
Concord, NH 03301-6312
(603) 271-2211   Toll Free: (800) 778-3816
Fax: (603) 271-5352
E-mail: adjutantnh@amlegion.state.nh.us
Web: www.nhlegion.org

Summary To provide financial assistance to the children of members of the New Hampshire Department of the American Legion or American Legion Auxiliary who are interested in studying education at a college in any state.

Eligibility This program is open to residents of New Hampshire who are entering their first year at an accredited 4-year college or university in any state to work on a bachelor's degree in the field of education. Applicant's parent must be a member of the American Legion or its Auxiliary (or if deceased have been a member at time of death). They must have a GPA of 3.0 or higher in their junior and senior high school years. Financial need is considered in the selection process.

Financial data The stipend is $2,000.

Duration 1 year.

Number awarded 1 each year.

Deadline April of each year.

[398]
ALEXANDER KREIGLOWA NAVY AND MARINE CORPS DEPENDENTS EDUCATION FOUNDATION SCHOLARSHIP

Navy League of the United States-San Diego Council
Attn: Scholarship Committee
2115 Park Boulevard
San Diego, CA 92101
(619) 230-0301   Fax: (619) 230-0302
Web: www.navyleague-sd.com/Scholarship.htm

Summary To provide financial assistance to high school seniors in California who are children of Naval Service personnel and interested in attending college in any state.

Eligibility This program is open to seniors graduating from high schools in California in the top 10% of their class. Applicants must be the dependent child of an active-duty, retired, or deceased member of the Naval Service (U.S. Navy or U.S. Marine Corps). They must be planning to enroll at an accredited 4-year college or university in any state. Along with their

application, they must submit an essay of 1 to 2 pages describing their high school experience and accomplishments and how those will help them as they pursue a college education. Financial need is considered in the selection process.

Financial data The stipend ranges up to $15,000 per year.

Duration 1 year; may be renewed up to 3 additional years.

Number awarded 1 each year.

Deadline March of each year.

[399]
ALLIE MAE ODEN MEMORIAL SCHOLARSHIP

Ladies Auxiliary of the Fleet Reserve Association
Attn: Membership Service Administrator
P.O. Box 2086
Shingle Springs, CA 95682-2086
(530) 677-3925   E-mail: laframsa@att.net
Web: www.la-fra.org/scholarship.html

Summary To provide financial assistance for college to the children and grandchildren of members of the Fleet Reserve Association (FRA).

Eligibility This program is open to the children and grandchildren of deceased FRA members or of persons who were eligible to be FRA members at the time of their death. Applicants must submit an essay on their life experiences, career objectives, and what motivated them to select those objectives. Selection is based on academic record, financial need, extracurricular activities, leadership skills, and participation in community activities. U.S. citizenship is required.

Financial data The stipend is $2,500.

Duration 1 year; may be renewed.

Additional information Membership in the FRA is open to active-duty, retired, and Reserve members of the Navy, Marine Corps, and Coast Guard.

Number awarded 1 each year.

Deadline April of each year.

[400]
AMERICAL DIVISION VETERANS ASSOCIATION SCHOLARSHIP

Americal Division Veterans Association
c/o Ron Green, Scholar Fund Chair
141 River Bend Drive
Oconee, TN 37361
E-mail: ron_green46@yahoo.com
Web: www.americal.org/scholor.html

Summary To provide financial assistance for college to the dependents of members of the Americal Division Veterans Association.

Eligibility This program is open to the children and grandchildren of members of the Americal Division Veterans Association and to the children of Americal Division veterans who were killed in action or died while on active duty with the Division. Applicants must submit an essay of 200 to 300 words on subjects pertaining to national pride. Financial need is not considered in the selection process.

Financial data Recently, stipends ranged from $1,000 to $3,000 per year.

Duration 1 year; recipients may reapply.

Number awarded Varies each year; recently, 35 of these scholarships were available: 1 at $3,000, 2 at $2,000, 6 at $1,500, and 26 at $1,000.

Deadline March of each year.

[401]
AMERICAN GI FORUM WOMEN'S RE-ENTRY SCHOLARSHIPS

American GI Forum of the United States
2870 North Speer Boulevard, Suite 103
Denver, CO 80211
(303) 458-1700   Toll Free: (866) 244-3628
Fax: (303) 458-1634   E-mail: agifnat@gmail.com
Web: www.agifusa.org/women

Summary To provide financial assistance to mature women who are members of the American GI Forum and interested in returning to college.

Eligibility This program is open to women who have been members of a women's chapter of the American GI Forum for at least 2 years. Applicants must be at least 25 years of age and enrolled or planning to enroll at a college or university as a full- or part-time student. Along with their application, they must submit transcripts, 3 letters of recommendation, proof of income, and a biographical essay.

Financial data A stipend is awarded (amount not specified).

Duration 1 year; recipients may reapply.

Additional information The American GI Forum is the largest federally-charter Hispanic veterans organization in the United States.

Number awarded 1 or more each year.

Deadline Deadline not specified.

[402]
AMERICAN LEGION AUXILIARY EMERGENCY FUND

American Legion Auxiliary
Attn: AEF Program Case Manager
8945 North Meridian Street
Indianapolis, IN 46260
(317) 569-4544   Fax: (317) 569-4502
E-mail: aef@alaforveterans.org
Web: www.alaforveterans.org

Summary To provide funding to members of the American Legion Auxiliary who are facing temporary emergency needs.

Eligibility This program is open to members of the American Legion Auxiliary who have maintained their membership for the immediate past 2 consecutive years and have paid their dues for the current year. Applicants must need emergency assistance for the following purposes: 1) food, shelter, and utilities during a time of financial crisis; 2) food and shelter because of weather-related emergencies and natural disasters; or 3) educational training for eligible members who lack the necessary skills for employment or to upgrade competitive work force skills. They must have exhausted all other sources of financial assistance, including funds and/or services available through the local Post and/or Unit, appropriate community welfare agencies, or state and federal financial aid for education. Grants are not available to settle already existing or accumulated debts, handle catastrophic illness, resettle disaster victims, or other similar problems.

Financial data The maximum grant is $2,400. Payments may be made directly to the member or to the mortgage company or utility. Educational grants may be paid directly to the educational institution.

Duration Grants are expended over no more than 3 months.

Additional information This program began in 1969. In 1981, it was expanded to include the Displaced Homemaker Fund (although that title is no longer used).

Number awarded Varies each year.

Deadline Applications may be submitted at any time.

[403]
AMERICAN LEGION AUXILIARY SCHOLARSHIP FOR NON-TRADITIONAL STUDENTS

American Legion Auxiliary
8945 North Meridian Street
Indianapolis, IN 46260
(317) 569-4500   Fax: (317) 569-4502
E-mail: alahq@alaforveterans.org
Web: www.alaforveterans.org

Summary To provide financial assistance for college to nontraditional students affiliated with the American Legion.

Eligibility This program is open to members of the American Legion, American Legion Auxiliary, or Sons of the American Legion who have paid dues for the 2 preceding years and the calendar year in which application is being made. Applicants must be nontraditional students who are either 1) returning to school after some period of time during which their formal education was interrupted, or 2) just beginning their education at a later point in life. Selection is based equally on scholastic standing and academics, character and leadership, goals, and need.

Financial data The stipend is $1,000, paid directly to the recipient's school.

Duration 1 year.

Additional information Applications are available from the president of the candidate's own unit or from the secretary or education chair of the department.

Number awarded 5 each year: 1 in each division of the American Legion Auxiliary.

Deadline Applications must be submitted to the unit president by February of each year.

[404]
AMERICAN LEGION LEGACY SCHOLARSHIPS

American Legion
Attn: Americanism and Children & Youth Division
700 North Pennsylvania Street
P.O. Box 1055
Indianapolis, IN 46206-1055
(317) 630-1212   Fax: (317) 630-1223
E-mail: acy@legion.org
Web: legion.org/scholarships/legacy

Summary To provide financial assistance for college to children of U.S. military personnel killed on active duty on or after September 11, 2001.

Eligibility This program is open to the children (including adopted children and stepchildren) of active-duty U.S. military personnel (including federalized National Guard and Reserve members) who died on active duty on or after September 11, 2001. Applicants must be high school seniors or graduates planning to enroll full time at an accredited institution of higher education in the United States. Selection is based on academic achievement, school and community activities, leadership skills, and financial need.

Financial data The stipend depends on the availability of funds.

Duration 1 year; may be renewed.

Additional information This program began in 2003.

Number awarded Varies each year.

Deadline April of each year.

[405]
AMERICAN LEGION NATIONAL EAGLE SCOUT OF THE YEAR

American Legion
Attn: Americanism and Children & Youth Division
700 North Pennsylvania Street
P.O. Box 1055
Indianapolis, IN 46206-1055
(317) 630-1202   Fax: (317) 630-1223
E-mail: acy@legion.org
Web: legion.org/scholarships/eaglescout

Summary To recognize and reward, with college scholarships, Eagle Scouts who are members of a troop associated with the American Legion or are the son or grandson of a member of the Legion.

Eligibility Applicants for this award must be either 1) a registered, active member of a Boy Scout Troop, Varsity Scout Team, or Venturing Crew chartered to an American Legion Post, Auxiliary Unit, or Sons of the American Legion Squadron, or 2) a registered active member of a Boy Scout Troop, Varsity Scout Team, or Venturing Crew and also the son or grandson of a member of the American Legion or American Legion Auxiliary. They must also 1) have received the Eagle Scout Award; 2) be active members of their religious institution and have received the appropriate religious emblem; 3) have demonstrated practical citizenship in church, school, Scouting, and community; 4) be at least 15 years of age and enrolled in high school; and 5) submit at least 4 letters of recommendation, including 1 each from leaders of their religious institution, school, community, and Scouting.

Financial data The Scout of the Year receives $10,000; each runner-up receives $2,500.

Duration The awards are presented annually; recipients are eligible to receive their scholarships immediately upon graduation from an accredited high school and must utilize the award within 4 years of their graduation date.

Additional information The recipients may use the scholarships at any school of their choice, provided it is accredited for education above the high school level and located within the United States or its possessions.

Number awarded 1 Scout of the Year and 3 runners-up are selected each year. In addition, many American Legion state departments offer scholarships to their residents who are Eagle Scouts, including Connecticut, Florida, Indiana, Iowa, New Jersey, New York, Tennessee, and Wisconsin.

Deadline Nominations must be received by the respective department headquarters by the end of February of each year and by the national headquarters before the end of March.

[406]
AMERICAN PATRIOT FREEDOM SCHOLARSHIP AWARD

Homefront America
27375 Paseo La Serna
San Juan Capistrano, CA 92675
(949) 248-9468   E-mail: info@homefrontamerica.org
Web: www.homefrontamerica.org

Summary To provide financial assistance to children of active, Reserve, disabled, deceased, or retired military personnel.

Eligibility This program is open to students between 18 and 21 years of age who are children of 1) full-time active duty or Reserve service members; 2) service members disabled as a direct result of injuries sustained during a military operation; 3) deceased service members killed in action during a military operation; or 4) service members who are retired with an honorable discharge. Applicants must be enrolled or planning to enroll at an accredited college, university, or vocational/technical institute to work on an undergraduate degree. Selection is based primarily on a 500-word essay on significant contributions of America's greatest generation to our country.

Financial data The stipend is $1,000.

Duration 1 year.

Number awarded 5 each year.

Deadline Applications may be submitted at any time, but they must be received in time for the announcement of recipients at the end of May of each year.

[407]
AMERICAN PATRIOT SCHOLARSHIPS

Military Officers Association of America
Attn: Educational Assistance Program
201 North Washington Street
Alexandria, VA 22314-2539
(703) 549-2311   Toll Free: (800) 234-MOAA
Fax: (703) 838-5819   E-mail: edassist@moaa.org
Web: www.moaa.org

Summary To provide financial assistance for undergraduate education to children of members of the uniformed services who have died.

Eligibility This program is open to children under 24 years of age of active, Reserve, and National Guard uniformed service personnel (Army, Navy, Air Force, Marines, Coast Guard, Public Health Service, or National Oceanographic and Atmospheric Administration) whose parent has died on active service. Applicants must be working on an undergraduate degree. They must have a GPA of 3.0 or higher. Selection is based on academic ability, activities, and financial need.

Financial data The stipend is currently $5,000 per year.

Duration 1 year; may be renewed up to 4 additional years.

Additional information The MOAA was formerly named The Retired Officers Association (TROA). It established this program in 2002 in response to the tragic events of September 11, 2001.

Number awarded Varies each year; recently, 64 of these scholarships were awarded. Since the program was established, it has awarded $1,485,000 to 168 children of deceased military personnel.

Deadline February of each year.

[408]
AMVETS JROTC SCHOLARSHIPS

AMVETS National Headquarters
Attn: Scholarships
4647 Forbes Boulevard
Lanham, MD 20706-3807
(301) 459-9600   Toll Free: (877) 7-AMVETS, ext. 3043
Fax: (301) 459-7924   E-mail: amvets@amvets.org
Web: www.amvets.org/programs/scholarships.html

Summary To provide money for college to the children and grandchildren of members of AMVETS who have participated in Junior Reserve Officers' Training Corps (JROTC) in high school.

Eligibility This program is open to graduating high school seniors who are JROTC cadets and the children or grandchildren of an AMVETS member or of a deceased veteran who would have been eligible to be an AMVETS member. U.S. citizenship is required. Applicants must be interested in working full time on an undergraduate degree at an accredited college, university, or technical/trade school. Selection is based on financial need, academic promise (GPA of 3.0 or higher), involvement in extracurricular activities, and an essay of 50 to 100 words on "What a Higher Education Means to Me."

Financial data The stipend is $1,000.
Duration 1 year; nonrenewable.
Number awarded 1 each year.
Deadline April of each year.

[409]
AMVETS NATIONAL LADIES AUXILIARY SCHOLARSHIPS

AMVETS National Ladies Auxiliary
Attn: Scholarship Officer
4647 Forbes Boulevard
Lanham, MD 20706-4380
(301) 459-6255   Fax: (301) 459-5403
E-mail: auxhdqs@amvets.org
Web: amvetsaux.org/scholarships.htm

Summary To provide funding to members and certain dependents of members of AMVETS Auxiliary who are already enrolled in college.

Eligibility Applicants must belong to AMVETS Auxiliary or be the child or grandchild of a member. They must be in at least the second year of undergraduate study at an accredited college or university. Applications must include 3 letters of recommendation and an essay (from 200 to 500 words) about their past accomplishments, career and educational goals, and objectives for the future. Selection is based on the letters of reference (15%), academic record (15%), the essay (25%), and financial need (45%).

Financial data Scholarships are $1,000 or $750 each.
Duration 1 year.
Number awarded Up to 7 each year: 2 at $1,000 and 5 at $750.
Deadline June of each year.

[410]
ANCA SCHOLARSHIPS

Army Nurse Corps Association
Attn: Education Committee
P.O. Box 39235
San Antonio, TX 78218-1235
(210) 650-3534   Fax: (210) 650-3494
E-mail: education@e-anca.org
Web: e-anca.org/ANCAEduc.htm

Summary To provide financial assistance to students who have a connection to the Army and are interested in working on an undergraduate or graduate degree in nursing.

Eligibility This program is open to U.S. citizens attending colleges or universities that have accredited programs offering associate, bachelor's, master's, or doctoral degrees in nursing. Applicants must be 1) nursing or anesthesia students who plan to enter a component of the U.S. Army and are not participating in a program funded by a component of the U.S. Army; 2) nursing or anesthesia students who have previously served in a component of the U.S. Army; 3) Army Nurse Corps officers enrolled in an undergraduate or graduate nursing program not funded by a component of the U.S. Army; 4) enlisted soldiers in a component of the U.S. Army who are working on a baccalaureate degree in nursing not funded by a component of the U.S. Army; or 5) nursing or anesthesia students whose parent(s), spouse, and/or children are serving or have served in a component of the U.S. Army. Along with their application, they must submit a personal statement on their professional career objectives, reasons for applying for this scholarship, financial need, special considerations, personal and academic interests, and why they are preparing for a nursing career.

Financial data The stipend is $3,000. Funds are sent directly to the recipient's school.
Duration 1 year.
Additional information Although the sponsoring organization is open to officers of the Army Nurse Corps, it does not have an official affiliation with the Army. Therefore, students who receive these scholarships do not incur any military service obligation.
Number awarded 1 or more each year.
Deadline March of each year.

[411]
ANCHOR SCHOLARSHIP FOUNDATION AWARD

Anchor Scholarship Foundation
4966 Euclid Road, Suite 109
Virginia Beach, VA 23462
(757) 671-3200, ext. 116   Fax: (757) 671-3300
E-mail: admin@anchorscholarship.com
Web: anchorscholarship.com

Summary To provide financial assistance for college to dependents of active-duty or retired personnel serving in the Naval Surface Forces.

Eligibility This program is open to dependents of active-duty or retired personnel who have served at least 6 years (need not be consecutive) in a unit under the administrative control of Commanders, Naval Surface Forces, U.S. Atlantic Fleet or U.S. Pacific Fleet. Applicants must be high school seniors or students already attending an accredited 4-year college or university and working on a bachelor's degree as a full-time student. Spouses are eligible if they are working full time on a first bachelor's degree. Selection is based on academic proficiency, extracurricular activities, character, all-around ability, and financial need.

Financial data Stipends range up to $2,000.

Duration 1 year; may be renewed.

Additional information This foundation was established in 1980 and limited to personnel who had served in the Atlantic Fleet. Its program was originally known as the SURFLANT Scholarship Foundation Award. In 2004, the program was expanded to include those who served in the Pacific Fleet and the current name was adopted. Requests for applications must be accompanied by a self-addressed stamped envelope.

Number awarded Varies each year; recently, 34 students received new or renewal scholarships.

Deadline February of each year.

[412]
ANNA GEAR JUNIOR SCHOLARSHIP

American Legion Auxiliary
Department of Virginia
Attn: Education Chair
1708 Commonwealth Avenue
Richmond, VA 23230
(804) 355-6410   Fax: (804) 353-5246
Web: vaauxiliary.org

Summary To provide financial assistance to junior members of the American Legion Auxiliary in Virginia who plan to attend college in any state.

Eligibility This program is open to seniors graduating from high schools in Virginia and planning to attend college in any state. Applicants must have been junior members of the American Legion Auxiliary for at least the 3 previous years. They must have completed at least 30 hours of volunteer service within their community and submit a 500-word article on "The Value of Volunteering in the Community."

Financial data The stipend is $1,000.

Duration 1 year.

Number awarded 1 each year.

Deadline March of each year.

[413]
A-OK STUDENT REWARD PROGRAM

U.S. Navy
Attn: Navy Exchange Service Command
3280 Virginia Beach Boulevard
Virginia Beach, VA 23452-5724
Toll Free: (800) NAV-EXCH
Web: www.mynavyexchange.com

Summary To provide financial assistance for college to children of active and retired military personnel who shop at Navy Exchange (NEX) stores.

Eligibility This program is open to dependent children of active-duty military members, Reservists, and military retirees who are enrolled in grades 1-12 and have a GPA of 3.0 or higher. Applicants submit an entry at the service desk of their NEX store. Winners are selected in a drawing.

Financial data Winners receive savings bonds for $5,000, $3,000, $2,000, or $1,000. Funds are intended to help pay expenses of college.

Duration Drawings are held 4 times a year (in February, May, August, and November).

Additional information This program began in 1997.

Number awarded 16 each year: at each drawing, 1 savings bond for each of the 4 denominations is awarded.

Deadline Deadline not specified.

[414]
ARKANSAS AMERICAN LEGION AUXILIARY ACADEMIC SCHOLARSHIP

American Legion Auxiliary
Department of Arkansas
Attn: Department Secretary
1415 West Seventh Street
Little Rock, AR 72201-2903
(501) 374-5836   Fax: (501) 372-0855
E-mail: arkaux@att.net
Web: auxiliary.arlegion.org/scholarships.html

Summary To provide financial assistance to descendants of veterans who are high school seniors in Arkansas and planning to attend college in any state.

Eligibility This program is open to the descendants of veterans in Arkansas who served during eligibility dates for membership in the American Legion. Both the student and the parent must be residents of Arkansas. Their total family income must be less than $55,000. The student must be a high school senior planning to attend college in any state. Along with their application, they must submit an essay of 800 to 1,000 words on what their country's flag means to them. Selection is based on character (15%), Americanism (15%), leadership (15%), financial need (15%), and scholarship (40%).

Financial data The stipend is $1,000; funds are paid in 2 equal installments.

Duration 1 year.

Number awarded 1 each year.

Deadline February of each year.

[415]
ARKANSAS MILITARY DEPENDENTS' SCHOLARSHIP PROGRAM

Arkansas Department of Higher Education
Attn: Financial Aid Division
114 East Capitol Avenue
Little Rock, AR 72201-3818
(501) 371-2050   Toll Free: (800) 54-STUDY
Fax: (501) 371-2001   E-mail: finaid@adhe.edu
Web: www.adhe.edu

Summary To provide financial assistance for educational purposes to dependents of certain categories of Arkansas veterans.

Eligibility This program is open to the natural children, adopted children, stepchildren, and spouses of Arkansas residents who have been declared to be a prisoner of war, killed in action, missing in action, killed on ordnance delivery, or 100% totally and permanently disabled during, or as a result of, active military service. Applicants and their parent or spouse must be residents of Arkansas. They must be working on, or planning to work on, a bachelor's degree or certificate of completion at a public college, university, or technical school in Arkansas.

Financial data The program pays for tuition, general registration fees, special course fees, activity fees, room and board (if provided in campus facilities), and other charges associated with earning a degree or certificate.

Duration 1 year; undergraduates may obtain renewal as long as they make satisfactory progress toward a baccalaureate degree; graduate students may obtain renewal as long as they maintain a minimum GPA of 2.0 and make satisfactory progress toward a degree.

Additional information This program was established in 1973 as the Arkansas Missing in Action/Killed in Action Dependents Scholarship Program to provide assistance to the dependents of veterans killed in action, missing in action, or declared a prisoner of war. In 2005, it was amended to include dependents of disabled veterans and given its current name. Applications must be submitted to the financial aid director at an Arkansas state-supported institution of higher education or state-supported technical/vocational school.

Number awarded Varies each year; recently, 4 of these scholarships were awarded.

Deadline May of each year for late summer and fall terms; October of each year for spring and early summer terms.

[416]
ARKANSAS SERVICE MEMORIAL FUND

Arkansas Community Foundation
1400 West Markham, Suite 206
Little Rock, AR 72201
(501) 372-1116　　　　　　　　Toll Free: (800) 220-ARCF
Fax: (501) 372-1166　　　　　　E-mail: arcf@arcf.org
Web: www.arcf.org/page12787.cfm

Summary To provide financial assistance for college to children of deceased veterans or other government officials in Arkansas.

Eligibility This program is open to seniors graduating from high schools in Arkansas whose parent died in service to the community, state, or nation. Applicants must be planning to attend an accredited 2- or 4-year college in Arkansas on a full-time basis. Selection is based on such factors as academics, school activities, community service, future goals, faculty and adviser recommendations, and financial need.

Financial data Stipends range from $500 to $5,000 per year.

Duration 1 year; may be renewed as long as the recipient is making satisfactory progress toward a degree.

Additional information This program began in 1984.

Number awarded Varies each year; since this program was established, it has awarded 124 scholarships worth $485,000.

Deadline April of each year.

[417]
ARMY AND AIR FORCE EXCHANGE SERVICE RETIRED EMPLOYEES ASSOCIATION SCHOLARSHIPS

AAFES Retired Employees Association
Attn: Scholarship Committee
7045 Rembrandt Drive
Plano, TX 75093
(972) 862-8099　　　　　　　E-mail: gall.tom@verizon.net
Web: www.shopmyexchange.com

Summary To provide financial assistance for college to high school seniors who have a tie to the Army and Air Force Exchange Service (AAFES).

Eligibility This program is open to high school seniors who are 1) the child of an active, retired, or deceased AAFES employee; 2) the child of assigned military personnel; or 3) an AAFES employee. Military retirees must have retired while on assignment with AAFES. Deceased parents must have died while an active or retired AAFES employee or military assignee. All retired parents must be members of the AAFES Retired Employees Association. Students who quality as an AAFES employee must have been employed for at least 1 year. At least 1 qualifying parent must have been an AAFES employee or military assignee for at least 1 year. Applicants must be planning to attend an accredited college or university or a U.S. military academy. They must have scores of at least 1750 on the SAT or 25 on the ACT. Along with their application, they must submit an essay on why they should be awarded this scholarship. Selection is based on that essay; academic honors and other recognition received; school activity participation; outside activities, hobbies, and special talents; and letters of recommendation.

Financial data Stipends range from $1,250 to $5,000.

Duration 1 year.

Additional information These scholarships were first awarded in 1985.

Number awarded Varies each year; recently, 16 of these scholarships were awarded: 2 at $5,000, 10 at $3,000, 1 at $1,500, and 3 at $1,250. Since the program began, it has awarded 254 scholarships, worth $475,795.

Deadline March of each year.

[418]
ARMY AVIATION ASSOCIATION OF AMERICA SCHOLARSHIPS

Army Aviation Association of America Scholarship Foundation
Attn: AAAA Scholarship Foundation
755 Main Street, Suite 4D
Monroe, CT 06468-2830
(203) 268-2450　　　　　　　　Fax: (203) 268-5870
E-mail: aaaa@quad-a.org
Web: www.quad-a.org

Summary To provide financial aid for undergraduate or graduate study to members of the Army Aviation Association of America and their relatives.

Eligibility This program is open to association members (or deceased members) and their spouses, unmarried siblings, unmarried children, and unmarried grandchildren. Applicants must be enrolled or accepted for enrollment as an undergraduate or graduate student at an accredited college or university. Graduate students must include a 250-word essay on their life experiences, work history, and aspirations. Some scholarships are specifically reserved for enlisted, warrant officer, company grade, and Department of the Army civilian members. Selection is based on academic merit and personal achievement.

Financial data Stipends range up to $3,000 per year.

Duration Scholarships may be for 1, 2, or 4 years.

Number awarded Varies each year; recently, $309,500 in scholarships was awarded to 209 students. Since the program began in 1963, the foundation has awarded more than $4.1 million to nearly 2,500 qualified applicants.

Deadline April of each year.

[419]
ARMY ENGINEER MEMORIAL AWARDS

Army Engineer Spouses' Club
c/o Nancy Temple, Chair
P.O. Box 6332
Alexandria, VA 22306-6332
E-mail: scholarships@armyengineerspouses.com
Web: armyengineerspouses.com

Summary To provide financial assistance for college to the children of officers who served in the Army Corps of Engineers.

Eligibility This program is open to children of 1) U.S. Army Corps of Engineers officers and warrant officers who are currently on active duty, retired, or deceased while on active duty or after retiring from active duty; or 2) current Department of the Army employees of the U.S. Army Corps of Engineers. Applicants must be high school seniors planning to attend a college, university, or technical/vocational school. Along with their application, they must submit an essay of 300 to 400 words on the event that has had the greatest impact on their life so far and how they think it will affect them in the future. Selection is based on academic and extracurricular achievement during high school. U.S. citizenship is required.

Financial data Stipends are $2,000 or $1,000.

Duration 1 year.

Additional information This program began in 1967.

Number awarded Varies each year; recently, 4 of these scholarships were awarded.

Deadline February of each year.

[420]
ARMY OFFICERS' WIVES' CLUB OF THE GREATER WASHINGTON AREA SCHOLARSHIP PROGRAM

Army Officers' Wives' Club of the Greater Washington Area
c/o Fort Myer Thrift Shop
Attn: Scholarship Committee Chair
P.O. Box 1124
Fort Myer, VA 22211
(703) 764-9656   E-mail: collegeaowcgwa@gmail.com
Web: www.aowcgwa.org/index.cfm?action=scholarships

Summary To provide financial assistance for college to the children and spouses of U.S. Army personnel and veterans in the Washington, D.C. metropolitan area.

Eligibility This program is open to 1) high school seniors who are children of Army personnel, 2) college students under 22 years of age who are children of Army personnel; and 3) spouses of Army personnel. High school seniors and spouses must reside with their sponsor in the Washington metropolitan area; the sponsor of college students must reside in that area. Sponsors may be active-duty, retired, or deceased, and officer or enlisted. Applicants must submit an essay of 200 to 300 words on a topic that changes annually but relates to their experience as the member of an Army family; a list of extracurricular activities, honors, church activities, community service, and employment; an official transcript that includes (for high school seniors) their SAT or ACT scores; and a letter of recommendation. Students who plan to

attend a service academy or receive another full scholarship are not eligible. Selection is based on scholastic merit and community involvement; financial need is not considered.

Financial data The maximum stipend is $2,000.

Duration 1 year.

Additional information The Washington metropolitan area is defined to include the Virginia cities of Alexandria, Fairfax, Falls Church, Manassas, and Manassas Park; the Virginia counties of Arlington, Fairfax, Fauquier, Loudoun, Prince William, and Stafford; the Maryland counties of Calvert, Charles, Frederick, Montgomery, and Prince George's; and the District of Columbia. This program is supported in part by the First Command Educational Foundation.

Number awarded Varies each year; recently, this sponsor awarded more than $170,000 in scholarships and community grants.

Deadline March of each year.

[421]
ARMY SCHOLARSHIP FOUNDATION SCHOLARSHIPS

Army Scholarship Foundation
11700 Preston Road, Suite 660-301
Dallas, TX 75230
E-mail: ContactUs@armyscholarshipfoundation.org
Web: www.armyscholarshipfoundation.org

Summary To provide financial assistance for undergraduate study to the children and spouses of Army personnel.

Eligibility This program is open to 1) children of regular active-duty, active-duty Reserve, and active-duty National Guard U.S. Army members in good standing; 2) spouses of serving enlisted regular active-duty, active-duty Reserve, and active-duty National Guard U.S. Army members in good standing; and 3) children of former U.S. Army members who received an honorable or medical discharge or were killed while serving in the U.S. Army. Applicants must be high school seniors, high school graduates, or undergraduates enrolled at an accredited college, university, or vocational/technical institute. They must be U.S. citizens and have a GPA of 2.0 or higher; children must be younger than 24 years of age. Financial need is considered in the selection process.

Financial data Stipends range from $500 to $2,000 per year.

Duration 1 year; recipients may reapply.

Additional information The Army Scholarship Foundation began in 2001. Among the general scholarships offered by the foundation are those designated the Captain Jennifer Shafer Odom Memorial Scholarship and the Lieutenant General Jack Costello Memorial Scholarship.

Number awarded 1 or more each year.

Deadline April of each year.

[422]
ARNOLD SOBEL SCHOLARSHIPS

U.S. Coast Guard
Attn: Office of Work-Life (CG-111)
2100 Second Street, S.W., Stop 7902
Washington, DC 20593-7902
(202) 475-5140   Toll Free: (800) 872-4957
Fax: (202) 475-5907
E-mail: HQS.SMB.FamilySupportServices@uscg.mil
Web: www.uscg.mil/worklife/scholarship.asp

Summary To provide financial assistance for college to the dependent children of Coast Guard enlisted personnel.
Eligibility This program is open to the dependent children of enlisted members of the U.S. Coast Guard on active duty, retired, or deceased, and of enlisted personnel in the Coast Guard Reserve currently on extended active duty 180 days or more. Applicants must be high school seniors or current undergraduates enrolled or planning to enroll full-time at a 4-year college, university, or vocational school. They must be under 24 years of age and registered in the Defense Enrollment Eligibility Reporting System (DEERS) system. Along with their application, they must submit their SAT or ACT scores, a letter of recommendation, transcripts, a financial information statement, and a 500-word essay on their personal and academic achievements, extracurricular activities, contributions to the community, and academic plans and career goals.
Financial data The stipend is $5,000 per year.
Duration 1 year; may be renewed up to 3 additional years.
Number awarded 4 each year.
Deadline March of each year.

[423]
ART AND ELEANOR COLONA SCHOLARSHIP GRANT

Chief Warrant and Warrant Officers Association
Attn: Executive Director
200 V Street, S.W.
Washington, DC 20024
(202) 554-7753   Toll Free: (800) 792-8447
Fax: (202) 484-0641   E-mail: cwoauscg@verizon.net
Web: www.cwoauscg.org/scholarship.htm

Summary To provide financial assistance for college to children of active or retired enlisted personnel of the U.S. Coast Guard.
Eligibility This program is open to the dependent sons and daughters of members of the U.S. Coast Guard (active duty or retired) or the Coast Guard Reserve serving on active duty. Applicants must be high school seniors or currently-enrolled full-time college students and have at least a 2.0 GPA. Along with their application, they must submit transcripts, letter of acceptance, an essay on their reasons for attending or desiring to attend an accredited institution of higher learning, support documentation if applicable, and a photograph (optional). Their parents' financial status is not considered in the selection process.
Financial data The stipend is $1,000 per year.
Duration 1 year; may be renewed up to 3 additional years.
Number awarded 1 or more each year.
Deadline May of each year.

[424]
ASSOCIATION OF GRADUATES DEPENDENT SCHOLARSHIPS

Association of Graduates
Attn: Vice President of Services
3116 Academy Drive, Suite 100
USAF Academy, CO 80840-4475
(719) 472-0300   Fax: (719) 333-4194
E-mail: Wayne.Taylor@aogusafa.org
Web: www.usafa.org/Membership/Scholarships

Summary To provide financial assistance for undergraduate education to children of Association of Graduates (AOG) members.
Eligibility This program is open to children of graduates of the U.S. Air Force Academy who either are paid-in-full life members or have maintained annual membership for at least the 5 consecutive years immediately preceding submission of the application package. Applicants must be either the graduate's natural child or legally adopted child (although they need not be financially dependent upon the graduate or his/her surviving spouse). They must have a GPA of 3.0 or higher and be working or planning to work full time on an undergraduate degree. Along with their application, they must an essay of 200 to 400 words on the importance of this scholarship to their education, transcripts, SAT and/or ACT scores, a list of extracurricular activities, a list of employment history, and a letter of recommendation. Selection is based on overall demonstrated merit, although financial need may also receive some consideration.
Financial data Stipends range from $500 to $2,000 per year. Funds are paid directly to the recipient.
Duration 1 year; recipients may reapply and be awarded 3 additional scholarships.
Number awarded Varies each year; recently, 18 of these scholarships were awarded.
Deadline March of each year.

[425]
ASSOCIATION OF THE UNITED STATES NAVY EDUCATIONAL ASSISTANCE PROGRAM

Association of the United States Navy
Attn: Educational Assistance Program
1619 King Street
Alexandria, VA 22314-2793
(703) 548-5800   Toll Free: (866) NAVY-411
Fax: (866) 683-3647   E-mail: cfo@ausn.org
Web: ausn.org

Summary To provide financial assistance for college to dependents of members of the Association of the United States Navy (formerly the Naval Reserve Association).
Eligibility This program is open to 1) dependent children, under 24 years of age, of association members; and 2) widows or widowers of deceased members. Applicants must be enrolled or planning to enroll full time at a college, university, or technical school. They must be U.S. citizens. Selection is based on academic and leadership ability, potential, character, personal qualities, and financial need.
Financial data The amounts of the stipends vary but recently averaged more than $4,000 per year.
Duration 1 year; may be renewed 1 additional year.
Additional information The Association of the United States Navy was formed in 2009 as a successor to the Naval Reserve Association.
Number awarded Varies each year.
Deadline April of each year.

[426]
BELVOIR OFFICERS' SPOUSES' CLUB SCHOLARSHIPS

Belvoir Officers' Spouses' Club
Attn: Scholarship Committee
P.O. Box 322
Fort Belvoir, VA 22060
(703) 799-1400   E-mail: info@belvoirosc.org
Web: www.belvoirosc.org/scholarship

Summary To provide financial assistance to children and spouses of military personnel in the greater Washington, D.C. area.

Eligibility This program is open to children and spouses of active-duty, retired, or deceased members of any branch of the armed forces (including Guard and Reserves) who reside in the greater Washington, D.C. area. Applicants must be high school seniors, current college students under 22 years of age, or spouses of any age who are attending or planning to attend a 2- or 4-year college or university in any state. Along with their application, they must submit a 250-word essay on 1) for high school seniors, how being a member of a military family has influenced their education choices; 2) for current college students, the experiences they have had since high school that have influenced their career goals; or 3) for souses, how their volunteer or professional experience has influenced their course of study. Selection is based on that essay, academic honors, extracurricular and community activities, paid or volunteer employment, and other honors and recognition.

Financial data A stipend is awarded (amount not specified).

Duration 1 year.

Number awarded Varies each year; recently, 17 of these scholarships, with a value of $12,000, were awarded.

Deadline March of each year.

[427]
BETTER CHANCE SCHOLARSHIP

Associates of Vietnam Veterans of America
Attn: Scholarship Program
8719 Colesville Road, Suite 100
Silver Spring, MD 20910
(301) 585-4000   Toll Free: (800) VVA-1316
Fax: (301) 585-0519
Web: www.avva.org/scholarship.html

Summary To provide money for college to members of Vietnam Veterans of America (VVA) and Associates of Vietnam Veterans of America (AVVA), their families, and the families of Vietnam veterans killed or missing in action.

Eligibility This program is open to members of VVA and AVVA; their spouses, children, and grandchildren; and the spouses, children, and grandchildren of Vietnam veterans killed in action (KIA) or missing in action (MIA). Especially encouraged to apply are average students who are not eligible for academic scholarships but who can demonstrate financial need. Applicants must submit essays on their goals, work experience, and community service.

Financial data Stipends are $1,000, $750, or $500.

Duration 1 year.

Additional information This program began in 1998.

Number awarded Normally 3 each year: 1 at $1,000, 1 at $750, and 1 at $500.

Deadline June of each year.

[428]
BG BENJAMIN B. TALLEY SCHOLARSHIP

Society of American Military Engineers-Anchorage Post
Attn: BG B.B. Talley Scholarship Endowment Fund
P.O. Box 6409
Anchorage, AK 99506-6409
(907) 244-8063   E-mail: cturletes@gci.net
Web: www.sameanchorage.org/h_about/scholinfo.html

Summary To provide financial assistance to student members of the Society of American Military Engineers (SAME) from Alaska who are working on a bachelor's or master's degree in designated fields of engineering or the natural sciences.

Eligibility This program is open to members of the Anchorage Post of SAME who are residents of Alaska, attending college in Alaska, an active-duty military member stationed in Alaska, or a dependent of an active-duty military member stationed in Alaska. Applicants must be 1) sophomores, juniors, or seniors majoring in engineering, architecture, construction or project management, natural sciences, physical sciences, applied sciences, or mathematics at an accredited college or university; or 2) students working on a master's degree in those fields. They must have a GPA of 2.5 or higher. U.S. citizenship is required. Along with their application, they must submit an essay of 250 to 500 words on their career goals. Selection is based on that essay, academic achievement, participation in school and community activities, and work/family activities; financial need is not considered.

Financial data Stipends range up to $3,000.

Duration 1 year.

Additional information This program began in 1997.

Number awarded Varies each year; at least 1 scholarship is reserved for a master's degree students.

Deadline December of each year.

[429]
BLACKHORSE SCHOLARSHIP

Blackhorse Association
P.O. Box 223
Hemphill, TX 75948-0223
E-mail: info@blackhorse.org
Web: www.blackhorse.org/scholarships.cfm

Summary To provide financial assistance for college to children of members of the Blackhorse Association who are currently serving or have served with the 11th Armored Cavalry Regiment (ACR).

Eligibility This program is open to the natural and adopted children of current or former 11th ACR solders who are also members of the association. Applicants must be attending or planning to attend college. In the selection process, first priority is given to children who lost a parent in service of the regiment; second priority is given to children of those incapacitated by wounds or injury while serving the regiment; third priority is given based on financial need of the applicant and family.

Financial data The stipend is $3,000 per year.

Duration 1 year; may be renewed up to 3 additional years.

Additional information The Blackhorse Association was founded in 1970 by veterans of the 11th ACR who had served in Vietnam.

Number awarded Varies each year; recently, 14 of these scholarships were awarded. Since this program was established, it has awarded more than $500,000 in scholarships.
Deadline March of each year.

[430]
BOOZ ALLEN HAWAII SCHOLARSHIP FUND
Hawai'i Community Foundation
Attn: Scholarship Department
827 Fort Street Mall
Honolulu, HI 96813
(808) 537-6333   Toll Free: (888) 731-3863
Fax: (808) 521-6286
E-mail: scholarships@hcf-hawaii.org
Web: www.hawaiicommunityfoundation.org/scholarships

Summary To provide financial assistance to residents of Hawaii and dependents of military personnel stationed in the state who are attending college in any state.
Eligibility This program is open to residents of Hawaii and dependents of military personnel stationed in the state. Applicants must be attending a 4-year accredited college or university in any state as a full-time undergraduate student. They must be able to demonstrate academic achievement (GPA of 3.0 or higher), good moral character, and financial need. Along with their application, they must submit a short statement indicating their reasons for attending college, their planned course of study, their career goals, and what community service means to them.
Financial data The amounts of the awards depend on the availability of funds and the need of the recipient. Recently, the average value of each of the scholarships awarded by the foundation was more than $2,000.
Duration 1 year.
Number awarded Varies each year.
Deadline February of each year.

[431]
BOWFIN MEMORIAL SCHOLARSHIPS
Pearl Harbor Submarine Officers' Wives' Club
c/o Lana Vargas
Pearl Harbor Submarine Memorial Association
11 Arizona Memorial Drive
Honolulu, HI 96818
(808) 423-1341   Fax: (808) 422-5201
E-mail: submariescholarships@ymail.com
Web: www.pearlharborsosa.org/?page_id=9

Summary To provide financial assistance to the children of submarine force personnel who live in Hawaii and plan to attend college in any state.
Eligibility This program is open to the children of submarine force personnel (active duty, retired, or deceased) who are under 23 years of age. Applicants may attend school anywhere in the United States, but their submarine sponsor or surviving parent must live in Hawaii. Selection is based on academic achievement, extracurricular activities, community involvement, motivation and goals, and financial need.
Financial data Stipends range from $250 to $5,000 per year.
Duration 1 year; may be renewed upon annual reapplication.

Additional information This program was established in 1985 to honor the 3,505 submariners and 52 submarines lost during World War II.
Number awarded Varies each year; recently, 11 of these scholarships were awarded.
Deadline February of each year.

[432]
BUCKINGHAM MEMORIAL SCHOLARSHIPS
Air Traffic Control Association
Attn: Scholarship Fund
1101 King Street, Suite 300
Alexandria, VA 22314
(703) 299-2430   Fax: (703) 299-2437
E-mail: info@atca.org
Web: www.atca.org/ATCA-Scholarship

Summary To provide financial assistance for college or graduate school to children of current or former air traffic control specialists serving with the military or at other facilities.
Eligibility This program is open to U.S. citizens who are the children, natural or adopted, of a person currently or formerly serving as an air traffic control specialist with the U.S. government, with the U.S. military, or in a private facility in the United States. Applicants must be enrolled or planning to enroll at least half time in a baccalaureate or graduate program at an accredited college or university and have at least 30 semester hours to be completed before graduation. Along with their application, they must submit a 500-word essay on how they will blend their career with community service in their adult life. Financial need is considered in the selection process.
Financial data The amounts of the awards depend on the availability of funds and the number, qualifications, and need of the applicants.
Duration 1 year; may be renewed.
Additional information This program was formerly known as the Children of Air Traffic Control Specialists Scholarship Program.
Number awarded Varies each year; recently, 5 of these scholarships were awarded.
Deadline April of each year.

[433]
BUICK ACHIEVERS SCHOLARSHIP PROGRAM
Scholarship America
Attn: Scholarship Management Services
One Scholarship Way
P.O. Box 297
St. Peter, MN 56082
(507) 931-1682   Toll Free: (866) 243-4644
Fax: (507) 931-9168
E-mail: buickachievers@scholarshipamerica.org
Web: www.buickachievers.com

Summary To provide financial assistance to students (particularly veterans and their dependents) who are entering college for the first time and planning to major in specified fields related to engineering, design, or business.
Eligibility This program is open to high school seniors and graduates who are planning to enroll full time at an accredited 4-year college or university as first-time freshmen. Applicants must be planning to major in accounting, business administration, engineering (chemical, controls, electrical, environ-

mental, industrial, manufacturing, mechanical, plastic/polymers, or engineering technology), design (graphic, industrial, product, or transportation), ergonomics, finance, industrial hygiene, labor and industrial relations, management (logistics, manufacturing, operations, or supply chain), marketing, mathematics, occupational health and safety, or statistics. U.S. citizenship or permanent resident status is required. Selection is based on academic achievement, financial need, participation and leadership in community and school activities, work experience, educational and career goals, and other unusual circumstances. Special consideration is given to first-generation college students, women, minorities, military veterans, and dependents of military personnel.

Financial data   Stipends are $25,000 or $2,000 per year.

Duration   1 year; renewable up to 3 more years (or 4 years if entering a 5-year engineering program).

Additional information   This program is funded by the General Motors Foundation.

Number awarded   1,100 each year: 100 at $25,000 and 1,000 at $2,000.

Deadline   March of each year.

[434]
CALIFORNIA FEE WAIVER PROGRAM FOR CHILDREN OF VETERANS

California Department of Veterans Affairs
Attn: Division of Veterans Services
1227 O Street, Room 105
P.O. Box 942895
Sacramento, CA 94295
(916) 653-2573   Toll Free: (877) 741-8532
Fax: (916) 653-2563   TDD: (800) 324-5966
Web: www.cdva.ca.gov/VetServices/Education.aspx

Summary   To provide financial assistance for college to the children of disabled or deceased veterans in California.

Eligibility   Eligible for this program are the children of veterans who 1) died of a service-connected disability; 2) had a service-connected disability at the time of death; or 3) currently have a service-connected disability of any level of severity. Applicants must plan to attend a community college in California, branch of the California State University system, or campus of the University of California. Their income, including the value of support received from parents, cannot exceed $11,369. The veteran is not required to have a connection to California for this program. Dependents in college who are eligible to receive federal education benefits from the U.S. Department of Veterans Affairs are not eligible for these fee waivers.

Financial data   This program provides for waiver of registration fees to students attending any publicly-supported community or state college or university in California.

Duration   1 year; may be renewed.

Number awarded   Varies each year.

Deadline   Deadline not specified.

[435]
CALIFORNIA FEE WAIVER PROGRAM FOR DEPENDENTS OF DECEASED OR DISABLED NATIONAL GUARD MEMBERS

California Department of Veterans Affairs
Attn: Division of Veterans Services
1227 O Street, Room 105
P.O. Box 942895
Sacramento, CA 94295
(916) 653-2573   Toll Free: (877) 741-8532
Fax: (916) 653-2563   TDD: (800) 324-5966
Web: www.cdva.ca.gov/VetServices/Education.aspx

Summary   To provide financial assistance for college to dependents of disabled and deceased members of the California National Guard.

Eligibility   Eligible for this program are dependents, unremarried surviving spouses, and current registered domestic partners (RDPs) of members of the California National Guard who, in the line of duty and in the active service of the state, were killed, died of a disability, or became permanently disabled. Applicants must be attending or planning to attend a community college, branch of the California State University system, or campus of the University of California.

Financial data   Full-time college students receive a waiver of tuition and registration fees at any publicly-supported community or state college or university in California.

Duration   1 year; may be renewed.

Number awarded   Varies each year.

Deadline   Deadline not specified.

[436]
CALIFORNIA FEE WAIVER PROGRAM FOR DEPENDENTS OF TOTALLY DISABLED VETERANS

California Department of Veterans Affairs
Attn: Division of Veterans Services
1227 O Street, Room 105
P.O. Box 942895
Sacramento, CA 94295
(916) 653-2573   Toll Free: (877) 741-8532
Fax: (916) 653-2563   TDD: (800) 324-5966
Web: www.cdva.ca.gov/VetServices/Education.aspx

Summary   To provide financial assistance for college to dependents of disabled and other California veterans.

Eligibility   Eligible for this program are spouses, children, and unremarried spouses or registered domestic partners (RDPs) of veterans who are currently totally service-connected disabled (or are being compensated for a service-connected disability at a rate of 100%) or who died of a service-connected cause or disability. The veteran parent must have served during a qualifying war period and must have been discharged or released from military service under honorable conditions. Children must be younger than 27 years of age (extended to 30 if the child is a veteran); there are no age restrictions for spouses, surviving spouses, or RDPs. This program does not have an income limit. Dependents in college are not eligible if they are qualified to receive educational benefits from the U.S. Department of Veterans Affairs. Applicants must be attending or planning to attend a community college, branch of the California State University system, or campus of the University of California.

Financial data Full-time college students receive a waiver of tuition and registration fees at any publicly-supported community or state college or university in California.

Duration Children of eligible veterans may receive post-secondary benefits until the needed training is completed or until the dependent reaches 27 years of age (extended to 30 if the dependent serves in the armed forces). Spouses and surviving spouses are limited to a maximum of 48 months' full-time training or the equivalent in part-time training.

Number awarded Varies each year.

Deadline Deadline not specified.

[437]
CALIFORNIA FEE WAIVER PROGRAM FOR RECIPIENTS OF THE MEDAL OF HONOR AND THEIR CHILDREN

California Department of Veterans Affairs
Attn: Division of Veterans Services
1227 O Street, Room 101
P.O. Box 942895
Sacramento, CA 94295
(916) 653-2573   Toll Free: (877) 741-8532
Fax: (916) 653-2563   TDD: (800) 324-5966
Web: www.cdva.ca.gov/VetServices/Education.aspx

Summary To provide money for college to veterans in California who received the Medal of Honor and their children.

Eligibility This program is open to recipients of the Medal of Honor and their children younger than 27 years of age reside in California. Applicants must be attending or planning to attend a community college or a university in the California State University or the University of California system.

Financial data Full-time college students receive a waiver of tuition and registration fees at any publicly-supported community or state college or university in California.

Duration 1 year; may be renewed.

Number awarded Varies each year.

Deadline Deadline not specified.

[438]
CALIFORNIA LEGION AUXILIARY EDUCATIONAL ASSISTANCE

American Legion Auxiliary
Department of California
Veterans War Memorial Building
401 Van Ness Avenue, Room 113
San Francisco, CA 94102-4586
(415) 861-5092   Fax: (415) 861-8365
E-mail: calegionaux@calegionaux.org
Web: www.calegionaux.org/scholarships.htm

Summary To provide financial assistance to high school seniors in California who are the children of veterans or military personnel and require assistance to continue their education.

Eligibility This program is open to seniors graduating from high schools in California who are the children of active-duty military personnel or veterans who served during wartime. Applicants must be planning to continue their education at a college, university, or business/trade school in California. Each high school in California may nominate only 1 student for these scholarships; the faculty selects the nominee if more than 1 student wishes to apply. Selection is based on the

application (25%), scholarship (25%), character and leadership (25%), and financial need (25%).

Financial data Stipends are $1,000 or $500 per year.

Duration 1 year; 1 of the scholarships may be renewed 1 additional year.

Number awarded 8 each year: 1 at $1,000 that may be renewed 1 additional year, 4 at $1,000 that are nonrenewable, and 3 at $500 that are nonrenewable.

Deadline March of each year.

[439]
CALIFORNIA LEGION AUXILIARY PAST DEPARTMENT PRESIDENT'S JUNIOR SCHOLARSHIP

American Legion Auxiliary
Department of California
Veterans War Memorial Building
401 Van Ness Avenue, Room 113
San Francisco, CA 94102-4586
(415) 861-5092   Fax: (415) 861-8365
E-mail: calegionaux@calegionaux.org
Web: www.calegionaux.org/scholarships.htm

Summary To provide money for college to the daughters and other female descendants of California veterans who are active in the American Legion Junior Auxiliary.

Eligibility This program is open to the daughters, grand-daughters, and great- granddaughters of veterans who served during wartime. Applicants must be in their senior year at an accredited high school, must have been members of the Junior Auxiliary for at least 3 consecutive years, and must be residents of California (if eligibility for Junior Auxiliary membership is by a current member of the American Legion or Auxiliary in California, the applicant may reside elsewhere). They must be planning to attend college in California. Selection is based on scholastic merit (20%); active participation in Junior Auxiliary (15%); record of service or volunteerism within the applicant's community, school, and/or unit (35%); a brief description of the applicant's desire to pursue a higher education (15%); and 3 letters of reference (15%).

Financial data The stipend depends on the availability of funds but ranges from $300 to $1,000.

Duration 1 year.

Number awarded 1 each year.

Deadline April of each year.

[440]
CALIFORNIA LEGION AUXILIARY PAST PRESIDENTS' PARLEY NURSING SCHOLARSHIPS

American Legion Auxiliary
Department of California
Veterans War Memorial Building
401 Van Ness Avenue, Room 113
San Francisco, CA 94102-4586
(415) 861-5092   Fax: (415) 861-8365
E-mail: calegionaux@calegionaux.org
Web: www.calegionaux.org/scholarships.htm

Summary To provide funding to California residents who are current military personnel, veterans, or members of their families and interested in studying nursing in the state.

Eligibility This program is open to California residents who are currently serving on active military duty, veterans who served during wartime, or the spouse, widow(er), or child of such a veteran. Applicants must be entering or continuing students of nursing at an accredited institution of higher learning in California. Selection is based on the application (25%), scholarship (25%), character and leadership (25%), and financial need (25%).

Financial data Stipends range up to $2,000.

Duration 1 year.

Number awarded Varies each year.

Deadline March of each year.

[441]
CALIFORNIA LEGION AUXILIARY SCHOLARSHIPS FOR CONTINUING AND/OR REENTRY STUDENTS

American Legion Auxiliary
Department of California
Veterans War Memorial Building
401 Van Ness Avenue, Room 113
San Francisco, CA 94102-4586
(415) 861-5092   Fax: (415) 861-8365
E-mail: calegionaux@calegionaux.org
Web: www.calegionaux.org/scholarships.htm

Summary To provide funding to California residents who are active-duty military personnel, veterans, or children of veterans and require assistance to continue their education.

Eligibility This program is open to California residents who are 1) active-duty military personnel; 2) veterans of World War I, World War II, Korea, Vietnam, Grenada/Lebanon, Panama, or Desert Shield/Desert Storm; and 3) children of veterans who served during those periods of war. Applicants must be continuing or reentry students at a college, university, or business/trade school in California. Selection is based on the application (25%), scholarship (25%), character and leadership (25%), and financial need (25%).

Financial data The stipend is $1,000 or $500.

Duration 1 year.

Additional information This program includes 1 scholarship designated as the Mel Foronda Memorial Scholarship.

Number awarded 5 each year: 3 at $1,000 and 2 at $500.

Deadline March of each year.

[442]
CAPTAIN CALIENDO COLLEGE ASSISTANCE FUND SCHOLARSHIP

U.S. Coast Guard Chief Petty Officers Association
Attn: CCCAF Scholarship Committee
5520-G Hempstead Way
Springfield, VA 22151-4009
(703) 941-0395   Fax: (703) 941-0397
E-mail: cgcpoa@aol.com
Web: www.uscgcpoa.org

Summary To recognize and reward, with college scholarships, children of members or deceased members of the U.S. Coast Guard Chief Petty Officers Association (CPOA) or the Coast Guard Enlisted Association (CGEA) who submit outstanding essays.

Eligibility This competition is open to children of members or deceased members of the CPOA or CGEA who are attending or planning to attend a college, university, or vocational school. Applicants may not be older than 24 years of age (the age limit does not apply to disabled children). They must submit an essay, up to 500 words, on a topic that changes annually; recently, students were asked to write on how they grew

from an unsuccessful experience and how they are a better person for it today. The author of the essay judged most outstanding receives this scholarship.

Financial data The award is a $5,000 scholarship.

Duration The competition is held annually.

Number awarded 1 each year.

Deadline February of each year.

[443]
CAPTAIN GERARD COOK SCHOLARSHIP

National Guard Association of Florida
Attn: Scholarship Committee
P.O. Box 3446
St. Augustine, FL 32085-3446
(904) 823-0628   Fax: (904) 839-2068
E-mail: ngafl1903@floridaguard.org
Web: www.floridaguard.org/florida-guard-scholarships.html

Summary To provide financial assistance to children of members of the Florida National Guard who are studying architecture or engineering at a college in any state.

Eligibility This program is open to children of members of the Florida National Guard who are attending an accredited college or university in any state. Applicants must be working on a degree in architecture or engineering. Along with their application, they must submit a 500-word essay explaining why they need the award and what they plan to do with their architecture or engineering degree. Selection is based on academic achievement, civic and moral leadership, character, and financial need.

Financial data The stipend is $1,000.

Duration 1 year.

Additional information This program is jointly sponsored by the National Guard Association of Florida (NGOA-FL) and the Enlisted National Guard Association of Florida (ENGAF).

Number awarded 1 each year.

Deadline May of each year.

[444]
CAROLINE HOWARTH SCHOLARSHIP

American Legion Auxiliary
Department of New Jersey
c/o Lucille M. Miller, Secretary/Treasurer
1540 Kuser Road, Suite A-8
Hamilton, NJ 08619
(609) 581-9580   Fax: (609) 581-8429

Summary To provide financial assistance to New Jersey residents who are the descendants of veterans and planning to attend college in any state.

Eligibility This program is open to the children, grandchildren, and great-grandchildren of veterans who served in the U.S. armed forces during specified periods of wartime. Applicants must be graduating high school seniors who have been residents of New Jersey for at least 2 years. They must be planning to attend a college or university in any state. Along with their application, they must submit a 1,000-word essay on a topic that changes annually; recently, students were asked to write on the topic, "The Importance of Helping Military Families in Your Community." Selection is based on academic achievement (40%), character (15%), leadership (15%), Americanism (15%), and financial need (15%).

Financial data Stipends range from $1,000 to $2,500.

Duration 1 year; nonrenewable.
Number awarded 1 each year.
Deadline April of each year.

[445]
CCME SPOUSE SCHOLARSHIPS

Council of College and Military Educators
c/o Cynthia Bruce, Scholarship Committee Chair
American Council on Education, Military Evaluations
One Dupont Circle, Suite 250
Washington, DC 20036
(202) 939-9432   E-mail: cynthia_bruce@ace.nche.edu
Web: www.ccmeonline.org/scholarships.aspx

Summary To provide financial assistance to spouses of members of the armed services who are interested in working on an undergraduate or master's degree.

Eligibility This program is open to spouses of members of the uniformed services, including active, National Guard, and Reserves, Their spouse must have completed basic military training or officer candidate school. Applicants must be currently enrolled full time at an accredited institution that is a member of the Council of College and Military Educators (CCME) and working on an associate, bachelor's, or master's degree. Undergraduates must have a GPA of 2.0 or higher and graduate students must have a GPA of 3.0 or higher. Along with their application, they must submit an essay of up to 300 words on how their academic goals and qualifications support the mission of CCME. Financial need is not considered in the selection process.

Financial data The stipend is $1,000.
Duration 1 year.
Number awarded 5 each year.
Deadline October of each year.

[446]
CHAPPIE HALL MEMORIAL SCHOLARSHIP PROGRAM

101st Airborne Division Association
32 Screaming Eagle Boulevard
P.O. Box 929
Fort Campbell, KY 42223-0929
(931) 431-0199   Fax: (931) 431-0195
E-mail: 101stairbornedivisionassociation@comcast.net
Web: www.screamingeagle.org/Scholarships.aspx

Summary To provide financial assistance for college to the spouses, children, and grandchildren of members of the 101st Airborne Division Association.

Eligibility This program is open to graduating high school seniors and current college students who maintained a GPA of 2.0 or higher during the preceding school year and whose parent, grandparent, or spouse is (or, if deceased, was) a regular or life (not associate) member of the 101st Airborne Division. Applicants must submit a 150-word essay on patriotism and a letter on their career objectives, community service, hobbies, interests, personal achievements, and how a higher education for them in their chosen field can benefit our nation. Selection is based on the letter, career objectives, academic record, and letters of recommendation.

Financial data A stipend is awarded (amount not specified).
Duration 1 year; may be renewed.

Additional information This program includes the Pratt Scholarships, the Knapp Family Scholarship, the Ellen Willis Martin Scholarships, the Catherine and Charles Kratz Scholarships, and the Paul Vallely Family Scholarship.
Number awarded Varies each year; recently, 18 of these scholarships were awarded.
Deadline May of each year.

[447]
CHARLES C. BLANTON AFBA FAMILY SURVIVOR COLLEGE SCHOLARSHIP

Armed Forces Benefit Association
AFBA Building
909 North Washington Street
Alexandria, VA 22314-1556
(703) 549-4455   Toll Free: (800) 776-2322
E-mail: info@afba.com
Web: www.afba.com

Summary To provide financial assistance for college to surviving spouses and children of members of the Armed Forces Benefit Association (AFBA) who were killed on duty.

Eligibility This program is open to surviving spouses and children of deceased members of AFBA. Membership in AFBA is open to active-duty, National Guard, or Reserve members of the armed forces; those who are retired or separated from service; and emergency service providers (law enforcement officers, fire fighters, and emergency medical service providers). The AFBA member's death must have been in a combat zone, as a result of combat action, as a result of acts of foreign or domestic terrorism, or at an event to which an emergency service provider is dispatched in a situation where there is the potential for loss of life. Applicants must be attending or planning to attend an undergraduate college or university.

Financial data The stipend is $10,000 per year.
Duration 1 year; may be renewed for up to 3 additional years.
Number awarded 1 or more each year.
Deadline Deadline not specified.

[448]
CHARLES W. AND ANNETTE HILL SCHOLARSHIP FUND

American Legion
Department of Kansas
1314 S.W. Topeka Boulevard
Topeka, KS 66612-1886
(785) 232-9315   Fax: (785) 232-1399
Web: www.ksamlegion.org/programs.htm

Summary To provide financial assistance for college to the children of members of the Kansas American Legion, particularly those interested in majoring in science, engineering, or business.

Eligibility This program is open to graduating seniors at high schools in Kansas who have a GPA of 3.0 or higher. Applicants must be a descendant of a member of the American Legion. Preference is given to applicants planning to major in science, engineering, or business administration at a Kansas college, university, junior college, or trade school. Selection is based on high school transcripts, 3 letters of recommendation, an essay of 250 to 500 words on "Why I Want to Go to College," and financial need.

Financial data The stipend is $1,000 per year.

Duration 1 year; may be renewed if the recipient maintains a GPA of 3.0 or higher.

Number awarded 1 each year.

Deadline February of each year.

[449]
CHIEF MASTER SERGEANTS OF THE AIR FORCE SCHOLARSHIPS

Air Force Sergeants Association
Attn: Scholarship Coordinator
5211 Auth Road
Suitland, MD 20746
(301) 899-3500   Toll Free: (800) 638-0594
Fax: (301) 899-8136   E-mail: balsobrooks@hqafsa.org
Web: www.hqafsa.org

Summary To provide financial assistance for college to the dependent children of enlisted Air Force personnel.

Eligibility This program is open to the unmarried children (including stepchildren and legally adopted children) of enlisted active-duty, retired, or veteran members of the U.S. Air Force, Air National Guard, or Air Force Reserves. Applicants must be attending or planning to attend an accredited academic institution. They must have an unweighted GPA of 3.5 or higher. Along with their application, they must submit 1) a paragraph on their life objectives and what they plan to do with the education they receive; and 2) an essay on the most urgent problem facing society today. High school seniors must also submit a transcript of all high school grades and a record of their SAT or ACT scores. Selection is based on academic record, character, leadership skills, writing ability, versatility, and potential for success. Financial need is not a consideration. A unique aspect of these scholarships is that applicants may supply additional information regarding circumstances that entitle them to special consideration; examples of such circumstances include student disabilities, financial hardships, parent disabled and unable to work, parent missing in action/killed in action/prisoner of war, or other unusual extenuating circumstances.

Financial data Stipends range from $1,000 to $3,000; funds may be used for tuition, room and board, fees, books, supplies, and transportation.

Duration 1 year; may be renewed if the recipient maintains full-time enrollment.

Additional information The Air Force Sergeants Association administers this program on behalf of the Airmen Memorial Foundation. It was established in 1987 and named in honor of CMSAF Richard D. Kisling, the late third Chief Master Sergeant of the Air Force. In 1997, following the deaths of CMSAF's (Retired) Andrews and Harlow, it was given its current name. The highest-ranked applicant receives the Paul W. Airey Memorial Scholarship.

Number awarded Varies each year; recently, 11 of these scholarships were awarded: 1 at $3,000, 1 at $2,500, 1 at $2,000, 1 at $1,500 and 7 at $1,000. Since this program began, it has awarded more than $250,000 in scholarships.

Deadline March of each year.

[450]
CHILDREN OF FALLEN PATRIOTS FOUNDATION ASSISTANCE

Children of Fallen Patriots Foundation
P.O. Box 181
Old Greenwich, CT 06870
Toll Free: (866) 917-CFPF   Fax: (203) 547-6243
E-mail: contact@fallenpatriots.org
Web: fallenpatriots.org/for-families/faqs

Summary To provide financial assistance to the children of military personnel killed in combat or training.

Eligibility This program is open to the children (natural, by marriage, or adopted) of military personnel who died in the line of duty. Applicants must be enrolled or planning to enroll at a college, university, community college, or vocational school. Applicants must submit documentation of their relationship to the deceased military member, bills or receipts for all covered expenses, transcripts that include GPA, and information on their U.S. Department of Veterans Affairs benefits.

Financial data The foundation attempts to pay for all costs of higher education not covered by other grants or scholarships.

Duration Until completion of a college degree or certificate.

Number awarded Varies each year.

Deadline Applications may be submitted at any time.

[451]
CHILDREN OF FALLEN SOLDIERS RELIEF FUND COLLEGE GRANTS

Children of Fallen Soldiers Relief Fund
P.O. Box 3968
Gaithersburg, MD 20885-3968
(301) 685-3421   Toll Free: (866) 96-CFSRF
Fax: (301) 630-0592   E-mail: grants@cfsrf.org
Web: www.cfsrf.org

Summary To provide financial assistance for college to children and spouses of military personnel killed or severely disabled during service in Iraq or Afghanistan.

Eligibility This program is open to spouses and children of military personnel killed or severely disabled as a result of service in Operation Iraqi Freedom or Operation Enduring Freedom. Applicants must be enrolled or planning to enroll at a college or university. They must have a GPA of 2.75 or higher and be able to demonstrate financial need.

Financial data Grants have ranged from $1,000 to $28,000, depending on the need of the recipient.

Duration These are 1-time grants.

Additional information This organization was founded in 2003.

Number awarded Varies each year; since the organization was founded, it has awarded 14 of these college grants.

Deadline Applications may be submitted at any time.

[452]
CHILDREN OF WARRIORS NATIONAL PRESIDENTS' SCHOLARSHIP

American Legion Auxiliary
8945 North Meridian Street
Indianapolis, IN 46260
(317) 569-4500   Fax: (317) 569-4502
E-mail: alahq@alaforveterans.org
Web: www.alaforveterans.org

Summary To provide financial assistance for college to the descendants of war veterans.

Eligibility This program is open to children, stepchildren, grandchildren, and great-grandchildren of veterans who served during wartime. Applicants must be high school seniors who have completed at least 50 hours of volunteer service within their community and plan to attend an accredited 4-year college or university. Each Department (state) organization of the American Legion Auxiliary nominates 1 candidate for this scholarship annually. Nominees must submit a 1,000-word essay on a topic that changes annually; recently, students were asked to write on "The Importance of Helping Military Families in Your Community." Selection is based on the essay (25%), character and leadership (25%), scholarship, (25%), and financial need (25%).

Financial data Stipends are $2,500, $2,000, or $1,500. Funds are paid directly to the recipient's school.

Duration 1 year; recipients may not reapply.

Additional information Applications are available from the local Unit or from the Department Secretary or Department Education Chair of the state in which the applicant resides. This program was previously named the American Legion Auxiliary National President's Scholarship.

Number awarded 15 each year: in each of the 5 divisions of the Auxiliary, 1 scholarship at $2,500, 1 at $2,000, and 1 at $1,500 are awarded.

Deadline February of each year.

[453]
CLAIRE OLIPHANT MEMORIAL SCHOLARSHIP

American Legion Auxiliary
Department of New Jersey
c/o Lucille M. Miller, Secretary/Treasurer
1540 Kuser Road, Suite A-8
Hamilton, NJ 08619
(609) 581-9580   Fax: (609) 581-8429

Summary To provide financial assistance to New Jersey residents who are the descendants of veterans and planning to attend college in any state.

Eligibility This program is open to the children, grandchildren, and great-grandchildren of veterans who served in the U.S. armed forces during specified periods of wartime. Applicants must be graduating high school seniors who have been residents of New Jersey for at least 2 years. They must be planning to attend a college or university in any state. Along with their application, they must submit a 1,000-word essay on a topic that changes annually; recently, students were asked to write on the topic, "The Importance of Helping Military Families in Your Community " Selection is based on academic achievement (40%), character (15%), leadership (15%), Americanism (15%), and financial need (15%).

Financial data The stipend is $1,800.

Duration 1 year.

Number awarded 1 each year.
Deadline April each year.

[454]
CLAY MAITLAND SCHOLARSHIP

U.S. Coast Guard
Attn: Office of Work-Life (CG-111)
2100 Second Street, S.W., Stop 7902
Washington, DC 20593-7902
(202) 475-5140   Toll Free: (800) 872-4957
Fax: (202) 475-5907
E-mail: HQS.SMB.FamilySupportServices@uscg.mil
Web: www.uscg.mil/worklife/scholarship.asp

Summary To provide financial assistance to the dependent children of Coast Guard enlisted personnel who are interested in studying marine science in college.

Eligibility This program is open to the dependent children of enlisted members of the U.S. Coast Guard on active duty, retired, or deceased and of enlisted personnel in the Coast Guard Reserve currently on extended active duty 180 days or more. Applicants must be high school seniors or current undergraduates enrolled or planning to enroll full-time at a 4-year college, university, or vocational school with a major in marine science. They must be under 24 years of age and registered in the Defense Enrollment Eligibility Reporting System (DEERS) system. Along with their application, they must submit their SAT or ACT scores, a letter of recommendation, transcripts, a financial information statement, and a 500-word essay on their personal and academic achievements, extracurricular activities, contributions to the community, and academic plans and career goals.

Financial data The stipend is $5,000.

Duration 1 year; nonrenewable.

Number awarded 1 each year.

Deadline March of each year.

[455]
COAST GUARD EXCHANGE SYSTEM SCHOLARSHIP PROGRAM

U.S. Coast Guard
Attn: Community Services Command
Battlefield Technology Center
510 Independence Parkway, Suite 500
Chesapeake, VA 23320-5191
(757) 842-4937   Fax: (757) 420-7185
E-mail: CHarrison@cg-exchange.com
Web: www.uscg.mil

Summary To provide financial assistance for college to high school seniors whose parent is affiliated with the Coast Guard.

Eligibility This program is open to graduating high school seniors and students in the final year of home schooling who are planning to enroll full time at an accredited college or university. Applicants must be the dependent children of active and Reserve Coast Guard members, retired Coast Guard members, civilian employees of the Coast Guard, or members of the Coast Guard Auxiliary. Along with their application, they must submit a 1-page essay explaining what they hope to achieve in their college career, including their educational, professional, and personal goals. Selection is based on that essay, SAT and/or ACT scores, GPA, class ranking, participation and leadership in school and community volunteer activities, personal accomplishments and interests, and letters of recommendation.

Financial data Stipends are $1,500, $750, or $500.
Duration 1 year.
Number awarded 3 each year: 1 at $1,500, 1 at $750, and 1 at $500.
Deadline February of each year.

[456]
COAST GUARD FALLEN HEROES SCHOLARSHIP

U.S. Coast Guard
Attn: Office of Work-Life (CG-111)
2100 Second Street, S.W., Stop 7902
Washington, DC 20593-7902
(202) 475-5140   Toll Free: (800) 872-4957
Fax: (202) 475-5907
E-mail: HQS.SMB.FamilySupportServices@uscg.mil
Web: www.uscg.mil/worklife/scholarship.asp

Summary To provide funding for college to children of Coast Guard personnel who died in the line of duty.
Eligibility This program is open to children of members of the U.S. Coast Guard (enlisted or commissioned) who died during official land, air, or sea operations. Applicants must be high school seniors or current undergraduates enrolled or planning to enroll full-time at a 4-year college, university, or vocational school. They must be under 24 years of age and registered in the Defense Enrollment Eligibility Reporting System (DEERS) system. Along with their application, they must submit their SAT or ACT scores, a letter of recommendation, transcripts, a financial information statement, and a 500-word essay on their personal and academic achievements, extracurricular activities, contributions to the community, and academic plans and career goals.
Financial data A stipend is awarded (amount not specified).
Duration 1 year; may be renewed up to 3 additional years.
Additional information This program began in 2005.
Number awarded 1 or more each year.
Deadline Applications may be submitted at any time.

[457]
COAST GUARD FOUNDATION SCHOLARSHIPS

U.S. Coast Guard
Attn: Office of Work-Life (CG-111)
2100 Second Street, S.W., Stop 7902
Washington, DC 20593-7902
(202) 475-5140   Toll Free: (800) 872-4957
Fax: (202) 475-5907
E-mail: HQS.SMB.FamilySupportServices@uscg.mil
Web: www.uscg.mil/worklife/scholarship.asp

Summary To provide financial assistance for college to the dependent children of Coast Guard enlisted personnel.
Eligibility This program is open to the dependent children of enlisted members of the U.S. Coast Guard on active duty, retired, or deceased, and of enlisted personnel in the Coast Guard Reserve currently on extended active duty 180 days or more. Applicants must be high school seniors or current undergraduates enrolled or planning to enroll full-time at a 4-year college, university, or vocational school. They must be under 24 years of age and registered in the Defense Enrollment Eligibility Reporting System (DEERS) system. Along with their application, they must submit their SAT or ACT

scores, a letter of recommendation, transcripts, a financial information statement, and a 500-word essay on their personal and academic achievements, extracurricular activities, contributions to the community, and academic plans and career goals.
Financial data Stipends range from $2,500 to $5,000 per year.
Duration 1 year; may be renewed up to 3 additional years.
Additional information This program is sponsored by the Coast Guard Foundation.
Number awarded Varies each year; recently, 14 of these scholarships were awarded.
Deadline March of each year.

[458]
COAST GUARD RESERVE USAA SCHOLARSHIP

U.S. Coast Guard
Attn: CG-131
2100 Second Street, S.W., Stop 7801
Washington, DC 20593-7801
(202) 475-5477   E-mail: george.m.rubesha@uscg.mil
Web: www.uscg.mil/RESERVE/docs/pay_benefits/usaa.asp

Summary To provide financial assistance for college or graduate school to members of the Coast Guard Reserves and their dependents.
Eligibility This program is open to Coast Guard enlisted reservists (SELRES or IRR) and their dependents who are registered in the Defense Enrollment Eligibility Reporting System (DEERS). Applicants must be enrolled or accepted for enrollment at 1) an accredited institution in a program leading to an associate, bachelor's, master's, or doctoral degree; or 2) a 2- or 4-year course of study at an accredited technical or vocational training school. Along with their application, they must submit a 1-page essay on how the participation of themselves, their spouse, or their parent in the Coast Guard Reserve has contributed to their success.
Financial data The stipend is $1,000.
Duration 1 year.
Additional information This program is sponsored by the United States Automobile Association (USAA) Insurance Corporation.
Number awarded 6 each year.
Deadline June of each year.

[459]
COL CARL F. BASWELL COMBAT WOUNDED ENGINEER SCHOLARSHIP

Army Engineer Association
Attn: Executive Director
P.O. Box 30260
Alexandria, VA 22310-8260
(703) 428-7084   Fax: (703) 428-6043
E-mail: xd@armyengineer.com
Web: www.armyengineer.com/scholarships.htm

Summary To provide financial assistance for college to children and spouses of Army Engineers who were wounded in combat in Iraq or Afghanistan.
Eligibility This program is open to the children and spouses of U.S. Army Engineers who were wounded in combat and received a Purple Heart during Operation Iraqi Freedom or Operation Enduring Freedom. Applicants must be

working on or planning to work on an associate, bachelor's, or master's degree at an accredited college or university. Selection is based primarily on financial need, although potential for academic success and standards of conduct as supported by personal references are also considered.

Financial data   The stipend is $2,500.

Duration   1 year.

Additional information   This program began in 2010.

Number awarded   1 each year.

Deadline   June of each year.

[460]
COL CARL F. BASWELL FALLEN ENGINEER MEMORIAL SCHOLARSHIP

Army Engineer Association
Attn: Executive Director
P.O. Box 30260
Alexandria, VA 22310-8260
(703) 428-7084   Fax: (703) 428-6043
E-mail: xd@armyengineer.com
Web: www.armyengineer.com/scholarships.htm

Summary   To provide financial assistance for college to children and spouses of Army Engineers who were killed in Iraq or Afghanistan.

Eligibility   This program is open to the children and spouses of U.S. Army Engineers who were killed in combat during Operation Iraqi Freedom or Operation Enduring Freedom. Applicants must be working on or planning to work on an associate, bachelor's, or master's degree at an accredited college or university. Selection is based primarily on financial need, although potential for academic success and standards of conduct as supported by personal references are also considered.

Financial data   The stipend is $2,500.

Duration   1 year.

Additional information   This program began in 2010.

Number awarded   1 each year.

Deadline   June of each year.

[461]
COLLEGE SCHOLARSHIPS FOR DEPENDENT CHILDREN

Air Force Officers' Wives' Club of Washington, D.C.
Attn: Scholarship Committee
P.O. Box 8490
Washington, DC 20032
(202) 239-1932   E-mail: scholarships@afowc.com
Web: www.afowc.com/scholarships

Summary   To provide financial assistance for undergraduate or graduate education in any state to the dependent children of Air Force members in the Washington, D.C. area.

Eligibility   This program is open to the dependent children of Air Force enlisted or commissioned personnel residing in the Washington, D.C. metropolitan area in the following categories: active duty, Reserve, Guard, retired, or deceased. Applicants must be currently enrolled at an accredited college, university, vocational/trade school, community college, or graduate school in any state. Along with their application, they must submit a 400-word essay on their choice of 3 assigned topics that change annually. Selection is based on their essay academic ability, extracurricular activities, service

activities, citizenship, and references; financial need is not considered. Applicants who receive an appointment to a service academy are not eligible.

Financial data   The stipend is $4,000. Funds may be used only for payment of tuition or academic fees.

Duration   1 year; nonrenewable.

Number awarded   Varies each year.

Deadline   February of each year.

[462]
COLONEL HAROLD M. BEARDSLEE MEMORIAL SCHOLARSHIP AWARDS

Army Engineer Association
Attn: Executive Director
P.O. Box 30260
Alexandria, VA 22310-8260
(703) 428-7084   Fax: (703) 428-6043
E-mail: xd@armyengineer.com
Web: www.armyengineer.com/scholarships.htm

Summary   To provide financial assistance for college to children and spouses of members of the Army Engineer Association (AEA).

Eligibility   This program is open to spouses and children of AEA members in the following 4 categories: 1) graduating high school seniors who are children of active-duty or civilian members (including active-duty retired); 2) graduating high school seniors who are children of Reserve or National Guard members (including Reserve or National Guard retired); 3) children and spouses of members in the second, third, or fourth year of a baccalaureate degree program; and 4) the next best qualified applicant, regardless of category, not receiving any of those awards. Applicants must be enrolled or planning to enroll full time at an accredited college or university. Along with their application, they must submit an essay on their reasons for seeking this award. Selection is based on the essay, scholastic aptitude, and letters of recommendation.

Financial data   The stipend is $1,000.

Duration   1 year; nonrenewable.

Number awarded   4 each year: 1 in each category.

Deadline   April of each year.

[463]
COLONEL HAZEL ELIZABETH BENN, USMC SCHOLARSHIP

Fleet Reserve Association
Attn: FRA Education Foundation
125 North West Street
Alexandria, VA 22314-2754
(703) 683-1400   Toll Free: (800) FRA-1924
Fax: (703) 549-6610   E-mail: scholars@fra.org
Web: www.fra.org

Summary   To provide financial assistance for college to children of members of the Fleet Reserve Association (FRA) serving in the Navy as an enlisted medical rating assigned to the United States Marine Corps (USMC).

Eligibility   This program is open to the dependent children of members of the association or persons who were members at the time of death. Applicants must be entering their freshman or sophomore year of college. Their parent must be serving and have served in the U.S. Navy as an enlisted medical rating assigned to the USMC. Selection is based on academic record, financial need, extracurricular activities, leadership skills, and participation in community activities. U.S. citizenship is required.

Financial data   The stipend is $2,000.

Duration   1 year.

Number awarded   1 or more each year.

Deadline   April of each year.

[464]
COLORADO DEPENDENTS TUITION ASSISTANCE PROGRAM

Colorado Commission on Higher Education
1560 Broadway, Suite 1600
Denver, CO 80202
(303) 866-2723   Fax: (303) 866-4266
E-mail: cche@state.co.us
Web: highered.colorado.gov

Summary   To provide financial assistance for college to the dependents of disabled or deceased Colorado National Guardsmen, law enforcement officers, and fire fighters.

Eligibility   Eligible for the program are dependents of Colorado law enforcement officers, fire fighters, and National Guardsmen disabled or killed in the line of duty, as well as dependents of prisoners of war or service personnel listed as missing in action. Students must be Colorado residents under 22 years of age enrolled at 1) a state-supported 2- or 4-year Colorado college or university; 2) a private college, university, or vocational school in Colorado approved by the commission; or 3) an out-of-state 4-year college. Financial need is considered in the selection process.

Financial data   Eligible students receive free tuition at Colorado public institutions of higher education. If the recipient wishes to attend a private college, university, or proprietary school, the award is limited to the amount of tuition at a comparable state-supported institution. Students who have applied to live in a dormitory, but have not been accepted because there is not enough space, may be provided supplemental assistance. Students who choose to live off-campus are not eligible for room reimbursement or a meal plan. Students who attend a nonresidential Colorado institution and do not live at home are eligible for a grant of $1,000 per semester to assist with living expenses. Students who attend an out-of-state institution are eligible for the amount of tuition equivalent to that at a comparable Colorado public institution, but they are not eligible for room and board.

Duration   Up to 6 years or until completion of a bachelor's degree, provided the recipient maintains a GPA of 2.5 or higher.

Additional information   Recipients must attend accredited postsecondary institutions in Colorado.

Number awarded   Varies each year; recently, nearly $365,000 was allocated to this program.

Deadline   Deadline not specified.

[465]
COLORADO LEGION AUXILIARY DEPARTMENT PRESIDENT'S SCHOLARSHIP FOR JUNIOR AUXILIARY MEMBERS

American Legion Auxiliary
Department of Colorado
7465 East First Avenue, Suite D
Denver, CO 80230
(303) 367-5388   Fax: (303) 367-5388
E-mail: dept-sec@alacolorado.com
Web: www.alacolorado.com/index_files/Forms.htm

Summary   To provide money for college to junior members of the American Legion Auxiliary in Colorado.

Eligibility   This program is open to seniors at high schools in Colorado who have been junior members of the auxiliary for the past 3 years. Applicants must be Colorado residents planning to attend college in the state. Along with their application, they must submit a 1,000-word essay on the topic, "My Obligations as an American." Selection is based on character (20%), Americanism (20%), leadership (20%), scholarship (20%), and financial need (20%).

Financial data   The stipend is $1,000.

Duration   1 year; nonrenewable.

Number awarded   1 each year.

Deadline   March of each year.

[466]
COLORADO LEGION AUXILIARY DEPARTMENT PRESIDENT'S SCHOLARSHIPS

American Legion Auxiliary
Department of Colorado
7465 East First Avenue, Suite D
Denver, CO 80230
(303) 367-5388   Fax: (303) 367-5388
E-mail: dept-sec@alacolorado.com
Web: www.alacolorado.com/index_files/Forms.htm

Summary   To provide financial assistance to children and grandchildren of veterans in Colorado who plan to attend college in the state.

Eligibility   This program is open to children and grandchildren of veterans who served in the armed forces during wartime eligibility dates for membership in the American Legion. Applicants must be residents of Colorado who are high school seniors planning to attend a college in the state. Along with their application, they must submit a 1,000-word essay on the topic, "My Obligations as an American." Selection is based on character (15%), Americanism (15%), leadership (15%), scholarship (15%), and financial need (40%).

Financial data   Stipends are $1,000 or $500.

Duration   1 year.

Number awarded   4 each year: 2 at 1,000 and 2 at $500.

Deadline   March of each year.

[467]
COLORADO LEGION AUXILIARY PAST PRESIDENT'S PARLEY NURSE'S SCHOLARSHIP

American Legion Auxiliary
Department of Colorado
7465 East First Avenue, Suite D
Denver, CO 80230
(303) 367-5388   Fax: (303) 367-5388
E-mail: dept-sec@alacolorado.com
Web: www.alacolorado.com/index_files/Forms.htm

Summary To provide funding to wartime veterans and their descendants in Colorado who are interested in attending school in the state to prepare for a career in nursing.

Eligibility This program is open to 1) daughters, sons, spouses, granddaughters, and great-granddaughters of veterans, and 2) veterans who served in the armed forces during eligibility dates for membership in the American Legion. Applicants must be Colorado residents who have been accepted by an accredited school of nursing in the state. Along with their application, they must submit a 500-word essay on the topic, "Americanism." Selection is based on that essay (25%), scholastic ability (25%), financial need (25%), references (13%), and dedication to chosen field (12%).

Financial data Stipends range from $500 to $1,000.

Duration 1 year; nonrenewable.

Number awarded Varies each year, depending on the availability of funds.

Deadline April of each year.

[468]
COMMANDER DANIEL J. CHRISTOVICH SCHOLARSHIP

U.S. Coast Guard
Attn: Office of Work-Life (CG-111)
2100 Second Street, S.W., Stop 7902
Washington, DC 20593-7902
(202) 475-5140   Toll Free: (800) 872-4957
Fax: (202) 475-5907
E-mail: HQS.SMB.FamilySupportServices@uscg.mil
Web: www.uscg.mil/worklife/scholarship.asp

Summary To provide financial assistance for college to the dependent children of Coast Guard enlisted personnel.

Eligibility This program is open to the dependent children of enlisted members of the U.S. Coast Guard on active duty, retired, or deceased and of enlisted personnel in the Coast Guard Reserve currently on extended active duty 180 days or more. Applicants must be high school seniors or current undergraduates enrolled or planning to enroll full-time at a 4-year college, university, or vocational school. Along with their application, they must submit their SAT or ACT scores, a letter of recommendation, transcripts, a financial information statement, and a 500-word essay on their personal and academic achievements, extracurricular activities, contributions to the community, and academic plans and career goals.

Financial data The stipend is $2,500.

Duration 1 year; nonrenewable.

Number awarded 1 each year.

Deadline March of each year.

[469]
COMMANDER RONALD J. CANTIN SCHOLARSHIP

U.S. Coast Guard
Attn: Office of Work-Life (CG-111)
2100 Second Street, S.W., Stop 7902
Washington, DC 20593-7902
(202) 475-5140   Toll Free: (800) 872-4957
Fax: (202) 475-5907
E-mail: HQS.SMB.FamilySupportServices@uscg.mil
Web: www.uscg.mil/worklife/scholarship.asp

Summary To provide financial assistance for college to the dependent children of Coast Guard enlisted personnel.

Eligibility This program is open to the dependent children of enlisted members of the U.S. Coast Guard on active duty, retired, or deceased and of enlisted personnel in the Coast Guard Reserve currently on extended active duty 180 days or more. Applicants must be high school seniors or current undergraduates enrolled or planning to enroll full-time at a 4-year college, university, or vocational school. They must be under 24 years of age and registered in the Defense Enrollment Eligibility Reporting System (DEERS) system. Along with their application, they must submit their SAT or ACT scores, a letter of recommendation, transcripts, a financial information statement, and a 500-word essay on their personal and academic achievements, extracurricular activities, contributions to the community, and academic plans and career goals.

Financial data The stipend is $2,500.

Duration 1 year; nonrenewable.

Number awarded 1 each year.

Deadline March of each year.

[470]
COMMANDER WILLIAM S. STUHR SCHOLARSHIPS

Commander William S. Stuhr Scholarship Fund
Attn: Executive Director
P.O. Box 1138
Kitty Hawk, NC 27949-1138
(252) 255-3013   Fax: (252) 255-3014
E-mail: stuhrstudents@earthlink.net

Summary To provide money for college to the dependent children of retired or active-duty military personnel.

Eligibility This program is open to the dependent children of military personnel who are serving on active duty or retired with pay after 20 years' service (not merely separated from service). Applicants must be high school seniors who rank in the top 10% of their class and have an SAT score of at least 1250 or an ACT score of at least 27. They must plan to attend a 4-year accredited college. Selection is based on academic performance, extracurricular activities, demonstrated leadership potential, and financial need.

Financial data The stipend is $1,200 per year.

Duration 4 years, provided the recipient makes the dean's list at their college at least once during their first 2 years.

Additional information This program began in 1965. Recipients and their families attend a scholarship awards function in late May or early June; the fund pays air transportation to the event. Applications may be obtained only by writing and enclosing a self-addressed stamped envelope. The fund does not respond to telephone, fax, or e-mail inquiries.

Number awarded 6 each year: 1 for a child of a military servicemember from each of the 6 branches (Air Force, Army,

Coast Guard, Marine Corps, Navy, and Reserves/National Guard).
Deadline January of each year.

[471]
CONGRESSIONAL MEDAL OF HONOR SOCIETY SCHOLARSHIPS

Congressional Medal of Honor Society
40 Patriots Point Road
Mt. Pleasant, SC 29464
(843) 884-8862   Fax: (843) 884-1471
E-mail: medalhq@earthlink.net
Web: www.cmohs.org

Summary To provide financial assistance to dependents of Congressional Medal of Honor winners who are interested in pursuing postsecondary education.
Eligibility Sons and daughters of Congressional Medal of Honor recipients are eligible to apply if they are high school seniors or graduates and have been accepted by an accredited college or university.
Financial data The stipend is $2,000 per year.
Duration 1 year; renewable for up to 3 more years.
Number awarded Varies; approximately 15 each year.
Deadline August or December of each year.

[472]
CONGRESSMAN DAVID L. HOBSON CIVIL ENGINEERING SCHOLARSHIP

Army Engineer Association
Attn: Executive Director
P.O. Box 30260
Alexandria, VA 22310-8260
(703) 428-7084   Fax: (703) 428-6043
E-mail: xd@armyengineer.com
Web: www.armyengineer.com/scholarships.htm

Summary To provide financial assistance to members of the Army Engineer Association (AEA) and their families interested in studying civil engineering in college.
Eligibility This program is open to AEA members and their families who are U.S. citizens. Applicants must be enrolled full time at an accredited college or university and working on a bachelor's degree in civil engineering. Along with their application, they must submit a 600-word essay that lists their academic and professional goals, extracurricular activities, and military service (if applicable). Selection is based on that essay, scholastic aptitude, and letters of recommendation.
Financial data The stipend is $3,000.
Duration 1 year; nonrenewable.
Additional information This program is sponsored by the engineering firm, Trimble.
Number awarded 4 each year.
Deadline July of each year.

[473]
CONNECTICUT NATIONAL GUARD FOUNDATION SCHOLARSHIPS

Connecticut National Guard Foundation, Inc.
Attn: Scholarship Committee
360 Broad Street
Hartford, CT 06105-3795
(860) 241-1550   Fax: (860) 293-2929
E-mail: scholarship.committee@ctngfoundation.org
Web: www.ctngfoundation.org/Scholarship.asp

Summary To provide money for college to members of the Connecticut National Guard and their families.
Eligibility This program is open to members of the Connecticut Army National Guard and Organized Militia, their children, and their spouses. Applicants must be enrolled or planning to enroll in an accredited college or technical program. Along with their application, they must submit a letter of recommendation, a list of extracurricular activities, high school or college transcripts, and a 200-word statement on their educational and future goals. Selection is based on achievement and citizenship.
Financial data Stipends are $2,000 or $1,000.
Duration 1 year.
Number awarded 5 at $2,000 and 5 at $1,000.
Deadline March of each year.

[474]
CONNECTICUT TUITION WAIVER FOR VETERANS

Connecticut Office of Financial and Academic Affairs for Higher Education
Attn: Student Financial Aid
61 Woodland Street
Hartford, CT 06105-2326
(860) 947-1855   Toll Free: (800) 842-0229 (within CT)
Fax: (860) 947-1311   E-mail: sfa@ctdhe.org
Web: www.ctohe.org/SFA/default.htm

Summary To provide money for college or graduate school to certain Connecticut veterans and military personnel or their dependents.
Eligibility This program is open to 1) honorably-discharged Connecticut veterans who served at least 90 days during specified periods of wartime; 2) active members of the Connecticut Army and Air National Guard; 3) Connecticut residents who are a dependent child or surviving spouse of a member of the armed forces killed in action on or after September 11, 2001 who was also a Connecticut resident; and 4) Connecticut residents who are dependent children of a person officially declared missing in action or a prisoner of war while serving in the armed forces after January 1, 1960. Applicants must be attending or planning to attend a public college or university in the state.
Financial data The program provides a waiver of 100% of tuition for students working on an undergraduate or graduate degree at the University of Connecticut, 100% of tuition for general fund courses at campuses of Connecticut State University, 50% of tuition for extension and summer courses at campuses of Connecticut State University, 100% of tuition at all Connecticut community colleges, and 50% or fees at Charter Oak State College.
Duration Up to 4 years.

Additional information This is an entitlement program; applications are available from the respective college financial aid offices.

Number awarded Varies each year.

Deadline Deadline not specified.

[475]
CONTINUING EDUCATION SCHOLARSHIPS FOR NON-MILITARY AIR FORCE SPOUSES

Air Force Officers' Wives' Club of Washington, D.C.
Attn: Scholarship Committee
P.O. Box 8490
Washington, DC 20032
(202) 239-1932   E-mail: scholarships@afowc.com
Web: www.afowc.com/scholarships

Summary To provide financial assistance for undergraduate or graduate study in any state to the non-military spouses of Air Force members in the Washington, D.C. area.

Eligibility This program is open to the non-military spouses of Air Force enlisted or commissioned personnel residing in the Washington, D.C. metropolitan area in the following categories: active duty, Reserve, Guard, retired, MIA/POW, or deceased. Applicants must be enrolled or planning to enroll as an undergraduate or graduate student at a college or university in any state. Along with their application, they must submit a 400-word essay on why they are pursuing higher education and how it will be of personal benefit to them in the future. Selection is based on their essay academic ability, extracurricular activities, service activities, citizenship, and references; financial need is not considered.

Financial data The stipend is $4,000. Funds may be used only for payment of tuition or academic fees.

Duration 1 year; nonrenewable.

Number awarded Varies each year.

Deadline February of each year.

[476]
COUDRET TRUST SCHOLARSHIPS

American Legion
Department of Arkansas
702 Victory Street
P.O. Box 3280
Little Rock, AR 72203
(501) 375-1104   Toll Free: (877) 243-9799
Fax: (501) 375-4236   E-mail: alegion@swbell.net
Web: www.arlegion.org/scholarships/coudret_trust.html

Summary To provide money for college to descendants of members of the American Legion in Arkansas.

Eligibility This program is open to the children, grandchildren, and great-grandchildren of living or deceased members of the American Legion in Arkansas. The Legionnaire, except veterans of Operation Enduring Freedom and Operation Iraqi Freedom era, must have been a member for at least 2 years. Applicants must be high school seniors or graduates of a 2-year college in Arkansas. They must sign a drug free pledge and a declaration of support for the Preamble to the Constitution of the American Legion. Selection is based on American spirit, character, leadership quality, scholastic endeavor, and financial need.

Financial data The stipend is $1,000 per year.

Duration 2 years.

Number awarded 4 each year.

Deadline March of each year.

[477]
CPO SCHOLARSHIP FUND

Senior Enlisted Academy Alumni Association
Attn: CPO Scholarship Fund
1269 Elliot Avenue
Newport, RI 02841-1525
E-mail: cposfboard@cposf.org
Web: www.cposf.org

Summary To provide financial assistance for college to the dependents of Navy Chief Petty Officers (CPOs).

Eligibility This program is open to the spouses and children (natural born, adopted, or step) of active, Reserve, retired, and deceased Navy CPOs. Applicants must be high school seniors or students currently enrolled at a college, university, or vocational/technical school with the goal of obtaining an associate or bachelor's degree or certificate. Along with their application, they must submit an autobiographical essay of 200 to 500 words that discusses their significant experiences, community involvement, and qualities of character and leadership important in achieving their goals. Selection is based on the essay, honors and awards received during high school, extracurricular activities, community activities, and employment experience; financial need is not considered. Members of the armed services are not eligible.

Financial data The stipend is $2,000.

Duration 1 year.

Additional information The applicant judged most outstanding receives the Tom Crow Memorial Scholarship.

Number awarded Varies each year; recently, 56 of these scholarships were awarded.

Deadline March of each year.

[478]
CSM VINCENT BALDASSARI MEMORIAL SCHOLARSHIPS

Enlisted Association National Guard of New Jersey
Attn: Scholarship Chair
3650 Saylors Pond Road
Fort Dix, NJ 08640
(609) 562-0260   Fax: (609) 562-0283
Web: www.eang-nj.org/scholarships.html

Summary To provide financial assistance to New Jersey National Guard members and their children who are interested in attending college in any state.

Eligibility This program is open to 1) children of New Jersey National Guard members who are also members of the Enlisted Association National Guard of New Jersey, and 2) drilling Guard members who are also members of the Association. Applicants must be attending or planning to attend a college or university in any state. Along with their application, they must submit 1) information on their church, school, and community activities; 2) a list of honors they have received; 3) letters of recommendation; 4) transcripts; and 5) a letter with specific facts about their desire to continue their education and specifying their career goals. Financial need is not considered in the selection process.

Financial data The stipend is $1,000.

Duration 1 year.

Number awarded Varies each year; recently, 5 of these scholarships were awarded.

Deadline May of each year.

[479]
CSM VIRGIL R. WILLIAMS SCHOLARSHIP PROGRAM

Enlisted Association of the National Guard of the United States
3133 Mount Vernon Avenue
Alexandria, VA 22305-2640
(703) 519-3846   Toll Free: (800) 234-EANG
Fax: (703) 519-3849   E-mail: eangus@eangus.org
Web: www.eangus.org/resources/scholarships_grants.aspx

Summary To provide financial assistance to National Guard members and their dependents who are members of the Enlisted Association of the National Guard of the United States (EANGUS) and entering or continuing in college.

Eligibility This program is open to high school seniors and current college students who are enrolled or planning to enroll as full-time undergraduate students. They must be 1) National Guard members who belong to EANGUS; 2) unmarried sons and daughters of EANGUS members; 3) spouses of EANGUS members; or 4) unremarried spouses and unmarried dependent children of deceased EANGUS members who were in good standing at the time of their death. Honorary, associate, or corporate membership alone does not qualify. Applicants must submit a copy of their school transcript, 3 letters of recommendation, a letter of academic reference (from their principal, dean, or counselor), a photocopy of the qualifying state and/or national membership card (parent's, spouse's or applicant's), and a personal letter with specific facts as to their desire to continue their education and why financial assistance is necessary. Application packets must be submitted to the state EANGUS association; acceptable packets are then sent to the national offices for judging. Selection is based on academic achievement, character, leadership, and financial need.

Financial data The stipend is $2,000.

Duration 1 year; nonrenewable.

Additional information Recent sponsors of this program included USAA Insurance Corporation, GEICO Insurance, the Armed Forces Benefit Association, and the Armed Forces Insurance Company.

Number awarded Varies each year; recently, 10 of these scholarships were awarded.

Deadline Applications must first be verified by the state office and then submitted by June to the national office.

[480]
DAEDALIAN FOUNDATION DESCENDANTS' SCHOLARSHIP PROGRAM

Daedalian Foundation
Attn: Scholarship Committee
55 Main Circle (Building 676)
P.O. Box 249
Randolph AFB, TX 78148-0249
(210) 945-2113   Fax: (210) 945-2112
E-mail: kristi@daedalians.org
Web: www.daedalians.org/foundation/scholarships.htm

Summary To provide financial assistance to descendants of members of the Order of Daedalians who wish to prepare for a career in military aviation or space.

Eligibility This program is open to descendants of members of the order who are working on or planning to work on a baccalaureate or higher degree. Applicants must be interested in and willing to commit to a career as a commissioned military pilot, flight crew member, astronaut, or commissioned officer in 1 of the armed forces of the United States in a discipline directly supporting aeronautics or astronautics. They must be physically and mentally qualified for flight and/or space; if they intend to pursue a non-flying career as a commissioned officer in a scientific or engineering discipline supporting aviation or space, they must pass a physical examination qualifying for active commissioned duty in the U.S. armed forces. Nominations must be submitted by a local chapter (Flight) of Daedalian. Selection is based on academic achievement and recognition, extracurricular activities, honors, and employment experience. Financial need may be considered if all other factors are equal.

Financial data The stipend is $2,000.

Additional information The Order of Daedalians was founded in 1934 as an organization of the nearly 14,000 aviators who served as military pilots during World War I and are still listed and designated as Founder Members. In the 1950s, the organization expanded eligibility to include 1) on a sponsorship basis, current and former commissioned military pilots from all services; and 2) on a hereditary basis, descendants of Founder Members.

Number awarded Up to 3 each year.

Deadline July of each year.

[481]
DANIEL E. LAMBERT MEMORIAL SCHOLARSHIP

American Legion
Department of Maine
P.O. Box 900
Waterville, ME 04903-0900
(207) 873-3229   Fax: (207) 872-0501
E-mail: legionme@mainelegion.org
Web: www.mainelegion.org

Summary To provide financial assistance to the children of veterans in Maine who plan to attend college in any state.

Eligibility This program is open to residents of Maine who are the child or grandchild of a veteran. Applicants must be attending or planning to attend an accredited college or vocational/technical school in any state. They must have demonstrated, by their past behavior, that they believe in the American way of life. U.S. citizenship is required. Financial need is considered in the selection process.

Financial data The stipend is $1,000.

Duration 1 year.

Number awarded 1 or 2 each year.

Deadline April of each year.

[482]
DATATEL ANGELFIRE SCHOLARSHIP

Datatel Scholars Foundation
4375 Fair Lakes Court
Fairfax, VA 22033
(703) 968-9000, ext. 4549   Toll Free: (800) 486-4332
Fax: (703) 968-4625   E-mail: scholars@datatel.com
Web: www.datatelscholars.org

Summary To provide funding to graduating high school seniors, college students, and graduate students who will be studying at a Datatel client school and are veterans, veterans' dependents, or refugees from southeast Asia.

Eligibility This program is open to 1) veterans who served in the Asian theater (Vietnam, Cambodia, or Laos) between 1964 and 1975; 2) their spouses and children; 3) refugees from Vietnam, Cambodia, or Laos; and 4) veterans who served in Operation Desert Storm, Operation Enduring Freedom, and/or Operation Iraqi Freedom. Applicants must attend a Datatel client college or university during the upcoming school year as a full- or part-time undergraduate or graduate student. They must first apply to their institution, which selects 2 semifinalists and forwards their applications to the sponsor. Along with their application, they must include a 1,000-word personal statement that discusses how the conflict has affected them personally, summarizes how the conflict has impacted their educational goals, and describes how being awarded this scholarship will help them achieve their goals. Selection is based on the quality of the personal statement (60%) and academic merit (40%).

Financial data The stipend is $1,700. Funds are paid directly to the institution.

Duration 1 year.

Additional information Datatel, Inc. produces advanced information technology solutions for higher education. It has more than 750 client sites in the United States and Canada. This scholarship was created to commemorate those who lost their lives in Vietnam or Iraq and is named after a memorial administered by the Disabled American Veterans Association in Angelfire, New Mexico.

Number awarded 10 each year.

Deadline Students must submit online applications to their institution or organization by January of each year.

[483]
DAUGHTERS OF THE CINCINNATI SCHOLARSHIP PROGRAM

Daughters of the Cincinnati
Attn: Scholarship Administrator
20 West 44th Street, Suite 508
New York, NY 10036
(212) 991-9945 E-mail: scholarships@daughters1894.org
Web: www.daughters1894.org

Summary To provide financial assistance for college to high school seniors who are the daughters of active-duty, deceased, or retired military officers.

Eligibility This program is open to high school seniors who are the daughters of career commissioned officers of the regular Army, Navy, Air Force, Coast Guard, or Marine Corps on active duty, deceased, or retired. Applicants must be planning to enroll at a college or university in any state. Along with their application, they must submit an official school transcript, SAT or ACT scores, a letter of recommendation, and documentation of financial need.

Financial data Scholarship amounts have recently averaged $4,000 per year. Funds are paid directly to the college of the student's choice.

Duration 1 year; may be renewed up to 3 additional years, provided the recipient remains in good academic standing.

Additional information This program was originally established in 1906.

Number awarded Approximately 12 each year.

Deadline March of each year.

[484]
DELAWARE EDUCATIONAL BENEFITS FOR CHILDREN OF DECEASED VETERANS AND OTHERS

Delaware Department of Education
Attn: Higher Education Office
401 Federal Street
Dover, DE 19901-3639
(302) 735-4120   Toll Free: (800) 292-7935
Fax: (302) 739-6765   E-mail: dheo@doe.k12.de.us
Web: www.doe.k12.de.us

Summary To provide financial assistance for undergraduate education to dependents of deceased Delaware veterans, state police officers, and Department of Transportation employees and members of the armed forces declared prisoners of war or missing in action.

Eligibility Applicants for this assistance must have been Delaware residents for at least 3 consecutive years and be the children, between 16 and 24 years of age, of members of the armed forces 1) whose cause of death was service-related, 2) who are being held or were held as a prisoner of war, or 3) who are officially declared missing in action. The parent must have been a resident of Delaware at the time of death or declaration of missing in action or prisoner of war status. Also eligible are children of Delaware state police officers whose cause of death was service-related and employees of the state Department of Transportation routinely employed in job-related activities upon the state highway system whose cause of death was job related. U.S. citizenship or eligible noncitizen status is required.

Financial data Eligible students receive full tuition at any state-supported institution in Delaware or, if the desired educational program is not available at a state-supported school, at any private institution in Delaware. If the desired educational program is not offered at either a public or private institution in Delaware, this program pays the full cost of tuition at the out-of-state school the recipient attends. Students who wish to attend a private or out-of-state school even though their program is offered at a Delaware public institution receive the equivalent of the average tuition and fees at the state school.

Duration 1 year; may be renewed for 3 additional years.

Number awarded Varies each year.

Deadline Applications may be submitted at any time, but they must be received at least 4 weeks before the beginning of classes.

[485]
DELLA VAN DEUREN MEMORIAL SCHOLARSHIPS

American Legion Auxiliary
Department of Wisconsin
Attn: Education Chair
2930 American Legion Drive
P.O. Box 140
Portage, WI 53901-0140
(608) 745-0124   Toll Free: (866) 664-3863
Fax: (608) 745-1947   E-mail: alawi@amlegionauxwi.org
Web: www.amlegionauxwi.org/Scholarships.htm

Summary To provide financial assistance to Wisconsin residents who are members or children of members of the American Legion Auxiliary and interested in attending college.

Eligibility This program is open to members and children of members of the American Legion Auxiliary in Wisconsin. Applicants must be high school seniors or graduates attending or planning to attend a college or university in any state. They must have a GPA of 3.5 or higher and be able to demonstrate financial need. Along with their application, they must submit a 300-word essay on "Education—An Investment in the Future."

Financial data The stipend is $1,000.

Duration 1 year; nonrenewable.

Number awarded 2 each year.

Deadline March of each year.

[486]
DISABLED AMERICAN VETERANS AUXILIARY NATIONAL EDUCATION SCHOLARSHIP FUND

Disabled American Veterans Auxiliary
Attn: National Education Scholarship Fund
3725 Alexandria Pike
Cold Spring, KY 41076
(859) 441-7300   Toll Free: (877) 426-2838, ext. 4020
Fax: (859) 442-2095   E-mail: dava@davmail.org
Web: auxiliary.dav.org/membership/Programs.aspx

Summary To provide financial assistance to members of the Disabled American Veterans (DAV) Auxiliary who are interested in attending college or graduate school.

Eligibility This program is open to paid life members of the auxiliary who are attending or planning to attend a college, university, or vocational school as a full- or part-time undergraduate or graduate student. Applicants must be at least seniors in high school, but there is no maximum age limit. Selection is based on academic achievement; participation in DAV activities; participation in other activities for veterans in their school, community, or elsewhere; volunteer work; membership in clubs or organizations; honors and awards; a statement of academic goals; and financial need.

Financial data Stipends are $1,500 per year for full-time students or $750 per year for part-time students.

Duration 1 year; may be renewed for up to 4 additional years, provided the recipient maintains a GPA of 2.5 or higher.

Additional information Membership in the DAV Auxiliary is available to extended family members of veterans eligible for membership in Disabled American Veterans (i.e., any man or woman who served in the armed forces during a period of war or under conditions simulating war and was wounded, disabled to any degree, or left with long-term illness as a result of military service and was discharged or retired from military service under honorable conditions). This program was established in September 2010 as a replacement for the educational loan program that the DAV Auxiliary operated from 1931 until August 2010.

Number awarded Varies each year.

Deadline March of each year.

[487]
DISTINGUISHED FLYING CROSS SOCIETY SCHOLARSHIPS

Distinguished Flying Cross Society
Attn: Scholarship Program
P.O. Box 530250
San Diego, CA 92153
Toll Free: (866) DFC-MEDAL
Web: www.dfcsociety.org/?page_id=790

Summary To provide financial assistance for college to descendants of members of the Distinguished Flying Cross Society (DFCS).

Eligibility This program is open to descendants (including legally adopted children) of DFCS members. Applicants must be working on an undergraduate degree at an accredited institution of higher education. Along with their application, they must submit a list of memberships in school-related organizations, a list of elected leadership positions they have held, information on activities that demonstrate community involvement, transcripts (including SAT scores), and a 500-word essay on why they feel they deserve this scholarship.

Financial data The stipend is $1,000.

Duration 1 year.

Additional information Membership in the sponsoring organization, founded in 1994, is limited to members of the U.S. armed forces who have been awarded the Distinguished Flying Cross as a result of deeds accomplished during aerial flight.

Number awarded 4 each year.

Deadline November of each year.

[488]
DKF VETERANS ASSISTANCE FOUNDATION SCHOLARSHIPS

DKF Veterans Assistance Foundation
P.O. Box 7166
San Carlos, CA 94070
(650) 595-3896   E-mail: admin@dkfveterans.com
Web: www.dkfveterans.com

Summary To provide financial assistance for college in any state to California residents who are veterans of Operation Enduring Freedom (OEF) in Afghanistan or Operation Iraqi Freedom (OIF) or the dependents of deceased or disabled veterans of those actions.

Eligibility This program is open to 1) veterans of the U.S. armed forces (including the Coast Guard) who served in support of OEF or OIF within the central command area of responsibility; and 2) dependents of those veterans who were killed in action or incurred disabilities rated as 75% or more. Applicants must be residents of California enrolled or planning to enroll full time at a college, university, community college, or trade institution in any state. Along with their application, they must submit a cover letter introducing themselves and their educational goals.

Financial data The stipend is $5,000 per year for students at universities and state colleges or $1,500 per year for students at community colleges and trade institutions.

Duration 1 year; may be renewed up to 3 additional years, provided the recipient maintains a GPA of 3.0 or higher.

Additional information This foundation began in 2005.

Number awarded A limited number are awarded.

Deadline Deadline not specified.

[489]
DOLPHIN SCHOLARSHIPS

Dolphin Scholarship Foundation
Attn: Scholarship Administrator
4966 Euclid Road, Suite 109
Virginia Beach, VA 23462
(757) 671-3200, ext. 111   Fax: (757) 671-3330
E-mail: scholars@dolphinscholarship.org
Web: www.dolphinscholarship.org

Summary   To provide financial assistance for college to the children of members or former members of the Submarine Force.

Eligibility   This program is open to the unmarried children and stepchildren under 24 years of age of 1) members or former members of the Submarine Force who qualified in submarines and served in the submarine force for at least 8 years; 2) Navy members who served in submarine support activities for at least 10 years; and 3) Submarine Force members who died on active duty. Applicants must be working or intending to work toward a bachelor's degree at an accredited 4-year college or university. Selection is based on academic proficiency, commitment and excellence in school and community activities, and financial need.

Financial data   The stipend is $3,400 per year.

Duration   1 year; may be renewed for 3 additional years.

Additional information   Since this program began in 1961, it has awarded more than $8 million to more than 1,000 students. It includes awards previously offered by U.S. Submarine Veterans of World War II. In 1991, that organization agreed to turn over its funds to the Dolphin Scholarship Foundation with the stipulation that it would award 3 scholarships each year, designated the U.S. Submarine Veterans of World War II Scholarship, the Wives of the U.S. Submarine Veterans of World War II Scholarship, and the Arnold Krippendorf Scholarship.

Number awarded   Varies each year; recently, 27 new and 100 renewal scholarships were awarded.

Deadline   March of each year.

[490]
DOROTHY KELLERMAN SCHOLARSHIP

American Legion Auxiliary
Department of New Jersey
c/o Lucille M. Miller, Secretary/Treasurer
1540 Kuser Road, Suite A-8
Hamilton, NJ 08619
(609) 581-9580   Fax: (609) 581-8429

Summary   To provide financial assistance to New Jersey residents who are the descendants of veterans and planning to attend college in any state.

Eligibility   This program is open to the children, grandchildren, and great-grandchildren of veterans who served in the U.S. armed forces during specified periods of wartime. Applicants must be graduating high school seniors who have been residents of New Jersey for at least 2 years. They must be planning to attend a college or university in any state. Along with their application, they must submit a 1,000-word essay on a topic that changes annually; recently, students were asked to write on the topic, "The Importance of Helping Military Families in Your Community " Selection is based on academic achievement (40%), character (15%), leadership (15%), Americanism (15%), and financial need (15%).

Financial data   Stipends range from $1,000 to $2,500.

Duration   1 year; nonrenewable.

Number awarded   1 each year.

Deadline   April of each year.

[491]
DR. HANNAH K. VUOLO MEMORIAL SCHOLARSHIP

American Legion
Department of New York
112 State Street, Suite 1300
Albany, NY 12207
(518) 463-2215   Toll Free: (800) 253-4466
Fax: (518) 427-8443   E-mail: info@nylegion.org
Web: www.ny.legion.org/scholar.htm

Summary   To provide financial assistance to descendants of members of the American Legion in New York who are interested in becoming secondary school teachers.

Eligibility   This program is open to the natural or adopted direct descendants of members or deceased members of the American Legion's New York Department. Applicants must be high school seniors or graduates under 21 years of age entering an accredited college in any state as freshmen with a commitment to earning a degree in secondary education. Preference is given to residents of New York. Selection is based on financial need (11 points), academic record (10 points), Americanism (9 points), participation in projects to help the elderly, needy, or disabled (8 points), self-help as demonstrated by work record (7 points), participation in social, political, religious, or athletic groups (6 points), neatness and correctness of letter (5 points), and New York residency (4 points).

Financial data   The stipend is $1,000.

Duration   1 year.

Number awarded   1 each year.

Deadline   April of each year.

[492]
DR. KATE WALLER BARRETT GRANT

American Legion Auxiliary
Department of Virginia
Attn: Education Chair
1708 Commonwealth Avenue
Richmond, VA 23230
(804) 355-6410   Fax: (804) 353-5246
Web: vaauxiliary.org

Summary   To provide financial assistance to Virginia residents who are children of veterans or of members of the American Legion Auxiliary and planning to attend college in any state.

Eligibility   This program is open to the children of veterans or of members of the American Legion Auxiliary who are high school seniors in Virginia planning to attend an accredited educational institution in any state. Along with their application, they must submit transcripts with SAT or ACT scores, 4 letters of recommendation, and a 500-word essay on their responsibilities as a citizen of the United States. Selection is based on citizenship (20%), leadership (20%), scholarship (40%), and financial need (20%).

Financial data   The stipend is $1,000.

Duration   1 year.

Number awarded   1 each year.

Deadline March of each year.

[493]
DRAGON HILL CHAPTER NCOA SCHOLARSHIPS

Non Commissioned Officers Association of the United
States of America-Dragon Hill Chapter 1507
PSC 450
Box 705
APO AP 96206-0705
E-mail: jterry@ncoakorea.org
Web: ncoakorea.org/scholarship.htm

Summary To provide financial assistance for college to
seniors at Department of Defense Dependents Schools
(DoDDS) in Korea who are children of enlisted military personnel or of members of the Non Commissioned Officers
Association (NCOA).

Eligibility This program is open to seniors at DoDDS high
schools in Korea who have a cumulative GPA of 3.25 or
higher and are planning to attend college. Applicants must be
the child of either a U.S. military enlisted service member or
an NCOA member. They must have performed at least 40
hours of community or volunteer service during their junior or
senior year of high school. Along with their application, they
must submit a 250-word autobiography that closes with a
paragraph on why they want to go to college, letters of recommendation, certification of community or volunteer service, a
copy of their high school transcript, and a copy of their SAT/
ACT scores.

Financial data The stipend is $1,000.

Duration 1 year.

Number awarded Up to 4 each year.

Deadline March of each year.

[494]
DRS GUARDIAN SCHOLARSHIP FUND

National Guard Educational Foundation
Attn: Scholarship Fund
One Massachusetts Avenue, N.W.
Washington, DC 20001
(202) 789-0031   Fax: (202) 682-9358
E-mail: ngef@ngaus.org
Web: www.drsfoundation.net/guard

Summary To provide financial assistance for college to
children of members of the National Guard who died in service.

Eligibility This program is open to 1) high school juniors
and seniors who have been accepted to an accredited community college, technical school, or 4-year college or university and have a GPA of 3.0 or higher; and 2) students who are
currently enrolled full time at an accredited community college, technical school, or 4-year college or university and
have a GPA of 2.5 or higher. Applicants must be the dependent child of a National Guard member who died in an operational or training mission in support of Operation Enduring
Freedom, Operation Iraqi Freedom, or Operation New Dawn.
The educational institution they are attending or planning to
attend must be located in the 50 states, the District of Columbia, Puerto Rico, the U.S. Virgin Islands, or Guam. Along with
their application, they must submit a 1-page essay on their
deceased parent, transcripts, and documentation of financial
need.

Financial data The stipend is $6,250 per year.

Duration 1 year; may be renewed 1 additional year by students at community colleges and technical schools and up to
3 additional years by students at 4-year colleges and universities.

Additional information This program was established in
2011 by DRS Technologies, Inc., a defense contractor head-
quartered in Parsippany, New Jersey.

Number awarded Varies each year.

Deadline June of each year.

[495]
E.A. BLACKMORE SCHOLARSHIP

American Legion
Department of Wyoming
1320 Hugur Avenue
Cheyenne, WY 82001-4817
(307) 634-3035   Fax: (307) 635-7093
E-mail: wylegion@qwestoffice.net
Web: www.wylegion.org

Summary To provide financial assistance to the children
and grandchildren of members of the American Legion in
Wyoming who are interested in attending college in any state.

Eligibility This program is open to the children and grandchildren of members and deceased members of the American Legion in Wyoming. Applicants must rank in the top 20%
of their high school graduating class and be able to demonstrate financial need.

Financial data The stipend is $1,000 per year. Funds are
paid directly to the recipient's school to be used for tuition,
room and board, textbooks, and other fees.

Duration 1 year; may be renewed up to 3 additional years.

Number awarded 1 each year.

Deadline May of each year.

[496]
EAGLES MEMORIAL FOUNDATION EDUCATIONAL GRANTS FOR MILITARY AND OTHER SERVICE PERSONNEL

Fraternal Order of Eagles
Attn: Eagles Memorial Foundation
1623 Gateway Circle South
Grove City, OH 43123
(614) 883-2200   Fax: (613) 883-2201
E-mail: memorialfoundation@foe.com
Web: www.foe.com

Summary To provide financial assistance for college to the
children of deceased members of the Fraternal Order of
Eagles or its Ladies Auxiliary who died in action.

Eligibility Applicants must be the minor (under 25 years of
age) unmarried children of a deceased parent who was a
member of the Fraternal Order of Eagles or its Ladies Auxiliary at the time of death; the member must have died from
injuries or diseases incurred or aggravated in the line of duty
while serving 1) in the armed forces of the United States or
Canada; 2) as volunteer law enforcement officers in the
United States; 3) as volunteer fire fighters; or 4) as volunteer
emergency medical service officers.

Financial data Stipends up to $6,000 per school year are
provided. Funds must be used for tuition, fees, books, and
course-related supplies. Room and board expenses are not
covered.

Duration 1 year; may be renewed for up to 4 additional years, provided the recipient maintains a GPA of 2.0 or higher and remains an unmarried dependent.
Number awarded Varies each year.
Deadline Deadline not specified.

[497]
EANGGA SCHOLARSHIP

Enlisted Association of the National Guard of Georgia
Attn: Executive Director
P.O. Box 602
Ellenwood, GA 30294
(678) 644-9245   E-mail: csmharber@comcast.net
Web: www.eangga.com

Summary To provide financial assistance to members of the Enlisted Association of the National Guard of Georgia (EANGGA) and their families who are interested in attending college in any state.
Eligibility This program is open to EANGGA who have been in good standing for at least 1 year and to their children and spouses. Applicants must be enrolled or planning to enroll at a college or university in any state. Selection is based primarily on an essay, up to 7 pages in length, on a patriotic theme (e.g., heritage of the U.S. flag, history of the National Guard or a National Guard unit, acts of heroism by American patriots, our Constitution or Bill of Rights, civil liberties and other issues in a democratic state).
Financial data A stipend is awarded (amount not specified).
Duration 1 year.
Number awarded 2 each year.
Deadline April of each year.

[498]
EANGTN SCHOLARSHIP PROGRAM

Enlisted Association of the National Guard of Tennessee
Attn: Scholarship Committee
4332 Kenilwood Drive, Suite B
Nashville, TN 37204-4401
(615) 781-2000   Fax: (615) 833-9173
E-mail: betty@eangtn.org
Web: www.eangtn.org/Scholarships.htm

Summary To provide financial assistance to members of the Enlisted Association of the National Guard of Tennessee (EANGTN) and to their dependents who are interested in attending college in any state.
Eligibility This program is open to students who are members of both the Tennessee National Guard and EANGTN or the dependent son, daughter, or spouse of a member in good standing. Children must be unmarried, unless they are also a member of the National Guard. Applicants must be entering or continuing at a college or university in any state. Along with their application, they must submit a transcript, a letter with specific facts as to their desire to continue their education and why financial assistance is required, 3 letters of recommendation, and a letter of academic reference.
Financial data The stipend is $1,000. Funds are paid to the recipient's school once enrollment is confirmed.
Duration 1 year.
Additional information In 1985, the National Guard Association of Tennessee (NGAT) agreed that the EANGTN

would fund the scholarships of both associations. Additional funding is also provided by USAA Insurance Corporation.
Number awarded 6 each year.
Deadline January of each year.

[499]
EANGUS AUXILIARY SCHOLARSHIP PROGRAM

Enlisted Association of the National Guard of the United States
Attn: Auxiliary
3133 Mount Vernon Avenue
Alexandria, VA 22305-2640
(703) 519-3846   Toll Free: (800) 234-EANG
Fax: (703) 519-3849   E-mail: eangus@eangus.org
Web: www.eangus.org

Summary To provide financial assistance to members of the Auxiliary of the Enlisted Association of the National Guard of the United States (EANGUS) and their dependents who are entering or continuing in college.
Eligibility This program is open to high school seniors and currently-enrolled college students who are EANGUS Auxiliary members, their unmarried children, or their spouses. Applicants must be enrolled or planning to enroll at a college, university, business school, or trade school and taking at least 8 accredited hours. Graduate students are not eligible. Along with their application, they must submit a copy of their school transcript, 3 letters of recommendation, a letter of academic reference (from their principal, dean, or counselor), and a letter with specific goals for continuing their education and why financial assistance is necessary. The sponsor's State Auxiliary must have made a donation to the EANGUS Auxiliary Scholarship fund for the current and prior years. Selection is based on academic achievement, character, leadership, and financial need.
Financial data Stipends are $1,250 or $1,000.
Duration 1 year; nonrenewable.
Additional information This program includes 1 scholarship donated by USAA Insurance Corporation.
Number awarded 4 each year: 1 at $1,250 and 3 at $1,000.
Deadline June of each year.

[500]
EANGUT SCHOLARSHIP

Enlisted Association of the National Guard of Utah
Attn: Scholarship Committee
17800 South Camp Williams Road
Riverton, UT 84065-4999
(801) 699-1680   E-mail: Derek.dimond1@us.army.mil
Web: www.eangut.org

Summary To provide financial assistance to National Guard members who are active members of the Enlisted Association National Guard of Utah (EANGUT) and their families entering or continuing in college in the state.
Eligibility This program is open to members of EANGUT, their spouses, their children, and the spouses and unmarried dependent children of deceased members. Applicants must be attending or planning to attend a college, university, or vocational/technical school in Utah. EANGUT members must have at least 1 year remaining on their enlistment or have completed 20 or more years of service. Along with their application, they must submit a brief statement on their desire to

continue their education and why financial assistance is requested. Selection is based on academic achievement, citizenship, and financial need.

Financial data The stipend is $1,000, including $500 contributed by EANGUT and $500 by USAA Insurance Corporation.

Duration 1 year.

Number awarded 1 or more each year.

Deadline July of each year.

[501]
EDUCATION FOUNDATION FOR THE COLORADO NATIONAL GUARD GRANTS

National Guard Association of Colorado
Attn: Education Foundation, Inc.
P.O. Box 440889
Aurora, CO 80044-0889
(303) 909-6369   Fax: (720) 535-5925
E-mail: BernieRogoff@comcast.net
Web: efcong.org/Grants

Summary To provide financial assistance to members of the Colorado National Guard and their families who are interested in attending college or graduate school in any state.

Eligibility This program is open to current and retired members of the Colorado National Guard and their dependent unmarried children and spouses. Applicants must be enrolled or planning to enroll full or part time at a college, university, trade school, business school, or graduate school in any state. Along with their application, they must submit an essay, up to 2 pages in length, on their desire to continue their education, what motivates them, their financial need, their commitment to academic excellence, and their current situation. Selection is based on academic achievement, community involvement, and financial need.

Financial data Stipends are at least $1,000 per year.

Duration 1 year; may be renewed.

Number awarded Varies each year; recently, 38 of these grants, with a total value of $50,000, were awarded.

Deadline July of each year for fall semester; January of each year for spring semester.

[502]
EDWARD T. CONROY MEMORIAL SCHOLARSHIP PROGRAM

Maryland Higher Education Commission
Attn: Office of Student Financial Assistance
6 North Liberty Street, Ground Suite
Baltimore, MD 21201
(410) 767-3300   Toll Free: (800) 974-0203
Fax: (410) 332-0250   TDD: (800) 735-2258
E-mail: osfamail@mhec.state.md.us
Web: www.mhec.state.md.us/financialAid/descriptions.asp

Summary To provide money for college or graduate school in Maryland to children and spouses of victims of the September 11, 2001 terrorist attacks and specified categories of veterans, public safety employees, and their children or spouses.

Eligibility This program is open to entering and continuing undergraduate and graduate students in the following categories: 1) children and surviving spouses of victims of the September 11, 2001 terrorist attacks who died in the World Trade Center in New York City, in the Pentagon in Virginia, or on United Airlines Flight 93 in Pennsylvania; 2) veterans who

have, as a direct result of military service, a disability of 25% or greater and have exhausted or are no longer eligible for federal veterans' educational benefits; 3) children of armed forces members whose death or 100% disability was directly caused by military service; 4) POW/MIA veterans of the Vietnam Conflict and their children; 5) state or local public safety officers or volunteers who became 100% disabled in the line of duty; and 6) children and unremarried surviving spouses of state or local public safety employees or volunteers who died or became 100% disabled in the line of duty. The parent, spouse, veteran, POW, or public safety officer or volunteer must have been a resident of Maryland at the time of death or when declared disabled. Financial need is not considered.

Financial data The amount of the award is equal to tuition and fees at a Maryland postsecondary institution, to a maximum of $19,000 for children and spouses of the September 11 terrorist attacks or $9,000 for all other recipients.

Duration Up to 5 years of full-time or 8 years of part-time study.

Additional information Recipients must enroll at a 2- or 4-year Maryland college or university as a full-time or part-time degree-seeking undergraduate or graduate student or attend a private career school.

Number awarded Varies each year.

Deadline July of each year.

[503]
E.E. MIXON SECOND DRAGOON FOUNDATION SCHOLARSHIPS

E.E. Mixon Second Dragoon Foundation
c/o Scott C. Pierce
217 Painted Fall Way
Cary, NC 27513
(203) 979-7083   E-mail: scott@2nddragoons.org
Web: 2nddragoons.org/index/?q=node/15

Summary To provide financial assistance for college to former members of the U.S. Army's Second Cavalry Regiment and the children of current and former members.

Eligibility This program is open to former members of the Second Cavalry Regiment and the children of current or former members. Members of other Army units and their children may also be considered, especially if they have a previous connection with the Second Cavalry Regiment or other U.S. Cavalry Regiments. Applicants must submit a 500-word essay on 1 of the following topics: 1) how our military presence in Europe contributed to the end of the Cold War; 2) the role of the non-commissioned officer corps in the U.S. military; 3) what America means to them; or 4) their strategy for the way forward in Afghanistan. They must be attending or planning to attend a college or university. Selection is based on the essay and a statement of their educational goals, projected or current field of study, and personal or family affiliation with a cavalry unit.

Financial data Stipends range from $250 to $1,000 per year. Funds are deposited directly into the recipient's college tuition account.

Duration 1 semester; may be renewed.

Number awarded Varies each year; recently, 3 of these scholarships were awarded.

Deadline July of each year.

[504]
EIRO YAMADA MEMORIAL SCHOLARSHIP

Go For Broke Memorial Education Center
P.O. Box 2590
Gardena, CA 90247
(310) 222-5710   Fax: (310) 222-5700
E-mail: Cayleen@goforbroke.org
Web: www.goforbroke.org

Summary To provide financial assistance for college or graduate school to residents of any state who are descendants of World War II Japanese American veterans.

Eligibility This program is open to residents of any state who are attending or planning to attend a trade school, community college, or 4-year college or university on the undergraduate or graduate school level. Applicants must be 1) a direct descendant of a Japanese American World War II veteran, or 2) a descendant once-removed (such as a grand-niece or a grand-nephew) of a Japanese American serviceman or servicewoman killed in action during World War II. Along with their application, they must submit a short essay on "The Values I Have Learned from My Japanese American Forefathers" or their personal reflections on the Japanese American experience during World War II.

Financial data Stipends range from $500 to $1,000.

Duration 1 year.

Number awarded Varies each year; recently, 12 of these scholarships were awarded.

Deadline April of each year.

[505]
ESSAY COMPETITION FOR CHILDREN OF PUBLIC EMPLOYEES

Civil Service Employees Insurance Group
Attn: Scholarship Contest
P.O. Box 8041
Walnut Creek, CA 94596-8041
Toll Free: (800) 282-6848
Web: www.cse-insurance.com/scholarship.htm

Summary To recognize and reward, with college scholarships, the best essays written on teenage automobile safety by the children of full-time public employees (including military personnel) in selected states.

Eligibility This competition is open to high school seniors in 3 geographic regions: southern California, northern California, and Arizona/Nevada. Applicants must have been accepted as a full-time student at an accredited 4-year college, university, or trade school in the United States. Applicants must have a cumulative GPA of 3.0 or higher. Their parent or legal guardian must be currently employed full time (or if retired or deceased, must have been employed full time) by a government entity, including, but not limited to, peace officers, fire fighters, educators, postal employees, military personnel, or federal, state, and local government workers. Qualified students are invited to write an essay (up to 500 words) that discusses the ways the teenage automobile accident rate can be reduced. Essays are evaluated on the basis of originality, creativity, and writing proficiency. Also required in the application process are an official transcript and letters of recommendation.

Financial data Prizes in each region are $1,500 scholarships for first place, $1,000 scholarships for second place, and $500 scholarships each for third through fifth places.

Duration The prizes are awarded annually.

Number awarded 15 each year: 5 in each region.

Deadline April of each year.

[506]
EXEMPTION FOR DEPENDENTS OF TEXAS VETERANS

Texas Higher Education Coordinating Board
Attn: Grants and Special Programs
1200 East Anderson Lane
P.O. Box 12788
Austin, TX 78711-2788
(512) 427-6340   Toll Free: (800) 242-3062
Fax: (512) 427-6420   E-mail: grantinfo@thecb.state.tx.us
Web: www.collegeforalltexans.com

Summary To exempt children and spouses of disabled or deceased U.S. veterans from payment of tuition at public universities in Texas.

Eligibility This program is open to residents of Texas whose parent or spouse was a resident of the state at the time of entry into the U.S. armed forces, the Texas National Guard, or the Texas Air National Guard. The veteran parent or spouse must have died as a result of service-related injuries or illness, be missing in action, or have become totally disabled as a result of service-related injury or illness. Applicants must have no remaining federal education benefits. They must be attending or planning to attend a public college or university in the state. Children of veterans must be 25 years of age or younger.

Financial data Eligible students are exempt from payment of tuition, dues, fees, and charges at state-supported colleges and universities in Texas.

Duration 1 year; may be renewed.

Additional information This program was established under provisions of the Hazlewood Act; it is also referred to as Hazlewood Exemption for Dependents of Texas Veterans.

Number awarded Varies each year; recently, 9 of these awards were granted.

Deadline Deadline not specified.

[507]
EXEMPTION FOR ORPHANS OF TEXAS MEMBERS OF THE U.S. ARMED FORCES OR NATIONAL GUARD

Texas Higher Education Coordinating Board
Attn: Grants and Special Programs
1200 East Anderson Lane
P.O. Box 12788
Austin, TX 78711-2788
(512) 427-6340   Toll Free: (800) 242-3062
Fax: (512) 427-6420   E-mail: grantinfo@thecb.state.tx.us
Web: www.collegeforalltexans.com

Summary To exempt residents of Texas whose parent died in service to the U.S. military or National Guard from payment of tuition at public universities in the state.

Eligibility This program is open to residents of Texas who are the dependent children of a parent who died as a result of injury or illness directly related to service in the U.S. military or the National Guard. Applicants must have used up all federal education benefits for which they are eligible. They must be attending or planning to attend a public college or university in the state.

Financial data Eligible students are exempt from payment of tuition, dues, fees, and charges at state-supported colleges and universities in Texas.
Duration 1 year; may be renewed.
Number awarded Varies each year.
Deadline Deadline not specified.

[508]
EXEMPTION FROM TUITION FEES FOR DEPENDENTS OF KENTUCKY VETERANS
Kentucky Department of Veterans Affairs
Attn: Field Operations Branch
321 West Main Street, Suite 390
Louisville, KY 40202
(502) 595-4447   Toll Free: (800) 928-4012 (within KY)
Fax: (502) 595-4448   E-mail: Pamela.Cypert@ky.gov
Web: www.veterans.ky.gov/benefits/tuitionwaiver.htm
Summary To provide financial assistance for undergraduate or graduate studies to the children or unremarried widow(er)s of deceased Kentucky veterans.
Eligibility This program is open to the children, stepchildren, adopted children, and unremarried widow(er)s of veterans who were residents of Kentucky when they entered military service or joined the Kentucky National Guard. The qualifying veteran must have been killed in action during a wartime period or died as a result of a service-connected disability incurred during a wartime period. Applicants must be attending or planning to attend a state-supported college or university in Kentucky to work on an undergraduate or graduate degree.
Financial data Eligible dependents and survivors are exempt from tuition and matriculation fees at any state-supported institution of higher education in Kentucky.
Duration There are no age or time limits on the waiver.
Number awarded Varies each year.
Deadline Deadline not specified.

[509]
EXPLOSIVE ORDNANCE DISPOSAL MEMORIAL SCHOLARSHIPS
Explosive Ordnance Disposal Memorial Foundation
Attn: Executive Director
822 Coldwater Creek Circle
Niceville, FL 32578
(813) 389-0351   E-mail: scholarship@eodmemorial.org
Web: www.eodmemorial.org/scholarship
Summary To provide financial assistance for college to spouses and other family members of technicians or military officers who have worked in explosive ordnance disposal.
Eligibility This program is open to children, stepchildren, spouses, grandchildren, and other recognized dependents of graduates of Naval School Explosive Ordnance Disposal (NAVSCOLEOD) who served or are serving in the Army, Navy, Air Force, or Marine Corps. Active-duty personnel and NAVSCOLEOD graduates are not eligible. Children or other dependents must be 23 years of age or younger; spouses may be of any age. Selection is based on GPA, community involvement and volunteerism, extracurricular activities, awards, paid employment, an essay, future goals, letters of recommendation, and overall impression. Applicants who are family members of an Explosive Ordnance Disposal

Wounded Warrior or Memorial Honoree are automatically granted scholarships.
Financial data A stipend is awarded (amount not specified). Funds are paid directly to the academic institution for the student's tuition, books, fees, and on-campus housing.
Duration 1 year; may be renewed up to 3 additional years.
Number awarded Varies each year; recently, 42 of these scholarships were awarded.
Deadline March of each year.

[510]
FCDA SCHOLARSHIPS
First Cavalry Division Association
Attn: Foundation
302 North Main Street
Copperas Cove, TX 76522-1703
(254) 547-6537   Fax: (254) 547-8853
E-mail: firstcav@1cda.org
Web: www.1cda.org/Foundation_Overview.htm
Summary To provide financial assistance for undergraduate education to soldiers currently or formerly assigned to the First Cavalry Division and their families.
Eligibility This program is open to children of soldiers who died or have been declared totally and permanently disabled from injuries incurred while serving with the First Cavalry Division during any armed conflict; children of soldiers who died while serving in the First Cavalry Division during peacetime; and active-duty soldiers currently assigned or attached to the First Cavalry Division and their spouses and children.
Financial data The stipend is $1,200 per year. The checks are made out jointly to the student and the school and may be used for whatever the student needs, including tuition, books, and clothing.
Duration 1 year; may be renewed up to 3 additional years.
Additional information Requests for applications must be accompanied by a self-addressed stamped envelope.
Number awarded Varies each year; since the program was established, it has awarded more than $783,800 to 468 children of disabled and deceased Cavalry members and more than $212,900 to 300 current members of the Division and their families.
Deadline June of each year.

[511]
FIFTH MARINE DIVISION ASSOCIATION SCHOLARSHIP
Fifth Marine Division Association Scholarship Fund
c/o Marine Corps Scholarship Foundation
909 North Washington Street, Suite 400
Alexandria, VA 22314
(703) 549-0060   Toll Free: (866) 496-5462
Fax: (703) 549-9474   E-mail: students@mcsf.org
Web: www.mcsf.org
Summary To provide financial assistance for college to the grandchildren of veterans who served with the Fifth Marine Division.
Eligibility This program is open to grandchildren of veterans who served with the Fifth Marine Division during World War II or Vietnam and are or were members of the Sixth Marine Division Association. Applicants must be high school seniors, high school graduates, or current college students. Along with their application, they must submit academic tran-

scripts, a copy of their grandparent's honorable discharge, and a 500-word essay on a topic that changes periodically. The family income of applicants must be less than $90,000 per year.

Financial data Stipends range from $500 to $2,500 per year.

Duration 1 year; may be renewed for up to 3 additional years.

Additional information Recipients may also accept scholarship aid from other sources.

Number awarded Varies each year; recently, 4 of these scholarships were awarded.

Deadline February of each year.

[512]
FIRST LIEUTENANT MICHAEL L. LEWIS, JR. MEMORIAL FUND SCHOLARSHIP

American Legion Auxiliary
Department of New York
112 State Street, Suite 1310
Albany, NY 12207
(518) 463-1162   Toll Free: (800) 421-6348
Fax: (518) 449-5406   E-mail: alanyterry@nycap.rr.com
Web: www.deptny.org/Scholarships.htm

Summary To provide financial assistance to members of the American Legion Auxiliary in New York who plan to attend college in any state.

Eligibility This program is open to 1) junior members of the New York Department of the American Legion Auxiliary who are high school seniors or graduates younger than 20 years of age; and 2) senior members who are continuing their education to further their studies or update their job skills. Applicants must be attending or planning to attend college in any state. Along with their application, they must submit a 200-word essay on "Why a college education is important to me," or "Why I want to continue my post high school education in a business or trade school." Selection is based on character (25%), Americanism (25%), leadership (25%), and scholarship (25%).

Financial data A stipend is awarded (amount not specified).

Duration 1 year.

Number awarded 2 each year: 1 to a junior member and 1 to a senior member. If no senior members apply, both scholarships are awarded to junior members.

Deadline March of each year.

[513]
FIRST LIEUTENANT SCOTT MCCLEAN LOVE MEMORIAL SCHOLARSHIP

Army Scholarship Foundation
11700 Preston Road, Suite 660-301
Dallas, TX 75230
E-mail: ContactUs@armyscholarshipfoundation.org
Web: www.armyscholarshipfoundation.org

Summary To provide financial assistance for undergraduate study to the children and spouses of Army personnel, especially those who major in the fine arts.

Eligibility This program is open to 1) children of regular active-duty, active-duty Reserve, and active-duty National Guard U.S. Army members in good standing; 2) spouses of serving enlisted regular active-duty, active-duty Reserve, and

active-duty National Guard U.S. Army members in good standing; and 3) children of former U.S. Army members who received an honorable or medical discharge or were killed while serving in the U.S. Army. Preference is given to students who are majoring or planning to major in the fine arts. Applicants must be high school seniors, high school graduates, or undergraduates enrolled at an accredited college, university, or vocational/technical institute. They must be U.S. citizens and have a GPA of 2.0 or higher; children must be younger than 24 years of age. Financial need is considered in the selection process.

Financial data The stipend ranges from $500 to $2,000 per year.

Duration 1 year; recipients may reapply.

Additional information The Army Scholarship Foundation was established in 2001.

Number awarded 1 each year.

Deadline April of each year.

[514]
FIRST MARINE DIVISION ASSOCIATION SCHOLARSHIPS

First Marine Division Association
403 North Freeman Street
Oceanside, CA 92054
(760) 967-8561   Toll Free: (877) 967-8561
Fax: (760) 967-8567   E-mail: oldbreed@sbcglobal.net
Web: www.1stmarinedivisionassociation.org

Summary To provide financial assistance for college to dependents of deceased or disabled veterans of the First Marine Division.

Eligibility This program is open to dependents of veterans who served in the First Marine Division or in a unit attached to that Division, are honorably discharged, and now are either totally and permanently disabled or deceased from any cause. Applicants must be attending or planning to attend an accredited college, university, or trade school as a full-time undergraduate student. Graduate students and students still in high school or prep school are not eligible.

Financial data The stipend is $1,750 per year.

Duration 1 year; may be renewed up to 3 additional years.

Additional information Award winners who marry before completing the course or who drop out for non-scholastic reasons must submit a new application before benefits can be resumed.

Number awarded Varies each year; recently, 28 of these scholarships were awarded.

Deadline Deadline not specified.

[515]
FLORIDA AMERICAN LEGION GENERAL SCHOLARSHIPS

American Legion
Department of Florida
Attn: Programs Director
1912A Lee Road
P.O. Box 547859
Orlando, FL 32854-7859
(407) 295-2631, ext. 222
Toll Free: (800) 393-3378 (within FL)
Fax: (407) 299-0901   E-mail: mail@floridalegion.org
Web: www.floridalegion.org/programs/scholarships

Summary To provide financial assistance to the descendants of American Legion members in Florida who plan to attend college in any state.

Eligibility This program is open to the direct descendants (children, grandchildren, great-grandchildren, and legally adopted children) of a member of the American Legion's Department of Florida or of a deceased U.S. veteran who would have been eligible for membership in the American Legion. Applicants must be seniors graduating from a Florida high school and planning to attend an accredited college or university in any state. Financial need is not considered in the selection process.

Financial data Stipends are $2,500, $1,500, $1,000, or $500.

Duration 1 year; nonrenewable.

Number awarded 7 each year: 1 at $2,500, 1 at $1,500, 1 at $1,000, and 4 at $500.

Deadline February of each year.

[516]
FLORIDA BOYS STATE SCHOLARSHIP

American Legion
Department of Florida
Attn: Programs Director
1912A Lee Road
P.O. Box 547859
Orlando, FL 32854-7859
(407) 295-2631, ext. 222
Toll Free: (800) 393-3378 (within FL)
Fax: (407) 299-0901   E-mail: mail@floridalegion.org
Web: www.floridalegion.org/programs/scholarships

Summary To provide financial assistance for college to the descendants of veterans who participate in Florida Boys State.

Eligibility This program is open to the direct descendants (sons, grandsons, great-grandsons, and legally adopted sons) of American war veterans who are selected as delegates to Florida Boys State.

Financial data The stipend is $1,000.

Duration 1 year; nonrenewable.

Additional information In addition to this scholarship that can be used at the college or university of the recipient's choice, Tallahassee Community College (TCC) and Florida State University (FSU) offer 5 scholarships to Boys State delegates who attend TCC for 2 years followed by 2 years at FSU.

Number awarded 1 each year.

Deadline Deadline not specified.

[517]
FLORIDA LEGION AUXILIARY DEPARTMENT SCHOLARSHIP

American Legion Auxiliary
Department of Florida
1912A Lee Road
P.O. Box 547917
Orlando, FL 32854-7917
(407) 293-7411   Fax: (407) 299-6522
E-mail: contact@alafl.org
Web: alafl.org/index.php?department-scholarship

Summary To provide financial assistance to the children of Florida veterans who are interested in attending college in the state.

Eligibility This program is open to children and stepchildren of honorably-discharged veterans who are Florida residents. Applicants must be enrolled or planning to enroll full time at a postsecondary school in the state. Financial need is considered in the selection process.

Financial data The stipends are up to $2,000 for a 4-year university or up to $1,000 for a community college or vocational/technical school. All funds are paid directly to the institution.

Duration 1 year; may be renewed if the recipient needs further financial assistance and has maintained a GPA of 2.5 or higher.

Number awarded Varies each year, depending on the availability of funds.

Deadline January of each year.

[518]
FLORIDA LEGION AUXILIARY MEMORIAL SCHOLARSHIP

American Legion Auxiliary
Department of Florida
1912A Lee Road
P.O. Box 547917
Orlando, FL 32854-7917
(407) 293-7411   Fax: (407) 299-6522
E-mail: contact@alafl.org
Web: alafl.org/index.php?memorial-scholarship

Summary To provide financial assistance to members and female dependents of members of the Florida American Legion Auxiliary who are interested in attending college in any state.

Eligibility Applicants must be members of the Florida Auxiliary or daughters or granddaughters of members who have at least 3 years of continuous membership. They must be sponsored by their local units, be Florida residents, and be enrolled or planning to enroll full time at a college, university, community college, or vocational/technical school in any state. Selection is based on academic record and financial need.

Financial data The stipends are up to $2,000 for a 4-year university or up to $1,000 for a community college or vocational/technical school. All funds are paid directly to the institution.

Duration 1 year; may be renewed if the recipient needs further financial assistance and has maintained at least a 2.5 GPA.

Number awarded Varies each year, depending on the availability of funds.

Deadline January of each year.

[519]
FLORIDA SCHOLARSHIPS FOR CHILDREN AND SPOUSES OF DECEASED OR DISABLED VETERANS

Florida Department of Education
Attn: Office of Student Financial Assistance
325 West Gaines Street
Tallahassee, FL 32399-0400
(850) 410-5160   Toll Free: (888) 827-2004
Fax: (850) 487-1809   E-mail: osfa@fldoe.org
Web: www.floridastudentfinancialaid.org

Summary To provide financial assistance for college to the children and spouses of Florida veterans who are disabled, deceased, or officially classified as prisoners of war (POW) or missing in action (MIA).

Eligibility This program is open to residents of Florida who are U.S. citizens or eligible noncitizens and the dependent children or spouses of veterans or service members who 1) died as a result of service-connected injuries, diseases, or disabilities sustained while on active duty during a period of war; 2) have a service-connected 100% total and permanent disability; or 3) were classified as POW or MIA by the U.S. armed forces or as civilian personnel captured while serving with the consent or authorization of the U.S. government during wartime service. The veteran or service member must have been a U.S. citizen or eligible noncitizens and a resident of Florida for at least 1 year before death, disability, or POW/MIA status. Children must be between 16 and 22 years of age. Spouses of deceased veterans or service members must be unremarried and must apply within 5 years of their spouse's death. Spouses of disabled veterans must have been married for at least 1 year.

Financial data Awards provide payment of tuition and registration fees at public institutions in Florida or an equivalent sum at private institutions.

Duration 1 quarter or semester; may be renewed for up to 110% of the required credit hours of an initial associate, baccalaureate, diploma, or certificate program, provided the student maintains a GPA of 2.0 or higher.

Number awarded Varies each year; recently, 295 new and 331 renewal scholarships were awarded.

Deadline March of each year.

[520]
FOLDS OF HONOR SCHOLARSHIPS

Folds of Honor Foundation
Attn: Scholarships
5800 North Patriot Drive
Owasso, OK 74055
(918) 591-2406   Fax: (918) 494-9826
E-mail: scholarships@foldsofhonor.org
Web: www.foldsofhonor.com/scholarships

Summary To provide financial assistance for college to the spouses and children of service members killed or disabled as a result of service in the Global War on Terror.

Eligibility This program is open to the spouses and children of 1) an active-duty or Reserve component soldier, sailor, airman, Marine, or Coast Guardsman killed or disabled in the Global War on Terror; 2) an active-duty or Reserve component soldier, sailor, airman, Marine, or Coast Guardsman who is currently classified as a POW or MIA; 3) a veteran who died from any cause while such service-connected dis-

ability was in existence; 4) a service member missing in action or captured in the line of duty by a hostile force; 5) a service member forcibly detained or interned in the line of duty by a foreign government or power; or 6) a service member who received a Purple Heart medal. Applicants must submit a 1-page personal essay that includes a short biography, a description of the service members disability or death, and a statement of what the scholarship would mean to them and how it will help them achieve their career goals. Immediate-use scholarships are available to spouses or dependents currently attending or accepted into a 2- or 4-year college or university or a vocational, technical, or other certification program. Future-use scholarships are available to young children of service members and held for them until they are ready to attend college.

Financial data Stipends range up to $2,500 per semester ($5,000 per year), depending on the need of the recipient. Funds are dispersed directly to the recipient's institution.

Duration 1 year.

Additional information These scholarships were first awarded in 2008.

Number awarded Varies each year; since the program was established, it has awarded 2,539 immediate-use scholarships and 99 future-use scholarships.

Deadline May or November of each year for immediate-use scholarships; May of each year for future-use scholarships.

[521]
FORCE RECON ASSOCIATION SCHOLARSHIPS

Force Recon Association
P.O. Box 425
Rowe, MA 01367
E-mail: commchief@forcerecon.com
Web: www.forcerecon.com

Summary To provide money for college to members of the Force Recon Association and their dependents.

Eligibility This program is open to members of the Force Recon Association and family members of a relative who served both in the U.S. Marine Corps and was or is assigned to a Force Reconnaissance Company. The relative must be either an active or deceased member of the Force Recon Association. Family members include wives and widows, sons and daughters (including adopted and stepchildren), grandchildren, and great-grandchildren. Applicants may be pursuing scholastic, vocational, or technical education. Along with their application, they must submit a personal statement on why they desire this scholarship, their proposed course of study, their progress in their current course of study, and their long-range career goals. Selection is based on academic achievement, letters of recommendation, demonstrated character, and the written statements.

Financial data A stipend is awarded (amount not specified).

Duration 1 year; may be renewed.

Number awarded 1 or more each year.

Deadline Applications must be received at least 2 weeks prior to the annual meeting of the Force Recon Association.

[522]
FOURTH MARINE DIVISION ASSOCIATION OF WWII SCHOLARSHIP

Fourth Marine Division Association of WWII
c/o Marine Corps Scholarship Foundation
909 North Washington Street, Suite 400
Alexandria, VA 22314
(703) 549-0060   Toll Free: (866) 496-5462
Fax: (703) 549-9474   E-mail: students@mcsf.org
Web: www.mcsf.org

Summary To provide financial assistance for college to the grandchildren of veterans who served with the Fourth Marine Division during World War II.

Eligibility This program is open to grandchildren of veterans who served with the Fourth Marine Division during World War II and are or were members of the Fourth Marine Division Association of World War II. Applicants must be high school seniors, high school graduates, or current college students. Along with their application, they must submit academic transcripts, a copy of their grandparent's honorable discharge, and a 500-word essay on a topic that changes periodically. Only undergraduate study is supported. The family income of applicants must be less than $90,000 per year.

Financial data Stipends depend on the need of the recipient and the availability of funds, but generally range from $500 to $2,500 per year.

Duration 1 year; may be renewed for up to 3 additional years.

Additional information The highest-ranked applicant receives an award that is designated the Thomas W. Morrow Scholarship.

Number awarded Varies each year; recently, 12 of these scholarships were awarded.

Deadline February of each year.

[523]
FRA NON-MEMBER SCHOLARSHIPS

Fleet Reserve Association
Attn: FRA Education Foundation
125 North West Street
Alexandria, VA 22314-2754
(703) 683-1400   Toll Free: (800) FRA-1924
Fax: (703) 549-6610   E-mail: scholars@fra.org
Web: www.fra.org

Summary To provide financial assistance for college or graduate school to current or former sea service personnel and their families.

Eligibility This program is open to 1) active-duty, Reserve, honorably-discharged veterans, and retired members of the U.S. Navy, Marine Corps, and Coast Guard; and 2) their spouses, children, and grandchildren. Applicants must be enrolled as full-time undergraduate or graduate students but they are not required to be members of the sponsoring organization. Along with their application, they must submit an essay on why they want to go to college and what they intend to accomplish with their degree. Selection is based on academic record, financial need, extracurricular activities, leadership skills, and participation in community activities. U.S. citizenship is required.

Financial data A stipend is awarded (amount not specified).

Duration 1 year; may be renewed.

Number awarded 1 or more each year.
Deadline April of each year.

[524]
FRA SCHOLARSHIPS

Fleet Reserve Association
Attn: FRA Education Foundation
125 North West Street
Alexandria, VA 22314-2754
(703) 683-1400   Toll Free: (800) FRA-1924
Fax: (703) 549-6610   E-mail: scholars@fra.org
Web: www.fra.org

Summary To provide financial assistance for college or graduate school to members of the Fleet Reserve Association (FRA) and their families.

Eligibility This program is open to members of the FRA and the dependent children, grandchildren, and spouses of living or deceased members. Applicants must be enrolled as full-time undergraduate or graduate students. Along with their application, they must submit an essay on why they want to go to college and what they intend to accomplish with their degree. Selection is based on academic record, financial need, extracurricular activities, leadership skills, and participation in community activities. U.S. citizenship is required.

Financial data The stipend is $5,000 per year.

Duration 1 year; may be renewed.

Additional information Membership in the FRA is restricted to active-duty, retired, and reserve members of the Navy, Marines, and Coast Guard.

Number awarded 6 each year.

Deadline April of each year.

[525]
FRANCIS P. MATTHEWS AND JOHN E. SWIFT EDUCATIONAL TRUST SCHOLARSHIPS

Knights of Columbus
Attn: Department of Scholarships
P.O. Box 1670
New Haven, CT 06507-0901
(203) 752-4332   Fax: (203) 772-2696
E-mail: info@kofc.org
Web: www.kofc.org/en/scholarships/matthews_swift.html

Summary To provide financial assistance at Catholic colleges or universities in any country to children of disabled or deceased veterans, law enforcement officers, or firemen who are/were also Knights of Columbus members.

Eligibility This program is open to children of members of the sponsoring organization who are high school seniors in any country planning to attend a 4-year Catholic college or university in their country. The parent must be a member of Knights of Columbus who 1) was serving in the military forces of their country and was killed by hostile action or wounded by hostile action, resulting within 2 years in permanent and total disability; 2) was a full-time law enforcement officer who became disabled or died as a result of criminal violence; or 3) was a fire fighter who became disabled or deceased in the line of duty.

Financial data The amounts of the awards vary but are designed to cover tuition, to a maximum of $25,000 per year, at the Catholic college or university of the recipient's choice in the country of their residence. Funds are not available for room, board, books, fees, transportation, dues, computers, or supplies.

Duration   1 year; may be renewed up to 3 additional years.

Additional information   This program was established in 1944 to provide scholarships to the children of Knights who became totally and permanently disabled through service during World War II. It has been modified on many occasions, most recently in 2007 to its current requirements.

Number awarded   Varies each year.

Deadline   February of each year.

[526]
FREEDOM ALLIANCE SCHOLARSHIPS

Freedom Alliance
Attn: Scholarship Fund
22570 Markey Court, Suite 240
Dulles, VA 20166-6915
(703) 444-7940   Toll Free: (800) 475-6620
Fax: (703) 444-9893
Web: www.freedomalliance.org

Summary   To provide financial assistance for college to the children of deceased and disabled military personnel.

Eligibility   This program is open to high school seniors, high school graduates, and undergraduate students under 26 years of age who are dependent children of military personnel (soldier, sailor, airman, Marine, or Guardsman). The military parent must 1) have been killed or permanently disabled as a result of an operational mission or training accident, or 2) be currently classified as a POW or MIA. For disabled parents, the disability must be permanent, service-connected, and rated at 100% by the U.S. Department of Veterans Affairs. Applicants must submit a 500-word essay on what their parent's service means to them.

Financial data   Stipends range up to $6,000 per year.

Duration   1 year; may be renewed up to 3 additional years, provided the recipient remains enrolled full time with a GPA of 2.0 or higher.

Number awarded   Varies each year; recently, 225 of these scholarships were awarded.

Deadline   July of each year.

[527]
GAMEWARDENS ASSOCIATION SCHOLARSHIP

Gamewardens Association, Vietnam to Present
c/o Glen Fry, Scholarship Program
230 P.R. 182 West
Heloted, TX 78023
(210) 301-4497   E-mail: normlguy@gmail.com
Web: www.tf116.org/scholarship.html

Summary   To provide financial assistance for college to the children or grandchildren of members of Gamewardens Association, Vietnam to Present.

Eligibility   This program is open to the children and grandchildren of living or deceased members of Gamewardens Association, Vietnam to Present. High school students (under 21 years of age) planning to enter college as full-time students and students already enrolled in college (under 23 years of age) are eligible. Selection is based on SAT or ACT scores, extracurricular activities, leadership positions held, work or volunteer experience, and financial need.

Financial data   Stipends are $2,000. Awards are paid directly to the college the student is attending.

Duration   1 year.

Additional information   Membership in Gamewardens Association, Vietnam to Present is open to 1) veterans who served in Vietnam in Task Force 116 or in support of Task Force 116, River Patrol Force; or 2) veterans or current Navy personnel serving as an Special Warfare Combatant-craft Crewman (SWCC) or Riverine Operator in any operation subsequent to Vietnam (including in Iraq). This program includes the YNC John Williams Scholarship and the River Division 551 and 534 Scholarship.

Number awarded   1 to 4 each year.

Deadline   July of each year.

[528]
GENERAL EMMETT PAIGE SCHOLARSHIPS

Armed Forces Communications and Electronics
  Association
Attn: AFCEA Educational Foundation
4400 Fair Lakes Court
Fairfax, VA 22033-3899
(703) 631-6138   Toll Free: (800) 336-4583, ext. 6138
Fax: (703) 631-4693   E-mail: scholarshipsinfo@afcea.org
Web: www.afcea.org/education/scholarships/military

Summary   To provide financial assistance to veterans, military personnel, and their family members who are majoring in specified scientific fields in college.

Eligibility   This program is open to veterans, persons on active duty in the uniformed military services, and their spouses or dependents who are currently enrolled full time in an accredited 4-year college or university in the United States. Graduating high school seniors are not eligible, but veterans entering college as freshmen may apply. Spouses or dependents must be sophomores or juniors. Applicants must be U.S. citizens, be of good moral character, have demonstrated academic excellence, be motivated to complete a college education, and be working toward a degree in engineering (aerospace, computer, electrical, or systems), computer engineering technology, electronics engineering technology, computer network systems, mathematics, physics, information systems security, information systems management, technology management, computer science, or other field directly related to the support of U.S. intelligence enterprises or national security. They must have a GPA of 3.0 or higher. Along with their application, they must provide a copy of Discharge Form DD214, Certificate of Service, or facsimile of their current Department of Defense or Coast Guard Identification Card. Financial need is not considered.

Financial data   The stipend is $2,500 per year.

Duration   1 year; may be renewed.

Number awarded   Varies each year; recently, 5 of these scholarships were awarded.

Deadline   April of each year.

[529]
GENERAL HENRY H. ARNOLD EDUCATION GRANT PROGRAM

Air Force Aid Society
Attn: Education Assistance Department
241 18th Street South, Suite 202
Arlington, VA 22202-3409
(703) 607-3072, ext. 51   Toll Free: (800) 769-8951
Fax: (703) 607-3022
Web: www.afas.org/Education/ArnoldEdGrant.cfm

Summary To provide financial assistance for college to dependents of active-duty, retired, disabled, or deceased Air Force personnel.

Eligibility This program is open to 1) dependent children of Air Force personnel who are active duty, Reservists on extended active duty, retired due to length of active-duty service or disability, or deceased while on active duty or in retired status; 2) spouses of active-duty Air Force members and Reservists on extended active duty; and 3) surviving spouses of Air Force members who died while on active duty or in retired status. Applicants must be enrolled or planning to enroll as full-time undergraduate students at an accredited college, university, or vocational/trade school. Spouses must be attending school within the 48 contiguous states. Selection is based on family income and education costs.

Financial data The stipend is $2,000.

Duration 1 year; may be renewed if the recipient maintains a GPA of 2.0 or higher.

Additional information Since this program began in the 1988-89 academic year, it has awarded more than 94,000 grants.

Number awarded Varies each year.

Deadline March of each year.

[530]
GENERAL JOHN PAUL RATAY EDUCATIONAL FUND GRANTS

Military Officers Association of America
Attn: Educational Assistance Program
201 North Washington Street
Alexandria, VA 22314-2539
(703) 549-2311   Toll Free: (800) 234-MOAA
Fax: (703) 838-5819   E-mail: edassist@moaa.org
Web: www.moaa.org

Summary To provide financial assistance to dependent children of surviving spouses of deceased members of Military Officers Association of America (MOAA) who are working on an undergraduate degree.

Eligibility This program is open to children of surviving spouses of deceased retired military officers. Applicants must be younger than 24 years of age. Applicants for the MOAA Educational Assistance Program loans are automatically considered for these scholarships; no separate application is necessary. Selection is based on scholastic ability (GPA of 3.0 or higher), participation, character, leadership, and financial need.

Financial data The stipend is $4,000 per year.

Duration 1 year; may be renewed for up to 4 additional years if the recipient remains enrolled full time and has not yet graduated.

Additional information The MOAA was formerly named The Retired Officers Association (TROA). No grants are made for graduate study.

Number awarded Varies each year.

Deadline February of each year.

[531]
GENERAL WILLIAM E. DEPUY MEMORIAL SCHOLARSHIP PROGRAM

Society of the First Infantry Division
Attn: 1st Infantry Division Foundation
1933 Morris Road
Blue Bell, PA 19422-1422
Toll Free: (888) 324-4733   Fax: (215) 661-1934
E-mail: Fdn1ID@aol.com
Web: 1stid.org/foundation/scholarships.cfm

Summary To provide financial assistance for college to the children of certain deceased members of the First Infantry Division.

Eligibility This program is open to the children of soldiers who served in the First Infantry Division and were killed while serving in combat with the Division or in peacetime training accidents. This is an entitlement program. All eligible applicants receive an award.

Financial data The stipend is $2,500 per year.

Duration 1 year; may be renewed up to 3 additional years.

Additional information This program was established during the Vietnam war to provide scholarships to children of soldiers killed while on duty with the active division; more than 1,300 children whose fathers died while serving in Vietnam received scholarships.

Number awarded Varies each year.

Deadline Deadline not specified.

[532]
GEORGIA DEPARTMENT AMERICAN LEGION SCHOLARSHIP

American Legion
Department of Georgia
3035 Mt. Zion Road
Stockbridge, GA 30281-4101
(678) 289-8883   E-mail: amerlegga@bellsouth.net
Web: www.galegion.org

Summary To provide financial assistance to children and grandchildren of members of the American Legion in Georgia who plan to attend college in any state.

Eligibility This program is open to seniors graduating from high schools in Georgia who have a GPA of 3.0 or higher in core subjects. Applicants must be children or grandchildren of members of the American Legion in the Department of Georgia who served in the military. They must be sponsored by a Georgia post of the American Legion. Financial need is not considered in the selection process.

Financial data The stipend is $1,000.

Duration 1 year.

Number awarded 6 each year.

Deadline June of each year.

[533]
GEORGIA LEGION AUXILIARY PAST PRESIDENT'S PARLEY NURSING SCHOLARSHIP

American Legion Auxiliary
Department of Georgia
3035 Mt. Zion Road
Stockbridge, GA 30281-4101
(678) 289-8446   Fax: (678) 289-9496
E-mail: secretary@galegionaux.org
Web: www.galegionaux.org

Summary To provide financial assistance to daughters of veterans in Georgia who are interested in attending college in any state to prepare for a career in nursing.

Eligibility This program is open to George residents who are 1) interested in nursing education and 2) the daughters of veterans. Applicants must be sponsored by a local unit of the American Legion Auxiliary. Selection is based on a statement explaining why they want to become a nurse and why they need a scholarship, a transcript of all high school or college grades, and 4 letters of recommendation (1 from a high school principal or superintendent, 1 from the sponsoring American Legion Auxiliary local unit, and 2 from other responsible people).

Financial data The amount of the award depends on the availability of funds.

Number awarded Varies, depending upon funds available.

Deadline April of each year.

[534]
GEORGIA'S HERO SCHOLARSHIP PROGRAM

Georgia Student Finance Commission
Attn: Scholarships and Grants Division
2082 East Exchange Place, Suite 200
Tucker, GA 30084-5305
(770) 724-9000   Toll Free: (800) 505-GSFC
Fax: (770) 724-9089   E-mail: gacollege411@gsfc.org
Web: www.gacollege411.org

Summary To provide financial assistance for college to members of the National Guard or Reserves in Georgia and their children and spouses.

Eligibility This program is open to Georgia residents who are active members of the Georgia National Guard or U.S. Military Reserves, were deployed outside the United States for active-duty service on or after February 1, 2003 to a location designated as a combat zone, and served in that combat zone for at least 181 consecutive days. Also eligible are 1) the children, younger than 25 years of age, of Guard and Reserve members who completed at least 1 term of service (of 181 days each) overseas on or after February 1, 2003; 2) the children, younger than 25 years of age, of Guard and Reserve members who were killed or totally disabled during service overseas on or after February 1, 2003, regardless of their length of service; and 3) the spouses of Guard and Reserve members who were killed in a combat zone, died as a result of injuries, or became 100% disabled as a result of injuries received in a combat zone during service overseas on or after February 1, 2003, regardless of their length of service. Applicants must be interested in attending a unit of the University System of Georgia, a unit of the Georgia Department of Technical and Adult Education, or an eligible private college or university in Georgia.

Financial data The stipend for full-time study is $2,000 per academic year, not to exceed $8,000 during an entire program of study. The stipend for part-time study is prorated appropriately.

Duration 1 year; may be renewed (if satisfactory progress is maintained) for up to 3 additional years.

Additional information This program, which stands for Helping Educate Reservists and their Offspring, began in 2005.

Number awarded Varies each year.

Deadline June of each year.

[535]
GERALDINE K. MORRIS AWARD

Army Engineer Spouses' Club
c/o Nancy Temple, Chair
P.O. Box 6332
Alexandria, VA 22306-6332
E-mail: scholarships@armyengineerspouses.com
Web: armyengineerspouses.com

Summary To provide financial assistance to the children of officers and civilians who served in the Army Corps of Engineers and are interested in studying nursing in college.

Eligibility This program is open to children of 1) U.S. Army Corps of Engineers officers and warrant officers who are on active duty, retired, or deceased while on active duty or after retiring from active duty; or 2) current Department of the Army employees of the U.S. Army Corps of Engineers. Applicants must be high school seniors planning to enroll in a program leading to a nursing degree or certification. Selection is based on academic and extracurricular achievement during high school. U.S. citizenship is required.

Financial data The stipend ranges from $1,000 to $2,000.

Duration 1 year.

Additional information This program began in 2006.

Number awarded 1 each year.

Deadline February of each year.

[536]
GLADYS MCPARTLAND SCHOLARSHIPS

United States Marine Corps Combat Correspondents Association
Attn: Executive Director
110 Fox Court
Wildwood, FL 34785
(352) 748-4698   E-mail: usmccca@cfl.rr.com
Web: www.usmccca.org/archives/4941

Summary To provide financial assistance to members of the U.S. Marine Corps Combat Correspondents Association (USMCCCA) or their dependents and Marines in designated occupational fields who are interested in studying any field in college.

Eligibility This program is open to 1) members of USMCCCA, their dependents, and their spouses; and 2) active-duty Marines in Occupational Fields 4300 and 4600 and their dependents who are USMCCCA members or will agree to become members if awarded a scholarship. Applicants must be enrolled or planning to enroll in an undergraduate program in any field. Along with their application, they must submit 500-word essays on 1) their noteworthy achievements and long-range goals; and 2) the United States I want to see in 15 years and my role in the transformation. Financial need is not considered in the selection process.

Financial data Stipends range up to $3,000; funds are disbursed directly to the recipient's institution to be used exclusively for tuition, books, and/or fees.

Duration 1 year.

Number awarded 1 or more each year.

Deadline May of each year.

[537]
GOLD STAR SCHOLARSHIP PROGRAMS

Navy-Marine Corps Relief Society
Attn: Education Division
875 North Randolph Street, Suite 225
Arlington, VA 22203-1757
(703) 696-4960   Fax: (703) 696-0144
E-mail: education@nmcrs.org
Web: www.nmcrs.org/education.html

Summary To provide financial assistance for college to the children and spouses of Navy or Marine Corps personnel who died while serving on active duty or after retirement.

Eligibility This program is open to children under 23 years of age and unremarried spouses of members of the Navy or Marine Corps who died while serving on active duty or after retirement. Applicants must be enrolled or planning to enroll full time at a college, university, or vocational/technical school. They must have a GPA of 2.0 or higher and be able to demonstrate financial need.

Financial data Stipends range from $500 to $2,500 per year. Funds are disbursed directly to the financial institution.

Duration 1 year; recipients may reapply.

Number awarded Varies each year.

Deadline March of each year.

[538]
GROGAN MEMORIAL SCHOLARSHIP

American Academy of Physician Assistants-Veterans
   Caucus
Attn: Veterans Caucus
P.O. Box 362
Danville, PA 17821-0362
(570) 271-0292   Fax: (570) 271-5850
E-mail: admin@veteranscaucus.org
Web: www.veteranscaucus.org

Summary To provide funding to veterans and their dependents studying to become physician assistants.

Eligibility This program is open to U.S. citizens who are currently enrolled in a physician assistant program. The program must be approved by the Commission on Accreditation of Allied Health Education. Applicants must be honorably discharged members of any branch of the military or the dependents of those members. Selection is based on military honors and awards received, civic and college honors and awards received, professional memberships and activities, and GPA. An electronic copy of the applicant's DD Form 214 must accompany the application.

Financial data The stipend is $2,000.

Duration 1 year.

Number awarded 1 each year.

Deadline February of each year.

[539]
HAD RICHARDS UDT-SEAL MEMORIAL SCHOLARSHIP

Navy Seal Foundation
Attn: Chief Financial Officer
1619 D Street, Building 5326
Virginia Beach, VA 23459
(757) 363-7490   Fax: (757) 363-7491
E-mail: info@navysealfoundation.org
Web: www.navysealfoundation.org

Summary To provide financial assistance for college to children of members of the UDT-SEAL Association.

Eligibility This program is open to children of members who are single, under 22 years of age, and a dependent of a sponsoring member of the association. Sponsors must be serving or have served in the armed forces and the Naval Special Warfare Community, been an association member for the last 4 consecutive years, and paid their dues for the current year. Applicants may be high school seniors, high school graduates, or undergraduate students. Along with their application, they must submit an essay, up to 2 pages in length, on a topic that changes annually; recently, students were asked to explore benevolence in their life and describe when they were able to demonstrate it. They may also indicate any special circumstances such as financial need, single parent status, or disabilities.

Financial data Stipends are $15,000 or $7,500 per year.

Duration 1 year; may be renewed.

Additional information Membership in the association is open to all officers and enlisted personnel of the armed forces (active, retired, discharged, or separated) who have served with a Navy Combat Demolition Unit (NCDU), Underwater Demolition Team (UDT), or SEAL Team.

Number awarded Varies each year; recently, the Navy Seal Foundation awarded 12 dependent scholarships for all of its programs: 3 for 4 years at $15,000 per year to high school seniors and graduates, 3 for 1 year at $7,500 to high school seniors and graduates, 3 for 1 year at $15,000 to current college students, and 3 for 1 year at $7,500 to current college students.

Deadline February of each year.

[540]
HAROLD DWIGHT HARRAH SCHOLARSHIPS

Vietnam Veterans of America-Chapter 522
P.O. Box 551
Indian Rocks Beach, FL 33785-0551
(727) 278-4111
Web: www.vva522.org/scholarship.html

Summary To provide financial assistance to high school seniors in Florida who are related to a veteran and interested in attending college in any state.

Eligibility This program is open to seniors graduating from public or private high schools in Florida and planning to attend college in any state. Applicants must be U.S. citizens and related to a veteran. They must have a GPA of 3.25 and be able to document financial need and volunteer work or community service activities within the past 12 months. Along with their application, they must submit a 1,000-word essay on how this scholarship will support their educational goals.

Financial data The stipend is $1,000. Funds are disbursed directly to the recipient's college or university.

Duration 1 year.

Additional information Chapter 522 is the Pinellas County Chapter of Vietnam Veterans of America (VVA), but the scholarship is available to all high school seniors in Florida.

Number awarded 3 each year.

Deadline March of each year.

[541]
HATTIE TEDROW MEMORIAL FUND SCHOLARSHIP

American Legion
Department of North Dakota
405 West Main Street, Suite 4A
P.O. Box 5057
West Fargo, ND 58078
(701) 293-3120   Fax: (701) 293-9951
E-mail: Programs@ndlegion.org
Web: www.ndlegion.org/children_youth.html

Summary To provide financial assistance to high school seniors in North Dakota who are direct descendants of veterans and interested in attending college in any state.

Eligibility This program is open to seniors graduating from high schools in North Dakota and planning to attend a college, university, trade school, or technical school in any state. Applicants must be the children, grandchildren, or great-grandchildren of veterans who served honorably in the U.S. armed forces. Along with their application, they must submit a 500-word essay on why they should receive this scholarship. Selection is based on the essay and academic performance; financial need is not considered.

Financial data The stipend is $2,000.

Duration 1 year; nonrenewable.

Number awarded 1 each year.

Deadline April of each year.

[542]
HELEN KLIMEK STUDENT SCHOLARSHIP

American Legion Auxiliary
Department of New York
112 State Street, Suite 1310
Albany, NY 12207
(518) 463-1162   Toll Free: (800) 421-6348
Fax: (518) 449-5406   E-mail: alanyterry@nycap.rr.com
Web: www.deptny.org/Scholarships.htm

Summary To provide financial assistance to New York residents who are the descendants of veterans and interested in attending college in any state.

Eligibility This program is open to residents of New York who are high school seniors or graduates and attending or planning to attend an accredited college or university in any state. Applicants must be the children, grandchildren, or great-grandchildren of veterans who served during specified periods of wartime. Along with their application they must submit a 700-word statement on the significance or value of volunteerism as a resource towards the positive development of their personal and professional future. Selection is based on character (20%), Americanism (15%), volunteer involvement (20%), leadership (15%), scholarship (15%), and financial need (15%). U.S. citizenship is required.

Financial data The stipend is $1,000. Funds are paid directly to the recipient's school.

Duration 1 year.

Number awarded 1 each year.

Deadline February of each year.

[543]
HENRY J. REILLY MEMORIAL SCHOLARSHIP FOR COLLEGE SOPHOMORES AND JUNIORS

Reserve Officers Association of the United States
Attn: Scholarship Program
One Constitution Avenue, N.E.
Washington, DC 20002-5618
(202) 646-7719   Toll Free: (800) 809-9448, ext. 719
Fax: (202) 547-1641   E-mail: scholarship@roa.org
Web: www.roa.org

Summary To provide financial assistance to members of the Reserve Officers Association (ROA) and their children or grandchildren who are completing the sophomore or junior year of college.

Eligibility Applicants for this scholarship must be active or associate members of the association or their children or grandchildren (under the age of 26). Children, age 21 or under, of deceased members who were active and paid up at the time of their death are also eligible. Spouses are not eligible, unless they are members of the association. ROTC members do not qualify as sponsors. Applicants must provide evidence of full-time enrollment at a regionally-accredited 4-year college or university, demonstrate leadership qualities, have earned a GPA of 3.3 or higher in high school and 3.0 or higher in college, have scored at least 1875 on the SAT or 55 on the English/math ACT, and (if appropriate) have registered for the draft. Community college students who are transferring to a 4-year college and university are also eligible. They must submit an application and a 500-word essay on career goals.

Financial data The stipend is $1,000 per year.

Duration 1 year; may be renewed.

Number awarded The sponsor awards a total of 30 scholarships each year.

Deadline May of each year.

[544]
HENRY J. REILLY MEMORIAL SCHOLARSHIP FOR FRESHMEN IN COLLEGE

Reserve Officers Association of the United States
Attn: Scholarship Program
One Constitution Avenue, N.E.
Washington, DC 20002-5618
(202) 646-7719   Toll Free: (800) 809-9448, ext. 719
Fax: (202) 547-1641   E-mail: scholarship@roa.org
Web: www.roa.org

Summary To provide financial assistance to children and grandchildren of members of the Reserve Officers Association (ROA) who are completing the freshman year of college.

Eligibility Applicants for these scholarships must be the children or grandchildren of active or associate members of the association. They must be completing the freshman year of full-time undergraduate study at a regionally-accredited 4-year college or university in the United States. Children, age 21 or under, of deceased members who were active and paid up at the time of their death are also eligible. Applicants must have earned a GPA of 3.3 or higher, have scored at least 1875 on the SAT or at least 55 on the combined English/math ACT, show evidence of good moral character, demonstrate leadership qualities, be in the top quarter of their graduating class, and (if appropriate) have registered for the draft. Along with their application, they must submit a 500-word essay on career goals.

Financial data The stipend is $1,000.

Duration 1 year; recipients may reapply as undergraduates.

Number awarded The sponsor awards a total of 30 scholarships each year.

Deadline May of each year.

[545]
HENRY J. REILLY MEMORIAL SCHOLARSHIP FOR GRADUATING HIGH SCHOOL SENIORS

Reserve Officers Association of the United States
Attn: Scholarship Program
One Constitution Avenue, N.E.
Washington, DC 20002-5618
(202) 646-7719   Toll Free: (800) 809-9448, ext. 719
Fax: (202) 547-1641   E-mail: scholarship@roa.org
Web: www.roa.org

Summary To provide financial assistance for college to children and grandchildren of members of the Reserve Officers Association (ROA) who are graduating high school seniors.

Eligibility Applicants for these scholarships must be the children or grandchildren of active or associate members of the association. They must be high school seniors accepted for full-time undergraduate study at a regionally-accredited 4-year college or university in the United States. Children, age 21 or under, of deceased members who were active and paid up at the time of their death are also eligible. Applicants must have earned a GPA of 3.3 or higher, have scored at least 1875 on the SAT or at least 55 on the combined English/math ACT, show evidence of good moral character, demonstrate leadership qualities, be in the top quarter of their graduating class, and (if appropriate) have registered for the draft. Along with their application, they must submit a 500-word essay on career goals.

Financial data The stipend is $1,000.

Duration 1 year; recipients may reapply as undergraduates.

Number awarded The sponsor awards a total of 30 scholarships each year.

Deadline May of each year.

[546]
HEROES LEGACY SCHOLARSHIPS

Fisher House Foundation
111 Rockville Pike, Suite 420
Rockville, MD 20850
Toll Free: (888) 294-8560
E-mail: bgawne@fisherhouse.org
Web: www.militaryscholar.org/legacy/index.html

Summary To provide financial assistance for college to the children of deceased and disabled veterans and military personnel.

Eligibility This program is open to the unmarried sons and daughters of U.S. military servicemembers (including active duty, retirees, Guard/Reserves, and survivors) who are high school seniors or full-time freshmen at an accredited college, university, or community college and younger than 23 years of age. Applicants must have at least 1 parent who, while

serving on active duty after September 11, 2001, either died or became disabled, defined as qualified for receipt of Traumatic Servicemembers Group Life Insurance (TSGLI) or rated as 100% permanently and totally disabled by the U.S. Department of Veterans Affairs. They must have a GPA of 2.5 or higher. Along with their application, they must submit a 500-word essay on a topic that changes annually; recently, students were asked to identify the 4 persons whose faces they would place on a 21st century Mount Rushmore type of monument and why. Selection is based on merit.

Financial data A stipend is awarded (amount not specified).

Duration 1 year.

Additional information This program was established in 2010 with proceeds from the sale of the book *Of Thee I Sing: A Letter to My Daughters* by President Barack Obama.

Number awarded Varies each year, depending on the availability of funds.

Deadline March of each year.

[547]
HEROES TRIBUTE SCHOLARSHIPS

Marine Corps Scholarship Foundation, Inc.
Attn: Scholarship Office
909 North Washington Street, Suite 400
Alexandria, VA 22314
(703) 549-0060   Toll Free: (866) 496-5462
Fax: (703) 549-9474   E-mail: students@mcsf.org
Web: www.mcsf.org

Summary To provide financial assistance for college to the children of Marines and Navy Corpsmen serving with the Marines who were killed on September 11, 2001 or in combat since that date.

Eligibility This program is open to the children of 1) Marines and former Marines killed in the terrorist attacks on September 11, 2001; and 2) Marines and U.S. Navy Corpsmen serving with the Marines who were killed in combat since September 11, 2001. Applicants must be high school seniors, high school graduates, or current undergraduates in an accredited college, university, or postsecondary vocational/technical school. They must submit academic transcripts (GPA of 2.0 or higher), documentation of their parent's service, and a 500-word essay on a topic that changes periodically. Only undergraduate study is supported. There is no maximum family income limitation. All qualified applicants receive scholarships.

Financial data The stipend is $7,500 per year.

Duration 4 years.

Number awarded Varies each year; recently, 4 of these scholarships were awarded.

Deadline February of each year.

[548]
HICKAM OFFICERS' SPOUSES' CLUB SCHOLARSHIPS

Hickam Officers' Spouses' Club
Attn: Scholarship Chair
PMB 168
P.O. Box 30800
Honolulu, HI 96820-0800
E-mail: scholarships@hickamosc.com
Web: www.hickamosc.com

Summary To provide financial assistance to dependents of current and former military personnel in Hawaii who are interested in attending college or graduate school in any state.
Eligibility This program is open to dependents of 1 of the following: 1) active-duty military members permanently stationed in Hawaii; 2) active-duty military members on a remote assignment from Hawaii; 3) retired military members resident in Hawaii; 4) full-time Hawaii National Guard and U.S. military Reserve members residing in Hawaii; and 5) survivors of deceased military members residing in Hawaii. Applicants must be seniors graduating from a Hawaii high school or accredited home school program based in Hawaii and planning to enroll at an accredited 2- or 4-year college, university, or vocational/technical school in any state; dependent children currently working on an undergraduate or graduate degree at a college or university in any state; or spouses currently working on an undergraduate or graduate degree at a college or university in any state. High school seniors must submit a 1-page essay on their greatest challenge, how they overcame it, and what lessons they learned. Spouses and other continuing students must submit a 1-page essay on what it means to live passionately and how they demonstrate it in their daily life. Selection is based on the essay, academic ability, extracurricular activities and work experience, service activities and citizenship, and a letter of recommendation.
Financial data A stipend is awarded (amount not specified).
Duration 1 year.
Number awarded 1 or more each year.
Deadline March of each year.

[549]
HIGH SCHOOL SCHOLARSHIPS FOR AIR FORCE DEPENDENTS

Air Force Officers' Wives' Club of Washington, D.C.
Attn: Scholarship Committee
P.O. Box 8490
Washington, DC 20032
(202) 239-1932   E-mail: scholarships@afowc.com
Web: www.afowc.com/scholarships

Summary To provide financial assistance for college to high school seniors who are dependents of Air Force members in the Washington, D.C. area.
Eligibility This program is open to high school seniors residing in the Washington, D.C. metropolitan area who are dependents of Air Force enlisted or commissioned personnel in the following categories: active duty, retired, Reserve, Guard, or deceased. Applicants must be planning to work on an accredited undergraduate degree at a college or university in any state. Along with their application, they must submit a 400-word essay on their choice of 3 assigned topics that change annually. Selection is based on their essay academic ability, extracurricular activities, service activities, citizenship, and references; financial need is not considered. Applicants who receive an appointment to a service academy are not eligible.
Financial data The stipend is $4,000. Funds may be used only for payment of tuition or academic fees.
Duration 1 year; nonrenewable.
Number awarded Varies each year.
Deadline February of each year.

[550]
HNGEA SCHOLARSHIP

Hawaii National Guard Enlisted Association
c/o Larnette H. Doi, Scholarship Committee Chair
360 Mamala Bay Drive
Hickam AFB, HI 9683-5517
E-mail: larnette.doi@hickam.af.mil
Web: www.hngea.net/Scholarship%20Webpage.htm

Summary To provide financial assistance for college to members of the Hawaii National Guard Enlisted Association (HNGEA) and their dependents.
Eligibility This program is open to HNGEA members and their dependent spouses and children. Applicants must be attending or interested in attending a college or university in Hawaii as an undergraduate student. They must have a GPA of at least 2.5 for the current semester and 2.0 overall. Along with their application, they must submit a letter describing their educational goals and need for the scholarship. Selection is based on that letter (10 points), academic achievement (50 points), participation in the organization (10 points), and financial need (30 points).
Financial data Stipends range from $500 to $2,000.
Duration 1 year.
Number awarded Varies each year.
Deadline June of each year.

[551]
HONOLULU POST SAME SCHOLARSHIPS

Society of American Military Engineers-Honolulu Post
P.O. Box 201445
Honolulu, HI 96820
Web: www.samehonolulu.org

Summary To provide financial assistance to residents of Hawaii, particularly those with ties to the military, who are interested in attending college in any state to work on an undergraduate or graduate degree in engineering or architecture.
Eligibility This program is open to residents of Hawaii who are graduating high school seniors or current undergraduates enrolled or planning to enroll full time at an accredited college or university in any state. Applicants must be planning to work on an undergraduate or graduate degree in engineering or architecture. They must be U.S. citizens and have a GPA of 3.0 or higher. Military affiliation or experience (i.e., ROTC, member or dependent of a member of the Society of Military Engineers (SAME), military dependent, Junior ROTC) is not required but is given preference. Along with their application, they must submit a transcript; a resume of work experience, academic activities, and extracurricular accomplishments; and a 1-page essay on how their engineering or architecture degree will impact our nation.
Financial data The stipend is $2,500.
Duration 1 year.
Number awarded Varies each year; recently, 6 of these scholarships were awarded.
Deadline March of each year.

[552]
HOPE FOR THE WARRIORS SPOUSE/CAREGIVER SCHOLARSHIPS

Hope for the Warriors
Attn: Spouse/Caregiver Scholarships Director
1011 South MacDill Avenue, Suite 812
Tampa, FL 33629
Toll Free: (877) 246-7349
E-mail: scholarship@hopeforthewarriors.org
Web: www.hopeforthewarriors.org/spouse.html

Summary To provide financial assistance for college to the spouses and caregivers of wounded or deceased military personnel or veterans.

Eligibility This program is open to spouses and caregivers of current and former service members who were wounded or killed in the line of duty since September 11, 2001. Applicants must be enrolled or planning to enroll full or part time at an accredited college, university, or trade school to work on a bachelor's degree, master's degree, or vocational certification. They must have a high school GPA of 2.6 or higher or a GED score of 650 or higher. Along with their application, they must submit a 500-word essay on how their life has been impacted by the Global War on Terror and how that impact played a role in their pursuit of higher education. Selection is based on that essay, academic achievement, personal goals, and letters of recommendation.

Financial data The stipend is $5,000 or $1,250 per year.

Duration 1 year; may be renewed up to 3 additional years.

Additional information This program includes the following named scholarships: the Shannon Maxwell Award, the Bonnie Amos Award, the Karin Dickerson Award, the Robin Kelleher-New Beginnings Award, and the Sidney Popkin Memorial Scholarship.

Number awarded 5 each year: 4 at $5,000 and 1 at $1,250.

Deadline March of each year.

[553]
HOWARD R. HARPER SCHOLARSHIPS

Enlisted Association of the National Guard of Iowa
c/o Jerald D. Hansen, Secretary
1409 East Coolbaugh Street
Red Oak, IA 51566
(712) 623-2804
Web: www.eangi.users01.com/index-4.html

Summary To provide funding to members of the Enlisted Association of the National Guard of Iowa (EANGI) and their dependents who are interested in attending college.

Eligibility This program is open to EANGI members and their spouses and children. Applicants must be attending or accepted at a VA-approved college or vocational/technical school (which may be in any state). Along with their application, they must submit a copy of their transcript, a letter with specific facts as to their desire to continue their education and why financial assistance is required, 3 letters of recommendation, and 1 academic reference.

Financial data The stipend is $1,500.

Duration 1 year.

Additional information Membership in EANGI is open to enlisted members of the Iowa Army or Air National Guard, active component members assigned to the Iowa Army or Air National Guard, and retired or honorably-discharged Iowa Army or Air National Guard enlisted personnel.

Number awarded 5 each year.

Deadline January of each year.

[554]
H.S. AND ANGELINE LEWIS SCHOLARSHIPS

American Legion Auxiliary
Department of Wisconsin
Attn: Education Chair
2930 American Legion Drive
P.O. Box 140
Portage, WI 53901-0140
(608) 745-0124   Toll Free: (866) 664-3863
Fax: (608) 745-1947   E-mail: alawi@amlegionauxwi.org
Web: www.amlegionauxwi.org/Scholarships.htm

Summary To provide financial assistance to Wisconsin residents who are related to veterans or members of the American Legion Auxiliary and interested in working on an undergraduate or graduate degree at a school in any state.

Eligibility This program is open to the children, wives, and widows of veterans who are high school seniors or graduates and have a GPA of 3.5 or higher. Grandchildren and great-grandchildren of members of the American Legion Auxiliary are also eligible. Applicants must be residents of Wisconsin and interested in working on an undergraduate or graduate degree at a school in any state. Along with their application, they must submit a 300-word essay on "Education—An Investment in the Future." Financial need is considered in the selection process.

Financial data The stipend is $1,000.

Duration 1 year; nonrenewable.

Number awarded 6 each year: 1 to a graduate student and 5 to undergraduates.

Deadline March of each year.

[555]
IA DRANG SCHOLARSHIP PROGRAM

First Cavalry Division Association
Attn: Foundation
302 North Main Street
Copperas Cove, TX 76522-1703
(254) 547-6537   Fax: (254) 547-8853
E-mail: firstcav@1cda.org
Web: www.1cda.org/Foundation_Overview.htm

Summary To provide financial assistance for undergraduate education to descendants of Army and Air Force personnel who fought in the battle of Ia Drang in 1965.

Eligibility This program is open to the children and grandchildren of members of designated Army and Air Force units who actually fought in the battle of the Ia Drang valley from November 3 through 19, 1965. For a list of the qualifying units, contact the sponsor. Children and grandchildren of personnel who were assigned to a unit that fought in the battles but were themselves at other locations during the specified dates are not eligible.

Financial data The stipend is $1,200 per year. The checks are made out jointly to the student and the school and may be used for whatever the student needs, including tuition, books, and clothing.

Duration 1 year; may be renewed up to 3 additional years.

Additional information This program began in 1994. Requests for applications must be accompanied by a self-addressed stamped envelope.

Number awarded Varies each year. Since the program was established, 183 of these scholarships, worth more than $351,000, have been awarded.

Deadline June of each year.

[556]
IDAHO FREEDOM SCHOLARSHIPS

Idaho State Board of Education
Len B. Jordan Office Building
650 West State Street, Room 307
P.O. Box 83720
Boise, ID 83720-0037
(208) 332-1574   Fax: (208) 334-2632
E-mail: scholarshiphelp@osbe.idaho.gov
Web: www.boardofed.idaho.gov/scholarship/freedom.asp

Summary To provide financial assistance for college to dependent children of Idaho veterans who are deceased or listed as prisoners of war or missing in action.

Eligibility Eligible for these scholarships are dependent children of Idaho veterans who have been determined by the federal government to have been 1) killed in action or died of injuries or wounds sustained in action, 2) prisoners of war (POW), or 3) missing in action (MIA) in southeast Asia (including Korea) or any area of armed conflict in which the United States is a party.

Financial data Each scholarship provides a full waiver of tuition and fees at public institutions of higher education or public vocational schools within Idaho, an allowance of $500 per semester for books, and on-campus housing and subsistence.

Duration Benefits are available for a maximum of 36 months.

Number awarded Varies each year.

Deadline Deadline not specified.

[557]
IDAHO LEGION AUXILIARY NURSES SCHOLARSHIP

American Legion Auxiliary
Department of Idaho
905 Warren Street
Boise, ID 83706-3825
(208) 342-7066   E-mail: idalegionaux@msn.com
Web: idahoala.org/scholarships.aspx

Summary To provide financial assistance to Idaho veterans and their descendants who are interested in studying nursing at a school in any state.

Eligibility This program is open to student nurses who are veterans or the children or grandchildren of veterans and are residents of Idaho. Applicants must be attending or planning to attend a school of nursing in any state. They may be traditional or nontraditional students between 17 and 35 years of age. Selection is based on need, academics, and deportment.

Financial data The stipend is $1,000.

Duration 1 year.

Number awarded 1 each year.

Deadline May of each year.

[558]
IDAHO LEGION SCHOLARSHIPS

American Legion
Department of Idaho
901 Warren Street
Boise, ID 83706-3825
(208) 342-7061   Fax: (208) 342-1964
E-mail: idlegion@mindspring.com
Web: idlegion.home.mindspring.com

Summary To provide financial assistance to the children and grandchildren of members of the American Legion or American Legion Auxiliary in Idaho who are planning to attend college in any state.

Eligibility This program is open to the children and grandchildren of members of the American Legion or American Legion Auxiliary in Idaho who have been members for at least 2 consecutive years. Applicants must be seniors at high schools in Idaho who plan to enroll full time at an accredited college, university, or vocational/technical school in any state.

Financial data A stipend is awarded (amount not specified).

Duration 1 year.

Number awarded Varies each year.

Deadline June of each year.

[559]
ILLINOIS AMERICAN LEGION AUXILIARY PAST PRESIDENTS PARLEY NURSES SCHOLARSHIP

American Legion Auxiliary
Department of Illinois
2720 East Lincoln Street
P.O. Box 1426
Bloomington, IL 61702-1426
(309) 663-9366   Fax: (309) 663-5827
E-mail: karen.boughan@ilala.org
Web: www.ilala.org/scholar.html

Summary To provide financial assistance to Illinois veterans and their descendants who are attending college in any state to prepare for a career as a nurse.

Eligibility This program is open to veterans who served during designated periods of wartime and their children, grandchildren, and great-grandchildren. Applicants must be currently enrolled at a college or university in any state and studying nursing. They must be residents of Illinois or members of the American Legion Family, Department of Illinois. Selection is based on commitment (25%), character (25%), academic rating (20%), and need (30%).

Financial data The stipend is $1,000.

Duration 1 year.

Additional information Applications may be obtained only from a local unit of the American Legion Auxiliary.

Number awarded 1 or more each year.

Deadline April of each year.

[560]
ILLINOIS AMVETS JUNIOR ROTC SCHOLARSHIPS

AMVETS-Department of Illinois
2200 South Sixth Street
Springfield, IL 62703
(217) 528-4713 Toll Free: (800) 638-VETS (within IL)
Fax: (217) 528-9896
Web: www.ilamvets.org/prog_scholarships.cfm

Summary To provide financial assistance for college to high school seniors in Illinois who have participated in Junior ROTC (JROTC), especially children and grandchildren of veterans.

Eligibility This program is open to seniors graduating from high schools in Illinois who have taken the ACT or SAT and have participated in the JROTC program. Financial need is considered in the selection process. Priority is given to children and grandchildren of veterans.

Financial data The stipend is $1,000.

Duration 1 year; nonrenewable.

Number awarded 5 each year: 1 in each of the sponsor's divisions.

Deadline February of each year.

[561]
ILLINOIS AMVETS SERVICE FOUNDATION SCHOLARSHIPS

AMVETS-Department of Illinois
2200 South Sixth Street
Springfield, IL 62703
(217) 528-4713 Toll Free: (800) 638-VETS (within IL)
Fax: (217) 528-9896
Web: www.ilamvets.org/prog_scholarships.cfm

Summary To provide financial assistance for college to high school seniors in Illinois, especially children and grandchildren of veterans.

Eligibility This program is open to seniors graduating from high schools in Illinois who have taken the ACT or SAT. Financial need is considered in the selection process. Priority is given to children and grandchildren of veterans.

Financial data The stipend is $1,000.

Duration 1 year; nonrenewable.

Number awarded Up to 30 each year: 6 in each of the sponsor's 5 divisions.

Deadline February of each year.

[562]
ILLINOIS AMVETS TRADE SCHOOL SCHOLARSHIPS

AMVETS-Department of Illinois
2200 South Sixth Street
Springfield, IL 62703
(217) 528-4713 Toll Free: (800) 638-VETS (within IL)
Fax: (217) 528-9896
Web: www.ilamvets.org/prog_scholarships.cfm

Summary To provide financial assistance to high school seniors in Illinois, especially children and grandchildren of veterans, who are interested in attending trade school.

Eligibility This program is open to seniors graduating from high schools in Illinois who have been accepted at an approved trade school. Financial need is considered in the

selection process. Priority is given to children and grandchildren of veterans.

Financial data The stipend is $5,000.

Duration 1 year; nonrenewable.

Number awarded 5 each year: 1 in each of the sponsor's divisions.

Deadline February of each year.

[563]
ILLINOIS CHILDREN OF VETERANS SCHOLARSHIPS

Illinois Department of Veterans' Affairs
833 South Spring Street
P.O. Box 19432
Springfield, IL 62794-9432
(217) 782-6641 Toll Free: (800) 437-9824 (within IL)
Fax: (217) 524-0344 TDD: (217) 524-4645
E-mail: webmail@dva.state.il.us
Web: www2.illinois.gov

Summary To provide financial assistance for college to the children of Illinois veterans (with preference given to the children of disabled or deceased veterans).

Eligibility Each county in the state is entitled to award an honorary scholarship to the child of a veteran of World War I, World War II, the Korean Conflict, the Vietnam Conflict, or after August 2, 1990. Preference is given to children of disabled or deceased veterans.

Financial data Students selected for this program receive free tuition at any branch of the University of Illinois.

Duration Up to 4 years.

Number awarded Each county in Illinois is entitled to award 1 scholarship. The Board of Trustees of the university may, from time to time, add to the number of honorary scholarships (when such additions will not create an unnecessary financial burden on the university).

Deadline Deadline not specified.

[564]
ILLINOIS FALLEN HEROES SCHOLARSHIP

Office of the State Treasurer
Attn: Bright Start Account Representative
400 West Monroe Street, Suite 401
Springfield, IL 62704
(217) 782-6540 Fax: (217) 524-3822
E-mail: fallenheroes@treasurer.state.il.us
Web: www.treasurer.il.gov

Summary To provide financial assistance for college to the children of Illinois service members killed in Iraq.

Eligibility This program is open to the children of fallen Illinois service members who served in Operation Iraqi Freedom or Operation Enduring Freedom. Applicants must be U.S. citizens of any age under 30 years. They may be planning to attend an accredited college or university anywhere in the United States or at selected institutions abroad. Children of all Illinois active and Reserve servicemen and women are eligible.

Financial data The stipend is $2,500. Funds are deposited into an age-based Bright Start portfolio (the Illinois 529 program) and are available when the student reaches college age. The older the child, the more conservative the investment becomes. Funds may be used only for tuition, fees, room, and board, and must be spent before the child reaches 30 years of age.

Duration   1 year.

Additional information   This program began in 2008.

Number awarded   Varies each year.

Deadline   May of each year.

[565]
ILLINOIS LEGION SCHOLARSHIPS

American Legion
Department of Illinois
2720 East Lincoln Street
P.O. Box 2910
Bloomington, IL 61702-2910
(309) 663-0361   Fax: (309) 663-5783
E-mail: hdqs@illegion.org
Web: www.illegion.org/scholarship.html

Summary   To provide financial assistance to the children and grandchildren of members of the American Legion in Illinois who plan to attend college in any state.

Eligibility   This program is open to students graduating from high schools in Illinois who plan to further their education at an accredited college, university, technical school, or trade school in any state. Applicants must be the children or grandchildren of living or deceased members of American Legion posts in Illinois. Selection is based on academic performance and financial need. U.S. citizenship is required.

Financial data   The stipend is $1,000.

Duration   1 year; nonrenewable.

Number awarded   20 each year: 4 in each of the Illinois department's 5 divisions.

Deadline   March of each year.

[566]
ILLINOIS LEGION TRADE SCHOOL SCHOLARSHIPS

American Legion
Department of Illinois
2720 East Lincoln Street
P.O. Box 2910
Bloomington, IL 61702-2910
(309) 663-0361   Fax: (309) 663-5783
E-mail: hdqs@illegion.org
Web: www.illegion.org/scholarship.html

Summary   To provide financial assistance to the children and grandchildren of members of the American Legion in Illinois who plan to attend trade school in any state.

Eligibility   This program is open to students graduating from high schools in Illinois who plan to further their education through a private career school, on-the-job training, apprenticeship, or cooperative training at a program in any state. Applicants must be the children or grandchildren of members of American Legion posts in Illinois. Selection is based on academic performance and financial need.

Financial data   The stipend is $1,000.

Duration   1 year; nonrenewable.

Number awarded   5 each year: 1 in each of the Illinois department's 5 divisions.

Deadline   March of each year.

[567]
ILLINOIS MIA/POW SCHOLARSHIP

Illinois Department of Veterans' Affairs
833 South Spring Street
P.O. Box 19432
Springfield, IL 62794-9432
(217) 782-6641   Toll Free: (800) 437-9824 (within IL)
Fax: (217) 524-0344   TDD: (217) 524-4645
E-mail: webmail@dva.state.il.us
Web: www2.illinois.gov

Summary   To provide financial assistance for 1) the undergraduate education of Illinois dependents of disabled or deceased veterans or those listed as prisoners of war or missing in action, and 2) the rehabilitation or education of disabled dependents of those veterans.

Eligibility   This program is open to the spouses, natural children, legally adopted children, or stepchildren of a veteran or servicemember who 1) has been declared by the U.S. Department of Defense or the U.S. Department of Veterans Affairs to be permanently disabled from service-connected causes with 100% disability, deceased as the result of a service-connected disability, a prisoner of war, or missing in action, and 2) at the time of entering service was an Illinois resident or was an Illinois resident within 6 months of entering such service. Special support is available for dependents who are disabled.

Financial data   An eligible dependent is entitled to full payment of tuition and certain fees at any Illinois state-supported college, university, or community college. In lieu of that benefit, an eligible dependent who has a physical, mental, or developmental disability is entitled to receive a grant to be used to cover the cost of treating the disability at 1 or more appropriate therapeutic, rehabilitative, or educational facilities. For all recipients, the total benefit cannot exceed the cost equivalent of 4 calendar years of full-time enrollment, including summer terms, at the University of Illinois.

Duration   This scholarship may be used for a period equivalent to 4 calendar years, including summer terms. Dependents have 12 years from the initial term of study to complete the equivalent of 4 calendar years. Disabled dependents who elect to use the grant for rehabilitative purposes may do so as long as the total benefit does not exceed the cost equivalent of 4 calendar years of full-time enrollment at the University of Illinois.

Additional information   An eligible child must begin using the scholarship prior to his or her 26th birthday. An eligible spouse must begin using the scholarship prior to 10 years from the effective date of eligibility (e.g., prior to August 12, 1989 or 10 years from date of disability or death).

Number awarded   Varies each year.

Deadline   Deadline not specified.

[568]
ILLINOIS SCHOLARSHIPS FOR JUNIOR MEMBERS

American Legion Auxiliary
Department of Illinois
2720 East Lincoln Street
P.O. Box 1426
Bloomington, IL 61702-1426
(309) 663-9366   Fax: (309) 663-5827
E-mail: karen.boughan@ilala.org
Web: www.ilala.org/scholar.html

Summary To provide financial assistance to high school seniors or graduates in Illinois who are junior members of the American Legion Auxiliary and planning to attend college in any state.

Eligibility This program is open to junior members of the Illinois American Legion Auxiliary who are daughters, granddaughters, great-granddaughters, or sisters of veterans who served during eligibility dates for membership in the American Legion. Applicants must be high school seniors or graduates who have not yet attended an institution of higher learning and are planning to attend college in any state. Along with their application, they must submit a 1,000-word essay on "The Veteran in My Life." Selection is based on that essay (25%) character and leadership (25%), scholarship (25%), and financial need (25%).

Financial data The stipend is $1,000.

Duration 1 year.

Number awarded Varies each year.

Deadline March of each year.

[569]
INDIANA AMERICAN LEGION FAMILY SCHOLARSHIP

American Legion
Department of Indiana
777 North Meridian Street
Indianapolis, IN 46204
(317) 630-1264   Fax: (317) 630-1277
Web: www.indlegion.org/?page_id=550

Summary To provide financial assistance to children and grandchildren of members of the American Legion family in Indiana who are interested in attending college in the state.

Eligibility This program is open to residents of Indiana who are the children or grandchildren of members of the American Legion, American Legion Auxiliary, Sons of the American Legion, or deceased members of those organizations who, at the time of death, were in current paid status. Applicants must be enrolled or accepted for enrollment at an Indiana college, university, junior college, community college, or technical school. Along with their application, they must submit a 500-word essay describing the reasons they wish to be considered for this scholarship, the purpose to which the funds will be put, their relationship to the Legion family and what it has meant to them, and how the citizens of Indiana and the members of the American Legion family will benefit in the future from their having achieved their educational goals with the assistance of this scholarship. Financial need is not considered in the selection process.

Financial data Stipends usually range from $700 to $1,000.

Duration 1 year.

Number awarded 3 each year: 1 to a high school senior who plans to attend a 4-year college or university, 1 to a high school senior who plans to attend a 2-year college, and 1 to a college freshman who plans to continue in that program.

Deadline March of each year.

[570]
INDIANA CHILD OF VETERAN AND PUBLIC SAFETY OFFICER SUPPLEMENTAL GRANT PROGRAM

State Student Assistance Commission of Indiana
Attn: Grants and Scholarships
W462 Indiana Government Center South
402 West Washington Street
Indianapolis, IN 46204
(317) 232-2355   Toll Free: (888) 528-4719 (within IN)
Fax: (317) 232-3260   E-mail: grants@ssaci.in.gov
Web: www.in.gov/ssaci/2338.htm

Summary To provide financial assistance to residents of Indiana who are the children or spouses of specified categories of deceased or disabled veterans or public safety officers and interested in attending college or graduate school in the state.

Eligibility This program is open to 1) children of deceased or disabled Indiana veterans, children of Purple Heart recipients, and children of Vietnam War veterans who were listed as POW or MIA; 2) children and spouses of members of the Indiana National Guard who suffered a service-connected death while serving on state active duty; 3) Indiana veterans who received a Purple Heart; 4) current and former students at the Indiana Soldiers' and Sailors' Children's Home (Morton Memorial High School); and 5) children and spouses of Indiana police officers, fire fighters, or emergency medical technicians killed in the line of duty or Indiana state police troopers permanently and totally disabled in the line of duty. The veterans and National Guard portions of this program are open to Indiana residents who are the natural or adopted children or spouses of veterans who served in the active-duty U.S. armed forces during a period of wartime.

Financial data Qualified applicants receive a 100% remission of tuition and all mandatory fees for undergraduate or graduate work at state-supported postsecondary schools and universities in Indiana. Support is not provided for such fees as room and board.

Duration Up to 124 semester hours of study.

Number awarded Varies each year.

Deadline Applications must be submitted at least 30 days before the start of the college term.

[571]
INDIANA SONS OF THE AMERICAN LEGION SCHOLARSHIP

Sons of the American Legion
Detachment of Indiana
Attn: Adjutant
777 North Meridian Street, Suite 104
Indianapolis, IN 46204
(317) 630-1363   Fax: (317) 237-9891
Web: www.in-sal.org/?p=1373

Summary To provide financial assistance to members of the Sons of the American Legion in Indiana who are interested in attending college in the state.

Eligibility This program is open to active members of a Squadron within the Indiana Detachment of the Sons of the American Legion. Applicants must be 1) seniors graduating from high school and planning to attend an accredited college, university, or trade school in Indiana, or 2) high school graduates attending or planning to attend an accredited college, university, or trade school in the state. Along with their application, they must submit an essay (up to 1,800 words) on the reasons why they feel they should receive this scholarship. Selection is based entirely on involvement in activities of the Sons of the American Legion.

Financial data   The stipend is $1,000.

Duration   1 year; nonrenewable.

Number awarded   1 each year.

Deadline   May of each year.

[572]
INDIANHEAD DIVISION SCHOLARSHIPS

Second (Indianhead) Division Association
Attn: Scholarship Foundation
c/o Jack Woodall
35 Wilkinson Drive
Landenberg, PA 19350
E-mail: warriorvet@verizon.net
Web: www.2ida.org/Scholarship.htm

Summary   To provide financial assistance for college to children and grandchildren of members of the Second (Indianhead) Division Association.

Eligibility   This program is open to 1) children and grandchildren of veterans who have been members of the association for the past 3 years and have a current membership, and 2) children and grandchildren of men or women killed in action while serving with the Second Division. Applicants may be high school seniors or currently-enrolled college students. They must submit a personal letter giving reasons for the request and plans for the future; a high school and, if appropriate, college transcript; ACT or SAT test scores; a statement from their school principal attesting to their character and involvement in extracurricular activities; 2 letters of recommendation from current teachers or professors; a 200- to 300-word essay on such subjects as "What Being an American Means to Me," "Why I Should Receive This Scholarship," or "What Significant Part of U.S. Army History Has the Second Infantry Division Contributed;" and a statement from their parents or guardians on the financial support they will be able to provide the applicant.

Financial data   The stipend is usually $1,000 per year.

Duration   1 year; may be renewed.

Number awarded   1 or more each year.

Deadline   May of each year.

[573]
INTERNATIONAL AUXILIARY EDUCATION GRANTS

Air Force Sergeants Association
Attn: Scholastic Coordinator
5211 Auth Road
Suitland, MD 20746
(301) 899-3500   Toll Free: (800) 638-0594
Fax: (301) 899-8136   E-mail: balsobrooks@hqafsa.org
Web: www.hqafsa.org

Summary   To provide financial assistance for college to members of the Air Force Sergeants Association (AFSA) Auxiliary.

Eligibility   This program is open to AFSA Auxiliary members who need assistance to enhance their income potential through formal education and/or training. Applicants must be seeking to obtain effective education and/or training to

acquire improved marketable skills. They must be 19 years of age or older.

Financial data   The current stipend is $1,000 per year. Funds are sent directly to the recipient's school to be used for tuition, room and board, fees, books, supplies, child care, meals, and transportation.

Duration   1 year; may be renewed if the student maintains full-time enrollment.

Additional information   This program began in 1990.

Number awarded   Varies each year; recently, 5 of these scholarships were awarded. Since the program began, it has awarded grants worth more than $117,000.

Deadline   March of each year.

[574]
IOWA WAR ORPHANS EDUCATIONAL AID FOR CHILDREN OF VETERANS WHO DIED ON OR AFTER SEPTEMBER 11, 2001

Iowa Department of Veterans Affairs
Camp Dodge, Building 3663
7105 N.W. 70th Avenue
Johnston, IA 50131-1824
(515) 242-5331   Toll Free: (800) VET-IOWA
Fax: (515) 242-5659   E-mail: idva.info@iowa.gov
Web: va.iowa.gov/benefits/war_orphans.html

Summary   To provide financial assistance for college in Iowa to the children of members of the armed forces from that state who died in service on or after September 11, 2001.

Eligibility   This program is open to children of veterans who died in service or as a result of such service on or after September 11, 2001. Eligibility also extends to children of deceased parents who were members of the Reserve components or of the National Guard who died or were killed while performing training or other duties. The deceased veteran must have been a resident of Iowa for at least 6 months prior to entering into active military service. The child must be attending or planning to attend a university, college, junior college, school of nursing, business school, or trade school located within Iowa and approved by the Iowa Department of Veterans Affairs. They must be younger than 31 years of age. This is an entitlement program. Aid is available to eligible orphans regardless of scholastic ability, number of years they plan to attend school, or marital status.

Financial data   The amount of assistance is equal to either 1) the highest resident undergraduate tuition rate for an institution of higher education under the control of the Iowa Board of Regents, less the amount of any state or federal education benefits, grants, or scholarships, or 2) the amount of the child's established financial need, whichever is less. Payments are made directly to the school by quarter, semester, or period, not to the recipient. Part-time students receive prorated amounts.

Duration   1 year; may be renewed until the recipient has received a total amount equal to 5 times the highest resident undergraduate tuition rate for an institution of higher education under the control of the Iowa Board of Regents, or until he or she reaches 31 years of age.

Number awarded   Varies each year.

Deadline   Deadline not specified.

[575]
IRAQ AND AFGHANISTAN SERVICE GRANTS

Department of Education
Attn: Federal Student Aid Information Center
P.O. Box 84
Washington, DC 20044-0084
(319) 337-5665   Toll Free: (800) 4-FED-AID
TDD: (800) 730-8913
Web: studentaid.ed.gov

Summary To provide financial assistance for undergraduate education to students whose parent was killed as a result of service in Iraq or Afghanistan.

Eligibility This program is open to students younger than 24 years of age whose parent or guardian was a member of the U.S. armed forces and died as a result of service performed in Iraq or Afghanistan after September 11, 2001. Applicants must be enrolled at least part time. The program is designed for students who do not qualify for Federal Pell Grants because of their family's financial situation.

Financial data The amount of the grant ranges up to that of a Federal Pell Grant, currently $5,550 per year.

Duration Up to 5 years of undergraduate study.

Number awarded Varies each year; recently, fewer than 1,000 students qualified for this program.

Deadline Students may submit applications between January of the current year through June of the following year.

[576]
ISABELLA M. GILLEN MEMORIAL SCHOLARSHIP

Aviation Boatswain's Mates Association
600 Montgomery Road
Westfield, MA 01085
E-mail: Scholarship@abma-usn.org
Web: www.abma-usn.org

Summary To provide financial assistance for college to the spouses and children of paid-up members of the Aviation Boatswains Mates Association (ABMA).

Eligibility Applicants must be dependents whose sponsor has been an active, dues-paying member of the ABMA for at least 2 years. They must prepare a statement describing their vocational or professional goals and relating how their past, present, and future activities make the accomplishment of those goals probable. Other submissions include transcripts, SAT or ACT scores, letters of recommendation, and honors received in scholarship, leadership, athletics, dramatics, community service, or other activities. Selection is based on financial need, character, leadership, and academic achievement.

Financial data The stipend is $3,500 per year.

Duration 1 year; may be renewed.

Additional information This program began in 1976. Membership in ABMA is open to all U.S. Navy personnel (active, retired, discharged, or separated) who hold or held the rating of aviation boatswains mate.

Number awarded 1 or 2 each year.

Deadline May of each year.

[577]
IVY DIVISION ASSOCIATION ANNUAL SCHOLARSHIP

National 4th Infantry (IVY) Division Association
c/o Don Kelby, Executive Director
P.O. Box 1914
St. Peters, MO 63376-0035
(314) 606-1969   E-mail: 4thidaed@swbell.net
Web: www.4thinfantry.org/content/scholarships-donations

Summary To provide money for college to members of the National 4th Infantry (IVY) Division Association and their families.

Eligibility This program is open to association members in good standing and all blood relatives of active association members in good standing. Recipients are chosen by lottery.

Financial data The stipend is $1,000.

Duration 1 year; may be renewed.

Additional information The trust fund from which these scholarships are awarded was created by the officers and enlisted men of the 4th Infantry Division as a living memorial to the men of the division who died in Vietnam. Originally, it was only open to children of members of the division who died in the line of duty in Vietnam between August 1, 1966 and December 31, 1977. When all those eligible had completed college, it adopted its current requirements.

Number awarded 1 or more each year.

Deadline June of each year.

[578]
IVY DIVISION ASSOCIATION MEMORIAL SCHOLARSHIP

National 4th Infantry (IVY) Division Association
c/o Don Kelby, Executive Director
P.O. Box 1914
St. Peters, MO 63376-0035
(314) 606-1969   E-mail: 4thidaed@swbell.net
Web: www.4thinfantry.org/content/scholarships-donations

Summary To provide financial assistance for college to descendants of soldiers who were killed while serving in the Fourth Infantry Division in the Global War on Terror (GWOT).

Eligibility This program is open to the children, stepchildren, and adopted children of soldiers who were killed while serving with the Fourth Infantry Division in Iraq, Afghanistan, and/or the GWOT. Membership in the sponsoring organization is not required. Recipients are chosen by lottery.

Financial data The stipend is $1,000.

Duration 1 year.

Number awarded 1 or more each year.

Deadline June of each year.

[579]
JACK E. BARGER, SR. MEMORIAL NURSING SCHOLARSHIPS

Pennsylvania State Nurses Association
Attn: Nursing Foundation of Pennsylvania
2578 Interstate Drive, Suite 101
Harrisburg, PA 17110
(717) 692-0542   Toll Free: (888) 707-PSNA
Fax: (717) 692-4540   E-mail: nfp@panurses.org
Web: www.panurses.org/2008/section.cfm?SID=21&ID=4

Summary To provide financial assistance to veterans, military personnel, and their dependents who are studying nursing in Pennsylvania.
Eligibility This program is open to veterans, active-duty military personnel, and the children and spouses of veterans and active-duty military personnel. Applicants must be residents of Pennsylvania and currently enrolled in an undergraduate professional school of nursing in the state. Recipients are selected by lottery from among the qualified applicants.
Financial data The stipend is $1,000.
Duration 1 year.
Additional information This program is sponsored by the Department of Pennsylvania Veterans of Foreign Wars (VFW). Recipients must attend the VFW Convention to accept the scholarship; travel, meals, and overnight expenses are paid by the VFW.
Number awarded 6 each year.
Deadline April of each year.

[580]
JAPANESE AMERICAN VETERANS ASSOCIATION MEMORIAL SCHOLARSHIPS

Japanese American Veterans Association
c/o Dave Buto
4226 Holborn Avenue
Annandale, VA 22003
(703) 503-3431   E-mail: admin@javadc.org
Web: www.javadc.org

Summary To provide financial assistance for college or graduate school to relatives of Japanese American veterans and military personnel.
Eligibility This program is open to graduating high school seniors and students currently working on an undergraduate or graduate degree at a college, university, or school of specialized study. Applicants must be related, by blood or marriage, to 1) a person who served with the 442nd Regimental Combat Team, the 100th Infantry Battalion, or other unit associated with those; 2) a person who served in the U.S. Military Intelligence Service during or after World War II; 3) a person of Japanese ancestry who is serving or has served in the U.S. armed forces and been honorable discharged; or 4) a member of the Japanese American Veterans Association (JAVA) whose membership extends back at least 1 year.
Financial data The stipend is $1,500.
Duration 1 year; recipients may reapply.
Additional information These scholarships, first awarded in 2008, include the following named awards: the Orville C. Shirey Memorial Scholarship, the Joseph Ichiuji Memorial Scholarship, the Sunao Phil Ishio Memorial Scholarship, the Kiyoko Tsuboi-Taubkin Memorial Scholarship, the Grant Hirabayashi Memorial Scholarship, the Teru Kamikawa Memorial Scholarship, the Mary Kozono Memorial Scholarship, and the Douglas Ishio Memorial Scholarship.
Number awarded 8 each year.
Deadline April of each year.

[581]
JEREMIAH TENHET US ARMY MILITARY INTELLIGENCE SCHOLARSHIP

American Academy of Physician Assistants-Veterans Caucus
Attn: Veterans Caucus
P.O. Box 362
Danville, PA 17821-0362
(570) 271-0292   Fax: (570) 271-5850
E-mail: admin@veteranscaucus.org
Web: www.veteranscaucus.org

Summary To provide financial assistance to Army veterans who served in Afghanistan and their dependents who are studying to become physician assistants.
Eligibility This program is open to U.S. citizens who are currently enrolled in a physician assistant program. The program must be approved by the Commission on Accreditation of Allied Health Education. Applicants must be honorably discharged members of the United States Army who served in Afghanistan or the dependents of those members. Selection is based on military honors and awards received, civic and college honors and awards received, professional memberships and activities, and GPA. An electronic copy of the applicant's DD Form 214 must accompany the application.
Financial data The stipend is $2,000.
Duration 1 year.
Number awarded 1 each year.
Deadline February of each year.

[582]
JEWELL HILTON BONNER SCHOLARSHIP

Navy League of the United States
Attn: Scholarships
2300 Wilson Boulevard, Suite 200
Arlington, VA 22201-5424
(703) 528-1775   Toll Free: (800) 356-5760
Fax: (703) 528-2333
E-mail: scholarships@navyleague.org
Web: www.navyleague.org

Summary To provide financial assistance for college to dependent children of sea service personnel, especially Native Americans.
Eligibility This program is open to U.S. citizens who are 1) dependents or direct descendants of an active, Reserve, retired, or honorably discharged member of the U.S. sea service (including the Navy, Marine Corps, Coast Guard, or Merchant Marines), or 2) current active members of the Naval Sea Cadet Corps. Applicants must be entering their freshman year at an accredited college or university. They must have a GPA of 3.0 or higher. Along with their application, they must submit transcripts, 2 letters of recommendation, SAT/ACT scores, documentation of financial need, proof of qualifying sea service duty, and a 1-page personal statement on why they should be considered for this scholarship. Preference is given to applicants of Native American heritage.
Financial data The stipend is $2,500 per year.
Duration 4 years, provided the recipient maintains a GPA of 3.0 or higher.
Number awarded 1 each year.
Deadline March of each year.

[583]
JEWISH WAR VETERANS NATIONAL EDUCATIONAL GRANTS

Jewish War Veterans of the U.S.A.
1811 R Street, N.W.
Washington, DC 20009-1659
(202) 265-6280   Fax: (202) 234-5662
E-mail: jwv@jwv.org
Web: www.jwv.org

Summary To provide money for college to descendants of members of the Jewish War Veterans of the U.S.A.

Eligibility This program is open to children, grandchildren, and great-grandchildren of members or of deceased members of Jewish War Veterans in good standing who are high school seniors. Applicants must have been accepted by an accredited 4-year college or university or a 3-year hospital school of nursing as a freshman. Selection is based on academic achievement, SAT and/or ACT test scores, class standing, and extracurricular and community activities.

Financial data First prize is the $1,000 Bernard Rotberg Memorial Scholarship; second prize is the $750 Louis S. Silvey Grant; third prize is $500.

Duration 1 year; nonrenewable.

Additional information Applications must be submitted through your Jewish War Veterans' department commander.

Number awarded 3 each year.

Deadline Applications must be submitted to the department commander by April of each year.

[584]
JOANNE HOLBROOK PATTON MILITARY SPOUSE SCHOLARSHIP PROGRAM

National Military Family Association, Inc.
Attn: Spouse Scholarship Program
2500 North Van Dorn Street, Suite 102
Alexandria, VA 22302-1601
(703) 931-NMFA   Toll Free: (800) 260-0218
Fax: (703) 931-4600
E-mail: scholarships@militaryfamily.org
Web: www.militaryfamily.org

Summary To provide financial assistance for postsecondary study to spouses of active and retired military personnel.

Eligibility This program is open to the spouses of military personnel (active, retired, Reserve, Guard, or survivor). Applicants must be attending or planning to attend an accredited postsecondary institution to work on an undergraduate or graduate degree, professional certification, vocational training, GED or ESL, or other postsecondary training. They may enroll part or full time and in-class or online. Along with their application, they must submit an essay on a question that changes annually; recently, applicants were asked to write about what they like most about the health care they are receiving as a military family member, what they like the least, and what they would recommend to change it. Selection is based on that essay, community involvement, and academic achievement.

Financial data The stipend is $1,000. Funds are paid directly to the educational institution to be used for tuition, fees, and school room and board. Support is not provided for books, rent, or previous education loans.

Duration 1 year; recipients may reapply.

Additional information This program began in 2004.

Number awarded Varies each year; recently, 484 of these scholarships were awarded.

Deadline January of each year.

[585]
JOHN A. HIGH CHILD WELFARE SCHOLARSHIP ENDOWMENT FUND

American Legion
Department of New Hampshire
State House Annex
25 Capitol Street, Room 431
Concord, NH 03301-6312
(603) 271-2211   Toll Free: (800) 778-3816
Fax: (603) 271-5352
E-mail: adjutantnh@amlegion.state.nh.us
Web: www.nhlegion.org

Summary To provide financial assistance to the sons of members of the New Hampshire Department of the American Legion or American Legion Auxiliary who plan to attend college.

Eligibility This program is open to male seniors graduating from high schools in New Hampshire who plan to attend college in any state. Applicants must be the son of a deceased veteran or of parents who have been members of the American Legion or the American Legion Auxiliary in New Hampshire for 3 continuous years. Along with their application, they must submit a 300-word essay on what this scholarship would mean to them. Selection is based on academic record (20%), Americanism (10%), financial need (50%), and character (20%).

Financial data The stipend is $2,000.

Duration 1 year.

Number awarded 1 each year.

Deadline April of each year.

[586]
JOHN CORNELIUS/MAX ENGLISH MEMORIAL SCHOLARSHIP AWARD

Marine Corps Tankers Association
c/o Buster Diggs, Scholarship Chair
1829 Ballentine Drive
Alpine, CA 91901
E-mail: Tigertanker2003@yahoo.com
Web: www.usmarinetankers.org/scholarship-program

Summary To provide financial assistance for college or graduate school to children and grandchildren of members of the Marine Corps Tankers Association and to Marine and Navy personnel currently serving in tank units.

Eligibility This program is open to high school seniors and graduates who are children, grandchildren, or under the guardianship of an active, Reserve, retired, or honorably discharged Marine who served in a tank unit. Marine or Navy Corpsmen currently assigned to tank units are also eligible. Applicants must be enrolled or planning to enroll full time at a college or graduate school. Their parent or grandparent must be a member of the Marine Corps Tankers Association or, if not a member, must join if the application is accepted. Along with their application, they must submit an essay on their educational goals, future aspirations, and concern for the future of our society and for the peoples of the world. Selection is based on that essay, academic record, school activities, leadership potential, and community service.

Financial data   The stipend is at least $2,000 per year.
Duration   1 year; recipients may reapply.
Number awarded   8 to 12 each year.
Deadline   March of each year.

[587]
JOHN KEYS KENTUCKY SONS OF THE AMERICAN LEGION SCHOLARSHIP

Sons of the American Legion
Detachment of Kentucky
Independence Squadron 275
P.O. Box 18791
Erlanger, KY 41018-0791
E-mail: SAL275@fuse.net
Web: moonbrothers275.org/indexSALhtml

Summary   To provide money for college to members of Kentucky squadrons of the Sons of the American Legion and to veterans who are residents of Kentucky.
Eligibility   This program is open to 1) members of the Sons of the American Legion who belong to a squadron in Kentucky, and 2) honorably-discharged veterans of the U.S. armed forces who are residents of Kentucky (regardless of length or period of service). Applicants must be enrolled (and have completed some course work) at a postsecondary institution in any state. Along with their application, they must submit a letter explaining their background, career objectives, current educational program, and financial need.
Financial data   The stipend varies, depending on the availability of funds; recently, they averaged $1,000. Awards are made directly to the recipient's institution.
Duration   1 year.
Additional information   This program began in 1988.
Number awarded   1 or 2 each year; since the program began, it has awarded more than 60 scholarships.
Deadline   March of each year.

[588]
JOLLY GREEN MEMORIAL SCHOLARSHIP

Jolly Green Association
Attn: Secretary
P.O. Box 965
O'Fallon, IL 62269-0965
E-mail: bill6100@aol.com
Web: www.jollygreen.org

Summary   To provide financial assistance for college to dependents of current and former members of the Air Force Combat Rescue or Support Forces.
Eligibility   This program is open to high school seniors who are dependents of current or former uniformed members of the USAF Combat Rescue or Support Forces. Applicants must have taken the ACT or SAT examinations and be eligible for admission to the college or university of their choice. Selection is based on academic achievement (40%), scholastic or public service achievements (10%), and financial need (50%).
Financial data   A stipend is awarded (amount not specified).
Duration   1 year.
Number awarded   1 or more each year.
Deadline   April of each year.

[589]
JON C. LADDA MEMORIAL FOUNDATION SCHOLARSHIP

Jon C. Ladda Memorial Foundation
P.O. Box 55
Unionville, CT 06085
E-mail: info@jonladda.org
Web: www.jonladda.org/scholarship.htm

Summary   To provide financial assistance for college to children of deceased and disabled U.S. Naval Academy graduates and members of the Navy submarine service.
Eligibility   This program is open to children of U.S. Naval Academy graduates and members of the U.S. Navy submarine service. The parent must have died on active duty or been medically retired with a 100% disability. Applicants must be enrolled or accepted at a 4-year college or university, including any of the service academies. Along with their application, they must submit an essay on a topic that changes annually. Selection is based on academic achievement, financial need, and merit.
Financial data   A stipend is awarded (amount not specified). Funds are disbursed directly to the recipient's institution.
Duration   1 year; may be renewed.
Number awarded   1 or more each year.
Deadline   March of each year.

[590]
JOSEPH A. MCALINDEN DIVERS' SCHOLARSHIP

Navy-Marine Corps Relief Society
Attn: Education Division
875 North Randolph Street, Suite 225
Arlington, VA 22203-1757
(703) 696-4960   Fax: (703) 696-0144
E-mail: education@nmcrs.org
Web: www.nmcrs.org/education.html

Summary   To provide financial assistance to current and former Navy and Marine Corps divers and their families who are interested in working on an undergraduate degree in a field related to ocean agriculture.
Eligibility   This program is open to Navy and Marine Corps active-duty and retired divers (includes Reservists serving on active duty for more than 90 days), their children under 23 years of age, and their spouses. Applicants must be working full time on their first undergraduate degree in oceanography, ocean agriculture, aquaculture, or a related field; they may also be engaged in advanced diver training, certification, or recertification. Financial need is considered.
Financial data   The stipend ranges from $500 to $3,000, depending on the need of the recipient.
Duration   1 year.
Number awarded   1 or more each year.
Deadline   Applications may be submitted at any time.

[591]
JOSEPH H. ELLINWOOD SCHOLARSHIP

American Legion
Department of Massachusetts
State House
24 Beacon Street, Suite 546-2
Boston, MA 02133-1044
(617) 727-2966   Fax: (617) 727-2969
E-mail: masslegion@verizon.net
Web: www.masslegion.org

Summary To provide financial assistance to the children and grandchildren of members of the American Legion in Massachusetts who plan to study nursing.

Eligibility This program is open to the children and grandchildren of members in good standing in the American Legion's Department of Massachusetts (or who were members in good standing at the time of death). Applicants must be entering their freshman year at a college or university in any state to prepare for a career as a nurse. Along with their application, they must submit a 100-word essay on their long-range goal and why they want to go to college. Financial need is considered in the selection process.

Financial data The stipend is $1,000. Funds are paid directly to the recipient.

Duration 1 year.

Number awarded 1 each year.

Deadline March of each year.

[592]
JOSEPH P. GAVENONIS SCHOLARSHIPS

American Legion
Department of Pennsylvania
Attn: Scholarship Endowment Fund
P.O. Box 2324
Harrisburg, PA 17105-2324
(717) 730-9100   Fax: (717) 975-2836
E-mail: hq@pa-legion.com
Web: www.pa-legion.com

Summary To provide financial assistance to the children of members of the American Legion in Pennsylvania who plan to attend college in the state.

Eligibility This program is open to seniors at high schools in Pennsylvania who are planning to attend a 4-year college or university in the state. Applicants must have a parent who has been in the military or is in the military and is a member of an American Legion Post in Pennsylvania. First preference is given to the children of Legion members who are deceased, killed in action, or missing in action. Financial need is considered in the selection process.

Financial data The stipend is $1,000 per year.

Duration 4 years, provided the recipient maintains a GPA of 2.5 or higher each semester.

Number awarded 1 or more each year.

Deadline May of each year.

[593]
JUDITH HAUPT MEMBER'S CHILD SCHOLARSHIP

Navy Wives Clubs of America
c/o NSA Mid-South
P.O. Box 54022
Millington, TN 38054-0022
Toll Free: (866) 511-NWCA
E-mail: nwca@navywivesclubsofamerica.org
Web: www.navywivesclubsofamerica.org/scholarships

Summary To provide financial assistance for college to the children of members of the Navy Wives Clubs of America.

Eligibility This program is open to students currently enrolled at accredited college or university who parent has been an association member for at least 1 year. Along with their application, they must submit a brief statement on why they feel they should be awarded this scholarship and any special circumstances (financial or other) they wish to have considered.

Financial data A stipend is provided (amount not specified).

Duration 1 year.

Additional information Membership in the association is open to spouses of enlisted personnel serving in the Navy, Marine Corps, Coast Guard, and the active Reserve units of those services; spouses of enlisted personnel who have been honorably discharged, retired, or transferred to the Fleet Reserve on completion of duty; and widows of enlisted personnel in those services.

Number awarded 1 or more each year.

Deadline May of each year.

[594]
JUNIOR GIRLS SCHOLARSHIPS

Ladies Auxiliary to the Veterans of Foreign Wars
c/o National Headquarters
406 West 34th Street
Kansas City, MO 64111
(816) 561-8655   Fax: (816) 931-4753
E-mail: info@ladiesauxvfw.org
Web: www.ladiesauxvfw.org/programs/scholarships.html

Summary To provide financial assistance for college to outstanding members of a Junior Girls Unit of the Ladies Auxiliary to the Veterans of Foreign Wars.

Eligibility Applicants must have been active members of a unit for 1 year, have held an office in the unit, and be between 13 and 16 years of age. Previous winners are not eligible, although former applicants who did not receive scholarships may reapply. Selection is based on participation in the Junior Girls Unit (40 points), school activities (30 points), and academic achievement (30 points).

Financial data The winner receives a $7,500 scholarship. Funds are paid directly to the college of the recipient's choice. In addition, $100 is awarded to each Junior Girl who is selected as the department winner and entered in the national competition.

Duration 1 year.

Number awarded 1 each year.

Deadline March of each year.

[595]
KANSAS TUITION WAIVER FOR DEPENDENTS AND SPOUSES OF DECEASED MILITARY PERSONNEL

Kansas Board of Regents
Attn: Student Financial Assistance
1000 S.W. Jackson Street, Suite 520
Topeka, KS 66612-1368
(785) 296-3518   Fax: (785) 296-0983
E-mail: dlindeman@ksbor.org
Web: www.kansasregents.org/scholarships_and_grants

Summary To provide financial assistance for college to residents of Kansas whose parent or spouse died on active military service after September 11, 2001.

Eligibility This program is open to residents of Kansas who are the dependent children or spouses of members of the U.S. armed forces who died on or after September 11, 2001 while, and as a result of, serving on active military duty. The deceased military member must have been a resident of Kansas at the time of death. Applicants must be enrolled or planning to enroll at a public educational institution in Kansas, including area vocational/technical schools and colleges, community colleges, the state universities, and Washburn University.

Financial data Qualifying students are permitted to enroll at an approved Kansas institution without payment of tuition or fees. They are responsible for other costs, such as books, room, and board.

Duration 1 year; may be renewed for a total of 10 semesters of undergraduate study.

Additional information This program began in 2005.

Number awarded Varies each year.

Deadline Deadline not specified.

[596]
KANSAS VETERANS OF FOREIGN WARS ENDOWMENT ASSOCIATION SCHOLARSHIP

Kansas Veterans of Foreign Wars
Attn: VFW Endowment Association
115 S.W. Gage Boulevard
P.O. Box 1008
Topeka, KS 66601-1008
(785) 272-6463   Fax: (785) 272-2629
E-mail: ksvfwhq@kvfw.kscoxmail.com
Web: www.ksvfw.org/Programs/index.shtml

Summary To provide financial assistance to residents of Kansas who are children or grandchildren of members of the Veterans of Foreign Wars (VFW) and interested in attending college in any state.

Eligibility This program is open to children and grandchildren of active and deceased members of a VFW Post or Ladies Auxiliary in Kansas. Applicants must be high school seniors, high school graduates or equivalent, or current undergraduate students. They must be attending or planning to attend a college, university, or vocational school in any state. Along with their application, they must submit a transcript that includes ACT scores (the ACT requirement is waived for applicants older than 25 years of age), a list of extracurricular activities, a statement on why they wish to further their education, and documentation of financial need.

Financial data The stipend ranges from $500 to $2,000 per year.

Duration 1 to 4 years.

Number awarded 1 or more each year.

Deadline January of each year.

[597]
KATHERN F. GRUBER SCHOLARSHIPS

Blinded Veterans Association
477 H Street, N.W.
Washington, DC 20001-2694
(202) 371-8880   Toll Free: (800) 669-7079
Fax: (202) 371-8258   E-mail: bva@bva.org
Web: www.bva.org/services.html

Summary To provide funds for undergraduate or graduate study to spouses and children of blinded veterans.

Eligibility This program is open to dependent children and spouses of blinded veterans of the U.S. armed forces. The veteran must be legally blind; the blindness may be either service connected or nonservice connected. Applicants must have been accepted or be currently enrolled as a full-time student in an undergraduate or graduate program at an accredited institution of higher learning. Along with their application, they must submit a 300-word essay on their career goals and aspirations. Financial need is not considered in the selection process.

Financial data The stipend is $2,000; funds are intended to be used to cover the student's expenses, including tuition, other academic fees, books, dormitory fees, and cafeteria fees. Funds are paid directly to the recipient's school.

Duration 1 year; recipients may reapply for up to 3 additional years.

Number awarded 6 each year.

Deadline April of each year.

[598]
KENTUCKIANA POST SAME SCHOLARSHIP

Society of American Military Engineers-Kentuckiana Post
c/o Erin Hall, Scholarship Committee Co-Chair
Messer Construction Company
11001 Plantside Drive
Louisville, KY 40299
(502) 261-9775   E-mail: ehall@messer.com
Web: posts.same.org/kentuckiana

Summary To provide financial assistance to students in Indiana and Kentucky, particularly those with ties to the military, who are interested in majoring in engineering in college.

Eligibility This program is open to students who fall into 1 of the following categories: a dependent of a current Society of American Military Engineers (SAME) Kentuckiana Post member; an employee or dependent of an employee of a Kentuckiana Post sustaining member firm; an employee or dependent of an employee of the Louisville District Corps of Engineers; a current student member of the Kentuckiana Post; a student whose permanent home address is within the Kentuckiana Post's geographic boundary (Kentucky and Indiana) and who is enrolled in an ROTC program or military academy; or an individual on active duty or the dependent of an individual on active duty who is assigned to an installation within the Kentuckiana Post's geographic boundary. Applicants must be U.S. citizens accepted at an undergraduate ABET-accredited engineering program; undergraduates enrolled in engineering technology programs are not eligible. Along with their application, they must submit an essay of 300 to 500 words on a topic that changes annually; recently, applicants were invited to write on how winning this scholarship would promote a promising future for their engineering career and how they might envision that career supporting the mission of SAME. Financial need is not considered in the selection process.

Financial data The stipend is $4,000 per year.

Duration 1 year; may be renewed 1 additional year.

Additional information Recipients are required to attend the scholarship luncheon ceremony in Louisville in May.

Number awarded Up to 5 each year.

Deadline March of each year.

[599]
KENTUCKY VETERANS TUITION WAIVER PROGRAM

Kentucky Department of Veterans Affairs
Attn: Field Operations Branch
321 West Main Street, Suite 390
Louisville, KY 40202
(502) 595-4447 Toll Free: (800) 928-4012 (within KY)
Fax: (502) 595-4448 E-mail: Pamela.Cypert@ky.gov
Web: www.veterans.ky.gov/benefits/tuitionwaiver.htm

Summary To provide financial assistance for college to the children, spouses, or unremarried widow(er)s of disabled or deceased Kentucky veterans.

Eligibility This program is open to the children, stepchildren, spouses, and unremarried widow(er)s of veterans who are residents of Kentucky (or were residents at the time of their death). The qualifying veteran must meet 1 of the following conditions: 1) died on active duty (regardless of wartime service); 2) died as a result of a service-connected disability (regardless of wartime service); 3) has a 100% service-connected disability; 4) is totally disabled (non-service connected) with wartime service; or 5) is deceased and served during wartime. The military service may have been as a member of the U.S. armed forces, the Kentucky National Guard, or a Reserve component; service in the Guard or Reserves must have been on state active duty, active duty for training, inactive duty training, or active duty with the U.S. armed forces. Children of veterans must be under 26 years of age; no age limit applies to spouses or unremarried widow(er)s. All applicants must be attending or planning to attend a 2-year, 4-year, or vocational technical school operated and funded by the Kentucky Department of Education.

Financial data Eligible dependents and survivors are exempt from tuition and matriculation fees at any state-supported institution of higher education in Kentucky.

Duration Tuition is waived until the recipient completes 45 months of training, receives a college degree, or (in the case of children of veterans) reaches 26 years of age, whichever comes first. Spouses and unremarried widow(er)s are not subject to the age limitation.

Number awarded Varies each year.

Deadline Deadline not specified.

[600]
KOREAN WAR VETERANS ASSOCIATION SCHOLARSHIPS

Korean War Veterans Association
Attn: Scholarship Coordinator
13730 Loumont Street
Whittier, CA 90601

Summary To provide financial assistance for college to descendants of Army veterans who served in Korea during or prior to the war there.

Eligibility This program is open to the children, grandchildren, and great-grandchildren of veterans who served on active duty in the U.S. Army in Korea between August 15, 1945 and December 31, 1955. Applicants must be attending or planning to attend an accredited college or university. Along with their application, they must submit an essay describing their educational and career goals, why they think they should receive this scholarship, and where they learned about it. Selection is based on academic achievement (GPA of 2.75 or higher), extracurricular activities, and financial need.

Financial data The stipend depends on the need of the recipient, to a maximum of $5,000 per year.

Duration 1 year; may be renewed up to 3 additional years or until completion of a bachelor's degree.

Number awarded Varies each year; recently, 5 of these scholarships were awarded.

Deadline April of each year.

[601]
LA FRA NATIONAL PRESIDENT'S SCHOLARSHIP

Ladies Auxiliary of the Fleet Reserve Association
Attn: Membership Service Administrator
P.O. Box 2086
Shingle Springs, CA 95682-2086
(530) 677-3925 E-mail: laframsa@att.net
Web: www.la-fra.org/scholarship.html

Summary To provide financial assistance for college to the children and grandchildren of naval personnel.

Eligibility Eligible to apply for these scholarships are the children and grandchildren of Navy, Marine, Coast Guard, active Fleet Reserve, Fleet Marine Corps Reserve, and Coast Guard Reserve personnel on active duty, retired with pay, or deceased while on active duty or retired with pay. Applicants must submit an essay on their life experiences, career objectives, and what motivated them to select those objectives. Selection is based on academic record, financial need, extracurricular activities, leadership skills, and participation in community activities. U.S. citizenship is required.

Financial data The stipend is $2,500.

Duration 1 year; may be renewed.

Number awarded 1 each year.

Deadline April of each year.

[602]
LA FRA SCHOLARSHIP

Ladies Auxiliary of the Fleet Reserve Association
Attn: Membership Service Administrator
P.O. Box 2086
Shingle Springs, CA 95682-2086
(530) 677-3925 E-mail: laframsa@att.net
Web: www.la-fra.org/scholarship.html

Summary To provide financial assistance for college to the daughters and granddaughters of naval personnel.

Eligibility Eligible to apply for these scholarships are the daughters and granddaughters of Navy, Marine, Coast Guard, active Fleet Reserve, Fleet Marine Corps Reserve, and Coast Guard Reserve personnel on active duty, retired with pay, or deceased while on active duty or retired with pay.

Applicants must submit an essay on their life experiences, career objectives, and what motivated them to select those objectives. Selection is based on academic record, financial need, extracurricular activities, leadership skills, and participation in community activities. U.S. citizenship is required.

Financial data   The stipend is $2,500.

Duration   1 year; may be renewed.

Number awarded   1 each year.

Deadline   April of each year.

[603]
LADIES AUXILIARY VFW CONTINUING EDUCATION SCHOLARSHIPS

Ladies Auxiliary to the Veterans of Foreign Wars
c/o National Headquarters
406 West 34th Street
Kansas City, MO 64111
(816) 561-8655   Fax: (816) 931-4753
E-mail: info@ladiesauxvfw.org
Web: www.ladiesauxvfw.org/programs/scholarships.html

Summary   To provide financial assistance for college to members of Ladies Auxiliary to the Veterans of Foreign Wars (VFW) and their families.

Eligibility   This program is open to members of the Ladies Auxiliary VFW and their children and spouses. Applicants must be 18 years of age or older and planning to work on a college degree or a career direction at a technical school. Along with their application, they must submit a 300-word essay describing their commitment to their goals and how this scholarship will help them attain those goals. The qualifying member must have belonged to the Auxiliary for at least 1 year prior to application. Financial need is considered in the selection process.

Financial data   The stipend is $1,000. Funds are paid directly to the college or vocational school.

Duration   1 year.

Number awarded   4 each year: 1 in each Ladies Auxiliary VFW Conference.

Deadline   February of each year.

[604]
LANGEA TONY LOPEZ SCHOLARSHIP

Louisiana National Guard Enlisted Association
c/o MSG Chad J. Anderson
Gillis Long Center
5445 Point Clair Road
Carville, LA 70721
(225) 319-4846   Fax: (225) 319-4880
E-mail: chad.j.anderson1@us.army.mil
Web: langea.org/templates/benefits/scholarship

Summary   To provide funding to members of the Louisiana National Guard Enlisted Association (LANGEA) and their dependents who plan to attend college in any state.

Eligibility   This program is open to members of the association, their spouses and unmarried dependent children, and the unremarried spouses and unmarried dependent children of deceased members who were in good standing at the time of their death. The qualifying LANGEA members must have at least 1 year remaining on their enlistment following completion of the school year for which the application is submitted or have served 20 years of more in the Louisiana National Guard. Applicants must be enrolled or planning to enroll full time at an accredited college, university, trade school, or business school in any state. Graduate students are not eligible. Selection is based on academic achievement, character, leadership, and financial need.

Financial data   The stipend is $2,000.

Duration   1 year; nonrenewable.

Number awarded   3 each year.

Deadline   February of each year.

[605]
LAURA BLACKBURN MEMORIAL SCHOLARSHIP

American Legion Auxiliary
Department of Kentucky
P.O. Box 5435
Frankfort, KY 40602-5435
(502) 352-2380   Fax: (502) 352-2381
Web: www.kyamlegionaux.org

Summary   To provide financial assistance to descendants of veterans in Kentucky who plan to attend college in any state.

Eligibility   This program is open to the children, grandchildren, and great-grandchildren of veterans who served in the armed forces during eligibility dates for membership in the American Legion. Applicants must be Kentucky residents enrolled in their senior year at an accredited high school. They must be planning to attend a college or university in any state. Selection is based on academic achievement (40%), character (20%), leadership (20%), and Americanism (20%).

Financial data   The stipend is $1,000.

Duration   1 year.

Number awarded   1 each year.

Deadline   March of each year.

[606]
LIEUTENANT GENERAL CLARENCE L. HUEBNER SCHOLARSHIPS

Society of the First Infantry Division
Attn: 1st Infantry Division Foundation
1933 Morris Road
Blue Bell, PA 19422-1422
Toll Free: (888) 324-4733   Fax: (215) 661-1934
E-mail: Fdn1ID@aol.com
Web: 1stid.org/foundation/scholarships.cfm

Summary   To provide financial support for college to the children or grandchildren of members of the First Infantry Division.

Eligibility   This program is open to high school seniors who are the children or grandchildren of soldiers who served in the First Infantry Division of the U.S. Army. Applicants must submit academic transcripts, letters of recommendation, and a 200-word essay on a major problem facing the country today and their recommendations for the solution of the problem. Selection is based on the essay, academic achievement, extracurricular activities, community service, and work experience.

Financial data   The stipend is $1,000 per year, payable to the recipient's school annually.

Duration   4 years.

Number awarded   Varies each year; recently, 3 of these scholarships were awarded.

Deadline   May of each year.

[607]
LILLIAN CAMPBELL MEDICAL SCHOLARSHIP

Wisconsin Veterans of Foreign Wars
P.O. Box 6128
Monona, WI 53716-0128
(608) 221-5276   Fax: (608) 221-5277
E-mail: wivfw@att.net
Web: vfwofwi.com/?w=wisconsin

Summary To provide financial assistance to students working on a degree in a medical field in Wisconsin who served in the military or are related to a person who did.

Eligibility This program is open to students who have completed at least 1 year of study in Wisconsin in a program in nursing, pharmacy, physician assistant, medical or surgical technology, physical or occupational therapy, dental assisting, radiology, or other related medical profession. Applicants or a member of their immediate family (parent, sibling, child, spouse, or grandparent) must have served in the military. They must have a high school diploma or GED but may be of any age. Along with their application, they must submit a 200-word essay on why they are studying this medical profession. Financial need is considered in the selection process.

Financial data The stipend is $1,000.

Duration 1 year.

Number awarded 1 or more each year.

Deadline April of each year.

[608]
LILLIE LOIS FORD SCHOLARSHIPS

American Legion
Department of Missouri
3341 American Avenue
P.O. Box 179
Jefferson City, MO 65102-0179
(573) 893-2353   Toll Free: (800) 846-9023
Fax: (573) 893-2980   E-mail: info@missourilegion.org
Web: www.missourilegion.org/default_016.htm

Summary To provide financial assistance for college to descendants of Missouri veterans who have participated in specified American Legion programs.

Eligibility This program is open to the unmarried children, grandchildren, and great-grandchildren under 21 years of age of honorably-discharged Missouri veterans who served at least 90 days on active duty. Applicants must be enrolled or planning to enroll at an accredited college or university in any state as a full-time student. Boys must have attended a complete session of Missouri Boys State or Cadet Patrol Academy. Girls must have attended a complete session of Missouri Girls State or Cadet Patrol Academy. Financial need is considered in the selection process.

Financial data The stipend is $1,000.

Duration 1 year (the first year of college).

Number awarded 2 each year: 1 for a boy and 1 for a girl.

Deadline April of each year.

[609]
LOUIS J. SCHOBER MEMORIAL SCHOLARSHIP

Society of American Military Engineers-Louisiana Post
c/o Anthony Goodgion, Education Committee Chair
Linfield, Hunter & Junius, Inc.
3608 18th Street, Suite 200
Metairie, LA 70002
(504) 833-5300   Fax: (504) 833-5350
E-mail: agoodgion@lhjunius.com
Web: posts.same.org/louisiana/YoungMembers.htm

Summary To provide financial assistance to engineering students at universities in Louisiana (particularly those with ties to the military) and to children of members of the Louisiana Post of the Society of American Military Engineers (SAME) at schools in any state.

Eligibility This program is open to students currently working on an undergraduate degree in engineering. Applicants must be either 1) enrolled at a college or university in Louisiana, or 2) the children of a member of the SAME Louisiana Post (who may be studying at a college or university in any state). Graduate students are not eligible; high school seniors may be considered if no suitable college students apply. Selection is based primarily on academic record and demonstration of leadership characteristics; other factors considered are participation in SAME posts and activities, enrollment in an ROTC program, former or current military service, and participation in school and community activities.

Financial data The stipend is $2,000.

Duration 1 year; nonrenewable.

Number awarded 1 or more each year.

Deadline May of each year.

[610]
LOUISIANA EDUCATIONAL BENEFITS FOR CHILDREN, SPOUSES, AND SURVIVING SPOUSES OF VETERANS

Louisiana Department of Veterans Affairs
Attn: Education Program
1885 Wooddale Boulevard, Room 1013
P.O. Box 94095, Capitol Station
Baton Rouge, LA 70804-9095
(225) 219-5000   Toll Free: (877) GEAUXVA
Fax: (225) 219-5590   E-mail: veteran@la.gov
Web: vetaffairs.la.gov/education

Summary To provide funding to children, spouses, and surviving spouses of certain disabled or deceased Louisiana veterans who plan to attend college in the state.

Eligibility This program is open to children (between 16 and 25 years of age), spouses, or surviving spouses of veterans who served during specified periods of wartime and 1) were killed in action or died in active service; 2) died of a service-connected disability; 3) are missing in action (MIA) or a prisoner of war (POW); 4) sustained a disability rated as 90% or more by the U.S. Department of Veterans Affairs; or 5) have been determined to be unemployable as a result of a service-connected disability. Deceased, MIA, and POW veterans must have resided in Louisiana for at least 12 months prior to entry into service. Living disabled veterans must have resided in Louisiana for at least 24 months prior to the child's or spouse's admission into the program.

Financial data Eligible persons accepted as full-time students at Louisiana state-supported colleges, universities, trade schools, or vocational/technical schools are admitted free and are exempt from payment of tuition, laboratory, athletic, medical, and other special fees. Free registration does not cover books, supplies, room and board, or fees assessed by the student body on themselves (such as yearbooks and weekly papers).

Duration Support is provided for a maximum of 4 school years, to be completed in not more than 5 years from date of original entry.

Additional information Attendance must be on a full-time basis. Surviving spouses must remain unremarried and must take advantage of the benefit within 10 years after eligibility is established.

Number awarded Varies each year.

Deadline Applications must be received no later than 3 months prior to the beginning of a semester.

[611]
LT. COL. ROMEO AND JOSEPHINE BASS FERRETTI SCHOLARSHIP

Air Force Association
Attn: Manager, National Aerospace Awards
1501 Lee Highway
Arlington, VA 22209-1198
(703) 247-5800, ext. 4807
Toll Free: (800) 727-3337, ext. 4807
Fax: (703) 247-5853   E-mail: lcross@afa.org
Web: www.afa.org/aef/aid/Ferretti.asp

Summary To provide financial assistance to dependents of Air Force enlisted personnel who are high school seniors planning to attend college to major in a field of science, technology, engineering, or mathematics (STEM).

Eligibility This program is open to dependents of Air Force active duty, Reserve, or Air National Guard enlisted personnel who are graduating high school seniors. Applicants must be planning to enroll full time at an accredited institute of higher education to work on an undergraduate degree in any area of STEM. Selection is based on academic achievement, character, and financial need.

Financial data The stipend is $2,500.

Duration 1 year; nonrenewable.

Number awarded Varies each year; recently, 4 of these scholarships were awarded.

Deadline June of each year.

[612]
LT. MICHAEL L. LEWIS, JR. MEMORIAL FUND

Sons of the American Legion
Detachment of New York
112 State Street, Suite 1300
Albany, NY 12207
(518) 463-2215   Fax: (518) 427-8443
E-mail: info@nylegion.org
Web: www.sonsdny.org

Summary To provide financial assistance to high school seniors and graduates in New York who are members of the Sons of the American Legion and plan to attend college in any state.

Eligibility This program is open to members of the Sons of the American Legion in New York. Applicants must be high school seniors or graduates and planning to attend college or trade school in any state. Along with their application, they must submit a 200-word essay either on why a college education is important to them or why they want to continue their postsecondary education in a business trade school. Selection is based on academics (25%), character (25%), leadership (25%), and Americanism (25%).

Financial data The stipend is $1,000.

Duration 1 year.

Number awarded 2 each year.

Deadline April of each year.

[613]
LTG AND MRS. JOSEPH M. HEISER SCHOLARSHIP

U.S. Army Ordnance Corps Association
Attn: Heiser Scholarship
P.O. Box 377
Aberdeen Proving Ground, MD 21005-0377
(410) 272-8540   Fax: (410) 272-8425
Web: www.usaocaweb.org/scholarships.htm

Summary To provide money for college to soldiers serving in the U.S. Army Ordnance Corps and members of the U.S. Army Ordnance Corps Association (OCA) and their families.

Eligibility This program is open to Ordnance soldiers (active and reserve), OCA members, and immediate family of OCA members. Applicants must be entering or attending a college or university to work on an associate or baccalaureate degree. Along with their application, they must submit 1) an essay of 1,000 to 1,500 words on the missions, heritage, or history of the U.S. Army Ordnance Corps; and 2) an essay of 300 to 500 words on their educational and career goals. Selection is based on the essays, scholastic aptitude, and grades.

Financial data The stipend is $1,000.

Duration 1 year.

Number awarded Varies each year; recently, 9 of these scholarships were awarded.

Deadline June of each year.

[614]
MADELINE PICKETT (HALBERT) COGSWELL NURSING SCHOLARSHIP

Daughters of the American Revolution-National Society
Attn: Committee Services Office, Scholarships
1776 D Street, N.W.
Washington, DC 20006-5303
(202) 628-1776
Web: www.dar.org/natsociety/edout_scholar.cfm

Summary To provide financial assistance for nursing education to active members of the Daughters of the American Revolution (DAR) and their descendants.

Eligibility This program is open to undergraduate students currently enrolled at accredited schools of nursing who are members, eligible for membership, or descendants of a member of DAR. Applicants must have completed at least 1 year of nursing school. They must be sponsored by a local chapter of DAR. Selection is based on academic excellence, commitment to field of study, and financial need. U.S. citizenship is required.

Financial data The stipend is $1,000.

Duration 1 year; nonrenewable.

Number awarded Varies each year.

Deadline February of each year.

[615]
MAINE VETERANS DEPENDENTS EDUCATIONAL BENEFITS

Bureau of Veterans' Services
117 State House Station
Augusta, ME 04333-0117
(207) 430-6035   Toll Free: (800) 345-0116 (within ME)
Fax: (207) 626-4471   E-mail: mainebvs@maine.gov
Web: www.maine.gov/dvem/bvs/educational_benefits.htm

Summary To provide financial assistance for undergraduate or graduate education to dependents of disabled and other Maine veterans.

Eligibility Applicants for these benefits must be children (high school seniors or graduates under 22 years of age), non-divorced spouses, or unremarried widow(er)s of veterans who meet 1 or more of the following requirements: 1) living and determined to have a total permanent disability resulting from a service-connected cause; 2) killed in action; 3) died from a service-connected disability; 4) died while totally and permanently disabled due to a service-connected disability but whose death was not related to the service-connected disability; or 5) a member of the armed forces on active duty who has been listed for more than 90 days as missing in action, captured, forcibly detained, or interned in the line of duty by a foreign government or power. The veteran parent must have been a resident of Maine at the time of entry into service or a resident of Maine for 5 years preceding application for these benefits. Children may be working on an associate or bachelor's degree. Spouses, widows, and widowers may work on an associate, bachelor's, or master's degree.

Financial data Recipients are entitled to free tuition at institutions of higher education supported by the state of Maine.

Duration Children may receive up to 8 semesters of support; they have 6 years from the date of first entrance to complete those 8 semesters. Continuation in the program is based on their earning a GPA of 2.0 or higher each semester. Spouses are entitled to receive up to 120 credit hours of educational benefits and have 10 years from the date of first entrance to complete their program.

Additional information College preparatory schooling and correspondence courses are not supported under this program.

Number awarded Varies each year.

Deadline Deadline not specified.

[616]
MAINE VIETNAM VETERANS SCHOLARSHIP FUND

Maine Community Foundation
Attn: Program Director
245 Main Street
Ellsworth, ME 04605
(207) 667-9735   Toll Free: (877) 700-6800
Fax: (207) 667-0447   E-mail: info@mainecf.org
Web: www.mainecf.org/statewidescholars.aspx

Summary To provide financial assistance for college or graduate school to Vietnam veterans or the dependents of Vietnam or other veterans in Maine.

Eligibility This program is open to residents of Maine who are Vietnam veterans or the descendants of veterans who served in the Vietnam Theater. As a second priority, children

of veterans from other time periods are also considered. Graduating high school seniors, nontraditional students, undergraduates, and graduate students are eligible to apply. Selection is based on financial need, extracurricular activities, work experience, academic achievement, and a personal statement of career goals and how the applicant's educational plans relate to them.

Financial data The stipend is $1,000 per year.

Duration 1 year.

Additional information This program began in 1985. There is a $3 processing fee.

Number awarded 3 to 6 each year.

Deadline April of each year.

[617]
MAJOR GENERAL DUANE L. "DUKE" CORNING MEMORIAL SCHOLARSHIP

South Dakota National Guard Enlisted Association
c/o Jody Smith
2823 West Main Street
Rapid City, SD 57702-8170
(605) 737-6224   E-mail: jody.smith2@us.army.mil
Web: www.sdngea.com/scholarship.html

Summary To provide financial assistance to current and retired members of the South Dakota National Guard Enlisted Association (SDNGEA), the National Guard Association of South Dakota (NGASD), and their dependents who are interested in attending college in any state.

Eligibility This program is open to current and retired members of the SDNGEA and the NGASD and the dependents of current and retired members of those associations. Applicants must be graduating high school seniors or full-time undergraduate students at a college or university in any state. They must submit a 300-page autobiography that includes their experiences to date and their hopes and plans for the future. Selection is based on the essay; awards, honors, and offices in high school, college, or trade school; GPA and ACT/SAT scores; letters of recommendation; and extracurricular and community activities and honors.

Financial data The stipend is $1,000.

Duration 1 year; nonrenewable.

Number awarded 1 each year.

Deadline March of each year.

[618]
MARIA C. JACKSON/GENERAL GEORGE A. WHITE SCHOLARSHIP

Oregon Student Access Commission
Attn: Grants and Scholarships Division
1500 Valley River Drive, Suite 100
Eugene, OR 97401-2146
(541) 687-7395   Toll Free: (800) 452-8807, ext. 7395
Fax: (541) 687-7414   TDD: (800) 735-2900
E-mail: awardinfo@osac.state.or.us
Web: www.oregonstudentaid.gov/scholarships.aspx

Summary To provide financial assistance to veterans and children of veterans and military personnel in Oregon who are interested in attending college or graduate school in the state.

Eligibility This program is open to residents of Oregon who served, or whose parents are serving or have served, in the U.S. armed forces. Applicants or their parents must have resided in Oregon at the time of enlistment. They must be enrolled or planning to enroll at a college or graduate school in the state. College and university undergraduates must have a GPA of 3.75 or higher, but there is no minimum GPA requirement for graduate students or those attending a technical school. Selection is based on academics and need.

Financial data Stipends for scholarships offered by the Oregon Student Access Commission (OSAC) range from $200 to $10,000 but recently averaged $2,300.

Number awarded Varies each year.

Deadline February of each year.

[619]
MARINE CORPS COUNTERINTELLIGENCE ASSOCIATION SCHOLARSHIPS

Marine Corps Counterintelligence Association
c/o Samuel L. Moyer, Scholarship Committee Chair
315 Palmdale Drive
Oldsmar, FL 34677
E-mail: oldjarhd@aol.com
Web: www.mccia.org

Summary To provide financial assistance for college to dependents of members of the Marine Corps Counterintelligence Association (MCCIA).

Eligibility This program is open to children, grandchildren, and spouses of 1) current MCCIA members; 2) deceased Marines who were MCCIA members at the time of death; and 3) counterintelligence Marines who lost their lives in the line of duty (whether they were a member of MCCIA or not). Spouses of deceased Marines must also be MCCIA Auxiliary members. Applicants must be enrolled or planning to enroll as a full-time undergraduate student at an accredited college or university and have a GPA of 3.0 or higher. Along with their application, they must submit a 1-page essay on a topic of their choice, letters of recommendation, SAT or ACT scores, transcripts, copies of awards and other honors, and evidence of acceptance at a college or university. Financial need is not considered.

Financial data Stipends range from $250 to $1,000. Funds must be used to help pay for tuition, books, fees, and materials; they may not be used for personal or living expenses.

Duration 1 year; may be renewed up to 4 additional years (need not be consecutive).

Number awarded Varies each year; recently, 7 of these scholarships, at $1,000 each, were awarded.

Deadline June of each year.

[620]
MARINE CORPS LEAGUE SCHOLARSHIPS

Marine Corps League
Attn: National Executive Director
P.O. Box 3070
Merrifield, VA 22116-3070
(703) 207-9588   Toll Free: (800) MCL-1775
Fax: (703) 207-0047   E-mail: mcl@mcleague.org
Web: www.mcleague.org

Summary To provide college aid to students whose parents served in the Marines and to members of the Marine Corps League or Marine Corps League Auxiliary.

Eligibility This program is open to 1) children of Marines who lost their lives in the line of duty; 2) spouses, children, grandchildren, great-grandchildren, and stepchildren of

active Marine Corps League and/or Auxiliary members; and 3) members of the Marine Corps League and/or Marine Corps League Auxiliary who are honorably discharged and in need of rehabilitation training not provided by government programs. Applicants must be seeking further education and training as a full-time student and be recommended by the commandant of an active chartered detachment of the Marine Corps League or the president of an active chartered unit of the Auxiliary. Financial need is not considered.

Financial data A stipend is awarded (amount not specified). Funds are paid directly to the recipient.

Duration 1 year; may be renewed up to 3 additional years (all renewals must complete an application and attach a transcript from the college or university).

Number awarded Varies, depending upon the amount of funds available each year.

Deadline June of each year.

[621]
MARINE CORPS SCHOLARSHIPS

Marine Corps Scholarship Foundation, Inc.
Attn: Scholarship Office
909 North Washington Street, Suite 400
Alexandria, VA 22314
(703) 549-0060   Toll Free: (866) 496-5462
Fax: (703) 549-9474   E-mail: students@mcsf.org
Web: www.mcsf.org

Summary To provide money for college to the children of present or former members of the U.S. Marine Corps.

Eligibility This program is open to the children of 1) Marines on active duty or in the Reserves who have served at least 90 days; 2) veteran Marines who have received an honorable discharge, received a medical discharge, were wounded, or were killed while serving in the U.S. Marines; 3) active-duty or Reserve U.S. Navy Corpsmen who are serving or have served with a U.S. Marine unit; and 4) U.S. Navy Corpsmen who have served with a U.S. Marine unit, have received an honorable discharge or medical discharge, were wounded, or were killed while serving in the U.S. Navy. Applicants must be high school seniors, high school graduates, or current undergraduates in an accredited college, university, or postsecondary vocational/technical school. They must submit academic transcripts (GPA of 2.0 or higher); a written statement of service from their parent's commanding officer or a copy of their parent's honorable discharge; and a 500-word essay on a topic that changes periodically. Only undergraduate study is supported. The family income of applicants must be less than $90,000 per year.

Financial data Stipends range from $1,500 to $10,000 per year.

Duration 1 year; may be renewed upon reapplication.

Number awarded Varies each year; recently, 1,636 of these scholarships were awarded.

Deadline February of each year.

[622]
MARINE GUNNERY SERGEANT JOHN DAVID FRY SCHOLARSHIP

Department of Veterans Affairs
Attn: Veterans Benefits Administration
810 Vermont Avenue, N.W.
Washington, DC 20420
(202) 418-4343   Toll Free: (888) GI-BILL1
Web: www.gibill.va.gov

Summary To provide financial assistance to children of military personnel who died in the line of duty on or after September 11, 2001.

Eligibility This program is open to the children of active-duty members of the Armed Forces who have died in the line of duty on or after September 11, 2001. Applicants must be planning to enroll as undergraduates at a college or university. They must be at least 18 years of age, even if they have completed high school.

Financial data Eligible students receive full payment of tuition and fees at public schools in their state of residence. For students attending a private or foreign university, the maximum payment for tuition and fees in most states is $17,500; students at private institutions in Arizona, Michigan, New Hampshire, New York, Pennsylvania, South Carolina, and Texas may be eligible for a higher tuition reimbursement rate. A monthly living stipend based on the military housing allowance for the zip code where the school is located and an annual book and supplies allowance of $1,000 are also provided.

Duration Participants receive up to 36 months of entitlement. They have 15 years in which to utilize the benefit.

Additional information This program began in 2009 as a component of the Post-9/11 GI Bill.

Number awarded Varies each year.

Deadline Deadline not specified.

[623]
MARINES' MEMORIAL ASSOCIATION SCHOLARSHIP FUND

Marines' Memorial Association
c/o Marines Memorial Club and Hotel
609 Sutter Street
San Francisco, CA 94102
(415) 673-6672   Fax: (415) 441-3649
E-mail: member@marineclub.com
Web: www.marineclub.com/membership/scholarship.php

Summary To provide money for college to members of the Marines' Memorial Association and their descendants.

Eligibility This program is open to active members of the association and their children and grandchildren. Applicants must be enrolled or planning to enroll in an undergraduate degree program at a college or university. Selection is based on academic merit, activities, and financial need.

Financial data Stipends are $5,000 or $2,500.

Duration 1 year.

Additional information Membership in the association is open to veterans of the Marines, Army, Navy, Air Force, or Coast Guard and to personnel currently serving in a branch of the armed forces. This program includes a number of named scholarships, including the Colonel Jack Barnes Scholarship, the Colonel Richard Hallock Scholarship, the Sergeants Henry and Jeanne Rose Scholarship, and the Evelyn Bukovac Hamilton Health Care Scholarship.

Number awarded 10 at $5,000 and 12 at $2,500.

Deadline April of each year.

[624]
MARION J. BAGLEY SCHOLARSHIP

American Legion Auxiliary
Department of New Hampshire
State House Annex
25 Capitol Street, Room 432
Concord, NH 03301-6312
(603) 271-2212   Toll Free: (800) 778-3816
Fax: (603) 271-5352
E-mail: nhalasec@amlegion.state.nh.us
Web: www.nhlegion.org

Summary To provide financial assistance to members of the American Legion Auxiliary and other New Hampshire residents who plan to attend college in any state.

Eligibility This program is open to New Hampshire residents and to members of a unit of the American Legion Auxiliary, Department of New Hampshire, who have been members for at least 3 consecutive years. Applicants must be graduating high school seniors, graduates of a high school or equivalent, or students currently attending an institution of higher learning in any state. Along with their application, they must submit 3 letters of recommendation; a list of school, church, and community activities or organizations in which they have participated; transcripts; and a 1,000-word essay on "My Obligations as an American." Financial need is considered in the selection process.

Financial data The stipend is $1,000.

Duration 1 year.

Number awarded 1 each year.

Deadline April of each year.

[625]
MARY BARRETT MARSHALL SCHOLARSHIP

American Legion Auxiliary
Department of Kentucky
P.O. Box 5435
Frankfort, KY 40602-5435
(502) 352-2380   Fax: (502) 352-2381
Web: www.kyamlegionaux.org

Summary To provide funding to female dependents of veterans in Kentucky who plan to attend college in the state.

Eligibility This program is open to the daughters, wives, sisters, widows, granddaughters, or great-granddaughters of veterans eligible for membership in the American Legion who are high school seniors or graduates and 5-year residents of Kentucky. Applicants must be planning to attend a college or university in Kentucky.

Financial data The stipend is $1,000. The funds may be used for tuition, registration fees, laboratory fees, and books, but not for room and board.

Duration 1 year.

Number awarded 1 each year.

Deadline March of each year.

[626]
MARY PAOLOZZI MEMBER'S SCHOLARSHIP

Navy Wives Clubs of America
c/o NSA Mid-South
P.O. Box 54022
Millington, TN 38054-0022
Toll Free: (866) 511-NWCA
E-mail: nwca@navywivesclubsofamerica.org
Web: www.navywivesclubsofamerica.org/scholarships

Summary To provide financial assistance for undergraduate or graduate study to members of the Navy Wives Clubs of America (NWCA).

Eligibility This program is open to NWCA members who can demonstrate financial need. Applicants must be 1) a high school graduate or senior planning to attend college full time next year; 2) currently enrolled in an undergraduate program and planning to continue as a full-time undergraduate; 3) a college graduate or senior planning to be a full-time graduate student next year; or 4) a high school graduate or GED recipient planning to attend vocational or business school next year. Along with their application, they must submit a brief statement on why they feel they should be awarded this scholarship and any special circumstances (financial or other) they wish to have considered. Financial need is also considered in the selection process.

Financial data Stipends range from $500 to $1,000 each year (depending upon the donations from the NWCA chapters).

Duration 1 year.

Additional information Membership in the NWCA is open to spouses of enlisted personnel serving in the Navy, Marine Corps, Coast Guard, and the active Reserve units of those services; spouses of enlisted personnel who have been honorably discharged, retired, or transferred to the Fleet Reserve on completion of duty; and widows of enlisted personnel in those services.

Number awarded 1 or more each year.

Deadline May of each year.

[627]
MARY ROWENA COOPER SCHOLARSHIP

Winston-Salem Foundation
Attn: Student Aid Department
860 West Fifth Street
Winston-Salem, NC 27101-2506
(336) 714-3445   Toll Free: (866) 227-1209
Fax: (336) 727-0581
E-mail: StudentAid@wsfoundation.org
Web: www.wsfoundation.org

Summary To provide financial assistance for college to children of veterans who served in Vietnam.

Eligibility This program is open to students currently enrolled at least half time at an accredited 2- or 4-year college, university, or vocational/technical school. Applicants must be the child of a living or deceased veteran who served in Vietnam. They must have a GPA of 2.0 or higher and have a family income less than 300% above the federal poverty guidelines. U.S. citizenship is required.

Financial data A stipend is awarded (amount not specified).

Duration 1 year; nonrenewable.

Additional information This program began in 1998. There is a $20 application fee (waived if the applicant is unable to pay).

Number awarded 1 or more each year.

Deadline August of each year.

[628]
MARYANN K. MURTHA MEMORIAL SCHOLARSHIP

American Legion Auxiliary
Department of New York
112 State Street, Suite 1310
Albany, NY 12207
(518) 463-1162   Toll Free: (800) 421-6348
Fax: (518) 449-5406   E-mail: alanyterry@nycap.rr.com
Web: www.deptny.org/Scholarships.htm

Summary To provide financial assistance to New York residents who are the descendants of veterans and interested in attending college in any state.

Eligibility This program is open to residents of New York who are high school seniors or graduates and attending or planning to attend an accredited college or university in any state. Applicants must be the children, grandchildren, or great-grandchildren of veterans who served during specified periods of wartime. Along with their application, they must submit a 700-word article describing their plans and goals for the future and how they hope to use their talent and education to help others. Selection is based on character (20%), Americanism (15%), community involvement (15%), leadership (15%), scholarship (20%), and financial need (15%). U.S. citizenship is required.

Financial data The stipend is $1,000. Funds are paid directly to the recipient's school.

Duration 1 year.

Number awarded 1 each year.

Deadline February of each year.

[629]
MARYLAND LEGION AUXILIARY CHILDREN AND YOUTH FUND SCHOLARSHIP

American Legion Auxiliary
Department of Maryland
1589 Sulphur Spring Road, Suite 105
Baltimore, MD 21227
(410) 242-9519   Fax: (410) 242-9553
E-mail: hq@alamd.org
Web: www.alamd.org/Home/Scholarships.html

Summary To provide financial assistance for college to the daughters of veterans who are Maryland residents and wish to study designated fields at a school in the state.

Eligibility This program is open to Maryland senior high school girls with a veteran parent who wish to study arts, sciences, business, public administration, education, or a medical field other than nursing at a college or university in the state. Preference is given to children of members of the American Legion or American Legion Auxiliary. Selection is based on character (30%), Americanism (20%), leadership (10%), scholarship (20%), and financial need (20%).

Financial data The stipend is $2,000.

Duration 1 year; may be renewed up to 3 additional years.

Number awarded 1 each year.

Deadline April of each year.

[630]
MARYLAND LEGION AUXILIARY PAST PRESIDENTS' PARLEY NURSING SCHOLARSHIP

American Legion Auxiliary
Department of Maryland
1589 Sulphur Spring Road, Suite 105
Baltimore, MD 21227
(410) 242-9519   Fax: (410) 242-9553
E-mail: hq@alamd.org
Web: www.alamd.org/Home/Scholarships.html

Summary To provide financial assistance to the female descendants of Maryland veterans who wish to study nursing at a school in any state.

Eligibility This program is open to Maryland residents who are the daughters, granddaughters, great-granddaughters, step-daughters, step-granddaughters, or step-great-grand-daughters of ex-servicewomen (or of ex-servicemen, if there are no qualified descendants of ex-servicewomen). Applicants must be interested in attending a school in any state to become a registered nurse and be able to show financial need. They must submit a 300-word essay on the topic "What a Nursing Career Means to Me."

Financial data The stipend is $2,000. Funds are sent directly to the recipient's school.

Duration 1 year; may be renewed for up to 3 additional years if the recipient remains enrolled full time.

Number awarded 1 each year.

Deadline April of each year.

[631]
MARYLAND SCHOLARSHIPS FOR VETERANS OF THE AFGHANISTAN AND IRAQ CONFLICTS

Maryland Higher Education Commission
Attn: Office of Student Financial Assistance
6 North Liberty Street, Ground Suite
Baltimore, MD 21201
(410) 767-3300   Toll Free: (800) 974-0203
Fax: (410) 332-0250   TDD: (800) 735-2258
E-mail: osfamail@mhec.state.md.us
Web: www.mhec.state.md.us/financialAid/descriptions.asp

Summary To provide financial assistance for college to residents of Maryland who have served in the armed forces in Afghanistan or Iraq and their children and spouses.

Eligibility This program is open to Maryland residents who are 1) a veteran who served at least 60 days in Afghanistan on or after October 24, 2001 or in Iraq on or after March 19, 2003; 2) an active-duty member of the armed forces who served at least 60 days in Afghanistan or Iraq on or after those dates; 3) a member of a Reserve component of the armed forces or the Maryland National Guard who was activated as a result of the Afghanistan or Iraq conflicts and served at least 60 days; and 4) the children and spouses of such veterans, active-duty armed forces personnel, or members of Reserve forces or Maryland National Guard. Applicants must be enrolled or accepted for enrollment in a regular undergraduate program at an eligible Maryland institution. In the selection process, veterans are given priority over dependent children and spouses.

Financial data The stipend is equal to 50% of the annual tuition, mandatory fees, and room and board of a resident undergraduate at a 4-year public institution within the University System of Maryland, currently capped at $9,430 per year.

The total amount of all state awards may not exceed the cost of attendance as determined by the school's financial aid office or $19,000, whichever is less.

Duration 1 year; may be renewed for an additional 4 years of full-time study or 7 years of part-time study, provided the recipient remains enrolled in an eligible program with a GPA of 2.5 or higher.

Additional information This program is scheduled to expire in 2016.

Number awarded Varies each year.

Deadline February of each year.

[632]
MASSACHUSETTS LEGION DEPARTMENT GENERAL SCHOLARSHIPS

American Legion
Department of Massachusetts
State House
24 Beacon Street, Suite 546-2
Boston, MA 02133-1044
(617) 727-2966   Fax: (617) 727-2969
E-mail: masslegion@verizon.net
Web: www.masslegion.org

Summary To provide financial assistance to the children and grandchildren of members of the American Legion in Massachusetts who are entering college in any state.

Eligibility This program is open to the children and grandchildren of members in good standing in the American Legion's Department of Massachusetts (or who were members in good standing at the time of death). Applicants must be entering their freshman year at a college or university in any state. Along with their application, they must submit a 100-word essay on their long-range goal and why they want to go to college. Financial need is considered in the selection process.

Financial data Stipends are $1,000 or $500.

Duration 1 year.

Additional information The $1,000 scholarships are designated as follows: the Frank R. Kelley Scholarship, the Robert (Sam) Murphy Scholarship, the H.P. Redden Scholarship, the Mayer/Murphy/Nee Scholarship, the Legionnaire Scholarship, the Past Department Commanders Scholarship, the Daniel J. Doherty Scholarship PNC, the John P. "Jake" Comer Scholarship PNC, and the Grace Fuller Olson Scholarship.

Number awarded 19 each year: 9 at $1,000 and 10 at $500.

Deadline March of each year.

[633]
MASSACHUSETTS PUBLIC SERVICE GRANT PROGRAM

Massachusetts Office of Student Financial Assistance
454 Broadway, Suite 200
Revere, MA 02151
(617) 391-6070   Fax: (617) 727-0667
E-mail: osfa@osfa.mass.edu
Web: www.osfa.mass.edu

Summary To provide financial assistance for college to children or widow(er)s of deceased public service officers and others (including selected veterans) in Massachusetts.

Eligibility This program is open to Massachusetts residents who are enrolled or planning to enroll full time at a college or university in the state. Applicants must be 1) the children or spouses of fire fighters, police officers, or corrections officers who were killed or died from injuries incurred in the line of duty; 2) children of prisoners of war or military service personnel missing in action in southeast Asia whose wartime service was credited to Massachusetts and whose service was between February 1, 1955 and the termination of the Vietnam campaign; or 3) children of veterans whose service was credited to Massachusetts and who were killed in action or died as a result of their service. U.S. citizenship or permanent resident status is required. This is an entitlement program; support is provided to all qualifying students, regardless of their academic achievement or financial need.

Financial data Scholarships provide up to the cost of tuition at a state-supported college or university in Massachusetts; if the recipient attends a private Massachusetts college or university, the scholarship is equivalent to tuition at a public institution, up to $2,500.

Duration 1 year; renewable.

Number awarded Varies each year.

Deadline April of each year.

[634]
MASSACHUSETTS SOLDIERS LEGACY FUND SCHOLARSHIPS

Massachusetts Soldiers Legacy Fund
P.O. Box 962061
Milk Street Post Office
Boston, MA 02196
Toll Free: (866) 856-5533   E-mail: info@mslfund.org
Web: www.mslfund.org

Summary To provide financial assistance for college or professional school to the children of service members from Massachusetts who were killed in Afghanistan or Iraq.

Eligibility This program is open to children of members of the U.S. armed forces who died while deployed on operations Enduring Freedom or Iraqi Freedom. The parent's home of record must have been Massachusetts. Applicants must be enrolled or planning to enroll at a 2- or 4-year college or university, professional school, or trade school in any state. All qualified children receive this assistance; there is no selection process.

Financial data The stipend is $10,000 per year.

Duration 1 year; may be renewed up to 3 additional years.

Additional information This program began in 2004.

Number awarded Varies each year.

Deadline Deadline not specified.

[635]
MCIA/JOHN J. GUENTHER MERIT SCHOLARSHIP

Marine Corps Intelligence Association, Inc.
Attn: Marine Corps Intelligence Educational Foundation
P.O. Box 1028
Quantico, VA 22134-1028
E-mail: scholarship@mcia-inc.org
Web: www.mcia-inc.org/7.html

Summary To provide financial assistance for college to members of the Marine Corps Intelligence Association (MCIA) and their dependent children.

Eligibility This program is open to current MCIA members, their dependent children, and their survivors. Applicants must be attending or planning to attend an accredited 4-year col-

lege or university as a full-time student. They must submit a 300-word essay on a risk that has led to a significant change in their personal or intellectual life, the most challenging obstacles they have had to overcome and what they learned from the experience, and where they envision themselves in 10 years. Selection is based on the essay, academic achievement, extracurricular activities, and work experience. Financial need is not considered.

Financial data The stipend is $2,000.

Duration 1 year.

Additional information Membership in the MCIA is open to Marine Corps intelligence personnel, including active duty, Reserve, and retired.

Number awarded At least 1 each year.

Deadline July of each year.

[636]
MG JAMES URSANO SCHOLARSHIP FUND

Army Emergency Relief
200 Stovall Street
Alexandria, VA 22332-0600
(703) 428-0000   Toll Free: (866) 878-6378
Fax: (703) 325-7183   E-mail: ursano@aerhq.org
Web: www.aerhq.org

Summary To provide financial assistance for college to the dependent children of Army personnel.

Eligibility This program is open to dependent unmarried children under 23 years of age (including stepchildren and legally adopted children) of soldiers on active duty, retired, or deceased while on active duty or after retirement. Applicants must be working or planning to work full time on a 4-year degree at an accredited college or university. They must have a GPA of 2.0 or higher. Selection is based primarily on financial need, but academic achievements and individual accomplishments are also considered.

Financial data The amount varies, depending on the needs of the recipient, but ranges from $1,000 to $5,200 per academic year. Recently, awards averaged more than $3,000.

Duration 1 year; renewable for up to 3 additional years, if the recipient maintains a GPA of 2.0 or higher.

Additional information Army Emergency Relief is a private nonprofit organization dedicated to "helping the Army take care of its own." Its primary mission is to provide financial assistance to Army people and their dependents in time of valid emergency need; its educational program was established as a secondary mission to meet a need of Army people for their dependents to pursue vocational training, preparation for acceptance by service academies, or an undergraduate education. It established this program in 1976.

Number awarded Varies; recently, 3,310 of these scholarships, with a value of $9,961,826, were awarded.

Deadline March of each year.

[637]
MICA SCHOLARSHIPS

Military Intelligence Corps Association
Attn: Scholarship Committee
P.O. Box 13020
Fort Huachuca, AZ 85670-3020
(520) 227-3894   E-mail: execdir@micorps.org
Web: www.micastore.com/Scholarships.html

Summary To provide financial assistance for college to members of the Military Intelligence Corps Association (MICA) and their immediate family.

Eligibility This program is open to active-duty, Reserve, National Guard, and retired military intelligence soldiers who are MICA members and to their immediate family (spouses, children, or other relatives living with and supported by the MICA member). Applicants must be attending or accepted for attendance at an accredited college, university, vocational school, or technical institution. Along with their application, they must submit a 1-page essay on their reasons for applying for the scholarship, including their educational plans, ambitions, goals, and personal attributes or experiences they feel will enable them to reach their goals. Financial need is not considered in the selection process.

Financial data Stipend amounts vary depending on the availability of funds and the number of qualified applicants, but recently were $5,000. Funds are to be used for tuition, books, and classroom fees; support is not provided for housing, board, travel, or administrative purposes.

Duration 1 year; recipients may reapply.

Number awarded Varies each year; recently, 4 of these scholarships were awarded.

Deadline May of each year.

[638]
MICHIGAN CHILDREN OF VETERANS TUITION GRANTS

Michigan Department of Treasury
Michigan Higher Education Assistance Authority
Attn: Office of Scholarships and Grants
P.O. Box 30462
Lansing, MI 48909-7962
(517) 373-0457   Toll Free: (888) 4-GRANTS
Fax: (517) 241-5835   E-mail: osg@michigan.gov
Web: www.michigan.gov/mistudentaid

Summary To provide financial assistance for college to the children of Michigan veterans who are totally disabled or deceased as a result of service-connected causes.

Eligibility This program is open to natural and adopted children of veterans who have been totally and permanently disabled as a result of a service-connected illness or injury prior to death and have now died, have died or become totally and permanently disabled as a result of a service-connected illness or injury, have been killed in action or died from another cause while serving in a war or war condition, or are listed as missing in action in a foreign country. The veteran must have been a legal resident of Michigan immediately before entering military service and did not reside outside of Michigan for more than 2 years, or must have established legal residency in Michigan after entering military service. Applicants must be between 16 and 26 years of age and must have lived in Michigan at least 12 months prior to the date of application. They must be enrolled or planning to enroll at least half time at a community college, public university, or independent degree-granting college or university in Michigan. U.S. citizenship or permanent resident status is required.

Financial data Recipients are exempt from payment of the first $2,800 per year of tuition or any other fee that takes the place of tuition.

Duration 1 year; may be renewed for up to 3 additional years if the recipient maintains full-time enrollment and a GPA of 2.25 or higher.

Additional information This program was formerly known as the Michigan Veterans Trust Fund Tuition Grants, administered by the Michigan Veterans Trust Fund within the Department of Military and Veterans Affairs. It was transferred to the Office of Scholarships and Grants in 2006.

Number awarded Varies each year; recently, 400 of these grants were awarded.

Deadline Deadline not specified.

[639]
MICHIGAN LEGION AUXILIARY NATIONAL PRESIDENT'S SCHOLARSHIP

American Legion Auxiliary
Department of Michigan
212 North Verlinden Avenue, Suite B
Lansing, MI 48915
(517) 267-8809   Fax: (517) 371-3698
E-mail: info@michalaux.org
Web: www.michalaux.org

Summary To provide financial assistance to children of veterans in Michigan who plan to attend college in any state.

Eligibility This program is open to Michigan residents who are the children of veterans who served during designated periods of wartime. Applicants must be in their senior year or graduates of an accredited high school and may not yet have attended an institution of higher learning. They must have completed 50 hours of community service during their high school years. Selection is based on scholarship, character, leadership, Americanism, and financial need. The winner competes for the American Legion National President's Scholarship. If the Michigan winners are not awarded the national scholarship, then they receive this departmental scholarship.

Financial data The stipend ranges from $1,000 to $2,500.

Duration 1 year.

Number awarded 1 each year.

Deadline February of each year.

[640]
MIKE NASH MEMORIAL SCHOLARSHIP FUND

Vietnam Veterans of America
Attn: Mike Nash Scholarship Program
8719 Colesville Road, Suite 100
Silver Spring, MD 20910-3919
(301) 585-4000   Toll Free: (800) VVA-1316
Fax: (301) 585-0519   E-mail: finance@vva.org
Web: www.vva.org/scholarship.html

Summary To provide financial assistance for college to members of Vietnam Veterans of America (VVA), their families, and the families of other Vietnam veterans.

Eligibility This program is open to 1) members of VVA; 2) the spouses, children, stepchildren, and grandchildren of VVA members; and 3) the spouses, children, stepchildren, and grandchildren of MIA, KIA, or deceased Vietnam veterans. Applicants must be enrolled or planning to enroll at least half time at an accredited college, university, or technical institution. Along with their application, they must submit high school or college transcripts; SAT, ACT, or other recognized test scores; a statement of current educational goals and objectives; a 500-word essay on "What a Veteran Means to Me;" and documentation of financial need.

Financial data   The stipend is $1,500 per year.

Duration   1 year; renewable up to 3 additional years.

Additional information   This program began in 1991 and given its current name in 1997.

Number awarded   Varies each year; recently, 9 of these scholarships were awarded.

Deadline   May of each year.

[641]
MILDRED R. KNOLES SCHOLARSHIPS

American Legion Auxiliary
Department of Illinois
2720 East Lincoln Street
P.O. Box 1426
Bloomington, IL 61702-1426
(309) 663-9366   Fax: (309) 663-5827
E-mail: karen.boughan@ilala.org
Web: www.ilala.org/scholar.html

Summary   To provide funding to Illinois veterans and their descendants who are attending college in any state.

Eligibility   This program is open to veterans who served during designated periods of wartime and their children, grandchildren, and great-grandchildren. Applicants must be currently enrolled at a college or university in any state and studying any field except nursing. They must be residents of Illinois or members of the American Legion Family, Department of Illinois. Along with their application, they must submit a 1,000-word essay on "What My Education Will Do for Me." Selection is based on that essay (25%) character and leadership (25%), scholarship (25%), and financial need (25%).

Financial data   The stipend is $1,000.

Duration   1 year.

Additional information   Applications may be obtained only from a local unit of the American Legion Auxiliary.

Number awarded   Varies each year.

Deadline   March of each year.

[642]
MILITARY BENEFIT ASSOCIATION SCHOLARSHIPS

Military Benefit Association
Attn: Member Services Department
14605 Avion Parkway
P.O. Box 221110
Chantilly, VA 20153-1110
(703) 968-6200   Toll Free: (800) 336-0100
Fax: (703) 968-6423
Web: www.militarybenefit.org/MemberBenefits/Scholarships

Summary   To provide money for college to children of members of the Military Benefit Association (MBA).

Eligibility   This program is open to dependent children of MBA members who are enrolled or planning to enroll as a full-time undergraduate student at an accredited 2- or 4-year college, university, or vocational/technical school. Applicants must have a GPA of 2.5 or higher. Race, color, creed, religion, gender, disability, and national origin are not considered in the selection process.

Financial data   The stipend is $2,500.

Duration   1 year.

Additional information   The MBA is an organization that provides insurance to military personnel and civilian employees of the U.S. government and their spouses. This program is administered by Scholarship Management Services.

Number awarded   5 each year.

Deadline   February of each year.

[643]
MILITARY COMMANDERS' SCHOLARSHIP FUND

Scholarship America
Attn: Scholarship Management Services
One Scholarship Way
P.O. Box 297
St. Peter, MN 56082
(507) 931-1682   Toll Free: (800) 537-4180
Fax: (507) 931-9168
E-mail: militarycommanders@scholarshipamerica.org
Web: www.scholarshipamerica.org/militarycommanders

Summary   To provide financial assistance for college to children of active and retired military personnel.

Eligibility   This program is open to children of active-duty, Reserve, National Guard, and retired members of the U.S. military. Applicants must be high school seniors or graduates who plan to enroll full time as entering freshmen at an accredited 2- or 4-year college or university. They must have a cumulative GPA of 3.5 or higher. Selection is based on academic record, demonstrated leadership and participation in school and community activities, honors, work experience, a statement of goals and aspirations, unusual personal or family circumstances, an outside appraisal, and financial need.

Financial data   The stipend is $5,000.

Duration   1 year; nonrenewable.

Additional information   This program is administered by Scholarship Management Services on behalf of the New York Chapter of the American Logistics Association.

Number awarded   Up to 10 each year: 2 from each branch of the armed forces (Air Force, Army, Coast Guard, Marines, Navy).

Deadline   February of each year.

[644]
MILITARY FAMILY SUPPORT TRUST SCHOLARSHIPS

Military Family Support Trust
1010 American Eagle Boulevard
P.O. Box 301
Sun City Center, FL 33573
(813) 634-4675   Fax: (813) 633-2412
E-mail: president@mobc-online.org
Web: www.mobc-online.org/scholarships.html

Summary   To provide money for college to children and grandchildren of retired and deceased officers who served in the military or designated public service agencies.

Eligibility   This program is open to graduating high school seniors who have a GPA of 3.0 and a minimum score of 21 on the ACT or 1500 on the 3-part SAT. Applicants must have a parent, guardian, or grandparent who is 1) a retired active-duty, National Guard, or Reserve officer or former officer of the U.S. Army, Navy, Marine Corps, Air Force, Coast Guard, Public Health Service, or National Oceanic and Atmospheric Administration, at the rank of O-1 through O-10, WO-1 through WO-5, or E-5 through E-9; 2) an officer who died while on active duty in service to the country; 3) a recipient of the Purple Heart, regardless of pay grade or length of service; 4) a World War II combat veteran of the Merchant Marine; 5) a federal employee at the grade of GS-7 or higher; 6) a Foreign Service Officer at the grade of FSO-8 or lower; or 7) an honorably discharged or retired foreign military officer of friendly nations meeting the service and disability retirement criteria of the respective country and living in the United States. Applicants must have been accepted to an accredited program at a college or university. Selection is based on leadership (40%), scholarship (30%), and financial need (30%).

Financial data Stipends range from $500 to $3,000 per year.

Duration 4 years, provided the recipient maintains a GPA of 3.0 or higher.

Additional information This foundation began in 1992 as the Military Officers' Benevolent Corporation. It changed its name in 2008 to the current usage.

Number awarded 16 each year: 4 at $3,000 per year, 1 at $2,500 per year, 1 at $2,000 per year, 2 at $1,500 per year, 1 at $1,000 per year, and 7 at $500 per year.

Deadline February of each year.

[645]
MILITARY NONRESIDENT TUITION WAIVER AFTER ASSIGNMENT IN TEXAS

Texas Higher Education Coordinating Board
Attn: Grants and Special Programs
1200 East Anderson Lane
P.O. Box 12788
Austin, TX 78711-2788
(512) 427-6340   Toll Free: (800) 242-3062
Fax: (512) 427-6420   E-mail: grantinfo@thecb.state.tx.us
Web: www.collegeforalltexans.com

Summary To provide educational assistance to the spouses and children of Texas military personnel assigned elsewhere.

Eligibility This program is open to the spouses and dependent children of members of the U.S. armed forces or commissioned officers of the Public Health Service who remain in Texas when the member is reassigned to duty outside of the state. The spouse or dependent child must reside continuously in Texas. Applicants must be attending or planning to attend a Texas public college or university.

Financial data Eligible students are entitled to pay tuition and fees at the resident rate at publicly-supported colleges and universities in Texas.

Duration The waiver remains in effect for the duration of the member's first assignment outside of Texas.

Additional information This program became effective in 2003.

Number awarded Varies each year.

Deadline Deadline not specified.

[646]
MILITARY NONRESIDENT TUITION WAIVER FOR MEMBERS, SPOUSES OR CHILDREN ASSIGNED TO DUTY IN TEXAS

Texas Higher Education Coordinating Board
Attn: Grants and Special Programs
1200 East Anderson Lane
P.O. Box 12788
Austin, TX 78711-2788
(512) 427-6340   Toll Free: (800) 242-3062
Fax: (512) 427-6420   E-mail: grantinfo@thecb.state.tx.us
Web: www.collegeforalltexans.com

Summary To exempt military personnel stationed in Texas and their dependents from the payment of nonresident tuition at public institutions of higher education in the state.

Eligibility Eligible for these waivers are members of the U.S. armed forces and commissioned officers of the Public Health Service from states other than Texas, their spouses, and dependent children. Applicants must be assigned to Texas and attending or planning to attend a public college or university in the state.

Financial data Although persons eligible under this program are classified as nonresidents, they are entitled to pay the resident tuition at Texas institutions of higher education, regardless of their length of residence in Texas.

Duration 1 year; may be renewed.

Number awarded Varies each year.

Deadline Deadline not specified.

[647]
MILITARY NONRESIDENT TUITION WAIVER FOR MEMBERS, SPOUSES OR CHILDREN WHO REMAIN CONTINUOUSLY ENROLLED IN HIGHER EDUCATION IN TEXAS

Texas Higher Education Coordinating Board
Attn: Grants and Special Programs
1200 East Anderson Lane
P.O. Box 12788
Austin, TX 78711-2788
(512) 427-6340   Toll Free: (800) 242-3062
Fax: (512) 427-6420   E-mail: grantinfo@thecb.state.tx.us
Web: www.collegeforalltexans.com

Summary To waive nonresident tuition at Texas public colleges and universities for members of the armed forces and their families who are no longer in the military.

Eligibility Eligible for these waivers are members of the U.S. armed forces, commissioned officers of the Public Health Service (PHS), their spouses, and their children. Applicants must have previously been eligible to pay tuition at the resident rate while enrolled in a degree or certificate program at a Texas public college or university because they were a member, spouse, or child of a member of the armed forces or PHS. This waiver is available after the servicemember, spouse, or parent is no longer a member of the armed forces or a commissioned officer of the PHS. The student must remain continuously enrolled in the same degree or certificate program in subsequent terms or semesters.

Financial data The student's eligibility to pay tuition and fees at the rate provided for Texas students does not terminate because the member, spouse, or parent is no longer in the service.

Duration 1 year.

Additional information This program became effective in September 2003.

Number awarded Varies each year.

Deadline Deadline not specified.

[648]
MILITARY SPOUSE CAREER ADVANCEMENT ACCOUNTS (MYCAA) PROGRAM

Department of Defense
Attn: Spouse Education and Career Opportunities
1400 Defense Pentagon
Washington, DC 20301-1400
(703) 253-7599　　　Toll Free: (800) 342-9647
TDD: (866) 607-6794
E-mail: MyCAAFeedback@militaryonesource.com
Web: https://aiportal.acc.af.mil/mycaa

Summary To provide financial assistance to military spouses who are interested in obtaining additional education that will improve their employment opportunities.

Eligibility This program is open to military spouses who are enrolled or planning to enroll in educational or training course that leads to an associate degree, license, certificate, or certification at an accredited college, university, or technical school in the United States or an approved testing organization that expands employment or portable career opportunities for military spouses. Applicants must be spouses of service members on active duty in pay grades E-1 to E-5, W-1 to W-2, or O-1 to O-2 who can start and complete their course work while their military sponsor is on Title 10 military orders, including spouses married to members of the National Guard and Reserve components. Support is not available for a bachelor's, master's, or doctoral degree; general studies, liberal arts, or interdisciplinary associate degrees that do not have a concentration; personal enrichment courses; transportation, lodging, child care, or medical services; study abroad programs; or high school completion programs. Spouses who are themselves in the military or married to members of the Coast Guard are not eligible.

Financial data The maximum support per fiscal year is $2,000; spouses may receive a lifetime total of $4,000 from this program. Funds are paid directly to schools.

Duration Associate degrees must be completed in 12 months and licenses and certificates within 18 months. The times of study may be extended over a 3-year period.

Additional information This program began in March 2009 but was suspended in February 2010 when an unexpected large number of spouses applied. It was resumed for spouses who had already applied in March 2010 and for new enrollees in October 2010.

Number awarded More than 136,000 military spouses and more than 3,000 schools are currently participating in this program.

Deadline Applications may be submitted at any time.

[649]
MINNESOTA G.I. BILL PROGRAM

Minnesota Office of Higher Education
Attn: Manager of State Financial Aid Programs
1450 Energy Park Drive, Suite 350
St. Paul, MN 55108-5227
(651) 642-0567　　　Toll Free: (800) 657-3866
Fax: (651) 642-0675　　　TDD: (800) 627-3529
E-mail: Ginny.Dodds@state.mn.us
Web: www.ohe.state.mn.us/mPg.cfm?pageID=891

Summary To provide financial assistance for college or graduate school in the state to residents of Minnesota who served in the military after September 11, 2001 and the families of deceased or disabled military personnel.

Eligibility This program is open to residents of Minnesota enrolled at colleges and universities in the state as undergraduate or graduate students. Applicants must be 1) a veteran who is serving or has served honorably in a branch of the U.S. armed forces at any time on or after September 11, 2001; 2) a non-veteran who has served honorably for a total of 5 years or more cumulatively as a member of the Minnesota National Guard or other active or Reserve component of the U.S. armed forces, and any part of that service occurred on or after September 11, 2001; or 3) a surviving child or spouse of a person who has served in the military at any time on or after September 11, 2001 and who has died or has a total and permanent disability as a result of that military service. Financial need is considered in the selection process.

Financial data The stipend is $1,000 per semester for full-time study or $500 per semester for part-time study. The maximum award is $3,000 per fiscal year or $10,000 per lifetime.

Duration 1 year; may be renewed, provided the recipient continues to make satisfactory academic progress.

Additional information This program was established by the Minnesota Legislature in 2007.

Number awarded Varies each year.

Deadline Deadline not specified.

[650]
MINNESOTA LEGION AUXILIARY DEPARTMENT SCHOLARSHIPS

American Legion Auxiliary
Department of Minnesota
State Veterans Service Building
20 West 12th Street, Room 314
St. Paul, MN 55155-2069
(651) 224-7634　　　Toll Free: (888) 217-9598
Fax: (651) 224-5243　　　E-mail: deptoffice@mnala.org
Web: www.mnala.org/ala/scholarship.asp

Summary To provide financial assistance to the children and grandchildren of Minnesota veterans who are interested in attending college in the state.

Eligibility This program is open to the children and grandchildren of veterans who served during designated periods of wartime. Applicants must be a resident of Minnesota or a member of an American Legion post, American Legion Auxiliary unit, or Sons of the American Legion detachment in the Department of Minnesota. They must be high school seniors or graduates, have a GPA of 2.0 or higher, be able to demonstrate financial need, and be planning to attend a vocational or business school, college, or university in Minnesota. Along with their application, they must submit a brief essay, telling of their plans for college, career goals, and extracurricular and community activities.

Financial data The stipend is $1,000. Funds are to be used to pay for tuition or books and are sent directly to the recipient's school.

Duration 1 year.

Number awarded 7 each year.

Deadline March of each year.

[651]
MINNESOTA LEGION AUXILIARY PAST PRESIDENTS PARLEY HEALTH CARE SCHOLARSHIP

American Legion Auxiliary
Department of Minnesota
State Veterans Service Building
20 West 12th Street, Room 314
St. Paul, MN 55155-2069
(651) 224-7634   Toll Free: (888) 217-9598
Fax: (651) 224-5243   E-mail: deptoffice@mnala.org
Web: www.mnala.org/ala/scholarship.asp

Summary To provide financial assistance for education in health care fields to members of the American Legion Auxiliary in Minnesota.

Eligibility This program is open to residents of Minnesota who have been members of the American Legion Auxiliary for at least 3 years. Applicants must have a GPA of 2.0 or higher and be planning to study in Minnesota. Their proposed major may be in any phase of health care, including nursing assistant, registered nursing, licensed practical nurse, X-ray or other technician, physical or other therapist, dental hygienist, or dental assistant.

Financial data The stipend is $1,000. Funds are sent directly to the recipient's school after satisfactory completion of the first quarter.

Duration 1 year.

Number awarded Up to 10 each year.

Deadline March of each year.

[652]
MINNESOTA NATIONAL GUARD SURVIVOR ENTITLEMENT TUITION REIMBURSEMENT PROGRAM

Department of Military Affairs
Attn: Education Services Officer
JFMN-J1-ARED
20 West 12th Street
St. Paul, MN 55155-2098
(651) 282-4589   Toll Free: (800) 657-3848
Fax: (651) 282-4694 E-mail: ngmneducation@ng.army.mil
Web: www.minnesotanationalguard.org

Summary To provide financial assistance for college or graduate school to survivors of members of the Minnesota National Guard who were killed on active duty.

Eligibility This program is open to surviving spouses and children of members of the Minnesota Army or Air National Guard who were killed while performing military duty. Dependent children are eligible until their 24th birthday; surviving spouses are eligible regardless of age or remarriage; all survivors remain eligible even if they move out of state and become non-Minnesota residents. The Guard member's death must have occurred within the scope of assigned duties

while in a federal duty status or on state active service. Applicants must be enrolled as undergraduate or graduate students at colleges or universities in Minnesota. Reimbursement is provided only for undergraduate courses completed with a grade of "C" or better or for graduate courses completed with a grade of "B" or better.

Financial data The maximum reimbursement rate is 100% of the undergraduate tuition rate at the University of Minnesota Twin Cities campus, with a maximum benefit of $10,000 per fiscal year.

Duration 1 academic term, to a maximum of 18 credits per term; may be renewed for a total of 144 semester credits or 208 quarter credits.

Additional information This program became effective in 1992.

Number awarded Varies each year.

Deadline Participants must request reimbursement within 60 days of the last official day of the term.

[653]
MISSISSIPPI EDUCATIONAL ASSISTANCE FOR MIA/POW DEPENDENTS

Mississippi State Veterans Affairs Board
3466 Highway 80
P.O. Box 5947
Pearl, MS 39288-5947
(601) 576-4850   Toll Free: (877) 203-5632
Fax: (601) 576-4868
Web: www.vab.ms.gov

Summary To provide financial assistance for college to the children of Mississippi residents who are POWs or MIAs.

Eligibility This entitlement program is open to the children of members of the armed services whose official home of record and residence is in Mississippi and who are officially reported as being either a prisoner of a foreign government or missing in action. Applicants must be attending or planning to attend a state-supported college or university in Mississippi.

Financial data This assistance covers all costs of college attendance.

Duration Up to 8 semesters.

Number awarded Varies each year.

Deadline Deadline not specified.

[654]
MISSOURI VIETNAM VETERAN SURVIVOR GRANT PROGRAM

Missouri Department of Higher Education
Attn: Student Financial Assistance
205 Jefferson Street
P.O. Box 1469
Jefferson City, MO 65102-1469
(573) 526-7958   Toll Free: (800) 473-6757
Fax: (573) 751-6635   E-mail: info@dhe.mo.gov
Web: www.dhe.mo.gov/ppc/grants/vietnamveterans.php

Summary To provide financial assistance to survivors of certain deceased Missouri Vietnam veterans who plan to attend college in the state.

Eligibility This program is open to surviving spouses and children of veterans who served in the military in Vietnam or the war zone in southeast Asia, who were residents of Missouri when first entering military service and at the time of death, whose death was attributed to or caused by exposure to toxic chemicals during the Vietnam conflict, and who served in the Vietnam Theater between 1961 and 1972. Applicants must be Missouri residents enrolled in a program leading to a certificate, associate degree, or baccalaureate degree at an approved postsecondary institution in the state. Students working on a degree or certificate in theology or divinity are not eligible. U.S. citizenship or permanent resident status is required.

Financial data The maximum annual grant is the lesser of 1) the actual tuition charged at the school where the recipient is enrolled, or 2) the amount of tuition charged to a Missouri undergraduate resident enrolled full time in the same class level and in the same academic major as an applicant at the Missouri public 4-year regional institutions.

Duration 1 semester; may be renewed until the recipient has obtained a baccalaureate degree, has received the award for 10 semesters, or has completed 150 semester credit hours, whichever comes first. Dependent children remain eligible until they reach 25 years of age. Spouses remain eligible until the fifth anniversary of the veteran's death.

Additional information Awards are not available for summer study.

Number awarded Up to 12 each year.

Deadline There is no application deadline, but early submission of the completed application is encouraged.

[655]
MISSOURI WARTIME VETERAN'S SURVIVOR GRANT PROGRAM

Missouri Department of Higher Education
Attn: Student Financial Assistance
205 Jefferson Street
P.O. Box 1469
Jefferson City, MO 65102-1469
(573) 526-7958   Toll Free: (800) 473-6757
Fax: (573) 751-6635   E-mail: info@dhe.mo.gov
Web: www.dhe.mo.gov/ppc/grants/wartimevetsurvivor.php

Summary To provide financial assistance to survivors of deceased or disabled Missouri post-September 11, 2001 veterans who plan to attend college in the state.

Eligibility This program is open to spouses and children of veterans whose deaths or injuries were a result of combat action or were attributed to an illness that was contracted while serving in combat action, or who became 80% disabled as a result of injuries or accidents sustained in combat action since September 11, 2001. The veteran must have been a Missouri resident when first entering military service or at the time of death or injury. The spouse or child must be a U.S. citizen or permanent resident or otherwise lawfully present in the United States; children of veterans must be younger than 25 years of age. All applicants must be enrolled or accepted for enrollment at least half time at participating public college or university in Missouri.

Financial data The maximum annual grant is the lesser of 1) the actual tuition charged at the school where the recipient is enrolled, or 2) the amount of tuition charged to a Missouri resident enrolled in the same number of hours at the University of Missouri at Columbia. Additional allowances provide up to $2,000 per semester for room and board and the lesser of the actual cost for books or $500.

Duration 1 year. May be renewed, provided the recipient maintains a GPA of 2.5 or higher and makes satisfactory academic progress; children of veterans are eligible until they turn 25 years of age or receive their first bachelor's degree, whichever occurs first.

Number awarded Up to 25 each year.

Deadline There is no application deadline, but early submission of the completed application is encouraged.

[656]
MONTANA WAR ORPHANS WAIVER

Office of the Commissioner of Higher Education
Attn: Montana University System
State Scholarship Coordinator
2500 Broadway
P.O. Box 203201
Helena, MT 59620-3201
(406) 444-0638   Toll Free: (800) 537-7508
Fax: (406) 444-1469   E-mail: snewlun@montana.edu
Web: www.mus.edu

Summary To provide financial assistance for undergraduate education to the children of Montana veterans who died in the line of duty or as a result of service-connected disabilities.

Eligibility This program is open to children of members of the U.S. armed forces who served on active duty during World War II, the Korean Conflict, the Vietnam Conflict, the Afghanistan Conflict, or the Iraq Conflict; were legal residents of Montana at the time of entry into service; and were killed in action or died as a result of injury, disease, or other disability while in the service. Applicants must be no older than 25 years of age. Financial need is considered in the selection process.

Financial data Students eligible for this benefit are entitled to attend any unit of the Montana University System without payment of undergraduate registration or incidental fees.

Duration Undergraduate students are eligible for continued fee waiver as long as they maintain reasonable academic progress as full-time students.

Number awarded Varies each year.

Deadline Deadline not specified.

[657]
MONTFORD POINT MARINE ASSOCIATION SCHOLARSHIP

Montford Point Marine Association
c/o James Maillard, National Scholarship Director
7714 113th Street, Number 2G
Forest Hills, NY 11375-7119
(718) 261-9640   Fax: (718) 261-3021
E-mail: Scholarships@montfordpointmarines.com
Web: www.montfordpointmarines.com

Summary To provide financial assistance to high school seniors, high school graduates, and current undergraduates who have a connection to the Montford Point Marine Association (MPMA).

Eligibility This program is open to high school seniors, high school graduates, or current college students who have a connection to the MPMA. Along with their application, they must submit academic transcripts, information on their connection to MPMA, and a 500-word essay on a topic that changes periodically. Only undergraduate study is supported.

The family income of applicants must be less than $90,000 per year.

Financial data Stipends depend on the need of the recipient and the availability of funds, but generally range from $500 to $2,500 per year.

Duration 1 year.

Additional information Membership in the MPMA is restricted to former Marines and the families of Marines who served at Camp Montford Point, North Carolina where African Americans trained during the days of segregation from 1942 to 1949. This scholarship program, which began in 2003, operates in coordination with the Marine Corps Scholarship Foundation.

Number awarded 1 or more each year.

Deadline Deadline not specified.

[658]
MOPH SCHOLARSHIP PROGRAM

Military Order of the Purple Heart
Attn: Scholarships
5413-B Backlick Road
Springfield, VA 22151-3960
(703) 642-5360   Toll Free: (888) 668-1656
Fax: (703) 642-2054
E-mail: scholarship@purpleheart.org
Web: www.purpleheart.org/Scholarships/Default.aspx

Summary To provide financial assistance for college or graduate school to members of the Military Order of the Purple Heart (MOPH) and their families.

Eligibility This program is open to 1) members of the MOPH; 2) direct descendants (children, stepchildren, adopted children, grandchildren, and great- grandchildren) of veterans who are MOPH members or who were members at the time of death; 3) direct descendants of veterans killed in action or who died of wounds but did not have the opportunity to join the order; and 4) spouses and widows of MOPH members, veterans killed in action, and veterans who died of wounds. Applicants must be graduating seniors or graduates of an accredited high school who are enrolled or accepted for enrollment in a full-time program of study in a college, university, or trade school. They must have a GPA of 2.75 or higher. U.S. citizenship is required. Along with their application, they must submit an essay of 200 to 300 words on a topic that changes annually but recently was, "The Price of Freedom." Financial need is not considered in the selection process.

Financial data The stipend is $3,000 per year.

Duration 1 year; may be renewed up to 2 additional years.

Additional information Membership in MOPH is open to all veterans who received a Purple Heart Medal and were discharged under conditions other than dishonorable. A processing fee of $15 is required.

Number awarded Varies each year; recently, 83 of these scholarships were awarded.

Deadline February of each year.

[659]
MSNCOA SCHOLARSHIPS

Mississippi National Guard Noncommissioned Officers Association
Attn: Executive Director
P.O. Box 699
Brandon, MS 39043-0699
(601) 824-0304   Toll Free: (800) 205-5797
Fax: (601) 824-4970   E-mail: msngnco@bellsouth.net
Web: www.msncoa.org/Scholarships.htm

Summary To provide financial assistance to dependents of members of the Mississippi National Guard Noncommissioned Officers Association who are interested in attending college in any state.

Eligibility This program is open to the unmarried dependent children and spouses of annual, enlisted, retired, and life members of the association and of deceased members who were annual, enlisted, retired, or life members at the time of death. Applicants must be high school seniors or undergraduate students with at least 1 full semester remaining before graduation. They must be attending or planning to attend an accredited university, college, community college, vocational/technical, business, or trade school in any state. Along with their application, they must submit a personal letter about themselves, letters of recommendation, transcripts, a copy of their sponsor's association membership card, and a copy of their ACT score.

Financial data The stipend depends on the availability of funds.

Duration 1 year.

Number awarded Varies each year.

Deadline January of each year.

[660]
NANNIE W. NORFLEET SCHOLARSHIP

American Legion Auxiliary
Department of North Carolina
P.O. Box 25726
Raleigh, NC 27611-5726
(919) 832-4051   Fax: (919) 832-1888
E-mail: ala1_nc@bellsouth.net
Web: nclegion.org/auxil.htm

Summary To provide funding to members of the American Legion Auxiliary in North Carolina and their children or grandchildren who plan to attend college in any state.

Eligibility This program is open to North Carolina residents who are either adult members of the American Legion Auxiliary or high school seniors (with preference to the children and grandchildren of members). Applicants must be interested in attending college in any state. They must be able to demonstrate financial need.

Financial data The stipend is $1,000.

Duration 1 year.

Number awarded 1 each year.

Deadline March of each year.

[661]
NARRAGANSETT BAY POST SAME SCHOLARSHIP

Society of American Military Engineers-Narragansett Bay
   Post
Attn: Scholarship Committee
15 Mohegan Avenue
New London, CT 06320
(860) 444-8312   Fax: (860) 444-8219
E-mail: Gregory.j.carabine@uscg.mil
Web: posts.same.org/Narragansett/scholarship.htm

Summary   To provide financial assistance to residents of
New England, particularly those with ties to the military, who
are interested in working on a bachelor's degree in construction-related fields at colleges in any state.

Eligibility   This program is open to residents of New England (preferably Connecticut, Massachusetts, and Rhode
Island) who are graduating high school seniors or students
currently enrolled at a college or university in any state. Applicants must be interested in working on a bachelor's degree in
an accredited engineering or architectural program, preferably in civil engineering, environmental engineering, architecture, or other construction-related program. Preference is
given to students who 1) are dependents of or sponsored by
a member of the Narragansett Bay Post of the Society of
American Military Engineers (SAME); 2) are enrolled in
ROTC (preferably not a recipient of an ROTC scholarship);
and 3) have prior U.S. military service and/or public service.
Along with their application, they must submit a 500-word
essay about themselves, their achievements, or their situation. Selection is based on that essay, grades and class rank,
school or community honors, extracurricular activities, leadership, volunteer activities, and completeness and quality of the
application. U.S. citizenship is required.

Financial data   The stipend is $1,000.
Duration   1 year.
Number awarded   1 each year.
Deadline   May of each year.

[662]
NATIONAL GUARD ASSOCIATION OF ARIZONA
SCHOLARSHIPS

National Guard Association of Arizona
Attn: Scholarship Committee
5640 East McDowell Road
Phoenix, AZ 85008
(602) 275-8305   Fax: (602) 275-9254
E-mail: ngaofaz@aol.com
Web: www.ngaaz.org/scholarship.html

Summary   To provide financial assistance to students at
colleges and universities in Arizona who have a connection to
the National Guard and the National Guard Association of
Arizona (NGAAZ).

Eligibility   This program is open to full-time students at colleges, universities, and community colleges in Arizona. Applicants must be a member of 1 of the following categories: 1) a
current enlisted member of the Arizona National Guard; 2) a
current officer member of the Arizona National Guard who is
also a member of the NGAAZ; or 3) children or spouses of
NGAAZ members. Applicants must submit 2 letters of recommendation and verification of good standing from the first
commander in the chain of command of the Arizona National
Guard. Selection is based on GPA (25%), community service

(15%), letters of recommendation (15%), knowledge of
National Guard philosophy (15%), and financial need (30%).
Financial data   The stipend is $1,500.
Duration   1 year; nonrenewable.
Number awarded   3 each year: 1 to each category of
applicant.
Deadline   April of each year.

[663]
NATIONAL GUARD ASSOCIATION OF CALIFORNIA
SCHOLARSHIPS

National Guard Association of California
Attn: Executive Director
3336 Bradshaw Road, Suite 230
Sacramento, CA 95827-2615
(916) 362-3411   Toll Free: (800) 647-0018
Fax: (916) 362-3707
Web: ngac.org

Summary   To provide funding to members or former members of the National Guard in California and their dependents
interested in attending college in any state.

Eligibility   This program is open to 1) dependents of service members of the California National Guard who have
died, have been wounded, are currently serving, or have
served in the Global War on Terrorism; 2) medically or honorably discharged California National Guard veterans who
served in Operation Enduring Freedom (OEF) or Operation
Iraqi Freedom (OIF); 3) California National Guard service
members who are currently serving or have served in the
Global War on Terrorism; or 4) dependents of retired California National Guard service members who are life members of
the National Guard Association of California. Applicants must
be attending or planning to attend a college, university, or
trade school in any state. Along with their application, they
must submit a 500-word essay on the greatest challenge they
have faced and how it has impacted them. Selection is based
on that essay; unweighted GPA; extracurricular activities,
honors, and/or awards; recommendations; and (if case of a
tie) SAT or ACT scores.

Financial data   Stipends range from $250 to $1,000.
Funds are paid directly to the recipient.
Duration   1 year.
Number awarded   Varies each year; recently, 19 of these
scholarships were awarded.
Deadline   May of each year.

[664]
NATIONAL GUARD ASSOCIATION OF
CONNECTICUT SCHOLARSHIP PROGRAM

National Guard Association of Connecticut
Attn: Scholarship Committee
360 Broad Street
Hartford, CT 06105-3795
(860) 247-5000   Fax: (860) 247-5000
E-mail: ngact_scholarship@ngact.org
Web: www.ngact.org/scholarships.htm

Summary   To provide financial assistance to members and
the family of members of the National Guard Association of
Connecticut (NGACT) who are interested in attending college
in any state.

Eligibility   This program is open to 1) NGACT members; 2)
unmarried children and grandchildren of NGACT members;

3) spouses of NGACT members; and 4) unremarried spouses and unmarried dependent children and grandchildren of deceased NGACT members who were members in good standing at the time of their death. Applicants must be attending or planning to attend, on a part- or full-time basis, a college, university, trade school, or business school in any state. Graduate students are not eligible to apply. Along with their application, they must submit: an official transcript, a letter on their desire to continue their education and why financial assistance is required, 2 letters of recommendation, and 1 letter of academic reference. Selection is based on academic record, character, leadership, and need.

Financial data A stipend is awarded (amount not specified). Funds are sent to the recipient but are made payable to the recipient's choice of school. To receive the awards, proof of enrollment must be presented.

Duration 1 year.

Number awarded Varies each year.

Deadline February of each year.

[665]
NATIONAL GUARD ASSOCIATION OF FLORIDA AND ENLISTED NATIONAL GUARD ASSOCIATION OF FLORIDA SCHOLARSHIP PROGRAM

National Guard Association of Florida
Attn: Scholarship Committee
P.O. Box 3446
St. Augustine, FL 32085-3446
(904) 823-0628　　　　　　Fax: (904) 839-2068
E-mail: ngafl1903@floridaguard.org
Web: www.floridaguard.org/florida-guard-scholarships.html

Summary To provide financial assistance to members of the Florida National Guard and their families who are also members of either the National Guard Association of Florida (NGOA-FL) or the Enlisted National Guard Association of Florida (ENGAF) and interested in attending college in the state.

Eligibility This program is open to active members of the Florida National Guard (enlisted, officer, and warrant officer), their spouses, and children, but preference is given to Guard members. Applicants must be residents of Florida attending or planning to attend an accredited college, university, or vocational/technical school in the state. They must also be a member, spouse of a member, or child of a member of their respective association. Selection is based on academic achievement, civic and moral leadership, character, and financial need.

Financial data Scholarships are $1,000 for full-time students or $500 for part-time students; funds are paid directly to the recipient's institution.

Duration 1 year; may be renewed.

Additional information This program is jointly sponsored by the respective associations.

Number awarded 15 each year.

Deadline June of each year.

[666]
NATIONAL GUARD ASSOCIATION OF INDIANA EDUCATIONAL GRANTS

National Guard Association of Indiana
Attn: Educational Grant Committee
2002 South Holt Road, Building 9
Indianapolis, IN 46241-4839
(317) 247-3196　　　　　Toll Free: (800) 219-2173
Fax: (317) 247-3575　　　E-mail: membership@ngai.net
Web: www.ngai.net/membership

Summary To provide financial assistance to members of the National Guard Association of Indiana (NGAI) and their dependents who plan to attend college in any state.

Eligibility This program is open to NGAI members who are currently serving in the Indiana National Guard and their dependents. Children and widow(er)s of former Guard members killed or permanently disabled while on duty with the Indiana National Guard are also eligible. Applicants must be attending or planning to attend a college or university in any state. Along with their application, they must submit 2 letters of recommendation, a copy of high school or college transcripts, SAT or ACT scores (if taken), a letter of acceptance from a college or university (if not currently attending college), and a 2-page essay on the educational program they intend to pursue and the goals they wish to attain. Selection is based on academic achievement, commitment and desire to achieve, extracurricular activities, accomplishments, goals, and financial need.

Financial data The stipend is $1,000.

Duration 1 year; recipients may reapply.

Number awarded 10 each year: 5 to military members and 5 to dependents.

Deadline March of each year.

[667]
NATIONAL GUARD ASSOCIATION OF MARYLAND SCHOLARSHIPS

National Guard Association of Maryland
Attn: Scholarship Committee
P.O. Box 16675
Baltimore, MD 21221-0675
(410) 557-2606　　　　　　Toll Free: (800) 844-1394
Fax: (410) 893-7529 E-mail: executivedirector@ngam.net
Web: www.ngam.net/benefits/scholarships.html

Summary To provide funding to current and former members of the Maryland National Guard and their dependents who are interested in attending college in any state.

Eligibility This program is open to active and retired members of the Maryland National Guard and their spouses and children. Applicants must be enrolled or planning to enroll in an accredited college, university, or vocational/technical school in any state on either a part-time or full-time basis. They must submit a resume in which they outline their academic background, activities in which they have participated, and honors they have received; 3 letters of recommendation; the name of the college; and information on financial need.

Financial data The stipend is $1,000. Funds are paid directly to the recipient's university for tuition, fees, and books.

Duration 1 year; recipients may reapply.

Number awarded Varies each year; recently, 17 of these scholarships were awarded.

Deadline   March of each year.

[668]
NATIONAL GUARD ASSOCIATION OF MASSACHUSETTS SCHOLARSHIPS

National Guard Association of Massachusetts
Attn: Education Services Office
50 Maple Street
Milford, MA 01757
(508) 735-6544   E-mail: contact@ngama.org
Web: www.ngama.org/scholarships

Summary   To provide financial assistance to members of the Massachusetts National Guard and their dependents who are interested in attending college in any state.

Eligibility   This program is open to 1) current members of the Massachusetts National Guard; 2) children and spouses of current members of the National Guard Association of Massachusetts (NGAMA); and 3) children and spouses of current members of the Massachusetts National Guard. Applicants must be enrolled in or planning to enroll in an accredited college or technical program in any state. Along with their application, they must submit a letter of recommendation, a list of extracurricular activities and other significant accomplishments, high school or college transcripts, and an essay on a topic that changes annually but relates to the National Guard.

Financial data   The stipend is $1,000.

Duration   1 year.

Number awarded   4 each year: 2 to members of the Massachusetts National Guard, 1 to a dependent of an NGAMA member, and 1 to a dependent of a Massachusetts National Guard member.

Deadline   March of each year.

[669]
NATIONAL GUARD ASSOCIATION OF NEW HAMPSHIRE SCHOLARSHIPS

National Guard Association of New Hampshire
Attn: Scholarship Committee
P.O. Box 22031
Portsmouth, NH 03802-2031
(603) 540-9608   E-mail: info@nganh.org
Web: www.nganh.org

Summary   To provide money to members of the National Guard Association of New Hampshire and their dependents who are interested in attending college.

Eligibility   This program is open to current members of the National Guard Association of New Hampshire (officer, enlisted, or retired) and their dependents. Applicants must be attending or planning to attend an accredited college or university in any state. Along with their application, they must submit a 1-page essay on a topic that changes annually; recently, they were asked to give their thoughts on whether or not United States efforts to support and stabilize democratic governments in Afghanistan and Iraq will lead to greater stability in the Southwest Asian region.

Financial data   The stipend is $1,000.

Duration   1 year.

Number awarded   1 each year.

Deadline   April of each year.

[670]
NATIONAL GUARD ASSOCIATION OF NEW JERSEY SCHOLARSHIP PROGRAM

National Guard Association of New Jersey
Attn: Executive Director
P.O. Box 266
Wrightstown, NJ 08562
(973) 541-6776   Fax: (973) 541-6909
E-mail: nganj@aol.com
Web: nganj.org/about.htm

Summary   To provide financial assistance to members of the National Guard Association of New Jersey (NGANJ) or their dependents who are interested in attending college or graduate school in any state.

Eligibility   This program is open to 1) active members of the NGANJ currently enrolled full time at an approved community college, school of nursing, or 4-year college in any state; and 2) the spouses, children, and grandchildren of active, retired, or deceased members entering or attending a 4-year college or university in any state. Applicants must submit transcripts, information on the civic and academic activities in which they have participated, and a list of offices, honors, awards, and special recognitions they have received. Selection is based on academic accomplishment, leadership, and citizenship.

Financial data   Stipends up to $1,000 are available.

Duration   1 year; nonrenewable.

Number awarded   Varies each year; recently, 10 of these scholarships were awarded.

Deadline   April of each year.

[671]
NATIONAL GUARD ASSOCIATION OF SOUTH CAROLINA AUXILIARY COLLEGE SCHOLARSHIP PROGRAM

National Guard Association of South Carolina Auxiliary
c/o National Guard Association of South Carolina
132 Pickens Street
Columbia, SC 29205
(803) 254-8456   Toll Free: (800) 822-3235
Fax: (803) 254-3869   E-mail: nginfo@ngasc.org
Web: www.ngasc.org/?page_id=11

Summary   To provide funding to members of the National Guard Association of South Carolina Auxiliary and their dependents who are interested in attending college.

Eligibility   This program is open to members of the auxiliary and their dependents who are related to an active, retired, or deceased member of the South Carolina National Guard. Applicants must be attending or planning to attend a college or university in any state. Along with their application, they must submit transcripts and documentation of financial need.

Financial data   A stipend is awarded (amount not specified).

Duration   1 year.

Number awarded   1 or more each year.

Deadline   January of each year.

[672]
NATIONAL GUARD ASSOCIATION OF SOUTH CAROLINA SCHOLARSHIPS

National Guard Association of South Carolina
Attn: NGASC Scholarship Foundation
132 Pickens Street
Columbia, SC 29205
(803) 254-8456   Toll Free: (800) 822-3235
Fax: (803) 254-3869   E-mail: nginfo@ngasc.org
Web: www.ngasc.org/?page_id=11

Summary To provide funding to current and former South Carolina National Guard members and their dependents who are interested in attending college or graduate school.

Eligibility This program is open to undergraduate students who are 1) current, retired, or deceased members of the South Carolina National Guard; 2) their dependents; and 3) members of the National Guard Association of South Carolina (NGASC). Graduate students are also eligible if they are members of the South Carolina National Guard. Applicants must be attending or interested in attending a college or university in any state as a full-time student. Several of the scholarships include additional restrictions on school or academic major; some are granted only for academic excellence, but most are based on both academics and financial need.

Financial data The stipend is $1,500 or $1,000.

Duration 1 year; may be renewed up to 3 additional years.

Number awarded Varies each year; recently, 42 of these scholarships were awarded: 1 at $1,500 and 41 at $1,000.

Deadline January of each year.

[673]
NATIONAL GUARD ASSOCIATION OF TENNESSEE AUXILIARY SCHOLARSHIP PROGRAM

National Guard Association of Tennessee Auxiliary
Attn: Scholarship Committee
4332 Kenilwood Drive
Nashville, TN 37204-4401
(615) 833-9100   Toll Free: (888) 642-8448 (within TN)
Fax: (615) 833-9173   E-mail: ngatauxiliary@aol.com
Web: www.ngatn.org

Summary To provide financial assistance to spouses of members of the Tennessee National Guard who are interested in attending college in any state.

Eligibility This program is open to spouses of current members of the Tennessee National Guard who are attending or planning to attend college in any state. Applicants must submit a personal statement on their reason for requesting the scholarship, their educational and career goals, and how this award can help them attain those goals. Financial need is also considered in the selection process.

Financial data The stipends are $1,500.

Duration 1 year.

Additional information This program includes the Margene Mogan Proctor Scholarship and the General Jerry Wyatt Memorial Scholarship.

Number awarded 2 each year.

Deadline June of each year.

[674]
NATIONAL GUARD ASSOCIATION OF TENNESSEE SCHOLARSHIP PROGRAM

National Guard Association of Tennessee
Attn: Scholarship Committee
4332 Kenilwood Drive
Nashville, TN 37204-4401
(615) 833-9100   Toll Free: (888) 642-8448 (within TN)
Fax: (615) 833-9173   E-mail: larry@ngatn.org
Web: www.ngatn.org

Summary To provide financial assistance for college to members or dependents of members of the National Guard Association of Tennessee (NGATN).

Eligibility This program is open to active Tennessee National Guard members and to active annual or life members of the NGATN. If no active Guard or association member qualifies, the scholarships may be awarded to the child of a Guard or association member, including life members who have retired or are deceased. All applicants must be high school seniors or graduates who meet entrance or continuation requirements at a Tennessee college or university. Selection is based on leadership in school and civic activities, motivation for continued higher education, academic achievement in high school and/or college, and financial need.

Financial data The stipends are $1,500.

Duration 1 year.

Number awarded 6 each year: 1 to an active National Guard member; 2 to current association members or their dependents; 2 to active National Guard members or their dependents; and 1 to a current Guard member who was mobilized for Operations Desert Storm, Noble Eagle, Enduring Freedom, or Iraqi Freedom.

Deadline June of each year.

[675]
NATIONAL GUARD ASSOCIATION OF TEXAS SCHOLARSHIP PROGRAM

National Guard Association of Texas
Attn: NGAT Educational Foundation
3706 Crawford Avenue
Austin, TX 78731-6803
(512) 454-7300   Toll Free: (800) 252-NGAT
Fax: (512) 467-6803   E-mail: rlindner@ngat.org
Web: www.ngat.org

Summary To provide funding to members and dependents of members of the National Guard Association of Texas who are interested in attending college or graduate school.

Eligibility This program is open to annual and life members of the association and their spouses and children (associate members and their dependents are not eligible). Applicants may be high school seniors, undergraduate students, or graduate students, either enrolled or planning to enroll at an institution of higher education in any state. Along with their application, they must submit an essay on their desire to continue their education. Selection is based on scholarship, citizenship, and leadership.

Financial data Stipends range from $500 to $5,000.

Duration 1 year (nonrenewable).

Additional information This program includes 1 scholarship sponsored by USAA Insurance Corporation.

Number awarded   Varies each year; recently, 13 of these scholarships were awarded: 1 at $5,000, 3 at $2,500, 1 at $2,000, 3 at $1,250, 4 at $1,000, and 1 at $500.
Deadline   February of each year.

[676]
NATIONAL GUARD ASSOCIATION OF UTAH "MINUTEMAN" SCHOLARSHIPS

National Guard Association of Utah
12953 South Minuteman Drive, Room 19835
P.O. Box 435
Draper, UT 84020
(801) 631-6314   E-mail: ngautah@ngaut.org
Web: www.ngaut.org/Scholarship.php

Summary   To provide financial assistance to members of the Utah National Guard and their dependents who are interested in attending college in the state.
Eligibility   This program is open to members of the Utah National Guard and their dependents who are enrolled for at least 6 credit hours at a college or university in the state. Applicants must submit 1) a 150-word description of their educational and career goals; 2) a 200- to 300-word description of leadership and extracurricular activities that they may have had or currently enjoy; 3) a 300-word essay on how the military has influenced their life; 4) a 1-page cover letter or resume; and 5) 2 letters of reference.
Financial data   The stipend is $1,000. Funds are sent to the recipient's school and must be used for tuition, laboratory fees, and curriculum-required books and supplies.
Duration   1 year.
Number awarded   5 each year.
Deadline   March of each year.

[677]
NATIONAL GUARD ASSOCIATION OF VERMONT SCHOLARSHIPS

National Guard Association of Vermont
Attn: Capt John Geno, President
P.O. Box 694
Essex Junction, VT 05452
(802) 338-3397   E-mail: john.geno@us.army.mil
Web: www.ngavt.org/scholarInfo.shtml

Summary   To provide funding to members of the Vermont National Guard (VTNG) and their children or spouses who are interested in attending college or graduate school.
Eligibility   This program is open to current members of the VTNG, their spouses, and their unmarried children. Applicants must be working, or planning to work, on an associate, undergraduate, technical, or graduate degree as a full-time student at a school in any state. Along with their application, they must submit an essay on their commitment to selfless public service or their plan for pursuing it in the future. Selection is based on academic performance, overall potential for a commitment to selfless public service, and financial need.
Financial data   The stipend is $1,000. Funds are sent directly to the recipient.
Duration   1 year; recipients may reapply.
Number awarded   4 each year: 3 to undergraduates and 1 to a graduate student.
Deadline   May of each year.

[678]
NATIONAL GUARD CHAPTER ASMC DEPENDENT SCHOLARSHIPS

American Society of Military Comptrollers-National Guard Chapter
c/o CW3 Carl Jackson, Continuing Education Committee
United States Property and Fiscal Officer for Georgia
Resource Management Division
P.O. Box 17882
Atlanta, GA 30316-0882
(678) 569-6399   E-mail: carl.stefan.jackson@us.army.mil
Web: www.ng-asmc.org

Summary   To provide funding to dependents of members of the National Guard Chapter of the American Society of Military Comptrollers (ASMC) who are interested in studying a field related to financial and resource management.
Eligibility   This program is open to graduating high school seniors and current college students entering a field of study related to financial and resource management (e.g., accounting, business administration, computer science, economics, finance, operations research related to financial management, public administration). Applicants must be a dependent of an ASMC member who has been a member of its National Guard Chapter for at least 24 months. Along with their application, they must submit 2 letters of recommendation, transcripts that include ACT and/or SAT scores, and a 250-word essay on their career and academic goals and financial need.
Financial data   Stipends are $1,500 or $1,000.
Duration   1 year.
Additional information   Membership in ASMC is open to military and civilian personnel involved in the field of military comptrollership. The National Guard Chapter serves ASMC members who are associated with the Army National Guard or Air National Guard in any state.
Number awarded   2 each year: 1 at $1,500 and 1 at $1,000.
Deadline   February of each year.

[679]
NATIONAL GUARD OF GEORGIA SCHOLARSHIP FUND FOR COLLEGES OR UNIVERSITIES

Georgia Guard Insurance Trust
P.O. Box 889
Mableton, GA 30126
(770) 739-9651   Toll Free: (800) 229-1053
Fax: (770) 745-0673   E-mail: director@ngaga.org
Web: www.ngaga.org/scholarships.html

Summary   To provide funding to members of the Georgia National Guard and their spouses, children, and grandchildren who are interested in attending college.
Eligibility   This program is open to policyholders with the Georgia Guard Insurance Trust (GGIT) who are members of the National Guard Association of Georgia (NGAGA) or the Enlisted Association of the National Guard of Georgia (EANGGA); spouses, children, and grandchildren of NGAGA and EANGGA members are also eligible. Applicants must be enrolled or planning to enroll full time at a college or university in any state and have received an academic honor while in high school. Graduating high school seniors must have a combined mathematics and critical reading SAT score of at least 1000 or a GPA of 3.0 or higher. Students already enrolled at a college or university must have a cumulative

GPA of 3.0 or higher. Along with their application, they must submit transcripts, a letter with personal specific facts regarding their desire to continue their education, 2 letters of recommendation, a letter of academic reference, and an agreement to retain insurance with the GGIT for at least 2 years following completion of the school year for which the scholarship is awarded. Selection is based on academics, character, and moral and personal traits.

Financial data   The stipend is $3,000.

Duration   1 year.

Number awarded   Recently, this sponsor awarded a total of 10 scholarships for all of its programs.

Deadline   April of each year.

[680]
NATIONAL GUARD OF GEORGIA SCHOLARSHIP FUND FOR VOCATIONAL OR BUSINESS SCHOOLS

Georgia Guard Insurance Trust
P.O. Box 889
Mableton, GA 30126
(770) 739-9651   Toll Free: (800) 229-1053
Fax: (770) 745-0673   E-mail: director@ngaga.org
Web: www.ngaga.org/scholarships.html

Summary   To provide financial assistance to members of the Georgia National Guard and their spouses, children, and grandchildren who are interested in attending business or vocational school in any state.

Eligibility   This program is open to policyholders with the Georgia Guard Insurance Trust (GGIT) who are members of the National Guard Association of Georgia (NGAGA) or the Enlisted Association of the National Guard of Georgia (EANGGA); spouses, children, and grandchildren of NGAGA and EANGGA members are also eligible. Applicants must be interested in enrolling full time in day or evening classes at a business or vocational school in any state. They must be able to meet program-specific admission standards and institutional requirements and complete all admission procedures for admission to a degree/diploma program in regular program status. Along with their application, they must submit transcripts, a letter with personal specific facts regarding their desire to continue their education, 2 letters of recommendation, and an agreement to retain insurance with the GGIT for at least 2 years following completion of the school year for which the scholarship is awarded. Selection is based on academics, character, and moral and personal traits.

Financial data   The stipend is $3,000.

Duration   1 year.

Number awarded   Recently, this sponsor awarded a total of 10 scholarships for all of its programs.

Deadline   April of each year.

[681]
NATIONAL SCHOLARSHIPS FOR ENTERING COLLEGE FRESHMEN

AMVETS National Headquarters
Attn: Scholarships
4647 Forbes Boulevard
Lanham, MD 20706-3807
(301) 459-9600   Toll Free: (877) 7-AMVETS, ext. 3043
Fax: (301) 459-7924   E-mail: amvets@amvets.org
Web: www.amvets.org/programs/scholarships.html

Summary   To provide funding to the children and grandchildren of members of AMVETS who are entering college.

Eligibility   This program is open to graduating high school seniors who are the children or grandchildren of an AMVETS member or of a deceased veteran who would have been eligible to be an AMVETS member. Applicants must be planning to enroll full time at a college, university, or accredited technical/trade school. U.S. citizenship is required. Selection is based on financial need, academic promise (GPA of 3.0 or higher), involvement in extracurricular activities, and an essay of 50 to 100 words on "What a Higher Education Means to Me."

Financial data   The stipend is $1,000 per year.

Duration   4 years (provided the recipient maintains a GPA of 2.0 or higher).

Additional information   Requests for applications must be accompanied by a self-addressed stamped envelope.

Number awarded   6 each year (1 in each AMVETS national district).

Deadline   April of each year.

[682]
NAUS SCHOLARSHIP PROGRAM

National Association for Uniformed Services
Attn: Scholarship Committee
5535 Hempstead Way
Springfield, VA 22151
(703) 750-1342   Toll Free: (800) 842-3451, ext. 1803
Fax: (703) 354-4380   E-mail: scholarship@naus.org
Web: www.naus.org

Summary   To provide financial assistance for college to members of the National Association for Uniformed Services (NAUS) and their families.

Eligibility   This program is open to NAUS members, their spouses, and their children. Applicants must be high school seniors or undergraduates enrolled full or part time in a degree- or certificate-granting program. High school seniors must have a GPA of 3.0 or higher and undergraduates must have a GPA of 2.5 or higher. Along with their application, they must submit statements, up to 100 words each, on 1) their reasons for enrolling in a postsecondary education program; and 2) a list of academic achievements, personal achievements, extracurricular activities, and any community service performed in the past 2 years. Financial need is not considered in the selection process.

Financial data   The stipend is $2,000.

Duration   1 year.

Additional information   Membership in NAUS is open to members of the armed forces, veterans, retirees, their spouses, and their widow(er)s.

Number awarded   5 each year.

Deadline   April of each year.

[683]
NAVAL ENLISTED RESERVE ASSOCIATION SCHOLARSHIPS

Naval Enlisted Reserve Association
Attn: Scholarship Committee
6703 Farragut Avenue
Falls Church, VA 22042-2189
(703) 534-1329   Toll Free: (800) 776-9020
Fax: (703) 534-3617   E-mail: members@nera.org
Web: www.nera.org

Summary To provide financial assistance for college to members of the Naval Enlisted Reserve Association (NERA) and their families.

Eligibility This program is open to regular or associate NERA members, the spouses of regular members, and the unmarried children and grandchildren under 23 years of age of regular members. Applicants must be graduating high school seniors or undergraduates currently attending an accredited 2- or 4-year college or university as a full- or part-time student. Along with their application, they must submit a 500-word essay on either 1) their career goals and objectives for their education; or 2) why Reservists are important to America. Financial need is not considered in the selection process.

Financial data The stipend is $2,500.

Duration 1 year.

Additional information This program is funded in part by USAA Insurance Corporation.

Number awarded 4 each year.

Deadline June of each year.

[684]
NAVAL HELICOPTER ASSOCIATION REGIONAL SCHOLARSHIPS

Naval Helicopter Association
Attn: Scholarship Fund
P.O. Box 180578
Coronado, CA 92178-0578
(619) 435-7139   Fax: (619) 435-7354
Web: nhascholarshipfund.org/scholarships-available.html

Summary To provide financial assistance for college to students who have an affiliation with the rotary wing activities of the sea services.

Eligibility This program is open to high school seniors and current undergraduates who are children, grandchildren, or spouses of active-duty, former, or retired Navy, Marine Corps, or Coast Guard rotary wing aviators, aircrewmen, or support personnel. Applicants must submit a personal statement on their academic and career aspirations. Selection is based on that statement, academic proficiency, scholastic achievements and awards, extracurricular activities, employment history, and letters of recommendation.

Financial data Stipends are $2,000.

Duration 1 year.

Number awarded 5 each year: 1 in each of 5 regions of the country.

Deadline February of each year.

[685]
NAVAL HELICOPTER ASSOCIATION UNDERGRADUATE SCHOLARSHIPS

Naval Helicopter Association
Attn: Scholarship Fund
P.O. Box 180578
Coronado, CA 92178-0578
(619) 435-7139   Fax: (619) 435-7354
Web: nhascholarshipfund.org/scholarships-available.html

Summary To provide financial assistance for college to students who have an affiliation with the rotary wing activities of the sea services.

Eligibility This program is open to high school seniors and current undergraduates who are children, grandchildren, or spouses of active-duty, former, or retired Navy, Marine Corps, or Coast Guard rotary wing aviators, aircrewmen, or support personnel. Applicants must submit a personal statement on their academic and career aspirations. Selection is based on that statement, academic proficiency, scholastic achievements and awards, extracurricular activities, employment history, and letters of recommendation.

Financial data Stipends are approximately $2,000.

Duration 1 year.

Additional information This program includes the DPA Thousand Points of Light Award (sponsored by D.P. Associates Inc. and L-3 Communications), the Sergei Sikorsky Scholarship, the Edward and Veronica Ream Memorial Scholarship, a scholarship sponsored by Lockheed Martin, and a scholarship sponsored by Raytheon Corporation.

Number awarded 5 each year.

Deadline February of each year.

[686]
NAVAL OFFICERS' SPOUSES' CLUB OF WASHINGTON, D.C. SCHOLARSHIP PROGRAM

Naval Officers' Spouses' Club of Washington, D.C.
Attn: Jenny Werner, Scholarship Committee
1009 Merlins Court
Herndon, VA 20170
(703) 992-8381   E-mail: scholarship@noscdc.com
Web: www.noscdc.com

Summary To provide financial assistance to the children of naval personnel and veterans in Naval District Washington who plan to attend college in any state.

Eligibility This program is open to dependent children of active-duty, retired, or deceased U.S. Navy personnel who are 1) residing and serving in a command within the boundaries of Naval District Washington; 2) retired and had served in a command in Naval District Washington; or 3) deceased and had served in a command in Naval District Washington. Applicants must be high school seniors at an accredited high school in Naval District Washington, U.S. citizens, and planning to enroll full time at an accredited 2- or 4-year undergraduate college or university, visual or performing arts school, or vocational/technical school in any state. Along with their application, they must submit a 600-word essay that covers 1) their personal goals and objectives; 2) how they feel furthering their education will help them accomplish their goals; and 3) how being a military dependent has affected those goals. Selection is based on that essay, GPA, SAT and/or ACT scores, extracurricular activities and awards, and school and community involvement; financial need is not considered.

Financial data The stipend is $2,000. Funds may be used only for tuition.

Duration 1 year; nonrenewable.

Additional information Naval District Washington covers the District of Columbia; the Maryland counties of Calvert, Charles, Montgomery, Prince George's, and St. Mary's; and the Virginia counties of Arlington, Fairfax, Fauquier, King George, Loudoun, Prince William, and Stafford (plus the independent cities within their boundaries).

Number awarded Varies each year; recently, 13 of these scholarships were awarded.

Deadline March of each year.

[687]
NAVAL SPECIAL WARFARE DEVELOPMENT GROUP SCHOLARSHIPS

Navy Seal Foundation
Attn: DEVGRU Scholarship Committee
1619 D Street, Building 5326
Virginia Beach, VA 23459
(757) 363-7490   Fax: (757) 363-7491
E-mail: info@navysealfoundation.org
Web: www.navysealfoundation.org

Summary To provide financial assistance for college to the children and spouses of personnel assigned to the Naval Special Warfare Development Group (DEVGRU).

Eligibility This program is open to the dependent children and spouses of former and present Navy SEAL, Special Warfare Combat Crewman (SWCC), or Military Direct Support person who is or has been assigned to DEVGRU. Applicants must be enrolled or planning to enroll at a trade school, technical/vocational institute, or undergraduate college. Along with their application, they must submit an essay on their plans as related to their educational and career objectives and long-term goals. Selection is based on merit (as measured by GPA, SAT scores, class rank, extracurricular activities, volunteer community involvement, leadership positions held, military service record, and after school employment, as appropriate) and academic potential.

Financial data Stipends are $15,000, $7,500, or $5,000 per year.

Duration 1 year; may be renewed.

Number awarded Varies each year; recently, the Navy Seal Foundation awarded 16 scholarships for all of its programs: 3 for 4 years at $15,000 per year to high school seniors and graduates, 3 for 1 year at $7,500 to high school seniors and graduates, 3 for 1 year at $15,000 to current college students, 3 for 1 year at $7,500 to current college students, and 4 for 1 year at $5,000 to spouses.

Deadline January of each year.

[688]
NAVY COUNSELOR ASSOCIATION EDUCATIONAL SCHOLARSHIP FUND

Navy Counselor Association
Attn: National Headquarters
P.O. Box 15233
Norfolk, VA 23511-0233
Web: www.usnca.org

Summary To provide money for college to dependent children of members of the Navy Counselor Association (NCA).

Eligibility This program is open to the dependent children of active NCA members. Applicants must be entering or attending an accredited college, university, or vocational/technical school. Along with their application, they must submit a 500-word essay on their educational goals and how those goals will benefit them and their community. Selection is based on the essay, academics, civic involvement, extracurricular activities, and goals.

Financial data The stipend is $1,500 per year.

Duration 1 year; may be renewed 1 additional year.

Additional information More information on this program can also be obtained from the NCA at the parent's current duty station (or last duty station, if deceased).

Number awarded Varies each year; recently, 4 of these scholarships were awarded.

Deadline June of each year.

[689]
NAVY LEAGUE FOUNDATION SCHOLARSHIPS

Navy League of the United States
Attn: Scholarships
2300 Wilson Boulevard, Suite 200
Arlington, VA 22201-5424
(703) 528-1775   Toll Free: (800) 356-5760
Fax: (703) 528-2333
E-mail: scholarships@navyleague.org
Web: www.navyleague.org

Summary To provide financial assistance for college to dependent children of sea service personnel.

Eligibility This program is open to U.S. citizens who are 1) dependents or direct descendants of an active, Reserve, retired, or honorably discharged member of the U.S. sea service (including the Navy, Marine Corps, Coast Guard, or Merchant Marine), or 2) currently an active member of the Naval Sea Cadet Corps. Applicants must be entering their freshman year at an accredited college or university. They must have a GPA of 3.0 or higher. Along with their application, they must submit transcripts, 2 letters of recommendation, SAT/ACT scores, documentation of financial need, proof of qualifying sea service duty, and a 1-page personal statement on why they should be considered for this scholarship.

Financial data The stipend is $2,500 per year.

Duration 4 years, provided the recipient maintains a GPA of 3.0 or higher.

Additional information This program includes the following named awards: the John G. Brokaw Scholarship, the Jack and Eileen Anderson Scholarship, the Ann E. Clark Foundation Scholarship, the Albert Levinson Scholarship, the Wesley C. Cameron Scholarship, and the United Armed Forces Association Scholarship.

Number awarded Approximately 25 each year.

Deadline March of each year.

[690]
NAVY/MARINE CORPS/COAST GUARD ENLISTED DEPENDENT SPOUSE SCHOLARSHIP

Navy Wives Clubs of America
c/o NSA Mid-South
P.O. Box 54022
Millington, TN 38054-0022
Toll Free: (866) 511-NWCA
E-mail: nwca@navywivesclubsofamerica.org
Web: www.navywivesclubsofamerica.org/scholarships

Summary To provide financial assistance for undergraduate or graduate study to spouses of naval personnel.

Eligibility This program is open to the spouses of active-duty Navy, Marine Corps, or Coast Guard members who can demonstrate financial need. Applicants must be 1) a high school graduate or senior planning to attend college full time next year; 2) currently enrolled in an undergraduate program and planning to continue as a full-time undergraduate; 3) a college graduate or senior planning to be a full-time graduate student next year; or 4) a high school graduate or GED recipient planning to attend vocational or business school next year. Along with their application, they must submit a brief statement on why they feel they should be awarded this scholarship and any special circumstances (financial or other) they wish to have considered. Financial need is also considered in the selection process.

Financial data The stipends range from $500 to $1,000 each year (depending upon the donations from chapters of the Navy Wives Clubs of America).

Duration 1 year.

Number awarded 1 or more each year.

Deadline May of each year.

[691]
NAVY SEAL FOUNDATION SCHOLARSHIPS

Navy Seal Foundation
Attn: Chief Financial Officer
1619 D Street, Building 5326
Virginia Beach, VA 23459
(757) 363-7490   Fax: (757) 363-7491
E-mail: info@navysealfoundation.org
Web: www.navysealfoundation.org

Summary To provide financial assistance for college to Naval Special Warfare (NSW) personnel and their families.

Eligibility This program is open to active-duty Navy SEALS, Special Warfare Combat Crewmen (SWCC), and military personnel assigned to other NSW commands. Their dependent children and spouses are also eligible. Applicants must be entering or continuing full or part-time students working on an associate or bachelor's degree. Along with their application, they must submit an essay, up to 2 pages in length, on a topic that changes annually; recently, students were asked to explore benevolence in their life and describe when they were able to demonstrate it. They may also indicate any special circumstances such as financial need, single parent status, or disabilities.

Financial data Stipends are $15,000, $7,500, or $5,000 per year.

Duration 1 year; may be renewed.

Number awarded Varies each year; recently, the Navy Seal Foundation awarded 16 scholarships for all of its programs: 3 for 4 years at $15,000 per year to high school

seniors and graduates, 3 for 1 year at $7,500 to high school seniors and graduates, 3 for 1 year at $15,000 to current college students, 3 for 1 year at $7,500 to current college students, and 4 for 1 year at $5,000 to spouses.

Deadline February of each year.

[692]
NAVY SUPPLY CORPS FOUNDATION MEMORIAL SCHOLARSHIPS

Navy Supply Corps Foundation
Attn: Administrator
P.O. Box 6228
Athens, GA 30604-6228
(706) 354-4111   Fax: (706) 354-0334
E-mail: foundationadmin@usnscf.com
Web: www.usnscf.com/programs/scholarships.aspx

Summary To provide funding for college to children of Navy Supply Corps personnel who died on active duty.

Eligibility This program is open to children of Navy Supply Corps personnel who died on active duty after 2001. The program applies to Active Duty Supply Corps Officers as well as Reserve Supply Corps Officers in the following categories: Mobilization, Active Duty for Special Work (ADSW), Active Duty for Training (ADT), Annual Training (AT), and Inactive Duty for Training (IDT). Applicants must be attending or planning to attend a 2- or 4-year accredited college on a full-time basis and have a GPA of 2.5 or higher in high school and/or college. Selection is based on character, leadership, academic achievement, extracurricular activities, and need.

Financial data The stipend is $2,500.

Duration 1 year.

Number awarded Varies each year; recently, 5 of these scholarships were awarded.

Deadline March of each year.

[693]
NAVY SUPPLY CORPS FOUNDATION NIB/NISH SCHOLARSHIPS

Navy Supply Corps Foundation
Attn: Administrator
P.O. Box 6228
Athens, GA 30604-6228
(706) 354-4111   Fax: (706) 354-0334
E-mail: foundationadmin@usnscf.com
Web: www.usnscf.com/programs/scholarships.aspx

Summary To provide financial assistance for college to blind or disabled relatives of current or former Navy Supply Corps personnel.

Eligibility This program is open to dependents (child, grandchild, or spouse) of a living or deceased regular, retired, reserve, or prior Navy Supply Corps officer, warrant officer, or enlisted personnel. Enlisted ratings that apply are AK (Aviation Storekeeper), SK (Storekeeper), MS (Mess Specialist), DK (Disbursing Clerk), SH (Ship Serviceman), LI (Lithographer), and PC (Postal Clerk). Applicants must be attending or planning to attend a 2- or 4-year accredited college on a full-time basis and have a GPA of 2.5 or higher in high school and/or college. They must be able to document blindness or severe disability. Selection is based on character, leadership, academic achievement, extracurricular activities, and financial need.

Financial data Stipends range from $1,000 to $5,000.

Duration 1 year.

Additional information This program was established in 2005 with support from National Industries for the Blind (NIB) and NISH (formerly the National Industries for the Severely Handicapped).

Number awarded 1 or more each year.

Deadline March of each year.

[694]
NAVY SUPPLY CORPS FOUNDATION SCHOLARSHIPS

Navy Supply Corps Foundation
Attn: Administrator
P.O. Box 6228
Athens, GA 30604-6228
(706) 354-4111   Fax: (706) 354-0334
E-mail: foundationadmin@usnscf.com
Web: www.usnscf.com/programs/scholarships.aspx

Summary To provide financial assistance for college to relatives of current or former Navy Supply Corps personnel.

Eligibility This program is open to dependents (child, grandchild, or spouse) of a living or deceased regular, retired, Reserve, or prior Navy Supply Corps officer, warrant officer, or enlisted personnel. Enlisted ratings that apply are AK (Aviation Storekeeper), SK (Storekeeper), MS (Mess Specialist), DK (Disbursing Clerk), SH (Ship Serviceman), LI (Lithographer), and PC (Postal Clerk). Applicants must be attending or planning to attend a 2- or 4-year accredited college on a full-time basis and have a GPA of 2.5 or higher in high school and/or college. Selection is based on character, leadership, academic achievement, extracurricular activities, and financial need.

Financial data Stipends range from $1,000 to $12,500 per year.

Duration 1 year; some scholarships may be renewed for 3 additional years.

Additional information This program began in 1971.

Number awarded Varies each year; recently, the foundation awarded 82 scholarships: 1 4-year scholarship at $12,500 per year, 6 4-year scholarships at $5,000 per year, 8 4-year scholarships at $2,500 per year, 12 1-year scholarships at $5,000, 34 1-year scholarships at $2,500, and 21 1-year scholarships at $1,000. Since the program was established, it has awarded 1,942 scholarships with a total value of more than $3,900,000.

Deadline March of each year.

[695]
NAVY WIVES CLUBS OF AMERICA NATIONAL SCHOLARSHIPS

Navy Wives Clubs of America
c/o NSA Mid-South
P.O. Box 54022
Millington, TN 38054-0022
Toll Free: (866) 511-NWCA
E-mail: nwca@navywivesclubsofamerica.org
Web: www.navywivesclubsofamerica.org/scholarships

Summary To provide financial assistance for college or graduate school to the children of naval personnel.

Eligibility Applicants for these scholarships must be the children (natural born, legally adopted, or stepchildren) of enlisted members of the Navy, Marine Corps, or Coast Guard on active duty, retired with pay, or deceased. Applicants must be attending or planning to attend an accredited college or university as a full-time undergraduate or graduate student. They must have a GPA of 2.5 or higher. Along with their application, they must submit an essay on their career objectives and the reasons they chose those objectives. Selection is based on academic standing, moral character, and financial need. Some scholarships are reserved for students majoring in special education, medical students, and children of members of Navy Wives Clubs of America (NWCA).

Financial data The stipend is $1,500.

Duration 1 year; may be renewed up to 3 additional years.

Additional information Membership in the NWCA is open to spouses of enlisted personnel serving in the Navy, Marine Corps, Coast Guard, and the active Reserve units of those services; spouses of enlisted personnel who have been honorably discharged, retired, or transferred to the Fleet Reserve on completion of duty; and widows of enlisted personnel in those services.

Number awarded 30 each year, including at least 4 to freshmen, 4 to current undergraduates applying for the first time, 2 to medical students, 1 to a student majoring in special education, and 4 to children of NWCA members.

Deadline May of each year.

[696]
NCPOA/BART LONGO MEMORIAL SCHOLARSHIPS

National Chief Petty Officers' Association
c/o Marjorie Hays, Treasurer
1014 Ronald Drive
Corpus Christi, TX 78412-3548
Web: www.goatlocker.org/ncpoa/scholarship.htm

Summary To provide financial assistance for college or graduate school to members of the National Chief Petty Officers' Association (NCPOA) and their families.

Eligibility This program is open to members of the NCPOA and the children, stepchildren, and grandchildren of living or deceased members. Applicants may be high school seniors or graduates entering a college or university or students currently enrolled full time as undergraduate or graduate students. Selection is based on academic achievement and participation in extracurricular activities; need is not considered.

Financial data The stipend is $1,000.

Duration 1 year.

Additional information Membership in the NCPOA is limited to men and women who served or are serving as Chief Petty Officers in the U.S. Navy, U.S. Coast Guard, or their Reserve components for at least 30 days.

Number awarded 2 each year: 1 to a high school senior or graduate and 1 to an undergraduate or graduate student.

Deadline May of each year.

[697]
NEBRASKA WAIVER OF TUITION FOR VETERANS' DEPENDENTS

Department of Veterans' Affairs
State Office Building
301 Centennial Mall South, Sixth Floor
P.O. Box 95083
Lincoln, NE 68509-5083
(402) 471-2458   Fax: (402) 471-2491
E-mail: john.hilgert@nebraska.gov
Web: www.vets.state.ne.us/benefits.html

Summary To provide financial assistance for college to dependents of deceased and disabled veterans and military personnel in Nebraska.

Eligibility Eligible are spouses, widow(er)s, and children who are residents of Nebraska and whose parent, stepparent, or spouse was a member of the U.S. armed forces and 1) died of a service-connected disability; 2) died subsequent to discharge as a result of injury or illness sustained while in service; 3) is permanently and totally disabled as a result of military service; or 4) is classified as missing in action or as a prisoner of war during armed hostilities. Applicants must be attending or planning to attend a branch of the University of Nebraska, a state college, or a community college in Nebraska.

Financial data Tuition is waived at public institutions in Nebraska.

Duration The waiver is valid for 1 degree, diploma, or certificate from a community college and 1 baccalaureate degree.

Additional information Applications may be submitted through 1 of the recognized veterans' organizations or any county service officer.

Number awarded Varies each year; recently, 311 of these grants were awarded.

Deadline Deadline not specified.

[698]
NEW HAMPSHIRE SCHOLARSHIPS FOR ORPHANS OF VETERANS

New Hampshire Department of Education
Attn: Higher Education Commission
Walker Building, Suite 20
21 Fruit Street
Concord, NH 03301-2450
(603) 271-2695   Toll Free: (888) 747-2382, ext. 119
Fax: (603) 271-1953   E-mail: Amy.Slattery@doe.nh.gov
Web: www.education.nh.gov/highered/finanical/index.htm

Summary To provide financial assistance to the children of New Hampshire veterans who died of service-connected causes and plan to attend college in the state.

Eligibility This program is open to New Hampshire residents between 16 and 25 years of age whose parent(s) died while on active duty or as a result of a service-related disability incurred during World War II, the Korean Conflict, the southeast Asian Conflict (Vietnam), or the Gulf Wars. Parents must have been residents of New Hampshire at the time of death. Applicants must be enrolled at least half time as undergraduate students at a public college or university in New Hampshire. Financial need is not considered in the selection process.

Financial data The stipend is $2,500 per year, to be used for the payment of room, board, books, and supplies. Recipients are also eligible to receive a tuition waiver from the institution.

Duration 1 year; may be renewed for up to 3 additional years.

Additional information This program began in 1943.

Number awarded Varies each year; recently, 2 of these scholarships were awarded.

Deadline Deadline not specified.

[699]
NEW JERSEY AMERICAN LEGION SCHOLARSHIPS

American Legion
Department of New Jersey
Attn: Scholarship Judges
135 West Hanover Street
Trenton, NJ 08618
(609) 695-5418   Fax: (609) 394-1532
E-mail: newjersey@legion.org
Web: www.njamericanlegion.org

Summary To provide financial assistance to the descendants of members of the New Jersey Department of the American Legion who plan to attend college in any state.

Eligibility This program is open to high school seniors who are the natural or adopted children, grandchildren, or great-grandchildren of members of the American Legion's New Jersey Department. Applicants must be planning to attend a college or university in any state. Along with their application, they must submit a brief statement on the reasons for their choice of vocation. Selection is based on character (20%), Americanism and community service (20%), leadership (20%), scholarship (20%), and financial need (20%).

Financial data The stipend is $1,000 per year.

Duration These scholarships are for 4 years, 2 years, or 1 year.

Additional information These scholarships were formerly designated the Lawrence Luterman Memorial Scholarships and the Stutz Memorial Scholarship.

Number awarded 8 each year: 2 for 4 years, 4 for 2 years, and 2 for 1 year.

Deadline February of each year.

[700]
NEW JERSEY BANKERS EDUCATION FOUNDATION SCHOLARSHIPS

New Jersey Bankers Association
Attn: New Jersey Bankers Education Foundation, Inc.
411 North Avenue East
Cranford, NJ 07016-2436
(908) 272-8500, ext. 614   Fax: (908) 272-6626
E-mail: j.meredith@njbankers.com
Web: www.njbankers.com

Summary To provide financial assistance to dependents of deceased and disabled military personnel who have a connection to New Jersey and are interested in attending college in any state.

Eligibility This program is open to the spouses, children, stepchildren, and grandchildren of members of the armed services who died or became disabled while on active duty; it is not required that the military person died in combat. Applicants must have a high school or equivalency diploma and be attending college in any state. Adult dependents who wish to obtain a high school equivalency diploma are also eligible. Either the dependent or the servicemember must have a connection to New Jersey; the applicant's permanent address must be in New Jersey or the servicemember's last permanent address or military base must have been in the state. Financial need is considered in the selection process.

Financial data A stipend is awarded (amount not specified).

Duration 1 year; may be renewed if the recipient maintains a "C" average.

Additional information This program began in 2005.

Number awarded 1 or more each year.

Deadline June of each year.

[701]
NEW JERSEY LEGION AUXILIARY PAST PRESIDENTS' PARLEY NURSES SCHOLARSHIPS

American Legion Auxiliary
Department of New Jersey
c/o Lucille M. Miller, Secretary/Treasurer
1540 Kuser Road, Suite A-8
Hamilton, NJ 08619
(609) 581-9580   Fax: (609) 581-8429

Summary To provide financial assistance to New Jersey residents who are the descendants of veterans and interested in studying nursing at a school in any state.

Eligibility This program is open to the children, grandchildren, and great-grandchildren of veterans who served in the U.S. armed forces during specified periods of wartime. Applicants must be graduating high school seniors who have been residents of New Jersey for at least 2 years. They must be planning to study nursing at a school in any state. Along with their application, they must submit a 1,000-word essay on a topic that changes annually; recently, students were asked to write on the topic, "The Importance of Helping Military Families in Your Community." Selection is based on academic achievement (40%), character (15%), leadership (15%), Americanism (15%), and financial need (15%).

Financial data A stipend is awarded (amount not specified).

Duration 1 year.

Number awarded 1 or more each year.

Deadline April of each year.

[702]
NEW JERSEY NATIONAL GUARD TUITION PROGRAM

New Jersey Department of Military and Veterans Affairs
Attn: New Jersey Army National Guard Education Center
3650 Saylors Pond Road
Fort Dix, NJ 08640-7600
(609) 562-0654   Toll Free: (888) 859-0352
Fax: (609) 562-0201
Web: www.state.nj.us/military/education/NJNGTP.htm

Summary To provide financial assistance for college or graduate school to New Jersey National Guard members and the surviving spouses and children of deceased members.

Eligibility This program is open to active members of the New Jersey National Guard who have completed Initial Active Duty for Training (IADT). Applicants must be New Jersey residents who have been accepted into a program of undergrad-

uate or graduate study at any of 31 public institutions of higher education in the state. The surviving spouses and children of deceased members of the Guard who had completed IADT and were killed in the performance of their duties while a member of the Guard are also eligible if the school has classroom space available.

Financial data Tuition for up to 15 credits per semester is waived for full-time recipients in state-supported colleges or community colleges in New Jersey.

Duration 1 semester; may be renewed.

Number awarded Varies each year.

Deadline Deadline not specified.

[703]
NEW JERSEY POW/MIA TUITION BENEFIT PROGRAM

New Jersey Department of Military and Veterans Affairs
Attn: Division of Veterans Programs
101 Eggert Crossing Road
P.O. Box 340
Trenton, NJ 08625-0340
(609) 530-7045   Toll Free: (800) 624-0508 (within NJ)
Fax: (609) 530-7075
Web: www.state.nj.us/military/veterans/programs.html

Summary To provide money for college to the children of New Jersey military personnel reported as missing in action or prisoners of war during the southeast Asian conflict.

Eligibility Eligible to apply for this assistance are New Jersey residents attending or accepted at a New Jersey public or independent postsecondary institution whose parents were military service personnel officially declared prisoners of war or missing in action after January 1, 1960.

Financial data This program entitles recipients to full undergraduate tuition at any public or independent postsecondary educational institution in New Jersey.

Duration Assistance continues until completion of a bachelor's degree.

Number awarded Varies each year.

Deadline February of each year for the spring term and September for the fall and spring terms.

[704]
NEW MEXICO CHILDREN OF DECEASED MILITARY AND STATE POLICE PERSONNEL SCHOLARSHIPS

New Mexico Department of Veterans' Services
Attn: Benefits Division
407 Galisteo Street, Room 142
P.O. Box 2324
Santa Fe, NM 87504-2324
(505) 827-6374   Toll Free: (866) 433-VETS
Fax: (505) 827-6372   E-mail: alan.martinez@state.nm.us
Web: www.dvs.state.nm.us/benefits.html

Summary To provide financial assistance for college or graduate school to the children of deceased military and state police personnel in New Mexico.

Eligibility This program is open to the children of 1) military personnel killed in action or as a result of such action during a period of armed conflict; 2) members of the New Mexico National Guard killed while on active duty; and 3) New Mexico State Police killed on active duty. Applicants must be between the ages of 16 and 26 and enrolled in a state-supported school in New Mexico. Children of deceased veterans must be nominated by the New Mexico Veterans' Service Commission; children of National Guard members must be nominated by the adjutant general of the state; children of state police must be nominated by the New Mexico State Police Board. Selection is based on merit and financial need.

Financial data The scholarships provide full waiver of tuition at state-funded postsecondary schools in New Mexico. A stipend of $150 per semester ($300 per year) provides assistance with books and fees.

Duration 1 year; may be renewed.

Deadline Deadline not specified.

[705]
NEW MEXICO LEGION AUXILIARY PAST PRESIDENTS PARLEY SCHOLARSHIPS

American Legion Auxiliary
Department of New Mexico
1215 Mountain Road, N.E.
Albuquerque, NM 87102-2716
(505) 242-9918   Fax: (505) 247-0478
E-mail: alauxnm@netscape.com

Summary To provide financial assistance to residents of New Mexico who are the children of veterans and studying nursing or a related medical field at a school in any state.

Eligibility This program is open to New Mexico residents who are attending college in any state. Applicants must be the children of veterans who served during specified periods of wartime. They must be studying nursing or a related medical field. Selection is based on scholarship, character, leadership, Americanism, and financial need.

Financial data A stipend is awarded (amount not specified).

Deadline April of each year.

[706]
NEW YORK LEGION AUXILIARY DEPARTMENT SCHOLARSHIP

American Legion Auxiliary
Department of New York
112 State Street, Suite 1310
Albany, NY 12207
(518) 463-1162   Toll Free: (800) 421-6348
Fax: (518) 449-5406   E-mail: alanyterry@nycap.rr.com
Web: www.deptny.org/Scholarships.htm

Summary To provide funding to New York residents who are the descendants of veterans and interested in attending college.

Eligibility This program is open to residents of New York who are high school seniors or graduates and attending or planning to attend an accredited college or university in any state. Applicants must be the children, grandchildren, or great-grandchildren of veterans who served during specified periods of wartime. Along with their application, they must submit a 500-word essay on a subject of their choice. Selection is based on character (20%), Americanism (20%), leadership (20%), scholarship (15%), and financial need (25%). U.S. citizenship is required.

Financial data The stipend is $1,000. Funds are paid directly to the recipient's school.

Duration 1 year.

Number awarded 1 each year.

Deadline February of each year.

[707]
NEW YORK LEGION AUXILIARY DISTRICT SCHOLARSHIPS

American Legion Auxiliary
Department of New York
112 State Street, Suite 1310
Albany, NY 12207
(518) 463-1162   Toll Free: (800) 421-6348
Fax: (518) 449-5406   E-mail: alanyterry@nycap.rr.com
Web: www.deptny.org/Scholarships.htm

Summary To provide financial assistance to descendants of veterans in New York who are interested in attending college in any state.

Eligibility This program is open to residents of New York who are high school seniors or graduates and attending or planning to attend an accredited college or university in any state. Applicants must be the children, grandchildren, or great-grandchildren of veterans who served during specified periods of wartime. Along with their application, they must submit a 500-word essay on why they chose to further their education. Selection is based on character (30%), Americanism (20%), leadership (10%), scholarship (30%), and financial need (20%). U.S. citizenship is required.

Financial data The stipend is $1,000. Funds are paid directly to the recipient's school.

Duration 1 year.

Number awarded 10 each year: 1 in each of the 10 judicial districts in New York.

Deadline February of each year.

[708]
NEW YORK LEGION AUXILIARY PAST PRESIDENTS PARLEY STUDENT SCHOLARSHIP IN MEDICAL FIELD

American Legion Auxiliary
Department of New York
112 State Street, Suite 1310
Albany, NY 12207
(518) 463-1162   Toll Free: (800) 421-6348
Fax: (518) 449-5406   E-mail: alanyterry@nycap.rr.com
Web: www.deptny.org/Scholarships.htm

Summary To provide funding to descendants of wartime veterans in New York who are interested in attending college to prepare for a career in a medical field.

Eligibility This program is open to residents of New York who are high school seniors or graduates and attending or planning to attend an accredited college or university in any state to prepare for a career in a medical field. Applicants must be the children, grandchildren, or great-grandchildren of veterans who served during specified periods of wartime. Along with their application, they must submit a 500-word essay on why they selected the medical field. Selection is based on character (30%), Americanism (20%), leadership (10%), scholarship (20%), and financial need (20%). U.S. citizenship is required.

Financial data The stipend is $1,000. Funds are paid directly to the recipient's school.

Duration 1 year.

Number awarded 2 each year.

Deadline February of each year.

[709]
NEW YORK STATE MILITARY SERVICE RECOGNITION SCHOLARSHIPS

New York State Higher Education Services Corporation
Attn: Student Information
99 Washington Avenue
Albany, NY 12255
(518) 473-1574   Toll Free: (888) NYS-HESC
Fax: (518) 473-3749   TDD: (800) 445-5234
E-mail: webmail@hesc.com
Web: www.hesc.com

Summary To provide funding to disabled veterans and the family members of deceased or disabled veterans who are residents of New York and interested in attending college in the state.

Eligibility This program is open to New York residents who served in the armed forces of the United States or state organized militia at any time on or after August 2, 1990 and became severely and permanently disabled as a result of injury or illness suffered or incurred in a combat theater or combat zone or during military training operations in preparation for duty in a combat theater or combat zone of operations. Also eligible are the children, spouses, or financial dependents of members of the armed forces of the United States or state organized militia who at any time after August 2, 1990 1) died, became severely and permanently disabled as a result of injury or illness suffered or incurred, or are classified as missing in action in a combat theater or combat zone of operations; 2) died as a result of injuries incurred in those designated areas; or 3) died or became severely and permanently disabled as a result of injury or illness suffered or incurred during military training operations in preparation for duty in a combat theater or combat zone of operations. Applicants must be attending or accepted at an approved program of study as full-time undergraduates at a public college or university or private institution in New York.

Financial data At public colleges and universities, this program provides payment of actual tuition and mandatory educational fees; actual room and board charged to students living on campus or an allowance for room and board for commuter students; and allowances for books, supplies, and transportation. At private institutions, the award is equal to the amount charged at the State University of New York (SUNY) for 4-year tuition and average mandatory fees (or the student's actual tuition and fees, whichever is less) plus allowances for room, board, books, supplies, and transportation.

Duration This program is available for 4 years of full-time undergraduate study (or 5 years in an approved 5-year bachelor's degree program).

Number awarded Varies each year.

Deadline April of each year.

[710]
NON COMMISSIONED OFFICERS ASSOCIATION SCHOLARSHIP FUND

Non Commissioned Officers Association of the United States of America
Attn: Scholarship Fund
P.O. Box 33790
San Antonio, TX 78265-3790
Toll Free: (800) 662-2620
E-mail: membsvc@ncoausa.org
Web: www.ncoausa.org

Summary To provide financial assistance for college to spouses and children of members of the Non Commissioned Officers Association.

Eligibility This program is open to spouses and children (under 25 years of age) of members of the association. Children must submit 2 letters of recommendation from teachers, a personal recommendation from an adult who is not a relative, a handwritten autobiography, a certified transcript of high school or college grades, ACT or SAT scores, and a composition on Americanism. Spouses must submit a copy of their high school diploma or GED equivalent; a certified transcript of all college courses completed (if any); a certificate of completion for any other courses or training; a brief biographical background statement; and a letter of intent that includes a description of their proposed course of study for a degree, plans for completion of a degree, and a paragraph on "What a College Degree Means to Me." Financial need is not normally considered in the selection process and no applicant will be rejected because of a lack of need, but in some cases of extreme need it may be used as a factor. Each year, 2 special awards are presented: the Mary Barraco Scholarship to the student submitting the best essay on Americanism, and the William T. Green Scholarship to the student with the best high school academic record.

Financial data The scholarship stipend is $900 for children of members or $1,000 for spouses of members; the special awards are $1,000. Funds are paid directly to the designated school to be used for the recipient's room and board, tuition, library fees, textbooks, and related instructional material.

Duration 1 year; may be renewed if the student maintains a GPA of 3.0 or higher and carries at least 15 hours.

Additional information Spouses who receive a grant must apply for membership in 1 of the NCOA membership categories (regular, associate, veteran, or auxiliary).

Number awarded 15 each year: 9 scholarships to children of members, 4 scholarships to spouses of members, and 2 special awards.

Deadline March of each year.

[711]
NONRESIDENT TUITION WAIVERS FOR VETERANS AND THEIR DEPENDENTS WHO MOVE TO TEXAS

Texas Higher Education Coordinating Board
Attn: Grants and Special Programs
1200 East Anderson Lane
P.O. Box 12788
Austin, TX 78711-2788
(512) 427-6340   Toll Free: (800) 242-3062
Fax: (512) 427-6420   E-mail: grantinfo@thecb.state.tx.us
Web: www.collegeforalltexans.com

Summary To exempt veterans who move to Texas and their dependents from the payment of nonresident tuition at public institutions of higher education in the state.

Eligibility Eligible for these waivers are former members of the U.S. armed forces and commissioned officers of the Public Health Service who are retired or have been honorably discharged, their spouses, and dependent children. Applicants must have moved to Texas upon separation from the service and be attending or planning to attend a public college or university in the state. They must have indicated their intent to become a Texas resident by registering to vote and doing 1 of the following: owning real property in Texas, registering an automobile in Texas, or executing a will indicating that they are a resident of the state.

Financial data Although persons eligible under this program are still classified as nonresidents, they are entitled to pay the resident tuition at Texas institutions of higher education on an immediate basis.

Duration 1 year.

Number awarded Varies each year.

Deadline Deadline not specified.

[712]
NORTH CAROLINA NATIONAL GUARD ASSOCIATION SCHOLARSHIPS

North Carolina National Guard Association
Attn: Educational Foundation, Inc.
7410 Chapel Hill Road
Raleigh, NC 27607-5047
(919) 851-3390   Toll Free: (800) 821-6159 (within NC)
Fax: (919) 859-4990
E-mail: peggyncngaef@bellsouth.net
Web: ncnga.org

Summary To provide financial assistance to members and dependents of members of the North Carolina National Guard Association who plan to attend college in any state.

Eligibility This program is open to active and associate members of the association as well as the spouses, children, grandchildren, and legal dependents of active, associate, or deceased members. Applicants must be high school seniors, high school graduates, or students currently enrolled at a college or university in any state. Selection is based on financial need, academic achievement, citizenship, leadership, and other application information. The most outstanding applicants receive scholarships provided by the SECU Foundation. Applicants who meet specified additional requirements qualify for various memorial and special scholarships.

Financial data Stipends are $10,000 or $5,000 for the SECU Foundation Scholarships, $1,000 for memorial and special scholarships, $1,000 for citizenship awards, $800 for general scholarships, or $400 for community college scholarships.

Duration 1 year; may be renewed.

Additional information This program, which began in 1968, includes a number of named memorial and special scholarships. Other scholarships are funded by the SECU Foundation of the State Employees' Credit Union and the USAA Insurance Corporation. The association also funds the Academic Excellence Leadership Award ($1,000) for outstanding applicants and the Special Population Scholarship ($1,000) for applicants with disabilities.

Number awarded Varies each year; recently, 37 of these scholarships were awarded: 2 SECU Foundation Scholarships (1 at $10,000 and 1 at $5,000), 18 memorial and special scholarships at $1,000, 2 citizenship awards are $1,000, 10 general scholarships at $800, and 5 community college scholarships at $400.

Deadline January of each year for high school graduates and college students; February for high school seniors.

[713]
NORTH CAROLINA SCHOLARSHIPS FOR CHILDREN OF WAR VETERANS

Division of Veterans Affairs
Albemarle Building
325 North Salisbury Street, Suite 1065
1315 Mail Service Center
Raleigh, NC 27699-1315
(919) 733-3851   Fax: (919) 733-2834
E-mail: ncdva.aso@ncmail.net
Web: www.ncveterans.com/benefitlist.aspx

Summary To provide financial assistance to the children of disabled and other classes of North Carolina veterans who plan to attend college in the state.

Eligibility Eligible applicants come from 5 categories: Class I-A: the veteran parent died in wartime service or as a result of a service-connected condition incurred in wartime service; Class I-B: the veteran parent is rated by the U.S. Department of Veterans Affairs (VA) as 100% disabled as a result of wartime service and currently or at the time of death was drawing compensation for such disability; Class II: the veteran parent is rated by the VA as much as 20% but less than 100% disabled due to wartime service, or was awarded a Purple Heart medal for wounds received, and currently or at the time of death drawing compensation for such disability; Class III: the veteran parent is currently or was at the time of death receiving a VA pension for total and permanent disability, or the veteran parent is deceased but does not qualify under any other provisions, or the veteran parent served in a combat zone or waters adjacent to a combat zone and received a campaign badge or medal but does not qualify under any other provisions; Class IV: the veteran parent was a prisoner of war or missing in action. For all classes, applicants must 1) be under 25 years of age and have a veteran parent who was a resident of North Carolina at the time of entrance into the armed forces; or 2) be the natural child, or adopted child prior to age 15, who was born in North Carolina, has been a resident of the state continuously since birth, and is the child of a veteran whose disabilities occurred during a period of war.

Financial data Students in Classes I-A, II, III, and IV receive $4,500 per academic year if they attend a private college or junior college; if attending a public postsecondary institution, they receive free tuition, a room allowance, a board allowance, and exemption from certain mandatory fees. Students in Class I-B receive $1,500 per academic year if they attend a private college or junior college; if attending a public postsecondary institution, they receive free tuition and exemption from certain mandatory fees.

Duration 4 academic years.

Number awarded An unlimited number of awards are made under Classes I-A, I-B, and IV. Classes II and III are limited to 100 awards each year in each class.

Deadline Applications for Classes I-A, I-B, and IV may be submitted at any time; applications for Classes II and III must be submitted by February of each year.

[714]
NORTH CAROLINA VIETNAM VETERANS SCHOLARSHIP PROGRAM

North Carolina Vietnam Veterans, Inc.
c/o Bud Gross, Treasurer
601 Compton Road
Raleigh, NC 27609
(919) 787-7228   E-mail: info@ncvvi.org
Web: www.ncvvi.org

Summary To provide financial assistance to North Carolina residents who are Vietnam veterans or the dependents of veterans and interested in attending college in any state.

Eligibility This program is open to current residents of Chatham, Durham, Franklin, Granville, Harnett, Johnston, Nash, or Wake counties in North Carolina who are either a Vietnam veteran or the veteran's spouse, child, foster child, adopted child, or grandchild. Families of members of North Carolina Vietnam Veterans, Inc. (NCVVI) who live in any county of the state are also eligible. Applicants must be attending or planning to attend a college, university, community college, or trade school in any state. They must submit a copy of the Department of Defense Form DD214 to document Vietnam service; a birth certificate and/or marriage license (as needed); a personal statement about themselves, including work experience, anticipated career, and goals; a list of current activities and awards; and an essay of 600 to 900 words on a topic that changes annually; recently, the topic was "Why was the transition from Vietnam to the United States a major problem for many veterans and still lingers to this date?"

Financial data Stipends range from $500 to $1,500. Funds are paid on a reimbursement basis (presentation of paid receipts for tuition, fees, and/or books).

Duration 1 year.

Additional information This program includes the Mike Hooks Memorial Scholarship.

Number awarded 1 or more each year.

Deadline February of each year.

[715]
NORTH DAKOTA EDUCATIONAL ASSISTANCE FOR DEPENDENTS OF VETERANS

Department of Veterans Affairs
4201 38th Street S.W., Suite 104
P.O. Box 9003
Fargo, ND 58106-9003
(701) 239-7165   Toll Free: (866) 634-8387
Fax: (701) 239-7166
Web: www.nd.gov/veterans/benefits/waiver.html

Summary To provide financial assistance for college to the spouses, widow(er)s, and children of disabled and other North Dakota veterans and military personnel.

Eligibility This program is open to the spouses, widow(er)s, and dependent children of veterans who were killed in action, died from wounds or other service-connected causes, were totally disabled as a result of service-connected causes, died from service-connected disabilities, were a prisoners of war, or were declared missing in action. Veteran par-

ents must have been born in and lived in North Dakota until entrance into the armed forces (or must have resided in the state for at least 6 months prior to entrance into military service) and must have served during wartime.

Financial data Eligible dependents receive free tuition and are exempt from fees at any state-supported institution of higher education, technical school, or vocational school in North Dakota.

Duration Up to 45 months or 10 academic semesters.

Number awarded Varies each year.

Deadline Deadline not specified.

[716]
NORTH DAKOTA NATIONAL GUARD ENLISTED ASSOCIATION SCHOLARSHIPS

North Dakota National Guard Enlisted Association
c/o MSG Joe Lovelace
4900 107th Avenue S.E.
Minot, ND 58701-9207
E-mail: joseph.m.lovelace@us.army.mil
Web: www.ndngea.org

Summary To provide financial assistance to members of the North Dakota National Guard Enlisted Association (NDNGEA) and their families who are interested in attending college in any state.

Eligibility This program is open to association members who have at least 1 year remaining on their enlistment or have completed 20 or more years in service. Also eligible are their unmarried dependent children and spouses and the unremarried spouses and unmarried dependent children of deceased NDNGEA members who were in good standing at the time of death. Applicants must be attending or planning to attend a university, college, or trade/business school in any state. Graduate students are not eligible. Selection is based on academic achievement, leadership, character, and financial need.

Financial data The stipend is $1,000. Funds are sent directly to the school in the recipient's name.

Duration 1 year.

Number awarded 1 or more each year.

Deadline November of each year.

[717]
NORTH DAKOTA VETERANS DEPENDENTS FEE WAIVER

North Dakota University System
Attn: Director of Financial Aid
State Capitol, Tenth Floor
600 East Boulevard Avenue, Department 215
Bismarck, ND 58505-0230
(701) 328-4114   Fax: (701) 328-2961
E-mail: nathan.stratton@ndus.edu
Web: www.ndus.edu/students/military-veterans-families

Summary To waive tuition and fees for dependents of deceased or other veterans at public institutions in North Dakota.

Eligibility Eligible for this benefit are the dependents of veterans who were North Dakota residents when they entered the armed forces and died of service-related causes, were killed in action, were prisoners of war, or were declared missing in action. Applicants must be attending or planning to attend a public college or university in North Dakota.

Financial data Qualified students are entitled to a waiver of all tuition and fees (except fees charged to retire outstanding bonds) at public institutions in North Dakota.
Duration 1 academic year; renewable.
Number awarded Varies each year.
Deadline Deadline not specified.

[718]
NYALPA SCHOLARSHIP

New York American Legion Press Association
Attn: Scholarship Chair
P.O. Box 650
East Aurora, NY 14052-0650
E-mail: CStarberry@cs.com
Web: www.nyalpa.webs.com

Summary To provide financial assistance to residents of New York who have a connection with the American Legion and are interested in careers in communications.
Eligibility This program is open to New York residents who are 1) children of members of the American Legion or American Legion Auxiliary, 2) members of the Sons of the American Legion, 3) junior members of the American Legion Auxiliary, or 4) graduates of the New York Boys State or Girls State. Applicants must be entering or attending an accredited 4-year college or university, working on a degree in communications (including public relations, journalism, reprographics, newspaper design or management, or other related fields acceptable to the scholarship committee). Along with their application, they must submit a 500-word essay on why they chose the field of communications as a future vocation. Financial need and class standing are not considered.
Financial data The stipend is $1,000.
Duration 1 year.
Number awarded 1 each year.
Deadline April of each year.

[719]
OHIO LEGION AUXILIARY DEPARTMENT PRESIDENT'S SCHOLARSHIP

American Legion Auxiliary
Department of Ohio
1100 Brandywine Boulevard, Suite D
P.O. Box 2760
Zanesville, OH 43702-2760
(740) 452-8245   Fax: (740) 452-2620
E-mail: ala_katie@rrohio.com
Web: www.alaohio.org/Scholarships

Summary To provide funding to veterans and their descendants in Ohio who are interested in attending college.
Eligibility This program is open to honorably-discharged veterans and the children, grandchildren, and great-grandchildren of living, deceased, or disabled honorably-discharged veterans who served during designated periods of wartime. Applicants must be residents of Ohio, seniors at an accredited high school, planning to enter a college in any state, and sponsored by an American Legion Auxiliary Unit. Along with their application, they must submit an original article (up to 500 words) written by the applicant on a topic that changes annually. Recently, students were asked to write on "Education and the American Dream." Selection is based on character, Americanism, leadership, scholarship, and need.

Financial data Stipends are $1,500 or $1,000. Funds are paid to the recipient's school.
Duration 1 year.
Number awarded 1 at $1,500 and 1 at $1,000.
Deadline February of each year.

[720]
OHIO LEGION SCHOLARSHIPS

American Legion
Department of Ohio
60 Big Run Road
P.O. Box 8007
Delaware, OH 43015
(740) 362-7478   Fax: (740) 362-1429
E-mail: legion@ohiolegion.com
Web: www.ohiolegion.com/scholarships/info.htm

Summary To provide financial assistance to residents of Ohio who are members of the American Legion, their families, or dependents of deceased military personnel and interested in attending college in any state.
Eligibility This program is open to residents of Ohio who are Legionnaires, direct descendants of living or deceased Legionnaires, or surviving spouses or children of deceased U.S. military personnel who died on active duty or of injuries received on active duty. Applicants must be attending or planning to attend colleges, universities, or other approved post-secondary schools in any state with a vocational objective. Selection is based on academic achievement as measured by course grades, scholastic test scores, difficulty of curriculum, participation in outside activities, and the judging committee's general impression.
Financial data Stipends are $2,500 or $1,500.
Duration 1 year.
Number awarded Varies each year; recently, 9 of these scholarships were awarded: 1 at $2,500 and 8 at $1,500.
Deadline April of each year.

[721]
OHIO NATIONAL GUARD ASSOCIATION LEADERSHIP GRANTS

Ohio National Guard Association
Attn: Leadership Grant Committee
1299 Virginia Avenue
P.O. Box 8070
Columbus, OH 43201
Toll Free: (800) 642-6642
E-mail: ONGAKoper@prodigy.net
Web: ohionga.org/scholarship.html

Summary To provide financial assistance to members of the Ohio National Guard Association (ONGA) and their families who are interested in attending college in any state.
Eligibility This program is open to active members (either officers or warrant officers) of the ONGA and the dependents of active, life, retired, or deceased members. Applicants must be enrolled or planning to enroll at a college or university in any state. Along with their application, they must submit transcripts, SAT/ACT scores, and a 2-page essay explaining why they should be selected to receive a grant. Selection is based on grades, future plans, membership and leadership, honors and awards, need, and overall impression.
Financial data A stipend is awarded (amount not specified).

Duration 1 year; nonrenewable.
Additional information This program began in 1996.
Number awarded Varies each year; recently, 5 of these grants were awarded.
Deadline November of each year.

[722]
OHIO SAFETY OFFICERS COLLEGE MEMORIAL FUND

Ohio Board of Regents
Attn: State Grants and Scholarships
30 East Broad Street, 36th Floor
Columbus, OH 43215-3414
(614) 466-6000   Toll Free: (888) 833-1133
Fax: (614) 466-5866 E-mail: hotline@regents.state.oh.us
Web: students.ohio.highered.org/paying/state-scholarship

Summary To provide funding to Ohio residents interested in attending college in the state and whose parent or spouse was killed in the line of duty as a safety officer or member of the armed forces.
Eligibility This program is open to Ohio residents whose parent or spouse was 1) a peace officer, fire fighter, or other safety officer killed in the line of duty anywhere in the United States; or 2) a member of the U.S. armed forces killed in the line of duty during Operation Enduring Freedom, Operation Iraqi Freedom, or other designated combat zone. Applicants must be interested in attending a participating Ohio college or university. Children and spouses of military personnel are eligible for this program only if they do not qualify for the Ohio War Orphans Scholarship.
Financial data At Ohio public colleges and universities, the program provides full payment of tuition. At Ohio private colleges and universities, the stipend is equivalent to the average amounts paid to students attending public institutions, currently $3,990 per year.
Duration 1 year; may be renewed up to 3 additional years.
Additional information Eligible institutions are Ohio state-assisted colleges and universities and Ohio institutions approved by the Board of Regents. This program was established in 1980.
Number awarded Varies each year; recently, 54 students received benefits from this program.
Deadline Application deadlines are established by each participating college and university.

[723]
OHIO WAR ORPHANS SCHOLARSHIP

Ohio Board of Regents
Attn: State Grants and Scholarships
30 East Broad Street, 36th Floor
Columbus, OH 43215-3414
(614) 752-9528   Toll Free: (888) 833-1133
Fax: (614) 466-5866
E-mail: jabdullah-simmons@regents.state.oh.us
Web: students.ohio.highered.org/paying/state-scholarship

Summary To provide financial assistance to the children of deceased or disabled Ohio veterans who plan to attend college in the state.
Eligibility This program is open to residents of Ohio who are under 25 years of age and interested in enrolling full time at an eligible college or university in the state. Applicants must be the child of a veteran who 1) was a member of the

U.S. armed forces, including the organized Reserves and Ohio National Guard, for a period of 90 days or more (or discharged because of a disability incurred after less than 90 days of service); 2) served during specified periods of war time ; 3) entered service as a resident of Ohio; and 4) as a result of that service, either was killed or became at least 60% service-connected disabled. Also eligible are children of veterans who have a permanent and total non-service connected disability and are receiving disability benefits from the U.S. Department of Veterans Affairs. If the veteran parent served only in the organized Reserves or Ohio National Guard, the parent must have been killed or became permanently and totally disabled while at a scheduled training assembly, field training period (of any duration or length), or active duty for training, pursuant to bona fide orders issued by a competent authority. Financial need is considered in the selection process.
Financial data At Ohio public colleges and universities, the program provides payment of 80% of tuition and fees. At Ohio private colleges and universities, the stipend is $4,797 per year (or 80% of the average amount paid to students attending public institutions).
Duration 1 year; may be renewed up to 4 additional years, provided the recipient maintains a GPA of 2.0 or higher.
Additional information Eligible institutions are Ohio state-assisted colleges and universities and Ohio institutions approved by the Board of Regents. This program was established in 1957.
Number awarded Varies, depending upon the funds available. If sufficient funds are available, all eligible applicants are given a scholarship. Recently, 861 students received benefits from this program.
Deadline June of each year.

[724]
OKLAHOMA TUITION WAIVER FOR PRISONERS OF WAR, PERSONS MISSING IN ACTION, AND DEPENDENTS

Oklahoma State Regents for Higher Education
Attn: Director of Scholarship and Grant Programs
655 Research Parkway, Suite 200
P.O. Box 108850
Oklahoma City, OK 73101-8850
(405) 225-9239   Toll Free: (800) 858-1840
Fax: (405) 225-9230   E-mail: studentinfo@osrhe.edu
Web: www.okcollegestart.org

Summary To provide financial assistance for college to Oklahoma residents (or their dependents) who were declared prisoners of war or missing in action.
Eligibility Applicants for this assistance must be veterans who were declared prisoners of war or missing in action after January 1, 1960 and were residents of Oklahoma at the time of entrance into the armed forces or when declared POW/MIA. Dependent children of those veterans are also eligible as long as they are under 24 years of age. Selection is based on financial need, academic aptitude and achievement, student activity participation, academic level, and academic discipline or field of study.
Financial data Eligible applicants are entitled to receive free tuition at any Oklahoma state-supported postsecondary educational, technical, or vocational school.

Duration Assistance continues for 5 years or until receipt of a bachelor's degree, whichever occurs first.
Additional information This assistance is not available to persons eligible to receive federal benefits.
Number awarded Varies each year.
Deadline Deadline not specified.

[725]
ONE PUKA PUKA ACHIEVEMENT SCHOLARSHIP

Club 100 Veterans
Attn: Scholarship Committee
520 Kamoku Street
Honolulu, HI 96826-5120
(808) 946-0272   E-mail: daisyy@hgea.net

Summary To provide financial assistance for college to family members of veterans who served in the 100th Infantry Battalion of World War II.
Eligibility This program is open to direct family members and descendants of 100th Infantry Battalion World War II veterans. Applicants must be high school seniors planning to attend an institution of higher learning or full-time undergraduate students at community colleges, vocational/trade schools, 4-year colleges, and universities. Along with their application, they must submit an essay on a topic that changes annually but relates to the experience of the Nisei men who fought in the racially-segregated 100th Infantry Battalion during World War II. Selection is based on that essay, academic achievement, extracurricular activities, and community service. Financial need is not considered.
Financial data The stipend is $3,000.
Duration 1 year; nonrenewable.
Number awarded 1 each year.
Deadline April of each year.

[726]
ONGEA SCHOLARSHIP PROGRAM

Ohio National Guard Enlisted Association
Attn: Scholarship Chair
1299 Virginia Avenue
Columbus, OH 43212
(740) 574-5932   Toll Free: (800) 642-6642
Fax: (614) 486-2216   E-mail: ongea@juno.com
Web: www.ongea.org/12.html

Summary To provide financial assistance to members of the Ohio National Guard Enlisted Association (ONGEA) and children of members of the ONGEA Auxiliary who are interested in attending college in any state.
Eligibility This program is open to 1) children of ONGEA and ONGEA Auxiliary members (ONGEA member spouses must be Auxiliary members in order for a child to be eligible); 2) unmarried dependent children of deceased ONGEA and ONGEA Auxiliary members who were in good standing the time of their death; and 3) ONGEA members (if married, the spouse must also be a member of the Auxiliary). Applicants must be enrolling as full-time undergraduate students at a college, university, trade school, or business school in any state. Selection is based on academic record, character, leadership, and financial need.
Financial data Stipends are $1,000 or $500. After verification of enrollment is provided, checks are sent to the recipient and made out to the recipient's school.
Duration 1 year; nonrenewable.

Additional information This program is sponsored jointly by ONGEA, the ONGEA Auxiliary, USAA Insurance Corporation, and the First Cleveland Cavalry Association.
Number awarded 5 to 10 each year, depending upon the availability of funds.
Deadline March of each year.

[727]
OPERATION ENDURING FREEDOM AND OPERATION IRAQI FREEDOM SCHOLARSHIP

Vermont Student Assistance Corporation
Attn: Scholarship Programs
10 East Allen Street
P.O. Box 2000
Winooski, VT 05404-2601
(802) 654-3798   Toll Free: (888) 253-4819
Fax: (802) 654-3765   TDD: (800) 281-3341 (within VT)
E-mail: info@vsac.org
Web: services.vsac.org/wps/wcm/connect/vsac/VSAC

Summary To provide financial assistance to residents of Vermont whose parent has served or is serving in Operating Enduring Freedom in Afghanistan or Operation Iraqi Freedom.
Eligibility This program is open to residents of Vermont who are children of a member of any branch of the armed forces or National Guard whose residence or home of record is in Vermont. Applicants must plan to enroll full time in a certificate, associate degree, or bachelor's degree program at an accredited postsecondary school in any state. The parent must have served or currently be serving in Operation Enduring Freedom or Operation Iraqi Freedom. Preference is given to applicants whose parent was killed, was wounded, or became permanently disabled as a result of their service. Along with their application, they must submit 1) a 100-word essay on any significant barriers that limit their access to education; and 2) a 250-word essay on their short- and long-term academic, educational, career, vocational, and/or employment goals. Selection is based on those essays, a letter of recommendation, and financial need.
Financial data The stipend ranges from $3,500 to $7,000 per year.
Duration 1 year; may be renewed up to 3 additional years.
Additional information This program, established in 2007, is sponsored by the Hoehl Family Foundation.
Number awarded Varies each year; recently, 14 of these scholarships were awarded.
Deadline March of each year.

[728]
OREGON LEGION AUXILIARY DEPARTMENT NURSES SCHOLARSHIP

American Legion Auxiliary
Department of Oregon
30450 S.W. Parkway Avenue
P.O. Box 1730
Wilsonville, OR 97070-1730
(503) 682-3162   Fax: (503) 685-5008
E-mail: contact@alaoregon.org
Web: www.alaoregon.org

Summary To provide financial assistance to the wives, widows, and children of Oregon veterans who are interested in studying nursing at a school in any state.

Eligibility This program is open to Oregon residents who are the wives or children of veterans with disabilities or the widows of deceased veterans. Applicants must have been accepted by an accredited hospital or school of nursing in any state. Selection is based on ability, aptitude, character, determination, seriousness of purpose, and need.

Financial data The stipend is $1,500.

Duration 1 year; may be renewed.

Number awarded 1 each year.

Deadline May of each year.

[729]
OREGON LEGION AUXILIARY DEPARTMENT SCHOLARSHIPS

American Legion Auxiliary
Department of Oregon
30450 S.W. Parkway Avenue
P.O. Box 1730
Wilsonville, OR 97070-1730
(503) 682-3162   Fax: (503) 685-5008
E-mail: contact@alaoregon.org
Web: www.alaoregon.org

Summary To provide funding to the dependents of Oregon veterans who are interested in attending college.

Eligibility This program is open to Oregon residents who are children or wives of disabled veterans or widows of veterans. Applicants must be interested in obtaining education beyond the high school level at a college, university, business school, vocational school, or any other accredited postsecondary school in the state of Oregon. Selection is based on ability, aptitude, character, seriousness of purpose, and financial need.

Financial data The stipend is $1,000.

Duration 1 year; nonrenewable.

Number awarded 3 each year; 1 of these is to be used for vocational or business school.

Deadline March of each year.

[730]
ORNGA SCHOLARSHIPS

Oregon National Guard Association
Attn: Scholarship Committee
1776 Militia Way, S.E.
P.O. Box 14350
Salem, OR 97309-5047
(503) 584-3456   Fax: (503) 584-3052
E-mail: info@ornga.org
Web: www.ornga.org/scholar_about.htm

Summary To provide financial assistance to members of the Oregon National Guard, the Oregon National Guard Association (ORNGA), and their children and spouses who are interested in attending college in any state.

Eligibility This program is open to active members of the Oregon Army and Air National Guard, members of the ORNGA, and their children and spouses. Applicants must be high school seniors, graduates, or GED recipients and interested in working on an undergraduate degree at a college, university, or trade school in any state. The parent, spouse, or applicant must have an ETS date beyond the end of the academic year for which the scholarship is used. Selection is based on demonstrated qualities of leadership, civic action, and academic achievement.

Financial data The stipend is $1,500.

Duration 1 year.

Number awarded 10 each year.

Deadline February of each year.

[731]
PARALYZED VETERANS OF AMERICA EDUCATIONAL SCHOLARSHIP PROGRAM

Paralyzed Veterans of America
Attn: Education and Training Foundation
801 18th Street, N.W.
Washington, DC 20006-3517
(202) 416-7651   Toll Free: (800) 424-8200, ext. 776
Fax: (202) 416-7641   TDD: (800) 795-HEAR
E-mail: christih@pva.org
Web: www.pva.org

Summary To provide money for college to members of the Paralyzed Veterans of America and their families.

Eligibility This program is open to association members, spouses of members, and unmarried dependent children of members under 24 years of age. Applicants must be attending or planning to attend an accredited U.S. college or university. They must be U.S. citizens. Along with their application, they must submit a personal statement explaining why they wish to further their education, short- and long-term academic goals, how this will meet their career objectives, and how it will affect the PVA membership. Selection is based on that statement, academic records, letters of recommendation, and extracurricular and community activities.

Financial data Stipends are $1,000 for full-time students or $500 for part-time students.

Duration 1 year.

Additional information This program began in 1986.

Number awarded Varies each year; recently 14 full-time and 3 part-time students received these scholarships. Since this program was established, it has awarded more than $300,000 in scholarships.

Deadline May of each year.

[732]
PAST NATIONAL PRESIDENT FRANCES BOOTH MEDICAL SCHOLARSHIP

Veterans of Foreign Wars of Maine
c/o Sheila Webber
P.O. Box 492
Old Orchard Beach, ME 04064
(207) 934-2405   E-mail: swebber2@maine.rr.com

Summary To provide financial assistance to children and grandchildren of members of the Veterans of Foreign Wars (VFW) and its Ladies Auxiliary in Maine who are studying a medical field in college.

Eligibility This program is open to Maine residents who are the children, grandchildren, stepchildren, or foster children of current or immediate past year members of the VFW or its Ladies Auxiliary in Maine. Applicants must be enrolled at a 2- or 4-year college, university, or vocational school and majoring in a field related to medicine.

Financial data The stipend is $1,000 or $500 per year. Funds are paid to the school of the recipient's choice.

Duration 1 year; may be renewed.

Number awarded 1 or more each year.

Deadline March of each year.

[733]
PAT TILLMAN MILITARY SCHOLARS PROGRAM

Pat Tillman Foundation
2121 South Mill Avenue, Suite 214
Tempe, AZ 85282
(480) 621-4074   Fax: (480) 621-4075
E-mail: scholarships@pattillmanfoundation.org
Web: www.pattillmanfoundation.org/tillman-military-scholars

Summary To provide financial assistance to veterans, active servicemembers, and their spouses who are interested in working on an undergraduate or graduate degree.

Eligibility This program is open to veterans and active servicemembers of all branches of the armed forces from both the pre- and post-September 11 era and their spouses; children are not eligible. Applicants must be enrolled or planning to enroll full time at a 4-year public or private college or university to work on an undergraduate, graduate, or postgraduate degree. Current and former servicemembers must submit 400-word essays on 1) their motivation and decision to serve in the U.S. military and how that decision and experience has changed their life and ambitions; and 2) their educational and career goals, how they will incorporate their military service experience into those goals, and how they intend to continue their service to others and the community. Spouses must submit 400-word essays on 1) their previous service to others and the community; and 2) their educational and career goals, how they will incorporate their service experiences and the impact of their spouse's military service into those goals, and how they intend to continue their service to others and the community. Selection is based on those essays, educational and career ambitions, record of military service, record of personal achievement, demonstration of service to others in the community, desire to continue such service, and leadership potential.

Financial data The stipend depends on the need of the recipient and the availability of funds.

Duration 1 year; may be renewed, provided the recipient maintains a GPA of 3.0 or higher, remains enrolled full time, and participates in civic action or community service.

Additional information This program began in 2009.

Number awarded Varies each year; recently, 60 students received a total of $916,000 through this program.

Deadline March of each year.

[734]
PAULINE LANGKAMP MEMORIAL SCHOLARSHIP

Navy Wives Clubs of America
P.O. Box 54022
Millington, TN 38053-6022
Toll Free: (866) 511-NWCA
E-mail: nwca@navywivesclubsofamerica.org
Web: www.navywivesclubsofamerica.org/scholarinfo.htm

Summary To provide money for college to the adult children of members of the Navy Wives Clubs of America (NWCA).

Eligibility This program is open to children of NWCA members who no longer carry a military ID card because they have reached adult status. Applicants must be attending or planning to attend an accredited college or university. Along with their application, they must submit a brief statement on why they feel they should be awarded this scholarship and any special circumstances (financial or other) they wish to have considered.

Financial data A stipend is provided (amount not specified).

Duration 1 year.

Additional information Membership in the NWCA is open to spouses of enlisted personnel serving in the Navy, Marine Corps, Coast Guard, and the active Reserve units of those services; spouses of enlisted personnel who have been honorably discharged, retired, or transferred to the Fleet Reserve on completion of duty; and widows of enlisted personnel in those services.

Number awarded 1 or more each year.

Deadline May of each year.

[735]
PENNSYLVANIA EDUCATIONAL GRATUITY FOR VETERANS' DEPENDENTS

Office of the Deputy Adjutant General for Veterans Affairs
Building S-0-47, FTIG
Annville, PA 17003-5002
(717) 865-8910   Toll Free: (800) 54 PA VET (within PA)
Fax: (717) 861-8589   E-mail: RA-VA-Info@pa.gov
Web: www.dmva.state.pa.us

Summary To provide financial assistance for college to the children of disabled or deceased Pennsylvania veterans.

Eligibility This program is open to children (between 16 and 23 years of age) of honorably-discharged veterans who are rated totally and permanently disabled as a result of wartime service or who have died of such a disability. Applicants must have lived in Pennsylvania for at least 5 years immediately preceding the date of application, be able to demonstrate financial need, and have been accepted or be currently enrolled in a Pennsylvania state or state-aided secondary or postsecondary educational institution.

Financial data The stipend is $500 per semester ($1,000 per year). The money is paid directly to the recipient's school and is to be applied to the costs of tuition, board, room, books, supplies, and/or matriculation fees.

Duration The allowance is paid for up to 4 academic years or for the duration of the course of study, whichever is less.

Number awarded Varies each year.

Deadline Deadline not specified.

[736]
PENNSYLVANIA GRANTS FOR CHILDREN OF SOLDIERS DECLARED POW/MIA

Pennsylvania Higher Education Assistance Agency
Attn: Special Programs
1200 North Seventh Street
P.O. Box 8157
Harrisburg, PA 17105-8157
(717) 720-2800   Toll Free: (800) 692-7392
Fax: (717) 720-5786   TDD: (800) 654-5988
Web: www.pheaa.org

Summary To provide financial assistance for college to the children of POWs/MIAs from Pennsylvania.

Eligibility This program is open to dependent children of members or former members of the U.S. armed services who served on active duty after January 31, 1955, who are or have been prisoners of war or are or have been listed as missing in action, and who were residents of Pennsylvania for at least 12 months preceding service on active duty. Eligible children must be enrolled in a program of at least 1 year in duration on at least a half-time basis at an approved school. Financial need is not considered in the selection process.

Financial data The maximum grant is $1,200.

Duration 1 year; may be renewed for 3 additional years.

Additional information With certain exceptions, recipients may attend any accredited college in the United States. Excluded from coverage are 2-year public colleges located outside Pennsylvania and schools in states bordering Pennsylvania that do not allow their state grant recipients to attend Pennsylvania schools (i.e., New York, Maryland, and New Jersey).

Number awarded Varies each year.

Deadline April of each year for students at colleges, universities, and transferable programs at community colleges; July of each year for students at business schools, trade/technical schools, hospital schools of nursing, and nontransferable programs at community colleges.

[737]
PENNSYLVANIA POSTSECONDARY EDUCATIONAL GRATUITY PROGRAM

Pennsylvania Higher Education Assistance Agency
Attn: Special Programs
1200 North Seventh Street
P.O. Box 8157
Harrisburg, PA 17105-8157
(717) 720-2800   Toll Free: (800) 692-7392
Fax: (717) 720-5786   TDD: (800) 654-5988
E-mail: pegp@pheaa.org
Web: www.pheaa.org

Summary To provide financial assistance for college to the children of Pennsylvania public service personnel who died in the line of service.

Eligibility This program is open to residents of Pennsylvania who are the children of 1) Pennsylvania police officers, fire fighters, rescue and ambulance squad members, corrections facility employees, or National Guard members who died in the line of duty after January 1, 1976; or 2) Pennsylvania sheriffs, deputy sheriffs, National Guard members, and certain other individuals on federal or state active military duty who died after September 11, 2001 as a direct result of performing their official duties. Applicants must be 25 years of age or younger and enrolled or accepted at a Pennsylvania community college, state-owned institution, or state-related institution as a full-time student working on an associate or baccalaureate degree. They must have already applied for other scholarships, including state and federal grants and financial aid from the postsecondary institution to which they are applying.

Financial data Grants cover tuition, fees, room, and board charged by the institution, less awarded scholarships and federal and state grants.

Duration Up to 5 years.

Additional information This program began in the 1998-99 winter/spring term to cover service personnel who died after January 1, 1976. It was amended in 2004 to cover additional service personnel who died after September 11, 2001.

Number awarded Varies each year.

Deadline March of each year.

[738]
PETER CONNACHER MEMORIAL SCHOLARSHIPS

Oregon Student Access Commission
Attn: Grants and Scholarships Division
1500 Valley River Drive, Suite 100
Eugene, OR 97401-2146
(541) 687-7395   Toll Free: (800) 452-8807, ext. 7395
Fax: (541) 687-7414   TDD: (800) 735-2900
E-mail: awardinfo@osac.state.or.us
Web: www.oregonstudentaid.gov/scholarships.aspx

Summary To provide money for college or graduate school to ex-prisoners of war and their descendants.

Eligibility Applicants must be U.S. citizens who 1) were military or civilian prisoners of war; or 2) are the descendants of ex-prisoners of war. They must be full-time undergraduate or graduate students. A copy of the ex-prisoner of war's discharge papers from the U.S. armed forces must accompany the application. In addition, written proof of POW status must be submitted, along with a statement of the relationship between the applicant and the ex-prisoner of war (father, grandfather, etc.). Selection is based on academic record and financial need. Preference is given to Oregon residents or their dependents.

Financial data Stipends for scholarships offered by the Oregon Student Access Commission (OSAC) range from $200 to $10,000 but recently averaged $2,300.

Duration 1 year; may be renewed for up to 3 additional years for undergraduate students or 2 additional years for graduate students. Renewal is dependent on evidence of continued financial need and satisfactory academic progress.

Additional information This program is administered by the OSAC with funds provided by the Oregon Community Foundation. Funds are also provided by the Columbia River Chapter of American Ex-prisoners of War, Inc.

Number awarded Varies each year; recently, 4 of these scholarships were awarded.

Deadline February of each year.

[739]
PNGAS SCHOLARSHIP FUND

Pennsylvania National Guard Associations
Attn: Pennsylvania National Guard Scholarship Fund
Biddle Hall (Building 9-109)
Fort Indiantown Gap
Annville, PA 17003-5002
(717) 865-9631   Toll Free: (800) 997-8885
Fax: (717) 861-5560   E-mail: oswalddean@aol.com
Web: www.pngas.net

Summary To provide funding to Pennsylvania National Guard members and the children of disabled or deceased members who are interested in attending college in any state.

Eligibility This program is open to active members of the Pennsylvania Army or Air National Guard. Children of members of the Guard who died or were permanently disabled while on Guard duty are also eligible. Applicants must be entering their first year of higher education as a full-time student or presently attending a college or vocational school in any state as a full-time student. Along with their application, they must submit an essay that outlines their military and civilian plans for the future. Selection is based on that essay, academics, leadership, and contributions to citizenship.

Financial data Stipends range from $500 to $2,000.

Duration 1 year.

Additional information The sponsoring organization includes the National Guard Association of Pennsylvania (NGAP) and the Pennsylvania National Guard Enlisted Association (PNGEA). This program, which began in 1977, includes the following named scholarships: the BG Richard E. Thorn Memorial Scholarship, the Murtha Memorial Scholarship, the BG Hugh S. Niles Memorial Scholarship, the PNGEA USAA Scholarship (sponsored by USAA Insurance), and the 28th Infantry Division Scholarship.

Number awarded Varies each year; recently, 13 of these scholarships were awarded: 2 at $2,000, 1 at $1,500, 1 at $1,000, and 9 at $500.

Deadline June of each year.

[740]
POPASMOKE SCHOLARSHIPS

USMC/Combat Helicopter Association
c/o Marine Corps Scholarship Foundation
909 North Washington Street, Suite 400
Alexandria, VA 22314
(703) 549-0060   Toll Free: (866) 496-5462
Fax: (703) 549-9474   E-mail: students@mcsf.org
Web: www.popasmoke.com/scholarship.html

Summary To provide financial assistance for college to the children and grandchildren of members of the USMC/Combat Helicopter Association.

Eligibility This program is open to children and grandchildren of members of the USMC/Combat Helicopter Association who are high school seniors, high school graduates, undergraduates enrolled at an accredited college or university, or students enrolled at an accredited postsecondary vocational/technical school. Applicants must be the child or grandchild of 1) a Marine on active duty, in the Reserve, retired, or deceased; or 2) a Marine or Marine Reservist who has received an honorable discharge, medical discharge, or was killed on active duty. Along with their application, they must submit academic transcripts, a copy of their parent's or grandparent's honorable discharge (if appropriate), and a 500-word essay on a topic that changes periodically. Only undergraduate study is supported. The family income of applicants must be less than $90,000 per year.

Financial data Stipends range up to $1,000 per year.

Duration 1 year; renewable up to 3 additional years.

Additional information This program includes the MGYSGT George T. Curtis Scholarship, established in 2006, the LTCOL Hubert "Black Bart" Bartels Scholarship, established in 2008, and the PFC Mike Clausen Scholarship, established in 2010.

Number awarded 3 each year.

Deadline March of each year.

[741]
PRAIRIE MINUTEMAN SCHOLARSHIP

National Guard Association of Illinois
Attn: Executive Director
1301 North MacArthur Boulevard
Springfield, IL 62701-2317
(217) 836-5251   Fax: (217) 483-5469
E-mail: execdir@ngai.com
Web: www.ngai.com/service.html

Summary To provide financial assistance to dependents of members of the National Guard Association of Illinois (NGAI) who are interested in attending college in any state.

Eligibility This program is open to dependents (children and spouses) of NGAI members in good standing. Applicants may be high school seniors, high school graduates, or currently-enrolled students at a college or university in any state. They must submit a completed application form, official transcripts, 2 letters of recommendation, a verified copy of their ACT/SAT scores, and a 250-word essay on their scholastic and professional goals and aspirations. Financial need is also considered in the selection process.

Financial data The stipend is $1,000 or $500.

Duration 1 year.

Number awarded 3 each year: 1 at $1,000 to an Illinois Army National Guard dependent, 1 at $1,000 to an Illinois Air National Guard dependent, and 1 at $500 (sponsored by USAA Insurance Corporation) to an enlisted Illinois National Guard dependent who is also a member of NGAI.

Deadline Applications must be submitted at least 45 days prior to the sponsor's annual conference. The conference is usually in late April, so applications are due in mid-March.

[742]
RADM WILLIAM A. SULLIVAN, USN (RET.) SCHOLARSHIP

Navy League of the United States
Attn: Scholarships
2300 Wilson Boulevard, Suite 200
Arlington, VA 22201-5424
(703) 528-1775   Toll Free: (800) 356-5760
Fax: (703) 528-2333
E-mail: scholarships@navyleague.org
Web: www.navyleague.org

Summary To provide financial assistance for college to dependent children of sea service personnel and veterans.

Eligibility This program is open to U.S. citizens who are 1) dependents or direct descendants of an active, Reserve, retired, or honorably discharged member of the U.S. sea service (including the Navy, Marine Corps, Coast Guard, or Merchant Marines), or 2) currently an active member of the Naval Sea Cadet Corps. Applicants must be entering their freshman year at an accredited college or university. They must have a GPA of 3.0 or higher. Along with their application, they must submit transcripts, 2 letters of recommendation, SAT/ACT scores, documentation of financial need, proof of qualifying sea service duty, and a 1-page personal statement on why they should be considered for this scholarship. Preference is given to applicants who reside in or near the San Diego, California area.

Financial data The stipend is $2,500 per year.

Duration 4 years, provided the recipient maintains a GPA of 3.0 or higher.

Number awarded 1 each year.

Deadline March of each year.

[743]
RANGER MEMORIAL SCHOLARSHIPS
National Ranger Memorial Foundation
Attn: Executive Secretary
P.O. Box 53369
Fort Benning, GA 31995
(706) 687-0906   E-mail: rangermemorial@gmail.com
Web: rangermemorial.com/scholarship_application.aspx

Summary To provide money for college to current and former U.S. Army Rangers and their descendants.

Eligibility This program is open to Rangers from any era and their descendants; awards are limited to descendants of Rangers who served during the World War II era for Ranger Battalions Association of WWII scholarships. Applicants must be graduating high school seniors or students currently enrolled at an accredited 2- or 4-year educational or technical institution. They must have a GPA of 3.0 or higher. Along with their application, they must submit information on their leadership activities, future goals and how they plan to attain those, and honors and awards received to date. Financial need is not considered in the selection process.

Financial data The stipend is $1,000.

Duration 1 year.

Additional information The National Ranger Memorial Foundation began awarding scholarships in 1999. The Ranger Battalions Association of WWII became a partner in 2007 and offered additional scholarships to descendants of World War II era Rangers.

Number awarded 49 each year: 45 offered by the National Ranger Memorial Foundation and 4 by the Ranger Battalions Association of WWII.

Deadline May of each year.

[744]
RAYMOND T. WELLINGTON, JR. MEMORIAL SCHOLARSHIP
American Legion Auxiliary
Department of New York
112 State Street, Suite 1310
Albany, NY 12207
(518) 463-1162   Toll Free: (800) 421-6348
Fax: (518) 449-5406   E-mail: alanyterry@nycap.rr.com
Web: www.deptny.org/Scholarships.htm

Summary To provide financial assistance to New York residents who are the descendants of veterans and interested in attending college in any state.

Eligibility This program is open to residents of New York who are high school seniors or graduates and attending or planning to attend an accredited college or university in any state. Applicants must be the children, grandchildren, or great-grandchildren of veterans who served during specified periods of wartime. Along with their application, they must submit a 700-word autobiography that includes their interests, experiences, long-range plans, and goals. Selection is based on character (15%), Americanism (15%), community involvement (15%), leadership (15%), scholarship (20%), and financial need (20%). U.S. citizenship is required.

Financial data The stipend is $1,000. Funds are paid directly to the recipient's school.

Duration 1 year.

Number awarded 1 each year.

Deadline February of each year.

[745]
RED RIVER VALLEY FIGHTER PILOTS ASSOCIATION SCHOLARSHIP GRANT PROGRAM
Red River Valley Association Foundation
Attn: Executive Director
P.O. Box 1553
Front Royal, VA 22630-0033
(540) 639-9798   Toll Free: (866) 401-7287
Fax: (540) 636-9776   E-mail: RRVARiverRats@aol.com
Web: www.river-rats.org/about_us/scholarship.php

Summary To provide financial assistance for college or graduate school to the spouses and children of selected service personnel and members of the Red River Valley Fighter Pilots Association.

Eligibility This program is open to the spouses and children of 1) servicemembers missing in action (MIA) or killed in action (KIA) in combat situations involving U.S. military forces from August 1964 through the present; 2) U.S. military aircrew members killed in a non-combat aircraft accident in which they were performing aircrew duties; and 3) current members of the association and deceased members who were in good standing at the time of their death. Scholarships are also available to students in fields related to aviation and space, even if they have no kinship relationship to a deceased aviator or member of the association. Applicants must be enrolled or planning to enroll full or part time at an accredited college, university, vocational/technical institute, or career school to work on an undergraduate or graduate degree. They must be 30 years of age or younger, although the age limit is extended to 40 for current and former military personnel. Selection is based on demonstrated academic achievement, SAT or ACT scores, financial need, and accomplishments in school, church, civic, and social activities.

Financial data The amount awarded varies, depending upon the need of the recipient. Recently, undergraduate stipends have ranged from $500 to $3,500 and averaged $1,725; graduate stipends have ranged from $500 to $2,000 and averaged $1,670. Funds are paid directly to the recipient's institution and are to be used for tuition, fees, books, and room and board for full-time students.

Duration 1 year; may be renewed if the recipient maintains a GPA of 2.0 or higher.

Additional information This program was established in 1970, out of concern for the families of aircrews (known as "River Rats") who were killed or missing in action in the Red River Valley of North Vietnam.

Number awarded Varies each year; since this program was established, it has awarded more than 1,000 scholarships worth more than $1,700,000.

Deadline May of each year.

[746]
REDUCED TUITION FOR CHILDREN AND SPOUSES OF SOUTH DAKOTA NATIONAL GUARDSMEN DISABLED OR DECEASED IN THE LINE OF DUTY
South Dakota Board of Regents
Attn: Scholarship Committee
306 East Capitol Avenue, Suite 200
Pierre, SD 57501-2545
(605) 773-3455   Fax: (605) 773-2422
E-mail: info@sdbor.edu
Web: www.sdbor.edu/students/redtuit_nationalguard.htm

Summary   To provide reduced tuition at public universities in South Dakota to the children and spouses of disabled and deceased members of the National Guard.
Eligibility   This program is open to the spouses and children (24 years of age or younger) of members of the South Dakota Army or Air National Guard who died or sustained a total and permanent disability while on state active duty, federal active duty, or any authorized duty training. Applicants must be proposing to work on an undergraduate degree at a public institution of higher education in South Dakota.
Financial data   Qualifying applicants are granted a 100% tuition waiver at state-supported postsecondary institutions in South Dakota. The waiver applies only to tuition, not fees.
Duration   8 semesters or 12 quarters of either full- or part-time study.
Number awarded   Varies each year.
Deadline   Deadline not specified.

[747]
RENEE FELDMAN SCHOLARSHIPS

Blinded Veterans Association Auxiliary
c/o Hazel C. Compton, Scholarship Chair
P.O. Box 267
Richlands, VA 24641
(276) 963-3745
Web: www.bvaaux.org

Summary   To provide financial assistance for college to spouses and children of blinded veterans.
Eligibility   This program is open to children and spouses of blinded veterans who are enrolled or planning to enroll full time at a college, university, community college, or vocational school. The veteran is not required to be a member of the Blinded Veterans Association. Applicants must submit a 300-word essay on their career goals and aspirations. Selection is based on that essay, academic achievement, and letters of reference.
Financial data   Stipends are $2,000 or $1,000 per year. Funds are paid directly to the recipient's school to be applied to tuition, books, and general fees.
Duration   1 year; may be renewed up to 3 additional years.
Number awarded   3 each year: 2 at $2,000 and 1 at $1,000.
Deadline   April of each year.

[748]
ROBERT H. CONNAL EDUCATION AWARDS

Enlisted Association of the New York National Guard, Inc.
Attn: Educational Award Chair
330 Old Niskayuna Road
Latham, NY 12110-2224
(518) 344-2670   E-mail: awards@eanyng.org
Web: www.eanyng.org/AwardsandScholarships.html

Summary   To provide financial assistance to members of the Enlisted Association of the New York National Guard (EANYNG) and their families who are interested in attending college in any state.
Eligibility   This program is open to EANYNG members and their spouses, children, and grandchildren. Applicants must be high school seniors or current undergraduates at a college or university in any state. The applicant or sponsor must have belonged to EANYNG for more than 1 year. Membership in EANYNG is limited to enlisted personnel in the New York Air

or Army National Guard. Selection is based on academic achievement, community service, extracurricular activities, and leadership abilities.
Financial data   Stipends are $1,000 or $500.
Duration   1 year; nonrenewable.
Additional information   Funding for this program is provided by the production of the association's yearly journal, members' dues, and a donation from USAA Insurance Corporation.
Number awarded   7 each year: 1 statewide scholarship at $1,000 and 6 at $500 in each region of the state.
Deadline   February of each year.

[749]
ROSEDALE POST 346 SCHOLARSHIP FUND

American Legion
Department of Kansas
1314 S.W. Topeka Boulevard
Topeka, KS 66612-1886
(785) 232-9315   Fax: (785) 232-1399
Web: www.ksamlegion.org/programs.htm

Summary   To provide financial assistance to the children of members of the Kansas American Legion or American Legion Auxiliary who are interested in attending college in any state.
Eligibility   This program is open to high school seniors and college freshmen and sophomores who are attending or planning to attend an approved college, university, junior college, or trade school in any state. Applicants must have an average or better academic record. At least 1 of their parents must be a veteran and have been a member of an American Legion post or Auxiliary in Kansas for at least 3 consecutive years. Along with their application, they must submit an essay of 250 to 500 words on "Why I Want to Go to College." Financial need is also considered in the selection process.
Financial data   The stipend is $1,500.
Duration   1 year; nonrenewable.
Number awarded   2 each year.
Deadline   February of each year.

[750]
ROY C. AND DOROTHY JEAN OLSON MEMORIAL SCHOLARSHIP

International Military Community Executives' Association
Attn: Scholarship
P.O. Box 7286
Alexandria, VA 22307-0286
(571) 207-8893   Fax: (866) 369-2435
E-mail: imcea@imcea.org
Web: www.imcea.org/scholarship.html

Summary   To provide financial assistance to children of members of the International Military Community Executives' Association (IMCEA) who are interested in attending college.
Eligibility   This program is open to dependent children of regular IMCEA members who are graduating from high school or already enrolled at a college or university. Along with their application, they must submit a 2-page essay on the appropriate role of the U.S. military in the world today. Selection is based on that essay, participation in extracurricular activities over the past 4 years, participation in community activities over the past 4 year, and commendations and honors received during the past 4 years.

Financial data The stipend is $1,000.
Duration 1 year.
Additional information Regular membership in IMCEA is open to Army, Air Force, Navy, Marine Corps, and Coast Guard personnel who provide MWR services at military installations and bases worldwide.
Number awarded 1 each year.
Deadline April of each year.

[751]
RUBY LORRAINE PAUL SCHOLARSHIP FUND
American Legion Auxiliary
Department of Nebraska
P.O. Box 5227
Lincoln, NE 68505-0227
(402) 466-1808   Fax: (402) 466-0182
E-mail: neaux@windstream.net
Web: www.nebraskalegionaux.net
Summary To provide funding to students in Nebraska who have a connection to the American Legion and plan to attend college in any state and study any field except nursing.
Eligibility Applicants must have been residents of Nebraska for at least 3 years and either 1) have been a member for at least 2 years of the American Legion, American Legion Auxiliary, or Sons of the American Legion, or 2) be the child, grandchild, or great-grandchild of an American Legion or American Legion Auxiliary member who has been a member for at least 2 years. They must be high school seniors or graduates who maintained a GPA of 3.0 or higher during the last 2 semesters of high school and have been accepted at an accredited college or university in any state to study any field except nursing. Along with their application, they must submit a brief essay describing their chosen field and how this scholarship will help them achieve their goals. Financial need is considered in the selection process.
Financial data A stipend is awarded (amount not specified).
Duration 1 year.
Number awarded 1 each year.
Deadline February of each year.

[752]
RUBY PAUL CAMPAIGN FUND SCHOLARSHIP
American Legion Auxiliary
Department of Nebraska
P.O. Box 5227
Lincoln, NE 68505-0227
(402) 466-1808   Fax: (402) 466-0182
E-mail: neaux@windstream.net
Web: www.nebraskalegionaux.net
Summary To provide financial assistance to students in Nebraska who have a connection to the American Legion and plan to attend college in any state.
Eligibility Applicants must have been residents of Nebraska for at least 3 years and either 1) have been a member for at least 2 years of the American Legion, American Legion Auxiliary, or Sons of the American Legion, or 2) be the child, grandchild, or great-grandchild of an American Legion or American Legion Auxiliary member who has been a member for at least 2 years. They must be high school seniors or graduates who maintained a GPA of 3.0 or higher during the last 2 semesters of high school and have been accepted at an

accredited college or university in any state. Along with their application, they must submit a brief essay describing their chosen field and how this scholarship will help them achieve their goals. Financial need is considered.
Financial data A stipend is awarded (amount not specified).
Duration 1 year.
Number awarded 1 each year.
Deadline February of each year.

[753]
SABAN MILITARY WIFE EDUCATIONAL SCHOLARSHIPS
Operation Homefront
8930 Fourwinds Drive, Suite 340
San Antonio, TX 78239
(210) 659-7756   Toll Free: (800) 722-6098
Fax: (210) 566-7544
Web: www.operationhomefront.net/scholarship
Summary To provide financial assistance to wives of military personnel who are interested in studying a medical-related field at a vocational school.
Eligibility This program is open to wives of military members currently serving on active duty, including Reserve and National Guard members who have served at least 180 combined days of full-time military duty since January 1, 2008. Applicants must be enrolled or planning to enroll in a vocational training program as a dental assistance, medical assistant, medical billing and coding specialist, medical insurance technician, patient care assistant/technician, nurse assistant, vocational nurse, or medical transcriber. Along with their application, they must submit a 300-word essay on how, besides being a military wife, they have contributed to making their community a better place. Selection is based on the essay and commitment to volunteerism.
Financial data Maximum stipends are $30,000, $10,000, or $8,500. Funds may be used for tuition only; books and other fees are not covered.
Duration The program of study must be completed within 48 months.
Additional information Recipients must perform at least 12 hours of community service in the year when they receive the scholarship.
Number awarded 22 each year: 2 at $30,000 (for nursing students only), 5 at $10,000, and 15 at $8,500.
Deadline April of each year.

[754]
SAD SACKS NURSING SCHOLARSHIP
AMVETS-Department of Illinois
2200 South Sixth Street
Springfield, IL 62703
(217) 528-4713   Toll Free: (800) 638-VETS (within IL)
Fax: (217) 528-9896
Web: www.ilamvets.org/prog_scholarships.cfm
Summary To provide financial assistance for nursing education to Illinois residents, especially descendants of disabled or deceased veterans.
Eligibility This program is open to seniors at high schools in Illinois who have been accepted to an approved nursing program and students already enrolled in an approved school of nursing in Illinois. Priority is given to dependents of

deceased or disabled veterans. Selection is based on academic record, character, interest and activity record, and financial need. Preference is given to students in the following order: third-year students, second-year students, and first-year students.

Financial data A stipend is awarded (amount not specified).

Duration 1 year.

Number awarded Varies each year; recently, 2 of these scholarships were awarded.

Deadline February of each year.

[755]
SAM ROSE MEMORIAL SCHOLARSHIP

Ladies Auxiliary of the Fleet Reserve Association
Attn: Membership Service Administrator
P.O. Box 2086
Shingle Springs, CA 95682-2086
(530) 677-3925   E-mail: laframsa@att.net
Web: www.la-fra.org/scholarship.html

Summary To provide financial assistance for college to the children and grandchildren of deceased members of the Fleet Reserve Association (FRA).

Eligibility This program is open to children and grandchildren of deceased members of the association or those who were eligible to be members at the time of death. Applicants must submit an essay on their life experiences, career objectives, and what motivated them to select those objectives. Selection is based on academic record, financial need, extracurricular activities, leadership skills, and participation in community activities. U.S. citizenship is required.

Financial data The stipend is $2,500.

Duration 1 year.

Additional information Membership in the FRA is open to active-duty, retired, and Reserve members of the Navy, Marine Corps, and Coast Guard.

Number awarded 1 each year.

Deadline April of each year.

[756]
SAMSUNG AMERICAN LEGION SCHOLARSHIPS

American Legion
Attn: Americanism and Children & Youth Division
700 North Pennsylvania Street
P.O. Box 1055
Indianapolis, IN 46206-1055
(317) 630-1202   Fax: (317) 630-1223
E-mail: acy@legion.org
Web: legion.org/scholarships/samsung

Summary To provide financial assistance for college to descendants of veterans who participate in Girls State or Boys State.

Eligibility This program is open to students entering their senior year of high school who are selected to participate in Girls State or Boys State, sponsored by the American Legion Auxiliary or American Legion in their state. Applicants must be the child, grandchild, or great-grandchild of a veteran who saw active-duty service during specified periods of wartime. Finalists are chosen at each participating Girls and Boys State, and they are then nominated for the national awards. Selection is based on academic record, community service, involvement in school and community activities, and financial

need. Special consideration is given to descendants of U.S. veterans of the Korean War.

Financial data Stipends are $20,000 or $1,100.

Duration 4 years.

Additional information These scholarships were first presented in 1996, following a gift in July 1995 to the American Legion from Samsung Corporation of Korea, as an act of appreciation for U.S. involvement in the Korean War.

Number awarded Varies each year; recently, 9 scholarships at $20,000 and 89 at $1,100 were awarded.

Deadline Deadline not specified.

[757]
SCHNEIDER-EMANUEL AMERICAN LEGION SCHOLARSHIPS

American Legion
Department of Wisconsin
2930 American Legion Drive
P.O. Box 388
Portage, WI 53901-0388
(608) 745-1090   Fax: (608) 745-0179
E-mail: info@wilegion.org
Web: www.wilegion.org

Summary To provide financial assistance to members of the American Legion in Wisconsin and their children or grandchildren who plan to attend college in any state.

Eligibility This program is open to seniors and graduates from accredited Wisconsin high schools. Applicants must be at least 1 of the following 1) a child whose father, mother, or legal guardian is a member of the Department of Wisconsin of the American Legion, American Legion Auxiliary, or Sons of the American Legion; 2) a grandchild whose grandfather, grandmother, or legal guardian is a member of the Department of Wisconsin of the American Legion, American Legion Auxiliary, or Sons of the American Legion; 3) a member of the Sons of the American Legion, American Legion Auxiliary, or Junior American Legion Auxiliary; or 4) a veteran and an American Legion member in Wisconsin. Applicants must have participated in Legion and Auxiliary youth programs. They must be planning to attend a college or university in any state to work on a baccalaureate degree. Selection is based on moral character; scholastic excellence (GPA of 3.0 or higher); participation and accomplishment in American Legion affiliated activities; and personality, leadership, and participation in general extracurricular activities.

Financial data The stipend is $1,000.

Duration 1 year.

Additional information This program began in 1968.

Number awarded 3 each year.

Deadline February of each year.

[758]
SCHOLARSHIPS FOR MILITARY CHILDREN

Fisher House Foundation
111 Rockville Pike, Suite 420
Rockville, MD 20850
Toll Free: (888) 294-8560
E-mail: JWeiskopf@fisherhouse.org
Web: www.militaryscholar.org/sfmc/index.html

Summary To provide financial assistance for college to the children of veterans and military personnel.

Eligibility This program is open to sons and daughters of U.S. military servicemembers (including active duty, retirees, Guard/Reserves, and survivors of deceased members) who are enrolled or accepted for enrollment as a full-time undergraduate at a college or university. Applicants must be younger than 23 years of age and enrolled in the Defense Enrollment Eligibility Reporting System (DEERS). They must have a GPA of 3.0 or higher. Along with their application, they must submit a 500-word essay on a topic that changes annually; recently, students were asked to identify the 4 persons whose faces they would place on a 21st century Mount Rushmore type of monument and why. Selection is based on merit.

Financial data The stipend is $1,500.

Duration 1 year; recipients may reapply.

Additional information This program, established in 2001, is administered by the Fisher House Foundation on behalf of the Defense Commissary Agency.

Number awarded At least 1 scholarship is allocated for each of the commissaries worldwide operated by the Defense Commissary Agency (DeCA); more than 1 scholarship per commissary may be available, depending on donations from suppliers and manufacturers whose products are sold at commissaries. Recently, the program awarded more than $1 million to 670 students.

Deadline February of each year.

[759]
SCHOLARSHIPS FOR USPHS COMMISSIONED CORPS DEPENDENTS

Commissioned Officers Association of the USPHS Inc.
Attn: PHS Commissioned Officers Foundation for the
 Advancement of Public Health
8201 Corporate Drive, Suite 200
Landover, MD 20785
(301) 731-9080   Fax: (301) 731-9084
E-mail: info@phscof.org
Web: www.phscof.org/education.html

Summary To provide financial assistance for college or graduate school to dependents of officers of the United States Public Health Service (USPHS) Commissioned Corps.

Eligibility This program is open to dependent children and dependent spouses of active-duty, retired, or deceased officers of the USPHS Commissioned Corps. Applicants must be entering or continuing full-time students at a college or graduate school. They must be U.S. citizens and have a GPA of 3.0 or higher. Along with their application, they must submit an essay on why they want to go to college and what they intend to accomplish with their degree. Financial need is not considered in the selection process.

Financial data Stipends range up to $1,000.

Duration 1 year.

Additional information The highest-ranked applicant receives the Ronald Lessing Memorial Scholarship.

Number awarded Varies each year; recently, 12 of these scholarships were awarded.

Deadline May of each year.

[760]
SCHUYLER S. PYLE SCHOLARSHIP

Fleet Reserve Association
Attn: FRA Education Foundation
125 North West Street
Alexandria, VA 22314-2754
(703) 683-1400   Toll Free: (800) FRA-1924
Fax: (703) 549-6610   E-mail: scholars@fra.org
Web: www.fra.org

Summary To provide financial assistance for college or graduate school to members of the Fleet Reserve Association (FRA) and their families.

Eligibility This program is open to members of the FRA and the dependent children, grandchildren, and spouses of living or deceased members. Applicants must be enrolled as full-time undergraduate or graduate students. Along with their application, they must submit an essay on why they want to go to college and what they intend to accomplish with their degree. Selection is based on academic record, financial need, extracurricular activities, leadership skills, and participation in community activities. U.S. citizenship is required.

Financial data The stipend is $5,000 per year.

Duration 1 year; may be renewed.

Additional information Membership in the FRA is restricted to active-duty, retired, and Reserve members of the Navy, Marine Corps, and Coast Guard.

Number awarded 1 each year.

Deadline April of each year.

[761]
SCOTT B. LUNDELL TUITION WAIVER FOR MILITARY MEMBERS' SURVIVING DEPENDENTS

Utah Department of Veteran's Affairs
Attn: Director
550 Foothill Boulevard, Room 202
Salt Lake City, UT 84108
(801) 326-2372   Toll Free: (800) 894-9497 (within UT)
Fax: (801) 326-2369   E-mail: veterans@utah.gov
Web: veterans.utah.gov/homepage/stateBenefits/index.html

Summary To provide a tuition waiver to residents of Utah who are dependents of deceased military personnel and attending a public institution in the state.

Eligibility This program is open to residents of Utah who are dependents of military members killed in the line of duty after September 11, 2001. Applicants must be working on an undergraduate degree at a public college or university in the state.

Financial data Tuition is waived for qualified dependents.

Duration Tuition is waived until completion of a bachelor's degree.

Additional information This program began in 2007.

Number awarded Varies each year.

Deadline Deadline not specified.

[762]
SEABEE MEMORIAL SCHOLARSHIP ASSOCIATION PROGRAM

Seabee Memorial Scholarship Association
P.O. Box 6574
Silver Spring, MD 20916
(301) 570-2850   Fax: (301) 570-2873
E-mail: smsa@erols.com
Web: www.seabee.org/scholarships.shtml

Summary   To provide financial assistance for college to the children or grandchildren of active or deceased members of the Naval Construction Battalion (Seabees) or Navy Civil Engineering Corps.

Eligibility   This program is open to the children, stepchildren, and grandchildren of regular, Reserve, retired, or deceased officers and enlisted members who are now serving in or have been honorably discharged from the Naval Construction Force (Seabees) or Navy Civil Engineering Corps. Applicants may be high school seniors, high school graduates, or students currently enrolled full-time at a 4-year college or university. Selection is based on financial need, citizenship, leadership, and scholastic record.

Financial data   The stipend is $1,900 per year.

Duration   1 year; may be renewed for 3 additional years.

Number awarded   Varies each year; recently, 20 new scholarships were awarded through this program.

Deadline   April of each year.

[763]
SECOND MARINE DIVISION ASSOCIATION MEMORIAL SCHOLARSHIP

Second Marine Division Association
Attn: Memorial Scholarship Fund
P.O. Box 8180
Camp Lejeune, NC 28547-8180
(910) 451-3167
Web: www.2dmardiv.com/Scholarship.html

Summary   To provide financial assistance for college to the children and grandchildren of veterans or members of the Second Marine Division.

Eligibility   This program is open to unmarried dependent children and grandchildren of individuals who are serving or have served in the Second Marine Division or in a unit attached to it (e.g., hospital corpsmen, aviation, logistics). Applicants must be high school seniors, high school graduates, or full-time undergraduate students in accredited colleges or vocational/technical schools. They must have a family income of less than $65,000 and a GPA of 2.75 or higher.

Financial data   The stipend is $1,200 per year.

Duration   1 year; may be renewed.

Number awarded   Varies each year.

Deadline   March of each year.

[764]
SERGEANT ANDREW EDMUND TOPHAM MEMORIAL SCHOLARSHIP

Army Scholarship Foundation
11700 Preston Road, Suite 660-301
Dallas, TX 75230
E-mail: ContactUs@armyscholarshipfoundation.org
Web: www.armyscholarshipfoundation.org

Summary   To provide financial assistance for undergraduate study to the children and spouses of Army personnel, especially those who served in the Global War on Terrorism.

Eligibility   This program is open to 1) children of regular active-duty, active-duty Reserve, and active-duty National Guard U.S. Army members in good standing; 2) spouses of serving enlisted regular active-duty, active-duty Reserve, and active-duty National Guard U.S. Army members in good standing; and 3) children of former U.S. Army members who received an honorable or medical discharge or were killed while serving in the U.S. Army. Preference is given to students who are family members of soldiers who served in either Afghanistan or Iraq as part of the Global War on Terrorism. Applicants must be high school seniors, high school graduates, or undergraduates enrolled at an accredited college, university, or vocational/technical institute. They must be U.S. citizens and have a GPA of 2.0 or higher; children must be younger than 24 years of age. Financial need is considered in the selection process.

Financial data   The stipend ranges from $500 to $2,000 per year.

Duration   1 year; recipients may reapply.

Additional information   The Army Scholarship Foundation was established in 2001.

Number awarded   1 each year.

Deadline   April of each year.

[765]
SERGEANT FELIX M. DELGRECO, JR. SCHOLARSHIP FUND

Connecticut Community Foundation
43 Field Street
Waterbury, CT 06702-1906
(203) 753-1315   Fax: (203) 756-3054
E-mail: jcarey@conncf.org
Web: www.conncf.org/scholarships

Summary   To provide financial assistance to high school seniors and current college students whose parents are members of the Connecticut Army National Guard.

Eligibility   This program is open to the children of members of the Connecticut Army National Guard who are attending or planning to attend college in any state. Applicants must have a grade average of "B-" or higher. Selection is based on academic motivation, extracurricular activities, work experience, a letter of recommendation, financial need, and an essay. U.S. citizenship is required.

Financial data   The stipend is $4,000 per year. Funds are paid directly to the recipient's school.

Duration   1 year; recipients may reapply up to the minimum number of years required to complete an undergraduate degree in their course of study, provided they maintain a grade average of "C+" or higher.

Additional information   This program is supported by the Connecticut National Guard Foundation.

Number awarded   Varies each year.

Deadline   March of each year.

[766]
SERGEANT MAJOR DOUGLAS R. DRUM MEMORIAL SCHOLARSHIP

American Military Retirees Association, Inc.
Attn: Scholarship Committee
5436 Peru Street, Suite 1
Plattsburgh, NY 12901
(518) 563-9479   Toll Free: (800) 424-2969
Fax: (518) 324-5204   E-mail: info@amra1973.org
Web: www.amra1973.org/Scholarship

Summary To provide financial assistance for college to members of the American Military Retirees Association (AMRA) and their dependents.

Eligibility This program is open to current members of AMRA and their dependents, children, and grandchildren. Applicants must be attending or planning to attend an accredited college or university. Along with their application, they must submit a 750-word essay on why they deserve this scholarship. Selection is based on academics, leadership, character, citizenship, and community service.

Financial data Stipends are $5,000, $2,500, or $1,000.

Duration 1 year.

Additional information Membership in AMRA is open to all retired members of the armed forces, regardless of rank.

Number awarded Varies each year; recently, 24 of these scholarships were awarded: 12 to incoming freshmen (1 at $5,000, 1 at $2,500, and 10 at $1,000) and 12 to returning college students (1 at $5,000, 1 at $2,500, and 10 at $1,000).

Deadline February of each year.

[767]
SIXTH MARINE DIVISION ASSOCIATION SCHOLARSHIP

Sixth Marine Division Association
c/o Marine Corps Scholarship Foundation
909 North Washington Street, Suite 400
Alexandria, VA 22314
(703) 549-0060   Toll Free: (866) 496-5462
Fax: (703) 549-9474   E-mail: students@mcsf.org
Web: www.mcsf.org

Summary To provide financial assistance for college to the grandchildren of veterans who served with the Sixth Marine Division during World War II.

Eligibility This program is open to grandchildren of veterans who served with the Sixth Marine Division during World War II and are or were members of the Sixth Marine Division Association. Applicants must be high school seniors, high school graduates, or current college students. Along with their application, they must submit academic transcripts, a copy of their grandparent's honorable discharge, and a 500-word essay on a topic that changes periodically. Only undergraduate study is supported. The family income of applicants must be less than $90,000 per year.

Financial data Stipends depend on the need of the recipient and the availability of funds, but generally range from $500 to $2,500 per year.

Duration 1 year; may be renewed for up to 3 additional years.

Additional information The highest-ranked applicant receives an award that is designated the Peter Mucci Memorial Scholarship.

Number awarded Varies each year; recently, 3 of these scholarships were awarded.

Deadline February of each year.

[768]
SOCIETY OF DAUGHTERS OF THE UNITED STATES ARMY SCHOLARSHIPS

Society of Daughters of the United States Army
c/o Janet B. Otto, Scholarship Chair
7717 Rockledge Court
Springfield, VA 21152

Summary To provide financial assistance for college to daughters and granddaughters of active, retired, or deceased career Army warrant and commissioned officers.

Eligibility This program is open to the daughters, adopted daughters, stepdaughters, or granddaughters of career commissioned officers or warrant officers of the U.S. Army (active, regular, or Reserve) who 1) are currently on active duty, 2) retired after 20 years of active duty or were medically retired, or 3) died while on active duty or after retiring from active duty with 20 or more years of service. Applicants must have at least a 3.0 GPA and be studying or planning to study at the undergraduate level. Selection is based on depth of character, leadership, seriousness of purpose, academic achievement, and financial need.

Financial data Scholarships, to a maximum of $1,000, are paid directly to the college or school for tuition, laboratory fees, books, or other expenses.

Duration 1 year; may be renewed up to 4 additional years if the recipient maintains at least a 3.0 GPA.

Additional information Recipients may attend any accredited college, professional, or vocational school. This program includes named scholarships from the following funds: the Colonel Hayden W. Wagner Memorial Fund, the Eugenia Bradford Roberts Memorial Fund, the Daughters of the U.S. Army Scholarship Fund, the Gladys K. and John K. Simpson Scholarship Fund, and the Margaret M. Prickett Scholarship Fund. Requests for applications must be accompanied by a self-addressed stamped envelope.

Number awarded Varies each year.

Deadline February of each year.

[769]
SOCIETY OF THE 3RD INFANTRY DIVISION SCHOLARSHIPS

Society of the 3rd Infantry Division
Attn: Scholarship Foundation
2010 Worcester Lane
Garland, TX 75040-3331
(972) 595-1704   E-mail: ldball1@msn.com
Web: 3idscholarshipfoundation.org

Summary To provide financial assistance for college to descendants of members of the Society of the 3rd Infantry Division and spouses of deceased 3rd Infantry Division members.

Eligibility This program is open to 1) children, grandchildren, and great-grandchildren of members of the society; and 3) children, grandchildren, and unremarried spouses of 3rd Infantry Division soldiers killed in action or died of wounds while on active duty. Applicants must be enrolled or planning to enroll as an undergraduate student. Along with their application, they must submit an essay of 2 to 4 pages on the history of the 3rd Infantry Division, national pride, loyalty to the nation, patriotism, or a related subject. Selection is based on the essay, academic accomplishment, extracurricular activities, community service involvement, goals after graduation, and financial need.

Financial data The stipend is $1,000.

Duration 1 year; recipients may reapply.

Additional information These scholarships were first awarded in 2005.

Number awarded Varies each year; recently, 10 of these scholarships were awarded.

Deadline April of each year.

[770]
SONS OF UNION VETERANS OF THE CIVIL WAR SCHOLARSHIPS

Sons of Union Veterans of the Civil War
P.O. Box 1865
Harrisburg, PA 17105
(717) 232-7000   E-mail: webmaster@suvcw.org
Web: suvcw.org/scholar.htm

Summary To provide financial assistance for college to descendants of Union Civil War veterans.

Eligibility This program is open to high school seniors and students currently enrolled at a 4-year college or university. Applicants must 1) rank in the upper quarter of their high school graduating class (preferably in the upper tenth); 2) have a record of performance in school and community activities; 3) have an interest in and positive attitude toward college; 4) provide 3 letters of recommendation; and 5) submit an official grade transcript. Males must be a current member or associate of Sons of Union Veterans of the Civil War. Females must be the daughter or granddaughter of a current member or associate of Sons of Union Veterans of the Civil War and a current member of at least 1 of the following organizations: Woman's Relief Corps, Ladies of the Grand Army of the Republic, Daughters of Union Veterans of the Civil War 1861-1865, or Auxiliary to the Sons of Union Veterans of the Civil War. Financial need is not considered in the selection process.

Financial data The stipend is $1,000. Funds are to be used for tuition and books. Checks are mailed directly to the recipient's school.

Duration 1 year.

Number awarded 2 each year.

Deadline March of each year.

[771]
SOUTH CAROLINA TUITION PROGRAM FOR CHILDREN OF CERTAIN WAR VETERANS

South Carolina Office of Veterans Affairs
c/o VA Regional Office Building
6437 Garners Ferry Road, Suite 1126
Columbia, SC 29209
(803) 647-2434   Fax: (803) 647-2312
E-mail: va@oepp.sc.gov
Web: www.govoepp.state.sc.us/va/benefits.html

Summary To provide free college tuition to the children of disabled and other South Carolina veterans.

Eligibility This program is open to the children of wartime veterans who were legal residents of South Carolina both at the time of entry into military or naval service and during ser-

vice, or who have been residents of South Carolina for at least 1 year. Veteran parents must 1) be permanently and totally disabled as determined by the U.S. Department of Veterans Affairs; 2) have been a prisoner of war; 3) have been killed in action; 4) have died from other causes while in service; 5) have died of a disease or disability resulting from service; 6) be currently missing in action; 7) have received the Congressional Medal of Honor; 8) have received the Purple Heart Medal from wounds received in combat; or 9) now be deceased but qualified under categories 1 or 2 above. The veteran's child must be 26 years of age or younger and working on an undergraduate degree.

Financial data Children who qualify are eligible for free tuition at any South Carolina state-supported college, university, or postsecondary technical education institution. The waiver applies to tuition only. The costs of room and board, certain fees, and books are not covered.

Duration Students are eligible to receive this support as long as they are younger than 26 years of age and working on an undergraduate degree.

Number awarded Varies each year.

Deadline Deadline not specified.

[772]
SOUTH DAKOTA REDUCED TUITION FOR CHILDREN OF DECEASED SERVICEMEN/WOMEN

South Dakota Board of Regents
Attn: Scholarship Committee
306 East Capitol Avenue, Suite 200
Pierre, SD 57501-2545
(605) 773-3455   Fax: (605) 773-2422
E-mail: info@sdbor.edu
Web: www.sdbor.edu/students/redtuit_childservice.htm

Summary To provide free tuition at South Dakota public colleges and universities to children of military personnel who died while in service.

Eligibility This program is open to residents of South Dakota younger than 25 years of age. The applicant's parent must have been killed in action or died of other causes while on active duty and must have been a resident of South Dakota for at least 6 months immediately preceding entry into active service.

Financial data Qualifying applicants are granted a 100% tuition waiver at state-supported postsecondary institutions in South Dakota. The waiver applies only to tuition, not fees.

Duration 8 semesters or 12 quarters of either full- or part-time study.

Number awarded Varies each year.

Deadline Deadline not specified.

[773]
SOUTH DAKOTA REDUCED TUITION FOR DEPENDENTS OF PRISONERS OF WAR OR MISSING IN ACTION

South Dakota Board of Regents
Attn: Scholarship Committee
306 East Capitol Avenue, Suite 200
Pierre, SD 57501-2545
(605) 773-3455   Fax: (605) 773-2422
E-mail: info@sdbor.edu
Web: www.sdbor.edu/students/redtuit_deppowmia.htm

Summary To provide free tuition at South Dakota public colleges and universities to dependents of prisoners of war (POWs) and persons missing in action (MIAs).

Eligibility This program is open to residents of South Dakota who are the dependents of POWs or of MIAs who are officially listed as residents of the state. Dependents include 1) children born before or during the period of time when the parent was declared MIA or POW; 2) children legally adopted or in legal custody of the parent during the period of time when the parent was declared MIA or POW; and 3) the spouse (if not legally separated) of the individual who is MIA or POW. Applicants must be attending or planning to attend a state-supported school in South Dakota.

Financial data For those who qualify, tuition and mandatory fees are waived.

Duration 8 semesters or 12 quarters of either full- or part-time study.

Number awarded Varies each year.

Deadline Deadline not specified.

[774]
SPECIAL OPERATIONS WARRIOR FOUNDATION SCHOLARSHIPS

Special Operations Warrior Foundation
4409 El Prado Boulevard
P.O. Box 13483
Tampa, FL 33681-3483
(813) 805-9400   Toll Free: (877) 337-7693
Fax: (813) 805-0567   E-mail: warrior@specialops.org
Web: www.specialops.org/?page=collegescholarship

Summary To provide financial assistance for college to the children of Special Operations personnel who died in training or operational missions.

Eligibility This program is open to the children of parents who served in Special Operations and were killed in a training accident or an operational mission. This is an entitlement program; all eligible students receive support.

Financial data A stipend is awarded (amount not specified). Funding is intended to cover expenses not included in the Marine Gunnery Sergeant John David Fry Scholarship or for dependents whose Special Operations parent was killed prior to September 11, 2001.

Duration 4 years or more.

Additional information This program was established in 1980 because of the high casualty rates experienced by personnel of U.S. Special Operations Command.

Number awarded Varies each year.

Deadline Applications may be submitted at any time.

[775]
SPIRIT OF YOUTH SCHOLARSHIP FOR JUNIOR MEMBERS

American Legion Auxiliary
8945 North Meridian Street
Indianapolis, IN 46260
(317) 569-4500   Fax: (317) 569-4502
E-mail: alahq@alaforveterans.org
Web: www.alaforveterans.org

Summary To provide financial assistance for college to junior members of the American Legion Auxiliary.

Eligibility Applicants for this scholarship must have been junior members of the Auxiliary for at least the past 3 years. They must be seniors at an accredited high school in the United States, have a GPA of 3.0 or higher, and be planning to enroll full time at a college, university, or professional or technical school that awards a certificate upon completion of an accredited course. Along with their application, they must submit a 1,000-word essay on a topic that changes annually; recently, students were asked to write on "The Future-Serving My Community and Our Veterans." Selection is based on that essay (30%), character and leadership (30%), and academic record (40%). Each unit of the Auxiliary may select a candidate for application to the department level, and each department submits a candidate for the national award.

Financial data The stipend is $1,000 per year.

Duration 4 years.

Additional information Applications are available from the president of the candidate's own unit or from the secretary or education chair of the department.

Number awarded 5 each year: 1 in each division of the American Legion Auxiliary.

Deadline Applications must be submitted to the unit president by February of each year.

[776]
SPOUSE EDUCATION ASSISTANCE PROGRAM

Army Emergency Relief
200 Stovall Street
Alexandria, VA 22332-0600
(703) 428-0000   Toll Free: (866) 878-6378
Fax: (703) 325-7183   E-mail: Spouse@aerhq.org
Web: www.aerhq.org

Summary To provide financial assistance for college to the dependent spouses of Army personnel.

Eligibility This program is open to spouses of Army soldiers on active duty, widow(er)s of soldiers who died while on active duty, spouses of retired soldiers, and widow(er)s of soldiers who died while in a retired status. Applicants may be residing in the United States or overseas. They must be working full or part time on a 4-year college degree and have a GPA of 2.0 or higher. Study for a second undergraduate or graduate degree is not supported. Selection is based primarily on financial need.

Financial data The maximum stipend is $2,800 per academic year.

Duration 1 year; may be renewed up to 3 additional years of full-time study or up to 7 additional years of part-time study.

Additional information Army Emergency Relief is a private nonprofit organization dedicated to "helping the Army take care of its own." It previously operated separate educational assistance programs for stateside and overseas spouses, but combined those effective in December, 2011.

Number awarded Varies each year; recently, approximately 2,000 spouses received support annually.

Deadline March of each year.

[777]
STANLEY A. DORAN MEMORIAL SCHOLARSHIPS

Fleet Reserve Association
Attn: FRA Education Foundation
125 North West Street
Alexandria, VA 22314-2754
(703) 683-1400   Toll Free: (800) FRA-1924
Fax: (703) 549-6610   E-mail: scholars@fra.org
Web: www.fra.org

Summary To provide financial assistance for college or graduate school to children of members of the Fleet Reserve Association (FRA).

Eligibility This program is open to the dependent children of FRA members who are in good standing (or were at the time of death, if deceased). Applicants must be working on or planning to work full time on an undergraduate or graduate degree. Along with their application, they must submit an essay on why they want to go to college and what they intend to accomplish with their degree. Selection is based on academic record, financial need, extracurricular activities, leadership skills, and participation in community activities. U.S. citizenship is required.

Financial data The amount awarded varies, depending on the needs of the recipient and the funds available.

Duration 1 year; may be renewed.

Additional information Membership in the FRA is restricted to active-duty, retired, and Reserve members of the Navy, Marine Corps, and Coast Guard.

Number awarded 3 each year.

Deadline April of each year.

[778]
SURVIVING DEPENDENTS OF MONTANA NATIONAL GUARD MEMBER WAIVER

Office of the Commissioner of Higher Education
Attn: Montana University System
State Scholarship Coordinator
2500 Broadway
P.O. Box 203201
Helena, MT 59620-3201
(406) 444-0638   Toll Free: (800) 537-7508
Fax: (406) 444-1469   E-mail: snewlun@montana.edu
Web: www.mus.edu

Summary To provide financial assistance for undergraduate study to dependents of deceased National Guard members in Montana.

Eligibility Eligible for this benefit are residents of Montana who are surviving spouses or children of Montana National Guard members killed as a result of injury, disease, or other disability incurred in the line of duty while serving on state active duty. Financial need is considered.

Financial data Students eligible for this benefit are entitled to attend any unit of the Montana University System without payment of undergraduate registration or incidental fees.

Duration Undergraduate students are eligible for continued fee waiver as long as they maintain reasonable academic progress as full-time students.

Additional information The waiver does not apply if the recipient is eligible for educational benefits from any governmental or private program that provides comparable benefits.

Number awarded Varies each year.

Deadline Deadline not specified.

[779]
SURVIVORS' AND DEPENDENTS' EDUCATIONAL ASSISTANCE PROGRAM

Department of Veterans Affairs
Attn: Veterans Benefits Administration
810 Vermont Avenue, N.W.
Washington, DC 20420
(202) 418-4343   Toll Free: (888) GI-BILL1
Web: www.gibill.va.gov/benefits/other_programs/dea.html

Summary To provide financial assistance for undergraduate or graduate study to children and spouses of deceased and disabled veterans, MIAs, and POWs.

Eligibility Eligible for this assistance are spouses and children of 1) veterans who died or are permanently and totally disabled as the result of active service in the armed forces; 2) veterans who died from any cause while rated permanently and totally disabled from a service-connected disability; 3) servicemembers listed as missing in action or captured in the line of duty by a hostile force; 4) servicemembers listed as forcibly detained or interned by a foreign government or power; and 5) servicemembers who are hospitalized or receiving outpatient treatment for a service-connected permanent and total disability and are likely to be discharged for that disability. Children must be between 18 and 26 years of age, although extensions may be granted. Spouses and children over 14 years of age with physical or mental disabilities are also eligible.

Financial data Monthly stipends for study at an academic institution are $957 for full time, $718 for three-quarter time, or $476 for half-time. Other rates apply for apprenticeship and on-the-job training, farm cooperative training, and special restorative training.

Duration Up to 45 months (or the equivalent in part-time training). Spouses must complete their training within 10 years of the date they are first found eligible. For spouses of servicemembers who died on active duty, benefits end 20 years from the date of death.

Additional information Benefits may be used to work on associate, bachelor's, or graduate degrees at colleges and universities, including independent study, cooperative training, and study abroad programs. Courses leading to a certificate or diploma from business, technical, or vocational schools may also be taken. Other eligible programs include apprenticeships, on-the-job training programs, farm cooperative courses, and correspondence courses (for spouses only). Remedial, deficiency, and refresher courses may be approved under certain circumstances.

Number awarded Varies each year.

Deadline Applications may be submitted at any time.

[780]
TAILHOOK EDUCATIONAL FOUNDATION SCHOLARSHIPS

Tailhook Educational Foundation
9696 Businesspark Avenue
P.O. Box 26626
San Diego, CA 92196-0626
(858) 689-9223   Toll Free: (800) 322-4665
E-mail: tag@tailhook.net
Web: www.tailhook.org/Foundation.html

Summary To provide financial assistance for college to personnel associated with naval aviation and their children.

Eligibility This program is open to 1) the children (natural, step, and adopted) of current or former U.S. Navy or Marine Corps personnel who served as an aviator, flight officer, or air crewman, or 2) personnel and children of personnel who are serving or have served on board a U.S. Navy aircraft carrier as a member of the ship's company or air wing. Applicants must be enrolled or accepted for enrollment at an accredited college or university. Selection is based on educational and extracurricular achievements, merit, and citizenship.

Financial data Stipend range from $1,500 to $15,000.

Duration 1 to 2 years.

Number awarded Varies each year; recently, 71 of these scholarships were awarded.

Deadline March of each year.

[781]
TEXAS AMERICAN LEGION AUXILIARY PAST PRESIDENT'S PARLEY SCHOLARSHIPS

American Legion Auxiliary
Department of Texas
P.O. Box 140407
Austin, TX 78714-0407
(512) 476-7278   Fax: (512) 482-8391
E-mail: alatexas@txlegion.org
Web: alatexas.org/scholarship/ppp.html

Summary To provide financial assistance to descendants of Texas veterans who wish to study a field related to medicine at a school in the state.

Eligibility This program is open to the children, grandchildren, and great-grandchildren of veterans who served during specified periods of wartime. Applicants must be residents of Texas studying or planning to study a medical field at a postsecondary institution in the state. Selection is based on need, goals, character, citizenship, and objectives.

Financial data The stipend is $1,000.

Duration 1 year.

Additional information Applications for these scholarships must be submitted through local units of the American Legion Auxiliary in Texas.

Number awarded 1 or more each year.

Deadline April of each year.

[782]
TEXAS B-ON-TIME LOAN PROGRAM

Texas Higher Education Coordinating Board
Attn: Hinson-Hazlewood College Student Loan Program
1200 East Anderson Lane
P.O. Box 12788
Austin, TX 78711-2788
(512) 427-6340   Toll Free: (800) 242-3062
Fax: (512) 427-6423   E-mail: loaninfo@thecb.state.tx.us
Web: www.hhloans.com/borrowers/BOTfactsheet.cfm

Summary To provide funding to students in Texas who are residents of the state or entitled to pay resident tuition as a dependent child of a member of the U.S. armed forces.

Eligibility This program is open to residents of Texas and residents of other states who are entitled to pay resident tuition as a dependent child of a member of the U.S. armed forces. Applicants must 1) have graduated from a public or accredited private high school in Texas or from a high school operated by the U.S. Department of Defense; or 2) earned an associate degree from an eligible Texas institution. They must be enrolled full time in an undergraduate degree or certificate program at an eligible college, university, junior college, or public technical college in Texas.

Financial data Eligible students may borrow up to $3,550 per semester ($7,100 per year) for a 4-year public or private institution, $945 per semester ($1,780 per year) for a 2-year public or private junior college, or $1,575 per semester ($3,150 per year) for a public technical college. A 3% origination fee is deducted from the loan proceeds. No interest is charged. Loans are forgiven if the students 1) graduate with a cumulative GPA of 3.0 or higher within 4 calendar years after they initially enroll; within 5 calendar years after they initially enroll in a degree program in architecture, engineering, or other field that normally requires more than 4 years for completion; or within 2 calendar years if they initially enroll in a public or private 2-year institution; or 2) graduate with a cumulative GPA of 3.0 or higher with a total number of credit hours that is no more than 6 hours beyond what is required to complete the degree or certificate.

Duration 1 year. May be renewed after the first year if the recipient makes satisfactory academic progress toward a degree or certificate. May be renewed after the second and subsequent years if the recipient completes at least 75% of the semester credit hours attempted and has a cumulative GPA of 2.5 or higher on all course work. Loans are available for a maximum of 150 credit hours.

Number awarded Varies each year.

Deadline Deadline not specified.

[783]
TEXAS CHILDREN OF U.S. MILITARY WHO ARE MISSING IN ACTION OR PRISONERS OF WAR EXEMPTION PROGRAM

Texas Higher Education Coordinating Board
Attn: Grants and Special Programs
1200 East Anderson Lane
P.O. Box 12788
Austin, TX 78711-2788
(512) 427-6340   Toll Free: (800) 242-3062
Fax: (512) 427-6420   E-mail: grantinfo@thecb.state.tx.us
Web: www.collegeforalltexans.com

Summary To provide educational assistance to the children of Texas military personnel declared prisoners of war or missing in action.

Eligibility Eligible are dependent children of Texas residents who are either prisoners of war or missing in action. Applicants must be under 21 years of age, or under 25 if they receive the majority of support from their parent(s).

Financial data Eligible students are exempted from the payment of all dues, fees, and tuition charges at publicly-supported colleges and universities in Texas.

Duration Up to 8 semesters.

Number awarded Varies each year; recently, 4 of these exemptions were granted.

Deadline Deadline not specified.

[784]
TEXAS WAIVERS OF NONRESIDENT TUITION FOR MILITARY SURVIVORS

Texas Higher Education Coordinating Board
Attn: Grants and Special Programs
1200 East Anderson Lane
P.O. Box 12788
Austin, TX 78711-2788
(512) 427-6340   Toll Free: (800) 242-3062
Fax: (512) 427-6420   E-mail: grantinfo@thecb.state.tx.us
Web: www.collegeforalltexans.com

Summary   To provide a partial tuition exemption to the surviving spouses and dependent children of deceased military personnel who move to Texas following the servicemember's death.

Eligibility   Eligible for these waivers are the surviving spouses and dependent children of members of the U.S. armed forces and commissioned officers of the Public Health Service who died while in service. Applicants must move to Texas within 60 days of the date of the death of the servicemember. They must be attending or planning to attend a public college or university in the state. Children are eligible even if the surviving parent does not accompany them to Texas.

Financial data   Although persons eligible under this program are still classified as nonresidents, they are entitled to pay the resident tuition at Texas institutions of higher education on an immediate basis.

Duration   1 year.

Additional information   This program became effective in 2003.

Number awarded   Varies each year.

Deadline   Deadline not specified.

[785]
THANKSUSA SCHOLARSHIPS

ThanksUSA
1390 Chain Bridge Road, Suite 260
McLean, VA 22101
Toll Free: (877) THX-USAS
Web: www.thanksusa.org/main/scholarships.html

Summary   To provide financial assistance for college to children and spouses of military personnel who served after September 11, 2001.

Eligibility   This program is open to dependent children 24 years of age or younger and spouses of active-duty military personnel. The parent or spouse must 1) have served on active duty for at least 180 days since September 11, 2001; 2) have been killed or wounded in action since that date; 3) be a member of the military Reserves activated to full-time duty; or 4) be a member of the National Guard who have been federalized. Applicants must be entering or attending an accredited 2- or 4-year college, university, vocational school, or technical school as a full-time student. They must have a GPA of 2.0 or higher. Selection is based on financial need, academic record, and demonstrated leadership and participation in school and community activities.

Financial data   The stipend is $3,000.

Duration   1 year.

Additional information   This program began in 2006. Selection of recipients is made by Scholarship Management Services, a division of Scholarship America.

Number awarded   Varies each year; recently, more than 250 of these scholarship were awarded. Since the program was established, it has awarded 2,200 scholarships with a value of nearly $6.5 million.

Deadline   May of each year.

[786]
THIRD MARINE DIVISION ASSOCIATION MEMORIAL SCHOLARSHIP FUND

Third Marine Division Association, Inc.
P.O. Box 254
Chalfont, PA 18914-0254
(215) 822-9094   E-mail: supertop@aol.com
Web: www.caltrap.org/3rd_MarDivAssoc/scholarship.asp

Summary   To provide financial assistance for college to children and some spouses of members of the Third Marine Division Association.

Eligibility   This program is open to dependent unmarried children whose sponsoring parent has been a member of the association for at least 2 years. Associate members do not qualify, except for widows of deceased regular or life member who had qualifying Third Marine Division service and association membership. Dependent children of military personnel who served in any Third Marine Division unit and lost their lives as a result of combat actions while serving in the operations known as Desert Shield, Desert Storm, or any other southwest Asia operation after August 2, 1990, are also eligible. Applicants must be interested in attending a college or university in the United States or Canada. They must be between 16 and 23 years of age and able to demonstrate financial need. Grandchildren of members are not eligible.

Financial data   Stipends range from $400 to $2,400, depending upon need.

Duration   1 year; may be renewed for up to 3 additional years for undergraduate study or until the recipient reaches 26 years of age, provided a "C" average is maintained.

Additional information   This program began in 1969.

Number awarded   20 to 25 each year.

Deadline   April of each year.

[787]
TRANSFER OF POST-9/11 GI-BILL BENEFITS TO DEPENDENTS

Department of Veterans Affairs
Attn: Veterans Benefits Administration
810 Vermont Avenue, N.W.
Washington, DC 20420
(202) 418-4343   Toll Free: (888) GI-BILL1
Web: www.gibill.va.gov

Summary   To provide financial assistance to dependents of military personnel who qualify for Post-9/11 GI Bill benefits and agree to transfer unused benefits to their spouse or child.

Eligibility   This program is open to dependents of current military personnel whose parent or spouse 1) has at least 6 years of service in the armed forces (active duty and/or Selected Reserve) and agrees to serve 4 additional years; 2) has at least 10 years of service, is precluded by either standard policy or statute from committing to 4 additional years, but agrees to serve for the maximum amount of time allowed by such policy or statute; or 3) is or becomes retirement eligible during the period following August 1, 2009 and agrees to serve for an additional period up to 3 years, depending on the date of retirement eligibility. The military parent or spouse must agree to transfer unused months of educational benefits to a dependent while still serving on active duty. Dependents must be enrolled or planning to enroll in an educational program, including work on an undergraduate or graduate degree, vocational/technical training, on-the-job training, flight training, correspondence training, licensing and national testing programs, entrepreneurship training, and tutorial assistance.

Financial data Dependents working on an undergraduate or graduate degree at public institutions in their state receive full payment of tuition and fees. For dependents who attend private institutions in most states, tuition and fee reimbursement is capped at $17,500 per academic year; the reimbursement rate is higher at private schools in Arizona, Michigan, New Hampshire, New York, Pennsylvania, South Carolina, and Texas. Benefits for other types of training programs depend on the amount for which the spouse or parent qualified under prior educational programs. Dependents also receive a monthly housing allowance based on the national average Basic Allowance for Housing (BAH) for an E-5 with dependents (currently $673.50) or $1,347 per month at schools in foreign countries); an annual book allowance of $1,000; and (for participants who live in a rural county remote from an educational institution) a rural benefit payment of $500 per year.

Duration Military members may transfer all or a portion of their 36 months of entitlement to a dependent. Spouses may start to use the benefit immediately, may use the benefit while the member remains in the armed forces or after separation from active duty, are not eligible for the housing or book allowances while the member is still serving on active duty, and can use the benefit for up to 15 years after the service member's last separation from active duty. Children may use the benefit only after they have completed high school (or equivalency certificate) or reached 18 years of age, may use the benefit only after the parent has completed 10 years of service, may use the benefit while the member remains in the armed forces or after separation from active duty, are entitled to the housing and book allowances even while the parent is on active duty, and are not subject to the 15-year limit but may not use the benefit after reaching 26 years of age.

Additional information This supplement was added to the Post-9/11 GI Bill program as a result of legislation passed by Congress in 2010.

Number awarded Varies each year.

Deadline Deadline not specified.

[788]
TREA NATIONAL SCHOLARSHIPS

The Retired Enlisted Association
Attn: National Scholarship Committee
1111 South Abilene Court
Aurora, CO 80012-4909
(303) 752-0660   Toll Free: (800) 338-9337
Fax: (303) 752-0835   E-mail: treahq@trea.org
Web: www.trea.org/Committees/Scholarship.html

Summary To provide financial assistance for college to the dependents of members of The Retired Enlisted Association (TREA).

Eligibility This program is open to dependent children and grandchildren of association or auxiliary members or

deceased members who were in good standing at the time of their death. Applicants must be high school seniors or full-time college students and interested in attending a 2- or 4-year college or university. They must have a GPA of 2.5 or higher. Along with their application, they must submit an essay on a topic that changes annually; recently, students were asked to explain why they chose to attend college instead of going into the military or public service. Selection is based on that essay, 2 letters of recommendation, educational accomplishments, extracurricular activities, work experience, and financial need.

Financial data The stipend is $1,000 per year.

Duration 1 year; recipients may reapply.

Number awarded 40 each year.

Deadline April of each year.

[789]
TUITION WAIVER FOR DISABLED CHILDREN OF KENTUCKY VETERANS

Kentucky Department of Veterans Affairs
Attn: Field Operations Branch
321 West Main Street, Suite 390
Louisville, KY 40202
(502) 595-4447   Toll Free: (800) 928-4012 (within KY)
Fax: (502) 595-4448   E-mail: Pamela.Cypert@ky.gov
Web: www.veterans.ky.gov/benefits/tuitionwaiver.htm

Summary To provide financial assistance for college to the children of Kentucky veterans who have a disability related to their parent's military service.

Eligibility This program is open to the children of veterans who have acquired a disability as a direct result of their parent's military service. The disability must have been designated by the U.S. Department of Veterans Affairs as compensable (currently defined as spina bifida). The veteran parent must 1) have served on active duty with the U.S. armed forces or in the National Guard or Reserve component on state active duty, active duty for training, or inactive duty training; and 2) be (or if deceased have been) a resident of Kentucky. Applicants must have been admitted to a state-supported university, college, or vocational training institute in Kentucky.

Financial data Eligible children are exempt from payment of tuition at state-supported institutions of higher education in Kentucky.

Duration There are no age or time limits on the waiver.

Number awarded Varies each year.

Deadline Deadline not specified.

[790]
UDT-SEAL SCHOLARSHIP

Navy Seal Foundation
Attn: Chief Financial Officer
1619 D Street, Building 5326
Virginia Beach, VA 23459
(757) 363-7490   Fax: (757) 363-7491
E-mail: info@navysealfoundation.org
Web: www.navysealfoundation.org

Summary To provide financial assistance for college to children of members of the UDT-SEAL Association.

Eligibility This program is open to children of members who are single, under 22 years of age, and a dependent of a sponsoring member of the association. Sponsors must be serving or have served in the armed forces and the Naval Special Warfare Community, have been an association member for the last 4 consecutive years, and have paid their dues for the current year. Applicants may be high school seniors, high school graduates, or undergraduate students. Along with their application, they must submit an essay, up to 2 pages in length, on a topic that changes annually; recently, students were asked to explore benevolence in their life and describe when they were able to demonstrate it. They may also indicate any special circumstances such as financial need, single parent status, or disabilities.

Financial data   Stipends are $15,000 or $7,500 per year.

Duration   1 year; may be renewed.

Additional information   Membership in the association is open to all officers and enlisted personnel of the armed forces (active, retired, discharged, or separated) who have served with a Navy Combat Demolition Unit (NCDU), Underwater Demolition Team (UDT), or SEAL Team.

Number awarded   Varies each year; recently, the Navy Seal Foundation awarded 12 dependent scholarships for all of its programs: 3 for 4 years at $15,000 per year to high school seniors and graduates, 3 for 1 year at $7,500 to high school seniors and graduates, 3 for 1 year at $15,000 to current college students, and 3 for 1 year at $7,500 to current college students.

Deadline   February of each year.

[791]
UNITED STATES ARMY WARRANT OFFICERS ASSOCIATION FAMILY MEMBER SCHOLARSHIP PROGRAM

United States Army Warrant Officers Association
Attn: USAWOA Scholarship Foundation
462 Herndon Parkway, Suite 207
Herndon, VA 20170-5235
(703) 742-7727   Toll Free: (800) 5-USAWOA
Fax: (703) 742-7728   E-mail: usawoasf@cavetel.net
Web: www.usawoa.org/WOASF/index.htm

Summary   To provide financial assistance for college to dependents of members of the United States Army Warrant Officers Association.

Eligibility   This program is open to children, grandchildren, and dependent stepchildren, under 23 years of age, of regular members of the association. Spouses of members are also eligible. Applicants must be enrolled or planning to enroll full time at an accredited U.S. college, university, or vocational/technical institution. They must have a GPA of 3.0 or higher. Along with their application, they must submit transcripts, SAT/ACT scores, letters of recommendation, a list of extracurricular activities, information on any special circumstances that would impact their attending college, and an essay of 800 to 1,000 words describing their educational goals and how reaching those goals will benefit the world around them. Financial need is not considered in the selection process.

Financial data   The stipend is at least $1,000.

Duration   1 year; may be renewed.

Number awarded   Varies each year; recently, 15 of these scholarships were awarded.

Deadline   April of each year.

[792]
UNITED WARRIOR SURVIVOR FOUNDATION EDUCATION FUND GRANTS

United Warrior Survivor Foundation
Attn: Executive Director
P.O. Box 181097
Coronado, CA 92118
(619) 437-1137   Toll Free: (800) 804-UWSF
Fax: (413) 677-1143   E-mail: Elizabeth@uwsf.org
Web: www.uwsf.org/support.html

Summary   To provide financial assistance for college to the spouses of Special Operations military personnel killed in the line of duty after September 11, 2001.

Eligibility   This program is open to the surviving spouses of soldiers, sailors, airmen, and marines who were serving under a U.S. military Special Operations command or directly supporting a Special Operations mission and were killed after September 11, 2001. Applicants must be enrolled or planning to enroll at an accredited college or technical school or in a professional licensure or certification program. They must have a GPA of 3.0 or higher. Along with their application, they must submit a 500-word essay explaining why they have chosen their intended program of study and how that program of study will contribute to their immediate or long-range career plans. Selection is based on the essay, merit, academic potential, and financial need.

Financial data   The stipend is $2,500 per year. Funds are paid directly to the recipient to be used for payment of tuition, books, supplies, child care costs, and transportation expenses.

Duration   1 year; may be renewed up to 3 additional years.

Number awarded   1 or more each year.

Deadline   July of each year.

[793]
U.S. ARMY WOMEN'S FOUNDATION LEGACY SCHOLARSHIPS

U.S. Army Women's Foundation
Attn: Scholarship Committee
P.O. Box 5030
Fort Lee, VA 23801-0030
(804) 734-3078   E-mail: info@awfdn.org
Web: www.awfdn.org/programs/legacyscholarships.shtml

Summary   To provide money for college to women who are serving or have served in the Army and their children.

Eligibility   This program is open to 1) women who have served or are serving honorably in the U.S. Army, U.S. Army Reserve, or Army National Guard; and 2) children of women who served honorably in the U.S. Army, U.S. Army Reserve, or Army National Guard. Applicants must be 1) upper-division students at an accredited college or university and have a GPA of 3.0 or higher; or 2) high school graduates or GED recipients enrolled at a community college and have a GPA of 2.5 or higher. Along with their application, they must submit a 2-page essay on why they should be considered for this scholarship, their future plans as related to their program of study, and information about their community service, activities, and work experience. Selection is based on merit, academic potential, community service, and financial need.

Financial data   The stipend is $2,500 for college and university students or $1,000 for community college students.

Duration   1 year.

Number awarded 5 to 10 each year.
Deadline January of each year.

[794]
USFAA SCHOLARSHIPS

United States Field Artillery Association
Attn: Scholarship Committee
Building 758, McNair Avenue
P.O. Box 33027
Fort Sill, OK 73503-0027
(580) 355-4677   Toll Free: (866) 355-4677
Fax: (580) 355-8745   E-mail: amy@fieldartillery.org
Web: www.fieldartillery.org/usfaa_scholarship/index.html

Summary To provide financial assistance for college to members of the United States Field Artillery Association (USFAA) and their immediate family.

Eligibility This program is open to 3 categories of students: USFAA members (officer or enlisted), immediate family of enlisted members, and immediate family of officer members. Applicants must have been accepted for admission as an undergraduate at an accredited college, university, or vocational program. Along with their application, they must submit an essay explaining their educational goals and how this scholarship will help meet those goals. Financial need is also considered in the selection process. The highest-ranked applicant receives the GEN Donald R. Keith Scholarship.

Financial data Stipends range from $1,000 to $2,500.
Duration 1 year.
Additional information The USFAA services the field artillery branch of the military.

Number awarded Varies each year; recently, 11 of these scholarships were awarded: 1 at $2,500 (the GEN Donald R. Keith Scholarship), 4 at $1,500, and 6 at $1,000.
Deadline March of each year.

[795]
USMCCCA SCHOLARSHIPS

United States Marine Corps Combat Correspondents
  Association
Attn: Executive Director
110 Fox Court
Wildwood, FL 34785
(352) 748-4698   E-mail: usmccca@cfl.rr.com
Web: www.usmccca.org/archives/4941

Summary To provide financial assistance to members of the U.S. Marine Corps Combat Correspondents Association (USMCCCA) or their dependents and Marines in designated occupational fields who are interested in studying communications in college.

Eligibility This program is open to 1) members of USMCCCA, their dependents, and their spouses; and 2) active-duty Marines in Occupational Fields 4300 and 4600 and their dependents who are USMCCCA members or will agree to become members if awarded a scholarship. Applicants must be enrolled or planning to enroll in an undergraduate program in communications. Along with their application, they must submit 500-word essays on 1) their noteworthy achievements and long-range goals; and 2) the United States I want to see in 15 years and my role in the transformation. Financial need is not considered in the selection process.

Financial data Stipends range up to $3,000; funds are disbursed directly to the recipient's institution to be used exclusively for tuition, books, and/or fees.
Duration 1 year.
Number awarded 1 or more each year.
Deadline May of each year.

[796]
USO DESERT STORM EDUCATION FUND

USO World Headquarters
Attn: Scholarship Program
Washington Navy Yard, Building 198
901 M Street, S.E.
Washington, DC 20374
(202) 610-5700   Fax: (202) 610-5699
Web: www.desert-storm.com/soldiers/uso.html

Summary To provide financial assistance for academic or vocational education to spouses and children of military personnel who died in the Persian Gulf War.

Eligibility This program is open to the spouses and children of armed service personnel killed, either through accidental causes or in combat, during Operations Desert Shield and Desert Storm. Department of Defense guidelines will be used to determine those service personnel who were taking part in either of these operations at the time of their deaths. This is an entitlement program; neither financial need nor academic achievement are factors in allocating support from the fund. All eligible candidates are contacted directly.

Financial data It is the purpose of the fund to provide as much financial support as possible to all eligible persons. To this end, USO will distribute all of the funds to the eligible persons in equal amounts.
Duration There will be a 1-time distribution of these funds.
Number awarded All eligible survivors will receive funding.
Deadline Deadline not specified.

[797]
USSVI SCHOLARSHIPS

United States Submarine Veterans, Inc.
Attn: Charitable Foundation
P.O. Box 3870
Silverdale, WA 98383-3870
(360) 337-2978   E-mail: info@ussvcf.org
Web: www.ussvi.org/Scholarship.asp

Summary To provide financial assistance for college to the children and grandchildren of members of the United States Submarine Veterans, Inc. (USSVI).

Eligibility This program is open to children and grandchildren of USSVI members who are high school seniors planning to attend college or already enrolled as college students. Applicants must be unmarried and under 21 years of age (or 23 if currently enrolled in a full-time course of study). Along with their application, they must submit a 400-word essay on why they should be awarded a scholarship and how they would use it. Selection is based on that essay, academic achievement, extracurricular activities, personal recommendations, and financial need.

Financial data Stipends vary; recently, they were $1,500, $1,250, or $950.
Duration 1 year.

Number awarded Varies each year; recently, 18 of these scholarships were awarded: 2 at $1,500, 6 at $1,250, and 10 at $950.

Deadline April of each year.

[798]
UTAH LEGION AUXILIARY NATIONAL PRESIDENT'S SCHOLARSHIP

American Legion Auxiliary
Department of Utah
350 North State Street, Suite 80
P.O. Box 148000
Salt Lake City, UT 84114-8000
(801) 539-1015   Toll Free: (877) 345-6780
Fax: (801) 521-9191   E-mail: alaut@yahoo.com
Web: www.utlegion.org/Auxiliary/aux1.htm

Summary To provide financial assistance to children of veterans in Utah who plan to attend college in any state.

Eligibility This program is open to Utah residents who are the children of veterans who served during specified periods of wartime. They must be high school seniors or graduates who have not yet attended an institution of higher learning. Selection is based on character, Americanism, leadership, scholarship, and financial need. The winners then compete for the American Legion Auxiliary National President's Scholarship. If the Utah winners are not awarded a national scholarship, then they receive this departmental scholarship.

Financial data The stipend is $1,500.

Duration 1 year.

Number awarded 1 each year.

Deadline February of each year.

[799]
VA MORTGAGE CENTER.COM MILITARY EDUCATION SCHOLARSHIP PROGRAM

VA Mortgage Center.com
2101 Chapel Plaza Court, Suite 107
Columbia, MO 65203
(573) 876-2729   Toll Free: (800) 405-6682
E-mail: jbuerck@vamc.com
Web: www.vamortgagecenter.com/scholarships.html

Summary To provide financial assistance for college to students who have a tie to the military.

Eligibility This program is open to 1) current and prospective ROTC program students; 2) active-duty military personnel with plans to attend college; 3) honorably-discharged veterans of the U.S. military; and 4) children of veterans or active-duty military. Applicants must be attending or planning to attend college as a full-time student. Selection is based primarily on an essay.

Financial data The stipend is $1,000.

Duration 1 year.

Additional information This program began in 2007.

Number awarded 10 each year: 5 each term.

Deadline April or October of each year.

[800]
VAA/ANGEA SCHOLARSHIP

Virginia Army/Air National Guard Enlisted Association
Attn: SMSgt Lori W. Flinn Scholarship Chair
15249 Fountain Road
Ashland, VA 23005
(804) 519-6491   E-mail: Scholarship@vaaangea.org
Web: www.vaaangea.org

Summary To provide financial assistance to members of the Virginia Army/Air National Guard Enlisted Association (VaA/ANGEA) and their families who are interested in attending college in any state.

Eligibility This program is open to 1) enlisted soldiers or enlisted airmen currently serving as a member of the Virginia National Guard (VNG) who are also a member of the VaA/ANGEA; 2) retired enlisted soldiers or retired enlisted airmen of the VNG who are also a member of the VaA/ANGEA; 3) spouses of current enlisted soldiers or enlisted airmen of the VNG who are also a member of the VaA/ANGEA; 4) spouses of retired enlisted soldiers or retired enlisted airmen of the VNG who are also a member of the VaA/ANGEA; and 5) dependents of current or retired enlisted soldiers or airmen of the VNG (a copy of the dependency decree may be required) who are also a member of the VaA/ANGEA. Applicants must submit a copy of their school transcript (high school or college), a letter with specific facts about their desire to continue their education and their need for assistance, 3 letters of recommendation, a letter of academic reference, and a photocopy of their VaA/ANGEA membership card. Selection is based on academics (15 points), personal statement (15 points), letters of recommendation (16 points), school involvement (15 points), community involvement (15 points), responsibility (15 points), and financial need (9 points).

Financial data Generally, stipends are $1,000 or $500.

Duration 1 year; recipients may reapply.

Number awarded Generally, 2 scholarships at $1,000 and 4 scholarships at $500 are awarded each year.

Deadline March of each year.

[801]
VADM ROBERT L. WALTERS SCHOLARSHIP

Surface Navy Association
2550 Huntington Avenue, Suite 202
Alexandria, VA 22303
(703) 960-6800   Toll Free: (800) NAVY-SNA
Fax: (703) 960-6807   E-mail: navysna@aol.com
Web: www.navysna.org

Summary To provide financial assistance for college or graduate school to dependents of members of the Surface Navy Association (SNA).

Eligibility This program is open to the children, stepchildren, wards, and spouses of SNA members. The SNA member must 1) be in the second or subsequent consecutive year of membership; 2) be serving, retired, or honorably discharged; 3) be a Surface Warfare Officer or Enlisted Surface Warfare Specialist; and 4) have served for at least 3 years on a surface ship of the U.S. Navy or Coast Guard. Applicants must be enrolled or planning to enroll full time at an accredited undergraduate or graduate institution; the full-time requirement may be waived for spouses. Along with their application, they must submit a 500-word essay on why they should be selected to receive this scholarship. High school seniors should also include a transcript of high school grades and a copy of ACT or SAT scores. Current college students should also include a transcript of the grades from their most recent 4 semesters of school. Selection is based on academic proficiency, non-scholastic activities, scholastic and non-scholastic awards, character, and financial need.

Financial data The stipend is $2,000 per year.

Duration 4 years, provided the recipient maintains a GPA of 3.0 or higher.

Number awarded Varies each year.

Deadline February of each year.

[802]
VETERANS OF THE VIETNAM WAR NATIONAL SCHOLARSHIP PROGRAM

Veterans of the Vietnam War, Inc.
Attn: Assistance in Education Program
805 South Township Boulevard
Pittston, PA 18640-3327
(570) 603-9740   Fax: (570) 603-9741
Web: www.vvnw.org

Summary To provide money for college to members of Veterans of the Vietnam War (VVnW) and their families.

Eligibility This program is open to members of the VVnW in good standing for at least 1 year and their spouses, children, adopted children, foster children, and other immediate descendants. Applicants must be enrolled in or accepted to a program of postsecondary education. Selection is based on a random drawing; financial need and merit are not considered.

Financial data The stipend is $1,000. Funds are paid directly to the recipient.

Duration 1 year.

Number awarded 1 or more each year, depending on the availability of funds.

Deadline October of each year.

[803]
VII CORPS DESERT STORM VETERANS ASSOCIATION SCHOLARSHIP

VII Corps Desert Storm Veterans Association
Attn: Scholarship Committee
Army Historical Foundation
2425 Wilson Boulevard
Arlington, VA 22201
(703) 978-6867   E-mail: viicorpsdsva@aol.com
Web: www.desertstormvets.org/Scholarship.html

Summary To provide financial assistance for college to students who served, or are the spouses or other family members of individuals who served, with VII Corps in Operations Desert Shield, Desert Storm, or related activities.

Eligibility Applicants must have served, or be a family member of those who served, with VII Corps in Operations Desert Shield/Desert Storm, Provide Comfort, or 1 of the support base activities. Scholarships are limited to students entering or enrolled in accredited technical institutions (trade or specialty), 2-year colleges, and 4-year colleges or universities. Awards will not be made to individuals receiving military academy appointments or full 4-year scholarships. Letters of recommendation and a transcript are required. Selection is not based solely on academic standing; consideration is also given to extracurricular activities and other self-development skills and abilities obtained through on-the-job training or cor-

respondence courses. Priority is given to survivors of VII Corps soldiers who died during Operations Desert Shield/Desert Storm or Provide Comfort, veterans who are also members of the VII Corps Desert Storm Veterans Association, and family members of veterans who are also members of the VII Corps Desert Storm Veterans Association.

Financial data The stipend ranges from $1,000 to $5,000 per year. Funds are paid to the recipients upon proof of admission or registration at an accredited academic institution.

Duration 1 year; recipients may reapply.

Additional information This program began in 1998.

Number awarded Approximately 3 each year.

Deadline January of each year.

[804]
VIRGINIA LEGION AUXILIARY NURSES SCHOLARSHIP

American Legion Auxiliary
Department of Virginia
Attn: Education Chair
1708 Commonwealth Avenue
Richmond, VA 23230
(804) 355-6410   Fax: (804) 353-5246
Web: vaauxiliary.org

Summary To provide funding to descendants of veterans in Virginia planning to study nursing in college.

Eligibility This program is open to seniors graduating from high schools in Virginia and to graduates of those high schools who have not yet attended a postsecondary institution. Applicants must be the children or grandchildren of veterans who served during eligibility dates for membership in the American Legion. They must be planning to attend college in any state to study nursing. Along with their application, they must submit a 500-word essay on a topic of their choice. Selection is based on academics, character, and Americanism.

Financial data The stipend is $1,000.

Duration 1 year.

Number awarded 1 each year.

Deadline April of each year.

[805]
VIRGINIA MILITARY SURVIVORS AND DEPENDENTS EDUCATION PROGRAM

Virginia Department of Veterans Services
270 Franklin Road, Room 810
Roanoke, VA 24011-2215
(540) 597-1730   Fax: (540) 857-7573
Web: www.dvs.virginia.gov/veterans-benefits.shtml

Summary To provide funding to the children and spouses of disabled and other Virginia veterans or service personnel.

Eligibility This program is open to residents of Virginia whose parent or spouse served in the U.S. armed forces (including the Reserves, the Virginia National Guard, or the Virginia National Guard Reserves) during any armed conflict subsequent to December 6, 1941, as a result of a terrorist act, during military operations against terrorism, or on a peacekeeping mission. The veterans must have been killed, missing in action, taken prisoner of war, or become at least 90% disabled as a result of such service. Applicants must have been accepted at a public college or university in Virginia as an undergraduate or graduate student. Children must be between 16 and 29 years of age; there are no age restrictions for spouses. The veteran must have been a resident of Virginia at the time of entry into active military service or for at least 5 consecutive years immediately prior to the date of application or death. Surviving spouses must have been residents of Virginia for at least 5 years prior to marrying the veteran or for at least 5 years immediately prior to the date on which the application was submitted.

Financial data   The program provides 1) waiver of tuition and all required fees at public institutions of higher education in Virginia; and 2) a stipend up to $1,500 per year to offset the costs of room, board, books, and supplies at those institutions. If more students qualify, the stipend is reduced; recently, it was $675 per semester ($1,350 per year) for full-time enrollment, $450 per semester for enrollment less than full-time but at least half-time, or $225 per semester for enrollment less than half-time.

Duration   Entitlement extends to a maximum of 36 months (4 years).

Additional information   Individuals entitled to this benefit may use it to pursue any vocational, technical, undergraduate, or graduate program of instruction. Generally, programs listed in the academic catalogs of state-supported institutions are acceptable, provided they have a clearly-defined educational objective (such as a certificate, diploma, or degree). This program was formerly known as the Virginia War Orphans Education Program.

Number awarded   Varies each year; recently, funding allowed for a total of 667 stipends at $1,500, but 740 students actually qualified and received a reduced stipend.

Deadline   Applications may be submitted at any time, but they must be received at least 30 days prior to the start of the term.

[806]
VIRGINIA NATIONAL GUARD ASSOCIATION SCHOLARSHIP

Virginia National Guard Association
Attn: Scholarship Committee
5901 Beulah Road
Sandston, VA 23150-6112
(804) 350-0175
Web: www.vnga.org/scholarship.shtml

Summary   To provide financial assistance to members of the Virginia National Guard Association (VNGA) and their families who are interested in attending college in any state.

Eligibility   Applicants must have been enrolled at a college or university in any state for 1 year and qualify under 1 of the following conditions: 1) an officer or warrant officer in the Virginia National Guard and a VNGA member; 2) the dependent child or spouse of an officer or warrant officer in the Virginia National Guard who is a VNGA member; 3) the dependent child or spouse of a retired officer or warrant officer who is a VNGA member; 4) the dependent child or spouse of a deceased retired officer or warrant officer, or 5) the dependent child or spouse of a Virginia National Guard officer or warrant officer who died while in the Virginia National Guard. Along with their application, they must submit a brief description of their educational and/or military objectives, a list of their leadership positions and honors, and a brief statement of their financial need.

Financial data   A stipend is awarded; the amount is determined annually.

Duration   1 year; may be renewed for 2 additional years.

Additional information   The association also offers a special scholarship in memory of CW4 William C. Singletary who, in rescuing 2 elderly women from drowning, gave his own life.

Number awarded   Varies each year.

Deadline   September of each year.

[807]
WAIVERS OF NONRESIDENT TUITION FOR DEPENDENTS OF MILITARY PERSONNEL MOVING TO TEXAS

Texas Higher Education Coordinating Board
Attn: Grants and Special Programs
1200 East Anderson Lane
P.O. Box 12788
Austin, TX 78711-2788
(512) 427-6340   Toll Free: (800) 242-3062
Fax: (512) 427-6420   E-mail: grantinfo@thecb.state.tx.us
Web: www.collegeforalltexans.com

Summary   To exempt dependents of military personnel who move to Texas from the payment of nonresident tuition at public institutions of higher education in the state.

Eligibility   Eligible for these waivers are the spouses and dependent children of members of the U.S. armed forces and commissioned officers of the Public Health Service who move to Texas while the servicemember remains assigned to another state. Applicants must be attending or planning to attend a public college or university in the state. They must indicate their intent to become a Texas resident. For dependent children to qualify, the spouse must also move to Texas.

Financial data   Although persons eligible under this program are still classified as nonresidents, they are entitled to pay the resident tuition at Texas institutions of higher education on an immediate basis.

Duration   1 year.

Additional information   This program became effective in 2003.

Number awarded   Varies each year.

Deadline   Deadline not specified.

[808]
WAIVERS OF NONRESIDENT TUITION FOR DEPENDENTS OF MILITARY PERSONNEL WHO PREVIOUSLY LIVED IN TEXAS

Texas Higher Education Coordinating Board
Attn: Grants and Special Programs
1200 East Anderson Lane
P.O. Box 12788
Austin, TX 78711-2788
(512) 427-6340   Toll Free: (800) 242-3062
Fax: (512) 427-6420   E-mail: grantinfo@thecb.state.tx.us
Web: www.collegeforalltexans.com

Summary   To provide a partial tuition exemption to the spouses and dependent children of military personnel who are Texas residents but are not assigned to duty in the state.

Eligibility   Eligible for these waivers are the spouses and dependent children of members of the U.S. armed forces who are not assigned to duty in Texas but have previously resided in the state for at least 6 months. Servicemembers must verify that they remain Texas residents by designating Texas as their place of legal residence for income tax purposes, registering to vote in the state, and doing 1 of the following: owning real property in Texas, registering an automobile in Texas, or executing a will indicating that they are a resident of the state. The spouse or dependent child must be attending or planning to attend a Texas public college or university.

Financial data Although persons eligible under this program are classified as nonresidents, they are entitled to pay the resident tuition at Texas institutions of higher education, regardless of their length of residence in Texas.

Duration 1 year.

Number awarded Varies each year.

Deadline Deadline not specified.

[809]
WALTER BEALL SCHOLARSHIP

Walter Beall Scholarship Foundation
c/o W. Ralph Holcombe, Secretary/Treasurer
4911 Fennell Court
Suffolk, VA 23435
(757) 484-7403   Fax: (757) 686-5952
E-mail: info@walterbeallscholarship.org
Web: www.walterbeallscholarship.org

Summary To provide financial assistance to members of the Fleet Reserve Association (FRA) and their families who are interested in studying engineering, aeronautical engineering, or aviation in college.

Eligibility This program is open to FRA members who have been in good standing for at least the past 2 consecutive years and their spouses, children, and grandchildren. Students in a Reserve officer candidate program receiving aid or attending a military academy are not eligible. Applicants must be enrolled at an accredited college, university, or technical institution in the United States in a program related to general engineering, aviation, or aeronautical engineering. Selection is based on GPA, scholastic aptitude test scores, curriculum goals, interests, community activities, awards, and financial need. U.S. citizenship is required.

Financial data The amounts of the awards depend on the availability of funds and the need of the recipients; they range from $2,000 to $5,000.

Duration 1 year; recipients may reapply.

Additional information The Walter Beall Scholarship Foundation is sponsored by the Past Regional Presidents Club of the Fleet Reserve Association. Membership in the FRA is restricted to active-duty, retired, and Reserve members of the Navy, Marine Corps, and Coast Guard.

Number awarded 1 or more each year.

Deadline April of each year.

[810]
WASHINGTON LEGION CHILDREN AND YOUTH SCHOLARSHIPS

American Legion
Department of Washington
3600 Ruddell Road S.E.
P.O. Box 3917
Lacey, WA 98509-3917
(360) 491-4373   Fax: (360) 491-7442
E-mail: administrator@walegion.org
Web: www.walegion.org/cy.htm

Summary To provide financial assistance to the children of members of the American Legion or American Legion Auxiliary in Washington who plan to attend college in the state.

Eligibility This program is open to sons and daughters of Washington Legionnaires or Auxiliary members, living or deceased, who are high school seniors. Applicants must be planning to attend an accredited institution of higher education, trade, or vocational school in the state of Washington. Selection is based on presentation, initiative, goals, commitment to goals, and financial need.

Financial data The stipend is $2,500 or $1,500, payable in equal amounts per semester.

Duration 1 year.

Number awarded 2 each year: 1 at $2,500 and 1 at $1,500.

Deadline March of each year.

[811]
WEST VIRGINIA STATE WAR ORPHANS EDUCATIONAL PROGRAM

West Virginia Department of Veteran's Assistance
Attn: Executive Secretary
1321 Plaza East, Suite 109
Charleston, WV 25301-1400
(304) 558-3661   Toll Free: (866) WV4-VETS (within WV)
Fax: (304) 558-3662 E-mail: Angela.S.Meadows@wv.gov
Web: www.veterans.wv.gov

Summary To provide financial assistance for college to the children and spouses of deceased West Virginia veterans.

Eligibility This program is open to residents of West Virginia who are children between 16 and 25 years of age or spouses of deceased veterans. The veteran must have entered service as a resident of West Virginia; served during specified periods of war time; and died during that wartime period or, if subsequent to discharge, as a result of disability incurred in that wartime service. Applicants must be attending or planning to attend a college or university in West Virginia.

Financial data The state appropriates $5,000 per year for the educational expenses of each qualifying child or spouse. That includes a waiver of tuition and fees at state-supported colleges and universities.

Duration 1 year; may be renewed upon reapplication if the student maintains a cumulative GPA of at least 2.0.

Number awarded Varies each year.

Deadline July of each year for the fall semester; November of each year for the spring semester.

[812]
WESTBROOK SCHOLARSHIP FUND

U.S. Coast Guard
Attn: Office of Work-Life (CG-111)
2100 Second Street, S.W., Stop 7902
Washington, DC 20593-7902
(202) 475-5140   Toll Free: (800) 872-4957
Fax: (202) 475-5907
E-mail: HQS.SMB.FamilySupportServices@uscg.mil
Web: www.uscg.mil/worklife/scholarship.asp

Summary To provide financial assistance for college to the dependent children of Coast Guard enlisted personnel.

Eligibility This program is open to the dependent children of enlisted members of the U.S. Coast Guard on active duty, retired, or deceased and of enlisted personnel in the Coast Guard Reserve currently on extended active duty 180 days or more. Applicants must be high school seniors or current undergraduates enrolled or planning to enroll full-time at a 4-year college, university, or vocational school. They must be under 24 years of age and registered in the Defense Enrollment Eligibility Reporting System (DEERS) system. Along with their application, they must submit their SAT or ACT scores, a letter of recommendation, transcripts, a financial information statement, and a 500-word essay on their personal and academic achievements, extracurricular activities, contributions to the community, and academic plans and career goals.

Financial data   The stipend is $2,500.

Duration   1 year; nonrenewable.

Number awarded   1 each year.

Deadline   March of each year.

[813]
WILLIAM F. JOHNSON MEMORIAL SCHOLARSHIP

Sons of the American Legion
Detachment of West Virginia
2016 Kanawha Boulevard, East
P.O. Box 3191
Charleston, WV 25332-3191
(304) 343-7591   Toll Free: (888) 534-4667
Fax: (304) 343-7592
E-mail: wvlegion@suddenlinkmail.com
Web: www.wvlegion.org

Summary   To provide financial assistance to high school seniors in West Virginia who have a family link to the American Legion and are planning to attend college in the state.

Eligibility   This program is open to seniors graduating from high schools in West Virginia who are the child or grandchild of a member of the American Legion, American Legion Auxiliary, or Sons of the American Legion. The member may be a resident of any state and belong to any department of the national organization, but the student must be planning to attend a college or university in West Virginia. Along with their application, they must submit a transcript and a 500-word essay on how they can assist a veteran's family and volunteer while the soldier is deployed far from home and family.

Financial data   The stipend is $1,000 or $500. Funds are paid directly to the students, but only after they have completed their first semester of college.

Duration   1 year; nonrenewable.

Number awarded   2 each year: 1 at $1,000 and 1 at $500.

Deadline   May of each year.

[814]
WILLIAM P. O'CONNELL MEMORIAL VETERANS REHABILITATION SCHOLARSHIP

Sons of the American Legion
Detachment of New York
112 State Street, Suite 1300
Albany, NY 12207
(518) 463-2215   Fax: (518) 427-8443
E-mail: info@nylegion.org
Web: www.sonsdny.org

Summary   To provide financial assistance to high school seniors and graduates in New York who are have been active

in veterans rehabilitation activities of the Sons of the American Legion and plan to attend college in any state.

Eligibility   This program is open to members of the Sons of the American Legion in New York who have been active in its veterans rehabilitation activities. Applicants must be high school seniors or graduates and planning to attend college or trade school in any state. Along with their application, they must submit a 200-word essay either on why a college education is important to them or why they want to continue their postsecondary education in a business trade school. Selection is based on academics (25%), character (25%), community service (25%), and veterans rehabilitation activities (25%).

Financial data   The stipend is $1,000.

Duration   1 year.

Number awarded   2 each year.

Deadline   April of each year.

[815]
WILMA D. HOYAL/MAXINE CHILTON SCHOLARSHIPS

American Legion Auxiliary
Department of Arizona
4701 North 19th Avenue, Suite 100
Phoenix, AZ 85015-3727
(602) 241-1080   Fax: (602) 604-9640
E-mail: secretary@aladeptaz.org
Web: aladeptaz.org/Scholarships.html

Summary   To provide financial assistance to veterans, the dependents of veterans, and other students who are majoring in selected subjects at Arizona public universities.

Eligibility   This program is open to second-year or upper-division full-time students majoring in political science, public programs, or special education at public universities in Arizona (the University of Arizona, Northern Arizona University, or Arizona State University). Applicants must have been Arizona residents for at least 1 year. They must have a GPA of 3.0 or higher. U.S. citizenship is required. Honorably-discharged veterans and immediate family members of veterans receive preference. Selection is based on scholarship (25%), financial need (40%), character (20%), and leadership (15%).

Financial data   The stipend is $1,000.

Duration   1 year; renewable.

Number awarded   1 to each of the 3 universities.

Deadline   May of each year.

[816]
WINGS OVER AMERICA SCHOLARSHIPS

Wings Over America Scholarship Foundation
Attn: Scholarship Administrator
4966 Euclid Road, Suite 109
Virginia Beach, VA 23462
(757) 671-3200, ext. 118
E-mail: scholarship@wingsoveramerica.us
Web: www.wingsoveramerica.us

Summary   To provide financial assistance for college to dependents of naval aviators.

Eligibility   This program is open to 1) children of a military sponsor who are graduating high school seniors planning to enroll in college full time to work on a bachelor's degree or who are already enrolled in such a program; and 2) spouses of a military sponsor currently enrolled full or part time and working on an associate or bachelor's degree at an accredited college or university. Children must be unmarried and younger than 23 years of age. The military sponsor must have completed at least 8 years of active-duty service in a Naval air forces or subordinate command and be currently on active duty, retired, or deceased. Also eligible are children of members of the U.S. Navy who died while on active duty serving with a Naval air force unit, regardless of the length of service of the deceased parent. Selection is based on academic proficiency, extracurricular activities, community contributions, and life experience and character of the applicant. The highest ranked applicant receives the CAPT Neil Kinnear Scholarship.

Financial data The CAPT Neil Kinnear Scholarship is $3,000 per year. Other stipend amounts depend on the availability of funds.

Duration 1 year; may be renewed.

Additional information This program began in 1987.

Number awarded Varies each year; recently, 43 of these scholarships were awarded: 20 high school seniors, 16 college students, and 7 spouses. Since the program was established, it has awarded more than $440,000 in scholarships.

Deadline March of each year.

[817]
WISCONSIN G.I. BILL TUITION REMISSION PROGRAM

Wisconsin Department of Veterans Affairs
201 West Washington Avenue
P.O. Box 7843
Madison, WI 53707-7843
(608) 266-1311   Toll Free: (800) WIS-VETS
Fax: (608) 267-0403   E-mail: WDVAInfo@dva.state.wi.us
Web: www.dva.state.wi.us/Ben_education.asp

Summary To provide financial assistance for college or graduate school to Wisconsin veterans and their dependents.

Eligibility This program is open to current residents of Wisconsin who 1) were residents of the state when they entered or reentered active duty in the U.S. armed forces, or 2) have moved to the state and have been residents for any consecutive 12-month period after entry or reentry into service. Applicants must have served on active duty for at least 2 continuous years or for at least 90 days during specified wartime periods. Also eligible are 1) qualifying children and unremarried surviving spouses of Wisconsin veterans who died in the line of duty or as the direct result of a service-connected disability; and 2) children and spouses of Wisconsin veterans who have a service-connected disability rated by the U.S. Department of Veterans Affairs as 30% or greater. Children must be between 17 and 25 years of age (regardless of the date of the veteran's death or initial disability rating) and be a Wisconsin resident for tuition purposes. Spouses remain eligible for 10 years following the date of the veteran's death or initial disability rating; they must be Wisconsin residents for tuition purposes but they may enroll full or part time. Students may attend any institution, center, or school within the University of Wisconsin (UW) System or the Wisconsin Technical College System (WCTS). There are no income limits, delimiting periods following military service during which the benefit must be used, or limits on the level of study (e.g., vocational, undergraduate, professional, or graduate).

Financial data Veterans who qualify as a Wisconsin resident for tuition purposes are eligible for a remission of 100% of standard academic fees and segregated fees at a UW campus or 100% of program and material fees at a WCTS institution. Veterans who qualify as a Wisconsin veteran for purposes of this program but for other reasons fail to meet the definition of a Wisconsin resident for tuition purposes at the UW system are eligible for a remission of 100% of non-resident fees. Spouses and children of deceased or disabled veterans are entitled to a remission of 100% of tuition and fees at a UW or WCTS institution.

Duration Up to 8 semesters or 128 credits, whichever is greater.

Additional information This program was established in 2005 as a replacement for Wisconsin Tuition and Fee Reimbursement Grants.

Number awarded Varies each year.

Deadline Applications must be submitted within 14 days from the office start of the academic term: in October for fall, March for spring, or June for summer.

[818]
WISCONSIN JOB RETRAINING GRANTS

Wisconsin Department of Veterans Affairs
201 West Washington Avenue
P.O. Box 7843
Madison, WI 53707-7843
(608) 266-1311   Toll Free: (800) WIS-VETS
Fax: (608) 267-0403   E-mail: WDVAInfo@dva.state.wi.us
Web: www.dva.state.wi.us/Ben_retraininggrants.asp

Summary To provide funds to recently unemployed Wisconsin veterans or their families who need financial assistance while being retrained for employment.

Eligibility This program is open to current residents of Wisconsin who 1) were residents of the state when they entered or reentered active duty in the U.S. armed forces, or 2) have moved to the state and have been residents for any consecutive 12-month period after entry or reentry into service. Applicants must have served on active duty for at least 2 continuous years or for at least 90 days during specified wartime periods. Unremarried spouses and minor or dependent children of deceased veterans who would have been eligible for the grant if they were living today may also be eligible. The applicant must, within the year prior to the date of application, have become unemployed (involuntarily laid off or discharged, not due to willful misconduct) or underemployed (experienced an involuntary reduction of income). Underemployed applicants must have current annual income from employment that does not exceed federal poverty guidelines (currently $14,521 for a family of 1, rising to $50,557 for a family of 8). All applicants must be retraining at accredited schools in Wisconsin or in a structured on-the-job program. Course work toward a college degree does not qualify. Training does not have to be full time, but the program must be completed within 2 years and must reasonably be expected to lead to employment.

Financial data The maximum grant is $3,000 per year; the actual amount varies, depending upon the amount of the applicant's unmet need. In addition to books, fees, and tuition, the funds may be used for living expenses.

Duration 1 year; may be renewed 1 additional year.

Number awarded   Varies each year.

Deadline   Applications may be submitted at any time.

[819]
WISCONSIN LEGION AUXILIARY DEPARTMENT PRESIDENT'S SCHOLARSHIP

American Legion Auxiliary
Department of Wisconsin
Attn: Education Chair
2930 American Legion Drive
P.O. Box 140
Portage, WI 53901-0140
(608) 745-0124   Toll Free: (866) 664-3863
Fax: (608) 745-1947   E-mail: alawi@amlegionauxwi.org
Web: www.amlegionauxwi.org/Scholarships.htm

Summary   To provide financial assistance to Wisconsin residents who are members or children of members of the American Legion Auxiliary and interested in attending college in any state.

Eligibility   This program is open to members and children of members of the American Legion Auxiliary in Wisconsin. Applicants must be high school seniors or graduates and attending or planning to attend a college or university in any state. They must have a GPA of 3.5 or higher and be able to demonstrate financial need. Along with their application, they must submit a 300-word essay on "Education—An Investment in the Future."

Financial data   The stipend is $1,000.

Duration   1 year.

Number awarded   3 each year.

Deadline   March of each year.

[820]
WISCONSIN LEGION AUXILIARY MERIT AND MEMORIAL SCHOLARSHIPS

American Legion Auxiliary
Department of Wisconsin
Attn: Education Chair
2930 American Legion Drive
P.O. Box 140
Portage, WI 53901-0140
(608) 745-0124   Toll Free: (866) 664-3863
Fax: (608) 745-1947   E-mail: alawi@amlegionauxwi.org
Web: www.amlegionauxwi.org/Scholarships.htm

Summary   To provide financial assistance to Wisconsin residents who are related to veterans or members of the American Legion Auxiliary and interested in working on an undergraduate degree at a school in any state.

Eligibility   This program is open to the children, wives, and widows of veterans who are high school seniors or graduates and have a GPA of 3.5 or higher. Grandchildren and great-grandchildren of members of the American Legion Auxiliary are also eligible. Applicants must be residents of Wisconsin and interested in working on an undergraduate degree at a school in any state. Along with their application, they must submit a 300-word essay on "Education—An Investment in the Future." Financial need is also considered.

Financial data   The stipend is $1,000.

Duration   1 year; nonrenewable.

Additional information   This program includes the following named scholarships: the Harriet Hass Scholarship, the Adalin Macauley Scholarship, the Eleanor Smith Scholarship,

the Pearl Behrend Scholarship, the Barbara Kranig Scholarship, and the Jan Pulvermacher-Ryan Scholarship.

Number awarded   7 each year.

Deadline   March of each year.

[821]
WISCONSIN LEGION AUXILIARY PAST PRESIDENTS PARLEY HEALTH CAREER SCHOLARSHIPS

American Legion Auxiliary
Department of Wisconsin
Attn: Education Chair
2930 American Legion Drive
P.O. Box 140
Portage, WI 53901-0140
(608) 745-0124   Toll Free: (866) 664-3863
Fax: (608) 745-1947   E-mail: alawi@amlegionauxwi.org
Web: www.amlegionauxwi.org/Scholarships.htm

Summary   To provide financial assistance for health-related education at a school in any state to the dependents and descendants of veterans in Wisconsin.

Eligibility   This program is open to the children, wives, and widows of veterans who are attending or entering a hospital, university, or technical school in any state to prepare for a health-related career. Grandchildren and great-grandchildren of veterans are eligible if they are members of the American Legion Auxiliary. Applicants must be residents of Wisconsin and have a GPA of 3.5 or higher. Along with their application, they must submit a 300-word essay on "The Importance of Health Careers Today." Financial need is also considered.

Financial data   The stipend is $1,200.

Duration   1 year; nonrenewable.

Number awarded   2 each year.

Deadline   March of each year.

[822]
WISCONSIN LEGION AUXILIARY PAST PRESIDENTS PARLEY REGISTERED NURSE SCHOLARSHIPS

American Legion Auxiliary
Department of Wisconsin
Attn: Education Chair
2930 American Legion Drive
P.O. Box 140
Portage, WI 53901-0140
(608) 745-0124   Toll Free: (866) 664-3863
Fax: (608) 745-1947   E-mail: alawi@amlegionauxwi.org
Web: www.amlegionauxwi.org/Scholarships.htm

Summary   To provide financial assistance to the dependents and descendants of Wisconsin veterans who are interested in studying nursing at a school in any state.

Eligibility   This program is open to the wives, widows, and children of Wisconsin veterans who are enrolled or have been accepted in an accredited school of nursing in any state to prepare for a career as a registered nurse. Grandchildren and great-grandchildren of veterans are also eligible if they are American Legion Auxiliary members. Applicants must be Wisconsin residents and have a GPA of 3.5 or higher. Along with their application, they must submit a 300-word essay on "The Need for Trained Nurses Today." Financial need is considered in the selection process.

Financial data   The stipend is $1,200.

Duration 1 year.
Number awarded 3 each year.
Deadline March of each year.

[823]
WISCONSIN NATIONAL GUARD ENLISTED ASSOCIATION COLLEGE GRANT PROGRAM

Wisconsin National Guard Enlisted Association
Attn: Executive Director
2400 Wright Street
Madison, WI 53704
(608) 242-3112 E-mail: WNGEA@yahoo.com
Web: www.wngea.org/MAIN/PROG/prosch.htm

Summary To provide financial assistance to members of the Wisconsin National Guard Enlisted Association (WNGEA) and their spouses and children who are interested in attending college or graduate school in any state.

Eligibility This program is open to WNGEA members, the unmarried children and spouses of WNGEA members, and the unmarried children and spouses of deceased WNGEA members. WNGEA member applicants, as well as the parents or guardians of unmarried children who are applicants, must have at least 1 year remaining on their enlistment following completion of the school year for which application is submitted (or they must have 20 or more years of service). Applicants must be enrolled at a college, university, graduate school, trade school, or business school in any state. Selection is based on need, leadership, and moral character.

Financial data Stipends are $1,000 or $500 per year.

Duration 1 year; recipients may not reapply for 2 years.

Additional information This program includes 1 scholarship sponsored by the USAA Insurance Corporation.

Number awarded Varies each year; recently, 4 of these scholarships were awarded: the Raymond A. Matera Scholarship at $1,000 and 3 others at $500 each.

Deadline April of each year.

[824]
WISCONSIN SONS OF THE AMERICAN LEGION SCHOLARSHIP

Sons of the American Legion
Detachment of Wisconsin
P.O. Box 388
Portage, WI 53901
(608) 745-1090 E-mail: adjutant@wisal.org
Web: www.wisal.org

Summary To provide financial assistance to members of the Wisconsin Detachment of the Sons of the American Legion (SAL) who plan to attend college in any state.

Eligibility This program is open to members of the SAL in Wisconsin who are seniors in high school or within 1 year of graduation from high school. Applicants must have at least 3 years of consecutive membership. They must be planning to attend a 4-year college or university or a 2-year technical school in any state. Along with their application, they must submit a 100-word essay on their educational objectives, the life's work for which they desire to prepare by attending college, and the value and contribution this scholarship would make toward the realization of those goals. Selection is based on that essay, academic record, contributions to school and community, SAL involvement, and financial need.

Financial data The stipend is $1,000, paid directly to the recipient's school.

Duration 1 year.
Number awarded 1 each year.
Deadline March of each year.

[825]
WOMEN MARINES ASSOCIATION SCHOLARSHIP PROGRAM

Women Marines Association
P.O. Box 377
Oaks, PA 19456-0377
Toll Free: (888) 525-1943
E-mail: scholarship@womenmarines.org
Web: www.womenmarines.org/scholarships.aspx

Summary To provide money for college or graduate school to students with ties to the military who are sponsored by members of the Women Marines Association (WMA).

Eligibility Applicants must be sponsored by a WMA member and fall into 1 of the following categories: 1) have served or are serving in the U.S. Marine Corps, regular or Reserve; 2) are a direct descendant by blood or legal adoption or a stepchild of a Marine on active duty or who has served honorably in the U.S. Marine Corps, regular or Reserve; 3) are a sibling or a descendant of a sibling by blood or legal adoption or a stepchild of a Marine on active duty or who has served honorably in the U.S. Marine Corps, regular or Reserve; or 4) have completed 2 years in a Marine Corps JROTC program. WMA members may sponsor an unlimited number of applicants per year. High school seniors must submit transcripts (GPA of 3.0 or higher) and SAT or ACT scores. Undergraduate and graduate students must have a GPA of 3.0 or higher.

Financial data The stipend is $1,500 per year.

Duration 1 year; may be renewed 1 additional year.

Additional information This program includes the following named scholarships: the WMA Memorial Scholarships, the Lily H. Gridley Memorial Scholarship, the Ethyl and Armin Wiebke Memorial Scholarship, the Maj. Megan Malia McClung Memorial Scholarship, the Agnes Sopcak Memorial Scholarship, the Virginia Guveyan Memorial Scholarship, and the LaRue A. Ditmore Music Scholarships. Applicants must know a WMA member to serve as their sponsor; the WMA will not supply listings of the names or addresses of chapters or individual members.

Number awarded Varies each year.
Deadline January of each year.

[826]
WOMEN'S ARMY CORPS VETERANS' ASSOCIATION SCHOLARSHIP

Women's Army Corps Veterans' Association
P.O. Box 5577
Fort McClellan, AL 36205-5577
(256) 820-6824 E-mail: info@armywomen.org
Web: www.armywomen.org

Summary To provide financial assistance for college to the relatives of Army military women.

Eligibility This program is open to high school seniors who are the children, grandchildren, nieces, or nephews of Army service women. Applicants must have a cumulative GPA of 3.5 or higher and be planning to enroll full time at an accredited college or university in the United States. They must submit a 500-word biographical sketch that includes their future goals and how the scholarship would be used. Selection is based on academic achievement, leadership ability as expressed through co-curricular activities and community involvement, the biographical sketch, and recommendations. Financial need is not considered. U.S. citizenship is required.

Financial data The stipend is $1,500.

Duration 1 year.

Number awarded 1 or more each year.

Deadline April of each year.

[827]
WORLD WAR II ILLINOIS DESCENDANTS SCHOLARSHIP

Sangamon County Community Foundation
Attn: Scholarship Coordinator
205 South Fifth Street, Suite 930
Springfield, IL 62701
(217) 789-4431   Fax: (217) 789-4635
E-mail: scholarships@sccf.us
Web: www.sccf.us/scholarshipfunds.html

Summary To provide financial assistance to high school seniors in Illinois who are the direct descendant of a veteran of World War II and plan to attend college in any state.

Eligibility This program is open to seniors graduating from high schools in Illinois who are the direct descendant (i.e., grandchild or great-grandchild, but not a great niece or nephew) of an Illinois veteran of World War II. Applicants must be planning to enroll full time at an accredited community college or 4-year college or university in any state. They must have an unweighted GPA of 4.0 or be projected to be the valedictorian or salutatorian of their class.

Financial data The stipend is $2,000.

Duration 1 year.

Number awarded 2 each year.

Deadline March of each year.

[828]
WYOMING COMBAT VETERAN SURVIVING ORPHAN TUITION BENEFIT

Wyoming Veterans Commission
Attn: Executive Director
5410 Bishop Boulevard
Cheyenne, WY 82009
(307) 777-8151   Toll Free: (800) 833-5987
Fax: (307) 777-8150   E-mail: larry.barttelbort@wyo.gov
Web: sites.google.com

Summary To provide financial assistance to children of deceased, POW, or MIA Wyoming veterans who are interested in attending college in the state.

Eligibility This program is open to children of veterans whose parent had been a resident of Wyoming for at least 1 year at the time of entering service and received the armed forces expeditionary medal or a campaign medal for service in an armed conflict in a foreign country. The veteran parent must 1) have died during active service during armed conflict in a foreign country; 2) be listed officially as being a POW or MIA as a result of active service with the military forces of the United States; or 3) have been honorably discharged from the military and subsequently died of an injury or disease incurred while in service and was a Wyoming resident at the time of death. Applicants must have been younger than 21 years of age when the veteran died or was listed as POW or MIA and younger than 22 years of age when they enter college. They must be attending or planning to attend the University of Wyoming or a community college in the state.

Financial data Qualifying veterans' children are eligible for free resident tuition at the University of Wyoming or at any of the state's community colleges.

Duration Up to 10 semesters.

Additional information Applications may be obtained from the institution the applicant is or is planning to attend.

Number awarded Varies each year.

Deadline Applications may be submitted at any time, but they should be received 2 or 3 weeks before the beginning of the semester.

[829]
WYOMING COMBAT VETERAN SURVIVING SPOUSE TUITION BENEFIT

Wyoming Veterans Commission
Attn: Executive Director
5410 Bishop Boulevard
Cheyenne, WY 82009
(307) 777-8151   Toll Free: (800) 833-5987
Fax: (307) 777-8150   E-mail: larry.barttelbort@wyo.gov
Web: sites.google.com

Summary To provide financial assistance to surviving spouses of deceased, POW, or MIA Wyoming veterans who are interested in attending college in the state.

Eligibility This program is open to spouses of veterans whose spouse had been a resident of Wyoming for at least 1 year at the time of entering service and received the armed forces expeditionary medal or a campaign medal for service in an armed conflict in a foreign country. The veteran spouse must 1) have died during active service during armed conflict in a foreign country; 2) be listed officially as being a POW or MIA as a result of active service with the military forces of the United States; or 3) have been honorably discharged from the military and subsequently died of an injury or disease incurred while in service and was a Wyoming resident at the time of death. Applicants must enroll at the University of Wyoming or a community college in the state within 10 years following the death of the combat veteran.

Financial data Qualifying veterans' spouses are eligible for free resident tuition at the University of Wyoming or at any of the state's community colleges.

Duration Up to 10 semesters.

Additional information Applications may be obtained from the institution the applicant is or is planning to attend.

Number awarded Varies each year.

Deadline Applications may be submitted at any time, but they should be received 2 or 3 weeks before the beginning of the semester.

[830]
WYOMING VIETNAM VETERAN SURVIVING CHILD TUITION BENEFIT

Wyoming Veterans Commission
Attn: Executive Director
5410 Bishop Boulevard
Cheyenne, WY 82009
(307) 777-8151   Toll Free: (800) 833-5987
Fax: (307) 777-8150   E-mail: larry.barttelbort@wyo.gov
Web: sites.google.com

Summary To provide financial assistance to children of deceased, POW, or MIA Wyoming veterans of the Vietnam era who are interested in attending college in the state.

Eligibility This program is open to children of veterans whose parent had been a resident of Wyoming for at least 1 year at the time of entering service, served between August 5, 1964 and May 7, 1975, and received the Vietnam service medal. The veteran parent must 1) have died as a result of service-connected causes; 2) be listed officially as being a POW or MIA as a result of active service with the military forces of the United States; or 3) have been honorably discharged from the military and subsequently died of an injury or disease incurred while in service and was a Wyoming resident at the time of death. Applicants must be attending or planning to attend the University of Wyoming or a community college in the state.

Financial data Qualifying veterans' children are eligible for free resident tuition at the University of Wyoming or at any of the state's community colleges.

Duration Up to 10 semesters.

Additional information Applications may be obtained from the institution the applicant is or is planning to attend.

Number awarded Varies each year.

Deadline Applications may be submitted at any time, but they should be received 2 or 3 weeks before the beginning of the semester.

[831]
WYOMING VIETNAM VETERAN SURVIVING SPOUSE TUITION BENEFIT

Wyoming Veterans Commission
Attn: Executive Director
5410 Bishop Boulevard
Cheyenne, WY 82009
(307) 777-8151   Toll Free: (800) 833-5987
Fax: (307) 777-8150   E-mail: larry.barttelbort@wyo.gov
Web: sites.google.com

Summary To provide funding to surviving spouses of deceased, POW, or MIA Wyoming veterans of the Vietnam era who want to attend college in the state.

Eligibility This program is open to spouses of veterans whose spouse had been a resident of Wyoming for at least 1 year at the time of entering service, served between August 5, 1964 and May 7, 1975, and received the Vietnam service medal. The veteran spouse must 1) have died as a result of service-connected causes; 2) be listed officially as being a POW or MIA as a result of active service with the military forces of the United States; or 3) have been honorably discharged from the military and subsequently died of an injury or disease incurred while in service and was a Wyoming resident at the time of death. Applicants must be attending or planning to attend the University of Wyoming or a community college in the state.

Financial data Qualifying veterans' surviving spouses are eligible for free resident tuition at the University of Wyoming or at any of the state's community colleges.

Duration Up to 10 semesters.

Additional information Applications may be obtained from the institution the applicant is or is planning to attend.

Number awarded Varies each year.

Deadline Applications may be submitted at any time, but they should be received 2 or 3 weeks before the beginning of the semester.

[832]
YELLOW RIBBON PROGRAM OF THE POST-9/11 GI BILL

Department of Veterans Affairs
Attn: Veterans Benefits Administration
810 Vermont Avenue, N.W.
Washington, DC 20420
(202) 418-4343   Toll Free: (888) GI-BILL1
Web: www.gibill.va.gov

Summary To provide financial assistance to veterans and their dependents who qualify for the Post-9/11 GI Bill and wish to attend a high cost private or out-of-state college or graduate school.

Eligibility Maximum Post-9/11 GI Bill benefits are available to veterans who 1) served on active duty for at least 36 aggregate months after September 11, 2001; or 2) were honorably discharged for a service-connected disability and served at least 30 continuous days after September 11, 2001. Military personnel currently on active duty and their spouses may qualify for Post-9/11 GI Bill benefits but are not eligible for the Yellow Ribbon Program. This program is available to veterans who qualify for those benefits at the 100% rate, the children of those veterans to whom they wish to transfer their benefits, and the children and spouses of active-duty personnel who qualify for benefits at the 100% rate to whom they wish to transfer those benefits. Applicants must be working on or planning to work on an undergraduate or graduate degree at a private or out-of-state public institution that charges tuition in excess of the $17,500 cap imposed by the Post-9/11 GI Bill and that has agreed with the Department of Veterans Affairs (VA) to participate in this program.

Financial data Colleges and universities that charge more than $17,500 per academic year in tuition and fees (or a higher amount at schools in Arizona, Michigan, New Hampshire, New York, Pennsylvania, South Carolina, and Texas) agree to waive tuition (up to 50%) for qualifying veterans and dependents. The amount that the college or university waives is matched by VA.

Duration Most participants receive up to 36 months of entitlement under this program. Benefits are payable for up to 15 years following release from active duty.

Number awarded Varies each year.

Deadline Deadline not specified.

[833]
YOUNG PATRIOT SCHOLARSHIP

Idaho Enlisted Association of the National Guard of the
    United States
c/o Steve Vinsonhaler
7054 West Saxton Drive
Boise, ID 83714-2366
(208) 407-4887   E-mail: svinsonhaler@imd.idaho.gov
Web: eangusidaho.org/Scholarships.php

Summary   To provide financial assistance to members of
the Idaho Enlisted Association of the National Guard of the
United States and their family members who are interested in
attending college in any state.

Eligibility   This program is open to 1) members of the association; 2) dependent unmarried children of members; 3)
spouses of members; and 4) unmarried spouses and unmarried dependent children of deceased members who were in
good standing at the time of death. Association members
must also be enlisted members of the Idaho National Guard
with at least 1 year remaining on their enlistment or have 20
or more years of military service. Applicants must be enrolled
or planning to enroll full time at a college, university, trade
school, or business school in any state. Along with their application, they must submit a 2-page essay about an activity or
interest that has been meaningful to them, a personal letter
providing information about themselves and their families, 2
letters of recommendation, an academic letter of recommendation, and a copy of the sponsor's current membership card
or number. Family income is considered in the selection process.

Financial data   The stipend is $1,500.

Duration   1 year; nonrenewable.

Number awarded   1 each year.

Deadline   August of each year.

Fellowships

Veterans •

Military Personnel •

Family Members •

Described here are 233 programs available to veterans, military personnel, and their family members who are or will be pursuing graduate or postdoctoral study or research in the United States. All of this is "free" money. Not one dollar will need to be repaid (provided, of course, that recipients meet all program requirements). Of these listings, 54 are set aside specifically for veterans, 105 for military personnel, and 74 for their family members (spouses, children, grandchildren, parents, and other relatives). If you are looking for a particular program and don't find it in this section, be sure to check the Program Title Index to see if it is covered elsewhere in the directory.

Veterans

[834]
AIR FORCE ROTC GRADUATE LAW PROGRAM

U.S. Air Force
Attn: Headquarters AFROTC/RRUC
551 East Maxwell Boulevard
Maxwell AFB, AL 36112-5917
(334) 953-2091   Toll Free: (866) 4-AFROTC
Fax: (334) 953-6167   E-mail: afrotc1@maxwell.af.mil
Web: afrotc.com

Summary To provide financial assistance for law school to veterans, military personnel, and others who are interested in joining Air Force ROTC and are willing to serve as Air Force officers following completion of their professional degree.

Eligibility Applicants must be U.S. citizens who are currently enrolled in the first year of law school at a college or university with an Air Force ROTC unit on campus or a college with a cross-enrollment agreement with such a school. They may be veterans, current military personnel, or first-year law students without military experience. The law school must be accredited by the American Bar Association. Applicants must agree to serve for at least 4 years as active-duty Air Force officers following graduation from law school. Selection is based on academic performance, extracurricular activities, work experience, community service, military record (if appropriate), and recommendations.

Financial data Students are paid during summer field training and also receive a tax-free stipend of $450 per month during the second year of law school or $500 per month during the third year of law school. No other scholarship assistance is provided.

Duration 2 years.

Additional information Participants attend a field training encampment (4 weeks for students with prior military service, 5 weeks for students with no prior military experience) during the summer between their first and second year of law school. They then complete the normal academic requirements for the 2-year AFROTC program while completing law school. After graduation, participants enter active duty as a first lieutenant (with promotion after 6 months).

Deadline March of each year.

[835]
ALASKA NATIONAL GUARD STATE TUITION REIMBURSEMENT PROGRAM

Alaska National Guard
Attn: Education Services Officer
P.O. Box 5800
Fort Richardson, AK 99505-5800
(907) 428-6477   Fax: (907) 428-6929
E-mail: ngmneducation@ng.army.mil
Web: www.akguard.com

Summary To provide financial assistance to current and former members of the Alaska National Guard who wish to work on a bachelor's or master's degree in the state.

Eligibility This program is open to members of the Alaska National Guard (Air and Army) and Naval Militia who have a rating of E-1 through O-5, including warrant officers, and are attending a university program in Alaska. Eligibility extends to members who 1) have satisfactorily completed their service contract and who served honorably in federal active service or federally-funded state active service after September 11, 2001; or 2) have been separated or discharged from the Guard because of a service-connected injury, disease, or disability. First priority is given to undergraduates; if funding is available, students working on a second bachelor's degree or a master's degree may be supported. Non-prior servicemembers must complete Initial Active Duty for Training (IADT); prior servicemembers are eligible immediately.

Financial data Recipients are entitled to reimbursement equivalent to 100% of the cost of tuition and fees at the University of Alaska, to a maximum of $7,500 per fiscal year.

Duration 1 semester; may be renewed for a total of 144 semester credits.

Number awarded Varies each year.

Deadline Applications may be submitted at any time, but they must be received at least 90 days after the last official day of the class or term.

[836]
AMVETS NATIONAL SCHOLARSHIPS FOR VETERANS

AMVETS National Headquarters
Attn: Scholarships
4647 Forbes Boulevard
Lanham, MD 20706-3807
(301) 459-9600   Toll Free: (877) 7-AMVETS, ext. 3043
Fax: (301) 459-7924   E-mail: amvets@amvets.org
Web: www.amvets.org/programs/scholarships.html

Summary To provide money for college or graduate school to certain veterans who are members of AMVETS.

Eligibility This program is open to AMVETS members who are veterans and U.S. citizens. Applicants must be interested in working full time on an undergraduate degree, graduate degree, or certification from an accredited technical/trade school. They must have exhausted all other government aid. Selection is based on financial need, academic promise, military duty and awards, volunteer activities, community services, jobs held during the past 4 years, and an essay of 50 to 100 words on "What a Higher Education Means to Me."

Financial data The stipend is $1,000 per year.

Duration Up to 4 years.

Additional information Requests for applications must be accompanied by a self-addressed stamped envelope.

Number awarded 3 each year.

Deadline April of each year.

[837]
ANCA SCHOLARSHIPS

Army Nurse Corps Association
Attn: Education Committee
P.O. Box 39235
San Antonio, TX 78218-1235
(210) 650-3534   Fax: (210) 650-3494
E-mail: education@e-anca.org
Web: e-anca.org/ANCAEduc.htm

Summary To provide financial assistance to students who have a connection to the Army and are interested in working on an undergraduate or graduate degree in nursing.

Eligibility This program is open to U.S. citizens attending colleges or universities that have accredited programs offering associate, bachelor's, master's, or doctoral degrees in nursing. Applicants must be 1) nursing or anesthesia students who plan to enter a component of the U.S. Army and are not participating in a program funded by a component of the U.S. Army; 2) nursing or anesthesia students who have previously served in a component of the U.S. Army; 3) Army Nurse Corps officers enrolled in an undergraduate or graduate nursing program not funded by a component of the U.S. Army; 4) enlisted soldiers in a component of the U.S. Army who are working on a baccalaureate degree in nursing not funded by a component of the U.S. Army; or 5) nursing or anesthesia students whose parent(s), spouse, and/or children are serving or have served in a component of the U.S. Army. Along with their application, they must submit a personal statement on their professional career objectives, reasons for applying for this scholarship, financial need, special considerations, personal and academic interests, and why they are preparing for a nursing career.

Financial data The stipend is $3,000. Funds are sent directly to the recipient's school.

Duration 1 year.

Additional information Although the sponsoring organization is open to officers of the Army Nurse Corps, it does not have an official affiliation with the Army. Therefore, students who receive these scholarships do not incur any military service obligation.

Number awarded 1 or more each year.

Deadline March of each year.

[838]
ARMY AVIATION ASSOCIATION OF AMERICA SCHOLARSHIPS

Army Aviation Association of America Scholarship Foundation
Attn: AAAA Scholarship Foundation
755 Main Street, Suite 4D
Monroe, CT 06468-2830
(203) 268-2450   Fax: (203) 268-5870
E-mail: aaaa@quad-a.org
Web: www.quad-a.org

Summary To provide financial aid for undergraduate or graduate study to members of the Army Aviation Association of America and their relatives.

Eligibility This program is open to association members (or deceased members) and their spouses, unmarried siblings, unmarried children, and unmarried grandchildren. Applicants must be enrolled or accepted for enrollment as an undergraduate or graduate student at an accredited college or university. Graduate students must include a 250-word essay on their life experiences, work history, and aspirations. Some scholarships are specifically reserved for enlisted, warrant officer, company grade, and Department of the Army civilian members. Selection is based on academic merit and personal achievement.

Financial data Stipends range up to $3,000 per year.

Duration Scholarships may be for 1, 2, or 4 years.

Number awarded Varies each year; recently, $309,500 in scholarships was awarded to 209 students. Since the program began in 1963, the foundation has awarded more than $4.1 million to nearly 2,500 qualified applicants.

Deadline April of each year.

[839]
ASSE FOUNDATION MILITARY SERVICE SCHOLARSHIP

American Society of Safety Engineers
Attn: ASSE Foundation
1800 East Oakton Street
Des Plaines, IL 60018
(847) 768-3435   Fax: (847) 768-3434
E-mail: agabanski@asse.org
Web: www.asse.org

Summary To provide financial assistance to upper-division and graduate student members of the American Society of Safety Engineers (ASSE), especially those who have served in the military.

Eligibility This program is open to ASSE student members who are working on an undergraduate or graduate degree in occupational safety, health, and environment or a closely-related field (e.g., industrial or environmental engineering, environmental science, industrial hygiene, occupational health nursing). Priority is given to students who have served in the military. Applicants must be full-time students who have completed at least 60 semester hours with a GPA of 3.0 or higher as undergraduates or at least 9 semester hours with a GPA of 3.5 or higher as graduate students. Along with their application, they must submit 2 essays of 300 words or less: 1) why they are seeking a degree in occupational safety and health or a closely-related field, a brief description of their current activities, and how those relate to their career goals and objectives; and 2) why they should be awarded this scholarship (including career goals and financial need). U.S. citizenship is not required.

Financial data The stipend is $1,000 per year.

Duration 1 year; recipients may reapply.

Number awarded 1 each year.

Deadline November of each year.

[840]
CAPTAIN SEAN P. GRIMES PHYSICIAN ASSISTANT EDUCATIONAL SCHOLARSHIP AWARD

Society of Army Physician Assistants
c/o Harold Slusher
6762 Candlewood Drive
P.O. Box 07490
Fort Myers, FL 33919
(239) 482-2162   Fax: (239) 482-2162
E-mail: hal.shusher@juno.com
Web: www.sapa.org/SeanScholarshipPage.htm

Summary To provide funding to current and former Army personnel interested in training as a physician assistant.

Eligibility This program is open to Army veterans, Army active-duty soldiers, Army National Guard soldiers, and Army Reservists. Soldiers may be of any enlisted or officer rank from E-5 through O-4. Applicants may be seeking initial training as a physician assistant or current physician assistants working on a baccalaureate, master's, or doctoral degree. They must have a GPA of 2.5 or higher. Candidates for initial training must be enrolled in an ARC-PA approved program. Other candidates must be enrolled at an accredited college or university. Financial need is considered.

Financial data The stipend is $6,000.

Duration 1 year.

Additional information This program began in 2006.

Number awarded 1 each year.

Deadline January of each year.

[841]
CONNECTICUT TUITION WAIVER FOR VETERANS

Connecticut Office of Financial and Academic Affairs for
Higher Education
Attn: Student Financial Aid
61 Woodland Street
Hartford, CT 06105-2326
(860) 947-1855   Toll Free: (800) 842-0229 (within CT)
Fax: (860) 947-1311   E-mail: sfa@ctdhe.org
Web: www.ctohe.org/SFA/default.htm

Summary To provide money for college or graduate school to certain Connecticut veterans and military personnel or their dependents.

Eligibility This program is open to 1) honorably-discharged Connecticut veterans who served at least 90 days during specified periods of wartime; 2) active members of the Connecticut Army and Air National Guard; 3) Connecticut residents who are a dependent child or surviving spouse of a member of the armed forces killed in action on or after September 11, 2001 who was also a Connecticut resident; and 4) Connecticut residents who are dependent children of a person officially declared missing in action or a prisoner of war while serving in the armed forces after January 1, 1960. Applicants must be attending or planning to attend a public college or university in the state.

Financial data The program provides a waiver of 100% of tuition for students working on an undergraduate or graduate degree at the University of Connecticut, 100% of tuition for general fund courses at campuses of Connecticut State University, 50% of tuition for extension and summer courses at campuses of Connecticut State University, 100% of tuition at all Connecticut community colleges, and 50% or fees at Charter Oak State College.

Duration Up to 4 years.

Additional information This is an entitlement program; applications are available from the respective college financial aid offices.

Number awarded Varies each year.

Deadline Deadline not specified.

[842]
DARLENE HOOLEY SCHOLARSHIP FOR OREGON VETERANS

Oregon Student Access Commission
Attn: Grants and Scholarships Division
1500 Valley River Drive, Suite 100
Eugene, OR 97401-2146
(541) 687-7395   Toll Free: (800) 452-8807, ext. 7395
Fax: (541) 687-7414   TDD: (800) 735-2900
E-mail: awardinfo@osac.state.or.us
Web: www.oregonstudentaid.gov/scholarships.aspx

Summary To provide financial assistance to veterans in Oregon who served during the Global War on Terror and are interested in working on an undergraduate or graduate degree at a college in the state.

Eligibility This program is open to Oregon veterans who served during the Global War on Terror; there is no minimum length of service requirement. Preference is given to members of active-duty Reserves and the National Guard who were deployed to an overseas conflict. Applicants must be enrolled or planning to enroll at least half time as an undergraduate or graduate student at a college or university in Oregon. Financial need is considered in the selection process.

Financial data Stipends for scholarships offered by the Oregon Student Access Commission (OSAC) range from $200 to $10,000 but recently averaged $2,300.

Duration 1 year; recipients may reapply.

Additional information This program is administered by OSAC with funds from the Oregon Community Foundation.

Number awarded Varies each year.

Deadline February of each year.

[843]
DATATEL ANGELFIRE SCHOLARSHIP

Datatel Scholars Foundation
4375 Fair Lakes Court
Fairfax, VA 22033
(703) 968-9000, ext. 4549   Toll Free: (800) 486-4332
Fax: (703) 968-4625   E-mail: scholars@datatel.com
Web: www.datatelscholars.org

Summary To provide funding to graduating high school seniors, college students, and graduate students who will be studying at a Datatel client school and are veterans, veterans' dependents, or refugees from southeast Asia.

Eligibility This program is open to 1) veterans who served in the Asian theater (Vietnam, Cambodia, or Laos) between 1964 and 1975; 2) their spouses and children; 3) refugees from Vietnam, Cambodia, or Laos; and 4) veterans who served in Operation Desert Storm, Operation Enduring Freedom, and/or Operation Iraqi Freedom. Applicants must attend a Datatel client college or university during the upcoming school year as a full- or part-time undergraduate or graduate student. They must first apply to their institution, which selects 2 semifinalists and forwards their applications to the sponsor. Along with their application, they must include a 1,000-word personal statement that discusses how the conflict has affected them personally, summarizes how the conflict has impacted their educational goals, and describes how being awarded this scholarship will help them achieve their goals. Selection is based on the quality of the personal statement (60%) and academic merit (40%).

Financial data The stipend is $1,700. Funds are paid directly to the institution.

Duration 1 year.

Additional information Datatel, Inc. produces advanced information technology solutions for higher education. It has more than 750 client sites in the United States and Canada. This scholarship was created to commemorate those who lost their lives in Vietnam or Iraq and is named after a memorial administered by the Disabled American Veterans Association in Angelfire, New Mexico.

Number awarded 10 each year.

Deadline Students must submit online applications to their institution or organization by January of each year.

[844]
DR. WILLIAM WALKER MEMORIAL SCHOLARSHIP

Community Foundation of the Ozarks
Attn: Scholarship Coordinator
421 East Trafficway
P.O. Box 8960
Springfield, MO 65801-8960
(417) 864-6199   Toll Free: (888) 266-6815
Fax: (417) 864-8344   E-mail: jbillings@cfozarks.org
Web: www.cfozarks.org

Summary To provide financial assistance to students (preference given to veterans) at medical schools in Missouri and Iowa.

Eligibility This program is open to students entering their final year in the top 15% of their class at a medical school in Missouri or Iowa. Applicants must be natural born U.S. citizens who can demonstrate superior clinical skills and the ability to communicate with patients effectively and with empathy. Preference is given to veterans, especially U.S. Marines.

Financial data The stipend is $5,000.

Duration 1 year.

Number awarded 1 each year.

Deadline June of each year.

[845]
EDUCATION FOUNDATION FOR THE COLORADO NATIONAL GUARD GRANTS

National Guard Association of Colorado
Attn: Education Foundation, Inc.
P.O. Box 440889
Aurora, CO 80044-0889
(303) 909-6369   Fax: (720) 535-5925
E-mail: BernieRogoff@comcast.net
Web: efcong.org/Grants

Summary To provide financial assistance to members of the Colorado National Guard and their families who are interested in attending college or graduate school in any state.

Eligibility This program is open to current and retired members of the Colorado National Guard and their dependent unmarried children and spouses. Applicants must be enrolled or planning to enroll full or part time at a college, university, trade school, business school, or graduate school in any state. Along with their application, they must submit an essay, up to 2 pages in length, on their desire to continue their education, what motivates them, their financial need, their commitment to academic excellence, and their current situation. Selection is based on academic achievement, community involvement, and financial need.

Financial data Stipends are at least $1,000 per year.

Duration 1 year; may be renewed.

Number awarded Varies each year; recently, 38 of these grants, with a total value of $50,000, were awarded.

Deadline July of each year for fall semester; January of each year for spring semester.

[846]
EDWARD T. CONROY MEMORIAL SCHOLARSHIP PROGRAM

Maryland Higher Education Commission
Attn: Office of Student Financial Assistance
6 North Liberty Street, Ground Suite
Baltimore, MD 21201
(410) 767-3300   Toll Free: (800) 974-0203
Fax: (410) 332-0250   TDD: (800) 735-2258
E-mail: osfamail@mhec.state.md.us
Web: www.mhec.state.md.us/financialAid/descriptions.asp

Summary To provide money for college or graduate school in Maryland to children and spouses of victims of the September 11, 2001 terrorist attacks and specified categories of veterans, public safety employees, and their children or spouses.

Eligibility This program is open to entering and continuing undergraduate and graduate students in the following categories: 1) children and surviving spouses of victims of the September 11, 2001 terrorist attacks who died in the World Trade Center in New York City, in the Pentagon in Virginia, or on United Airlines Flight 93 in Pennsylvania; 2) veterans who have, as a direct result of military service, a disability of 25% or greater and have exhausted or are no longer eligible for federal veterans' educational benefits; 3) children of armed forces members whose death or 100% disability was directly caused by military service; 4) POW/MIA veterans of the Vietnam Conflict and their children; 5) state or local public safety officers or volunteers who became 100% disabled in the line of duty; and 6) children and unremarried surviving spouses of state or local public safety employees or volunteers who died or became 100% disabled in the line of duty. The parent, spouse, veteran, POW, or public safety officer or volunteer must have been a resident of Maryland at the time of death or when declared disabled. Financial need is not considered.

Financial data The amount of the award is equal to tuition and fees at a Maryland postsecondary institution, to a maximum of $19,000 for children and spouses of the September 11 terrorist attacks or $9,000 for all other recipients.

Duration Up to 5 years of full-time or 8 years of part-time study.

Additional information Recipients must enroll at a 2- or 4-year Maryland college or university as a full-time or part-time degree-seeking undergraduate or graduate student or attend a private career school.

Number awarded Varies each year.

Deadline July of each year.

[847]
EXEMPTION FOR TEXAS VETERANS

Texas Higher Education Coordinating Board
Attn: Grants and Special Programs
1200 East Anderson Lane
P.O. Box 12788
Austin, TX 78711-2788
(512) 427-6340   Toll Free: (800) 242-3062
Fax: (512) 427-6420   E-mail: grantinfo@thecb.state.tx.us
Web: www.collegeforalltexans.com

Summary To exempt Texas veterans from payment of tuition for undergraduate or graduate study at public universities in the state.

Eligibility Eligible are veterans who currently reside in Texas and were legal residents of the state when they entered the U.S. armed forces and served for at least 181 days of active military duty, excluding basic training, during specified periods of wartime. Applicants must have received an honorable discharge or separation or a general discharge under honorable conditions. They must be enrolled at a public college or university in Texas and all their other federal veterans education benefits (not including Pell and SEOG grants) may not exceed the value of this exemption.

Financial data Veterans who are eligible for this benefit are entitled to free tuition and fees at state-supported colleges and universities in Texas.

Duration Exemptions may be claimed up to 150 credit hours, including undergraduate and graduate study.

Additional information This program was established under provisions of the Hazlewood Act, and is also referred to as Hazlewood Exemption for Texas Veterans.

Number awarded Varies each year; recently, 8,885 of these awards were granted.

Deadline Deadline not specified.

[848]
FIRST SERGEANT DOUGLAS AND CHARLOTTE DEHORSE SCHOLARSHIP

> Catching the Dream
> 8200 Mountain Road, N.E., Suite 203
> Albuquerque, NM 87110-7835
> (505) 262-2351   Fax: (505) 262-0534
> E-mail: NScholarsh@aol.com
> Web: www.catchingthedream.org

Summary To provide financial assistance to American Indians who have ties to the military and are working on an undergraduate or graduate degree.

Eligibility This program is open to American Indians who 1) have completed 1 year of an Army, Navy, or Air Force Junior Reserve Officer Training (JROTC) program; 2) are enrolled in an Army, Navy, or Air Force Reserve Officer Training (ROTC) program; or 3) are a veteran of the U.S. Army, Navy, Air Force, Marines, Merchant Marine, or Coast Guard. Applicants must be enrolled in college or graduate school. They must submit an application, personal essay, high school transcripts, and letters of recommendation.

Financial data A stipend is awarded (amount not specified).

Duration 1 year.

Additional information This program began in 2007.

Number awarded 1 or more each year.

Deadline April of each year for fall semester or quarter; September of each year for spring semester or winter quarter.

[849]
FRA NON-MEMBER SCHOLARSHIPS

> Fleet Reserve Association
> Attn: FRA Education Foundation
> 125 North West Street
> Alexandria, VA 22314-2754
> (703) 683-1400   Toll Free: (800) FRA-1924
> Fax: (703) 549-6610   E-mail: scholars@fra.org
> Web: www.fra.org

Summary To provide financial assistance for college or graduate school to current or former sea service personnel and their families.

Eligibility This program is open to 1) active-duty, Reserve, honorably-discharged veterans, and retired members of the U.S. Navy, Marine Corps, and Coast Guard; and 2) their spouses, children, and grandchildren. Applicants must be enrolled as full-time undergraduate or graduate students but they are not required to be members of the sponsoring organization. Along with their application, they must submit an essay on why they want to go to college and what they intend to accomplish with their degree. Selection is based on academic record, financial need, extracurricular activities, leadership skills, and participation in community activities. U.S. citizenship is required.

Financial data A stipend is awarded (amount not specified).

Duration 1 year; may be renewed.

Number awarded 1 or more each year.

Deadline April of each year.

[850]
FRA SCHOLARSHIPS

> Fleet Reserve Association
> Attn: FRA Education Foundation
> 125 North West Street
> Alexandria, VA 22314-2754
> (703) 683-1400   Toll Free: (800) FRA-1924
> Fax: (703) 549-6610   E-mail: scholars@fra.org
> Web: www.fra.org

Summary To provide financial assistance for college or graduate school to members of the Fleet Reserve Association (FRA) and their families.

Eligibility This program is open to members of the FRA and the dependent children, grandchildren, and spouses of living or deceased members. Applicants must be enrolled as full-time undergraduate or graduate students. Along with their application, they must submit an essay on why they want to go to college and what they intend to accomplish with their degree. Selection is based on academic record, financial need, extracurricular activities, leadership skills, and participation in community activities. U.S. citizenship is required.

Financial data The stipend is $5,000 per year.

Duration 1 year; may be renewed.

Additional information Membership in the FRA is restricted to active-duty, retired, and reserve members of the Navy, Marines, and Coast Guard.

Number awarded 6 each year.

Deadline April of each year.

[851]
GLENN F. GLEZEN SCHOLARSHIP

> Fleet Reserve Association
> Attn: FRA Education Foundation
> 125 North West Street
> Alexandria, VA 22314-2754
> (703) 683-1400   Toll Free: (800) FRA-1924
> Fax: (703) 549-6610   E-mail: scholars@fra.org
> Web: www.fra.org

Summary To provide financial assistance for graduate school to members of the Fleet Reserve Association (FRA) and their families.

Eligibility This program is open to members of the FRA and the dependent children, grandchildren, and spouses of living or deceased members. Applicants must be enrolled as full-time graduate students. Along with their application, they must submit an essay on why they want to go to college and what they intend to accomplish with their degree. Selection is based on academic record, financial need, extracurricular activities, leadership skills, and participation in community activities. U.S. citizenship is required.

Financial data The stipend is $5,000 per year.

Duration 1 year; may be renewed.

Additional information Membership in the FRA is restricted to active-duty, retired, and Reserve members of the Navy, Marine Corps, and Coast Guard. This program was established in 2001.

Number awarded 1 each year.

Deadline April of each year.

[852]
GOOGLE-SVA SCHOLARSHIP

Student Veterans of America
P.O. Box 77673
Washington, DC 20013
E-mail: SVA@studentveterans.org
Web: www.studentveterans.org/?page=Programs

Summary To provide funding to veterans working on a bachelor's or graduate degree in a computer-related field.

Eligibility This program is open to sophomores, juniors, seniors, and graduate students at U.S. colleges and universities who are veterans (must possess a DD-214) and were honorably discharged or are still in good standing with their branch of service. Applicants must be working full time on a degree in computer science, computer engineering, or a closely-related technical field (e.g., software engineering, electrical engineering (with a heavy computer science course load), information systems, information technology, applied networking, system administration). Along with their application, they must submit a 1,000-word personal statement that covers their reasons for applying for this scholarship, their reasons for choosing their major, their professional objectives as they relate to their degree, their role as a leader in their community and/or chapter, and any additional community service initiatives in which they have been involved. Financial need is not considered in the selection process.

Financial data The stipend is $10,000.

Duration 1 year.

Additional information This program is sponsored by Google.

Number awarded 8 each year.

Deadline March of each year.

[853]
HENRY J. REILLY MEMORIAL GRADUATE SCHOLARSHIP

Reserve Officers Association of the United States
Attn: Scholarship Program
One Constitution Avenue, N.E.
Washington, DC 20002-5618
(202) 646-7719   Toll Free: (800) 809-9448, ext. 719
Fax: (202) 547-1641   E-mail: scholarship@roa.org
Web: www.roa.org

Summary To provide financial support for graduate study to members of the Reserve Officers Association (ROA).

Eligibility This program is open to active or associate members of the association who are enrolled in or accepted for enrollment in graduate studies at an accredited U.S. institution of higher education. Applicants for a master's degree must have earned a GPA of 3.2 or higher as an undergraduate; applicants for a doctoral degree must have received a master's degree or been accepted into a doctoral program. Applications must include 3 letters of recommendation: 1 from a military or civilian superior regarding the applicant's leadership ability or potential and 2 from persons qualified to assess academic ability.

Financial data The stipend is $1,000 per year.

Duration 1 year; may be renewed up to 3 additional years if the recipient maintains a GPA of 3.3 or higher.

Number awarded The sponsor awards a total of 30 scholarships each year.

Deadline May of each year.

[854]
ILLINOIS NATIONAL GUARD GRANT PROGRAM

Illinois Student Assistance Commission
Attn: Scholarship and Grant Services
1755 Lake Cook Road
Deerfield, IL 60015-5209
(847) 948-8550   Toll Free: (800) 899-ISAC
Fax: (847) 831-8549   TDD: (800) 526-0844
E-mail: isac.studentservices@isac.illinois.gov
Web: www.collegeillinois.org

Summary To provide financial assistance to current or former members of the Illinois National Guard who are interested in attending college or graduate school in the state.

Eligibility This program is open to members of the Illinois National Guard who are 1) currently active or 2) have been active for at least 5 consecutive years, have been called to federal active duty for at least 6 months, and are within 12 months after their discharge date. Applicants must also be enrolled at an Illinois public 2- or 4-year college or university and have served at least 1 full year in the Guard.

Financial data Recipients are eligible for payment of tuition and some fees for either undergraduate or graduate study at an Illinois state-supported college or university.

Duration This assistance extends for 8 semesters or 12 quarters (or the equivalent in part-time study).

Number awarded Varies each year.

Deadline September of each year for the academic year; February of each year for spring semester, winter quarter, or spring quarter; June of each year for summer term.

[855]
ILLINOIS VETERAN GRANT PROGRAM

Illinois Student Assistance Commission
Attn: Scholarship and Grant Services
1755 Lake Cook Road
Deerfield, IL 60015-5209
(847) 948-8550   Toll Free: (800) 899-ISAC
Fax: (847) 831-8549   TDD: (800) 526-0844
E-mail: isac.studentservices@isac.illinois.gov
Web: www.collegeillinois.org

Summary To provide financial assistance to Illinois veterans who are interested in attending college or graduate school in the state.

Eligibility This program is open to Illinois residents who served in the U.S. armed forces (including members of the Reserves and the Illinois National Guard) for at least 1 year on active duty and have been honorably discharged. The 1-year service requirement does not apply to veterans who 1) served in a foreign country in a time of hostilities in that country, 2) were medically discharged for service-related reasons, or 3) were discharged prior to August 11, 1967. Applicants must have been Illinois residents for at least 6 months before entering service and they must have returned to Illinois within 6 months after separation from service. Current members of the Reserve Officer Training Corps are not eligible.

Financial data This program pays tuition and certain fees at Illinois public colleges, universities, and community colleges.

Duration This scholarship may be used for the equivalent of up to 4 years of full-time enrollment, provided the recipient maintains the minimum GPA required by their school.

Additional information This is an entitlement program; once eligibility has been established, no further applications are necessary.

Number awarded Varies each year.

Deadline Applications may be submitted at any time.

[856]
JOSEPH R. BARANSKI SCHOLARSHIP

Fleet Reserve Association
Attn: FRA Education Foundation
125 North West Street
Alexandria, VA 22314-2754
(703) 683-1400   Toll Free: (800) FRA-1924
Fax: (703) 549-6610   E-mail: scholars@fra.org
Web: www.fra.org

Summary To provide financial assistance for graduate school to members of the Fleet Reserve Association (FRA) and their families.

Eligibility This program is open to members of the FRA and the dependent children, grandchildren, and spouses of living or deceased members. Applicants must be enrolled as full-time graduate students. Along with their application, they must submit an essay on why they want to go to college and what they intend to accomplish with their degree. Selection is based on academic record, financial need, extracurricular activities, leadership skills, and participation in community activities. U.S. citizenship is required.

Financial data The stipend is $5,000.

Duration 1 year; may be renewed.

Additional information Membership in the FRA is restricted to active-duty, retired, and Reserve members of the Navy, Marine Corps, and Coast Guard. This program was established in 2001.

Number awarded 1 each year.

Deadline April of each year.

[857]
KAISER PERMANENTE COLORADO DIVERSITY SCHOLARSHIP PROGRAM

Kaiser Permanente
Attn: Physician Recruitment Services
10350 East Dakota Avenue
Denver, CO 80231-1314
(303) 344-7299   Toll Free: (866) 239-1677
Fax: (303) 344-7818
E-mail: co-diversitydevelopment@kp.org
Web: scholarselect.com

Summary To provide funding to veterans and other Colorado residents who come from diverse backgrounds and are interested in working on an undergraduate or graduate degree in a health care field at a public college in the state.

Eligibility This program is open to all residents of Colorado, including those who identify as 1 or more of the following: African American, Asian Pacific, Latino, lesbian, gay, bisexual, transgender, intersex, Native American, U.S. veteran, and/or a person with a disability. Applicants must be enrolled or planning to enroll full time at a publicly-funded college, university, or technical school in Colorado as 1) a graduating high school senior with a GPA of 2.7 or higher; 2) a GED recipient with a GED score of 520 or higher; 3) an undergraduate student; or 4) a graduate or doctoral student. They must be preparing for a career in health care (e.g., athletic training, audiology, cardiovascular perfusion technology, clinical medical assisting, cytotechnology, dental assisting, dental hygiene, diagnostic medicine, dietetics, emergency medical technology, medicine, nursing, occupational therapy, pharmacy, phlebotomy, physical therapy, physician assistant, radiology, respiratory therapy, social work, sports medicine, surgical technology). Along with their application, they must submit 300-word essays on 1) a brief story from their childhood and the aspects of their experience that will contribute to their become a good health care provided; 2) what giving back to the community means to them and their experiences in community involvement that demonstrate their commitment to health care; and 3) what they consider the most pressing issue in health care today. Selection is based on academic achievement, character qualities, community outreach and volunteering, and financial need. U.S. citizenship is required.

Financial data Stipends range from $1,400 to $2,600.

Duration 1 year.

Number awarded Varies each year; recently, 17 of these scholarships were awarded.

Deadline February of each year.

[858]
LANCASTER SCHOLARSHIP

Susquehanna Foundation for the Blind
244 North Queen Street
Lancaster, PA 17603
(717) 291-5951
Web: www.sabvi.org/Grants%20and%20Scholarships

Summary To provide funding to Pennsylvania residents who are legally blind veterans and interested in working on a undergraduate or graduate degree at a college in any state.

Eligibility This program is open to veterans who are residents of Pennsylvania and legally blind. Applicants must be attending or planning to attend an institution of higher education at any level in any state. Along with their application, they must submit a brief description of their career goal. Financial need is considered in the selection process.

Financial data The stipend is $1,000 per year.

Duration 1 year; may be renewed up to 3 additional years.

Number awarded 1 or more each year.

Deadline January of each year.

[859]
MAINE VIETNAM VETERANS SCHOLARSHIP FUND

Maine Community Foundation
Attn: Program Director
245 Main Street
Ellsworth, ME 04605
(207) 667-9735   Toll Free: (877) 700-6800
Fax: (207) 667-0447   E-mail: info@mainecf.org
Web: www.mainecf.org/statewidescholars.aspx

Summary To provide financial assistance for college or graduate school to Vietnam veterans or the dependents of Vietnam or other veterans in Maine.

Eligibility This program is open to residents of Maine who are Vietnam veterans or the descendants of veterans who served in the Vietnam Theater. As a second priority, children of veterans from other time periods are also considered. Graduating high school seniors, nontraditional students, undergraduates, and graduate students are eligible to apply. Selection is based on financial need, extracurricular activities, work experience, academic achievement, and a personal statement of career goals and how the applicant's educational plans relate to them.

Financial data The stipend is $1,000 per year.

Duration 1 year.

Additional information This program began in 1985. There is a $3 processing fee.

Number awarded 3 to 6 each year.

Deadline April of each year.

[860]
MARIA C. JACKSON/GENERAL GEORGE A. WHITE SCHOLARSHIP

Oregon Student Access Commission
Attn: Grants and Scholarships Division
1500 Valley River Drive, Suite 100
Eugene, OR 97401-2146
(541) 687-7395   Toll Free: (800) 452-8807, ext. 7395
Fax: (541) 687-7414   TDD: (800) 735-2900
E-mail: awardinfo@osac.state.or.us
Web: www.oregonstudentaid.gov/scholarships.aspx

Summary To provide financial assistance to veterans and children of veterans and military personnel in Oregon who are interested in attending college or graduate school in the state.

Eligibility This program is open to residents of Oregon who served, or whose parents are serving or have served, in the U.S. armed forces. Applicants or their parents must have resided in Oregon at the time of enlistment. They must be enrolled or planning to enroll at a college or graduate school in the state. College and university undergraduates must have a GPA of 3.75 or higher, but there is no minimum GPA requirement for graduate students or those attending a technical school. Selection is based on academics and need.

Financial data Stipends for scholarships offered by the Oregon Student Access Commission (OSAC) range from $200 to $10,000 but recently averaged $2,300.

Number awarded Varies each year.

Deadline February of each year.

[861]
MG EUGENE C. RENZI, USA (RET.)/MANTECH INTERNATIONAL CORPORATION TEACHER'S SCHOLARSHIP

Armed Forces Communications and Electronics Association
Attn: AFCEA Educational Foundation
4400 Fair Lakes Court
Fairfax, VA 22033-3899
(703) 631-6138   Toll Free: (800) 336-4583, ext. 6138
Fax: (703) 631-4693   E-mail: scholarshipinfo@afcea.org
Web: www.afcea.org

Summary To provide financial assistance to undergraduate and graduate students (especially veterans) who are preparing for a career as a teacher of science and mathematics.

Eligibility This program is open to full-time sophomores, juniors, seniors, and graduate students at accredited colleges and universities in the United States. Applicants must be U.S. citizens preparing for a career as a teacher of science, mathematics, or information technology at a middle or secondary school. They must have a GPA of 3.0 or higher. In the selection process, first consideration is given to wounded or disabled veterans, then to honorably discharged veterans. Financial need is not considered.

Financial data The stipend is $2,500.

Duration 1 year.

Additional information This program was established in 2008 with support from ManTech International Corporation.

Number awarded 1 each year.

Deadline March of each year.

[862]
MINNESOTA G.I. BILL PROGRAM

Minnesota Office of Higher Education
Attn: Manager of State Financial Aid Programs
1450 Energy Park Drive, Suite 350
St. Paul, MN 55108-5227
(651) 642-0567   Toll Free: (800) 657-3866
Fax: (651) 642-0675   TDD: (800) 627-3529
E-mail: Ginny.Dodds@state.mn.us
Web: www.ohe.state.mn.us/mPg.cfm?pageID=891

Summary To provide financial assistance for college or graduate school in the state to residents of Minnesota who served in the military after September 11, 2001 and the families of deceased or disabled military personnel.

Eligibility This program is open to residents of Minnesota enrolled at colleges and universities in the state as undergraduate or graduate students. Applicants must be 1) a veteran who is serving or has served honorably in a branch of the U.S. armed forces at any time on or after September 11, 2001; 2) a non-veteran who has served honorably for a total of 5 years or more cumulatively as a member of the Minnesota National Guard or other active or Reserve component of the U.S. armed forces, and any part of that service occurred on or after September 11, 2001; or 3) a surviving child or spouse of a person who has served in the military at any time on or after September 11, 2001 and who has died or has a total and permanent disability as a result of that military service. Financial need is considered in the selection process.

Financial data The stipend is $1,000 per semester for full-time study or $500 per semester for part-time study. The maximum award is $3,000 per fiscal year or $10,000 per lifetime.

Duration 1 year; may be renewed, provided the recipient continues to make satisfactory academic progress.

Additional information This program was established by the Minnesota Legislature in 2007.

Number awarded Varies each year.

Deadline Deadline not specified.

[863]
MONTANA HONORABLY DISCHARGED VETERAN WAIVER

Office of the Commissioner of Higher Education
Attn: Montana University System
State Scholarship Coordinator
2500 Broadway
P.O. Box 203201
Helena, MT 59620-3201
(406) 444-0638   Toll Free: (800) 537-7508
Fax: (406) 444-1469   E-mail: snewlun@montana.edu
Web: www.mus.edu

Summary To provide financial assistance for undergraduate or graduate studies to selected Montana veterans.

Eligibility This program is open to honorably-discharged veterans who served with the U.S. armed forces and who are residents of Montana. Only veterans who at some time qualified for U.S. Department of Veterans Affairs (VA) educational benefits, but who are no longer eligible or have exhausted their benefits, are entitled to this waiver. Veterans who served any time prior to May 8, 1975 are eligible to work on undergraduate or graduate degrees. Veterans whose service began after May 7, 1975 are eligible only to work on their first undergraduate degree. They must have received an Armed Forces Expeditionary Medal for service in Lebanon, Grenada, or Panama; served in a combat theater in the Persian Gulf between August 2, 1990 and April 11, 1991 and received the Southwest Asia Service Medal; were awarded the Kosovo Campaign Medal; or served in a combat theater in Afghanistan or Iraq after September 11, 2001 and received the Global War on Terrorism Expeditionary Medal, the Afghanistan Campaign Medal, or the Iraq Campaign Medal. Financial need must be demonstrated.

Financial data Veterans eligible for this benefit are entitled to attend any unit of the Montana University System without payment of registration or incidental fees.

Duration Students are eligible for continued fee waiver as long as they make academic progress as full-time students.

Number awarded Varies each year.

Deadline Deadline not specified.

[864]
MONTGOMERY GI BILL (ACTIVE DUTY)

Department of Veterans Affairs
Attn: Veterans Benefits Administration
810 Vermont Avenue, N.W.
Washington, DC 20420
(202) 418-4343   Toll Free: (888) GI-BILL1
Web: www.gibill.va.gov

Summary To provide financial assistance for college, graduate school, and other types of postsecondary schools to new enlistees in any of the armed forces after they have completed their service obligation.

Eligibility This program is open to veterans who received an honorable discharge and have a high school diploma, a GED, or, in some cases, up to 12 hours of college credit; veterans who already have a bachelor's degree are eligible to work on a master's degree or higher. Applicants must also meet the requirements of 1 of the following categories: 1) entered active duty for the first time after June 30, 1985, had military pay reduced by $100 per month for the first 12 months, and continuously served for 3 years, or 2 years if that was their original enlistment, or 2 years if they entered Selected Reserve within a year of leaving active duty and served 4 years (the 2 by 4 program); 2) entered active duty before January 1, 1977, had remaining entitlement under the Vietnam Era GI Bill on December 31, 1989, served at least 1 day between October 19, 1984 and June 30, 1985, and stayed on active duty through June 30, 1988 (or June 30, 1987 if they entered Selected Reserve within 1 year of leaving active duty and served 4 years); 3) on active duty on September 30, 1990 and separated involuntarily after February 2, 1991, involuntarily separated on or after November 30, 1993, or voluntarily separated under either the Voluntary Separation Incentive (VSI) or Special Separation Benefit (SSB) program, and before separation had military pay reduced by $1,200; or 4) on active duty on October 9, 1996, had money remaining in an account from the Veterans Educational Assistance Program (VEAP), elected Montgomery GI Bill (MGIB) by October 9, 1997, and paid $1,200. Certain National Guard members may also qualify under category 4 if they served on full-time active duty between July 1, 1985 and November 28, 1989, elected MGIB between October 9, 1996 and July 8, 1997, and paid $1,200. Following completion of their service obligation, participants may enroll in colleges or universities for associate, bachelor, or graduate degrees; in courses leading to a certificate or diploma from business, technical, or vocational schools; for apprenticeships or on-the-job training programs; in correspondence courses; in flight training; for preparatory courses necessary for admission to a college or graduate school; for licensing and certification tests approved for veterans; or in state-approved teacher certification programs. Veterans who wish to enroll in certain high-cost technology programs (life science, physical science, engineering, mathematics, engineering and science technology, computer specialties, and engineering, science, and computer management) may be eligible for an accelerated payment.

Financial data For veterans in categories 1, 3, and 4 who served on active duty for 3 years or more, the current monthly stipend for college or university work is $1,473 for full-time study. For enlistees whose initial active-duty obligation was less than 3 years, the current monthly stipend for college or university work is $1,196. For veterans in category 2 with remaining eligibility, the current monthly stipend for institutional study full time is $1,661 for no dependents, $1,697 with 1 dependent, $1,728 with 2 dependents, and $16 for each additional dependent. Lower rates apply for less than full-time study, apprenticeships and on-the-job training, cooperative education, correspondence courses, and flight training.

Duration 36 months; active-duty servicemembers must utilize the funds within 10 years of leaving the armed services; Reservists may draw on their funds while still serving.

Additional information This was the basic VA education program, referred to as Chapter 30, until the passage of the Post-9/11 GI Bill in 2009. Veterans who have remaining benefits available from this program may utilize those or transfer them to the new program.

Number awarded Varies each year.

Deadline Deadline not specified.

[865]
NATIONAL GUARD ASSOCIATION OF SOUTH CAROLINA SCHOLARSHIPS

National Guard Association of South Carolina
Attn: NGASC Scholarship Foundation
132 Pickens Street
Columbia, SC 29205
(803) 254-8456   Toll Free: (800) 822-3235
Fax: (803) 254-3869   E-mail: nginfo@ngasc.org
Web: www.ngasc.org/?page_id=11

Summary To provide funding to current and former South Carolina National Guard members and their dependents who are interested in attending college or graduate school.

Eligibility This program is open to undergraduate students who are 1) current, retired, or deceased members of the South Carolina National Guard; 2) their dependents; and 3) members of the National Guard Association of South Carolina (NGASC). Graduate students are also eligible if they are members of the South Carolina National Guard. Applicants must be attending or interested in attending a college or university in any state as a full-time student. Several of the scholarships include additional restrictions on school or academic major; some are granted only for academic excellence, but most are based on both academics and financial need.

Financial data The stipend is $1,500 or $1,000.

Duration 1 year; may be renewed up to 3 additional years.

Number awarded Varies each year; recently, 42 of these scholarships were awarded: 1 at $1,500 and 41 at $1,000.

Deadline January of each year.

[866]
NATIONAL GUARD ASSOCIATION OF TEXAS SCHOLARSHIP PROGRAM

National Guard Association of Texas
Attn: NGAT Educational Foundation
3706 Crawford Avenue
Austin, TX 78731-6803
(512) 454-7300   Toll Free: (800) 252-NGAT
Fax: (512) 467-6803   E-mail: rlindner@ngat.org
Web: www.ngat.org

Summary To provide funding to members and dependents of members of the National Guard Association of Texas who are interested in attending college or graduate school.

Eligibility This program is open to annual and life members of the association and their spouses and children (associate members and their dependents are not eligible). Applicants may be high school seniors, undergraduate students, or graduate students, either enrolled or planning to enroll at an institution of higher education in any state. Along with their application, they must submit an essay on their desire to continue their education. Selection is based on scholarship, citizenship, and leadership.

Financial data Stipends range from $500 to $5,000.

Duration 1 year (nonrenewable).

Additional information This program includes 1 scholarship sponsored by USAA Insurance Corporation.

Number awarded Varies each year; recently, 13 of these scholarships were awarded: 1 at $5,000, 3 at $2,500, 1 at $2,000, 3 at $1,250, 4 at $1,000, and 1 at $500.

Deadline February of each year.

[867]
NAVAL RESEARCH LABORATORY BROAD AGENCY ANNOUNCEMENT

Naval Research Laboratory
Attn: Contracting Division
4555 Overlook Avenue, S.W.
Washington, DC 20375-5320
(202) 767-5227   Fax: (202) 767-0494
Web: heron.nrl.navy.mil/contracts/home.htm

Summary To provide funding to investigators (especially veterans) who are interested in conducting scientific research of interest to the U.S. Navy.

Eligibility This program is open to investigators qualified to perform research in designated scientific and technical areas. Topics cover a wide range of technical and scientific areas; recent programs included radar technology, information technology, optical sciences, tactical electronic warfare, materials science and component technology, chemistry, computational physics and fluid dynamics, plasma physics, electronics science and technology, biomolecular science and engineering, ocean and atmospheric science and technology, acoustics, remote sensing, oceanography, marine geosciences, marine meteorology, and space science. Proposals may be submitted by any non-governmental entity, including commercial firms, institutions of higher education with degree-granting programs in science or engineering, or by consortia led by such concerns. The Naval Research Laboratory (NRL) encourages participation by small businesses, small disadvantaged business concerns, women-owned small businesses, veteran-owned small businesses, service-disabled veteran-owned small businesses, HUBZone small businesses, Historically Black Colleges and Universities, and Minority Institutions. Selection is based on the degree to which new and creative solutions to technical issues important to NRL programs are proposed and the feasibility of the proposed approach and technical objectives; the offeror's ability to implement the proposed approach; the degree to which technical data and/or computer software developed under the proposed contract are to be delivered to the NRL with rights compatible with NRL research and development objectives; and proposed cost and cost realism.

Financial data The typical range of funding is from $100,000 to $2,000,000.

Duration 1 year.

Additional information The Naval Research Laboratory conducts most of its research in its own facilities in Washington, D.C., Stennis Space Center, Mississippi, and Monterey, California, but it also funds some related research.

Number awarded Varies each year.

Deadline Each program establishes its own application deadline; for a complete list of all the programs, including their deadlines, contact the NRL.

[868]
NCPOA/BART LONGO MEMORIAL SCHOLARSHIPS

National Chief Petty Officers' Association
c/o Marjorie Hays, Treasurer
1014 Ronald Drive
Corpus Christi, TX 78412-3548
Web: www.goatlocker.org/ncpoa/scholarship.htm

Summary To provide financial assistance for college or graduate school to members of the National Chief Petty Officers' Association (NCPOA) and their families.

Eligibility This program is open to members of the NCPOA and the children, stepchildren, and grandchildren of living or deceased members. Applicants may be high school seniors or graduates entering a college or university or students currently enrolled full time as undergraduate or graduate students. Selection is based on academic achievement and participation in extracurricular activities; need is not considered.

Financial data The stipend is $1,000.

Duration 1 year.

Additional information Membership in the NCPOA is limited to men and women who served or are serving as Chief Petty Officers in the U.S. Navy, U.S. Coast Guard, or their Reserve components for at least 30 days.

Number awarded 2 each year: 1 to a high school senior or graduate and 1 to an undergraduate or graduate student.

Deadline May of each year.

[869]
NEW MEXICO VIETNAM VETERAN SCHOLARSHIPS

New Mexico Department of Veterans' Services
Attn: Benefits Division
407 Galisteo Street, Room 142
P.O. Box 2324
Santa Fe, NM 87504-2324
(505) 827-6374   Toll Free: (866) 433-VETS
Fax: (505) 827-6372   E-mail: alan.martinez@state.nm.us
Web: www.dvs.state.nm.us/benefits.html

Summary To provide funding to Vietnam veterans in New Mexico who are interested in working on an undergraduate or master's degree at a public college in the state.

Eligibility This program is open to Vietnam veterans who have been residents of New Mexico for at least 10 years. Applicants must have been honorably discharged and have been awarded the Vietnam Service Medal or the Vietnam Campaign Medal. They must be planning to attend a state-supported college, university, or community college in New Mexico to work on an undergraduate or master's degree. Awards are granted on a first-come, first-served basis.

Financial data The scholarships provide full payment of tuition and purchase of required books at any state-funded postsecondary institution in New Mexico.

Duration 1 year.

Deadline Deadline not specified.

[870]
NEW YORK VETERANS TUITION AWARDS

New York State Higher Education Services Corporation
Attn: Student Information
99 Washington Avenue
Albany, NY 12255
(518) 473-1574   Toll Free: (888) NYS-HESC
Fax: (518) 473-3749   TDD: (800) 445-5234
E-mail: webmail@hesc.com
Web: www.hesc.com

Summary To provide tuition assistance to eligible veterans enrolled in a college or graduate school in New York.

Eligibility This program is open to veterans who served in the U.S. armed forces in 1) Indochina between February 28, 1961 and May 7, 1975; 2) hostilities that occurred after February 28, 1961 as evidenced by receipt of an Armed Forces Expeditionary Medal, Navy Expeditionary Medal, or Marine Corps Expeditionary Medal; 3) the Persian Gulf on or after August 2, 1990; or 4) Afghanistan on or after September 11, 2001. Applicants must have been discharged from the service under honorable conditions, must be a New York resident, must be a U.S. citizen or eligible noncitizen, must be enrolled full or part time at an undergraduate or graduate degree-granting institution in New York or in an approved vocational training program in the state, must be charged at least $200 tuition per year, and must apply for a New York Tuition Assistance Program (TAP) award.

Financial data For full-time study, the maximum stipend is tuition or $5,295, whichever is less. For part-time study, the stipend is based on the number of credits certified and the student's actual part-time tuition.

Duration For undergraduate study, up to 8 semesters, or up to 10 semesters for a program requiring 5 years for completion; for graduate study, up to 6 semesters; for vocational programs, up to 4 semesters. Award limits are based on full-time study or equivalent part-time study.

Additional information If a TAP award is also received, the combined academic year award cannot exceed tuition costs. If it does, the TAP award will be reduced accordingly.

Number awarded Varies each year.

Deadline April of each year.

[871]
NHA ACTIVE DUTY SCHOLARSHIPS

Naval Helicopter Association
Attn: Scholarship Fund
P.O. Box 180578
Coronado, CA 92178-0578
(619) 435-7139   Fax: (619) 435-7354
Web: nhascholarshipfund.org/scholarships-available.html

Summary To provide money for college or graduate school to active-duty and former personnel who are working or have worked in rotary wing activities of the sea services.

Eligibility This program is open to active-duty or former Navy, Marine Corps, or Coast Guard rotary wing aviators, aircrewmen, or support personnel. Applicants must be working on or planning to work on an undergraduate or graduate degree in any field. Along with their application, they must submit a personal statement on their academic and career aspirations. Selection is based on that statement, academic proficiency, scholastic achievements and awards, extracurricular activities, employment history, and recommendations.

Financial data   Stipends are approximately $2,000.

Duration   1 year.

Number awarded   4 each year: 2 to undergraduates and 2 to graduate students.

Deadline   February of each year.

[872]
PAT TILLMAN MILITARY SCHOLARS PROGRAM

Pat Tillman Foundation
2121 South Mill Avenue, Suite 214
Tempe, AZ 85282
(480) 621-4074   Fax: (480) 621-4075
E-mail: scholarships@pattillmanfoundation.org
Web: www.pattillmanfoundation.org/tillman-military-scholars

Summary   To provide financial assistance to veterans, active servicemembers, and their spouses who are interested in working on an undergraduate or graduate degree.

Eligibility   This program is open to veterans and active servicemembers of all branches of the armed forces from both the pre- and post-September 11 era and their spouses; children are not eligible. Applicants must be enrolled or planning to enroll full time at a 4-year public or private college or university to work on an undergraduate, graduate, or postgraduate degree. Current and former servicemembers must submit 400-word essays on 1) their motivation and decision to serve in the U.S. military and how that decision and experience has changed their life and ambitions; and 2) their educational and career goals, how they will incorporate their military service experience into those goals, and how they intend to continue their service to others and the community. Spouses must submit 400-word essays on 1) their previous service to others and the community; and 2) their educational and career goals, how they will incorporate their service experiences and the impact of their spouse's military service into those goals, and how they intend to continue their service to others and the community. Selection is based on those essays, educational and career ambitions, record of military service, record of personal achievement, demonstration of service to others in the community, desire to continue such service, and leadership potential.

Financial data   The stipend depends on the need of the recipient and the availability of funds.

Duration   1 year; may be renewed, provided the recipient maintains a GPA of 3.0 or higher, remains enrolled full time, and participates in civic action or community service.

Additional information   This program began in 2009.

Number awarded   Varies each year; recently, 60 students received a total of $916,000 through this program.

Deadline   March of each year.

[873]
PETER CONNACHER MEMORIAL SCHOLARSHIPS

Oregon Student Access Commission
Attn: Grants and Scholarships Division
1500 Valley River Drive, Suite 100
Eugene, OR 97401-2146
(541) 687-7395   Toll Free: (800) 452-8807, ext. 7395
Fax: (541) 687-7414   TDD: (800) 735-2900
E-mail: awardinfo@osac.state.or.us
Web: www.oregonstudentaid.gov/scholarships.aspx

Summary   To provide money for college or graduate school to ex-prisoners of war and their descendants.

Eligibility   Applicants must be U.S. citizens who 1) were military or civilian prisoners of war; or 2) are the descendants of ex-prisoners of war. They must be full-time undergraduate or graduate students. A copy of the ex-prisoner of war's discharge papers from the U.S. armed forces must accompany the application. In addition, written proof of POW status must be submitted, along with a statement of the relationship between the applicant and the ex-prisoner of war (father, grandfather, etc.). Selection is based on academic record and financial need. Preference is given to Oregon residents or their dependents.

Financial data   Stipends for scholarships offered by the Oregon Student Access Commission (OSAC) range from $200 to $10,000 but recently averaged $2,300.

Duration   1 year; may be renewed for up to 3 additional years for undergraduate students or 2 additional years for graduate students. Renewal is dependent on evidence of continued financial need and satisfactory academic progress.

Additional information   This program is administered by the OSAC with funds provided by the Oregon Community Foundation. Funds are also provided by the Columbia River Chapter of American Ex-prisoners of War, Inc.

Number awarded   Varies each year; recently, 4 of these scholarships were awarded.

Deadline   February of each year.

[874]
POST-9/11 GI BILL

Department of Veterans Affairs
Attn: Veterans Benefits Administration
810 Vermont Avenue, N.W.
Washington, DC 20420
(202) 418-4343   Toll Free: (888) GI-BILL1
Web: www.gibill.va.gov/benefits/post_911_gibill/index.html

Summary   To provide funding to veterans or military personnel who entered service on or after September 11, 2001.

Eligibility   This program is open to current and former military personnel who 1) served on active duty for at least 90 aggregate days after September 11, 2001; or 2) were discharged with a service-connected disability after 30 days. Applicants must be planning to enroll in an educational program, including work on an undergraduate or graduate degree, vocational/technical training, on-the-job training, flight training, correspondence training, licensing and national testing programs, and tutorial assistance.

Financial data   Participants working on an undergraduate or graduate degree at public institutions in their state receive full payment of tuition and fees. For participants who attend private institutions in most states, tuition and fee reimbursement is capped at $17,500 per academic year; the reimbursement rate is higher at private schools in Arizona, Michigan, New Hampshire, New York, Pennsylvania, South Carolina, and Texas. Benefits for other types of training programs depend on the amount for which the veteran qualified under prior educational programs. Veterans also receive a monthly housing allowance based on the national average Basic Allowance for Housing (BAH) for an E-5 with dependents (currently $673.50) or $1,347 per month at schools in foreign countries; an annual book allowance of $1,000; and (for participants who live in a rural county remote from an educational institution) a rural benefit payment of $500 per year.

Duration Most participants receive up to 36 months of entitlement under this program. Benefits are payable for up to 15 years following release from active duty.

Additional information This program, referred to as Chapter 33, began in 2009 as a replacement for previous educational programs for veterans and military personnel (e.g., Montgomery GI Bill, REAP). Current participants in those programs may be able to transfer benefits from those programs to this new plan. To qualify for 100% of Post 9/11-GI Bill benefits, transferees must have at least 36 months of active-duty service. Transferees with less service are entitled to smaller percentages of benefits, ranging down to 40% for those with only 90 days of service.

Number awarded Varies each year; since the program began, it has awarded nearly $4 billion in benefits to more than 295,000 veterans.

Deadline Deadline not specified.

[875]
ROBERT W. NOLAN SCHOLARSHIP

Fleet Reserve Association
Attn: FRA Education Foundation
125 North West Street
Alexandria, VA 22314-2754
(703) 683-1400   Toll Free: (800) FRA-1924
Fax: (703) 549-6610   E-mail: scholars@fra.org
Web: www.fra.org

Summary To provide financial assistance for graduate school to members of the Fleet Reserve Association (FRA) and their families.

Eligibility This program is open to members of the FRA and the dependent children, grandchildren, and spouses of living or deceased members. Applicants must be enrolled as full-time graduate students. Along with their application, they must submit an essay on why they want to go to college and what they intend to accomplish with their degree. Selection is based on academic record, financial need, extracurricular activities, leadership skills, and participation in community activities. U.S. citizenship is required.

Financial data The stipend is $5,000 per year.

Duration 1 year; may be renewed.

Additional information Membership in the FRA is restricted to active-duty, retired, and Reserve members of the Navy, Marine Corps, and Coast Guard. This program was established in 2001.

Number awarded 1 each year.

Deadline April of each year.

[876]
RUTH LANG FITZGERALD MEMORIAL SCHOLARSHIP

Massachusetts Association of Registered Nurses
P.O. Box 285
Milton, MA 02186
(617) 990-2856   Toll Free: (866) MARN-ANA
E-mail: info@marnonline.org
Web: www.marnonline.org

Summary To provide funding to members of the Massachusetts Association of Registered Nurses (MARN), particularly those with ties to the military, who are interested in working on a special project or attending a conference.

Eligibility This program is open to registered nurses who have been members of MARN for at least 1 year. Applicants must be interested in pursuing an area of interest or special project that will be beneficial to them and/or the association. The award may be used to attend an educational conference, the American Nurses Association convention, or some other educational activity. It may also be used to participate in a humanitarian aid project. Preference is given to applicants who have current or prior military service, work or hope to work with a senior population, or have an interest in legislative issues.

Financial data The grant is $1,000.

Duration 1 year; nonrenewable.

Number awarded 1 each year.

Deadline October of each year.

[877]
SCHUYLER S. PYLE SCHOLARSHIP

Fleet Reserve Association
Attn: FRA Education Foundation
125 North West Street
Alexandria, VA 22314-2754
(703) 683-1400   Toll Free: (800) FRA-1924
Fax: (703) 549-6610   E-mail: scholars@fra.org
Web: www.fra.org

Summary To provide financial assistance for college or graduate school to members of the Fleet Reserve Association (FRA) and their families.

Eligibility This program is open to members of the FRA and the dependent children, grandchildren, and spouses of living or deceased members. Applicants must be enrolled as full-time undergraduate or graduate students. Along with their application, they must submit an essay on why they want to go to college and what they intend to accomplish with their degree. Selection is based on academic record, financial need, extracurricular activities, leadership skills, and participation in community activities. U.S. citizenship is required.

Financial data The stipend is $5,000 per year.

Duration 1 year; may be renewed.

Additional information Membership in the FRA is restricted to active-duty, retired, and Reserve members of the Navy, Marine Corps, and Coast Guard.

Number awarded 1 each year.

Deadline April of each year.

[878]
SCOTT DOMINGUEZ-CRATERS OF THE MOON CHAPTER SCHOLARSHIP

American Society of Safety Engineers
Attn: ASSE Foundation
1800 East Oakton Street
Des Plaines, IL 60018
(847) 768-3435   Fax: (847) 768-3434
E-mail: agabanski@asse.org
Web: www.asse.org

Summary To provide financial assistance to undergraduate and graduate student members of the American Society of Safety Engineers (ASSE), particularly those with ties to the military, who are from designated western states.

Eligibility This program is open to ASSE members who are working on an undergraduate or graduate degree in occupational safety, health, and environment or a closely-related field (e.g., industrial or environmental engineering, environmental science, industrial hygiene, occupational health nursing). First priority is given to residents within the service area of Craters of the Moon Chapter in Idaho; second priority is given to residents of other states in ASSE Region II (Arizona, Colorado, Montana, Nevada, New Mexico, Utah, and Wyoming). Special consideration is also given to 1) employees of a sponsoring organization or their dependents; 2) students who are serving their country through active duty in the armed forces or are honorably discharged; 3) former members of the Boy Scouts, Girl Scouts, FFA, or 4-H; 4) recipients of awards from service organizations; and 5) students who have provided volunteer service to an ASSE chapter in a leadership role. Undergraduates must have completed at least 60 semester hours with a GPA of 3.0 or higher. Graduate students must have completed at least 9 semester hours with a GPA of 3.5 or higher and have had a GPA of 3.0 or higher as an undergraduate. Full-time students must be ASSE student members; part-time students must be ASSE general or professional members. Along with their application, they must submit 2 essays of 300 words or less: 1) why they are seeking a degree in occupational safety and health or a closely-related field, a brief description of their current activities, and how those relate to their career goals and objectives; and 2) why they should be awarded this scholarship (including career goals and financial need). U.S. citizenship is not required.

Financial data The stipend is $1,000 per year.

Duration 1 year; recipients may reapply.

Additional information This program is sponsored by the ASSE Craters of the Moon Chapter.

Number awarded 1 each year.

Deadline November of each year.

[879]
STUDENT VETERANS OF AMERICA-ILLINOIS PATRIOT EDUCATION FUND

Student Veterans of America
P.O. Box 77673
Washington, DC 20013
E-mail: SVA@studentveterans.org
Web: www.studentveterans.org/?page=Programs

Summary To provide financial assistance to veterans from Illinois who are working on a bachelor's or graduate degree at a college or university in the state.

Eligibility This program is open to student veterans who are working on an undergraduate or graduate degree at a college or university in Illinois. Applicants must have a strong Illinois connection (e.g., lived in the state prior to service). Selection is based on academic achievement, participation in Student Veterans of America (SVA), community involvement, and a personal essay.

Financial data The stipend is $1,000.

Duration 1 year.

Additional information These program, first awarded in 2012, is supported by the Illinois Patriot Education Fund (IPEF).

Number awarded Varies each year; recently 7 of these scholarships were awarded.

Deadline January of each year.

[880]
SUPPLEMENTS TO PROMOTE REENTRY INTO BIOMEDICAL AND BEHAVIORAL RESEARCH CAREERS

National Institutes of Health
Attn: Office of Research on Women's Health
6707 Democracy Boulevard, Suite 400
Bethesda, MD 20892-5484
(301) 402-1770   Fax: (301) 402-1798
TDD: (301) 451-5936
E-mail: ODORWH-research@mail.nih.gov
Web: grants.nih.gov/grants/guide/index.html

Summary To provide research grants to support individuals with high potential who wish to reenter an active research career after taking time off for military service or other activities.

Eligibility Principal investigators on various research awards from the National Institutes of Health (NIH) may submit a request for an administrative supplement to support an eligible candidate interested in reestablishing a research career. The parent grant must have at least 2 years of support remaining. Candidates must have a doctoral degree (M.D., D.D.S., Ph.D., O.D., D.V.M., or equivalent) and sufficient prior research experience to qualify for a doctoral-level research staff or faculty position. In general, they must have undergone a career interruption for at least 1 but no more than 8 years. Examples of qualifying career interruptions include child rearing; an incapacitating illness or injury of the candidate, spouse, partner, or member of the immediate family; relocation to accommodate a spouse, partner, or other family member; pursuit of non-research endeavors that would permit earlier retirement of debt incurred in obtaining a doctoral degree; and military service. Candidates who have begun the reentry process through a fellowship, traineeship, or similar mechanism are not eligible. The program is not intended to support additional graduate training or career changes from non-research to research careers. Only U.S. citizens, nationals, and permanent residents are eligible.

Financial data The proposed salary and fringe benefits for the candidate must be in accordance with the salary structure of the grantee institution, consistent with the level of effort. Up to $10,000 may be requested for supplies, domestic travel, and publication costs relevant to the proposed research.

Duration Up to 3 years.

Additional information Supplements provided under this program may be for either part-time or full-time support for the candidate; all supported time is to be spent updating and enhancing research skills. Awards under this program are available from all NIH agencies. The names and addresses of staff people at each agency are available from the NIH.

Number awarded Varies each year.

Deadline Applications may be submitted at any time.

[881]
UTAH TUITION WAIVER FOR PURPLE HEART RECIPIENTS

Utah Department of Veteran's Affairs
Attn: Director
550 Foothill Boulevard, Room 202
Salt Lake City, UT 84108
(801) 326-2372   Toll Free: (800) 894-9497 (within UT)
Fax: (801) 326-2369   E-mail: veterans@utah.gov
Web: veterans.utah.gov/homepage/stateBenefits/index.html

Summary To provide a tuition waiver to veterans in Utah who received a Purple Heart award and are interested in working on an undergraduate or graduate degree at a public institution in the state.

Eligibility This program is open to residents of Utah who received a Purple Heart award as a result of military service. Applicants must be working on an undergraduate or master's degree at a public college or university in the state.

Financial data Tuition at the rate for residents of the state is waived for qualified veterans.

Duration Tuition is waived until completion of a bachelor's or master's degree.

Number awarded Varies each year.

Deadline Deadline not specified.

[882]
VETERANS EDUCATIONAL ASSISTANCE PROGRAM (VEAP)

Department of Veterans Affairs
Attn: Veterans Benefits Administration
810 Vermont Avenue, N.W.
Washington, DC 20420
(202) 418-4343   Toll Free: (888) GI-BILL1
Web: www.gibill.va.gov/benefits/other_programs/veap.html

Summary To provide financial assistance for college or graduate school to veterans who first entered active duty between January 1, 1977 and June 30, 1985.

Eligibility Veterans who served and military servicemembers currently serving are eligible if they 1) entered active duty between January 1, 1977 and June 30, 1985; 2) were released under conditions other than dishonorable or continue on active duty; 3) served for a continuous period of 181 days or more (or were discharged earlier for a service-connected disability); and 4) have satisfactorily contributed to the program. No individuals on active duty could enroll in this program after March 31, 1987. Veterans who enlisted for the first time after September 7, 1980 or entered active duty as an officer or enlistee after October 16, 1981 must have completed 24 continuous months of active duty. Benefits are available for the pursuit of an associate, bachelor, or graduate degree at a college or university; a certificate or diploma from a business, technical, or vocational school; apprenticeship or on-the-job training programs; cooperative courses; correspondence school courses; tutorial assistance; remedial, refresher, and deficiency training; flight training; study abroad programs leading to a college degree; nontraditional training away from school; and work-study for students enrolled at least three-quarter time.

Financial data Participants contribute to the program, through monthly deductions from their military pay, from $25 to $100 monthly, up to a maximum of $2,700. They may also, while on active duty, make a lump sum contribution to the training fund. When the participant elects to use the benefits for an approved course of education or training, the Department of Veterans Affairs (VA) will match the contribution at the rate of $2 for every $1 made by the participant.

Duration Participants receive monthly payments for the number of months they contributed or for 36 months, whichever is less. The amount of the payments is determined by dividing the number of months benefits will be paid into the participant's training fund total. Participants have 10 years from the date of last discharge or release from active duty within which to use these benefits.

Additional information A participant may leave this program at the end of any 12-consecutive-month period of participation and those who do so may have their contributions refunded.

Number awarded Varies each year.

Deadline Applications may be submitted at any time.

[883]
VOCATIONAL REHABILITATION AND EMPLOYMENT VETSUCCESS PROGRAM

Department of Veterans Affairs
Attn: Veterans Benefits Administration
Vocational Rehabilitation and Employment Service
810 Vermont Avenue, N.W.
Washington, DC 20420
(202) 418-4343   Toll Free: (800) 827-1000
Web: www.vba.va.gov/bin/vre/index.htm

Summary To provide funding to veterans with service-connected disabilities who need assistance to find employment or, if seriously disabled, to live independently.

Eligibility This program is open to veterans who have a service-connected disability of at least 10% or a memorandum rating of 20% or more from the Department of Veterans Affairs (VA). They must qualify for services provided by the VA VetSuccess that include assistance finding and keeping a job, including the use of special employer incentives and job accommodations; on-the-job training, apprenticeships, and non-paid work experiences; postsecondary training at a college, vocational, technical, or business school; supportive rehabilitation services such as case management, counseling, and medical referrals; independent living services for veterans unable to work due to the severity of their disabilities.

Financial data While in training and for 2 months after, eligible disabled veterans may receive subsistence allowances in addition to their disability compensation or retirement pay. Generally, the current full-time monthly rate is $566.97 with no dependents, $703.28 with 1 dependent, $828.76 with 2 dependents, and $60.41 for each additional dependent; proportional rates apply for less than full-time training.

Duration Veterans remain eligible for these services up to 12 years from either the date of separation from active military service or the date the veteran was first notified by VA of a service-connected disability rating (whichever came later).

Number awarded Varies each year.

Deadline Applications are accepted at any time.

[884]
WISCONSIN G.I. BILL TUITION REMISSION PROGRAM

Wisconsin Department of Veterans Affairs
201 West Washington Avenue
P.O. Box 7843
Madison, WI 53707-7843
(608) 266-1311   Toll Free: (800) WIS-VETS
Fax: (608) 267-0403   E-mail: WDVAInfo@dva.state.wi.us
Web: www.dva.state.wi.us/Ben_education.asp

Summary To provide financial assistance for college or graduate school to Wisconsin veterans and their dependents.

Eligibility This program is open to current residents of Wisconsin who 1) were residents of the state when they entered or reentered active duty in the U.S. armed forces, or 2) have moved to the state and have been residents for any consecutive 12-month period after entry or reentry into service. Applicants must have served on active duty for at least 2 continuous years or for at least 90 days during specified wartime periods. Also eligible are 1) qualifying children and unremarried surviving spouses of Wisconsin veterans who died in the line of duty or as the direct result of a service-connected disability; and 2) children and spouses of Wisconsin veterans who have a service-connected disability rated by the U.S. Department of Veterans Affairs as 30% or greater. Children must be between 17 and 25 years of age (regardless of the date of the veteran's death or initial disability rating) and be a Wisconsin resident for tuition purposes. Spouses remain eligible for 10 years following the date of the veteran's death or initial disability rating; they must be Wisconsin residents for tuition purposes but they may enroll full or part time. Students may attend any institution, center, or school within the University of Wisconsin (UW) System or the Wisconsin Technical College System (WCTS). There are no income limits, delimiting periods following military service during which the benefit must be used, or limits on the level of study (e.g., vocational, undergraduate, professional, or graduate).

Financial data Veterans who qualify as a Wisconsin resident for tuition purposes are eligible for a remission of 100% of standard academic fees and segregated fees at a UW campus or 100% of program and material fees at a WCTS institution. Veterans who qualify as a Wisconsin veteran for purposes of this program but for other reasons fail to meet the definition of a Wisconsin resident for tuition purposes at the UW system are eligible for a remission of 100% of non-resident fees. Spouses and children of deceased or disabled veterans are entitled to a remission of 100% of tuition and fees at a UW or WCTS institution.

Duration Up to 8 semesters or 128 credits, whichever is greater.

Additional information This program was established in 2005 as a replacement for Wisconsin Tuition and Fee Reimbursement Grants.

Number awarded Varies each year.

Deadline Applications must be submitted within 14 days from the office start of the academic term: in October for fall, March for spring, or June for summer.

[885]
WISCONSIN JOB RETRAINING GRANTS

Wisconsin Department of Veterans Affairs
201 West Washington Avenue
P.O. Box 7843
Madison, WI 53707-7843
(608) 266-1311   Toll Free: (800) WIS-VETS
Fax: (608) 267-0403   E-mail: WDVAInfo@dva.state.wi.us
Web: www.dva.state.wi.us/Ben_retraininggrants.asp

Summary To provide funds to recently unemployed Wisconsin veterans or their families who need financial assistance while being retrained for employment.

Eligibility This program is open to current residents of Wisconsin who 1) were residents of the state when they entered or reentered active duty in the U.S. armed forces, or 2) have moved to the state and have been residents for any consecutive 12-month period after entry or reentry into service. Applicants must have served on active duty for at least 2 continuous years or for at least 90 days during specified wartime periods. Unremarried spouses and minor or dependent children of deceased veterans who would have been eligible for the grant if they were living today may also be eligible. The applicant must, within the year prior to the date of application, have become unemployed (involuntarily laid off or discharged, not due to willful misconduct) or underemployed (experienced an involuntary reduction of income). Underemployed applicants must have current annual income from employment that does not exceed federal poverty guidelines (currently $14,521 for a family of 1, rising to $50,557 for a family of 8). All applicants must be retraining at accredited schools in Wisconsin or in a structured on-the-job program. Course work toward a college degree does not qualify. Training does not have to be full time, but the program must be completed within 2 years and must reasonably be expected to lead to employment.

Financial data The maximum grant is $3,000 per year; the actual amount varies, depending upon the amount of the applicant's unmet need. In addition to books, fees, and tuition, the funds may be used for living expenses.

Duration 1 year; may be renewed 1 additional year.

Number awarded Varies each year.

Deadline Applications may be submitted at any time.

[886]
WOMEN MARINES ASSOCIATION SCHOLARSHIP PROGRAM

Women Marines Association
P.O. Box 377
Oaks, PA 19456-0377
Toll Free: (888) 525-1943
E-mail: scholarship@womenmarines.org
Web: www.womenmarines.org/scholarships.aspx

Summary To provide money for college or graduate school to students with ties to the military who are sponsored by members of the Women Marines Association (WMA).

Eligibility Applicants must be sponsored by a WMA member and fall into 1 of the following categories: 1) have served or are serving in the U.S. Marine Corps, regular or Reserve; 2) are a direct descendant by blood or legal adoption or a stepchild of a Marine on active duty or who has served honorably in the U.S. Marine Corps, regular or Reserve; 3) are a sibling or a descendant of a sibling by blood or legal adoption or a stepchild of a Marine on active duty or who has served honorably in the U.S. Marine Corps, regular or Reserve; or 4) have completed 2 years in a Marine Corps JROTC program. WMA members may sponsor an unlimited number of applicants per year. High school seniors must submit transcripts (GPA of 3.0 or higher) and SAT or ACT scores. Undergraduate and graduate students must have a GPA of 3.0 or higher.

Financial data The stipend is $1,500 per year.

Duration 1 year; may be renewed 1 additional year.

Additional information This program includes the following named scholarships: the WMA Memorial Scholarships, the Lily H. Gridley Memorial Scholarship, the Ethyl and Armin Wiebke Memorial Scholarship, the Maj. Megan Malia McClung Memorial Scholarship, the Agnes Sopcak Memorial Scholarship, the Virginia Guveyan Memorial Scholarship, and the LaRue A. Ditmore Music Scholarships. Applicants must know a WMA member to serve as their sponsor; the WMA will not supply listings of the names or addresses of chapters or individual members.

Number awarded Varies each year.

Deadline January of each year.

[887]
YELLOW RIBBON PROGRAM OF THE POST-9/11 GI BILL

Department of Veterans Affairs
Attn: Veterans Benefits Administration
810 Vermont Avenue, N.W.
Washington, DC 20420
(202) 418-4343   Toll Free: (888) GI-BILL1
Web: www.gibill.va.gov

Summary To provide financial assistance to veterans and their dependents who qualify for the Post-9/11 GI Bill and wish to attend a high cost private or out-of-state college or graduate school.

Eligibility Maximum Post-9/11 GI Bill benefits are available to veterans who 1) served on active duty for at least 36 aggregate months after September 11, 2001; or 2) were honorably discharged for a service-connected disability and served at least 30 continuous days after September 11, 2001. Military personnel currently on active duty and their spouses may qualify for Post-9/11 GI Bill benefits but are not eligible for the Yellow Ribbon Program. This program is available to veterans who qualify for those benefits at the 100% rate, the children of those veterans to whom they wish to transfer their benefits, and the children and spouses of active-duty personnel who qualify for benefits at the 100% rate to whom they wish to transfer those benefits. Applicants must be working on or planning to work on an undergraduate or graduate degree at a private or out-of-state public institution that charges tuition in excess of the $17,500 cap imposed by the Post-9/11 GI Bill and that has agreed with the Department of Veterans Affairs (VA) to participate in this program.

Financial data Colleges and universities that charge more than $17,500 per academic year in tuition and fees (or a higher amount at schools in Arizona, Michigan, New Hampshire, New York, Pennsylvania, South Carolina, and Texas) agree to waive tuition (up to 50%) for qualifying veterans and dependents. The amount that the college or university waives is matched by VA.

Duration Most participants receive up to 36 months of entitlement under this program. Benefits are payable for up to 15 years following release from active duty.

Number awarded Varies each year.

Deadline Deadline not specified.

Military Personnel

[888]
AIR FORCE FINANCIAL ASSISTANCE PROGRAM

U.S. Air Force
Attn: Air Force Institute of Technology
2950 P Street, Building 642
Wright-Patterson AFB, OH 45433-7765
(937) 255-5824, ext. 3036   Toll Free: (800) 588-5260
Fax: (937) 656-7156   E-mail: afit.cimj3@afit.edu
Web: www.airforce.com

Summary To provide financial assistance to future Air Force officers who are currently participating in a medical or dental residency.

Eligibility This program is open to U.S. citizens who are currently at any point in residency training in a medical or dental specialty that meets the needs of the U.S. Air Force. Upon acceptance into the program, applicants are commissioned as officers in the U.S. Air Force Reserve; after completion of school, they must perform active-duty service as a doctor or dentist in the Air Force.

Financial data This program pays an annual grant of more than $45,000 and a stipend of $2,088 per month.

Additional information Participants must spend 14 days each year in an Active Duty Tour (ADT) assignment. Medical doctors incur an active-duty obligation of 1 year for each year of support plus 1 additional year. Dentists incur an active-duty obligation of 1 year for each year of support, with a minimum of 3 years.

Number awarded Varies each year.

Deadline Applications may be submitted at any time.

[889]
AIR FORCE HEALTH PROFESSIONS SCHOLARSHIP PROGRAM

U.S. Air Force
Attn: Air Force Institute of Technology
2950 P Street, Building 642
Wright-Patterson AFB, OH 45433-7765
(937) 255-5824, ext. 3036   Toll Free: (800) 588-5260
Fax: (937) 656-7156   E-mail: afit.cimj3@afit.edu
Web: www.airforce.com

Summary To provide financial assistance for education in a medical or scientific field to future Air Force medical officers.

Eligibility This program is open to U.S. citizens who are accepted to or already enrolled in a health care professional program. They must be working on a degree that will prepare them for service in Air Force Biomedical Science Corps specialties (pharmacists, optometrists, clinical psychologists, or public health officers), Nurse Corps specialties, Medical Corps, or Dental Corps. Upon acceptance into the program, applicants are commissioned as officers in the U.S. Air Force; after completion of medical school, they must perform at least 3 years of active-duty service in the U.S. Air Force.

Financial data This program pays full tuition at any school of medicine or osteopathy located in the United States or Puerto Rico, and it also covers the cost of fees, books, and other required equipment. In addition, recipients are awarded a stipend of $2,088 per month for 10 1/2 months of the year; for the other 1 1/2 months of each year, they perform active-duty service, usually at an Air Force medical facility, and receive the normal pay of a Second Lieutenant.

Duration 1 or 2 years for Biomedical Service Corps specialties, 2 or 3 years for Nurse Corps specialties, 3 or 4 years for Medical Corps or Dental Corps.

Additional information Following receipt of the degree, students serve an internship and residency either in an Air Force hospital (in which case they receive Air Force active-duty pay) or, if not selected for Air Force graduate medical education, in a civilian hospital (where they receive only the regular salary paid by the civilian institution). Only after completion of the residency, in either an Air Force or a civilian hospital, do the students begin the active-duty service obligation. That obligation is equal to the number of years of support received plus 1 year.

Number awarded Approximately 325 each year.

Deadline Deadline not specified.

[890]
AIR FORCE JUDGE ADVOCATE GENERAL'S DEPARTMENT FUNDED LEGAL EDUCATION PROGRAM

U.S. Air Force
Attn: HQ USAF/JAX
112 Luke Street, Suite 104
Bolling AFB, DC 20032-6400
Toll Free: (800) JAG-USAF
E-mail: afsana.ahmed@pentagon.af.mil
Web: www.jagusaf.hq.af.mil

Summary To provide financial assistance to Air Force officers interested in attending law school.

Eligibility This program is open to commissioned officers in the U.S. Air Force who have at least 2 but no more than 6 years of active-duty military service (including both enlisted and commissioned time) and have graduated from an accredited college or university with a bachelor's degree. Applicants must be currently in the pay grade of O-3 or below. They must submit transcripts from undergraduate (and/or graduate) schools, their LSAT results, and proof of an application or acceptance to an ABA-accredited law school.

Financial data Selectees continue to receive their regular pay and allowances during participation in this program. They also receive payment of tuition (to a maximum of $12,000 per year) and a book allowance.

Duration Until completion of a law degree.

Additional information Selectees are required to perform legal internships each summer they are in law school. Following completion of law school and passage of a bar examination, they enter service as an Air Force judge advocate with an active-duty obligation of 2 years for each year of legal training supported by this program.

Number awarded Varies each year; recently, 8 officers received support from this program.

Deadline February of each year.

[891]
AIR FORCE ONE-YEAR COLLEGE PROGRAM (OYCP)

U.S. Air Force
Attn: HQ USAF/JAX
112 Luke Street, Suite 104
Bolling AFB, DC 20032-6400
Toll Free: (800) JAG-USAF
E-mail: afsana.ahmed@pentagon.af.mil
Web: www.jagusaf.hq.af.mil

Summary To provide financial assistance to law students who are willing to join Air Force ROTC and serve as Air Force Judge Advocates following completion of their studies.

Eligibility This program is open to students in their second year at an ABA-approved law school that has, or is located near, an AFROTC detachment. Applicants must be in good academic standing and able to meet AFROTC entry standards (U.S. citizenship, weight and medical qualifications, and Air Force Officer Qualification Test minimum score). They must be younger than 35 years of age upon commissioning and entering active duty. Selection is based on academic performance, extracurricular activities, community service, prior military record (if any), work experience, and a recommendation by a staff judge advocate following an interview.

Financial data Participants receive a stipend for 10 months of the year at $450 per month if they qualify for the third year of AFROTC or $500 per month if they qualify for the fourth year of AFROTC and a salary at pay grade E-5 during summer field training. No other scholarship assistance is available.

Duration 1 year.

Additional information Selectees with no prior military experience attend field training encampment during the summer prior to entering the AFROTC program as contract cadets. Upon completion of their degree and legal licensing requirements, participants enter active duty as first lieutenants in the U.S. Air Force Judge Advocate General's Department. After 6 months of active duty, they are promoted to captain. The initial required active-duty service obligation is 4 years.

Number awarded Varies each year.

Deadline January of each year.

[892]
AIR FORCE RESERVE TUITION ASSISTANCE

U.S. Air Force Reserve
Attn: Air Reserve Personnel Center
Directorate of Personnel Services
6760 East Irvington Place
Denver, CO 80280-4000
(303) 676-7037   Toll Free: (800) 525-0102
Fax: (478) 327-2215
E-mail: arpc.contactcenter@arpc.denver.af.mil
Web: www.arpc.afrc.af.mil

Summary To provide financial assistance for college or graduate school to members of the Air Force Reserve.

Eligibility This program is open to Air Force Reserve members interested in working on an undergraduate or graduate degree either through distance learning or on-campus courses from an accredited postsecondary institution. Applicants must be actively participating (for pay and points) and in good standing (not have a UIF, not placed on a control roster, not pending or issued an Article 15, and/or not pending court martial). They must submit a degree plan specifying all classes for which they are seeking assistance. Enlisted students must have retainability that extends beyond the last course approved for assistance or they must extend or re-enlist; commissioned officers must have a mandatory separation date of not less than 24 months of service commitment starting at the end of the last course completed.

Financial data Undergraduates receive 100% of tuition, to a maximum of $250 per semester hour or $4,500 per year; graduate students receive 75% of tuition, to a maximum of $250 per semester hour or $4,500 per year.

Duration 1 year; may be renewed.

Number awarded Varies each year.

Deadline Applications may be submitted at any time.

[893]
AIR FORCE ROTC GRADUATE LAW PROGRAM

U.S. Air Force
Attn: Headquarters AFROTC/RRUC
551 East Maxwell Boulevard
Maxwell AFB, AL 36112-5917
(334) 953-2091   Toll Free: (866) 4-AFROTC
Fax: (334) 953-6167   E-mail: afrotc1@maxwell.af.mil
Web: afrotc.com

Summary To provide financial assistance for law school to veterans, military personnel, and others who are interested in joining Air Force ROTC and are willing to serve as Air Force officers following completion of their professional degree.

Eligibility Applicants must be U.S. citizens who are currently enrolled in the first year of law school at a college or university with an Air Force ROTC unit on campus or a college with a cross-enrollment agreement with such a school. They may be veterans, current military personnel, or first-year law students without military experience. The law school must be accredited by the American Bar Association. Applicants must agree to serve for at least 4 years as active-duty Air Force officers following graduation from law school. Selection is based on academic performance, extracurricular activities, work experience, community service, military record (if appropriate), and recommendations.

Financial data Students are paid during summer field training and also receive a tax-free stipend of $450 per month during the second year of law school or $500 per month during the third year of law school. No other scholarship assistance is provided.

Duration 2 years.

Additional information Participants attend a field training encampment (4 weeks for students with prior military service, 5 weeks for students with no prior military experience) during the summer between their first and second year of law school. They then complete the normal academic requirements for the 2-year AFROTC program while completing law school. After graduation, participants enter active duty as a first lieutenant (with promotion after 6 months).

Deadline March of each year.

[894]
AIR FORCE ROTC PROFESSIONAL OFFICER CORPS INCENTIVE

U.S. Air Force
Attn: Headquarters AFROTC/RRUC
551 East Maxwell Boulevard
Maxwell AFB, AL 36112-5917
(334) 953-2091   Toll Free: (866) 4-AFROTC
Fax: (334) 953-6167   E-mail: afrotc1@maxwell.af.mil
Web: afrotc.com/learn-about/programs-and-scholarships

Summary To provide financial assistance for undergraduate and graduate studies to individuals who have completed 2 years of college and who are willing to join Air Force ROTC and serve as Air Force officers following completion of their degree.

Eligibility Applicants must be U.S. citizens who have completed 2 years of the general military course at a college or university with an Air Force ROTC unit on campus or a college with a cross-enrollment agreement with such a college. They must be full-time students, have a GPA of 2.0 or higher both cumulatively and for the prior term, be enrolled in both Aerospace Studies class and Leadership Laboratory, pass the Air Force Officer Qualifying Test, meet Air Force physical fitness and weight requirements, and be able to be commissioned before they become 31 years of age. They must agree to serve for at least 4 years as active-duty Air Force officers following graduation from college with either a bachelor's or graduate degree.

Financial data This scholarship provides a monthly subsistence allowance of $450 as a junior or $500 as a senior.

Duration Until completion of a graduate degree.

Additional information Scholarship recipients must complete 4 years of aerospace studies courses at 1 of the 144 colleges and universities that have an Air Force ROTC unit on campus; students may also attend 984 other colleges that have cross-enrollment agreements with the institutions that have an Air Force ROTC unit on campus. Recipients must also attend a 4-week summer training camp at an Air Force base between their junior and senior year.

Number awarded Varies each year.

Deadline Deadline not specified.

[895]
AIR FORCE SERVICES CLUB MEMBERSHIP SCHOLARSHIP PROGRAM

Air Force Services Agency
Attn: HQ AFSVA/SVOFT
10100 Reunion Place, Suite 501
San Antonio, TX 78216-4138
(210) 395-7787
E-mail: web.clubs-operations@randolph.af.mil
Web: www.afclubs.net/CN_Scholarship.htm

Summary To recognize and reward, with academic scholarships, Air Force Club members and their families who submit outstanding essays.

Eligibility This program is open to Air Force Club members and their spouses, children, and stepchildren who have been accepted by or are enrolled at an accredited college or university. Grandchildren are eligible if they are the dependent of a club member. Applicants may be undergraduate or graduate students enrolled full or part time. They must submit an essay of up to 500 words on a topic that changes annually; a recent topic was "My Contribution to the Air Force." Applicants must also include a 1-page summary of their long-term career and life goals and previous accomplishments, including civic, athletic, and academic awards.

Financial data Awards are $1,000 scholarships.

Duration The competition is held annually.

Additional information This competition, first held in 1997, is sponsored by Chase Bank and the Coca-Cola Company.

Number awarded 25 each year.

Deadline Entries must be submitted to the member's base services commander or division chief by June of each year.

[896]
AIR FORCE TUITION ASSISTANCE PROGRAM

U.S. Air Force
Attn: Air Force Personnel Center
Headquarters USAF/DPPAT
550 C Street West, Suite 10
Randolph AFB, TX 78150-4712
Fax: (210) 565-2328
Web: www.airforce.com

Summary To provide financial assistance for college or graduate school to active-duty Air Force personnel.

Eligibility Eligible to apply for this program are active-duty Air Force personnel who have completed 2 years of their service obligation.

Financial data Air Force personnel chosen for participation in this program continue to receive their regular Air Force pay. The Air Force will pay 100% of the tuition costs in an approved program, to a maximum of $4,500 per year or $250 per semester hour, whichever is less.

Duration Up to 4 years.

Additional information Applications and further information about this program are available from counselors at the education centers on Air Force bases. Most Air Force personnel who receive tuition assistance participate in the Community College of the Air Force; there, participants earn a 2-year associate degree by combining on-the-job technical training or attendance at Air Force schools with enrollment in college courses at a civilian institution during off-duty hours. In addition, each Air Force base offers at least 4 subject areas in which selected Air Force personnel can receive tuition assistance for study leading to a bachelor's degree, and 2 disciplines in which they can pursue graduate study.

Number awarded Varies each year.

Deadline Deadline not specified.

[897]
AL PONTE SCHOLARSHIP AWARD

Association of Former Intelligence Officers
Attn: Scholarships Committee
6723 Whittier Avenue, Suite 200
McLean, VA 22101-4533
(703) 790-0320   Fax: (703) 991-1278
E-mail: afio@afio.com
Web: www.afio.com/13_scholarships.htm

Summary To provide financial assistance to members or the children or grandchildren of members of the Association of Former Intelligence Officers (AFIO) who are interested in working on a graduate degree in international relations and/or intelligence.

Eligibility This program is open to college seniors who are interested in attending graduate school to work on a degree in international relations and/or intelligence. Applicants must be AFIO members, the children or grandchildren of members, or the children or grandchildren of personnel currently serving in military intelligence. Selection is based on merit, character, estimated future potential, background, and relevance of their studies to the full spectrum of national security interests and career ambitions. U.S. citizenship is required.

Financial data The stipend is $1,000.

Duration 1 year.

Number awarded 1 each year.

Deadline June of each year.

[898]
ALABAMA NATIONAL GUARD EDUCATIONAL ASSISTANCE PROGRAM

Alabama Commission on Higher Education
Attn: Grants Coordinator
100 North Union Street
P.O. Box 302000
Montgomery, AL 36130-2000
(334) 242-2273   Fax: (334) 242-0268
E-mail: cheryl.newton@ache.alabama.gov
Web: www.ache.alabama.gov/StudentAsst/Programs.htm

Summary To provide financial assistance to members of the Alabama National Guard interested in attending college or graduate school in the state.

Eligibility This program is open to Alabama residents who are enrolled in an associate, baccalaureate, master's, or doctoral program at a public college, university, community college, technical college, or junior college in the state; are making satisfactory academic progress as determined by the eligible institution; and are members in good standing of the Alabama National Guard who have completed basic training and advanced individual training. Applicants may be receiving federal veterans benefits, but they must show a cost less aid amount of at least $25.

Financial data Scholarships cover tuition, educational fees, books, and supplies, up to a maximum of $1,000 per year. All Alabama Student Grant program proceeds for which the student is eligible are deducted from this award.

Duration Up to 12 years after the date of the first grant payment to the student through this program.

Number awarded Varies each year; awards are determined on a first-in, first-out basis as long as funds are available.

Deadline July of each year.

[899]
ALASKA NATIONAL GUARD STATE TUITION REIMBURSEMENT PROGRAM

Alaska National Guard
Attn: Education Services Officer
P.O. Box 5800
Fort Richardson, AK 99505-5800
(907) 428-6477   Fax: (907) 428-6929
E-mail: ngmneducation@ng.army.mil
Web: www.akguard.com

Summary To provide financial assistance to current and former members of the Alaska National Guard who wish to work on a bachelor's or master's degree in the state.

Eligibility This program is open to members of the Alaska National Guard (Air and Army) and Naval Militia who have a rating of E-1 through O-5, including warrant officers, and are attending a university program in Alaska. Eligibility extends to members who 1) have satisfactorily completed their service contract and who served honorably in federal active service or federally-funded state active service after September 11, 2001; or 2) have been separated or discharged from the Guard because of a service-connected injury, disease, or disability. First priority is given to undergraduates; if funding is available, students working on a second bachelor's degree or a master's degree may be supported. Non-prior servicemembers must complete Initial Active Duty for Training (IADT); prior servicemembers are eligible immediately.

Financial data Recipients are entitled to reimbursement equivalent to 100% of the cost of tuition and fees at the University of Alaska, to a maximum of $7,500 per fiscal year.

Duration 1 semester; may be renewed for a total of 144 semester credits.

Number awarded Varies each year.

Deadline Applications may be submitted at any time, but they must be received at least 90 days after the last official day of the class or term.

[900]
ANCA SCHOLARSHIPS

Army Nurse Corps Association
Attn: Education Committee
P.O. Box 39235
San Antonio, TX 78218-1235
(210) 650-3534   Fax: (210) 650-3494
E-mail: education@e-anca.org
Web: e-anca.org/ANCAEduc.htm

Summary To provide financial assistance to students who have a connection to the Army and are interested in working on an undergraduate or graduate degree in nursing.

Eligibility This program is open to U.S. citizens attending colleges or universities that have accredited programs offering associate, bachelor's, master's, or doctoral degrees in nursing. Applicants must be 1) nursing or anesthesia students who plan to enter a component of the U.S. Army and are not participating in a program funded by a component of the U.S. Army; 2) nursing or anesthesia students who have previously served in a component of the U.S. Army; 3) Army Nurse Corps officers enrolled in an undergraduate or graduate nursing program not funded by a component of the U.S. Army; 4) enlisted soldiers in a component of the U.S. Army who are working on a baccalaureate degree in nursing not funded by a component of the U.S. Army; or 5) nursing or anesthesia students whose parent(s), spouse, and/or children are serving or have served in a component of the U.S. Army. Along with their application, they must submit a personal statement on their professional career objectives, reasons for applying for this scholarship, financial need, special considerations, personal and academic interests, and why they are preparing for a nursing career.

Financial data The stipend is $3,000. Funds are sent directly to the recipient's school.

Duration 1 year.

Additional information Although the sponsoring organization is open to officers of the Army Nurse Corps, it does not have an official affiliation with the Army. Therefore, students who receive these scholarships do not incur any military service obligation.

Number awarded 1 or more each year.

Deadline March of each year.

[901]
ARMED FORCES HEALTH PROFESSIONS SCHOLARSHIPS

U.S. Navy
Attn: Navy Medicine Professional Development Center Code OH
8901 Wisconsin Avenue, Building 1, 13th Floor, Room 13132
Bethesda, MD 20889-5611
(301) 295-1217   Toll Free: (800) USA-NAVY
Fax: (301) 295-1811   E-mail: OH@med.navy.mil
Web: www.med.navy.mil

Summary To provide financial assistance for education in a medical field to future Navy medical officers.

Eligibility Applicants for this assistance must be U.S. citizens, under 36 years of age, who are enrolled in or accepted at an accredited medical, osteopathic, physician assistant, dental, or optometry school located in the United States or Puerto Rico. Upon acceptance into the program, applicants are commissioned as officers in the U.S. Navy Medical Corps Reserve; after completion of medical school, they must perform at least 3 years of active-duty service in the U.S. Navy.

Financial data This program pays full tuition at any school of medicine, osteopathy, dentistry, or optometry or a course leading to a master's degree as a physician assistant located in the United States or Puerto Rico, and also covers the cost of fees, books, and required equipment. In addition, recipients are awarded a stipend of $2,088 per month for 10 1/2 months of the year; for the other 1 1/2 months of each year, they perform active-duty service, usually at a Navy medical facility, and receive the normal pay of an Ensign.

Duration Assistance under this program continues until the student completes work for a doctorate degree in medicine, osteopathy, dentistry, or optometry or a master's degree as a physician assistant.

Additional information Following receipt of the doctorate degree, recipients serve an internship and residency either in a naval hospital (in which case they receive Navy active-duty pay) or, if not selected for naval graduate medical education, in a civilian hospital (where they receive only the regular salary of the civilian institution). After completion of the residency, the students must begin the active-duty service obligation. That obligation is 1 year for each year of participation in the program, with a minimum service obligation of 3 years.

Number awarded Varies each year.

Deadline August of each year.

[902]
ARMY ADVANCED CIVIL SCHOOLING PROGRAM

U.S. Army
Human Resources Command
Attn: OPCF ACS Program
1500 Spearhead Division Avenue
Fort Knox, KY 40122-5408
Toll Free: (888) ARMY-HRC
E-mail: acs2125@conus.army.mil
Web: myarmybenefits.us.army.mil/Home.html

Summary To provide financial assistance to Army officers interested in working on an advanced degree in selected fields.

Eligibility This program is open to Army officers who wish to work on an advanced degree at an approved civilian institution on a full-time basis. Applicants must have a regular Army commission or a United States Army Reserve (USAR) commission with Voluntary Indefinite Status (VI). They must have completed a bachelor's degree with a GPA of 2.5 or higher and must have a GMAT score of 500 or higher or a GRE score of 500 or higher in the quantitative and verbal categories plus a 4.0 or higher in the analytical category.

Financial data The officer continues to receive regular Army salary and allowances. The fellowship pays tuition up to $14,500 per year, a 1-time payment of $600 for application fees, and a book allotment of $200 per year.

Duration 12 to 22 months, depending on the program.

Additional information Participants in this program incur an additional service obligation of 3 days of service for each day of educational leave. Further information and applications are available from the applicant's assignment officer.

Number awarded Approximately 412 each year.

Deadline September of each year.

[903]
ARMY AVIATION ASSOCIATION OF AMERICA SCHOLARSHIPS

Army Aviation Association of America Scholarship
  Foundation
Attn: AAAA Scholarship Foundation
755 Main Street, Suite 4D
Monroe, CT 06468-2830
(203) 268-2450   Fax: (203) 268-5870
E-mail: aaaa@quad-a.org
Web: www.quad-a.org

Summary To provide financial aid for undergraduate or graduate study to members of the Army Aviation Association of America and their relatives.

Eligibility This program is open to association members (or deceased members) and their spouses, unmarried siblings, unmarried children, and unmarried grandchildren. Applicants must be enrolled or accepted for enrollment as an undergraduate or graduate student at an accredited college or university. Graduate students must include a 250-word essay on their life experiences, work history, and aspirations. Some scholarships are specifically reserved for enlisted, warrant officer, company grade, and Department of the Army civilian members. Selection is based on academic merit and personal achievement.

Financial data Stipends range up to $3,000 per year.

Duration Scholarships may be for 1, 2, or 4 years.

Number awarded Varies each year; recently, $309,500 in scholarships was awarded to 209 students. Since the program began in 1963, the foundation has awarded more than $4.1 million to nearly 2,500 qualified applicants.

Deadline April of each year.

[904]
ARMY HEALTH PROFESSIONS SCHOLARSHIP PROGRAM

U.S. Army
Human Resources Command, Health Services Division
Attn: AHRC-OPH-AN
1500 Spearhead Division Avenue
Fort Knox, KY 40122-5408
Toll Free: (888) ARMY-HRC
E-mail: askhrc@conus.army.mil
Web: www.goarmy.com/amedd/education/hpsp.html

Summary To provide financial assistance to future Army officers who are interested in preparing for a career in medically-related fields.

Eligibility This program is open to U.S. citizens under 35 years of age. Applicants must be enrolled in or accepted as a full-time student at an accredited professional school located in the United States or Puerto Rico in 1 of the following areas: allopathic or osteopathic medicine, dentistry, clinical or counseling psychology, optometry, veterinary science, or psychiatric nurse practitioner. Upon acceptance into the program, applicants are commissioned as officers in the U.S. Army Reserve; after completion of school, they must perform active-duty service in the U.S. Army Medical Corps, Dental Corps, Medical Service Corps (for clinical psychology and optometry), Nurse Corps, or Veterinary Corps.

Financial data This program pays full tuition at any school or college granting a doctoral or other relevant professional degree located in the United States or Puerto Rico and covers the cost of fees, books, and other required equipment. Recipients are also awarded a stipend of $2,088 per month for 10 1/2 months of the year. During the other 1 1/2 months of each year, they perform active-duty service, usually at an Army medical facility, and receive the normal pay of a Second Lieutenant.

Duration 1 to 4 years for the medical program; 1 to 4 years for the dental program; 2 or 3 years for the clinical or counseling psychology program; 2 to 4 years for the optometry program; and 1 to 3 years for the veterinary program.

Additional information Participants incur an active-duty obligation based on existing Department of Defense and Army Directives in effect at the time they sign their contract accepting support through this program. Recently, the obligation has been 1 year for each year of support and a minimum of 2 years for the medical program or 3 years for the dental, clinical or counseling psychology, optometry, or veterinary programs.

Number awarded Varies each year.

Deadline Applications may be submitted at any time.

[905]
ARMY JUDGE ADVOCATE GENERAL CORPS FUNDED LEGAL EDUCATION PROGRAM

U.S. Army
Attn: Office of the Judge Advocate General
DAJA-PT
2200 Army Pentagon, Room 2B517
Washington, DC 20310
(703) 588-6774   Toll Free: (866) ARMY-JAG
Fax: (703) 588-0100 E-mail: Yvonne.Caron@us.army.mil
Web: www.jagcnet.army.mil/law.goarmy.com

Summary To provide financial assistance to Army officers interested in obtaining a law degree.

Eligibility This program is open to commissioned active-duty Army officers who have graduated from an accredited college or university with a baccalaureate (or equivalent) degree. Applicants must have completed at least 2 but not more than 6 years of active duty (including warrant officer and enlisted service) and currently hold a rank of O-1 through O-3. They must be interested in attending a regular course of instruction leading to a J.D. or LL.B. degree at an approved civilian law school. U.S. citizenship is required. Selection is based on the "total person concept," including an evaluation of undergraduate and graduate school transcripts, LSAT score, ORB, OERs, SJA interview letter, and statement of motivation to attend law school.

Financial data While participating in this program, officers continue to receive their regular Army salary. The program also covers tuition, fees, and all other educational costs.

Duration 3 years.

Additional information Participants normally are expected to attend a state-supported law school where they qualify for in-state tuition or where military members are granted in-state tuition rates. Following completion of their law degree and admission to the bar, they incur a 2-year active-duty service obligation as an attorney in the Judge Advocate General's Corps (JAGC) for each academic year spent in law school. If they fail to pass the bar examination or are not assigned to the JAGC for any other reason, they are returned to their basic branch of assignment for completion of their service obligation. If they refuse to accept appointment in or assignment to the JAGC, they are returned to their basic branch of assignment for completion of their service obligation; they must also reimburse the government for all costs of their advanced education.

Number awarded The program is authorized to support up to 25 officers each year but normally selects only 15.

Deadline October of each year.

[906]
ARMY MEDICAL AND DENTAL SCHOOL STIPEND PROGRAM (MDSSP)

U.S. Army
Human Resources Command, Health Services Division
Attn: AHRC-OPH-AN
1500 Spearhead Division Avenue
Fort Knox, KY 40122-5408
Toll Free: (888) ARMY-HRC
E-mail: askhrc@conus.army.mil
Web: www.goarmy.com

Summary To provide financial assistance to students in designated medically-related fields who are interested in serving in the U.S. Army Reserve after graduation.

Eligibility This program is open to U.S. citizens under 35 years of age. Applicants must be enrolled in or accepted as a full-time student at an accredited professional school located in the United States or Puerto Rico in 1 of the following areas: allopathic or osteopathic medicine, dentistry, psychology (doctoral level only), optometry, or psychiatric nurse practitioner. Upon acceptance into the program, applicants are commissioned as officers in the U.S. Army Reserve; after completion of school, they must train as part of an Army Reserve unit and serve when needed.

Financial data This program pays a stipend of $2,088 per month.

Duration Until completion of a degree.

Additional information Participants incur an obligation to serve 1 year in the Selected Reserve for each 6 months of support received, including 12 days of annual training or active duty for training.

Number awarded Varies each year.

Deadline Applications may be submitted at any time.

[907]
ARMY MEDICAL DEPARTMENT FINANCIAL ASSISTANCE PROGRAM

U.S. Army
Human Resources Command, Health Services Division
Attn: AHRC-OPH-AN
1500 Spearhead Division Avenue
Fort Knox, KY 40122-5408
Toll Free: (888) ARMY-HRC
E-mail: askhrc@conus.army.mil
Web: www.goarmy.com

Summary To provide financial assistance to future Army officers who are currently participating in a medical or dental residency.

Eligibility This program is open to U.S. citizens who are currently at any point in residency training as a medical resident, oral surgeon, endodontist, periodontist, pedodontist, or orthodontist. Medical doctors must possess a permanent unrestricted license to practice medicine in the United States, the District of Columbia, Puerto Rico, or a U.S. territory. Upon acceptance into the program, applicants are commissioned as officers in the U.S. Army Reserve; after completion of training, they must perform active-duty service in the U.S. Army Medical Corps or Dental Corps.

Financial data This program pays an annual grant of more than $45,000 and a stipend of $2,088 per month.

Additional information Participants also spend 14 days each year in an Active-Duty-For-Training (ADFT) assignment. Medical doctors incur an active-duty obligation of 1 year for each year of support plus 1 additional year. Dentists incur an active-duty obligation of 1 year for each year of support and a minimum of 3 years.

Number awarded Varies each year.

Deadline Applications may be submitted at any time.

[908]
ARMY NATIONAL GUARD TUITION ASSISTANCE

U.S. Army National Guard
c/o DANTES
6490 Saufley Field Road
Pensacola, FL 32509-5243
(850) 452-1085   Fax: (850) 452-1161
E-mail: tahelp@voled.doded.mil
Web: www.nationalguard.com/benefits/money-for-college

Summary To provide financial assistance for college or graduate school to members of the Army National Guard in each state.

Eligibility This program is open to members of the Army National Guard in every state who are interested in attending a college, community college, or university within the state. Applicants must have sufficient time to complete the course before their Expiration Time of Service (ETS) date. They must be interested in working on a high school diploma or equivalent (GED), certificate, associate degree, bachelor's degree, master's degree, or first professional degree, including those in architecture, Certified Public Accountant (C.P.A.), podiatry, dentistry (D.D.S. or D.M.D.), medicine (M.D.), optometry, osteopathic medicine, pharmacy (Pharm.D.), or theology (M.Div. or M.H.L.). Commissioned officers must agree to remain in the Guard for at least 4 years following completion of the course for which assistance is provided, unless they are involuntarily separated from the service.

Financial data Assistance provides up to 100% of tuition (to a maximum of $250 per semester hour or $4,500 per person per fiscal year).

Duration Participants in Officer Candidate School (OCS), Warrant Officer Candidate School (WOCS), and ROTC Simultaneous Membership Program (SMP) may enroll in up to 15 semester hours per year until completion of a baccalaureate degree. Warrant Officers are funded to complete an associate degree.

Additional information Tuition assistance may be used along with federal Pell Grants but not with Montgomery GI Bill benefits. State tuition assistance programs can be used concurrently with this program, but not to exceed 100% of tuition costs.

Number awarded Varies each year; recently, more than 22,000 Guard members received tuition assistance.

Deadline Deadline not specified.

[909]
ARMY RESERVE TUITION ASSISTANCE

U.S. Army Reserve
Attn: Director, USAR Education
ARPC-PS
1 Reserve Way
St. Louis, MO 63132-5200
Toll Free: (800) 452-0201
Web: www.goarmy.com/reserve/benefits/education.html

Summary To provide financial assistance for college or graduate school to specified members of the U.S. Army Reserve (USAR).

Eligibility This program is open to USAR soldiers in the following categories: TPU, JRU, IMA, ROTC Simultaneous Membership Program Cadets (non-scholarship holders), and Chaplain Candidates. Members of the Active Guard Reserve (AGR) are covered by Regular Army tuition assistance and are not eligible for this program. Soldiers who have been flagged for weight control or because of the results of their Army Physical Fitness Test (APFT) are still eligible, but soldiers who have been flagged for adverse actions cannot receive this assistance. Applicants must be working on their first credential at the diploma, certificate associate, baccalaureate, or graduate level. Commissioned officers must agree to participate actively for 4 years in the Selected Reserve from the date of completion of the course for which tuition assistance is provided. Enlisted soldiers must certify that sufficient time remains within their Time In Service (TIS) to complete the course before their Expiration Term of Service (ETS).

Financial data Assistance is provided at the rate of $250 per credit hour, to a maximum of $4,500 per fiscal year.

Duration 1 year; may be renewed.

Number awarded Varies each year.

Deadline Applications may be submitted at any time.

[910]
ARMY SPECIALIZED TRAINING ASSISTANCE PROGRAM (STRAP)

U.S. Army
Human Resources Command, Health Services Division
Attn: AHRC-OPH-AN
1500 Spearhead Division Avenue
Fort Knox, KY 40122-5408
Toll Free: (888) ARMY-HRC
E-mail: askhrc@conus.army.mil
Web: www.goarmy.com/amedd/education.html

Summary To provide funding to members of the United States Army Reserve (USAR) or Army National Guard (ARNG) who are engaged in additional training in designated health care fields that are considered critical for wartime medical needs.

Eligibility This program is open to members of the USAR or ARNG who are currently 1) medical residents (in orthopedic surgery, family practice, emergency medicine, general surgery, obstetrics/gynecology, or internal medicine); 2) dental residents (in oral surgery, prosthodontics, or comprehensive dentistry); 3) nursing students working on a master's degree in critical care or nurse anesthesia; or 4) associate degree or diploma nurses working on a bachelor's degree. Applicants must agree to a service obligation of 1 year for every 6 months of support received.

Financial data This program pays a stipend of $2,088 per month.

Additional information During their obligated period of service, participants must attend Extended Combat Training (ECT) at least 12 days each year and complete the Officer Basic Leadership Course (OBLC) within the first year.

Number awarded Varies each year.

Deadline Applications may be submitted at any time.

[911]
ARMY TUITION ASSISTANCE BENEFITS

U.S. Army
Human Resources Command
AHRC-PDE-EI
Attn: Education Incentives and Counseling Branch
1500 Spearhead Division Avenue
Fort Knox, KY 40122-5408
Toll Free: (888) ARMY-HRC
E-mail: askhrc@conus.army.mil
Web: www.goarmyed.com

Summary To provide financial assistance to Army personnel interested in working on an undergraduate or graduate degree.

Eligibility This program is open to active-duty Army personnel, including members of the Army National Guard and Army Reserve on active duty. Applicants must first visit an education counselor to declare an educational goal and establish an educational plan. They may enroll in up to 15 semester hours of academic courses.

Financial data Those selected for participation in this program receive their regular Army pay and 100% of tuition at the postsecondary educational institution of their choice, but capped at $4,500 per year or $250 per semester hour, whichever is less.

Duration Until completion of a bachelor's or graduate degree.

Additional information This program is part of the Army Continuing Education System (ACES). Further information is available from counselors at the education centers at all Army installations with a troop strength of 750 or more.

Number awarded Varies each year.

Deadline Deadline not specified.

[912]
ASMC MEMBERS' CONTINUING EDUCATION PROGRAM AWARD

American Society of Military Comptrollers
Attn: National Awards Committee
415 North Alfred Street
Alexandria, VA 22314
(703) 549-0360   Toll Free: (800) 462-5637
Fax: (703) 549-3181   E-mail: lloyd@asmconline.org
Web: awards.asmconline.org

Summary To provide financial assistance for continuing education to members of the American Society of Military Comptrollers (ASMC).

Eligibility Applicants for this assistance must have been members of the society for at least 2 full years and must have been active in the local chapter at some level (e.g., board member, committee chair or member, volunteer for chapter events), They must be enrolled or planning to enroll at an academic institution in a field of study directly related to military comptrollership, including business administration, economics, public administration, accounting, or finance. Selection is based on individual merit.

Financial data Stipends are $3,000 or $1,500.

Duration 1 year.

Additional information The ASMC is open to all financial management professionals employed by the U.S. Department of Defense and Coast Guard, both civilian and military. The applicant whose service to the society is judged the most exceptional is designated the Dick Vincent Scholarship winner.

Number awarded 11 each year: 1 at $3,000 (the Dick Vincent Scholarship) and 10 at $1,500.

Deadline March of each year.

[913]
BG BENJAMIN B. TALLEY SCHOLARSHIP

Society of American Military Engineers-Anchorage Post
Attn: BG B.B. Talley Scholarship Endowment Fund
P.O. Box 6409
Anchorage, AK 99506-6409
(907) 244-8063   E-mail: cturletes@gci.net
Web: www.sameanchorage.org/h_about/scholinfo.html

Summary To provide financial assistance to student members of the Society of American Military Engineers (SAME) from Alaska who are working on a bachelor's or master's degree in designated fields of engineering or the natural sciences.

Eligibility This program is open to members of the Anchorage Post of SAME who are residents of Alaska, attending college in Alaska, an active-duty military member stationed in Alaska, or a dependent of an active-duty military member stationed in Alaska. Applicants must be 1) sophomores, juniors, or seniors majoring in engineering, architecture, construction or project management, natural sciences, physical sciences, applied sciences, or mathematics at an accredited college or university; or 2) students working on a master's degree in those fields. They must have a GPA of 2.5 or higher. U.S. citizenship is required. Along with their application, they must submit an essay of 250 to 500 words on their career goals. Selection is based on that essay, academic achievement, participation in school and community activities, and work/family activities; financial need is not considered.

Financial data Stipends range up to $3,000.

Duration 1 year.

Additional information This program began in 1997.

Number awarded Varies each year; at least 1 scholarship is reserved for a master's degree students.

Deadline December of each year.

[914]
CALIFORNIA NATIONAL GUARD EDUCATION ASSISTANCE AWARD PROGRAM

Office of the Adjutant General
Joint Force Headquarters
Attn: Katrina Beck
9800 Goethe Road, Box 37
Sacramento, CA 95826
(916) 854-4255   Fax: (916) 854-3739
E-mail: Katrina.beck2@us.army.mil
Web: www.calguard.ca.gov/education/Pages/default.aspx

Summary To provide financial assistance to members of the California National Guard who are interested in attending college or graduate school in the state.

Eligibility This program is open to residents of California who have served at least 2 years as active members of the California National Guard, the State Military Reserve, or the Naval Militia. Applicants must be planning to attend a college, university, community college, or vocational/technical institute in the state to obtain a certificate, degree (associate, bachelor's, master's, or doctoral) or diploma that they do not currently hold. They must agree to remain an active member of the Guard, Reserve, or Militia as long as they participate in the program.

Financial data The maximum stipends are equal to those provided by Cal Grants A and B; recently, those were $12,192 at branches of the University of California, $9,708 at nonpublic institutions, $5,472 at branches of the California State University system, or $1,551 at community colleges. Graduate students receive an additional stipend of $500 for books and supplies.

Duration 1 year; may be renewed, provided the recipient maintains a GPA of 2.0 or higher.

Additional information This program operates in partnership with the California Student Aid Commission.

Number awarded Up to 1,000 each year.

Deadline The priority deadline for new applications is June of each year.

[915]
CAPTAIN JODI CALLAHAN MEMORIAL GRADUATE SCHOLARSHIP

Air Force Association
Attn: Manager, National Aerospace Awards
1501 Lee Highway
Arlington, VA 22209-1198
(703) 247-5800, ext. 4807
Toll Free: (800) 727-3337, ext. 4807
Fax: (703) 247-5853   E-mail: lcross@afa.org
Web: www.afa.org/aef/aid/callahan.asp

Summary   To provide financial assistance for graduate education to Air Force personnel who are members of the Air Force Association.

Eligibility   This program is open to active-duty Air Force members and full-time Guard and Reserve personnel (officer or enlisted) who are also members of the association. Applicants must be working on a master's degree in a nontechnical field during off-duty time and have a GPA of 3.0 or higher. Along with their application, they must submit a 2-page essay describing their academic goals and how they expect their degree to enhance their service to the Air Force.

Financial data   The stipend is $1,000. Funds may be used for any reasonable expenses related to working on a degree, including tuition, lab fees, and books.

Duration   1 year; nonrenewable.

Number awarded   2 each year.

Deadline   June of each year.

[916]
CAPTAIN SEAN P. GRIMES PHYSICIAN ASSISTANT EDUCATIONAL SCHOLARSHIP AWARD

Society of Army Physician Assistants
c/o Harold Slusher
6762 Candlewood Drive
P.O. Box 07490
Fort Myers, FL 33919
(239) 482-2162   Fax: (239) 482-2162
E-mail: hal.shusher@juno.com
Web: www.sapa.org/SeanScholarshipPage.htm

Summary   To provide funding to current and former Army personnel interested in training as a physician assistant.

Eligibility   This program is open to Army veterans, Army active-duty soldiers, Army National Guard soldiers, and Army Reservists. Soldiers may be of any enlisted or officer rank from E-5 through O-4. Applicants may be seeking initial training as a physician assistant or current physician assistants working on a baccalaureate, master's, or doctoral degree. They must have a GPA of 2.5 or higher. Candidates for initial training must be enrolled in an ARC-PA approved program. Other candidates must be enrolled at an accredited college or university. Financial need is considered.

Financial data   The stipend is $6,000.

Duration   1 year.

Additional information   This program began in 2006.

Number awarded   1 each year.

Deadline   January of each year.

[917]
COAST GUARD TUITION ASSISTANCE PROGRAM

U.S. Coast Guard Institute
Attn: Commanding Officer
5900 S.W. 64th Street, Room 233
Oklahoma City, OK 73169-6990
(405) 954-1360   Fax: (405) 954-7245
E-mail: CGI-PF-Tuition_Assistance@uscg.mil
Web: www.uscg.mil

Summary   To provide financial assistance to members and employees of the Coast Guard who are interested in pursuing additional education during their off-duty hours.

Eligibility   This program is open to Coast Guard members who are interested in pursuing additional education at the high school, vocational/technical, undergraduate, graduate, or professional level. Civilian employees with at least 90 days of Coast Guard service and Selected Reservists are also eligible. Enlisted members must have at least 12 months remaining on their active-duty contracts or Selected Reserve obligation after completion of the course. Active-duty officers must agree to fulfill a 2-year service obligation following completion of the course; officers of the selected reserve must agree to fulfill a 4-year service obligation following completion of the course. Civilian employees must agree to retain employment with the Coast Guard for 1 month for each completed course credit hour. For military personnel, the command education services officer (ESO) must certify that the course of instruction is Coast Guard mission or career related. The supervisor of civilian employees must certify that the education is career related. All courses must be related to the mission of the Coast Guard or the individual's career or professional development.

Financial data   Active-duty, Reserve, and civilian Coast Guard members receive full payment of all expenses for completion of a high school degree or equivalent. For college courses (vocational/technical, undergraduate, and graduate), 100% of the cost of tuition is reimbursed, to a maximum of $250 per semester hour or $4,500 per fiscal year.

Duration   Until completion of a bachelor's or graduate degree.

Additional information   Graduate students must earn a grade of "B" or higher to receive reimbursement; undergraduates must earn a grade of "D" or higher.

Number awarded   Varies each year; recently, more than 10,000 Coast Guard active-duty members, Reservists, and civilian employees received tuition assistance worth approximately $14.5 million.

Deadline   Applications may be submitted at any time.

[918]
COLONEL JERRY W. ROSS SCHOLARSHIP

American Pharmacists Association
Attn: APhA Foundation
2215 Constitution Avenue, N.W.
Washington, DC 20037-2985
(202) 429-7565   Toll Free: (800) 237-APhA
Fax: (202) 783-2351   E-mail: info@aphafoundation.org
Web: www.pharmacist.com

Summary   To provide financial assistance for work on a degree in pharmacy to Air Force pharmacy technicians who are members of the Academy of Student Pharmacists of the

American Pharmacists Association (APhA-ASP) and their families.

Eligibility This program is open to full-time pharmacy students who are either 1) Air Force pharmacy technicians working on a degree in pharmacy, or 2) family members of an Air Force pharmacist or technician who is enrolled in an accredited college of pharmacy. Applicants must have been actively involved in their school's APhA-ASP chapter. They must have completed at least 1 year in the professional sequence of courses with a GPA of 2.75 or higher. Along with their application, they must submit a 500-word essay on a topic that changes annually but relates to the future of the pharmacy profession, 2 letters of recommendation, a current resume or curriculum vitae, and a list of pharmacy and non-pharmacy related activities. Preference is given to applicants who indicate further Air Force service.

Financial data The stipend is $1,000.

Duration 1 year; recipients may reapply.

Number awarded 1 each year.

Deadline November of each year.

[919]
COLORADO NATIONAL GUARD STATE TUITION ASSISTANCE

Department of Military and Veterans Affairs
Attn: CODAG-TA
6848 South Revere Parkway
Centennial, CO 80112-6703
(720) 250-1550   Fax: (720) 250-1559
E-mail: tuition@dmva.state.co.us
Web: www.dmva.state.co.us/page/ta

Summary To provide financial assistance for college or graduate school to members of the Colorado National Guard.

Eligibility This program is open to members of the Colorado National Guard who have completed at least 6 months of military service and are currently in drilling status. Applicants must be enrolled or planning to enroll at a public institution of higher education in Colorado to work on an associate, bachelor's, or master's degree.

Financial data This program provides payment of up to 100% of the in-state tuition at public institutions in Colorado.

Duration 1 semester; may be renewed as long as the recipient remains an active member of the Guard and maintains a GPA of 2.0 or higher. Assistance is limited to a total of 132 semester hours.

Additional information Recipients must serve 1 year in the Guard for each semester or quarter of assistance received.

Number awarded Varies each year.

Deadline June of each year for the fall semester; November of each year for the spring semester; April of each year for the summer term.

[920]
CONNECTICUT TUITION WAIVER FOR VETERANS

Connecticut Office of Financial and Academic Affairs for Higher Education
Attn: Student Financial Aid
61 Woodland Street
Hartford, CT 06105-2326
(860) 947-1855   Toll Free: (800) 842-0229 (within CT)
Fax: (860) 947-1311   E-mail: sfa@ctdhe.org
Web: www.ctohe.org/SFA/default.htm

Summary To provide money for college or graduate school to certain Connecticut veterans and military personnel or their dependents.

Eligibility This program is open to 1) honorably-discharged Connecticut veterans who served at least 90 days during specified periods of wartime; 2) active members of the Connecticut Army and Air National Guard; 3) Connecticut residents who are a dependent child or surviving spouse of a member of the armed forces killed in action on or after September 11, 2001 who was also a Connecticut resident; and 4) Connecticut residents who are dependent children of a person officially declared missing in action or a prisoner of war while serving in the armed forces after January 1, 1960. Applicants must be attending or planning to attend a public college or university in the state.

Financial data The program provides a waiver of 100% of tuition for students working on an undergraduate or graduate degree at the University of Connecticut, 100% of tuition for general fund courses at campuses of Connecticut State University, 50% of tuition for extension and summer courses at campuses of Connecticut State University, 100% of tuition at all Connecticut community colleges, and 50% or fees at Charter Oak State College.

Duration Up to 4 years.

Additional information This is an entitlement program; applications are available from the respective college financial aid offices.

Number awarded Varies each year.

Deadline Deadline not specified.

[921]
CSC DEFENSE GRADUATE SCHOLARSHIP

Armed Forces Communications and Electronics Association
Attn: AFCEA Educational Foundation
4400 Fair Lakes Court
Fairfax, VA 22033-3899
(703) 631-6138   Toll Free: (800) 336-4583, ext. 6138
Fax: (703) 631-4693 E-mail: scholarshipsinfo@afcea.org
Web: www.afcea.org

Summary To provide financial assistance to young professionals working on a graduate degree in designated scientific and engineering fields.

Eligibility This program is open to young professionals (35 years of age or younger) already employed in a field related to communications, computer science, or electronics. Applicants must be currently enrolled at an accredited college or university in the United States and committed to working on an advanced college degree (M.S. or Ph.D.) relating to communications, computer science, electronics engineering, electrical engineering, or systems engineering. They must have a GPA of 3.2 or higher and be preparing for a career in science or engineering. U.S. citizenship is required.

Financial data The stipend is $3,000.

Duration 1 year; may be renewed.

Additional information This program is sponsored by CSC Defense Group.

Number awarded 2 each year.

Deadline April of each year.

[922]
CSM ROBERT W. ELKEY AWARD

Army Engineer Association
Attn: Executive Director
P.O. Box 30260
Alexandria, VA 22310-8260
(703) 428-7084   Fax: (703) 428-6043
E-mail: xd@armyengineer.com
Web: www.armyengineer.com/scholarships.htm

Summary To provide financial assistance for college or graduate school to enlisted members of the Army Engineer Association (AEA).

Eligibility This program is open to AEA members serving in an active, Reserve, or National Guard component Army Engineer unit, school, or organization within the Corps of Engineers of the United States Army. Applicants must be enlisted personnel (PVT, PFC, SPC, CPL, SGT, or SSG). They must be working on or planning to work on an associate, bachelor's, or master's degree at an accredited college or university. Selection is based primarily on financial need, although potential for academic success and standards of conduct as supported by personal references are also considered.

Financial data The stipend is $1,000.

Duration 1 year.

Number awarded 3 each year.

Deadline June of each year.

[923]
DEDICATED ARMY NATIONAL GUARD SCHOLARSHIPS

U.S. Army National Guard
c/o DANTES
6490 Saufley Field Road
Pensacola, FL 32509-5243
(850) 452-1085   Fax: (850) 452-1161
Web: www.nationalguard.com

Summary To provide financial assistance to college and graduate students who are interested in enrolling in Army ROTC and serving in the Army National Guard following graduation.

Eligibility This program is open to full-time students entering their sophomore or junior year of college with a GPA of 2.5 or higher. High school seniors are also eligible if they plan to attend a military junior college (MJC), have a GPA of 2.5 or higher, and have scores of at least 19 on the ACT or 920 on the combined mathematics and critical reading SAT. Graduate students may also be eligible if they have only 2 years remaining for completion of their degree. Students who have been awarded an ROTC campus-based scholarship may apply to convert to this program during their freshman year. Applicants must meet all medical and moral character requirements for enrollment in Army ROTC. They must be

willing to enroll in the Simultaneous Membership Program (SMP) of an ROTC unit on their campus; the SMP requires simultaneous membership in Army ROTC and the Army National Guard.

Financial data Participants receive full reimbursement of tuition, a grant of $1,200 per year for books, plus an ROTC stipend for 10 months of the year at $350 per month during their sophomore year, $450 per month during their junior year, and $500 per month during their senior year. As a member of the Army National Guard, they also receive weekend drill pay at the pay grade of E-5 during their junior year or E-6 during their senior year.

Duration 2 or 3 years for college students; 2 years for high school seniors entering an MJC.

Additional information After graduation, participants serve 3 to 6 months on active duty in the Officer Basic Course (OBC). Following completion of OBC, they are released from active duty and are obligated to serve 8 years in the Army National Guard.

Number awarded Approximately 600 each year.

Deadline Deadline not specified.

[924]
DISTRICT OF COLUMBIA NATIONAL GUARD TUITION ASSISTANCE

District of Columbia National Guard
Attn: Education Services Office
2001 East Capitol Street, S.E.
Washington, DC 20003-1719
(202) 685-9825   Fax: (202) 685-9815
E-mail: joanne.thweatt@dc.ngb.army.mil
Web: states.ng.mil/sites/DC/education/Pages/tuition.aspx

Summary To provide financial assistance for college or graduate school (in selected fields) to current members of the District of Columbia National Guard.

Eligibility This program is open to traditional, technician, and AGR members of the District of Columbia Air and Army National Guard. Applicants must have a high school diploma or equivalency and currently be working on an associate, bachelor's, or master's degree at an accredited postsecondary education institution. In some instances, support may also be available for an M.D., D.O., P.A., or J.D. degree.

Financial data Army National Guard members are eligible for up to $4,500 per year in federal tuition assistance; they may supplement that with up to $1,500 per year in District tuition assistance. Air National Guard members do not have access to federal tuition assistance, so they may receive up to $6,000 in District tuition assistance. Funds must be used to pay for tuition, fees, and/or books.

Duration 1 semester; recipients may reapply.

Number awarded Varies each year.

Deadline July of each year for the fall session, October of each year for the spring session, or April of each year for the summer session.

[925]
EDUCATION FOUNDATION FOR THE COLORADO NATIONAL GUARD GRANTS

National Guard Association of Colorado
Attn: Education Foundation, Inc.
P.O. Box 440889
Aurora, CO 80044-0889
(303) 909-6369 Fax: (720) 535-5925
E-mail: BernieRogoff@comcast.net
Web: efcong.org/Grants

Summary To provide financial assistance to members of the Colorado National Guard and their families who are interested in attending college or graduate school in any state.

Eligibility This program is open to current and retired members of the Colorado National Guard and their dependent unmarried children and spouses. Applicants must be enrolled or planning to enroll full or part time at a college, university, trade school, business school, or graduate school in any state. Along with their application, they must submit an essay, up to 2 pages in length, on their desire to continue their education, what motivates them, their financial need, their commitment to academic excellence, and their current situation. Selection is based on academic achievement, community involvement, and financial need.

Financial data Stipends are at least $1,000 per year.

Duration 1 year; may be renewed.

Number awarded Varies each year; recently, 38 of these grants, with a total value of $50,000, were awarded.

Deadline July of each year for fall semester; January of each year for spring semester.

[926]
FIRST SERGEANT DOUGLAS AND CHARLOTTE DEHORSE SCHOLARSHIP

Catching the Dream
8200 Mountain Road, N.E., Suite 203
Albuquerque, NM 87110-7835
(505) 262-2351 Fax: (505) 262-0534
E-mail: NScholarsh@aol.com
Web: www.catchingthedream.org

Summary To provide financial assistance to American Indians who have ties to the military and are working on an undergraduate or graduate degree.

Eligibility This program is open to American Indians who 1) have completed 1 year of an Army, Navy, or Air Force Junior Reserve Officer Training (JROTC) program; 2) are enrolled in an Army, Navy, or Air Force Reserve Officer Training (ROTC) program; or 3) are a veteran of the U.S. Army, Navy, Air Force, Marines, Merchant Marine, or Coast Guard. Applicants must be enrolled in college or graduate school. They must submit an application, personal essay, high school transcripts, and letters of recommendation.

Financial data A stipend is awarded (amount not specified).

Duration 1 year.

Additional information This program began in 2007.

Number awarded 1 or more each year.

Deadline April of each year for fall semester or quarter; September of each year for spring semester or winter quarter.

[927]
FLORIDA NATIONAL GUARD EDUCATIONAL DOLLARS FOR DUTY (EDD) PROGRAM

Department of Military Affairs
Attn: Education Services Officer
82 Marine Street
St. Augustine, FL 32084-5039
(904) 823-0417 Toll Free: (800) 342-6528
Web: dma.myflorida.com

Summary To provide financial assistance for college graduate school to members of the Florida National Guard.

Eligibility This program is open to current members of the Florida National Guard. Applicants must be attending or planning to attend a college or university in Florida to work on an undergraduate or master's degree. College preparatory and vocational/technical programs also qualify. Guard members who already have a master's degree are not eligible.

Financial data The program provides for payment of 100% of tuition and fees at a public college or university or an equivalent amount at a private institution.

Duration 1 year; may be renewed.

Number awarded Varies each year; recently, approximately 765 Florida National Guard members utilized this program.

Deadline Deadline not specified.

[928]
FRA NON-MEMBER SCHOLARSHIPS

Fleet Reserve Association
Attn: FRA Education Foundation
125 North West Street
Alexandria, VA 22314-2754
(703) 683-1400 Toll Free: (800) FRA-1924
Fax: (703) 549-6610 E-mail: scholars@fra.org
Web: www.fra.org

Summary To provide financial assistance for college or graduate school to current or former sea service personnel and their families.

Eligibility This program is open to 1) active-duty, Reserve, honorably-discharged veterans, and retired members of the U.S. Navy, Marine Corps, and Coast Guard; and 2) their spouses, children, and grandchildren. Applicants must be enrolled as full-time undergraduate or graduate students but they are not required to be members of the sponsoring organization. Along with their application, they must submit an essay on why they want to go to college and what they intend to accomplish with their degree. Selection is based on academic record, financial need, extracurricular activities, leadership skills, and participation in community activities. U.S. citizenship is required.

Financial data A stipend is awarded (amount not specified).

Duration 1 year; may be renewed.

Number awarded 1 or more each year.

Deadline April of each year.

[929]
FRA SCHOLARSHIPS

Fleet Reserve Association
Attn: FRA Education Foundation
125 North West Street
Alexandria, VA 22314-2754
(703) 683-1400   Toll Free: (800) FRA-1924
Fax: (703) 549-6610   E-mail: scholars@fra.org
Web: www.fra.org

Summary To provide financial assistance for college or graduate school to members of the Fleet Reserve Association (FRA) and their families.

Eligibility This program is open to members of the FRA and the dependent children, grandchildren, and spouses of living or deceased members. Applicants must be enrolled as full-time undergraduate or graduate students. Along with their application, they must submit an essay on why they want to go to college and what they intend to accomplish with their degree. Selection is based on academic record, financial need, extracurricular activities, leadership skills, and participation in community activities. U.S. citizenship is required.

Financial data The stipend is $5,000 per year.

Duration 1 year; may be renewed.

Additional information Membership in the FRA is restricted to active-duty, retired, and reserve members of the Navy, Marines, and Coast Guard.

Number awarded 6 each year.

Deadline April of each year.

[930]
GLENN F. GLEZEN SCHOLARSHIP

Fleet Reserve Association
Attn: FRA Education Foundation
125 North West Street
Alexandria, VA 22314-2754
(703) 683-1400   Toll Free: (800) FRA-1924
Fax: (703) 549-6610   E-mail: scholars@fra.org
Web: www.fra.org

Summary To provide financial assistance for graduate school to members of the Fleet Reserve Association (FRA) and their families.

Eligibility This program is open to members of the FRA and the dependent children, grandchildren, and spouses of living or deceased members. Applicants must be enrolled as full-time graduate students. Along with their application, they must submit an essay on why they want to go to college and what they intend to accomplish with their degree. Selection is based on academic record, financial need, extracurricular activities, leadership skills, and participation in community activities. U.S. citizenship is required.

Financial data The stipend is $5,000 per year.

Duration 1 year; may be renewed.

Additional information Membership in the FRA is restricted to active-duty, retired, and Reserve members of the Navy, Marine Corps, and Coast Guard. This program was established in 2001.

Number awarded 1 each year.

Deadline April of each year.

[931]
HENRY J. REILLY MEMORIAL GRADUATE SCHOLARSHIP

Reserve Officers Association of the United States
Attn: Scholarship Program
One Constitution Avenue, N.E.
Washington, DC 20002-5618
(202) 646-7719   Toll Free: (800) 809-9448, ext. 719
Fax: (202) 547-1641   E-mail: scholarship@roa.org
Web: www.roa.org

Summary To provide financial support for graduate study to members of the Reserve Officers Association (ROA).

Eligibility This program is open to active or associate members of the association who are enrolled in or accepted for enrollment in graduate studies at an accredited U.S. institution of higher education. Applicants for a master's degree must have earned a GPA of 3.2 or higher as an undergraduate; applicants for a doctoral degree must have received a master's degree or been accepted into a doctoral program. Applications must include 3 letters of recommendation: 1 from a military or civilian superior regarding the applicant's leadership ability or potential and 2 from persons qualified to assess academic ability.

Financial data The stipend is $1,000 per year.

Duration 1 year; may be renewed up to 3 additional years if the recipient maintains a GPA of 3.3 or higher.

Number awarded The sponsor awards a total of 30 scholarships each year.

Deadline May of each year.

[932]
HONOLULU POST SAME SCHOLARSHIPS

Society of American Military Engineers-Honolulu Post
P.O. Box 201445
Honolulu, HI 96820
Web: www.samehonolulu.org

Summary To provide financial assistance to residents of Hawaii, particularly those with ties to the military, who are interested in attending college in any state to work on an undergraduate or graduate degree in engineering or architecture.

Eligibility This program is open to residents of Hawaii who are graduating high school seniors or current undergraduates enrolled or planning to enroll full time at an accredited college or university in any state. Applicants must be planning to work on an undergraduate or graduate degree in engineering or architecture. They must be U.S. citizens and have a GPA of 3.0 or higher. Military affiliation or experience (i.e., ROTC, member or dependent of a member of the Society of Military Engineers (SAME), military dependent, Junior ROTC) is not required but is given preference. Along with their application, they must submit a transcript; a resume of work experience, academic activities, and extracurricular accomplishments; and a 1-page essay on how their engineering or architecture degree will impact our nation.

Financial data The stipend is $2,500.

Duration 1 year.

Number awarded Varies each year; recently, 6 of these scholarships were awarded.

Deadline March of each year.

[933]
HOOVER INSTITUTION NATIONAL SECURITY AFFAIRS FELLOWS PROGRAM

Stanford University
Hoover Institution
Attn: National Fellows Program
434 Galvez Mall
Stanford, CA 94305-6010
(650) 723-3972   Toll Free: (877) Hooverl
Fax: (650) 723-1687   E-mail: weissbart@stanford.edu
Web: www.hoover.org

Summary To provide an opportunity for military personnel to conduct research at Stanford University's Hoover Institution.

Eligibility This program is open to active-duty military personnel nominated by their service. Applicants must be interested in conducting independent research at the institution on topics relevant to their respective branch of the service.

Financial data A stipend is provided (amount not specified).

Duration 1 year, beginning in September.

Additional information Fellows are expected to participate in the intellectual life of the Hoover Institution, including regular afternoon discussions, weekly seminars, and monthly dinners. Fellows are also expected to make at least 1 presentation on their research before an appropriate group of scholars.

Number awarded Up to 5 each year: 1 each from the Air Force, Army, Marines, Navy, and State Department.

Deadline January of each year.

[934]
ILLINOIS NATIONAL GUARD GRANT PROGRAM

Illinois Student Assistance Commission
Attn: Scholarship and Grant Services
1755 Lake Cook Road
Deerfield, IL 60015-5209
(847) 948-8550   Toll Free: (800) 899-ISAC
Fax: (847) 831-8549   TDD: (800) 526-0844
E-mail: isac.studentservices@isac.illinois.gov
Web: www.collegeillinois.org

Summary To provide financial assistance to current or former members of the Illinois National Guard who are interested in attending college or graduate school in the state.

Eligibility This program is open to members of the Illinois National Guard who are 1) currently active or 2) have been active for at least 5 consecutive years, have been called to federal active duty for at least 6 months, and are within 12 months after their discharge date. Applicants must also be enrolled at an Illinois public 2- or 4-year college or university and have served at least 1 full year in the Guard.

Financial data Recipients are eligible for payment of tuition and some fees for either undergraduate or graduate study at an Illinois state-supported college or university.

Duration This assistance extends for 8 semesters or 12 quarters (or the equivalent in part-time study).

Number awarded Varies each year.

Deadline September of each year for the academic year; February of each year for spring semester, winter quarter, or spring quarter; June of each year for summer term.

[935]
INTERNATIONAL SECURITY AND COOPERATION PROFESSIONAL FELLOWSHIPS

Stanford University
Center for International Security and Cooperation
Attn: Freeman Spogli Institute for International Studies
Encina Hall, Room C206-8
616 Serra Street
Stanford, CA 94305-6165
(650) 724-9132   Fax: (650) 723-0089
E-mail: CISACfellowship@stanford.edu
Web: cisac.stanford.edu/docs/cisac_fellowships

Summary To provide funding to professionals (particularly from the military) who are interested in conducting research in residence on topics of interest to Stanford University's Center for International Security and Cooperation.

Eligibility This program is open to mid-career professionals in journalism, law, the military, government, or international organizations, either from the United States or abroad. Applicants must be interested in conducting research in any discipline of the social sciences, humanities, natural sciences, or engineering that relates to international security problems. Relevant topics include nuclear weapons proliferation and risk, nuclear energy, war and civil conflict, global governance, migration and transnational flows, public health and the environment, cyber and biosecurity, international norms and ethics, and insurgency and homeland security.

Financial data The stipend depends on experience and is determined on a case-by-case basis. Additional funds may be available for dependents and travel.

Duration 9 months.

Additional information Fellows are expected to write a publishable article during their fellowship. They should not plan to spend any time conducting research abroad or in other parts of the country.

Number awarded Varies each year.

Deadline January of each year.

[936]
JOHN CORNELIUS/MAX ENGLISH MEMORIAL SCHOLARSHIP AWARD

Marine Corps Tankers Association
c/o Buster Diggs, Scholarship Chair
1829 Ballentine Drive
Alpine, CA 91901
E-mail: Tigertanker2003@yahoo.com
Web: www.usmarinetankers.org/scholarship-program

Summary To provide financial assistance for college or graduate school to children and grandchildren of members of the Marine Corps Tankers Association and to Marine and Navy personnel currently serving in tank units.

Eligibility This program is open to high school seniors and graduates who are children, grandchildren, or under the guardianship of an active, Reserve, retired, or honorably discharged Marine who served in a tank unit. Marine or Navy Corpsmen currently assigned to tank units are also eligible. Applicants must be enrolled or planning to enroll full time at a college or graduate school. Their parent or grandparent must be a member of the Marine Corps Tankers Association or, if not a member, must join if the application is accepted. Along with their application, they must submit an essay on their educational goals, future aspirations, and concern for the future

of our society and for the peoples of the world. Selection is based on that essay, academic record, school activities, leadership potential, and community service.
Financial data The stipend is at least $2,000 per year.
Duration 1 year; recipients may reapply.
Number awarded 8 to 12 each year.
Deadline March of each year.

[937]
JOSEPH R. BARANSKI SCHOLARSHIP
Fleet Reserve Association
Attn: FRA Education Foundation
125 North West Street
Alexandria, VA 22314-2754
(703) 683-1400   Toll Free: (800) FRA-1924
Fax: (703) 549-6610   E-mail: scholars@fra.org
Web: www.fra.org
Summary To provide financial assistance for graduate school to members of the Fleet Reserve Association (FRA) and their families.
Eligibility This program is open to members of the FRA and the dependent children, grandchildren, and spouses of living or deceased members. Applicants must be enrolled as full-time graduate students. Along with their application, they must submit an essay on why they want to go to college and what they intend to accomplish with their degree. Selection is based on academic record, financial need, extracurricular activities, leadership skills, and participation in community activities. U.S. citizenship is required.
Financial data The stipend is $5,000.
Duration 1 year; may be renewed.
Additional information Membership in the FRA is restricted to active-duty, retired, and Reserve members of the Navy, Marine Corps, and Coast Guard. This program was established in 2001.
Number awarded 1 each year.
Deadline April of each year.

[938]
KENTUCKY NATIONAL GUARD TUITION AWARD PROGRAM
Kentucky Higher Education Assistance Authority
Attn: Student Aid Branch
100 Airport Road
P.O. Box 798
Frankfort, KY 40602-0798
(502) 696-7392   Toll Free: (800) 928-8926, ext. 7392
Fax: (502) 696-7373   TDD: (800) 855-2880
E-mail: studentaid@kheaa.com
Web: www.kheaa.com/website/kheaa/military_ky?main=7
Summary To provide financial assistance for college or graduate school to members of the Kentucky National Guard.
Eligibility This program is open to active enlisted members of the Kentucky National Guard who are interested in working full or part time on an undergraduate or graduate degree. Applicants must have maintained standards of satisfactory membership in the Guard, including passing the most recent physical fitness test, meeting the height-weight standard, meeting attendance standards, having no unsatisfactory performance or absence-without-leave records, and having no other restrictions on their personnel file. Preference is given to applicants working on their first undergraduate degree.

Financial data The program provides payment of full tuition and fees at any state-supported university, community college, or vocational or technical school in Kentucky.
Duration 1 semester; may be renewed.
Number awarded Varies each year.
Deadline March of each year for summer or fall terms; September of each year for spring term.

[939]
LIFE'S CHOICES FOUNDATION GRADUATE SCHOLARSHIP AWARDS
Association of Former Intelligence Officers
Attn: Scholarships Committee
6723 Whittier Avenue, Suite 200
McLean, VA 22101-4533
(703) 790-0320   Fax: (703) 991-1278
E-mail: afio@afio.com
Web: www.afio.com/13_scholarships.htm
Summary To provide financial assistance to graduate students who are members or descendants of members of the U.S. intelligence community and interested in working on a degree in a field related to national security.
Eligibility This program is open to graduate students who apply in their senior undergraduate year or first graduate year. Applicants must be personnel serving in government agencies comprising the U.S. intelligence community or their children or grandchildren. They must be working on a degree in a field related to national security or intelligence studies and be, or planning to be, serving in the U.S. government. Along with their application, they must submit a cover letter that explains their need for assistance, their career goals and dreams, and their views of U.S. world standing and its intelligence community. Selection is based on merit, character, estimated future potential, background, and relevance of their studies to the full spectrum of national security interests and career ambitions. U.S. citizenship is required.
Financial data The stipend is $3,500.
Duration 1 year.
Additional information This program is sponsored by the Morris Family Charitable Corporation.
Number awarded 2 each year.
Deadline June of each year.

[940]
MAINE NATIONAL GUARD EDUCATION ASSISTANCE PROGRAM
Maine National Guard
Attn: Education
Camp Keyes
Augusta, ME 04333-0033
(207) 626-4370   Toll Free: (800) 462-3101 (within ME)
Fax: (207) 626-4509
Web: www.me.ngb.army.mil
Summary To provide financial assistance for undergraduate or graduate study to members of the Maine National Guard.
Eligibility This program is open to active members of the Maine National Guard who are interested in working on an undergraduate or graduate degree or certificate at a college or university within the state. Applicants must be Maine residents who have successfully completed basic training or received a commission. They may not have any unsatisfac-

tory record of participation in the Guard. First priority is given to Guard members who do not have a baccalaureate degree and are working on a degree; second priority is given to members without a graduate degree who are working on a degree, teacher certification, principal certification, or superintendent certification; third priority is for all others.

Financial data This program provides payment of up to 100% of tuition and fees at a Maine accredited public postsecondary institution. Recipients may also attend a private college or university in Maine, but the benefit is capped at the tuition rates at the University of Maine.

Duration 1 semester; may be renewed for a total of 150 credit hours, as long as the recipient maintains satisfactory participation in the Guard and an academic GPA of 2.0 or higher.

Number awarded Varies each year.

Deadline October of each year for college terms beginning from January through April; February of each year for college terms beginning from May through July; June of each year for college terms beginning in August or September.

[941]
MARINE CORPS FUNDED LAW EDUCATION PROGRAM

U.S. Marine Corps
Manpower and Reserve Affairs (MMOA-3)
Attn: Undergraduate and Graduate Education Programs
3280 Russell Road
Quantico, VA 22134-5103
(703) 784-9286   Fax: (703) 784-9844
E-mail: Diane.Rodgers@usmc.mil
Web: www.usmc.mil

Summary To allow selected commissioned Marine Corps officers to earn a law degree by providing financial assistance for full-time study.

Eligibility Eligible to participate in this program are commissioned Marine Corps officers at the rank of captain or below. Applicants must have at least 2 but no more than 6 years of total active service and be able to complete 20 years of active service before their 55th birthday. They must have graduated from an accredited college or university with a bachelor's degree, have taken the LSAT at their own arrangement and expense, and have been accepted at an accredited law school in the United States.

Financial data Commissioned officers selected to participate in this program receive their regular Marine Corps pay and allowances while attending a college or university on a full-time basis, as well as payment for the cost of tuition (to a maximum of $10,000 per year).

Duration Up to the equivalent of 2 academic years.

Number awarded Varies each year; recently, 3 Marines were selected to participate in this program.

Deadline October of each year.

[942]
MARINE CORPS TUITION ASSISTANCE PROGRAM

U.S. Marine Corps
Attn: Lifelong Learning Center
3098 Range Road
Quantico, VA 22134-5028
(703) 784-9550   E-mail: vernon.taylor@usmc.mil
Web: www.usmc-mccs.org/education/mta.cfm

Summary To provide financial assistance for undergraduate or graduate study to Marine Corps personnel.

Eligibility Eligible for assistance under this program are active-duty Marines who wish to take college courses for academic credit during off-duty time. Funding is available for vocational/technical, undergraduate, graduate, undergraduate development, independent study, and distance learning programs. Commissioned officers must agree to remain on active duty for 2 years after the completion of any funded courses. All students must successfully complete their courses with a satisfactory grade.

Financial data Those selected for participation in this program receive their regular Marine Corps pay and 100% of tuition at the postsecondary educational institution of their choice, but capped at $4,500 per year or $250 per semester hour, whichever is less.

Duration Until completion of a bachelor's or graduate degree.

Number awarded Varies each year; in recent years, approximately 20,000 Marines availed themselves of this funding.

Deadline Deadline not specified.

[943]
MARYLAND NATIONAL GUARD STATE TUITION ASSISTANCE

Maryland National Guard
Attn: Education Services Office
Fifth Regiment Armory
29th Division Street, Room D24
Baltimore, MD 21201-2288
(410) 576-6093   Toll Free: (800) 492-2526
Fax: (410) 576-6082
E-mail: mdng_education@md.ngb.army.mil
Web: www.goarmyed.com

Summary To provide partial tuition reimbursement to members of the Maryland National Guard working on an undergraduate or graduate degree at a college in the state.

Eligibility This program is open to members of the Maryland National Guard who have at least 24 months of service remaining in the Guard from the start of the course date. Priority is given to junior enlisted personnel (grades E-1 through E-6). Applicants must be attending or planning to attend a state-supported college or university or a designated private institution in Maryland to work on an undergraduate or graduate degree. They must agree to remain a member of the Guard for at least 2 years for receipt of a bachelor's or lower degree or for 4 years for receipt of a master's or higher degree.

Financial data Eligible Guard members receive an amount equal to 50% of their college/university tuition and related course fees, to a maximum of $5,000 per fiscal year.

Duration 1 semester; recipients may reapply.

Additional information Individuals must apply for reimbursement within 45 days after their course is completed. They must have earned at least a grade of "C" in the course to qualify for reimbursement.

Number awarded Varies each year.

Deadline Deadline not specified.

[944]
MARYLAND NATIONAL GUARD STATE TUITION WAIVER

Maryland National Guard
Attn: Education Services Office
Fifth Regiment Armory
29th Division Street, Room D24
Baltimore, MD 21201-2288
(410) 576-6093   Toll Free: (800) 492-2526
Fax: (410) 576-6082
E-mail: mdng_education@md.ngb.army.mil
Web: www.goarmyed.com

Summary   To waive tuition for members of the Maryland National Guard at colleges and universities in the state.
Eligibility   All state-supported colleges and universities and 2 private universities in Maryland have developed a tuition waiver program for members of the National Guard who are taking graduate or undergraduate courses.
Financial data   The amount of the waiver ranges from 25% to 50%. Most 4-year colleges waive 50% of tuition for up to 6 credits per semester.
Duration   1 semester; recipients may reapply.
Additional information   Some schools also limit the number of credits for which a Guard member can receive waivers during any semester.
Number awarded   Varies each year.
Deadline   Deadline not specified.

[945]
MASSACHUSETTS NATIONAL GUARD EDUCATIONAL ASSISTANCE PROGRAM

Massachusetts National Guard
Attn: Education Services Office
50 Maple Street
Milford, MA 01757-3604
(508) 233-6590   Toll Free: (888) 301-3103, ext. 6753
Fax: (508) 233-6781   E-mail: ma-education@ng.army.mil
Web: states.ng.mil

Summary   To provide financial assistance to members of the Massachusetts National Guard interested in working on an undergraduate or graduate degree at a college in the state.
Eligibility   This program is open to actively participating members of the Army or Air National Guard in Massachusetts. Applicants must have less than 9 AWOLs (Absence Without Leave) at all times and must not ETS (Expiration of Term of Service) during the period enrolled. They must be accepted for admission or enrolled at 1 of 28 Massachusetts public colleges, universities, or community colleges and working on an associate, bachelor's, master's, or doctoral degree. The institution must have a vacancy after all tuition-paying students and all students who are enrolled under any scholarship or tuition waiver provisions have enrolled.
Financial data   Eligible Guard members are exempt from any tuition payments at colleges or universities operated by the Commonwealth of Massachusetts and funded by the Massachusetts Board of Higher Education.
Duration   Up to a total of 130 semester hours.
Additional information   Recipients may enroll either part or full time in a Massachusetts state-supported institution. This program, commonly referred to as the 100% Tuition

Waiver Program, is funded through the Massachusetts Board of Higher Education.
Number awarded   Varies each year.
Deadline   Deadline not specified.

[946]
MCA CHAPLAIN CANDIDATE SCHOLARSHIPS

Military Chaplains Association of the United States of America
Attn: Chaplain Candidate Scholarship Committee
P.O. Box 7056
Arlington, VA 22207-7056
(703) 533-5890   E-mail: chaplains@mca-usa.org
Web: mca-usa.org/scholarships

Summary   To provide financial assistance to seminary students who are serving as chaplain candidates for the U.S. armed forces.
Eligibility   This program is open to full-time students in accredited seminaries who are currently approved as and serving as chaplain candidates in the armed forces (Army, Air Force, or Navy). Applicants must be able to demonstrate financial need. Along with their application, they must submit 500-word essays on 1) their sense of call to ministry with particular emphasis on their call to provide pastoral care for military personnel and their families; and 2) their understanding thus far of ministry in a religiously diverse environment (such as the armed forces of the United States).
Financial data   The stipend is $2,000.
Duration   1 year.
Additional information   This program began in 1992.
Number awarded   Varies each year. Since the program was established, it has awarded 63 scholarships.
Deadline   June of each year.

[947]
MEDICAL CORPS OPTION OF THE SEAMAN TO ADMIRAL-21 PROGRAM

U.S. Navy
Attn: Commander, Naval Service Training Command
250 Dallas Street, Suite A
Pensacola, FL 32508-5268
(850) 452-9433   Fax: (850) 452-2486
E-mail: PNSC_STA21@navy.mil
Web: www.sta-21.navy.mil

Summary   To allow outstanding enlisted Navy personnel to complete a bachelor's degree, be accepted to medical school, earn an M.D. or D.O. degree, and be commissioned in the Navy Medical Corps.
Eligibility   This program is open to U.S. citizens who are currently serving on active duty in the U.S. Navy or Naval Reserve, including Full Time Support (FTS), Selected Reserves (SELRES), and Navy Reservists on active duty, except for those on active duty for training (ACDUTRA). Applicants must be high school graduates (or GED recipients) who are able to 1) complete requirements for a baccalaureate degree within 36 months; 2) complete a medical degree through the Uniformed Services University of Health Services (USUHS) or the Health Professions Scholarship Program (HPSP); and 3) complete 20 years of active commissioned service as a physician by age 62. Within the past 3 years, they must have taken the SAT (and achieved scores of at least 500 on the mathematics section and 500 on the critical

reading section) or the ACT (and achieved a score of 41 or higher, including at least 21 on the mathematics portion and 20 on the English portion).

Financial data Awardees continue to receive their regular Navy pay and allowances while they attend college on a full-time basis. They also receive reimbursement for tuition, fees, and books up to $10,000 per year. If base housing is available, they are eligible to live there. Participants are not eligible to receive benefits under the Navy's Tuition Assistance Program (TA), the Montgomery GI Bill (MGIB), the Navy College Fund, or the Veterans Educational Assistance Program (VEAP).

Duration Selectees are supported for up to 36 months of full-time, year-round study or completion of a bachelor's degree, as long as they maintain a GPA of 3.0 or higher. They are then supported until completion of a medical degree.

Additional information Upon acceptance into the program, selectees attend the Naval Science Institute (NSI) in Newport, Rhode Island for an 8-week program in the fundamental core concepts of being a naval officer (navigation, engineering, weapons, military history and justice, etc.). They then enter an NROTC affiliated college or university with a pre-medical program that confers an accredited B.S. degree to pursue full-time study. They become members of and drill with the NROTC unit. After they complete their bachelor's degree, they are commissioned as an ensign in the Naval Reserve. They must apply to and be accepted at medical school, either the USUSH or a civilian medical school through the HPSP. Following completion of medical school, they are promoted to lieutenant and assigned to active duty in the Medical Corps. Selectees incur a service obligation of 5 years for their baccalaureate degree support plus whatever obligation they incur for medical degree support (usually 7 years if they attend USUSH or 4 years if they attend a civilian institution through HPSP).

Number awarded Varies each year.

Deadline June of each year.

[948]
MEDICAL SERVICE CORPS INSERVICE PROCUREMENT PROGRAM (MSC-IPP)

U.S. Navy
Attn: Navy Medicine Professional Development Center
Code O3C
8901 Wisconsin Avenue, 16th Floor, Tower 1
Bethesda, MD 20889-5611
(301) 319-4520   Fax: (301) 295-1783
E-mail: mscipp@nmetc.med.navy.mil
Web: www.med.navy.mil

Summary To provide funding to Navy and Marine enlisted personnel who wish to earn an undergraduate or graduate degree in selected health care specialties while continuing to receive their regular pay and allowances.

Eligibility This program is open to enlisted personnel who are serving on active duty in any rating in pay grade E-5 through E-9 of the U.S. Navy, U.S. Marine Corps, or the Marine Corps Reserve serving on active duty (including Full Time Support of the Reserve). Applicants must be interested in working on a degree to become commissioned in the following medical specialties: environmental health, health care administration, industrial hygiene, occupational therapy, pharmacy, physician assistant, radiation health, or social work. If they plan to work on a graduate degree, they must have scores of at least 1000 on the GRE or 500 on the GMAT; if they plan to work on a bachelor's or physician assistant degree, they must have scores of at least 1000 on the SAT (including 460 on the mathematics portion) or 42 on the ACT (21 on the English portion, 21 on the mathematics portion). They must be U.S. citizens who can be commissioned before they reach their 42nd birthday.

Financial data Participants receive payment of tuition, mandatory fees, a book allowance, and full pay and allowances for their enlisted pay grade. They are eligible for advancement while in college.

Duration 24 to 48 months of full-time, year-round study, until completion of a relevant degree.

Additional information Following graduation, participants are commissioned in the Medical Service Corps and attend Officer Indoctrination School. They incur an 8-year military service obligation, including at least 3 years served on active duty.

Number awarded Varies each year; recently, 36 of these positions were available: 2 in environmental health, 14 in health care administration, 1 in occupational therapy, 1 in pharmacy, 15 in physician assistant, 2 in radiation health, and 1 in social work.

Deadline August of each year.

[949]
MG LEIF J. SVERDRUP AWARD

Army Engineer Association
Attn: Executive Director
P.O. Box 30260
Alexandria, VA 22310-8260
(703) 428-7084   Fax: (703) 428-6043
E-mail: xd@armyengineer.com
Web: www.armyengineer.com/scholarships.htm

Summary To provide financial assistance for college or graduate school to officers who are members of the Army Engineer Association (AEA).

Eligibility This program is open to AEA members serving in an active, Reserve, or National Guard component Army Engineer unit, school, or organization within the Corps of Engineers of the United States Army. Applicants must be commissioned officers (2LT, 1LT, or CPT) or warrant officers (WO1 or WO2). They must be working on or planning to work on an associate, bachelor's, or master's degree at an accredited college or university. Selection is based primarily on financial need, although potential for academic success and standards of conduct as supported by personal references are also considered.

Financial data The stipend is $1,000.

Duration 1 year.

Number awarded 1 or 2 each year.

Deadline June of each year.

[950]
MINNESOTA G.I. BILL PROGRAM

Minnesota Office of Higher Education
Attn: Manager of State Financial Aid Programs
1450 Energy Park Drive, Suite 350
St. Paul, MN 55108-5227
(651) 642-0567   Toll Free: (800) 657-3866
Fax: (651) 642-0675   TDD: (800) 627-3529
E-mail: Ginny.Dodds@state.mn.us
Web: www.ohe.state.mn.us/mPg.cfm?pageID=891

Summary To provide financial assistance for college or graduate school in the state to residents of Minnesota who served in the military after September 11, 2001 and the families of deceased or disabled military personnel.

Eligibility This program is open to residents of Minnesota enrolled at colleges and universities in the state as undergraduate or graduate students. Applicants must be 1) a veteran who is serving or has served honorably in a branch of the U.S. armed forces at any time on or after September 11, 2001; 2) a non-veteran who has served honorably for a total of 5 years or more cumulatively as a member of the Minnesota National Guard or other active or Reserve component of the U.S. armed forces, and any part of that service occurred on or after September 11, 2001; or 3) a surviving child or spouse of a person who has served in the military at any time on or after September 11, 2001 and who has died or has a total and permanent disability as a result of that military service. Financial need is considered in the selection process.

Financial data The stipend is $1,000 per semester for full-time study or $500 per semester for part-time study. The maximum award is $3,000 per fiscal year or $10,000 per lifetime.

Duration 1 year; may be renewed, provided the recipient continues to make satisfactory academic progress.

Additional information This program was established by the Minnesota Legislature in 2007.

Number awarded Varies each year.

Deadline Deadline not specified.

[951]
MINNESOTA NATIONAL GUARD MEDICAL PROFESSIONAL STUDENT STATE TUITION REIMBURSEMENT PROGRAM

Department of Military Affairs
Attn: Education Services Officer
JFMN-J1-ARED
20 West 12th Street
St. Paul, MN 55155-2098
(651) 282-4589   Toll Free: (800) 657-3848
Fax: (651) 282-4694 E-mail: ngmneducation@ng.army.mil
Web: www.minnesotanationalguard.org

Summary To provide partial tuition reimbursement to medical, dental, and physician assistant students who are interested in serving in the Minnesota National Guard.

Eligibility This program is open to Minnesota Army and Air National Guard members who initially appoint as medical or dental student officers or are already commissioned officers and attain civilian physician assistant master's student status. Applicants must agree to accept a Medical Corps commission in the Guard after graduation.

Financial data This program provides reimbursement of the tuition charged, not to exceed 100% of the tuition costs at the University of Minnesota Twin Cities campus medical or

dental schools. Upon graduation from medical, dental, or physician assistant school, officers must serve the same number of years in the Minnesota National Guard that they participated in the program. Failure to fulfill that service obligation will result in recoupment of a prorated portion of the tuition reimbursed.

Duration The program provides funding for up to 144 semester or 208 quarter credits.

Number awarded The number of participants at any given time is limited to 15 Army Guard officers and 4 Air Guard officers.

Deadline Participants must request reimbursement within 60 days of the last official day of the term.

[952]
MINNESOTA NATIONAL GUARD STATE TUITION REIMBURSEMENT

Department of Military Affairs
Attn: Education Services Officer
JFMN-J1-ARED
20 West 12th Street
St. Paul, MN 55155-2098
(651) 282-4589   Toll Free: (800) 657-3848
Fax: (651) 282-4694 E-mail: ngmneducation@ng.army.mil
Web: www.minnesotanationalguard.org

Summary To provide financial assistance for college or graduate school to members of the Minnesota National Guard.

Eligibility Eligible for this program are members of the Minnesota Army or Air National Guard in grades E-1 through O-5 (including warrant officers) who are enrolled as undergraduate or graduate students at colleges or universities in Minnesota. Reimbursement is provided only for undergraduate courses completed with a grade of "C" or better or for graduate courses completed with a grade of "B" or better. Guard members who served on federal active status or federally-funded state active service after September 11, 2001 are eligible for this assistance for up to 2 years after completion of their service contract (or up to 8 years if they were separated or discharged because of a service-connected injury, disease, or disability).

Financial data The maximum reimbursement rate is 100% of the undergraduate tuition rate at the University of Minnesota Twin Cities campus, with a maximum benefit of $10,000 per fiscal year.

Duration 1 semester, to a maximum of 18 credits per semester; may be renewed until completion of an associate, bachelor's, master's, or doctoral degree or 144 semester credits, whichever comes first.

Number awarded Varies each year.

Deadline Deadline not specified.

[953]
MONTGOMERY GI BILL (SELECTED RESERVE)

Department of Veterans Affairs
Attn: Veterans Benefits Administration
810 Vermont Avenue, N.W.
Washington, DC 20420
(202) 418-4343   Toll Free: (888) GI-BILL1
Web: www.gibill.va.gov

Summary To provide financial assistance for college or graduate school to members of the Reserves or National Guard.

Eligibility Eligible to apply are members of the Reserve elements of the Army, Navy, Air Force, Marine Corps, and Coast Guard, as well as the Army National Guard and the Air National Guard. To be eligible, a Reservist must 1) have a 6-year obligation to serve in the Selected Reserves signed after June 30, 1985 (or, if an officer, to agree to serve 6 years in addition to the original obligation); 2) complete Initial Active Duty for Training (IADT); 3) meet the requirements for a high school diploma or equivalent certificate before completing IADT; and 4) remain in good standing in a drilling Selected Reserve unit. Reservists who enlisted after June 30, 1985 can receive benefits for undergraduate degrees, graduate training, or technical courses leading to certificates at colleges and universities. Reservists whose 6-year commitment began after September 30, 1990 may also use these benefits for a certificate or diploma from business, technical, or vocational schools; cooperative training; apprenticeship or on-the-job training; correspondence courses; independent study programs; tutorial assistance; remedial, deficiency, or refresher training; flight training; or state-approved alternative teacher certification programs.

Financial data The current monthly rate is $345 for full-time study, $258 for three-quarter time study, $171 for half-time study, or $86.25 for less than half-time study. For apprenticeship and on-the-job training, the monthly stipend is $258.75 for the first 6 months, $189.75 for the second 6 months, and $120.75 for the remainder of the program. Other rates apply for cooperative education, correspondence courses, and flight training.

Duration Up to 36 months for full-time study, 48 months for three-quarter study, 72 months for half-time study, or 144 months for less than half-time study. Benefits end 10 years from the date the Reservist became eligible for the program.

Additional information This program is frequently referred to as Chapter 1606 (formerly Chapter 106).

Number awarded Varies each year.

Deadline Applications may be submitted at any time.

[954]
NATIONAL GUARD ASSOCIATION OF NEW JERSEY SCHOLARSHIP PROGRAM

National Guard Association of New Jersey
Attn: Executive Director
P.O. Box 266
Wrightstown, NJ 08562
(973) 541-6776   Fax: (973) 541-6909
E-mail: nganj@aol.com
Web: nganj.org/about.htm

Summary To provide financial assistance to members of the National Guard Association of New Jersey (NGANJ) or their dependents who are interested in attending college or graduate school in any state.

Eligibility This program is open to 1) active members of the NGANJ currently enrolled full time at an approved community college, school of nursing, or 4-year college in any state; and 2) the spouses, children, and grandchildren of active, retired, or deceased members entering or attending a 4-year college or university in any state. Applicants must submit transcripts, information on the civic and academic activi-

ties in which they have participated, and a list of offices, honors, awards, and special recognitions they have received. Selection is based on academic accomplishment, leadership, and citizenship.

Financial data Stipends up to $1,000 are available.

Duration 1 year; nonrenewable.

Number awarded Varies each year; recently, 10 of these scholarships were awarded.

Deadline April of each year.

[955]
NATIONAL GUARD ASSOCIATION OF SOUTH CAROLINA SCHOLARSHIPS

National Guard Association of South Carolina
Attn: NGASC Scholarship Foundation
132 Pickens Street
Columbia, SC 29205
(803) 254-8456   Toll Free: (800) 822-3235
Fax: (803) 254-3869   E-mail: nginfo@ngasc.org
Web: www.ngasc.org/?page_id=11

Summary To provide funding to current and former South Carolina National Guard members and their dependents who are interested in attending college or graduate school.

Eligibility This program is open to undergraduate students who are 1) current, retired, or deceased members of the South Carolina National Guard; 2) their dependents; and 3) members of the National Guard Association of South Carolina (NGASC). Graduate students are also eligible if they are members of the South Carolina National Guard. Applicants must be attending or interested in attending a college or university in any state as a full-time student. Several of the scholarships include additional restrictions on school or academic major; some are granted only for academic excellence, but most are based on both academics and financial need.

Financial data The stipend is $1,500 or $1,000.

Duration 1 year; may be renewed up to 3 additional years.

Number awarded Varies each year; recently, 42 of these scholarships were awarded: 1 at $1,500 and 41 at $1,000.

Deadline January of each year.

[956]
NATIONAL GUARD ASSOCIATION OF TEXAS SCHOLARSHIP PROGRAM

National Guard Association of Texas
Attn: NGAT Educational Foundation
3706 Crawford Avenue
Austin, TX 78731-6803
(512) 454-7300   Toll Free: (800) 252-NGAT
Fax: (512) 467-6803   E-mail: rlindner@ngat.org
Web: www.ngat.org

Summary To provide funding to members and dependents of members of the National Guard Association of Texas who are interested in attending college or graduate school.

Eligibility This program is open to annual and life members of the association and their spouses and children (associate members and their dependents are not eligible). Applicants may be high school seniors, undergraduate students, or graduate students, either enrolled or planning to enroll at an institution of higher education in any state. Along with their application, they must submit an essay on their desire to continue their education. Selection is based on scholarship, citizenship, and leadership.

Financial data   Stipends range from $500 to $5,000.

Duration   1 year (nonrenewable).

Additional information   This program includes 1 scholarship sponsored by USAA Insurance Corporation.

Number awarded   Varies each year; recently, 13 of these scholarships were awarded: 1 at $5,000, 3 at $2,500, 1 at $2,000, 3 at $1,250, 4 at $1,000, and 1 at $500.

Deadline   February of each year.

[957]
NATIONAL GUARD ASSOCIATION OF VERMONT SCHOLARSHIPS

National Guard Association of Vermont
Attn: Capt John Geno, President
P.O. Box 694
Essex Junction, VT 05452
(802) 338-3397   E-mail: john.geno@us.army.mil
Web: www.ngavt.org/scholarInfo.shtml

Summary   To provide funding to members of the Vermont National Guard (VTNG) and their children or spouses who are interested in attending college or graduate school.

Eligibility   This program is open to current members of the VTNG, their spouses, and their unmarried children. Applicants must be working, or planning to work, on an associate, undergraduate, technical, or graduate degree as a full-time student at a school in any state. Along with their application, they must submit an essay on their commitment to selfless public service or their plan for pursuing it in the future. Selection is based on academic performance, overall potential for a commitment to selfless public service, and financial need.

Financial data   The stipend is $1,000. Funds are sent directly to the recipient.

Duration   1 year; recipients may reapply.

Number awarded   4 each year: 3 to undergraduates and 1 to a graduate student.

Deadline   May of each year.

[958]
NAVY ADVANCED EDUCATION VOUCHER PROGRAM

U.S. Navy
Naval Education and Training Command
Center for Personal and Professional Development
Attn: AEV Program Office
6490 Saufley Field Road
Pensacola, FL 32509-5204
(850) 452-7271   Fax: (850) 452-1272
E-mail: rick.cusimano@navy.mil
Web: www.navycollege.navy.mil/aev/aev_home.cfm

Summary   To provide financial assistance to Navy enlisted personnel who are interested in earning an undergraduate or graduate degree during off-duty hours.

Eligibility   This program is open to senior enlisted Navy personnel in ranks E-7 and E-8. Applicants should be transferring to, or currently on, shore duty with sufficient time ashore to complete a bachelor's or master's degree. Personnel at rank E-7 may have no more than 16 years in service and at E-8 no more than 18 years. The area of study must be certified by the Naval Postgraduate School as Navy-relevant.

Financial data   This program covers education costs (tuition, books, and fees), to a maximum of $6,700 per year or a total of $20,000 per participant for a bachelor's degree or

$20,000 per year or a total of $40,000 per participant for a master's degree.

Duration   Up to 36 months from the time of enrollment for a bachelor's degree; up to 24 months from the time of enrollment for a master's degree.

Additional information   Recently approved majors for bachelor's degrees included human resources, construction management, information technology, emergency and disaster management, paralegal, engineering, business administration, leadership and management, nursing, strategic foreign languages, and electrical/electronic technology. Approved fields of study for master's degrees included business administration, education and training management, emergency and disaster management, engineering and technology, homeland defense and security, human resources, information technology, leadership and management, project management, and systems analysis. Recipients of this assistance incur an obligation to remain on active duty following completion of the program for a period equal to 3 times the number of months of education completed, to a maximum obligation of 36 months.

Number awarded   Varies each year; recently, 20 of these vouchers were awarded: 15 for bachelor's degrees and 5 for master's degrees.

Deadline   May of each year.

[959]
NAVY GRADUATE EDUCATION VOUCHER PROGRAM

U.S. Navy
Naval Education and Training Command
Center for Personal and Professional Development
Attn: GEV Program Office
6490 Saufley Field Road
Pensacola, FL 32509-5204
(850) 452-1001, ext. 2247   Fax: (850) 452-1272
E-mail: marjoriette.dilworth@navy.mil
Web: www.navycollege.navy.mil/gev/gev_home.cfm

Summary   To provide financial assistance to Navy officers who are interested in earning a graduate degree in selected fields during off-duty hours.

Eligibility   This program is open to active-duty unrestricted line (URL) Navy officers in ranks O-3 through O-5. Applicants should be transferring to, or currently on, shore duty with sufficient time ashore to complete a master's degree program. Officers who already have a graduate degree funded through Department of Defense assistance or veteran's education benefits are not eligible. Officers currently enrolled in a qualifying master's degree program using the Navy Tuition Assistance Program, using any other financial assistance program, or paying privately are eligible to apply for this program, but they are not eligible for reimbursement of any previously-paid educational expenses. The area of study must be certified by the Naval Postgraduate School as Navy-relevant.

Financial data   This program covers graduate education costs (tuition, books, and fees), up to a maximum of $20,000 per year.

Duration   Up to 24 months from the time of enrollment, provided the student maintains a GPA of 3.0 or higher.

Additional information   This program began in 1999. Recently, support was provided for graduate study in chemistry, computer science, engineering, English, financial management, history, mathematics, operations analysis, operations research, and regional studies. Recipients of this assistance incur an obligation to remain on active duty following completion of the program for a period equal to 3 times the number of months of education completed, to a maximum obligation of 36 months.

Number awarded Varies each year; recently, 115 of these positions were available (40 for aviation officers, 30 for submarine officers, 40 for surface warfare officers, and 5 for special warfare and special operations officers.

Deadline Deadline not specified.

[960]
NAVY LAW EDUCATION PROGRAM

U.S. Navy
Attn: Naval Education and Training Command
Center for Personal and Professional Development
Code N2A2LEP
6490 Saufley Field Road
Pensacola, FL 32509-5204
(850) 452-1001, ext. 2219 E-mail: billie.colonna@navy.mil
Web: www.jag.navy.mil

Summary To provide financial assistance to Navy and Marine Corps officers who are interested in working on a law degree on a full-time basis.

Eligibility This program is open to active-duty Navy and Marine Corps commissioned officers in pay grade O-1 through O-3. Applicants must have served at least 2 but not more than 6 years on active duty and be able to complete 20 years of active service as a commissioned officer before their 62nd birthday. They must have a baccalaureate degree from an accredited institution and be interested in working on a degree at an ABA-accredited law school. U.S. citizenship is required.

Financial data This program provides payment of mandatory tuition and fees, up to $500 per year for required textbooks, and a 1-time payment of $1,500 for a bar examination review course. Recipients continue to earn full pay and benefits while attending law school.

Duration Participants must complete their law degree within 36 months.

Additional information Following completion of their law degree, participants serve as career judge advocates in the Navy for 2 years for each year of legal training from this program.

Number awarded 7 each year.

Deadline November of each year.

[961]
NAVY MEDICAL FINANCIAL ASSISTANCE PROGRAM

U.S. Navy
Attn: Navy Medicine Professional Development Center
Code OH
8901 Wisconsin Avenue, Building 1, 13th Floor, Room 13132
Bethesda, MD 20889-5611
(301) 295-1217   Toll Free: (800) USA-NAVY
Fax: (301) 295-1811   E-mail: oh@med.navy.mil
Web: www.med.navy.mil

Summary To provide financial assistance to future Navy officers who are currently participating in a medical or dental residency.

Eligibility This program is open to U.S. citizens who are currently at any point in residency training in a medical or dental specialty that meets the needs of the U.S. Navy. Recently, that included (for doctors) family practice, orthopedic surgery, internal medicine, and general surgery and (for dentists) oral surgery and endodontics. Upon acceptance into the program, applicants are commissioned as officers in the U.S. Navy Reserve; after completion of school, they must perform active-duty service as a doctor or dentist in the Navy.

Financial data This program pays an annual grant of $45,000 and a stipend of $2,088 per month.

Additional information Participants also spend 14 days each year in an Annual Training (AT) assignment. Medical doctors incur an active-duty obligation of 1 year for each year of support plus 1 additional year. Dentists incur an active-duty obligation of 1 year for each year of support and a minimum of 3 years.

Number awarded Varies each year.

Deadline Applications may be submitted at any time.

[962]
NAVY TUITION ASSISTANCE PROGRAM

U.S. Navy
Attn: Naval Education and Training Command
Center for Personal and Professional Development
Code N725
6490 Saufley Field Road
Pensacola, FL 32509-5241
(850) 452-7271   Toll Free: (877) 838-1659
Fax: (850) 452-1149   E-mail: ncc@navy.mil
Web: www.navycollege.navy.mil/nta.cfm

Summary To provide financial assistance for high school, vocational, undergraduate, or graduate studies to Navy personnel.

Eligibility This program is open to active-duty Navy officers and enlisted personnel, including Naval Reservists on continuous active duty, enlisted Naval Reservists ordered to active duty for 120 days or more, and Naval Reservist officers ordered to active duty for 2 years or more. Applicants must register to take courses at accredited civilian schools during off-duty time. They must be working on their first associate, bachelor's, master's, doctoral, or professional degree. Tuition assistance is provided for courses taken at accredited colleges, universities, vocational/technical schools, private schools, and through independent study/distance learning (but not for flight training).

Financial data Those selected for participation in this program receive their regular Navy pay and 100% of tuition at the postsecondary educational institution of their choice, but capped at $250 per semester hour and 12 semester hours per fiscal year (the 12-semester hour limit may be waived upon application), or a total of $4,500 per fiscal year.

Duration Until completion of a bachelor's or graduate degree.

Additional information Officers must agree to remain on active duty for at least 2 years after completion of courses funded by this program.

Number awarded Varies each year.

Deadline Deadline not specified.

[963]
NCPOA/BART LONGO MEMORIAL SCHOLARSHIPS

National Chief Petty Officers' Association
c/o Marjorie Hays, Treasurer
1014 Ronald Drive
Corpus Christi, TX 78412-3548
Web: www.goatlocker.org/ncpoa/scholarship.htm

Summary To provide financial assistance for college or graduate school to members of the National Chief Petty Officers' Association (NCPOA) and their families.

Eligibility This program is open to members of the NCPOA and the children, stepchildren, and grandchildren of living or deceased members. Applicants may be high school seniors or graduates entering a college or university or students currently enrolled full time as undergraduate or graduate students. Selection is based on academic achievement and participation in extracurricular activities; need is not considered.

Financial data The stipend is $1,000.

Duration 1 year.

Additional information Membership in the NCPOA is limited to men and women who served or are serving as Chief Petty Officers in the U.S. Navy, U.S. Coast Guard, or their Reserve components for at least 30 days.

Number awarded 2 each year: 1 to a high school senior or graduate and 1 to an undergraduate or graduate student.

Deadline May of each year.

[964]
NEVADA NATIONAL GUARD STATE TUITION WAIVER PROGRAM

Nevada National Guard
Attn: Education Officer
2460 Fairview Drive
Carson City, NV 89701-6807
(775) 887-7326   Fax: (775) 887-7279
Web: www.nv.ngb.army.mil/education.cfm

Summary To provide financial assistance to Nevada National Guard members who are interested in attending college or graduate school in the state.

Eligibility This program is open to active members of the Nevada National Guard who are interested in attending a public community college, 4-year college, or university in the state. Applicants must be residents of Nevada. Independent study, correspondence courses, and study at the William S. Boyd School of Law, the University of Nevada School of Medicine, and the UNLV School of Dental Medicine are not eligible.

Financial data This program provides a waiver of 100% of tuition at state-supported community colleges, colleges, or universities in Nevada.

Duration 1 year; may be renewed.

Additional information This program was established on a pilot basis in 2003 and became permanent in 2005. Recipients must attain a GPA of at least 2.0 or refund all tuition received.

Number awarded Varies each year.

Deadline Applications must be received at least 3 weeks prior to the start of classes.

[965]
NEW HAMPSHIRE NATIONAL GUARD TUITION WAIVER PROGRAM

Office of the Adjutant General
Attn: Education Office
State Military Reservation
4 Pembroke Road
Concord, NH 03301-5652
(603) 227-1550   Fax: (603) 225-1257
TDD: (800) 735-2964
E-mail: education@nharmyguard.com
Web: www.nh.ngb.army.mil/members/education

Summary To provide financial assistance to members of the New Hampshire National Guard who are interested in attending college or graduate school in the state.

Eligibility This program is open to active members of the New Hampshire National Guard who have completed advanced individual training or commissioning and have at least a 90% attendance rate at annual training and drill assemblies. Applicants may be working on any type of academic degree at public institutions in New Hampshire. They must apply for financial aid from their school, for the New Hampshire National Guard Scholarship Program, and for federal tuition assistance.

Financial data The program provides full payment of tuition.

Duration 1 year; may be renewed.

Additional information This program began in 1996.

Number awarded Varies each year, depending on availability of space.

Deadline Deadline not specified.

[966]
NEW JERSEY NATIONAL GUARD TUITION PROGRAM

New Jersey Department of Military and Veterans Affairs
Attn: New Jersey Army National Guard Education Center
3650 Saylors Pond Road
Fort Dix, NJ 08640-7600
(609) 562-0654   Toll Free: (888) 859-0352
Fax: (609) 562-0201
Web: www.state.nj.us/military/education/NJNGTP.htm

Summary To provide financial assistance for college or graduate school to New Jersey National Guard members and the surviving spouses and children of deceased members.

Eligibility This program is open to active members of the New Jersey National Guard who have completed Initial Active Duty for Training (IADT). Applicants must be New Jersey residents who have been accepted into a program of undergraduate or graduate study at any of 31 public institutions of higher education in the state. The surviving spouses and children of deceased members of the Guard who had completed IADT and were killed in the performance of their duties while a member of the Guard are also eligible if the school has classroom space available.

Financial data Tuition for up to 15 credits per semester is waived for full-time recipients in state-supported colleges or community colleges in New Jersey.

Duration 1 semester; may be renewed.

Number awarded Varies each year.

Deadline Deadline not specified.

[967]
NEW MEXICO NATIONAL GUARD ASSOCIATION MASTER'S/CONTINUING EDUCATION SCHOLARSHIPS

New Mexico National Guard Association
Attn: Executive Director
10 Bataan Boulevard
Santa Fe, NM 87508
(505) 474-1669   Fax: (505) 474-1671
E-mail: execdir@nganm.org
Web: www.nganm.org

Summary To provide financial assistance to members of the New Mexico National Guard Association and their dependents who are working on a master's or other advanced degree.

Eligibility This program is open to association members (with paid-up current dues) and their dependents. Applicants must have completed their postsecondary education and be working on their master's or other higher degree. They must submit an official college transcript with a GPA of 3.3 or higher, a completed application, and an original essay (from 800 to 1,200 words) on their past accomplishments and contributions and what contributions they intend to make with this education to better the community or the National Guard.

Financial data The stipend is $1,000. Funds are paid directly to the recipient's school.

Duration 1 year; nonrenewable.

Number awarded 2 each year.

Deadline April of each year.

[968]
NHA ACTIVE DUTY SCHOLARSHIPS

Naval Helicopter Association
Attn: Scholarship Fund
P.O. Box 180578
Coronado, CA 92178-0578
(619) 435-7139   Fax: (619) 435-7354
Web: nhascholarshipfund.org/scholarships-available.html

Summary To provide money for college or graduate school to active-duty and former personnel who are working or have worked in rotary wing activities of the sea services.

Eligibility This program is open to active-duty or former Navy, Marine Corps, or Coast Guard rotary wing aviators, aircrewmen, or support personnel. Applicants must be working on or planning to work on an undergraduate or graduate degree in any field. Along with their application, they must submit a personal statement on their academic and career aspirations. Selection is based on that statement, academic proficiency, scholastic achievements and awards, extracurricular activities, employment history, and recommendations.

Financial data Stipends are approximately $2,000.

Duration 1 year.

Number awarded 4 each year: 2 to undergraduates and 2 to graduate students.

Deadline February of each year.

[969]
NORTH CAROLINA NATIONAL GUARD TUITION ASSISTANCE PROGRAM

North Carolina National Guard
Attn: Education Services Office
4105 Reedy Creek Road
Raleigh, NC 27607-6410
(919) 664-6272   Toll Free: (800) 621-4136
Fax: (919) 664-6520   E-mail: nceso@ng.army.mil
Web: www.nc.ngb.army.mil

Summary To provide financial assistance to members of the North Carolina National Guard who plan to attend college or graduate school in the state.

Eligibility This program is open to active members of the North Carolina National Guard (officer, warrant officer, or enlisted) who have at least 2 years of enlistment remaining after the end of the academic period for which tuition assistance is provided. Applicants must be enrolled in an eligible business or trade school, private institution, or public college/ university in North Carolina. They may be working on a vocational, undergraduate, graduate, or doctoral degree.

Financial data The maximum stipend is based on the highest tuition and fees at the University of North Carolina at Chapel Hill; recently, that was $5,396 for undergraduates or $6,692 for graduate students.

Duration 1 year; may be renewed.

Number awarded Varies each year.

Deadline Deadline not specified.

[970]
NORTH DAKOTA NATIONAL GUARD TUITION ASSISTANCE PROGRAM

North Dakota National Guard
Attn: Education Services Office
P.O. Box 5511
Bismarck, ND 58506-5511
(701) 333-3064   E-mail: ngndj1esos@ng.army.mil
Web: www.ndguard.ngb.army.mil

Summary To provide financial assistance to members of the North Dakota National Guard who plan to attend college or graduate school in the state.

Eligibility This program is open to members of the North Dakota National Guard who have a record of satisfactory participation (no more than 9 unexcused absences in the past 12 months) and service remaining after completion of the class for which they are requesting assistance. Applicants must be seeking support for trade or vocational training or work on an associate, baccalaureate, or graduate degree. They must be attending or planning to attend a North Dakota higher education public institution or a participating private institution (currently, Jamestown College, University of Mary in Bismarck, MedCenter One College of Nursing, Rasmussen College, or Trinity Bible College). Full-time AGR personnel do not qualify for this program. This is an entitlement program, provided all requirements are met.

Financial data Participating colleges and universities waive 25% of tuition for eligible courses (undergraduate only), up to 25% of the tuition at the University of North Dakota. Through this program, the National Guard provides reimbursement of the remaining 75% of tuition for eligible courses (undergraduate and graduate), or up to 75% of the tuition at the University of North Dakota. The program also reimburses

100% of all regular fees, not to exceed 100% of the regular fees charged by the University of North Dakota. State reimbursements are paid directly to the student in the form of a check, based upon the number of credit hours successfully completed.

Duration Benefits are available for up to 144 semester credit hours or the completion of an undergraduate or graduate degree, provided the recipient earns a grade of "C" or higher in each undergraduate course or "B" or higher in each graduate course.

Number awarded Varies each year.

Deadline Applications should be submitted at least 30 days before the semester begins.

[971]
PAT TILLMAN MILITARY SCHOLARS PROGRAM

Pat Tillman Foundation
2121 South Mill Avenue, Suite 214
Tempe, AZ 85282
(480) 621-4074   Fax: (480) 621-4075
E-mail: scholarships@pattillmanfoundation.org
Web: www.pattillmanfoundation.org/tillman-military-scholars

Summary To provide financial assistance to veterans, active servicemembers, and their spouses who are interested in working on an undergraduate or graduate degree.

Eligibility This program is open to veterans and active servicemembers of all branches of the armed forces from both the pre- and post-September 11 era and their spouses; children are not eligible. Applicants must be enrolled or planning to enroll full time at a 4-year public or private college or university to work on an undergraduate, graduate, or postgraduate degree. Current and former servicemembers must submit 400-word essays on 1) their motivation and decision to serve in the U.S. military and how that decision and experience has changed their life and ambitions; and 2) their educational and career goals, how they will incorporate their military service experience into those goals, and how they intend to continue their service to others and the community. Spouses must submit 400-word essays on 1) their previous service to others and the community; and 2) their educational and career goals, how they will incorporate their service experiences and the impact of their spouse's military service into those goals, and how they intend to continue their service to others and the community. Selection is based on those essays, educational and career ambitions, record of military service, record of personal achievement, demonstration of service to others in the community, desire to continue such service, and leadership potential.

Financial data The stipend depends on the need of the recipient and the availability of funds.

Duration 1 year; may be renewed, provided the recipient maintains a GPA of 3.0 or higher, remains enrolled full time, and participates in civic action or community service.

Additional information This program began in 2009.

Number awarded Varies each year; recently, 60 students received a total of $916,000 through this program.

Deadline March of each year.

[972]
PENNSYLVANIA NATIONAL GUARD EDUCATIONAL ASSISTANCE PROGRAM

Pennsylvania Higher Education Assistance Agency
Attn: Special Programs
1200 North Seventh Street
P.O. Box 8157
Harrisburg, PA 17105-8157
(717) 720-2800   Toll Free: (800) 692-7392
Fax: (717) 720-5786   TDD: (800) 654-5988
Web: www.pheaa.org

Summary To provide money for college or graduate school to Pennsylvania National Guard members.

Eligibility This program is open to active members of the Pennsylvania National Guard who are Pennsylvania residents and serving as enlisted personnel, warrant officers, or commissioned officers of any grade. Applicants must accept an obligation to serve in the Pennsylvania National Guard for a period of 6 years from the date of entry into the program. Students who do not possess a baccalaureate degree must be enrolled full or part time in an approved program of education at an approved institution of higher learning in Pennsylvania. Master's degree students are supported on a part-time basis only. Guard members receiving an ROTC scholarship of any type are not eligible.

Financial data Full-time undergraduate students receive payment of 100% of tuition at a state-owned university. Part-time students receive either actual tuition charged or two-thirds of the full-time tuition charged to a Pennsylvania resident at a state-owned university, whichever is less. Graduate students receive either half the actual tuition charged or one-third of the full-time tuition charged to a Pennsylvania resident at a state-owned university, whichever is less. Recipients who fail to fulfill the service obligation must repay all funds received within 10 years, including interest at 7%.

Duration Up to 5 years.

Additional information This program, first offered in 1997, is jointly administered by the Pennsylvania Department of Military and Veterans Affairs and the Pennsylvania Higher Education Assistance Agency. Support for summer and graduate school is available only if funding permits.

Number awarded Varies each year; recently, 1,789 members of the Pennsylvania National Guard were enrolled in this program.

Deadline April of each year for students at colleges, universities, and transferable programs at community colleges; July of each year for students at business schools, trade/technical schools, hospital schools of nursing, and nontransferable programs at community colleges.

[973]
PLATOON LEADERS CLASS MARINE CORPS TUITION ASSISTANCE PROGRAM

U.S. Marine Corps
Attn: Marine Corps Recruiting Command
3280 Russell Road
Quantico, VA 22134-5103
(703) 784-9449   Fax: (703) 784-9859
E-mail: wendelrf@mcrc.usmc.mil
Web: www.usmc.mil

Summary To provide financial assistance to members of the Marine Corps Reserves interested in working on a bachelor's or law degree.
Eligibility This program is open to members of the Marine Corps Reserves enrolled full time in a bachelor's or law (J.D. or equivalent) degree program. Applicants must be a member of the Marine Corps Platoon Leader Class (PLC) Program and have completed 6 weeks (or more) of military training required by that program. They must agree to accept a commission in the active-duty Marine Corps and serve 5 years following completion of their degree.
Financial data This program provides reimbursement of tuition, books, and required fees, up to a maximum of $5,200 per academic year. If participants are also members of the Marine Corps Reserves, they may use any Montgomery GI Bill benefits to which they are entitled.
Duration Up to 3 consecutive years, or completion of a bachelor's or law degree.
Additional information Participants who successfully obtain a bachelor's or law degree and complete officer candidate training are commissioned as second lieutenants in the Regular Marine Corps. This program began in 1999.
Number awarded Up to 1,200 each year.
Deadline December of each year.

[974]
POST-9/11 GI BILL

Department of Veterans Affairs
Attn: Veterans Benefits Administration
810 Vermont Avenue, N.W.
Washington, DC 20420
(202) 418-4343   Toll Free: (888) GI-BILL1
Web: www.gibill.va.gov/benefits/post_911_gibill/index.html

Summary To provide funding to veterans or military personnel who entered service on or after September 11, 2001.
Eligibility This program is open to current and former military personnel who 1) served on active duty for at least 90 aggregate days after September 11, 2001; or 2) were discharged with a service-connected disability after 30 days. Applicants must be planning to enroll in an educational program, including work on an undergraduate or graduate degree, vocational/technical training, on-the-job training, flight training, correspondence training, licensing and national testing programs, and tutorial assistance.
Financial data Participants working on an undergraduate or graduate degree at public institutions in their state receive full payment of tuition and fees. For participants who attend private institutions in most states, tuition and fee reimbursement is capped at $17,500 per academic year; the reimbursement rate is higher at private schools in Arizona, Michigan, New Hampshire, New York, Pennsylvania, South Carolina, and Texas. Benefits for other types of training programs depend on the amount for which the veteran qualified under prior educational programs. Veterans also receive a monthly housing allowance based on the national average Basic Allowance for Housing (BAH) for an E-5 with dependents (currently $673.50) or $1,347 per month at schools in foreign countries; an annual book allowance of $1,000; and (for participants who live in a rural county remote from an educational institution) a rural benefit payment of $500 per year.

Duration Most participants receive up to 36 months of entitlement under this program. Benefits are payable for up to 15 years following release from active duty.
Additional information This program, referred to as Chapter 33, began in 2009 as a replacement for previous educational programs for veterans and military personnel (e.g., Montgomery GI Bill, REAP). Current participants in those programs may be able to transfer benefits from those programs to this new plan. To qualify for 100% of Post 9/11-GI Bill benefits, transferees must have at least 36 months of active-duty service. Transferees with less service are entitled to smaller percentages of benefits, ranging down to 40% for those with only 90 days of service.
Number awarded Varies each year; since the program began, it has awarded nearly $4 billion in benefits to more than 295,000 veterans.
Deadline Deadline not specified.

[975]
REDUCED TUITION FOR SOUTH DAKOTA
NATIONAL GUARD MEMBERS

South Dakota Board of Regents
Attn: Scholarship Committee
306 East Capitol Avenue, Suite 200
Pierre, SD 57501-2545
(605) 773-3455   Fax: (605) 773-2422
E-mail: info@sdbor.edu
Web: www.sdbor.edu

Summary To provide financial assistance for college or graduate school to members of the South Dakota National Guard.
Eligibility Eligible to apply for this assistance are members of the South Dakota Army or Air National Guard who are South Dakota residents, have satisfactorily completed Initial Active Duty for Training (IADT), meet the entrance requirements at 1 of the 6 state educational institutions or 4 state vocational/technical schools, maintain sustained membership in their National Guard unit, and maintain satisfactory academic progress.
Financial data Qualifying Guard members are eligible for a 50% reduction in tuition at any state-supported postsecondary institution in South Dakota.
Duration This assistance is available for up to 128 credit hours at the undergraduate level and up to 32 credit hours at the graduate level.
Additional information Students participating in the Army Continuing Education Systems (ACES) or the Montgomery GI Bill are not authorized to use this program.
Number awarded Varies each year.
Deadline Deadline not specified.

[976]
RESERVE EDUCATIONAL ASSISTANCE PROGRAM

Department of Veterans Affairs
Attn: Veterans Benefits Administration
810 Vermont Avenue, N.W.
Washington, DC 20420
(202) 418-4343   Toll Free: (888) GI-BILL1
Web: www.gibill.va.gov/benefits/other_programs/reap.html

Summary To provide financial assistance for college or graduate school to members of the Reserves or National

Guard who are called to active duty during a period of national emergency.

Eligibility This program is open to members of the Selected Reserve and Individual Ready Reserve (including Reserve elements of the Army, Navy, Air Force, Marine Corps, and Coast Guard, as well as the Army National Guard and the Air National Guard) who have served on active duty on or after September 11, 2001 for at least 90 consecutive days. Applicants must be interested in working on an undergraduate or graduate degree, vocational or technical training, on-the-job or apprenticeship training, correspondence training, or flight training.

Financial data For full-time study at a college or university, the current monthly rate is $589.20 for personnel with consecutive service of 90 days but less than 1 year, $883.80 for personnel with consecutive service of more than 1 year but less than 2 years, or $1,178.40 for those with consecutive service of 2 years or more. Reduced rates apply for part-time college or university study, apprenticeship and on-the-job training, licensing and certification training, cooperative education, correspondence courses, and flight training.

Duration Up to 36 months for full-time study. There is no fixed time for persons eligible for this program to utilize its benefits (except in the case of a member separated from the Ready Reserve for a disability, who are entitled to benefits for 10 years after the date of eligibility).

Additional information This program, established in 2005, is frequently referred to as Chapter 1607.

Number awarded Varies each year.

Deadline Applications may be submitted at any time.

[977]
RHODE ISLAND NATIONAL GUARD STATE TUITION ASSISTANCE PROGRAM

Rhode Island National Guard
Joint Force Headquarters
Attn: Education Service Officer
645 New London Avenue
Cranston, RI 02920-3097
(401) 275-4109   Fax: (401) 275-4014
E-mail: NGRIeduc@ng.army.mil
Web: states.ng.mil/sites/RI/education/default.aspx

Summary To provide financial support to members of the National Guard in Rhode Island interested in attending college or graduate school in the state.

Eligibility This program is open to active members of the Rhode Island National Guard in good standing who are currently satisfactorily participating in all unit training assemblies and annual training periods. Applicants must have at least 1 year of service remaining. They must be enrolled in or planning to enroll in an associate, bachelor's, or master's degree program at a public institution in the state.

Financial data Qualified Guard members receive payment of tuition for up to 5 courses per semester.

Duration 1 semester; may be renewed.

Additional information This program began in 1999.

Number awarded Varies each year.

Deadline Deadline not specified.

[978]
RHODE ISLAND NATIONAL GUARD STATE TUITION EXEMPTION PROGRAM

Rhode Island National Guard
Joint Force Headquarters
Attn: Education Service Officer
645 New London Avenue
Cranston, RI 02920-3097
(401) 275-4109   Fax: (401) 275-4014
E-mail: NGRIeduc@ng.army.mil
Web: states.ng.mil/sites/RI/education/default.aspx

Summary To provide financial support to members of the Rhode Island National Guard who attend public institutions in the state.

Eligibility This program is open to active members of the Rhode Island National Guard who attend all required unit training assemblies and annual training. Applicants must be residents of Rhode Island working toward an associate, bachelors, or master's degree at a designated public institution in the state. They must pass the Guard's height and weight standards, weapons qualification, and the APFT. They may not have more than 4 unexcused absences from military duty within a 12-month period or have tested positive for any illegal drug.

Financial data Qualified Guard members are entitled to tuition-free classes at public institutions in Rhode Island. The waiver does not cover books or fees.

Duration Upon enrollment, Guard members are entitled to 2 tuition-free classes per year.

Additional information This program began in 1994. The designated institutions are the University of Rhode Island, Rhode Island College, and the Community College of Rhode Island.

Number awarded Varies each year.

Deadline Deadline not specified.

[979]
ROBERT W. BRUNSMAN MEMORIAL SCHOLARSHIP

International Military Community Executives' Association
Attn: Scholarship
P.O. Box 7286
Alexandria, VA 22307-0286
(571) 207-8893   Fax: (866) 369-2435
E-mail: imcea@imcea.org
Web: www.imcea.org/scholarship.html

Summary To provide financial assistance to members of the International Military Community Executives' Association (IMCEA) who are working in the field of military morale, welfare, and recreation (MWR) and currently enrolled in college or graduate school.

Eligibility This program is open to regular IMCEA members who are currently employed in the field of military MWR. Applicants must be already enrolled at a college or university, either in-class or online, and taking undergraduate or graduate courses related to MWR. Along with their application, they must submit a 2-page essay on how all MWR services (e.g., clubs, bowling, golf, child care, libraries) might work together to create synergy and enhance the mission of IMCEA. Selection is based on that essay, participation in IMCEA activities, and involvement in military MWR services.

Financial data The stipend is $1,000.

Duration 1 year.

Additional information Regular membership in IMCEA is open to Army, Air Force, Navy, Marine Corps, and Coast Guard personnel who provide MWR services at military installations and bases worldwide.

Number awarded 1 each year.

Deadline April of each year.

[980]
ROBERT W. NOLAN SCHOLARSHIP

Fleet Reserve Association
Attn: FRA Education Foundation
125 North West Street
Alexandria, VA 22314-2754
(703) 683-1400   Toll Free: (800) FRA-1924
Fax: (703) 549-6610   E-mail: scholars@fra.org
Web: www.fra.org

Summary To provide financial assistance for graduate school to members of the Fleet Reserve Association (FRA) and their families.

Eligibility This program is open to members of the FRA and the dependent children, grandchildren, and spouses of living or deceased members. Applicants must be enrolled as full-time graduate students. Along with their application, they must submit an essay on why they want to go to college and what they intend to accomplish with their degree. Selection is based on academic record, financial need, extracurricular activities, leadership skills, and participation in community activities. U.S. citizenship is required.

Financial data The stipend is $5,000 per year.

Duration 1 year; may be renewed.

Additional information Membership in the FRA is restricted to active-duty, retired, and Reserve members of the Navy, Marine Corps, and Coast Guard. This program was established in 2001.

Number awarded 1 each year.

Deadline April of each year.

[981]
RUTH LANG FITZGERALD MEMORIAL SCHOLARSHIP

Massachusetts Association of Registered Nurses
P.O. Box 285
Milton, MA 02186
(617) 990-2856   Toll Free: (866) MARN-ANA
E-mail: info@marnonline.org
Web: www.marnonline.org

Summary To provide funding to members of the Massachusetts Association of Registered Nurses (MARN), particularly those with ties to the military, who are interested in working on a special project or attending a conference.

Eligibility This program is open to registered nurses who have been members of MARN for at least 1 year. Applicants must be interested in pursuing an area of interest or special project that will be beneficial to them and/or the association. The award may be used to attend an educational conference, the American Nurses Association convention, or some other educational activity. It may also be used to participate in a humanitarian aid project. Preference is given to applicants who have current or prior military service, work or hope to work with a senior population, or have an interest in legislative issues.

Financial data The grant is $1,000.

Duration 1 year; nonrenewable.

Number awarded 1 each year.

Deadline October of each year.

[982]
SAMUEL ELIOT MORISON NAVAL HISTORY SCHOLARSHIP

Naval History and Heritage Command
Attn: Senior Historian
Washington Navy Yard
805 Kidder Breese Street, S.E.
Washington Navy Yard, DC 20374-5060
(202) 433-3940   Fax: (202) 433-3593
Web: www.history.navy.mil/prizes/prize3.htm

Summary To provide financial assistance to Navy and Marine Corps officers who are working on a graduate degree in a field related to naval history.

Eligibility This program is open to active-duty commissioned officers of the U.S. Navy or U.S. Marine Corps who are working on a graduate degree in history, international relations, or a related field. Applications must be submitted through and endorsed by applicants' commanding officers. Selection is based on the relevance of the chosen area of study to U.S. naval history; demonstrated professional performance with particular emphasis on the officer's specialty; academic ability, including baccalaureate record; career needs of the officer; and potential for professional growth.

Financial data The stipend is $5,000; funds are to be used for expenses related to research, travel, and the purchase of books or other educational materials.

Duration 1 year.

Number awarded 1 each year.

Deadline March of each year.

[983]
SCHUYLER S. PYLE SCHOLARSHIP

Fleet Reserve Association
Attn: FRA Education Foundation
125 North West Street
Alexandria, VA 22314-2754
(703) 683-1400   Toll Free: (800) FRA-1924
Fax: (703) 549-6610   E-mail: scholars@fra.org
Web: www.fra.org

Summary To provide financial assistance for college or graduate school to members of the Fleet Reserve Association (FRA) and their families.

Eligibility This program is open to members of the FRA and the dependent children, grandchildren, and spouses of living or deceased members. Applicants must be enrolled as full-time undergraduate or graduate students. Along with their application, they must submit an essay on why they want to go to college and what they intend to accomplish with their degree. Selection is based on academic record, financial need, extracurricular activities, leadership skills, and participation in community activities. U.S. citizenship is required.

Financial data The stipend is $5,000 per year.

Duration 1 year; may be renewed.

Additional information Membership in the FRA is restricted to active-duty, retired, and Reserve members of the Navy, Marine Corps, and Coast Guard.

Number awarded 1 each year.
Deadline April of each year.

[984]
SCOTT DOMINGUEZ-CRATERS OF THE MOON CHAPTER SCHOLARSHIP

American Society of Safety Engineers
Attn: ASSE Foundation
1800 East Oakton Street
Des Plaines, IL 60018
(847) 768-3435   Fax: (847) 768-3434
E-mail: agabanski@asse.org
Web: www.asse.org

Summary To provide financial assistance to undergraduate and graduate student members of the American Society of Safety Engineers (ASSE), particularly those with ties to the military, who are from designated western states.

Eligibility This program is open to ASSE members who are working on an undergraduate or graduate degree in occupational safety, health, and environment or a closely-related field (e.g., industrial or environmental engineering, environmental science, industrial hygiene, occupational health nursing). First priority is given to residents within the service area of Craters of the Moon Chapter in Idaho; second priority is given to residents of other states in ASSE Region II (Arizona, Colorado, Montana, Nevada, New Mexico, Utah, and Wyoming). Special consideration is also given to 1) employees of a sponsoring organization or their dependents; 2) students who are serving their country through active duty in the armed forces or are honorably discharged; 3) former members of the Boy Scouts, Girl Scouts, FFA, or 4-H; 4) recipients of awards from service organizations; and 5) students who have provided volunteer service to an ASSE chapter in a leadership role. Undergraduates must have completed at least 60 semester hours with a GPA of 3.0 or higher. Graduate students must have completed at least 9 semester hours with a GPA of 3.5 or higher and have had a GPA of 3.0 or higher as an undergraduate. Full-time students must be ASSE student members; part-time students must be ASSE general or professional members. Along with their application, they must submit 2 essays of 300 words or less: 1) why they are seeking a degree in occupational safety and health or a closely-related field, a brief description of their current activities, and how those relate to their career goals and objectives; and 2) why they should be awarded this scholarship (including career goals and financial need). U.S. citizenship is not required.

Financial data The stipend is $1,000 per year.
Duration 1 year; recipients may reapply.
Additional information This program is sponsored by the ASSE Craters of the Moon Chapter.
Number awarded 1 each year.
Deadline November of each year.

[985]
UTAH NATIONAL GUARD STATE TUITION ASSISTANCE PROGRAM

Utah Army National Guard
Attn: UT-G1-ESO
12953 South Minuteman Drive
P.O. Box 1776
Draper, UT 84020-1776
(801) 523-4534   E-mail: ngut.sta@us.army.mil
Web: www.ut.ngb.army.mil/education2

Summary To provide tuition assistance for college or graduate school to currently-enrolled members of the Utah National Guard.

Eligibility This program is open to Utah residents who are MOS/AFSC qualified members of the Utah National Guard. Applicants must be seeking funding to obtain a 1) high school diploma or GED certification; 2) undergraduate, graduate, vocational, technical, or licensure certificate; 3) associate degree; 4) baccalaureate degree; or 5) master's or first professional degree, such as architecture, certified public accountant, podiatry (D.P.M.), dentistry (D.D.S. or D.M.D.), medicine (M.D.), optometry (O.D.), osteopathic medicine (D.O.), pharmacy (D.Pharm.), law (J.D.), or theology (M.Div. or M.H.L.). Enlisted personnel must have remaining obligation on their existing enlistment contract that will extend to or beyond the last date of course enrollment for these funds. Officers must have at least 4 years of Selected Reserve service remaining from the date of completion of the course for which this funding is provided.

Financial data Support is provided for 100% of the cost of tuition, to a maximum of $250 per hour or a maximum of $4,500 per year.
Duration 1 semester; recipients may renew.
Additional information Members of the Utah Air National Guard should contact the 151st MSF-DPH, 765 North 2200 West, Salt Lake City, UT 84116. Recipients of this funding may continue to receive any GI Bill funding to which they are entitled, but they may not simultaneously apply for this and federal Tuition Assistance benefits.
Number awarded Varies each year; recently, a total of $750,000 was available for this program.
Deadline March of each year for summer term; August of each year for fall term; November of each year for winter or spring term.

[986]
VIRGINIA NATIONAL GUARD TUITION ASSISTANCE PROGRAM

Virginia National Guard
Attn: Educational Services Officer
Fort Pickett, Building 316
Blackstone, VA 23824-6316
(434) 298-6222   Toll Free: (888) 483-2682
Fax: (434) 298-6296   E-mail: vaeducation@ng.army.mil
Web: vko.va.ngb.army.mil/VirginiaGuard

Summary To provide financial assistance to members of the Virginia National Guard who are interested in attending college or graduate school in the state.

Eligibility This program is open to active members of the Virginia National Guard who are residents of Virginia and interested in attending college or graduate school in the state. Awards are presented in the following priority order: 1) enlisted personnel who have previously received assistance through this program; 2) officers who need to complete a bachelor's degree in order to be eligible for promotion to captain; 3) warrant officers working on an associate or bachelor's degree; 4) any member working on an undergraduate degree; and 4) any member working on a graduate degree.

Financial data The program provides reimbursement of tuition at approved colleges, universities, and vocational/technical schools in Virginia, to a maximum of $2,000 per semester or $6,000 per year. Bookstore grants up to $350 per semester are also provided.

Duration 1 semester; may be renewed.

Additional information This program began in 1983. Recipients must remain in the Guard for at least 2 years after being funded.

Number awarded Varies each year.

Deadline March of each year for summer session; June of each year for fall semester; October of each year for spring semester.

[987]
WASHINGTON NATIONAL GUARD SCHOLARSHIP PROGRAM

Washington National Guard
Attn: Education Services Office
Building 15, G1-ED
Camp Murray, WA 98430
(253) 512-8838   Toll Free: (800) 606-9843 (within WA)
Fax: (253) 512-8941 E-mail: education@wa.ngb.army.mil
Web: washingtonguard.org/edu

Summary To provide funding to members of the Washington National Guard who wish to attend college or graduate school in the state.

Eligibility This program is open to members of the Washington National Guard who have already served for at least 1 year and have at least 2 years remaining on their current contract. Applicants must have a rank between E1 and O3. They must be attending an accredited college as a resident of Washington state and must already have utilized all available federal educational benefits. Army Guard members must have completed BCT/AIT and awarded initial MOS; Air Guard members must have completed BMT/initial tech school and been awarded "3-Level" AFSC. Graduate students are eligible, but undergraduates receive preference as long as they are making satisfactory progress toward a baccalaureate degree. The minimum GPA requirement is 2.5 for undergraduates or 3.0 for graduate students.

Financial data This program provides a stipend that is based on the number of credits completed but does not exceed the amount required for tuition, books, and fees at the University of Washington. Recipients incur a service obligation of 1 additional year in the Guard for the initial scholarship award and 1 additional year for each full year of academic credit completed with this assistance. The grant serves as a loan which is forgiven if the recipient completes the contracted service time in the Washington National Guard. Failure to meet the service obligation requires the recipient to repay the loan plus 8% interest.

Duration 1 year; may be renewed.

Number awarded Varies each year. A total of $100,000 is available for this program annually; scholarships are awarded on a first-come, first-served basis as long as funds are available.

Deadline June of each year.

[988]
WEST VIRGINIA NATIONAL GUARD EDUCATIONAL ENCOURAGEMENT PROGRAM

Office of the Adjutant General
Attn: Education Officer
1703 Coonskin Drive
Charleston, WV 25311-1085
(304) 561-6306   Toll Free: (866) 986-4326
Fax: (304) 561-6307   E-mail: kathy.kidd@us.army.mil
Web: www.wv.ngb.army.mil/education/benefits/default.aspx

Summary To provide financial assistance to members of the National Guard in West Virginia who are interested in attending college or graduate school in the state.

Eligibility This program is open to active members of the West Virginia National Guard who are residents of West Virginia and interested in attending a public or private college in the state. Applicants must have maintained satisfactory participation (90% attendance) in the Guard. They must be interested in working on a vocational, associate, bachelor's, or master's degree. In some instances, support may also be available to Guard members who are interested in working on an M.D., D.O., P.A., or J.D. degree.

Financial data The program provides payment of 100% of the tuition and fees at participating colleges and universities in West Virginia, to a maximum of $6,000 per year.

Duration 1 academic year; may be renewed.

Number awarded Varies each year.

Deadline Deadline not specified.

[989]
WILLIAM J. PERRY FELLOWSHIP IN INTERNATIONAL SECURITY

Stanford University
Center for International Security and Cooperation
Attn: Fellowship Coordinator
Encina Hall, Room C206-7
616 Serra Street
Stanford, CA 94305-6165
(650) 724-9132   Fax: (650) 723-0089
E-mail: perryfellows@stanford.edu
Web: cisac.stanford.edu/fellowships/perry_fellowship

Summary To provide funding to professionals (particularly those from the military) who are interested in conducting policy-relevant research on international security issues while in residence at Stanford University's Center for International Security and Cooperation.

Eligibility This program is open to early and mid-career professionals from academia, the public and private sectors, national laboratories, and the military, either from the United States or abroad. Applicants must have a record of outstanding work in natural science, engineering, or mathematics and a genuine interest and dedication to solving international security problems. Their proposed research may involve interlapping issues of nuclear weapons policy and nuclear proliferation, regional tensions, biosecurity, homeland security, and effective global engagement.

Financial data The stipend depends on experience and is determined on a case-by-case basis. Health care and other benefits are also provided.

Duration 9 months.

Additional information Fellows are expected to produce a publishable manuscript based on their research. They should not plan to spend any time conducting research abroad or in other parts of the country.

Number awarded 1 each year.

Deadline January of each year.

[990]
WISCONSIN NATIONAL GUARD ENLISTED ASSOCIATION COLLEGE GRANT PROGRAM

Wisconsin National Guard Enlisted Association
Attn: Executive Director
2400 Wright Street
Madison, WI 53704
(608) 242-3112   E-mail: WNGEA@yahoo.com
Web: www.wngea.org/MAIN/PROG/prosch.htm

Summary To provide financial assistance to members of the Wisconsin National Guard Enlisted Association (WNGEA) and their spouses and children who are interested in attending college or graduate school in any state.

Eligibility This program is open to WNGEA members, the unmarried children and spouses of WNGEA members, and the unmarried children and spouses of deceased WNGEA members. WNGEA member applicants, as well as the parents or guardians of unmarried children who are applicants, must have at least 1 year remaining on their enlistment following completion of the school year for which application is submitted (or they must have 20 or more years of service). Applicants must be enrolled at a college, university, graduate school, trade school, or business school in any state. Selection is based on need, leadership, and moral character.

Financial data Stipends are $1,000 or $500 per year.

Duration 1 year; recipients may not reapply for 2 years.

Additional information This program includes 1 scholarship sponsored by the USAA Insurance Corporation.

Number awarded Varies each year; recently, 4 of these scholarships were awarded: the Raymond A. Matera Scholarship at $1,000 and 3 others at $500 each.

Deadline April of each year.

[991]
WOMEN MARINES ASSOCIATION SCHOLARSHIP PROGRAM

Women Marines Association
P.O. Box 377
Oaks, PA 19456-0377
Toll Free: (888) 525-1943
E-mail: scholarship@womenmarines.org
Web: www.womenmarines.org/scholarships.aspx

Summary To provide money for college or graduate school to students with ties to the military who are sponsored by members of the Women Marines Association (WMA).

Eligibility Applicants must be sponsored by a WMA member and fall into 1 of the following categories: 1) have served or are serving in the U.S. Marine Corps, regular or Reserve; 2) are a direct descendant by blood or legal adoption or a stepchild of a Marine on active duty or who has served honorably in the U.S. Marine Corps, regular or Reserve; 3) are a sibling or a descendant of a sibling by blood or legal adoption or a stepchild of a Marine on active duty or who has served honorably in the U.S. Marine Corps, regular or Reserve; or 4) have completed 2 years in a Marine Corps JROTC program. WMA members may sponsor an unlimited number of applicants per year. High school seniors must submit transcripts (GPA of 3.0 or higher) and SAT or ACT scores. Undergraduate and graduate students must have a GPA of 3.0 or higher.

Financial data The stipend is $1,500 per year.

Duration 1 year; may be renewed 1 additional year.

Additional information This program includes the following named scholarships: the WMA Memorial Scholarships, the Lily H. Gridley Memorial Scholarship, the Ethyl and Armin Wiebke Memorial Scholarship, the Maj. Megan Malia McClung Memorial Scholarship, the Agnes Sopcak Memorial Scholarship, the Virginia Guveyan Memorial Scholarship, and the LaRue A. Ditmore Music Scholarships. Applicants must know a WMA member to serve as their sponsor; the WMA will not supply listings of the names or addresses of chapters or individual members.

Number awarded Varies each year.

Deadline January of each year.

[992]
WYOMING NATIONAL GUARD EDUCATIONAL ASSISTANCE PLAN

Wyoming National Guard
Attn: Education Services Officer
5410 Bishop Boulevard
Cheyenne, WY 82009
(307) 772-5939   Toll Free: (800) 832-1959, ext. 5939
Fax: (307) 772-5132 E-mail: wyomingguard@state.wy.us
Web: wyoguard.com/education/assistance

Summary To provide financial assistance to members of the Wyoming National Guard who are interested in attending college or graduate school in the state.

Eligibility This program is open to members of the Wyoming Army National Guard and the Wyoming Air National Guard who have spent at least 6 years in the Guard or are currently serving under their initial 6-year enlistment period. New enlistees who commit to serving 6 years are also eligible. Applicants may be pursuing, or planning to pursue, a degree at any level at the University of Wyoming, a Wyoming community college, or an approved technical institution in Wyoming.

Financial data The program provides full payment of tuition at eligible institutions.

Duration Guard members may continue to receive these benefits as long as they maintain a GPA of 2.0 or higher, keep up with Guard standards for drill attendance, and remain in good standing with the Guard.

Additional information The Wyoming legislature created this program in 2001. Recipients must agree to serve in the Guard for at least 2 years after they graduate or stop using the plan.

Number awarded Varies each year.

Deadline Deadline not specified.

Family Members

[993]
100TH INFANTRY BATTALION MEMORIAL SCHOLARSHIP FUND

Hawai'i Community Foundation
Attn: Scholarship Department
827 Fort Street Mall
Honolulu, HI 96813
(808) 537-6333   Toll Free: (888) 731-3863
Fax: (808) 521-6286
E-mail: scholarships@hcf-hawaii.org
Web: www.hawaiicommunityfoundation.org/scholarships

Summary To provide financial assistance for college or graduate school to descendants of 100th Infantry Battalion World War II veterans.

Eligibility This program is open to entering and continuing full-time undergraduate and graduate students at 2- and 4-year colleges and universities. Applicants must be a direct descendant of a World War II veteran of the 100th Infantry Battalion (which was comprised of Americans of Japanese descent). They must be able to demonstrate academic achievement (GPA of 3.5 or higher), an active record of extracurricular activities and community service, a willingness to promote the legacy of the 100th Infantry Battalion of World War II, and financial need. Along with their application, they must submit a short statement indicating their reasons for attending college, their planned course of study, their career goals, and what community service means to them. They must also submit a separate essay on the legacy of the 100th Infantry Battalion and how they will contribute to forwarding that legacy. Current residency in Hawaii is not required.

Financial data The amounts of the awards depend on the availability of funds and the need of the recipient. Recently, the average value of each of the scholarships awarded by the foundation was more than $2,000.

Duration 1 year.

Number awarded Varies each year; recently, 2 of these scholarships were awarded.

Deadline February of each year.

[994]
AIR FORCE SERVICES CLUB MEMBERSHIP SCHOLARSHIP PROGRAM

Air Force Services Agency
Attn: HQ AFSVA/SVOFT
10100 Reunion Place, Suite 501
San Antonio, TX 78216-4138
(210) 395-7787
E-mail: web.clubs-operations@randolph.af.mil
Web: www.afclubs.net/CN_Scholarship.htm

Summary To recognize and reward, with academic scholarships, Air Force Club members and their families who submit outstanding essays.

Eligibility This program is open to Air Force Club members and their spouses, children, and stepchildren who have been accepted by or are enrolled at an accredited college or university. Grandchildren are eligible if they are the dependent of a club member. Applicants may be undergraduate or graduate students enrolled full or part time. They must submit an essay of up to 500 words on a topic that changes annually; a recent topic was "My Contribution to the Air Force." Applicants must also include a 1-page summary of their long-term career and life goals and previous accomplishments, including civic, athletic, and academic awards.

Financial data Awards are $1,000 scholarships.

Duration The competition is held annually.

Additional information This competition, first held in 1997, is sponsored by Chase Bank and the Coca-Cola Company.

Number awarded 25 each year.

Deadline Entries must be submitted to the member's base services commander or division chief by June of each year.

[995]
AIR FORCE SPOUSE SCHOLARSHIPS

Air Force Association
Attn: Manager, National Aerospace Awards
1501 Lee Highway
Arlington, VA 22209-1198
(703) 247-5800, ext. 4807
Toll Free: (800) 727-3337, ext. 4807
Fax: (703) 247-5853   E-mail: lcross@afa.org
Web: www.afa.org/aef/aid/spouse.asp

Summary To provide financial assistance for undergraduate or graduate study to spouses of Air Force members.

Eligibility This program is open to spouses of active-duty Air Force, Air National Guard, or Air Force Reserve members. Spouses who are themselves military members or in ROTC are not eligible. Applicants must have a GPA of 3.5 or higher in college (or high school if entering college for the first time) and be able to provide proof of acceptance into an accredited undergraduate or graduate degree program. They must submit a 2-page essay on their academic and career goals, the motivation that led them to that decision, and how Air Force and other local community activities in which they are involved will enhance their goals. Selection is based on the essay and 2 letters of recommendation.

Financial data The stipend is $2,500; funds are sent to the recipients' schools to be used for any reasonable cost related to working on a degree.

Duration 1 year; nonrenewable.

Additional information This program began in 1995.

Number awarded Varies each year; recently, 3 of these scholarships were awarded.

Deadline April of each year.

[996]
AL AND WILLAMARY VISTE SCHOLARSHIP PROGRAM

101st Airborne Division Association
32 Screaming Eagle Boulevard
P.O. Box 929
Fort Campbell, KY 42223-0929
(931) 431-0199   Fax: (931) 431-0195
E-mail: 101stairbornedivisionassociation@comcast.net
Web: www.screamingeagle.org/Scholarships.aspx

Summary To provide financial assistance to the spouses, children, and grandchildren of members of the 101st Airborne Division Association who are upper-division or graduate students working on a degree in science.

Eligibility This program is open to college juniors, seniors, and graduate students who maintained a GPA of 3.75 or higher during the preceding school year and whose parent, grandparent, or spouse is (or, if deceased, was) a regular or life (not associate) member of the 101st Airborne Division. Preference is given to students working on a degree in a physical science, medical science, or other scientific research field. Applicants must submit a 500-word essay on what it means to be an American and a letter on their course of study, community service, hobbies, interests, personal achievements, and how a higher education for them in their chosen field can benefit our nation. Selection is based on the letter, career objectives, academic record, and letters of recommendation.

Financial data A stipend is awarded (amount not specified).

Duration 1 year; may be renewed.

Number awarded At least 1 each year.

Deadline May of each year.

[997]
AL PONTE SCHOLARSHIP AWARD

Association of Former Intelligence Officers
Attn: Scholarships Committee
6723 Whittier Avenue, Suite 200
McLean, VA 22101-4533
(703) 790-0320   Fax: (703) 991-1278
E-mail: afio@afio.com
Web: www.afio.com/13_scholarships.htm

Summary To provide financial assistance to members or the children or grandchildren of members of the Association of Former Intelligence Officers (AFIO) who are interested in working on a graduate degree in international relations and/or intelligence.

Eligibility This program is open to college seniors who are interested in attending graduate school to work on a degree in international relations and/or intelligence. Applicants must be AFIO members, the children or grandchildren of members, or the children or grandchildren of personnel currently serving in military intelligence. Selection is based on merit, character, estimated future potential, background, and relevance of their studies to the full spectrum of national security interests and career ambitions. U.S. citizenship is required.

Financial data The stipend is $1,000.

Duration 1 year.

Number awarded 1 each year.

Deadline June of each year.

[998]
ALABAMA G.I. DEPENDENTS' SCHOLARSHIP PROGRAM

Alabama Department of Veterans Affairs
770 Washington Avenue, Suite 470
Montgomery, AL 36102-1509
(334) 242-5077   Fax: (334) 242-5102
E-mail: willie.moore@va.state.al.us
Web: www.va.state.al.us/scholarship.htm

Summary To provide educational benefits to the dependents of disabled, deceased, and other Alabama veterans.

Eligibility This program is open to children, spouses, and unremarried widow(er)s of veterans who are currently rated as 20% or more service-connected disabled or were so rated at time of death, were a former prisoner of war, have been declared missing in action, died as the result of a service-connected disability, or died while on active military duty in the line of duty. The veteran must have been a permanent civilian resident of Alabama for at least 1 year prior to entering active military service and served honorably for at least 90 days during war time (or less, in case of death or service-connected disability). Veterans who were not Alabama residents at the time of entering active military service may also qualify if they have a 100% disability and were permanent residents of Alabama for at least 5 years prior to filing the application for this program or prior to death, if deceased. Children and step-children must be under the age of 26, but spouses and widow(er)s may be of any age. Spouses cease to be eligible if they become divorced from the qualifying veteran. Widow(er)s cease to be eligible if they remarry.

Financial data Eligible dependents may attend any state-supported Alabama institution of higher learning or enroll in a prescribed course of study at any Alabama state-supported trade school without payment of any tuition, book fees, or laboratory charges.

Duration This is an entitlement program for 5 years of full-time undergraduate or graduate study or part-time equivalent for all qualifying children and for spouses and unremarried widow(er)s who veteran spouse is or was rated 100% disabled or meets other qualifying requirements. Spouses and unremarried widow(er)s whose veteran spouse is or was rated between 20% and 90% disabled may attend only 3 standard academic years.

Additional information Benefits for children, spouses, and unremarried widow(er)s are available in addition to federal government benefits. Assistance is not provided for non-credit courses, placement testing, GED preparation, continuing educational courses, pre-technical courses, or state board examinations.

Number awarded Varies each year.

Deadline Applications may be submitted at any time.

[999]
ANCA SCHOLARSHIPS

Army Nurse Corps Association
Attn: Education Committee
P.O. Box 39235
San Antonio, TX 78218-1235
(210) 650-3534   Fax: (210) 650-3494
E-mail: education@e-anca.org
Web: e-anca.org/ANCAEduc.htm

Summary To provide financial assistance to students who have a connection to the Army and are interested in working on an undergraduate or graduate degree in nursing.

Eligibility This program is open to U.S. citizens attending colleges or universities that have accredited programs offering associate, bachelor's, master's, or doctoral degrees in nursing. Applicants must be 1) nursing or anesthesia students who plan to enter a component of the U.S. Army and are not participating in a program funded by a component of the U.S. Army; 2) nursing or anesthesia students who have previously served in a component of the U.S. Army; 3) Army Nurse Corps officers enrolled in an undergraduate or graduate nursing program not funded by a component of the U.S. Army; 4) enlisted soldiers in a component of the U.S. Army who are working on a baccalaureate degree in nursing not funded by a component of the U.S. Army; or 5) nursing or anesthesia students whose parent(s), spouse, and/or children are serving or have served in a component of the U.S. Army. Along with their application, they must submit a personal statement on their professional career objectives, reasons for applying for this scholarship, financial need, special considerations, personal and academic interests, and why they are preparing for a nursing career.

Financial data The stipend is $3,000. Funds are sent directly to the recipient's school.

Duration 1 year.

Additional information Although the sponsoring organization is open to officers of the Army Nurse Corps, it does not have an official affiliation with the Army. Therefore, students who receive these scholarships do not incur any military service obligation.

Number awarded 1 or more each year.

Deadline March of each year.

[1000]
ARMY AVIATION ASSOCIATION OF AMERICA SCHOLARSHIPS

Army Aviation Association of America Scholarship
  Foundation
Attn: AAAA Scholarship Foundation
755 Main Street, Suite 4D
Monroe, CT 06468-2830
(203) 268-2450   Fax: (203) 268-5870
E-mail: aaaa@quad-a.org
Web: www.quad-a.org

Summary To provide financial aid for undergraduate or graduate study to members of the Army Aviation Association of America and their relatives.

Eligibility This program is open to association members (or deceased members) and their spouses, unmarried siblings, unmarried children, and unmarried grandchildren. Applicants must be enrolled or accepted for enrollment as an undergraduate or graduate student at an accredited college or university. Graduate students must include a 250-word essay on their life experiences, work history, and aspirations. Some scholarships are specifically reserved for enlisted, warrant officer, company grade, and Department of the Army civilian members. Selection is based on academic merit and personal achievement.

Financial data Stipends range up to $3,000 per year.

Duration Scholarships may be for 1, 2, or 4 years.

Number awarded Varies each year; recently, $309,500 in scholarships was awarded to 209 students. Since the program began in 1963, the foundation has awarded more than $4.1 million to nearly 2,500 qualified applicants.

Deadline April of each year.

[1001]
BG BENJAMIN B. TALLEY SCHOLARSHIP

Society of American Military Engineers-Anchorage Post
Attn: BG B.B. Talley Scholarship Endowment Fund
P.O. Box 6409
Anchorage, AK 99506-6409
(907) 244-8063   E-mail: cturletes@gci.net
Web: www.sameanchorage.org/h_about/scholinfo.html

Summary To provide financial assistance to student members of the Society of American Military Engineers (SAME)

from Alaska who are working on a bachelor's or master's degree in designated fields of engineering or the natural sciences.

Eligibility This program is open to members of the Anchorage Post of SAME who are residents of Alaska, attending college in Alaska, an active-duty military member stationed in Alaska, or a dependent of an active-duty military member stationed in Alaska. Applicants must be 1) sophomores, juniors, or seniors majoring in engineering, architecture, construction or project management, natural sciences, physical sciences, applied sciences, or mathematics at an accredited college or university; or 2) students working on a master's degree in those fields. They must have a GPA of 2.5 or higher. U.S. citizenship is required. Along with their application, they must submit an essay of 250 to 500 words on their career goals. Selection is based on that essay, academic achievement, participation in school and community activities, and work/family activities; financial need is not considered.

Financial data Stipends range up to $3,000.

Duration 1 year.

Additional information This program began in 1997.

Number awarded Varies each year; at least 1 scholarship is reserved for a master's degree students.

Deadline December of each year.

[1002]
BUCKINGHAM MEMORIAL SCHOLARSHIPS

Air Traffic Control Association
Attn: Scholarship Fund
1101 King Street, Suite 300
Alexandria, VA 22314
(703) 299-2430   Fax: (703) 299-2437
E-mail: info@atca.org
Web: www.atca.org/ATCA-Scholarship

Summary To provide financial assistance for college or graduate school to children of current or former air traffic control specialists serving with the military or at other facilities.

Eligibility This program is open to U.S. citizens who are the children, natural or adopted, of a person currently or formerly serving as an air traffic control specialist with the U.S. government, with the U.S. military, or in a private facility in the United States. Applicants must be enrolled or planning to enroll at least half time in a baccalaureate or graduate program at an accredited college or university and have at least 30 semester hours to be completed before graduation. Along with their application, they must submit a 500-word essay on how they will blend their career with community service in their adult life. Financial need is considered in the selection process.

Financial data The amounts of the awards depend on the availability of funds and the number, qualifications, and need of the applicants.

Duration 1 year; may be renewed.

Additional information This program was formerly known as the Children of Air Traffic Control Specialists Scholarship Program.

Number awarded Varies each year; recently, 5 of these scholarships were awarded.

Deadline April of each year.

[1003]
CHAN-PADGETT SPECIAL FORCES MEMORIAL SCHOLARSHIP

American Academy of Physician Assistants-Veterans Caucus
Attn: Veterans Caucus
P.O. Box 362
Danville, PA 17821-0362
(570) 271-0292   Fax: (570) 271-5850
E-mail: admin@veteranscaucus.org
Web: www.veteranscaucus.org

Summary To provide financial assistance to children of veterans of the Army Special Forces who are studying to become physician assistants.

Eligibility This program is open to U.S. citizens who are currently enrolled in a physician assistant program. The program must be approved by the Commission on Accreditation of Allied Health Education. Applicants must be children of honorably discharged members of the Army Special Forces. Selection is based on military honors and awards received, civic and college honors and awards received, professional memberships and activities, and GPA. An electronic copy of the sponsor's DD Form 214 must accompany the application.

Financial data The stipend is $2,000.

Duration 1 year.

Additional information This program began in 2002.

Number awarded 1 each year.

Deadline February of each year.

[1004]
COL CARL F. BASWELL COMBAT WOUNDED ENGINEER SCHOLARSHIP

Army Engineer Association
Attn: Executive Director
P.O. Box 30260
Alexandria, VA 22310-8260
(703) 428-7084   Fax: (703) 428-6043
E-mail: xd@armyengineer.com
Web: www.armyengineer.com/scholarships.htm

Summary To provide financial assistance for college to children and spouses of Army Engineers who were wounded in combat in Iraq or Afghanistan.

Eligibility This program is open to the children and spouses of U.S. Army Engineers who were wounded in combat and received a Purple Heart during Operation Iraqi Freedom or Operation Enduring Freedom. Applicants must be working on or planning to work on an associate, bachelor's, or master's degree at an accredited college or university. Selection is based primarily on financial need, although potential for academic success and standards of conduct as supported by personal references are also considered.

Financial data The stipend is $2,500.

Duration 1 year.

Additional information This program began in 2010.

Number awarded 1 each year.

Deadline June of each year.

[1005]
COL CARL F. BASWELL FALLEN ENGINEER MEMORIAL SCHOLARSHIP

Army Engineer Association
Attn: Executive Director
P.O. Box 30260
Alexandria, VA 22310-8260
(703) 428-7084   Fax: (703) 428-6043
E-mail: xd@armyengineer.com
Web: www.armyengineer.com/scholarships.htm

Summary To provide financial assistance for college to children and spouses of Army Engineers who were killed in Iraq or Afghanistan.

Eligibility This program is open to the children and spouses of U.S. Army Engineers who were killed in combat during Operation Iraqi Freedom or Operation Enduring Freedom. Applicants must be working on or planning to work on an associate, bachelor's, or master's degree at an accredited college or university. Selection is based primarily on financial need, although potential for academic success and standards of conduct as supported by personal references are also considered.

Financial data The stipend is $2,500.

Duration 1 year.

Additional information This program began in 2010.

Number awarded 1 each year.

Deadline June of each year.

[1006]
COLLEGE SCHOLARSHIPS FOR DEPENDENT CHILDREN

Air Force Officers' Wives' Club of Washington, D.C.
Attn: Scholarship Committee
P.O. Box 8490
Washington, DC 20032
(202) 239-1932   E-mail: scholarships@afowc.com
Web: www.afowc.com/scholarships

Summary To provide financial assistance for undergraduate or graduate education in any state to the dependent children of Air Force members in the Washington, D.C. area.

Eligibility This program is open to the dependent children of Air Force enlisted or commissioned personnel residing in the Washington, D.C. metropolitan area in the following categories: active duty, Reserve, Guard, retired, or deceased. Applicants must be currently enrolled at an accredited college, university, vocational/trade school, community college, or graduate school in any state. Along with their application, they must submit a 400-word essay on their choice of 3 assigned topics that change annually. Selection is based on their essay academic ability, extracurricular activities, service activities, citizenship, and references; financial need is not considered. Applicants who receive an appointment to a service academy are not eligible.

Financial data The stipend is $4,000. Funds may be used only for payment of tuition or academic fees.

Duration 1 year; nonrenewable.

Number awarded Varies each year.

Deadline February of each year.

[1007]
COLONEL JERRY W. ROSS SCHOLARSHIP

American Pharmacists Association
Attn: APhA Foundation
2215 Constitution Avenue, N.W.
Washington, DC 20037-2985
(202) 429-7565   Toll Free: (800) 237-APhA
Fax: (202) 783-2351   E-mail: info@aphafoundation.org
Web: www.pharmacist.com

Summary To provide financial assistance for work on a degree in pharmacy to Air Force pharmacy technicians who are members of the Academy of Student Pharmacists of the American Pharmacists Association (APhA-ASP) and their families.

Eligibility This program is open to full-time pharmacy students who are either 1) Air Force pharmacy technicians working on a degree in pharmacy, or 2) family members of an Air Force pharmacist or technician who is enrolled in an accredited college of pharmacy. Applicants must have been actively involved in their school's APhA-ASP chapter. They must have completed at least 1 year in the professional sequence of courses with a GPA of 2.75 or higher. Along with their application, they must submit a 500-word essay on a topic that changes annually but relates to the future of the pharmacy profession, 2 letters of recommendation, a current resume or curriculum vitae, and a list of pharmacy and non-pharmacy related activities. Preference is given to applicants who indicate further Air Force service.

Financial data The stipend is $1,000.

Duration 1 year; recipients may reapply.

Number awarded 1 each year.

Deadline November of each year.

[1008]
CONNECTICUT TUITION WAIVER FOR VETERANS

Connecticut Office of Financial and Academic Affairs for
  Higher Education
Attn: Student Financial Aid
61 Woodland Street
Hartford, CT 06105-2326
(860) 947-1855   Toll Free: (800) 842-0229 (within CT)
Fax: (860) 947-1311   E-mail: sfa@ctdhe.org
Web: www.ctohe.org/SFA/default.htm

Summary To provide money for college or graduate school to certain Connecticut veterans and military personnel or their dependents.

Eligibility This program is open to 1) honorably-discharged Connecticut veterans who served at least 90 days during specified periods of wartime; 2) active members of the Connecticut Army and Air National Guard; 3) Connecticut residents who are a dependent child or surviving spouse of a member of the armed forces killed in action on or after September 11, 2001 who was also a Connecticut resident; and 4) Connecticut residents who are dependent children of a person officially declared missing in action or a prisoner of war while serving in the armed forces after January 1, 1960. Applicants must be attending or planning to attend a public college or university in the state.

Financial data The program provides a waiver of 100% of tuition for students working on an undergraduate or graduate degree at the University of Connecticut, 100% of tuition for general fund courses at campuses of Connecticut State University, 50% of tuition for extension and summer courses at campuses of Connecticut State University, 100% of tuition at all Connecticut community colleges, and 50% or fees at Charter Oak State College.

Duration Up to 4 years.

Additional information This is an entitlement program; applications are available from the respective college financial aid offices.

Number awarded Varies each year.

Deadline Deadline not specified.

[1009]
CONTINUING EDUCATION SCHOLARSHIPS FOR NON-MILITARY AIR FORCE SPOUSES

Air Force Officers' Wives' Club of Washington, D.C.
Attn: Scholarship Committee
P.O. Box 8490
Washington, DC 20032
(202) 239-1932   E-mail: scholarships@afowc.com
Web: www.afowc.com/scholarships

Summary To provide financial assistance for undergraduate or graduate study in any state to the non-military spouses of Air Force members in the Washington, D.C. area.

Eligibility This program is open to the non-military spouses of Air Force enlisted or commissioned personnel residing in the Washington, D.C. metropolitan area in the following categories: active duty, Reserve, Guard, retired, MIA/POW, or deceased. Applicants must be enrolled or planning to enroll as an undergraduate or graduate student at a college or university in any state. Along with their application, they must submit a 400-word essay on why they are pursuing higher education and how it will be of personal benefit to them in the future. Selection is based on their essay academic ability, extracurricular activities, service activities, citizenship, and references; financial need is not considered.

Financial data The stipend is $4,000. Funds may be used only for payment of tuition or academic fees.

Duration 1 year; nonrenewable.

Number awarded Varies each year.

Deadline February of each year.

[1010]
DAEDALIAN FOUNDATION DESCENDANTS' SCHOLARSHIP PROGRAM

Daedalian Foundation
Attn: Scholarship Committee
55 Main Circle (Building 676)
P.O. Box 249
Randolph AFB, TX 78148-0249
(210) 945-2113   Fax: (210) 945-2112
E-mail: kristi@daedalians.org
Web: www.daedalians.org/foundation/scholarships.htm

Summary To provide financial assistance to descendants of members of the Order of Daedalians who wish to prepare for a career in military aviation or space.

Eligibility This program is open to descendants of members of the order who are working on or planning to work on a baccalaureate or higher degree. Applicants must be interested in and willing to commit to a career as a commissioned military pilot, flight crew member, astronaut, or commissioned officer in 1 of the armed forces of the United States in a discipline directly supporting aeronautics or astronautics. They must be physically and mentally qualified for flight and/or space; if they intend to pursue a non-flying career as a commissioned officer in a scientific or engineering discipline supporting aviation or space, they must pass a physical examination qualifying for active commissioned duty in the U.S. armed forces. Nominations must be submitted by a local chapter (Flight) of Daedalian. Selection is based on academic achievement and recognition, extracurricular activities, honors, and employment experience. Financial need may be considered if all other factors are equal.

Financial data The stipend is $2,000.

Additional information The Order of Daedalians was founded in 1934 as an organization of the nearly 14,000 aviators who served as military pilots during World War I and are still listed and designated as Founder Members. In the 1950s, the organization expanded eligibility to include 1) on a sponsorship basis, current and former commissioned military pilots from all services; and 2) on a hereditary basis, descendants of Founder Members.

Number awarded Up to 3 each year.

Deadline July of each year.

[1011]
DATATEL ANGELFIRE SCHOLARSHIP

Datatel Scholars Foundation
4375 Fair Lakes Court
Fairfax, VA 22033
(703) 968-9000, ext. 4549   Toll Free: (800) 486-4332
Fax: (703) 968-4625   E-mail: scholars@datatel.com
Web: www.datatelscholars.org

Summary To provide funding to graduating high school seniors, college students, and graduate students who will be studying at a Datatel client school and are veterans, veterans' dependents, or refugees from southeast Asia.

Eligibility This program is open to 1) veterans who served in the Asian theater (Vietnam, Cambodia, or Laos) between 1964 and 1975; 2) their spouses and children; 3) refugees from Vietnam, Cambodia, or Laos; and 4) veterans who served in Operation Desert Storm, Operation Enduring Freedom, and/or Operation Iraqi Freedom. Applicants must attend a Datatel client college or university during the upcoming school year as a full- or part-time undergraduate or graduate student. They must first apply to their institution, which selects 2 semifinalists and forwards their applications to the sponsor. Along with their application, they must include a 1,000-word personal statement that discusses how the conflict has affected them personally, summarizes how the conflict has impacted their educational goals, and describes how being awarded this scholarship will help them achieve their goals. Selection is based on the quality of the personal statement (60%) and academic merit (40%).

Financial data The stipend is $1,700. Funds are paid directly to the institution.

Duration 1 year.

Additional information Datatel, Inc. produces advanced information technology solutions for higher education. It has more than 750 client sites in the United States and Canada. This scholarship was created to commemorate those who lost their lives in Vietnam or Iraq and is named after a memorial administered by the Disabled American Veterans Association in Angelfire, New Mexico.

Number awarded 10 each year.

Deadline Students must submit online applications to their institution or organization by January of each year.

[1012]
DISABLED AMERICAN VETERANS AUXILIARY NATIONAL EDUCATION SCHOLARSHIP FUND

Disabled American Veterans Auxiliary
Attn: National Education Scholarship Fund
3725 Alexandria Pike
Cold Spring, KY 41076
(859) 441-7300   Toll Free: (877) 426-2838, ext. 4020
Fax: (859) 442-2095   E-mail: dava@davmail.org
Web: auxiliary.dav.org/membership/Programs.aspx

Summary To provide financial assistance to members of the Disabled American Veterans (DAV) Auxiliary who are interested in attending college or graduate school.

Eligibility This program is open to paid life members of the auxiliary who are attending or planning to attend a college, university, or vocational school as a full- or part-time undergraduate or graduate student. Applicants must be at least seniors in high school, but there is no maximum age limit. Selection is based on academic achievement; participation in DAV activities; participation in other activities for veterans in their school, community, or elsewhere; volunteer work; membership in clubs or organizations; honors and awards; a statement of academic goals; and financial need.

Financial data Stipends are $1,500 per year for full-time students or $750 per year for part-time students.

Duration 1 year; may be renewed for up to 4 additional years, provided the recipient maintains a GPA of 2.5 or higher.

Additional information Membership in the DAV Auxiliary is available to extended family members of veterans eligible for membership in Disabled American Veterans (i.e., any man or woman who served in the armed forces during a period of war or under conditions simulating war and was wounded, disabled to any degree, or left with long-term illness as a result of military service and was discharged or retired from military service under honorable conditions). This program was established in September 2010 as a replacement for the educational loan program that the DAV Auxiliary operated from 1931 until August 2010.

Number awarded Varies each year.

Deadline March of each year.

[1013]
EDUCATION FOUNDATION FOR THE COLORADO NATIONAL GUARD GRANTS

National Guard Association of Colorado
Attn: Education Foundation, Inc.
P.O. Box 440889
Aurora, CO 80044-0889
(303) 909-6369   Fax: (720) 535-5925
E-mail: BernieRogoff@comcast.net
Web: efcong.org/Grants

Summary To provide financial assistance to members of the Colorado National Guard and their families who are interested in attending college or graduate school in any state.

Eligibility This program is open to current and retired members of the Colorado National Guard and their dependent unmarried children and spouses. Applicants must be enrolled or planning to enroll full or part time at a college, university, trade school, business school, or graduate school in any state. Along with their application, they must submit an essay, up to 2 pages in length, on their desire to continue their education, what motivates them, their financial need, their commitment to academic excellence, and their current situation. Selection is based on academic achievement, community involvement, and financial need.

Financial data Stipends are at least $1,000 per year.

Duration 1 year; may be renewed.

Number awarded Varies each year; recently, 38 of these grants, with a total value of $50,000, were awarded.

Deadline July of each year for fall semester; January of each year for spring semester.

[1014]
EDWARD T. CONROY MEMORIAL SCHOLARSHIP PROGRAM

Maryland Higher Education Commission
Attn: Office of Student Financial Assistance
6 North Liberty Street, Ground Suite
Baltimore, MD 21201
(410) 767-3300   Toll Free: (800) 974-0203
Fax: (410) 332-0250   TDD: (800) 735-2258
E-mail: osfamail@mhec.state.md.us
Web: www.mhec.state.md.us/financialAid/descriptions.asp

Summary To provide money for college or graduate school in Maryland to children and spouses of victims of the September 11, 2001 terrorist attacks and specified categories of veterans, public safety employees, and their children or spouses.

Eligibility This program is open to entering and continuing undergraduate and graduate students in the following categories: 1) children and surviving spouses of victims of the September 11, 2001 terrorist attacks who died in the World Trade Center in New York City, in the Pentagon in Virginia, or on United Airlines Flight 93 in Pennsylvania; 2) veterans who have, as a direct result of military service, a disability of 25% or greater and have exhausted or are no longer eligible for federal veterans' educational benefits; 3) children of armed forces members whose death or 100% disability was directly caused by military service; 4) POW/MIA veterans of the Vietnam Conflict and their children; 5) state or local public safety officers or volunteers who became 100% disabled in the line of duty; and 6) children and unremarried surviving spouses of state or local public safety employees or volunteers who died or became 100% disabled in the line of duty. The parent, spouse, veteran, POW, or public safety officer or volunteer must have been a resident of Maryland at the time of death or when declared disabled. Financial need is not considered.

Financial data The amount of the award is equal to tuition and fees at a Maryland postsecondary institution, to a maximum of $19,000 for children and spouses of the September 11 terrorist attacks or $9,000 for all other recipients.

Duration Up to 5 years of full-time or 8 years of part-time study.

Additional information Recipients must enroll at a 2- or 4-year Maryland college or university as a full-time or part-time degree-seeking undergraduate or graduate student or attend a private career school.

Number awarded Varies each year.

Deadline July of each year.

[1015]
EIRO YAMADA MEMORIAL SCHOLARSHIP

Go For Broke Memorial Education Center
P.O. Box 2590
Gardena, CA 90247
(310) 222-5710   Fax: (310) 222-5700
E-mail: Cayleen@goforbroke.org
Web: www.goforbroke.org

Summary To provide financial assistance for college or graduate school to residents of any state who are descendants of World War II Japanese American veterans.

Eligibility This program is open to residents of any state who are attending or planning to attend a trade school, community college, or 4-year college or university on the undergraduate or graduate school level. Applicants must be 1) a direct descendant of a Japanese American World War II veteran, or 2) a descendant once-removed (such as a grand-niece or a grand-nephew) of a Japanese American serviceman or servicewoman killed in action during World War II. Along with their application, they must submit a short essay on "The Values I Have Learned from My Japanese American Forefathers" or their personal reflections on the Japanese American experience during World War II.

Financial data Stipends range from $500 to $1,000.

Duration 1 year.

Number awarded Varies each year; recently, 12 of these scholarships were awarded.

Deadline April of each year.

[1016]
EXEMPTION FROM TUITION FEES FOR DEPENDENTS OF KENTUCKY VETERANS

Kentucky Department of Veterans Affairs
Attn: Field Operations Branch
321 West Main Street, Suite 390
Louisville, KY 40202
(502) 595-4447   Toll Free: (800) 928-4012 (within KY)
Fax: (502) 595-4448   E-mail: Pamela.Cypert@ky.gov
Web: www.veterans.ky.gov/benefits/tuitionwaiver.htm

Summary To provide financial assistance for undergraduate or graduate studies to the children or unremarried widow(er)s of deceased Kentucky veterans.

Eligibility This program is open to the children, stepchildren, adopted children, and unremarried widow(er)s of veterans who were residents of Kentucky when they entered military service or joined the Kentucky National Guard. The qualifying veteran must have been killed in action during a wartime period or died as a result of a service-connected disability incurred during a wartime period. Applicants must be attending or planning to attend a state-supported college or university in Kentucky to work on an undergraduate or graduate degree.

Financial data Eligible dependents and survivors are exempt from tuition and matriculation fees at any state-supported institution of higher education in Kentucky.

Duration There are no age or time limits on the waiver.

Number awarded Varies each year.

Deadline Deadline not specified.

[1017]
FLORIDA LEGION AUXILIARY MASTER'S PROGRAM GRANT

American Legion Auxiliary
Department of Florida
1912A Lee Road
P.O. Box 547917
Orlando, FL 32854-7917
(407) 293-7411   Fax: (407) 299-6522
E-mail: contact@alafl.org
Web: alafl.org/index.php?masters-award-scholarship

Summary To provide financial assistance to members of the Florida American Legion Auxiliary who are interested in working on a master's degree in any field at a university in any state.

Eligibility This program is open to residents of Florida who have been members of the American Legion Auxiliary for at least 5 consecutive years. Applicants must be planning to enroll in an accredited master's degree program in any field at a college or university in any state. They must be sponsored by the local American Legion Auxiliary unit. Selection is based on academic record and financial need.

Financial data The stipend is $2,500 per year. All funds are paid directly to the institution.

Duration 1 year; may be renewed 1 additional year if the recipient needs further financial assistance and has maintained at least a 2.5 GPA.

Number awarded 1 each year.

Deadline January of each year.

[1018]
FRA NON-MEMBER SCHOLARSHIPS

Fleet Reserve Association
Attn: FRA Education Foundation
125 North West Street
Alexandria, VA 22314-2754
(703) 683-1400   Toll Free: (800) FRA-1924
Fax: (703) 549-6610   E-mail: scholars@fra.org
Web: www.fra.org

Summary To provide financial assistance for college or graduate school to current or former sea service personnel and their families.

Eligibility This program is open to 1) active-duty, Reserve, honorably-discharged veterans, and retired members of the U.S. Navy, Marine Corps, and Coast Guard; and 2) their spouses, children, and grandchildren. Applicants must be enrolled as full-time undergraduate or graduate students but they are not required to be members of the sponsoring organization. Along with their application, they must submit an essay on why they want to go to college and what they intend to accomplish with their degree. Selection is based on academic record, financial need, extracurricular activities, leadership skills, and participation in community activities. U.S. citizenship is required.

Financial data A stipend is awarded (amount not specified).

Duration 1 year; may be renewed.

Number awarded 1 or more each year.

Deadline April of each year.

[1019]
FRA SCHOLARSHIPS

Fleet Reserve Association
Attn: FRA Education Foundation
125 North West Street
Alexandria, VA 22314-2754
(703) 683-1400   Toll Free: (800) FRA-1924
Fax: (703) 549-6610   E-mail: scholars@fra.org
Web: www.fra.org

Summary To provide financial assistance for college or graduate school to members of the Fleet Reserve Association (FRA) and their families.

Eligibility This program is open to members of the FRA and the dependent children, grandchildren, and spouses of living or deceased members. Applicants must be enrolled as full-time undergraduate or graduate students. Along with their application, they must submit an essay on why they want to go to college and what they intend to accomplish with their degree. Selection is based on academic record, financial need, extracurricular activities, leadership skills, and participation in community activities. U.S. citizenship is required.

Financial data The stipend is $5,000 per year.

Duration 1 year; may be renewed.

Additional information Membership in the FRA is restricted to active-duty, retired, and reserve members of the Navy, Marines, and Coast Guard.

Number awarded 6 each year.

Deadline April of each year.

[1020]
GLENN F. GLEZEN SCHOLARSHIP

Fleet Reserve Association
Attn: FRA Education Foundation
125 North West Street
Alexandria, VA 22314-2754
(703) 683-1400   Toll Free: (800) FRA-1924
Fax: (703) 549-6610   E-mail: scholars@fra.org
Web: www.fra.org

Summary To provide financial assistance for graduate school to members of the Fleet Reserve Association (FRA) and their families.

Eligibility This program is open to members of the FRA and the dependent children, grandchildren, and spouses of living or deceased members. Applicants must be enrolled as full-time graduate students. Along with their application, they must submit an essay on why they want to go to college and what they intend to accomplish with their degree. Selection is based on academic record, financial need, extracurricular activities, leadership skills, and participation in community activities. U.S. citizenship is required.

Financial data The stipend is $5,000 per year.

Duration 1 year; may be renewed.

Additional information Membership in the FRA is restricted to active-duty, retired, and Reserve members of the Navy, Marine Corps, and Coast Guard. This program was established in 2001.

Number awarded 1 each year.

Deadline April of each year.

[1021]
HICKAM OFFICERS' SPOUSES' CLUB SCHOLARSHIPS

Hickam Officers' Spouses' Club
Attn: Scholarship Chair
PMB 168
P.O. Box 30800
Honolulu, HI 96820-0800
E-mail: scholarships@hickamosc.com
Web: www.hickamosc.com

Summary To provide financial assistance to dependents of current and former military personnel in Hawaii who are interested in attending college or graduate school in any state.

Eligibility This program is open to dependents of 1 of the following: 1) active-duty military members permanently stationed in Hawaii; 2) active-duty military members on a remote assignment from Hawaii; 3) retired military members resident in Hawaii; 4) full-time Hawaii National Guard and U.S. military Reserve members residing in Hawaii; and 5) survivors of deceased military members residing in Hawaii. Applicants must be seniors graduating from a Hawaii high school or accredited home school program based in Hawaii and planning to enroll at an accredited 2- or 4-year college, university, or vocational/technical school in any state; dependent children currently working on an undergraduate or graduate degree at a college or university in any state; or spouses currently working on an undergraduate or graduate degree at a college or university in any state. High school seniors must submit a 1-page essay on their greatest challenge, how they overcame it, and what lessons they learned. Spouses and other continuing students must submit a 1-page essay on what it means to live passionately and how they demonstrate it in their daily life. Selection is based on the essay, academic ability, extracurricular activities and work experience, service activities and citizenship, and a letter of recommendation.

Financial data A stipend is awarded (amount not specified).

Duration 1 year.

Number awarded 1 or more each year.

Deadline March of each year.

[1022]
HONOLULU POST SAME SCHOLARSHIPS

Society of American Military Engineers-Honolulu Post
P.O. Box 201445
Honolulu, HI 96820
Web: www.samehonolulu.org

Summary To provide financial assistance to residents of Hawaii, particularly those with ties to the military, who are interested in attending college in any state to work on an undergraduate or graduate degree in engineering or architecture.

Eligibility This program is open to residents of Hawaii who are graduating high school seniors or current undergraduates enrolled or planning to enroll full time at an accredited college or university in any state. Applicants must be planning to work on an undergraduate or graduate degree in engineering or architecture. They must be U.S. citizens and have a GPA of 3.0 or higher. Military affiliation or experience (i.e., ROTC, member or dependent of a member of the Society of Military Engineers (SAME), military dependent, Junior ROTC) is not required but is given preference. Along with their application,

they must submit a transcript; a resume of work experience, academic activities, and extracurricular accomplishments; and a 1-page essay on how their engineering or architecture degree will impact our nation.

Financial data The stipend is $2,500.

Duration 1 year.

Number awarded Varies each year; recently, 6 of these scholarships were awarded.

Deadline March of each year.

[1023]
HOPE FOR THE WARRIORS SPOUSE/CAREGIVER SCHOLARSHIPS

Hope for the Warriors
Attn: Spouse/Caregiver Scholarships Director
1011 South MacDill Avenue, Suite 812
Tampa, FL 33629
Toll Free: (877) 246-7349
E-mail: scholarship@hopeforthewarriors.org
Web: www.hopeforthewarriors.org/spouse.html

Summary To provide financial assistance for college to the spouses and caregivers of wounded or deceased military personnel or veterans.

Eligibility This program is open to spouses and caregivers of current and former service members who were wounded or killed in the line of duty since September 11, 2001. Applicants must be enrolled or planning to enroll full or part time at an accredited college, university, or trade school to work on a bachelor's degree, master's degree, or vocational certification. They must have a high school GPA of 2.6 or higher or a GED score of 650 or higher. Along with their application, they must submit a 500-word essay on how their life has been impacted by the Global War on Terror and how that impact played a role in their pursuit of higher education. Selection is based on that essay, academic achievement, personal goals, and letters of recommendation.

Financial data The stipend is $5,000 or $1,250 per year.

Duration 1 year; may be renewed up to 3 additional years.

Additional information This program includes the following named scholarships: the Shannon Maxwell Award, the Bonnie Amos Award, the Karin Dickerson Award, the Robin Kelleher-New Beginnings Award, and the Sidney Popkin Memorial Scholarship.

Number awarded 5 each year: 4 at $5,000 and 1 at $1,250.

Deadline March of each year.

[1024]
H.S. AND ANGELINE LEWIS SCHOLARSHIPS

American Legion Auxiliary
Department of Wisconsin
Attn: Education Chair
2930 American Legion Drive
P.O. Box 140
Portage, WI 53901-0140
(608) 745-0124   Toll Free: (866) 664-3863
Fax: (608) 745-1947   E-mail: alawi@amlegionauxwi.org
Web: www.amlegionauxwi.org/Scholarships.htm

Summary To provide financial assistance to Wisconsin residents who are related to veterans or members of the American Legion Auxiliary and interested in working on an undergraduate or graduate degree at a school in any state.

Eligibility This program is open to the children, wives, and widows of veterans who are high school seniors or graduates and have a GPA of 3.5 or higher. Grandchildren and great-grandchildren of members of the American Legion Auxiliary are also eligible. Applicants must be residents of Wisconsin and interested in working on an undergraduate or graduate degree at a school in any state. Along with their application, they must submit a 300-word essay on "Education—An Investment in the Future." Financial need is considered in the selection process.

Financial data The stipend is $1,000.

Duration 1 year; nonrenewable.

Number awarded 6 each year: 1 to a graduate student and 5 to undergraduates.

Deadline March of each year.

[1025]
INDIANA CHILD OF VETERAN AND PUBLIC SAFETY OFFICER SUPPLEMENTAL GRANT PROGRAM

State Student Assistance Commission of Indiana
Attn: Grants and Scholarships
W462 Indiana Government Center South
402 West Washington Street
Indianapolis, IN 46204
(317) 232-2355   Toll Free: (888) 528-4719 (within IN)
Fax: (317) 232-3260   E-mail: grants@ssaci.in.gov
Web: www.in.gov/ssaci/2338.htm

Summary To provide financial assistance to residents of Indiana who are the children or spouses of specified categories of deceased or disabled veterans or public safety officers and interested in attending college or graduate school in the state.

Eligibility This program is open to 1) children of deceased or disabled Indiana veterans, children of Purple Heart recipients, and children of Vietnam War veterans who were listed as POW or MIA; 2) children and spouses of members of the Indiana National Guard who suffered a service-connected death while serving on state active duty; 3) Indiana veterans who received a Purple Heart; 4) current and former students at the Indiana Soldiers' and Sailors' Children's Home (Morton Memorial High School); and 5) children and spouses of Indiana police officers, fire fighters, or emergency medical technicians killed in the line of duty or Indiana state police troopers permanently and totally disabled in the line of duty. The veterans and National Guard portions of this program are open to Indiana residents who are the natural or adopted children or spouses of veterans who served in the active-duty U.S. armed forces during a period of wartime.

Financial data Qualified applicants receive a 100% remission of tuition and all mandatory fees for undergraduate or graduate work at state-supported postsecondary schools and universities in Indiana. Support is not provided for such fees as room and board.

Duration Up to 124 semester hours of study.

Number awarded Varies each year.

Deadline Applications must be submitted at least 30 days before the start of the college term.

[1026]
JAPANESE AMERICAN VETERANS ASSOCIATION MEMORIAL SCHOLARSHIPS

Japanese American Veterans Association
c/o Dave Buto
4226 Holborn Avenue
Annandale, VA 22003
(703) 503-3431   E-mail: admin@javadc.org
Web: www.javadc.org

Summary To provide financial assistance for college or graduate school to relatives of Japanese American veterans and military personnel.

Eligibility This program is open to graduating high school seniors and students currently working on an undergraduate or graduate degree at a college, university, or school of specialized study. Applicants must be related, by blood or marriage, to 1) a person who served with the 442nd Regimental Combat Team, the 100th Infantry Battalion, or other unit associated with those; 2) a person who served in the U.S. Military Intelligence Service during or after World War II; 3) a person of Japanese ancestry who is serving or has served in the U.S. armed forces and been honorable discharged; or 4) a member of the Japanese American Veterans Association (JAVA) whose membership extends back at least 1 year.

Financial data The stipend is $1,500.

Duration 1 year; recipients may reapply.

Additional information These scholarships, first awarded in 2008, include the following named awards: the Orville C. Shirey Memorial Scholarship, the Joseph Ichiuji Memorial Scholarship, the Sunao Phil Ishio Memorial Scholarship, the Kiyoko Tsuboi-Taubkin Memorial Scholarship, the Grant Hirabayashi Memorial Scholarship, the Teru Kamikawa Memorial Scholarship, the Mary Kozono Memorial Scholarship, and the Douglas Ishio Memorial Scholarship.

Number awarded 8 each year.

Deadline April of each year.

[1027]
JOANNE HOLBROOK PATTON MILITARY SPOUSE SCHOLARSHIP PROGRAM

National Military Family Association, Inc.
Attn: Spouse Scholarship Program
2500 North Van Dorn Street, Suite 102
Alexandria, VA 22302-1601
(703) 931-NMFA   Toll Free: (800) 260-0218
Fax: (703) 931-4600
E-mail: scholarships@militaryfamily.org
Web: www.militaryfamily.org

Summary To provide financial assistance for postsecondary study to spouses of active and retired military personnel.

Eligibility This program is open to the spouses of military personnel (active, retired, Reserve, Guard, or survivor). Applicants must be attending or planning to attend an accredited postsecondary institution to work on an undergraduate or graduate degree, professional certification, vocational training, GED or ESL, or other postsecondary training. They may enroll part or full time and in-class or online. Along with their application, they must submit an essay on a question that changes annually; recently, applicants were asked to write about what they like most about the health care they are receiving as a military family member, what they like the least, and what they would recommend to change it. Selection is based on that essay, community involvement, and academic achievement.

Financial data The stipend is $1,000. Funds are paid directly to the educational institution to be used for tuition, fees, and school room and board. Support is not provided for books, rent, or previous education loans.

Duration 1 year; recipients may reapply.

Additional information This program began in 2004.

Number awarded Varies each year; recently, 484 of these scholarships were awarded.

Deadline January of each year.

[1028]
JOHN CORNELIUS/MAX ENGLISH MEMORIAL SCHOLARSHIP AWARD

Marine Corps Tankers Association
c/o Buster Diggs, Scholarship Chair
1829 Ballentine Drive
Alpine, CA 91901
E-mail: Tigertanker2003@yahoo.com
Web: www.usmarinetankers.org/scholarship-program

Summary To provide financial assistance for college or graduate school to children and grandchildren of members of the Marine Corps Tankers Association and to Marine and Navy personnel currently serving in tank units.

Eligibility This program is open to high school seniors and graduates who are children, grandchildren, or under the guardianship of an active, Reserve, retired, or honorably discharged Marine who served in a tank unit. Marine or Navy Corpsmen currently assigned to tank units are also eligible. Applicants must be enrolled or planning to enroll full time at a college or graduate school. Their parent or grandparent must be a member of the Marine Corps Tankers Association or, if not a member, must join if the application is accepted. Along with their application, they must submit an essay on their educational goals, future aspirations, and concern for the future of our society and for the peoples of the world. Selection is based on that essay, academic record, school activities, leadership potential, and community service.

Financial data The stipend is at least $2,000 per year.

Duration 1 year; recipients may reapply.

Number awarded 8 to 12 each year.

Deadline March of each year.

[1029]
JOSEPH R. BARANSKI SCHOLARSHIP

Fleet Reserve Association
Attn: FRA Education Foundation
125 North West Street
Alexandria, VA 22314-2754
(703) 683-1400   Toll Free: (800) FRA-1924
Fax: (703) 549-6610   E-mail: scholars@fra.org
Web: www.fra.org

Summary To provide financial assistance for graduate school to members of the Fleet Reserve Association (FRA) and their families.

Eligibility This program is open to members of the FRA and the dependent children, grandchildren, and spouses of living or deceased members. Applicants must be enrolled as full-time graduate students. Along with their application, they must submit an essay on why they want to go to college and what they intend to accomplish with their degree. Selection is

based on academic record, financial need, extracurricular activities, leadership skills, and participation in community activities. U.S. citizenship is required.

Financial data The stipend is $5,000.

Duration 1 year; may be renewed.

Additional information Membership in the FRA is restricted to active-duty, retired, and Reserve members of the Navy, Marine Corps, and Coast Guard. This program was established in 2001.

Number awarded 1 each year.

Deadline April of each year.

[1030]
KATHERN F. GRUBER SCHOLARSHIPS

Blinded Veterans Association
477 H Street, N.W.
Washington, DC 20001-2694
(202) 371-8880   Toll Free: (800) 669-7079
Fax: (202) 371-8258   E-mail: bva@bva.org
Web: www.bva.org/services.html

Summary To provide funds for undergraduate or graduate study to spouses and children of blinded veterans.

Eligibility This program is open to dependent children and spouses of blinded veterans of the U.S. armed forces. The veteran must be legally blind; the blindness may be either service connected or nonservice connected. Applicants must have been accepted or be currently enrolled as a full-time student in an undergraduate or graduate program at an accredited institution of higher learning. Along with their application, they must submit a 300-word essay on their career goals and aspirations. Financial need is not considered in the selection process.

Financial data The stipend is $2,000; funds are intended to be used to cover the student's expenses, including tuition, other academic fees, books, dormitory fees, and cafeteria fees. Funds are paid directly to the recipient's school.

Duration 1 year; recipients may reapply for up to 3 additional years.

Number awarded 6 each year.

Deadline April of each year.

[1031]
LIFE'S CHOICES FOUNDATION GRADUATE SCHOLARSHIP AWARDS

Association of Former Intelligence Officers
Attn: Scholarships Committee
6723 Whittier Avenue, Suite 200
McLean, VA 22101-4533
(703) 790-0320   Fax: (703) 991-1278
E-mail: afio@afio.com
Web: www.afio.com/13_scholarships.htm

Summary To provide financial assistance to graduate students who are members or descendants of members of the U.S. intelligence community and interested in working on a degree in a field related to national security.

Eligibility This program is open to graduate students who apply in their senior undergraduate year or first graduate year. Applicants must be personnel serving in government agencies comprising the U.S. intelligence community or their children or grandchildren. They must be working on a degree in a field related to national security or intelligence studies and be, or planning to be, serving in the U.S. government.

Along with their application, they must submit a cover letter that explains their need for assistance, their career goals and dreams, and their views of U.S. world standing and its intelligence community. Selection is based on merit, character, estimated future potential, background, and relevance of their studies to the full spectrum of national security interests and career ambitions. U.S. citizenship is required.

Financial data   The stipend is $3,500.

Duration   1 year.

Additional information   This program is sponsored by the Morris Family Charitable Corporation.

Number awarded   2 each year.

Deadline   June of each year.

[1032]
MAINE VETERANS DEPENDENTS EDUCATIONAL BENEFITS

Bureau of Veterans' Services
117 State House Station
Augusta, ME 04333-0117
(207) 430-6035   Toll Free: (800) 345-0116 (within ME)
Fax: (207) 626-4471   E-mail: mainebvs@maine.gov
Web: www.maine.gov/dvem/bvs/educational_benefits.htm

Summary   To provide financial assistance for undergraduate or graduate education to dependents of disabled and other Maine veterans.

Eligibility   Applicants for these benefits must be children (high school seniors or graduates under 22 years of age), non-divorced spouses, or unremarried widow(er)s of veterans who meet 1 or more of the following requirements: 1) living and determined to have a total permanent disability resulting from a service-connected cause; 2) killed in action; 3) died from a service-connected disability; 4) died while totally and permanently disabled due to a service-connected disability but whose death was not related to the service-connected disability; or 5) a member of the armed forces on active duty who has been listed for more than 90 days as missing in action, captured, forcibly detained, or interned in the line of duty by a foreign government or power. The veteran parent must have been a resident of Maine at the time of entry into service or a resident of Maine for 5 years preceding application for these benefits. Children may be working on an associate or bachelor's degree. Spouses, widows, and widowers may work on an associate, bachelor's, or master's degree.

Financial data   Recipients are entitled to free tuition at institutions of higher education supported by the state of Maine.

Duration   Children may receive up to 8 semesters of support; they have 6 years from the date of first entrance to complete those 8 semesters. Continuation in the program is based on their earning a GPA of 2.0 or higher each semester. Spouses are entitled to receive up to 120 credit hours of educational benefits and have 10 years from the date of first entrance to complete their program.

Additional information   College preparatory schooling and correspondence courses are not supported under this program.

Number awarded   Varies each year.

Deadline   Deadline not specified.

[1033]
MAINE VIETNAM VETERANS SCHOLARSHIP FUND

Maine Community Foundation
Attn: Program Director
245 Main Street
Ellsworth, ME 04605
(207) 667-9735   Toll Free: (877) 700-6800
Fax: (207) 667-0447   E-mail: info@mainecf.org
Web: www.mainecf.org/statewidescholars.aspx

Summary   To provide financial assistance for college or graduate school to Vietnam veterans or the dependents of Vietnam or other veterans in Maine.

Eligibility   This program is open to residents of Maine who are Vietnam veterans or the descendants of veterans who served in the Vietnam Theater. As a second priority, children of veterans from other time periods are also considered. Graduating high school seniors, nontraditional students, undergraduates, and graduate students are eligible to apply. Selection is based on financial need, extracurricular activities, work experience, academic achievement, and a personal statement of career goals and how the applicant's educational plans relate to them.

Financial data   The stipend is $1,000 per year.

Duration   1 year.

Additional information   This program began in 1985. There is a $3 processing fee.

Number awarded   3 to 6 each year.

Deadline   April of each year.

[1034]
MARIA C. JACKSON/GENERAL GEORGE A. WHITE SCHOLARSHIP

Oregon Student Access Commission
Attn: Grants and Scholarships Division
1500 Valley River Drive, Suite 100
Eugene, OR 97401-2146
(541) 687-7395   Toll Free: (800) 452-8807, ext. 7395
Fax: (541) 687-7414   TDD: (800) 735-2900
E-mail: awardinfo@osac.state.or.us
Web: www.oregonstudentaid.gov/scholarships.aspx

Summary   To provide financial assistance to veterans and children of veterans and military personnel in Oregon who are interested in attending college or graduate school in the state.

Eligibility   This program is open to residents of Oregon who served, or whose parents are serving or have served, in the U.S. armed forces. Applicants or their parents must have resided in Oregon at the time of enlistment. They must be enrolled or planning to enroll at a college or graduate school in the state. College and university undergraduates must have a GPA of 3.75 or higher, but there is no minimum GPA requirement for graduate students or those attending a technical school. Selection is based on academics and need.

Financial data   Stipends for scholarships offered by the Oregon Student Access Commission (OSAC) range from $200 to $10,000 but recently averaged $2,300.

Number awarded   Varies each year.

Deadline   February of each year.

[1035]
MARY PAOLOZZI MEMBER'S SCHOLARSHIP

Navy Wives Clubs of America
c/o NSA Mid-South
P.O. Box 54022
Millington, TN 38054-0022
Toll Free: (866) 511-NWCA
E-mail: nwca@navywivesclubsofamerica.org
Web: www.navywivesclubsofamerica.org/scholarships

Summary To provide financial assistance for undergraduate or graduate study to members of the Navy Wives Clubs of America (NWCA).

Eligibility This program is open to NWCA members who can demonstrate financial need. Applicants must be 1) a high school graduate or senior planning to attend college full time next year; 2) currently enrolled in an undergraduate program and planning to continue as a full-time undergraduate; 3) a college graduate or senior planning to be a full-time graduate student next year; or 4) a high school graduate or GED recipient planning to attend vocational or business school next year. Along with their application, they must submit a brief statement on why they feel they should be awarded this scholarship and any special circumstances (financial or other) they wish to have considered. Financial need is also considered in the selection process.

Financial data Stipends range from $500 to $1,000 each year (depending upon the donations from the NWCA chapters).

Duration 1 year.

Additional information Membership in the NWCA is open to spouses of enlisted personnel serving in the Navy, Marine Corps, Coast Guard, and the active Reserve units of those services; spouses of enlisted personnel who have been honorably discharged, retired, or transferred to the Fleet Reserve on completion of duty; and widows of enlisted personnel in those services.

Number awarded 1 or more each year.

Deadline May of each year.

[1036]
MASSACHUSETTS SOLDIERS LEGACY FUND SCHOLARSHIPS

Massachusetts Soldiers Legacy Fund
P.O. Box 962061
Milk Street Post Office
Boston, MA 02196
Toll Free: (866) 856-5533   E-mail: info@mslfund.org
Web: www.mslfund.org

Summary To provide financial assistance for college or professional school to the children of service members from Massachusetts who were killed in Afghanistan or Iraq.

Eligibility This program is open to children of members of the U.S. armed forces who died while deployed on operations Enduring Freedom or Iraqi Freedom. The parent's home of record must have been Massachusetts. Applicants must be enrolled or planning to enroll at a 2- or 4-year college or university, professional school, or trade school in any state. All qualified children receive this assistance; there is no selection process.

Financial data The stipend is $10,000 per year.

Duration 1 year; may be renewed up to 3 additional years.

Additional information This program began in 2004.

Number awarded Varies each year.

Deadline Deadline not specified.

[1037]
MINNESOTA G.I. BILL PROGRAM

Minnesota Office of Higher Education
Attn: Manager of State Financial Aid Programs
1450 Energy Park Drive, Suite 350
St. Paul, MN 55108-5227
(651) 642-0567   Toll Free: (800) 657-3866
Fax: (651) 642-0675   TDD: (800) 627-3529
E-mail: Ginny.Dodds@state.mn.us
Web: www.ohe.state.mn.us/mPg.cfm?pageID=891

Summary To provide financial assistance for college or graduate school in the state to residents of Minnesota who served in the military after September 11, 2001 and the families of deceased or disabled military personnel.

Eligibility This program is open to residents of Minnesota enrolled at colleges and universities in the state as undergraduate or graduate students. Applicants must be 1) a veteran who is serving or has served honorably in a branch of the U.S. armed forces at any time on or after September 11, 2001; 2) a non-veteran who has served honorably for a total of 5 years or more cumulatively as a member of the Minnesota National Guard or other active or Reserve component of the U.S. armed forces, and any part of that service occurred on or after September 11, 2001; or 3) a surviving child or spouse of a person who has served in the military at any time on or after September 11, 2001 and who has died or has a total and permanent disability as a result of that military service. Financial need is considered in the selection process.

Financial data The stipend is $1,000 per semester for full-time study or $500 per semester for part-time study. The maximum award is $3,000 per fiscal year or $10,000 per lifetime.

Duration 1 year; may be renewed, provided the recipient continues to make satisfactory academic progress.

Additional information This program was established by the Minnesota Legislature in 2007.

Number awarded Varies each year.

Deadline Deadline not specified.

[1038]
MINNESOTA NATIONAL GUARD SURVIVOR ENTITLEMENT TUITION REIMBURSEMENT PROGRAM

Department of Military Affairs
Attn: Education Services Officer
JFMN-J1-ARED
20 West 12th Street
St. Paul, MN 55155-2098
(651) 282-4589   Toll Free: (800) 657-3848
Fax: (651) 282-4694 E-mail: ngmneducation@ng.army.mil
Web: www.minnesotanationalguard.org

Summary To provide financial assistance for college or graduate school to survivors of members of the Minnesota National Guard who were killed on active duty.

Eligibility This program is open to surviving spouses and children of members of the Minnesota Army or Air National Guard who were killed while performing military duty. Dependent children are eligible until their 24th birthday; surviving spouses are eligible regardless of age or remarriage; all survivors remain eligible even if they move out of state and become non-Minnesota residents. The Guard member's death must have occurred within the scope of assigned duties while in a federal duty status or on state active service. Applicants must be enrolled as undergraduate or graduate students at colleges or universities in Minnesota. Reimbursement is provided only for undergraduate courses completed with a grade of "C" or better or for graduate courses completed with a grade of "B" or better.

Financial data The maximum reimbursement rate is 100% of the undergraduate tuition rate at the University of Minnesota Twin Cities campus, with a maximum benefit of $10,000 per fiscal year.

Duration 1 academic term, to a maximum of 18 credits per term; may be renewed for a total of 144 semester credits or 208 quarter credits.

Additional information This program became effective in 1992.

Number awarded Varies each year.

Deadline Participants must request reimbursement within 60 days of the last official day of the term.

[1039]
NATIONAL GUARD ASSOCIATION OF NEW JERSEY SCHOLARSHIP PROGRAM

National Guard Association of New Jersey
Attn: Executive Director
P.O. Box 266
Wrightstown, NJ 08562
(973) 541-6776   Fax: (973) 541-6909
E-mail: nganj@aol.com
Web: nganj.org/about.htm

Summary To provide financial assistance to members of the National Guard Association of New Jersey (NGANJ) or their dependents who are interested in attending college or graduate school in any state.

Eligibility This program is open to 1) active members of the NGANJ currently enrolled full time at an approved community college, school of nursing, or 4-year college in any state; and 2) the spouses, children, and grandchildren of active, retired, or deceased members entering or attending a 4-year college or university in any state. Applicants must submit transcripts, information on the civic and academic activities in which they have participated, and a list of offices, honors, awards, and special recognitions they have received. Selection is based on academic accomplishment, leadership, and citizenship.

Financial data Stipends up to $1,000 are available.

Duration 1 year; nonrenewable.

Number awarded Varies each year; recently, 10 of these scholarships were awarded.

Deadline April of each year.

[1040]
NATIONAL GUARD ASSOCIATION OF SOUTH CAROLINA SCHOLARSHIPS

National Guard Association of South Carolina
Attn: NGASC Scholarship Foundation
132 Pickens Street
Columbia, SC 29205
(803) 254-8456   Toll Free: (800) 822-3235
Fax: (803) 254-3869   E-mail: nginfo@ngasc.org
Web: www.ngasc.org/?page_id=11

Summary To provide funding to current and former South Carolina National Guard members and their dependents who are interested in attending college or graduate school.

Eligibility This program is open to undergraduate students who are 1) current, retired, or deceased members of the South Carolina National Guard; 2) their dependents; and 3) members of the National Guard Association of South Carolina (NGASC). Graduate students are also eligible if they are members of the South Carolina National Guard. Applicants must be attending or interested in attending a college or university in any state as a full-time student. Several of the scholarships include additional restrictions on school or academic major; some are granted only for academic excellence, but most are based on both academics and financial need.

Financial data The stipend is $1,500 or $1,000.

Duration 1 year; may be renewed up to 3 additional years.

Number awarded Varies each year; recently, 42 of these scholarships were awarded: 1 at $1,500 and 41 at $1,000.

Deadline January of each year.

[1041]
NATIONAL GUARD ASSOCIATION OF TEXAS SCHOLARSHIP PROGRAM

National Guard Association of Texas
Attn: NGAT Educational Foundation
3706 Crawford Avenue
Austin, TX 78731-6803
(512) 454-7300   Toll Free: (800) 252-NGAT
Fax: (512) 467-6803   E-mail: rlindner@ngat.org
Web: www.ngat.org

Summary To provide funding to members and dependents of members of the National Guard Association of Texas who are interested in attending college or graduate school.

Eligibility This program is open to annual and life members of the association and their spouses and children (associate members and their dependents are not eligible). Applicants may be high school seniors, undergraduate students, or graduate students, either enrolled or planning to enroll at an institution of higher education in any state. Along with their application, they must submit an essay on their desire to continue their education. Selection is based on scholarship, citizenship, and leadership.

Financial data Stipends range from $500 to $5,000.

Duration 1 year (nonrenewable).

Additional information This program includes 1 scholarship sponsored by USAA Insurance Corporation.

Number awarded Varies each year; recently, 13 of these scholarships were awarded: 1 at $5,000, 3 at $2,500, 1 at $2,000, 3 at $1,250, 4 at $1,000, and 1 at $500.

Deadline February of each year.

[1042]
NATIONAL GUARD ASSOCIATION OF VERMONT SCHOLARSHIPS

National Guard Association of Vermont
Attn: Capt John Geno, President
P.O. Box 694
Essex Junction, VT 05452
(802) 338-3397   E-mail: john.geno@us.army.mil
Web: www.ngavt.org/scholarInfo.shtml

Summary To provide funding to members of the Vermont National Guard (VTNG) and their children or spouses who are interested in attending college or graduate school.
Eligibility This program is open to current members of the VTNG, their spouses, and their unmarried children. Applicants must be working, or planning to work, on an associate, undergraduate, technical, or graduate degree as a full-time student at a school in any state. Along with their application, they must submit an essay on their commitment to selfless public service or their plan for pursuing it in the future. Selection is based on academic performance, overall potential for a commitment to selfless public service, and financial need.
Financial data The stipend is $1,000. Funds are sent directly to the recipient.
Duration 1 year; recipients may reapply.
Number awarded 4 each year: 3 to undergraduates and 1 to a graduate student.
Deadline May of each year.

[1043]
NAVAL HELICOPTER ASSOCIATION GRADUATE SCHOLARSHIPS

Naval Helicopter Association
Attn: Scholarship Fund
P.O. Box 180578
Coronado, CA 92178-0578
(619) 435-7139   Fax: (619) 435-7354
Web: nhascholarshipfund.org/scholarships-available.html

Summary To provide financial assistance for graduate school to students who have an affiliation with the rotary wing activities of the sea services.
Eligibility This program is open to graduate students who are children, grandchildren, or spouses of active-duty, former, or retired Navy, Marine Corps, or Coast Guard rotary wing aviators, aircrewmen, or support personnel. Applicants must submit a personal statement on their academic and career aspirations. Selection is based on that statement, academic proficiency, scholastic achievements and awards, extracurricular activities, employment history, and letters of recommendation.
Financial data The stipend is $3,000.
Duration 1 year.
Number awarded 1 each year.
Deadline February of each year.

[1044]
NAVAL SPECIAL WARFARE DEVELOPMENT GROUP SCHOLARSHIPS

Navy Seal Foundation
Attn: DEVGRU Scholarship Committee
1619 D Street, Building 5326
Virginia Beach, VA 23459
(757) 363-7490   Fax: (757) 363-7491
E-mail: info@navysealfoundation.org
Web: www.navysealfoundation.org

Summary To provide financial assistance for college to the children and spouses of personnel assigned to the Naval Special Warfare Development Group (DEVGRU).
Eligibility This program is open to the dependent children and spouses of former and present Navy SEAL, Special Warfare Combat Crewman (SWCC), or Military Direct Support person who is or has been assigned to DEVGRU. Applicants must be enrolled or planning to enroll at a trade school, technical/vocational institute, or undergraduate college. Along with their application, they must submit an essay on their plans as related to their educational and career objectives and long-term goals. Selection is based on merit (as measured by GPA, SAT scores, class rank, extracurricular activities, volunteer community involvement, leadership positions held, military service record, and after school employment, as appropriate) and academic potential.
Financial data Stipends are $15,000, $7,500, or $5,000 per year.
Duration 1 year; may be renewed.
Number awarded Varies each year; recently, the Navy Seal Foundation awarded 16 scholarships for all of its programs: 3 for 4 years at $15,000 per year to high school seniors and graduates, 3 for 1 year at $7,500 to high school seniors and graduates, 3 for 1 year at $15,000 to current college students, 3 for 1 year at $7,500 to current college students, and 4 for 1 year at $5,000 to spouses.
Deadline January of each year.

[1045]
NAVY/MARINE CORPS/COAST GUARD ENLISTED DEPENDENT SPOUSE SCHOLARSHIP

Navy Wives Clubs of America
c/o NSA Mid-South
P.O. Box 54022
Millington, TN 38054-0022
Toll Free: (866) 511-NWCA
E-mail: nwca@navywivesclubsofamerica.org
Web: www.navywivesclubsofamerica.org/scholarships

Summary To provide financial assistance for undergraduate or graduate study to spouses of naval personnel.
Eligibility This program is open to the spouses of active-duty Navy, Marine Corps, or Coast Guard members who can demonstrate financial need. Applicants must be 1) a high school graduate or senior planning to attend college full time next year; 2) currently enrolled in an undergraduate program and planning to continue as a full-time undergraduate; 3) a college graduate or senior planning to be a full-time graduate student next year; or 4) a high school graduate or GED recipient planning to attend vocational or business school next year. Along with their application, they must submit a brief statement on why they feel they should be awarded this scholarship and any special circumstances (financial or other) they wish to have considered. Financial need is also considered in the selection process.
Financial data The stipends range from $500 to $1,000 each year (depending upon the donations from chapters of the Navy Wives Clubs of America).
Duration 1 year.
Number awarded 1 or more each year.
Deadline May of each year.

[1046]
NAVY WIVES CLUBS OF AMERICA NATIONAL SCHOLARSHIPS

Navy Wives Clubs of America
c/o NSA Mid-South
P.O. Box 54022
Millington, TN 38054-0022
Toll Free: (866) 511-NWCA
E-mail: nwca@navywivesclubsofamerica.org
Web: www.navywivesclubsofamerica.org/scholarships

Summary To provide financial assistance for college or graduate school to the children of naval personnel.

Eligibility Applicants for these scholarships must be the children (natural born, legally adopted, or stepchildren) of enlisted members of the Navy, Marine Corps, or Coast Guard on active duty, retired with pay, or deceased. Applicants must be attending or planning to attend an accredited college or university as a full-time undergraduate or graduate student. They must have a GPA of 2.5 or higher. Along with their application, they must submit an essay on their career objectives and the reasons they chose those objectives. Selection is based on academic standing, moral character, and financial need. Some scholarships are reserved for students majoring in special education, medical students, and children of members of Navy Wives Clubs of America (NWCA).

Financial data The stipend is $1,500.

Duration 1 year; may be renewed up to 3 additional years.

Additional information Membership in the NWCA is open to spouses of enlisted personnel serving in the Navy, Marine Corps, Coast Guard, and the active Reserve units of those services; spouses of enlisted personnel who have been honorably discharged, retired, or transferred to the Fleet Reserve on completion of duty; and widows of enlisted personnel in those services.

Number awarded 30 each year, including at least 4 to freshmen, 4 to current undergraduates applying for the first time, 2 to medical students, 1 to a student majoring in special education, and 4 to children of NWCA members.

Deadline May of each year.

[1047]
NCPOA/BART LONGO MEMORIAL SCHOLARSHIPS

National Chief Petty Officers' Association
c/o Marjorie Hays, Treasurer
1014 Ronald Drive
Corpus Christi, TX 78412-3548
Web: www.goatlocker.org/ncpoa/scholarship.htm

Summary To provide financial assistance for college or graduate school to members of the National Chief Petty Officers' Association (NCPOA) and their families.

Eligibility This program is open to members of the NCPOA and the children, stepchildren, and grandchildren of living or deceased members. Applicants may be high school seniors or graduates entering a college or university or students currently enrolled full time as undergraduate or graduate students. Selection is based on academic achievement and participation in extracurricular activities; need is not considered.

Financial data The stipend is $1,000.

Duration 1 year.

Additional information Membership in the NCPOA is limited to men and women who served or are serving as Chief

Petty Officers in the U.S. Navy, U.S. Coast Guard, or their Reserve components for at least 30 days.

Number awarded 2 each year: 1 to a high school senior or graduate and 1 to an undergraduate or graduate student.

Deadline May of each year.

[1048]
NEW JERSEY NATIONAL GUARD TUITION PROGRAM

New Jersey Department of Military and Veterans Affairs
Attn: New Jersey Army National Guard Education Center
3650 Saylors Pond Road
Fort Dix, NJ 08640-7600
(609) 562-0654　　　　　Toll Free: (888) 859-0352
Fax: (609) 562-0201
Web: www.state.nj.us/military/education/NJNGTP.htm

Summary To provide financial assistance for college or graduate school to New Jersey National Guard members and the surviving spouses and children of deceased members.

Eligibility This program is open to active members of the New Jersey National Guard who have completed Initial Active Duty for Training (IADT). Applicants must be New Jersey residents who have been accepted into a program of undergraduate or graduate study at any of 31 public institutions of higher education in the state. The surviving spouses and children of deceased members of the Guard who had completed IADT and were killed in the performance of their duties while a member of the Guard are also eligible if the school has classroom space available.

Financial data Tuition for up to 15 credits per semester is waived for full-time recipients in state-supported colleges or community colleges in New Jersey.

Duration 1 semester; may be renewed.

Number awarded Varies each year.

Deadline Deadline not specified.

[1049]
NEW MEXICO CHILDREN OF DECEASED MILITARY AND STATE POLICE PERSONNEL SCHOLARSHIPS

New Mexico Department of Veterans' Services
Attn: Benefits Division
407 Galisteo Street, Room 142
P.O. Box 2324
Santa Fe, NM 87504-2324
(505) 827-6374　　　　　Toll Free: (866) 433-VETS
Fax: (505) 827-6372　 E-mail: alan.martinez@state.nm.us
Web: www.dvs.state.nm.us/benefits.html

Summary To provide financial assistance for college or graduate school to the children of deceased military and state police personnel in New Mexico.

Eligibility This program is open to the children of 1) military personnel killed in action or as a result of such action during a period of armed conflict; 2) members of the New Mexico National Guard killed while on active duty; and 3) New Mexico State Police killed on active duty. Applicants must be between the ages of 16 and 26 and enrolled in a state-supported school in New Mexico. Children of deceased veterans must be nominated by the New Mexico Veterans' Service Commission; children of National Guard members must be nominated by the adjutant general of the state; children of state police must be nominated by the New Mexico State Police Board. Selection is based on merit and financial need.

Financial data The scholarships provide full waiver of tuition at state-funded postsecondary schools in New Mexico. A stipend of $150 per semester ($300 per year) provides assistance with books and fees.

Duration 1 year; may be renewed.

Deadline Deadline not specified.

[1050]
NEW MEXICO NATIONAL GUARD ASSOCIATION MASTER'S/CONTINUING EDUCATION SCHOLARSHIPS

New Mexico National Guard Association
Attn: Executive Director
10 Bataan Boulevard
Santa Fe, NM 87508
(505) 474-1669   Fax: (505) 474-1671
E-mail: execdir@nganm.org
Web: www.nganm.org

Summary To provide financial assistance to members of the New Mexico National Guard Association and their dependents who are working on a master's or other advanced degree.

Eligibility This program is open to association members (with paid-up current dues) and their dependents. Applicants must have completed their postsecondary education and be working on their master's or other higher degree. They must submit an official college transcript with a GPA of 3.3 or higher, a completed application, and an original essay (from 800 to 1,200 words) on their past accomplishments and contributions and what contributions they intend to make with this education to better the community or the National Guard.

Financial data The stipend is $1,000. Funds are paid directly to the recipient's school.

Duration 1 year; nonrenewable.

Number awarded 2 each year.

Deadline April of each year.

[1051]
PAT TILLMAN MILITARY SCHOLARS PROGRAM

Pat Tillman Foundation
2121 South Mill Avenue, Suite 214
Tempe, AZ 85282
(480) 621-4074   Fax: (480) 621-4075
E-mail: scholarships@pattillmanfoundation.org
Web: www.pattillmanfoundation.org/tillman-military-scholars

Summary To provide financial assistance to veterans, active servicemembers, and their spouses who are interested in working on an undergraduate or graduate degree.

Eligibility This program is open to veterans and active servicemembers of all branches of the armed forces from both the pre- and post-September 11 era and their spouses; children are not eligible. Applicants must be enrolled or planning to enroll full time at a 4-year public or private college or university to work on an undergraduate, graduate, or postgraduate degree. Current and former servicemembers must submit 400-word essays on 1) their motivation and decision to serve in the U.S. military and how that decision and experience has changed their life and ambitions; and 2) their educational and career goals, how they will incorporate their military service experience into those goals, and how they intend to continue their service to others and the community. Spouses must submit 400-word essays on 1) their previous service to others

and the community; and 2) their educational and career goals, how they will incorporate their service experiences and the impact of their spouse's military service into those goals, and how they intend to continue their service to others and the community. Selection is based on those essays, educational and career ambitions, record of military service, record of personal achievement, demonstration of service to others in the community, desire to continue such service, and leadership potential.

Financial data The stipend depends on the need of the recipient and the availability of funds.

Duration 1 year; may be renewed, provided the recipient maintains a GPA of 3.0 or higher, remains enrolled full time, and participates in civic action or community service.

Additional information This program began in 2009.

Number awarded Varies each year; recently, 60 students received a total of $916,000 through this program.

Deadline March of each year.

[1052]
PETER CONNACHER MEMORIAL SCHOLARSHIPS

Oregon Student Access Commission
Attn: Grants and Scholarships Division
1500 Valley River Drive, Suite 100
Eugene, OR 97401-2146
(541) 687-7395   Toll Free: (800) 452-8807, ext. 7395
Fax: (541) 687-7414   TDD: (800) 735-2900
E-mail: awardinfo@osac.state.or.us
Web: www.oregonstudentaid.gov/scholarships.aspx

Summary To provide money for college or graduate school to ex-prisoners of war and their descendants.

Eligibility Applicants must be U.S. citizens who 1) were military or civilian prisoners of war; or 2) are the descendants of ex-prisoners of war. They must be full-time undergraduate or graduate students. A copy of the ex-prisoner of war's discharge papers from the U.S. armed forces must accompany the application. In addition, written proof of POW status must be submitted, along with a statement of the relationship between the applicant and the ex-prisoner of war (father, grandfather, etc.). Selection is based on academic record and financial need. Preference is given to Oregon residents or their dependents.

Financial data Stipends for scholarships offered by the Oregon Student Access Commission (OSAC) range from $200 to $10,000 but recently averaged $2,300.

Duration 1 year; may be renewed for up to 3 additional years for undergraduate students or 2 additional years for graduate students. Renewal is dependent on evidence of continued financial need and satisfactory academic progress.

Additional information This program is administered by the OSAC with funds provided by the Oregon Community Foundation. Funds are also provided by the Columbia River Chapter of American Ex-prisoners of War, Inc.

Number awarded Varies each year; recently, 4 of these scholarships were awarded.

Deadline February of each year.

[1053]
RED RIVER VALLEY FIGHTER PILOTS ASSOCIATION SCHOLARSHIP GRANT PROGRAM

Red River Valley Association Foundation
Attn: Executive Director
P.O. Box 1553
Front Royal, VA 22630-0033
(540) 639-9798   Toll Free: (866) 401-7287
Fax: (540) 636-9776   E-mail: RRVARiverRats@aol.com
Web: www.river-rats.org/about_us/scholarship.php

Summary To provide financial assistance for college or graduate school to the spouses and children of selected service personnel and members of the Red River Valley Fighter Pilots Association.

Eligibility This program is open to the spouses and children of 1) servicemembers missing in action (MIA) or killed in action (KIA) in combat situations involving U.S. military forces from August 1964 through the present; 2) U.S. military aircrew members killed in a non-combat aircraft accident in which they were performing aircrew duties; and 3) current members of the association and deceased members who were in good standing at the time of their death. Scholarships are also available to students in fields related to aviation and space, even if they have no kinship relationship to a deceased aviator or member of the association. Applicants must be enrolled or planning to enroll full or part time at an accredited college, university, vocational/technical institute, or career school to work on an undergraduate or graduate degree. They must be 30 years of age or younger, although the age limit is extended to 40 for current and former military personnel. Selection is based on demonstrated academic achievement, SAT or ACT scores, financial need, and accomplishments in school, church, civic, and social activities.

Financial data The amount awarded varies, depending upon the need of the recipient. Recently, undergraduate stipends have ranged from $500 to $3,500 and averaged $1,725; graduate stipends have ranged from $500 to $2,000 and averaged $1,670. Funds are paid directly to the recipient's institution and are to be used for tuition, fees, books, and room and board for full-time students.

Duration 1 year; may be renewed if the recipient maintains a GPA of 2.0 or higher.

Additional information This program was established in 1970, out of concern for the families of aircrews (known as "River Rats") who were killed or missing in action in the Red River Valley of North Vietnam.

Number awarded Varies each year; since this program was established, it has awarded more than 1,000 scholarships worth more than $1,700,000.

Deadline May of each year.

[1054]
ROBERT W. NOLAN SCHOLARSHIP

Fleet Reserve Association
Attn: FRA Education Foundation
125 North West Street
Alexandria, VA 22314-2754
(703) 683-1400   Toll Free: (800) FRA-1924
Fax: (703) 549-6610   E-mail: scholars@fra.org
Web: www.fra.org

Summary To provide financial assistance for graduate school to members of the Fleet Reserve Association (FRA) and their families.

Eligibility This program is open to members of the FRA and the dependent children, grandchildren, and spouses of living or deceased members. Applicants must be enrolled as full-time graduate students. Along with their application, they must submit an essay on why they want to go to college and what they intend to accomplish with their degree. Selection is based on academic record, financial need, extracurricular activities, leadership skills, and participation in community activities. U.S. citizenship is required.

Financial data The stipend is $5,000 per year.

Duration 1 year; may be renewed.

Additional information Membership in the FRA is restricted to active-duty, retired, and Reserve members of the Navy, Marine Corps, and Coast Guard. This program was established in 2001.

Number awarded 1 each year.

Deadline April of each year.

[1055]
SCHUYLER S. PYLE SCHOLARSHIP

Fleet Reserve Association
Attn: FRA Education Foundation
125 North West Street
Alexandria, VA 22314-2754
(703) 683-1400   Toll Free: (800) FRA-1924
Fax: (703) 549-6610   E-mail: scholars@fra.org
Web: www.fra.org

Summary To provide financial assistance for college or graduate school to members of the Fleet Reserve Association (FRA) and their families.

Eligibility This program is open to members of the FRA and the dependent children, grandchildren, and spouses of living or deceased members. Applicants must be enrolled as full-time undergraduate or graduate students. Along with their application, they must submit an essay on why they want to go to college and what they intend to accomplish with their degree. Selection is based on academic record, financial need, extracurricular activities, leadership skills, and participation in community activities. U.S. citizenship is required.

Financial data The stipend is $5,000 per year.

Duration 1 year; may be renewed.

Additional information Membership in the FRA is restricted to active-duty, retired, and Reserve members of the Navy, Marine Corps, and Coast Guard.

Number awarded 1 each year.

Deadline April of each year.

[1056]
STANLEY A. DORAN MEMORIAL SCHOLARSHIPS

Fleet Reserve Association
Attn: FRA Education Foundation
125 North West Street
Alexandria, VA 22314-2754
(703) 683-1400   Toll Free: (800) FRA-1924
Fax: (703) 549-6610   E-mail: scholars@fra.org
Web: www.fra.org

Summary To provide financial assistance for college or graduate school to children of members of the Fleet Reserve Association (FRA).

Eligibility This program is open to the dependent children of FRA members who are in good standing (or were at the time of death, if deceased). Applicants must be working on or planning to work full time on an undergraduate or graduate degree. Along with their application, they must submit an essay on why they want to go to college and what they intend to accomplish with their degree. Selection is based on academic record, financial need, extracurricular activities, leadership skills, and participation in community activities. U.S. citizenship is required.

Financial data The amount awarded varies, depending on the needs of the recipient and the funds available.

Duration 1 year; may be renewed.

Additional information Membership in the FRA is restricted to active-duty, retired, and Reserve members of the Navy, Marine Corps, and Coast Guard.

Number awarded 3 each year.

Deadline April of each year.

[1057]
SURVIVORS' AND DEPENDENTS' EDUCATIONAL ASSISTANCE PROGRAM

Department of Veterans Affairs
Attn: Veterans Benefits Administration
810 Vermont Avenue, N.W.
Washington, DC 20420
(202) 418-4343   Toll Free: (888) GI-BILL1
Web: www.gibill.va.gov/benefits/other_programs/dea.html

Summary To provide financial assistance for undergraduate or graduate study to children and spouses of deceased and disabled veterans, MIAs, and POWs.

Eligibility Eligible for this assistance are spouses and children of 1) veterans who died or are permanently and totally disabled as the result of active service in the armed forces; 2) veterans who died from any cause while rated permanently and totally disabled from a service-connected disability; 3) servicemembers listed as missing in action or captured in the line of duty by a hostile force; 4) servicemembers listed as forcibly detained or interned by a foreign government or power; and 5) servicemembers who are hospitalized or receiving outpatient treatment for a service-connected permanent and total disability and are likely to be discharged for that disability. Children must be between 18 and 26 years of age, although extensions may be granted. Spouses and children over 14 years of age with physical or mental disabilities are also eligible.

Financial data Monthly stipends for study at an academic institution are $957 for full time, $718 for three-quarter time, or $476 for half-time. Other rates apply for apprenticeship and on-the-job training, farm cooperative training, and special restorative training.

Duration Up to 45 months (or the equivalent in part-time training). Spouses must complete their training within 10 years of the date they are first found eligible. For spouses of servicemembers who died on active duty, benefits end 20 years from the date of death.

Additional information Benefits may be used to work on associate, bachelor's, or graduate degrees at colleges and universities, including independent study, cooperative training, and study abroad programs. Courses leading to a certificate or diploma from business, technical, or vocational schools may also be taken. Other eligible programs include apprenticeships, on-the-job training programs, farm cooperative courses, and correspondence courses (for spouses only). Remedial, deficiency, and refresher courses may be approved under certain circumstances.

Number awarded Varies each year.

Deadline Applications may be submitted at any time.

[1058]
TRANSFER OF POST-9/11 GI-BILL BENEFITS TO DEPENDENTS

Department of Veterans Affairs
Attn: Veterans Benefits Administration
810 Vermont Avenue, N.W.
Washington, DC 20420
(202) 418-4343   Toll Free: (888) GI-BILL1
Web: www.gibill.va.gov

Summary To provide financial assistance to dependents of military personnel who qualify for Post-9/11 GI Bill benefits and agree to transfer unused benefits to their spouse or child.

Eligibility This program is open to dependents of current military personnel whose parent or spouse 1) has at least 6 years of service in the armed forces (active duty and/or Selected Reserve) and agrees to serve 4 additional years; 2) has at least 10 years of service, is precluded by either standard policy or statute from committing to 4 additional years, but agrees to serve for the maximum amount of time allowed by such policy or statute; or 3) is or becomes retirement eligible during the period following August 1, 2009 and agrees to serve for an additional period up to 3 years, depending on the date of retirement eligibility. The military parent or spouse must agree to transfer unused months of educational benefits to a dependent while still serving on active duty. Dependents must be enrolled or planning to enroll in an educational program, including work on an undergraduate or graduate degree, vocational/technical training, on-the-job training, flight training, correspondence training, licensing and national testing programs, entrepreneurship training, and tutorial assistance.

Financial data Dependents working on an undergraduate or graduate degree at public institutions in their state receive full payment of tuition and fees. For dependents who attend private institutions in most states, tuition and fee reimbursement is capped at $17,500 per academic year; the reimbursement rate is higher at private schools in Arizona, Michigan, New Hampshire, New York, Pennsylvania, South Carolina, and Texas. Benefits for other types of training programs depend on the amount for which the spouse or parent qualified under prior educational programs. Dependents also receive a monthly housing allowance based on the national average Basic Allowance for Housing (BAH) for an E-5 with dependents (currently $673.50) or $1,347 per month at schools in foreign countries); an annual book allowance of $1,000; and (for participants who live in a rural county remote from an educational institution) a rural benefit payment of $500 per year.

Duration Military members may transfer all or a portion of their 36 months of entitlement to a dependent. Spouses may start to use the benefit immediately, may use the benefit while the member remains in the armed forces or after separation from active duty, are not eligible for the housing or book allowances while the member is still serving on active duty, and can use the benefit for up to 15 years after the service member's last separation from active duty. Children may use the benefit only after they have completed high school (or equivalency certificate) or reached 18 years of age, may use the benefit only after the parent has completed 10 years of service, may use the benefit while the member remains in the armed forces or after separation from active duty, are entitled to the housing and book allowances even while the parent is on active duty, and are not subject to the 15-year limit but may not use the benefit after reaching 26 years of age.

Additional information This supplement was added to the Post-9/11 GI Bill program as a result of legislation passed by Congress in 2010.

Number awarded Varies each year.

Deadline Deadline not specified.

[1059]
VADM ROBERT L. WALTERS SCHOLARSHIP

Surface Navy Association
2550 Huntington Avenue, Suite 202
Alexandria, VA 22303
(703) 960-6800   Toll Free: (800) NAVY-SNA
Fax: (703) 960-6807   E-mail: navysna@aol.com
Web: www.navysna.org

Summary To provide financial assistance for college or graduate school to dependents of members of the Surface Navy Association (SNA).

Eligibility This program is open to the children, stepchildren, wards, and spouses of SNA members. The SNA member must 1) be in the second or subsequent consecutive year of membership; 2) be serving, retired, or honorably discharged; 3) be a Surface Warfare Officer or Enlisted Surface Warfare Specialist; and 4) have served for at least 3 years on a surface ship of the U.S. Navy or Coast Guard. Applicants must be enrolled or planning to enroll full time at an accredited undergraduate or graduate institution; the full-time requirement may be waived for spouses. Along with their application, they must submit a 500-word essay on why they should be selected to receive this scholarship. High school seniors should also include a transcript of high school grades and a copy of ACT or SAT scores. Current college students should also include a transcript of the grades from their most recent 4 semesters of school. Selection is based on academic proficiency, non-scholastic activities, scholastic and non-scholastic awards, character, and financial need.

Financial data The stipend is $2,000 per year.

Duration 4 years, provided the recipient maintains a GPA of 3.0 or higher.

Number awarded Varies each year.

Deadline February of each year.

[1060]
VIRGINIA MILITARY SURVIVORS AND DEPENDENTS EDUCATION PROGRAM

Virginia Department of Veterans Services
270 Franklin Road, Room 810
Roanoke, VA 24011-2215
(540) 597-1730   Fax: (540) 857-7573
Web: www.dvs.virginia.gov/veterans-benefits.shtml

Summary To provide funding to the children and spouses of disabled and other Virginia veterans or service personnel.

Eligibility This program is open to residents of Virginia whose parent or spouse served in the U.S. armed forces (including the Reserves, the Virginia National Guard, or the Virginia National Guard Reserves) during any armed conflict subsequent to December 6, 1941, as a result of a terrorist act, during military operations against terrorism, or on a peacekeeping mission. The veterans must have been killed, missing in action, taken prisoner of war, or become at least 90% disabled as a result of such service. Applicants must have been accepted at a public college or university in Virginia as an undergraduate or graduate student. Children must be between 16 and 29 years of age; there are no age restrictions for spouses. The veteran must have been a resident of Virginia at the time of entry into active military service or for at least 5 consecutive years immediately prior to the date of application or death. Surviving spouses must have been residents of Virginia for at least 5 years prior to marrying the veteran or for at least 5 years immediately prior to the date on which the application was submitted.

Financial data The program provides 1) waiver of tuition and all required fees at public institutions of higher education in Virginia; and 2) a stipend up to $1,500 per year to offset the costs of room, board, books, and supplies at those institutions. If more students qualify, the stipend is reduced; recently, it was $675 per semester ($1,350 per year) for full-time enrollment, $450 per semester for enrollment less than full-time but at least half-time, or $225 per semester for enrollment less than half-time.

Duration Entitlement extends to a maximum of 36 months (4 years).

Additional information Individuals entitled to this benefit may use it to pursue any vocational, technical, undergraduate, or graduate program of instruction. Generally, programs listed in the academic catalogs of state-supported institutions are acceptable, provided they have a clearly-defined educational objective (such as a certificate, diploma, or degree). This program was formerly known as the Virginia War Orphans Education Program.

Number awarded Varies each year; recently, funding allowed for a total of 667 stipends at $1,500, but 740 students actually qualified and received a reduced stipend.

Deadline Applications may be submitted at any time, but they must be received at least 30 days prior to the start of the term.

[1061]
WISCONSIN G.I. BILL TUITION REMISSION PROGRAM

Wisconsin Department of Veterans Affairs
201 West Washington Avenue
P.O. Box 7843
Madison, WI 53707-7843
(608) 266-1311   Toll Free: (800) WIS-VETS
Fax: (608) 267-0403   E-mail: WDVAInfo@dva.state.wi.us
Web: www.dva.state.wi.us/Ben_education.asp

Summary To provide financial assistance for college or graduate school to Wisconsin veterans and their dependents.

Eligibility This program is open to current residents of Wisconsin who 1) were residents of the state when they entered or reentered active duty in the U.S. armed forces, or 2) have moved to the state and have been residents for any consecutive 12-month period after entry or reentry into service. Applicants must have served on active duty for at least 2 continuous years or for at least 90 days during specified wartime periods. Also eligible are 1) qualifying children and unremarried surviving spouses of Wisconsin veterans who died in the line of duty or as the direct result of a service-connected disability; and 2) children and spouses of Wisconsin veterans who have a service-connected disability rated by the U.S. Department of Veterans Affairs as 30% or greater. Children must be between 17 and 25 years of age (regardless of the date of the veteran's death or initial disability rating) and be a Wisconsin resident for tuition purposes. Spouses remain eligible for 10 years following the date of the veteran's death or initial disability rating; they must be Wisconsin residents for tuition purposes but they may enroll full or part time. Students may attend any institution, center, or school within the University of Wisconsin (UW) System or the Wisconsin Technical College System (WCTS). There are no income limits, delimiting periods following military service during which the benefit must be used, or limits on the level of study (e.g., vocational, undergraduate, professional, or graduate).

Financial data Veterans who qualify as a Wisconsin resident for tuition purposes are eligible for a remission of 100% of standard academic fees and segregated fees at a UW campus or 100% of program and material fees at a WCTS institution. Veterans who qualify as a Wisconsin veteran for purposes of this program but for other reasons fail to meet the definition of a Wisconsin resident for tuition purposes at the UW system are eligible for a remission of 100% of non-resident fees. Spouses and children of deceased or disabled veterans are entitled to a remission of 100% of tuition and fees at a UW or WCTS institution.

Duration Up to 8 semesters or 128 credits, whichever is greater.

Additional information This program was established in 2005 as a replacement for Wisconsin Tuition and Fee Reimbursement Grants.

Number awarded Varies each year.

Deadline Applications must be submitted within 14 days from the office start of the academic term: in October for fall, March for spring, or June for summer.

[1062]
WISCONSIN JOB RETRAINING GRANTS

Wisconsin Department of Veterans Affairs
201 West Washington Avenue
P.O. Box 7843
Madison, WI 53707-7843
(608) 266-1311   Toll Free: (800) WIS-VETS
Fax: (608) 267-0403   E-mail: WDVAInfo@dva.state.wi.us
Web: www.dva.state.wi.us/Ben_retraininggrants.asp

Summary To provide funds to recently unemployed Wisconsin veterans or their families who need financial assistance while being retrained for employment.

Eligibility This program is open to current residents of Wisconsin who 1) were residents of the state when they entered or reentered active duty in the U.S. armed forces, or 2) have moved to the state and have been residents for any consecutive 12-month period after entry or reentry into service. Applicants must have served on active duty for at least 2 continuous years or for at least 90 days during specified wartime

periods. Unremarried spouses and minor or dependent children of deceased veterans who would have been eligible for the grant if they were living today may also be eligible. The applicant must, within the year prior to the date of application, have become unemployed (involuntarily laid off or discharged, not due to willful misconduct) or underemployed (experienced an involuntary reduction of income). Underemployed applicants must have current annual income from employment that does not exceed federal poverty guidelines (currently $14,521 for a family of 1, rising to $50,557 for a family of 8). All applicants must be retraining at accredited schools in Wisconsin or in a structured on-the-job program. Course work toward a college degree does not qualify. Training does not have to be full time, but the program must be completed within 2 years and must reasonably be expected to lead to employment.

Financial data The maximum grant is $3,000 per year; the actual amount varies, depending upon the amount of the applicant's unmet need. In addition to books, fees, and tuition, the funds may be used for living expenses.

Duration 1 year; may be renewed 1 additional year.

Number awarded Varies each year.

Deadline Applications may be submitted at any time.

[1063]
WISCONSIN LEGION AUXILIARY CHILD WELFARE SCHOLARSHIP

American Legion Auxiliary
Department of Wisconsin
Attn: Education Chair
2930 American Legion Drive
P.O. Box 140
Portage, WI 53901-0140
(608) 745-0124   Toll Free: (866) 664-3863
Fax: (608) 745-1947   E-mail: alawi@amlegionauxwi.org
Web: www.amlegionauxwi.org/Scholarships.htm

Summary To provide financial assistance for graduate training in special education at a school in any state to dependents and descendants of veterans in Wisconsin.

Eligibility This program is open to the children, wives, and widows of veterans who are college graduates and have a GPA of 3.5 or higher. Grandchildren and great-grandchildren of members of the American Legion Auxiliary are also eligible. Applicants must be residents of Wisconsin and interested in working on a graduate degree in special education at a school in any state. Along with their application, they must submit a 300-word essay on "Education—An Investment in the Future." Financial need is considered in the selection process.

Financial data The stipend is $1,000.

Duration 1 year; nonrenewable.

Number awarded 1 each year.

Deadline March of each year.

[1064]
WISCONSIN NATIONAL GUARD ENLISTED ASSOCIATION COLLEGE GRANT PROGRAM

Wisconsin National Guard Enlisted Association
Attn: Executive Director
2400 Wright Street
Madison, WI 53704
(608) 242-3112   E-mail: WNGEA@yahoo.com
Web: www.wngea.org/MAIN/PROG/prosch.htm

Summary   To provide financial assistance to members of the Wisconsin National Guard Enlisted Association (WNGEA) and their spouses and children who are interested in attending college or graduate school in any state.

Eligibility   This program is open to WNGEA members, the unmarried children and spouses of WNGEA members, and the unmarried children and spouses of deceased WNGEA members. WNGEA member applicants, as well as the parents or guardians of unmarried children who are applicants, must have at least 1 year remaining on their enlistment following completion of the school year for which application is submitted (or they must have 20 or more years of service). Applicants must be enrolled at a college, university, graduate school, trade school, or business school in any state. Selection is based on need, leadership, and moral character.

Financial data   Stipends are $1,000 or $500 per year.

Duration   1 year; recipients may not reapply for 2 years.

Additional information   This program includes 1 scholarship sponsored by the USAA Insurance Corporation.

Number awarded   Varies each year; recently, 4 of these scholarships were awarded: the Raymond A. Matera Scholarship at $1,000 and 3 others at $500 each.

Deadline   April of each year.

[1065]
WOMEN MARINES ASSOCIATION SCHOLARSHIP PROGRAM

Women Marines Association
P.O. Box 377
Oaks, PA 19456-0377
Toll Free: (888) 525-1943
E-mail: scholarship@womenmarines.org
Web: www.womenmarines.org/scholarships.aspx

Summary   To provide money for college or graduate school to students with ties to the military who are sponsored by members of the Women Marines Association (WMA).

Eligibility   Applicants must be sponsored by a WMA member and fall into 1 of the following categories: 1) have served or are serving in the U.S. Marine Corps, regular or Reserve; 2) are a direct descendant by blood or legal adoption or a stepchild of a Marine on active duty or who has served honorably in the U.S. Marine Corps, regular or Reserve; 3) are a sibling or a descendant of a sibling by blood or legal adoption or a stepchild of a Marine on active duty or who has served honorably in the U.S. Marine Corps, regular or Reserve; or 4) have completed 2 years in a Marine Corps JROTC program. WMA members may sponsor an unlimited number of applicants per year. High school seniors must submit transcripts (GPA of 3.0 or higher) and SAT or ACT scores. Undergraduate and graduate students must have a GPA of 3.0 or higher.

Financial data   The stipend is $1,500 per year.

Duration   1 year; may be renewed 1 additional year.

Additional information   This program includes the following named scholarships: the WMA Memorial Scholarships, the Lily H. Gridley Memorial Scholarship, the Ethyl and Armin Wiebke Memorial Scholarship, the Maj. Megan Malia McClung Memorial Scholarship, the Agnes Sopcak Memorial Scholarship, the Virginia Guveyan Memorial Scholarship, and the LaRue A. Ditmore Music Scholarships. Applicants must know a WMA member to serve as their sponsor; the WMA will not supply listings of the names or addresses of chapters or individual members.

Number awarded   Varies each year.

Deadline   January of each year.

[1066]
YELLOW RIBBON PROGRAM OF THE POST-9/11 GI BILL

Department of Veterans Affairs
Attn: Veterans Benefits Administration
810 Vermont Avenue, N.W.
Washington, DC 20420
(202) 418-4343   Toll Free: (888) GI-BILL1
Web: www.gibill.va.gov

Summary   To provide financial assistance to veterans and their dependents who qualify for the Post-9/11 GI Bill and wish to attend a high cost private or out-of-state college or graduate school.

Eligibility   Maximum Post-9/11 GI Bill benefits are available to veterans who 1) served on active duty for at least 36 aggregate months after September 11, 2001; or 2) were honorably discharged for a service-connected disability and served at least 30 continuous days after September 11, 2001. Military personnel currently on active duty and their spouses may qualify for Post-9/11 GI Bill benefits but are not eligible for the Yellow Ribbon Program. This program is available to veterans who qualify for those benefits at the 100% rate, the children of those veterans to whom they wish to transfer their benefits, and the children and spouses of active-duty personnel who qualify for benefits at the 100% rate to whom they wish to transfer those benefits. Applicants must be working on or planning to work on an undergraduate or graduate degree at a private or out-of-state public institution that charges tuition in excess of the $17,500 cap imposed by the Post-9/11 GI Bill and that has agreed with the Department of Veterans Affairs (VA) to participate in this program.

Financial data   Colleges and universities that charge more than $17,500 per academic year in tuition and fees (or a higher amount at schools in Arizona, Michigan, New Hampshire, New York, Pennsylvania, South Carolina, and Texas) agree to waive tuition (up to 50%) for qualifying veterans and dependents. The amount that the college or university waives is matched by VA.

Duration   Most participants receive up to 36 months of entitlement under this program. Benefits are payable for up to 15 years following release from active duty.

Number awarded   Varies each year.

Deadline   Deadline not specified.

Grants-in-Aid

Veterans ●

Military Personnel ●

Family Members ●

Described here are 362 programs that provide funding for personal needs, including property and income tax liabilities, travel, emergencies, service in dangerous military zones, loan repayment, burials, etc. All of this is "free" money. Not one dollar will need to be repaid (provided, of course, that recipients meet all program requirements).Of the programs listed here, 141 are open to veterans, 89 to military personnel, and 132 to their family members (spouses, children, grandchildren, parents, and other relatives). If you are looking for a particular program and don't find it in this section, be sure to check the Program Title Index to see if it is covered elsewhere in the directory.

Veterans

[1067]
AIR FORCE AID SOCIETY EMERGENCY FINANCIAL ASSISTANCE

Air Force Aid Society
Attn: Financial Assistance Department
241 18th Street South, Suite 202
Arlington, VA 22202-3409
(703) 607-3072, ext. 51   Toll Free: (800) 769-8951
Fax: (703) 607-3022
Web: www.afas.org/Assistance/HowWeCanHelp.cfm

Summary To provide loans and grants-in-aid to current and former Air Force personnel and their families who are facing emergency situations.

Eligibility This program is open to active-duty Air Force members and their dependents, retired Air Force personnel and their dependents, Air National Guard and Air Force Reserve personnel on extended duty over 15 days, and spouses and dependent children of deceased Air Force personnel who died on active duty or in retired status. Applicants must be facing problems, usually for relatively short periods, that affect their job or the essential quality and dignity of life the Air Force wants for its people. Examples of such needs include basic living expenses (food, rent, utilities), medical and dental care, funeral expenses, vehicle expenses, emergency travel, moving expenses, or child or respite care. Funding is generally not provided if it merely postpones a long-term inability to exist on present pay and allowances, for non-essentials, for continuing long-term assistance commitments, or to replace funds lost due to garnishment.

Financial data Assistance is provided as an interest-free loan, a grant, or a combination of both.

Number awarded Varies each year.

Deadline Applications may be submitted at any time.

[1068]
AIR WARRIOR COURAGE FOUNDATION GRANTS

Air Warrior Courage Foundation
P.O. Box 877
Silver Spring, MD 20918
(301) 588-3282   Fax: (540) 636-9776
E-mail: awcf@awcfoundation.com
Web: www.airwarriorcourage.org

Summary To provide emergency assistance to veterans, military personnel, and their families, especially members of the Red River Valley Fighter Pilots Association (RRVA), who are facing unusual situations.

Eligibility These grants are available to active, Guard, Reserve, retired, and former military and Coast Guard personnel and dependent family members. Applicants must be able to demonstrate financial and material needs unmet by insurance programs, community support, or other service agencies. Special consideration is given to applicants eligible for the RRVA scholarship program (spouses and children of servicemembers missing in action or killed in action in armed conflicts by U.S. forces since August 1964, of U.S. military aircrew members killed in a non-combat aircraft accident in which they were performing aircrew duties, and of current

members of the association). Assistance includes the following activities: the troop support 9/11 Terrorism Memorial Fund, which provides financial assistance, college savings programs, and/or material support to surviving family members of those lost or injured in the war on terror and military units performing humanitarian activities worldwide; grants for individuals, which provides emergency financial support for utilities, rent, transportation, auto repairs, and medical expenses; the Professional Association for Therapeutic Horsemanship (PATH) grants, which supports horseback riding for children with certain mental, physical, or developmental challenges; and the College Savings Plan (529) program, which opens College Savings Plan (529) accounts for children of aviators killed during the performance of aircrew duties.

Financial data The amount awarded varies. Recent grants included more than $900,000 for the troop support 9/11 Terrorism Memorial Fund, $63,000 in grants to 57 individuals, $88,000 to support 88 children through the PATH program, and the opening of 22 College Savings Plans (529) at $2,000 for combat deaths or $1,000 for training accidents.

Duration These are 1-time grants.

Additional information This foundation began in 1998 as a charitable organization affiliated with the RRVA.

Number awarded Varies each year.

Deadline Applications may be submitted at any time.

[1069]
ALABAMA AD VALOREM TAX EXEMPTION FOR SPECIALLY ADAPTED HOUSES

Alabama Department of Revenue
Attn: Property Tax Division
Gordon Persons Building
50 North Ripley Street, Room 4126
P.O. Box 327210
Montgomery, AL 36132-7210
(334) 242-1525
Web: www.ador.state.al.us

Summary To provide a property tax exemption to the owners of specially adapted housing (housing adapted for disabled veterans) in Alabama.

Eligibility The home of any veteran which is or was acquired pursuant to the provisions of Public Law 702, 80th Congress (specially adapted housing grants for veterans) as amended (38 USC) will be exempted from ad valorem taxation if the house is owned and occupied by the veteran or the veteran's unremarried widow(er).

Financial data Qualifying houses are exempt from all ad valorem taxation.

Duration This exemption continues as long as the veteran or the unremarried widow(er) resides in the house.

Number awarded Varies each year.

Deadline Deadline not specified.

[1070]
ALABAMA MILITARY RETIREE INCOME TAX EXEMPTION

Alabama Department of Revenue
Attn: Income Tax Division
Gordon Persons Building
50 North Ripley Street, Room 4212
P.O. Box 327410
Montgomery, AL 36132-7410
(334) 242-1105   Fax: (334) 242-0064
E-mail: erohelpdesk@revenue.state.al.us
Web: www.ador.state.al.us

Summary To exempt a portion of the income of veterans and their survivors from taxation in Alabama.

Eligibility Eligible are Alabama recipients of regular military retired pay or military survivors benefits. Recipients of benefits paid by the U.S. Department of Veterans Affairs (including disability retirement payments) are also eligible for this exemption.

Financial data All income received as military retired pay, veterans' disability payment, or military survivors benefits is exempt from state, county, or municipal income taxation.

Duration The exemption continues as long as the recipient resides in Alabama.

Deadline Deadline not specified.

[1071]
ALASKA PROPERTY TAX EXEMPTION

Division of Community and Regional Affairs
Attn: Office of the State Assessor
550 West Seventh Avenue, Suite 1790
Anchorage, AK 99501-3510
(907) 269-4605   Fax: (907) 269-4539
E-mail: Steve.VanSant@alaska.gov
Web: www.commerce.state.ak.us/dcra/osa/taxfacts.htm

Summary To exempt from taxation the property owned by veterans with disabilities in Alaska.

Eligibility This exemption is available to veterans in Alaska who have a disability that was incurred or aggravated in the line of duty and that has been rated as 50% or more by the military service or the U.S. Department of Veterans Affairs. Applicants must own and occupy their primary residence. Senior citizens (65 years of age or older) are also eligible for this exemption.

Financial data Recipients are exempt from taxation on the first $150,000 of assessed valuation on real property.

Duration The exemption continues as long as the veteran with a disability resides in Alaska.

Additional information Applications may be obtained from the local assessor's office. Since 1986, the cost of this program has exceeded the funding available for it. As a result, recipients may be granted a prorated level of payments.

Number awarded Varies each year; recently, more than 27,000 disabled veterans and senior citizens received an average exemption of $1,839 on their property, which had an average assessed value of $135,420.

Deadline Applications may be submitted at any time.

[1072]
ARIZONA INCOME TAX EXEMPTION FOR PUBLIC EMPLOYEE RETIRED PAY

Arizona Department of Revenue
1600 West Monroe Street
Phoenix, AZ 85007-2650
(602) 542-3572   Toll Free: (800) 352-4090 (within AZ)
TDD: (602) 542-4021
Web: www.azdor.gov

Summary To exempt a portion of the pay of retired military personnel and other public employees from state income taxes in Arizona.

Eligibility Eligible are retired military personnel classified as Arizona residents for the purpose of state income tax. Retired federal, state, and local government employees also qualify.

Financial data Qualified taxpayers are allowed to exempt the amount they received or $2,500, whichever is less, from their income for purposes of state taxation.

Duration The exemption continues as long as the recipient resides in Arizona.

Deadline Deadline not specified.

[1073]
ARIZONA MILITARY FAMILY RELIEF FUND

Arizona Department of Veterans' Services
Attn: Military Family Relief Fund
3839 North Third Street, Suite 209
Phoenix, AZ 85012
(602) 234-8403   E-mail: mfrf@azdvs.gov
Web: www.azdvs.gov/benefits/relief_fund.aspx

Summary To provide assistance to military service members from Arizona and their families who face financial difficulties that result from the deployment of the military member to a combat zone.

Eligibility This assistance is available to military service members who have been deployed to a combat zone since September 11, 2001, are currently deployed in a combat zone, or became deceased, wounded, or seriously ill after September 11, 2001 due to a deployment. Applicants must be Arizona residents, as evidenced by having been deployed from a military base in the state, entered active military service after September 11, 2001 from the state, claimed the state as home of record, or been a member of the Arizona National Guard at the time of deployment. Military service members who have been discharged must have done so under honorable conditions. Family members (spouses, widows and widowers, dependent children, siblings, and parents) are also eligible. All applicants must be able to demonstrate how deployment affected their financial situation. Family members of those who were killed in action may request up to 6 months' living expenses and other appropriate expenses; family members of those who were wounded in action may request temporary living expenses while care in being delivered to the qualifying military person and other appropriate expenses; families of service members who are experiencing financial hardship may request living or other appropriate expenses to resolve financial hardship caused by deployment and assist with transition to financial stability.

Financial data Grants up to $20,000 are available, of which $3,000 is available for emergency situations.

Duration The maximum grant of $20,000 is a lifetime limit.

Number awarded Varies each year.
Deadline Applications may be submitted at any time.

[1074]
ARKANSAS DISABLED VETERANS PROPERTY TAX EXEMPTION

Arkansas Assessment Coordination Department
1614 West Third Street
Little Rock, AR 72201-1815
(501) 324-9240   Fax: (501) 324-9242
E-mail: dasbury@acd.state.ar.us
Web: www.arkansas.gov/acd

Summary To exempt from taxation the property owned by blind or disabled veterans, surviving spouses, and minor dependent children in Arkansas.

Eligibility This program is open to disabled veterans in Arkansas who have been awarded special monthly compensation by the U.S. Department of Veterans Affairs and who have 1) the loss of or the loss of use of 1 or more limbs, 2) total blindness in 1 or both eyes, or 3) total and permanent disability. The benefit also extends to veterans' unremarried surviving spouses and their minor children.

Financial data Qualifying veterans (or their unremarried widows or dependent children) are exempt from payment of all state taxes on their homestead and personal property.

Duration This exemption continues as long as the qualifying veteran (or dependent) resides in Arkansas.

Number awarded Varies each year.

Deadline Applications may be submitted at any time.

[1075]
ARKANSAS INCOME TAX EXEMPTIONS FOR MILITARY COMPENSATION AND DISABILITY PAY

Arkansas Department of Finance and Administration
Attn: Office of Income Tax Administration
Joel Ledbetter Building, Room 2300
1816 West Seventh Street
P.O. Box 3628
Little Rock, AR 72203-3628
(501) 682-1100   Fax: (501) 682-7692
E-mail: individual.income@dfa.arkansas.gov
Web: www.dfa.arkansas.gov

Summary To exempt a portion of the income of military personnel and disabled veterans from Arkansas state income taxes.

Eligibility Eligible are residents of Arkansas receiving military compensation or military disability income.

Financial data The first $9,000 of U.S. military compensation pay or military disability income is exempt from state income taxation.

Duration The exemptions continue as long as the recipient resides in Arkansas.

Deadline Deadline not specified.

[1076]
ARMY EMERGENCY RELIEF LOANS/GRANTS

Army Emergency Relief
200 Stovall Street
Alexandria, VA 22332-0600
(703) 428-0000   Toll Free: (866) 878-6378
Fax: (703) 325-7183   E-mail: aer@aerhq.org
Web: www.aerhq.org/dnn563/FinancialAssistance.aspx

Summary To provide loans and grants-in-aid to help with the emergency financial needs of Army veterans, military personnel, and their dependents.

Eligibility Eligible to apply are active-duty soldiers (single or married) and their dependents, Army National Guard and Army Reserve soldiers on continuous active duty for more than 30 days and their dependents, soldiers retired from active duty for longevity or physical disability and their dependents, Army National Guard and Army Reserve soldiers who retired at age 60 and their dependents, and surviving spouses and orphans of soldiers who died while on active duty or after they retired. Applicants must be seeking assistance for such emergency needs as food, rent, and utilities; emergency transportation and vehicle repair; funeral expenses; medical and dental expenses; or personal needs when pay is delayed or stolen. Support is not available to help pay for nonessentials, finance ordinary leave or vacation, pay fines or legal expenses, help liquidate or consolidate debt, assist with house purchase or home improvements, cover bad checks, pay credit card bills, or acquire a vehicle.

Financial data Support is provided in the form of loans or grants (or a combination).

Duration Qualifying individuals can apply whenever they have a valid emergency need.

Additional information This organization began in 1942.

Number awarded Varies each year; recently, the organization helped more than 66,000 Army people with more than $70 million, including $60 million to 58,820 active-duty soldiers and their families, $7.3 million to 4,914 retired soldiers and their families, and $2.7 million to 2,304 widow(er)s and orphans of deceased soldiers. Since it was established, the organization has helped more than 3.2 million qualifying individuals with more than $1.2 billion in financial assistance.

Deadline Applications may be submitted at any time.

[1077]
AUTOMOBILE ALLOWANCE FOR DISABLED VETERANS

Department of Veterans Affairs
Attn: Veterans Benefits Administration
810 Vermont Avenue, N.W.
Washington, DC 20420
(202) 418-4343   Toll Free: (800) 827-1000
Web: www1.va.gov

Summary To provide funding to certain disabled veterans and current service personnel who require specially adapted automobiles.

Eligibility To be eligible for a grant for an automobile, a veteran or current servicemember must have a service-connected loss or permanent loss of use of 1 or both hands or feet or permanent impairment of vision of both eyes to a prescribed degree. For adaptive equipment eligibility only, veterans entitled to compensation for ankylosis of 1 or both knees, or 1 or both hips, also qualify.

Financial data The grant consists of a payment by the Department of Veterans Affairs (VA) of up to $18,900 toward the purchase of an automobile or other conveyance. The VA will also pay for the adaptive equipment, its repair, and the replacement or reinstallation required for the safe operation of the vehicle purchased with VA assistance or for a previously or subsequently acquired vehicle.

Duration This is a 1-time grant.

Number awarded Varies each year.

Deadline Applications may be submitted at any time.

[1078]
CALIFORNIA DISABLED VETERAN EXEMPTION FROM THE IN LIEU TAX FEE FOR A MANUFACTURED HOME OR MOBILEHOME

Department of Housing and Community Development
Attn: Registration and Titling
1800 Third Street
P.O. Box 2111
Sacramento, CA 95812-2111
(916) 323-9224   Toll Free: (800) 952-8356
Web: www.hcd.ca.gov

Summary To provide a special property tax exemption to blind or disabled California veterans and/or their spouses who own and occupy a mobile home.

Eligibility This program is open to disabled veterans and/ or their spouses in California who have a manufactured home or mobile home as their principal place of residence. Veterans must be disabled as a result of injury or disease incurred in military service and have been a resident of California 1) at the time of entry into the service and be blind, or have lost the use of 1 or more limbs, or be totally disabled; 2) on November 7, 1972 and be blind in both eyes, or have lost the use of 2 or more limbs; or 3) on January 1, 1975 and be totally disabled. The spouses and unremarried surviving spouses of those disabled veterans are also eligible.

Financial data The exemption applies to the first $20,000 of the assessed market value of the manufactured home or mobile home. Veterans and/or spouses whose income falls below a specified level are entitled to an additional $10,000 exemption. The amount of the exemption is 100% if the home is owned by a veteran only, a veteran and spouse, or a spouse only; 50% if owned by a veteran and another person other than a spouse or by a spouse and another person other than the veteran; 67% if owned by a veteran, the spouse, and another person; 34% if owned by a veteran and 2 other people other than a spouse or by a spouse and 2 other people; 50% if owned by a veteran, the spouse, and 2 other people; or 25% if owned by a veteran and 3 other people or by a spouse and 3 other people.

Duration The exemption is available annually as long as the applicant meets all requirements.

Number awarded Varies each year.

Deadline Deadline not specified.

[1079]
CALIFORNIA PROPERTY TAX EXEMPTIONS FOR VETERANS

California Department of Veterans Affairs
Attn: Division of Veterans Services
1227 O Street, Room 101
P.O. Box 942895
Sacramento, CA 94295
(916) 653-2573   Toll Free: (877) 741-8532
Fax: (916) 653-2563   TDD: (800) 324-5966
Web: www.cdva.ca.gov/VetServices/Benefits.aspx

Summary To exempt a portion of the property of blind or disabled veterans in California and their spouses from taxation.

Eligibility This exemption is available to homeowners in California who are wartime veterans in receipt of service-connected disability compensation that is 1) at the totally disabled rate, 2) for loss or loss of use of 2 or more limbs, or 3) for blindness. Unremarried surviving spouses, including registered domestic partners, of veterans who are in receipt of service-connected death benefits are also eligible.

Financial data For veterans and spouses whose total household income from all sources is greater than $51,669 per year, up to $115,060 of the assessed value of a home is exempt from taxation. For veterans and spouses whose total household income from all sources is less than $51,669 per year, up to $172,592 of the assessed value of a home is exempt from taxation.

Duration The exemption is available as long as the veteran or spouse owns a home in California.

Additional information Information is available from the local county assessor's office in each California county.

Number awarded Varies each year.

Deadline Applications may be submitted at any time.

[1080]
CHILDREN OF FALLEN SOLDIERS RELIEF FUND FINANCIAL ASSISTANCE GRANTS

Children of Fallen Soldiers Relief Fund
P.O. Box 3968
Gaithersburg, MD 20885-3968
(301) 685-3421   Toll Free: (866) 96-CFSRF
Fax: (301) 630-0592   E-mail: grants@cfsrf.org
Web: www.cfsrf.org

Summary To provide personal financial assistance to veterans severely disabled during service in Iraq or Afghanistan and to the families of military personnel killed or severely disabled in those countries.

Eligibility This program is open to 1) veterans severely disabled as a result of service in Operation Iraqi Freedom or Operation Enduring Freedom; and 2) the spouses and children of military personnel killed or severely disabled during that service. Applicants must submit a 1-page statement describing their reason for requesting funds, the amount requested, the intended use of the funds, a list of monthly income and expenses, 2 recent months of bank statements, and overdue bills.

Financial data Grants have ranged from $1,650 to $16,916, depending on the need of the recipient.

Duration These are 1-time grants.

Additional information This organization was founded in 2003.

Number awarded Varies each year; since the organization was founded, it has awarded 18 of these financial assistance grants.

Deadline Applications may be submitted at any time.

[1081]
COAST GUARD MUTUAL ASSISTANCE GRANTS-IN-AID

Coast Guard Mutual Assistance
4200 Wilson Boulevard, Suite 610
Arlington, VA 20598-7180
(202) 493-6621   Toll Free: (800) 881-2462
Fax: (202) 493-6686   E-mail: ARL-DG-CGMA@uscg.mil
Web: www.cgmahq.org/Assistance/programs.html

Summary To provide funding to members of the Coast Guard Mutual Assistance (CGMA) and their families who need temporary assistance.

Eligibility This program is open to CGMA members who are facing special needs. Categories of aid that are available include emergency assistance (basic living expenses, emergency home repair, emergency travel expenses, fire and other disasters, funeral expenses, loss of funds, temporary living expenses); general assistance (adoption, child support, child care, family in-home day care facility, financial counseling, government travel cards, household furnishings, immigration fees, insurance, loss of income, moving expenses, non-emergency travel, non-support or inadequate support, past due bills and expenses, pay and allotment problems, vehicle repair, vehicle other expenses); housing assistance (payment of settlement charges associated with purchasing a residence, rental assistance, utilities); and medical and dental assistance (provider won't proceed without payment; mental health and family counseling; patient's cost share; durable medical equipment; prosthetic devices; rehabilitation, nursing, home, or respite care; orthodontia; long-term dental care; travel, transportation, and incidental expenses). Applicants must be able to demonstrate a need for assistance.

Financial data The assistance depends on the nature of the need.

Duration These are 1-time grants. A new application must accompany each request for assistance.

Additional information CGMA membership is open to active-duty and retired members of the U.S. Coast Guard, civilian employees of the U.S. Coast Guard, U.S. Coast Guard Reserve members, U.S. Coast Guard Auxiliary members, Public Health Service officers serving with the U.S. Coast Guard, and family members of all of those.

Number awarded Varies each year.

Deadline Deadline not specified.

[1082]
COLORADO PENSION/ANNUITY SUBTRACTION

Colorado Department of Revenue
Attn: Taxpayer Service Division
1375 Sherman Street, Room 242A
Denver, CO 80261-0005
(303) 232-2446   Toll Free: (800) 811-0172
Web: www.colorado.gov

Summary To exempt a portion of the pensions or annuities of veterans, people with disabilities, and other persons over the age of 55 from state income taxation in Colorado.

Eligibility This exemption is available to taxpayers over the age of 55 who are classified as Colorado residents for purposes of state income taxation, and to beneficiaries (such as a widowed spouse or orphan child) who are receiving a pension or annuity because of the death of the person who earned the pension. To qualify, the payment must be a retirement benefit that arose from an employer/employee relationship, service in the uniformed services of the United States, or contributions to a retirement plan that are deductible for federal income tax purposes. Disability retirement payments received by persons 55 years of age or older also qualify.

Financial data For retirees who are at least 65 years of age, up to $24,000 of qualified pension or retirement income may be excluded from income for purposes of Colorado state taxation. For persons who are at least 55 but under 65 years of age, up to $20,000 of qualified pension or retirement income may be excluded.

Duration The exclusion continues as long as the recipient resides in Colorado.

Additional information Disability retirement payments received by persons under 55 years of age do not qualify for the pension exclusion.

Deadline Deadline not specified.

[1083]
COLORADO PROPERTY TAX EXEMPTION FOR DISABLED VETERANS

Division of Veterans Affairs
1355 South Colorado Boulevard, Building C, Suite 113
Denver, CO 80220
(303) 343-1268   Fax: (303) 343-7238
Web: www.dmva.state.co.us/page/va/prop_tax

Summary To provide a partial exemption of taxes on property owned by disabled veterans or their spouses in Colorado.

Eligibility This exemption is open to veterans who reside in Colorado and have been rated 100% permanent and total service-connected disabled by the U.S. Department of Veterans Affairs. Applicants must have been honorably discharged and must own property in Colorado which they use as their primary residence. The exemption also applies to members of the National Guard or Reserves who sustained their injury during a period in which they were called to active duty, property owned by a veteran's spouse if both occupy the property as their primary residence, and property owned by a trust or other legal entity if the veteran or spouse is a major of the trust or other legal entity, the property was transferred solely for estate planning purposes, and the veteran or spouse would otherwise be the owner of record.

Financial data For qualifying veterans, 50% of the first $200,000 of actual value of the primary residence is exempted from taxes.

Duration The exemption continues as long as the veteran resides in the property.

Additional information This program was approved by Colorado voters in 2006.

Number awarded Varies each year.

Deadline Applications must be submitted by June of the year for which the exemption is requested.

[1084]
COMBAT-RELATED SPECIAL COMPENSATION

Department of Defense
Attn: Defense Finance and Accounting Service
U.S. Military Annuitant Pay
P.O. Box 7131
London, KY 40742-7131
Toll Free: (877) 327-4457   Fax: (800) 982-8459
Web: www.dfas.mil/dfas/retiredmilitary/disability/crsc.html

Summary To provide supplemental compensation to military retirees who are receiving disability pay from the U.S. Department of Veterans Affairs (VA).

Eligibility This program is open to retirees from the U.S. uniformed services who 1) are entitled to and/or receiving military retired pay; 2) are rated at least 10% disabled by the U.S. Department of Veterans Affairs (VA); 3) are a Reservist at least 60 years of age or retired under Temporary Early Retirement Authorization (TERA); and 4) waive their VA pay from their retired pay. Applicants must have a disability rating of 10% or higher, be drawing retirement pay, and be receiving VA disability that is not just service-connected but also combat-related, including injuries incurred as a direct result of armed conflict, hazardous duty, an instrumentality of war, or simulated war. Spouses and other dependents are not eligible for this program.

Financial data Qualified veterans receive compensation that depends on their combat-related disability rating (which may differ from their VA service-connected disability rating). They continue to receive their full military retirement pay (unlike VA disability compensation, which acts as an offset for an equivalent reduction in military retirement pay). The compensation is non-taxable.

Duration This compensation is payable for the life of the veteran.

Additional information The Combat-Related Special Compensation Program (CRSC I) began in June, 2003. The program was revised to offer compensation to a larger group of retirees and CRSC II began in January, 2004. Another revision in January, 2008 again expanded eligibility requirements. Military retirees, including those from the other uniformed services (Coast Guard, National Oceanic and Atmospheric Administration, and Public Health Service) must apply through the armed forces branch in which they served.

Number awarded Varies each year. Currently, more than 50,000 retirees are receiving payments of more than $59 million per month.

Deadline Applications may be submitted at any time.

[1085]
CONNECTICUT PERSONAL PROPERTY TAX EXEMPTION FOR WARTIME VETERANS

Office of Policy and Management
Attn: Intergovernmental Policy Division
450 Capitol Avenue
Hartford, CT 06106-1308
(860) 418-6278   Toll Free: (800) 286-2214 (within CT)
Fax: (860) 418-6493   TDD: (860) 418-6456
E-mail: leeann.graham@ct.gov
Web: www.ct.gov/opm/cwp/view.asp?a=2985&Q=383132

Summary To exempt wartime veterans and their family members from a portion of their personal property taxes if they are Connecticut residents.

Eligibility Eligible to apply for this exemption are veterans with 90 days of wartime service who are residents of Connecticut. Spouses, minor children, and parents of deceased veterans may also be eligible. An additional exemption may be available to veterans and spouses whose total adjusted gross income is less than $32,300 if unmarried or $39,500 if married. If the veteran is rated as 100% disabled by the U.S. Department of Veterans Affairs (VA), the maximum income levels are $18,000 if unmarried or $21,000 if married.

Financial data Property to the amount of $1,000 belonging to, or held in trust for, an eligible veteran is exempt from taxation. The same exemption is available to the surviving unremarried spouse, minor children, and (if there is no surviving unremarried spouse) parent of a deceased veteran. If the death was service-connected and occurred while on active duty, the exemption for a surviving unremarried spouse or minor child is $3,000. Municipalities may provide veterans and spouses with an additional exemption up to $2,000 of the assessed value of the property, provided their income is less than the qualifying level. The additional municipality exemption for spouses and children of veterans who died on active duty of service-connected causes is $6,000. The additional municipality exemptions for veterans and family members who do not meet the income requirements are $500 and $1,500, respectively.

Duration 1 year; exemptions continue as long as the eligible resident lives in Connecticut.

Number awarded Varies each year; recently, a total of 19,669 veterans received property tax exemptions through this and other programs in Connecticut.

Deadline Applications for the additional municipality exemption must be submitted to the assessor's office of the town of residence by September of every other year.

[1086]
CONNECTICUT REAL ESTATE TAX EXEMPTION FOR DISABLED VETERANS

Office of Policy and Management
Attn: Intergovernmental Policy Division
450 Capitol Avenue
Hartford, CT 06106-1308
(860) 418-6278   Toll Free: (800) 286-2214 (within CT)
Fax: (860) 418-6493   TDD: (860) 418-6456
E-mail: leeann.graham@ct.gov
Web: www.ct.gov/opm/cwp/view.asp?a=2985&Q=383132

Summary To exempt disabled or blind Connecticut veterans and their surviving spouses from the payment of a portion of their local property taxes.

Eligibility There are 2 categories of Connecticut veterans who qualify for exemptions from their dwelling house and the lot on which it is located: 1) those with major service-connected disabilities (paraplegia or osteochondritis resulting in permanent loss of the use of both legs or permanent paralysis of both legs and lower parts of the body; hemiplegia with permanent paralysis of 1 leg and 1 arm or either side of the body resulting from injury to the spinal cord, skeletal structure, or brain, or from disease of the spinal cord not resulting from syphilis; total blindness; amputation of both arms, both legs, both hands or both feet, or the combination of a hand and a foot; sustained through enemy action or resulting from an accident occurring or disease contracted in such active service) and 2) those with less severe disabilities (loss of use of 1 arm or 1 leg because of service-connected injuries). Surviving unremarried spouses of eligible deceased veterans are entitled to the same exemption as would have been granted to the veteran, as long as they continue to be the legal owner/occupier of the exempted residence. An additional exemption is available to veterans and spouses whose total adjusted gross income is less than $32,300 if unmarried or $39,500 if married. If the veteran is rated as 100% disabled by the U.S. Department of Veterans Affairs (VA), the maximum income levels are $18,000 if unmarried or $21,000 if married.

Financial data Veterans in the first category receive an exemption from local property taxation of $10,000 of assessed valuation. Veterans in the second category receive exemptions of $5,000 of assessed valuation. For veterans whose income is less than the specified levels, additional exemptions of $20,000 for the first category or $10,000 for the second category are available from municipalities that choose to participate. For veterans whose income exceeds the specified levels, the additional exemption from participating municipalities is $5,000 for the first category or $2,500 for the second category. Connecticut municipalities may also elect to exempt from taxation specially adapted housing acquired or modified by a veteran under the provisions of Section 801 of Title 38 of the United States Code.

Duration 1 year; exemptions continue as long as the eligible resident (or surviving spouse) owns/occupies the primary residence and lives in Connecticut.

Number awarded Varies each year; recently, a total of 19,669 veterans received property tax exemptions through this and other programs in Connecticut.

Deadline Applications for the additional municipality exemption must be submitted to the assessor's office of the town or residence by September of every other year.

[1087]
CONNECTICUT SOLDIERS', SAILORS' AND MARINES' FUND

Connecticut Department of Veterans' Affairs
Attn: Soldiers', Sailors' and Marines' Fund
864 Wethersfield Avenue
Hartford, CT 06114-3184
(860) 296-0719   Toll Free: (800) 491-4941 (within CT)
Fax: (860) 296-0820   E-mail: john.monahan@po.state.ct.us
Web: www.state.ct.us/ssmf

Summary To provide temporary financial assistance to needy Connecticut veterans.

Eligibility This program is open to veterans who were honorably discharged after at least 90 days of service during specified periods of wartime and are currently residents of Connecticut. Applicants must be able to demonstrate need for the following types of assistance: medical expenses; emergent dental care; prescription medications; eye examinations and purchase of eyeglasses; audiological evaluations and hearing aids; assistance with rental payments or mortgage interest payments; utilities (including gas, water, electric, and fuel oil); funeral expenses; or durable medical equipment. Support is not provided for payment of taxes; payment of insurance premiums (except medical insurance); purchase of real estate or payments of principal on mortgages; payment of telephone or cable bills; purchase of equities, bonds, or mutual funds; alimony or child support payments; payment

of personal debts, credit card bills, past-due bills, loans, or other obligations; or purchase of furniture, automobiles, or other capital goods.

Financial data The fund provides payments in the form of short-term grants.

Duration The funds are provided for emergency situations only; the program does not assist with ongoing financial needs.

Additional information This program, established in 1919, is subsidized by the state of Connecticut but administered by the American Legion of Connecticut.

Number awarded Varies each year.

Deadline Applications may be submitted at any time.

[1088]
CONNECTICUT VETERANS' ADDITIONAL EXEMPTION TAX RELIEF PROGRAM

Office of Policy and Management
Attn: Intergovernmental Policy Division
450 Capitol Avenue
Hartford, CT 06106-1308
(860) 418-6278   Toll Free: (800) 286-2214 (within CT)
Fax: (860) 418-6493   TDD: (860) 418-6456
E-mail: leeann.graham@ct.gov
Web: www.ct.gov/opm/cwp/view.asp?a=2985&Q=383132

Summary To exempt disabled veterans and their surviving spouses who are residents of Connecticut from a portion of their personal property taxes.

Eligibility Eligible to apply for this exemption are Connecticut veterans who are rated as disabled by the U.S. Department of Veterans Affairs (VA). Unremarried surviving spouses of qualified veterans are also eligible. An additional exemption may be available to veterans and spouses whose total adjusted gross income is less than $32,300 if unmarried or $39,500 if married. If the veteran is rated as 100% disabled by the U.S. Department of Veterans Affairs (VA), the maximum income levels are $18,000 if unmarried or $21,000 if married.

Financial data The amount of the exemption depends on the level of the VA disability rating: for 10% to 25%, it is $1,500; for more than 25% to 50%, $2,000; for more than 50% to 75%, $2,500; for more than 75% and for veterans older than 65 years of age with any level of disability, $3,000. Municipalities may elect to provide an additional exemption, equal to twice the amount provided, to veterans and spouses whose income is less than the qualifying level. For veterans and spouses who do not meet the income requirement, the additional exemption from participating municipalities is equal to 50% of the basic state exemption.

Duration 1 year; exemptions continue as long as the eligible resident lives in Connecticut.

Number awarded Varies each year; recently, a total of 19,669 veterans received property tax exemptions through this and other programs in Connecticut.

Deadline Applications for the additional municipality exemption must be submitted to the assessor's office of the town of residence by September of every other year.

[1089]
C.W. "BILL" AND BEVERLY YOUNG FINANCIAL ASSISTANCE FUND

Armed Forces Foundation
Attn: Family Assistance Program
16 North Carolina Avenue, N.E.
Washington, DC 20003
(202) 547-4713   Fax: (202) 547-4712
E-mail: info@armedforcesfoundation.org
Web: www.armedforcesfoundation.org

Summary To provide financial assistance to active-duty military personnel and those recently discharged from service who need funds to pay for the needs of their families.

Eligibility This program is open to 1) military personnel currently on active duty and receiving active-duty pay; 2) Reservists or National Guardsmen activated for at least 6 months; and 3) veterans released or discharged from active duty within the last 18 months. Applicants must be able to demonstrate that they need funding to help cover such expenses as utility bills, rent or mortgage payments for civilian housing, car payments, childcare (during illness, surgery or recovery), or car insurance or registration payments.

Financial data The amount of the assistance depends on the nature of the need and the availability of funds.

Duration These are 1-time grants.

Number awarded Varies each year.

Deadline Applications may be submitted at any time.

[1090]
DELAWARE PENSION BENEFITS FOR PARAPLEGIC VETERANS

Delaware Commission of Veterans Affairs
Robbins Building
802 Silver Lake Boulevard, Suite 100
Dover, DE 19904
(302) 739-2792   Toll Free: (800) 344-9900 (within DE)
Fax: (302) 739-2794   E-mail: antonio.davila@state.de.us
Web: veteransaffairs.delaware.gov

Summary To provide a monthly pension to paraplegic veterans in Delaware.

Eligibility Eligible for this benefit are Delaware residents who are paraplegic as a result of service in the armed forces of the United States while it was officially at war or during a period when the United States was engaged in hostilities with another nation as a member of the United Nations. Applicants must be listed on the rolls of the U.S. Department of Veterans Affairs as totally disabled.

Financial data The pension is $3,000 per year.

Duration Recipients remain eligible for this pension as long as they reside in Delaware.

Deadline Deadline not specified.

[1091]
DISABILITY PENSION PROGRAM FOR VETERANS

Department of Veterans Affairs
Attn: Veterans Benefits Administration
810 Vermont Avenue, N.W.
Washington, DC 20420
(202) 418-4343   Toll Free: (800) 827-1000
Web: www.vba.va.gov/bin/21/compensation/index.htm

Summary To provide a pension for disabled or elderly veterans who served during wartime.

Eligibility This program is open to veterans who were discharged under conditions other than dishonorable and who had at least 90 days of active military service, at least 1 day of which was during a period of war. They must be permanently and totally disabled or older than 65 years of age. Veterans who enlisted after September 7, 1980 generally had to have served at least 24 months or the full period for which they were called to active duty. The countable income of veterans must be below specified limits.

Financial data The pension program pays the difference, in 12 monthly installments, between countable income and the specified income level. Currently, those limits are the following: veteran with no dependents, $12,256; veteran with 1 dependent, $16,051; veteran in need of regular aid and attendance with no dependents, $20,447; veteran in need of regular aid and attendance with 1 dependent, $24,239; veteran permanently housebound without dependents, $14,978; veteran permanently housebound with 1 dependent, $18,773; 2 veterans married to each other, $16,051; increase for each additional dependent child, $2,093.

Duration The pension is paid for the life of the recipient.

Number awarded Varies each year.

Deadline Applications are accepted at any time.

[1092]
DISTRICT OF COLUMBIA AND FEDERAL GOVERNMENT PENSION AND ANNUITY EXCLUSION

Office of Tax and Revenue
Attn: Customer Service Center
1101 Fourth Street, S.W., Suite W270
Washington, DC 20024
(202) 727-4TAX   Fax: (202) 442-6304
E-mail: taxhelp@dc.gov
Web: otr.cfo.dc.gov/otr/site/default.asp

Summary To exempt a portion of the income received as a pension or annuity, including military retirement pay, from local income taxation in the District of Columbia.

Eligibility This exemption is available to residents of the District of Columbia who are 62 years of age or older. Applicants must be receiving income as military retired pay, pension income, or annuity income from the District or the federal government.

Financial data Qualifying residents are entitled to deduct their military retirement pay from local taxation, to a maximum of $3,000.

Duration The exclusion continues as long as the recipient resides in the District of Columbia.

Number awarded Varies each year.

Deadline The exclusion is claimed as part of the local income return, due in April of each year.

[1093]
FALLEN PATRIOT FUND GRANTS

Fallen Patriot Fund
c/o Bank of America Private Bank
TX1-492-19-09
P.O. Box 832409
Dallas, TX 75283-2409
(214) 658-7125   Fax: (214) 696-6310
E-mail: info@fallenpatriotfund.org
Web: www.fallenpatriotfund.org

Summary To provide personal financial assistance to veterans disabled as a result of combat in Iraq and to spouses and children of military personnel injured or killed in action in Iraq.

Eligibility This program is open to 1) veterans who were wounded in combat in support of Operation Iraqi Free, have been medically discharged from military service, received a disability rating from the U.S. Department of Veterans Affairs of 75% or greater, and can demonstrate dire financial hardship; 2) spouses of military personnel injured or killed in action in support of Operation Iraqi Freedom who can demonstrate dire financial hardship; and 3) children under 18 years of age of military personnel injured or killed in action in support of Operation Iraqi Freedom. Applicants who are currently enrolled as full-time undergraduate or vocational school students must demonstrate that all funds will be used to meet basic living expenses, not educational expenses. Graduate students, spouses who have received SGLI life insurance benefits, parents of military personnel injured or killed in action in support of Operation Iraqi Freedom, children over 18 years of age, and children or spouses of deceased military personnel whose death was a result of suicide are all ineligible. All applicants must state the nature of their financial hardship and how the money will be spent if a grant is provided.

Financial data The maximum grant is $3,000.

Duration Each disabled veteran or surviving spouse is limited to a total of 3 separate grants.

Additional information This program was established by the Mark Cuban Foundation.

Number awarded Varies each year; since the program was established, it has awarded more than $4.8 million in grants.

Deadline Applications may be submitted at any time.

[1094]
FINANCIAL AND MEDICAL ASSISTANCE FOR MASSACHUSETTS VETERANS

Department of Veterans' Services
600 Washington Street, Seventh Floor
Boston, MA 02111
(617) 210-5927   Fax: (617) 210-5755
E-mail: mdvs@vet.state.ma.us
Web: www.mass.gov

Summary To provide financial and medical assistance to indigent veterans and their dependents in Massachusetts.

Eligibility This assistance is open to veterans who are residents of Massachusetts and served in the U.S. armed services on active duty either for 90 days during specified periods of wartime or for 180 days during peacetime. Members of the National Guard and Reserves are also eligible if they have been called to regular active duty. Also eligible are spouses of the veteran, widows or widowers of the veteran, dependent parents of the veteran, any person who acted as a parent to the veteran for 5 years immediately prior to entering wartime service, children of the veteran under 19 years of age, children of the veteran between 19 and 23 years of age who are attending high school or an institution of higher education, children of the veteran 19 years of age or older who are mentally or physically unable to support themselves and were affected by the disability prior to their 18th birthday, and legally adopted children of the veteran. Applicants must be able to demonstrate a need for assistance for food, shelter, clothing, housing supplies, and medical care.

Financial data Grants depend on the need of the recipient.

Duration These are 1-time grants.

Number awarded Varies each year.

Deadline Applications may be submitted at any time.

[1095]
FLORIDA DISABLED VETERANS' PROPERTY TAX DISCOUNT ON HOMESTEAD PROPERTY

Florida Department of Revenue
Attn: Taxpayer Services
5050 West Tennessee Street
Tallahassee, FL 32399-0100
(850) 617-8600   Toll Free: (800) 352-3671
E-mail: EMailDOR@dor.state.fl.us
Web: www.myflorida.com

Summary To provide elderly disabled veterans with a partial exemption from taxation on their homesteads in Florida.

Eligibility This exemption is available to Florida residents who have real estate that they own and use as a homestead. Applicants must be at least 65 years of age and honorably-discharged veterans who have a service-related permanent disability as rated by the U.S. Department of Veterans Affairs (VA). They must have been a resident of Florida at the time they entered the military.

Financial data Qualifying veterans are entitled to a percentage discount on their property taxes equal to the percentage disability rating as determined by VA. This discount is in addition to any other exemptions for which the homestead owner is eligible (e.g., senior citizen, disabled veteran, regular homestead).

Duration The exemption applies as long as the taxpayer owns the property in Florida.

Additional information This program began in 2007. Initial applications should be made in person at the appropriate county property appraiser's office.

Number awarded Varies each year.

Deadline Applications must be submitted by February of the year for which the exemption is sought.

[1096]
FLORIDA PROPERTY TAX DISABILITY EXEMPTION FOR EX-SERVICE MEMBERS

Florida Department of Revenue
Attn: Taxpayer Services
5050 West Tennessee Street
Tallahassee, FL 32399-0100
(850) 617-8600   Toll Free: (800) 352-3671
E-mail: EMailDOR@dor.state.fl.us
Web: www.myflorida.com

Summary To exempt a portion of the value of property owned by disabled veterans in Florida.

Eligibility This exemption is available to veterans who have at least a 10% disability as a result of wartime or other service-connected events and are Florida residents owning taxable property.

Financial data The exemption applies to $5,000 of the value of the property.

Duration The exemption applies as long as the taxpayer owns the property in Florida.

Additional information Initial applications should be made in person at the appropriate county property appraiser's office.

Number awarded Varies each year.

Deadline Applications must be submitted by February of the year for which the exemption is sought.

[1097]
FLORIDA SERVICE-CONNECTED TOTAL AND PERMANENT DISABILITY PROPERTY TAX EXEMPTION

Florida Department of Revenue
Attn: Taxpayer Services
5050 West Tennessee Street
Tallahassee, FL 32399-0100
(850) 617-8600   Toll Free: (800) 352-3671
E-mail: EMailDOR@dor.state.fl.us
Web: www.myflorida.com

Summary To exempt from property taxation real estate owned by disabled veterans and their surviving spouses.

Eligibility This exemption is available to Florida residents who have real estate that they own and use as a homestead. Applicants must be honorably-discharged veterans who have a total and permanent disability or require a wheelchair for mobility as a result of their military service. Under certain circumstances, the benefit of this exemption can carry over to a surviving spouse.

Financial data All real estate used and owned as a homestead, less any portion used for commercial purposes, is exempt from taxation.

Duration The exemption applies as long as the taxpayer owns the property in Florida.

Additional information Initial applications should be made in person at the appropriate county property appraiser's office.

Number awarded Varies each year.

Deadline Applications must be submitted by February of the year for which the exemption is sought.

[1098]
GEORGIA HOMESTEAD TAX EXEMPTION FOR DISABLED VETERANS

Georgia Department of Revenue
Attn: Property Tax Division
4245 International Parkway, Suite A
Hapeville, GA 30354-3918
(404) 968-0707   Fax: (404) 968-0778
E-mail: Local.Government.Services@dor.ga.gov
Web: etax.dor.ga.gov

Summary To exempt from property taxation a portion of the value of homesteads owned by disabled veterans in Georgia and their families.

Eligibility This program is open to residents of Georgia who qualify as a 100% disabled veteran under any of several provisions of state law. Surviving spouses and minor children are also eligible. Applicants must actually occupy a homestead and use it as their legal residence for all purposes.

Financial data The first $50,000 of assessed valuation of the homestead owned by disabled veterans or their family members is exempt from property taxes for state, county, municipal, and school purposes.

Duration The exemption remains in effect as long as the veteran or family member owns and resides in the homestead.

Number awarded Varies each year.

Deadline Applications must be filed with local tax officials by February of each year.

[1099]
HAWAII GRANTS FOR SPECIAL HOUSING FOR DISABLED VETERANS

Office of Veterans Services
Attn: Veterans Services Coordinator
459 Patterson Road
E-Wing, Room 1-A103
Honolulu, HI 96819-1522
(808) 433-0420   Fax: (808) 433-0385
E-mail: ovs@ovs.hawaii.gov
Web: hawaii.gov/dod/ovs/benefits/state-provided-benefits

Summary To provide grants to disabled veterans in Hawaii for purchasing or remodeling a home.

Eligibility This program is open to totally disabled veterans in Hawaii. Applicants must be proposing to purchase or remodel a home to improve handicapped accessibility.

Financial data Grants up to $5,000 are available.

Duration These are 1-time grants.

Deadline Deadline not specified.

[1100]
HAWAII PROPERTY TAX EXEMPTIONS FOR DISABLED VETERANS

Office of Veterans Services
Attn: Veterans Services Coordinator
459 Patterson Road
E-Wing, Room 1-A103
Honolulu, HI 96819-1522
(808) 433-0420   Fax: (808) 433-0385
E-mail: ovs@ovs.hawaii.gov
Web: hawaii.gov/dod/ovs/benefits/state-provided-benefits

Summary To exempt the homes of disabled veterans and surviving spouses in Hawaii from real estate taxation.

Eligibility This program is open to totally disabled veterans in Hawaii and their surviving spouses.

Financial data The real property owned and occupied as a home is exempt from taxation.

Duration The exemption applies as long as the disabled veteran or his/her widow(er) resides in Hawaii.

Deadline Deadline not specified.

[1101]
HOPE FOR THE WARRIORS IMMEDIATE NEEDS GRANTS

Hope for the Warriors
Attn: Immediate Needs
1335 Western Boulevard, Suite E
Jacksonville, NC 28546-5539
(910) 938-1817   Toll Free: (877) 246-7349
E-mail: imn@hopeforthewarriors.org
Web: www.hopeforthewarriors.org/immneeds.html

Summary To provide funding for immediate needs to disabled military personnel, veterans, and their families.

Eligibility This assistance is available to wounded service members and their families. Applicants must need assistance to meet such immediate needs as travel to bedside where the government does not provide assistance, rental cars, lodging assistance, groceries, gas, furniture, assistance with child care, emergency assistance with essentials to daily living (e.g., rent and utilities), or items that assist and/or supplement programs at military treatment facilities and Veterans Administration polytrauma units.

Financial data The amount of the grant depends on the need of the recipient. Payment is always made to a third party.

Duration Applicants may apply once a year.

Number awarded Varies each year.

Deadline Applications may be submitted at any time.

[1102]
IDAHO CIRCUIT BREAKER PROPERTY TAX REDUCTION

Idaho State Tax Commission
Attn: Public Information Office
800 Park Boulevard, Plaza IV
P.O. Box 36
Boise, ID 83722-0410
(208) 334-7736   Toll Free: (800) 972-7660
TDD: (800) 377-3529
E-mail: pamela.waters@tax.idaho.com
Web: tax.idaho.gov/i-1052.cfm

Summary To reduce a portion of the property tax of disabled, blind, and other veterans and other disabled or elderly residents of Idaho.

Eligibility Eligible for this property tax reduction are residents of Idaho who own and live in a primary residence in the state and have an annual income of $28,000 or less (after deducting designated forms of income, including compensation received by a veteran from the U.S. Department of Veterans Affairs for a 40% to 100% service-connected disability). Applicants must be in 1 or more of the following categories: disabled (as recognized by an appropriate federal agency), blind, former prisoner of war or hostage, veteran with at least 10% service-connected disability or receiving a VA pension for a nonservice-connected disability, 65 years of age or older, widow(er) of any age, or fatherless or motherless child under 18 years of age.

Financial data The maximum amount of reduction is the lesser of $1,320 or the actual taxes on the recipient's qualifying home. The minimum reduction is the lesser of $100 or the actual taxes on the home.

Duration Applications for this reduction must be submitted each year.

Additional information All recipients of this reduction automatically receive Idaho's Homeowner's Exemption, which reduces the taxable value of the home (excluding land) by 50% or $75,000, whichever is less. Solid waste, irrigation, or other fees charged by some counties are not taxes and cannot be reduced by this program.

Number awarded Varies each year.

Deadline April of each year.

[1103]
IDAHO RETIREMENT BENEFITS DEDUCTION

Idaho State Tax Commission
Attn: Public Information Office
800 Park Boulevard, Plaza IV
P.O. Box 36
Boise, ID 83722-0410
(208) 334-7660   Toll Free: (800) 972-7660
TDD: (800) 377-3529
Web: tax.idaho.gov/i-1039.cfm

Summary To deduct the retirement and disability income of certain residents from state income tax in Idaho.

Eligibility Eligible for this deduction are full-year residents of Idaho who are age 65 or older, or disabled and age 62 and older, and who are receiving the following annuities and benefits: 1) retirement annuities paid by the United States to a retired civil service employee or the unremarried widow of the employee; 2) retirement benefits paid from the firemen's retirement fund of the state of Idaho to a retired fireman or the unremarried widow of a retired fireman; 3) retirement benefits paid from the policeman's retirement fund of a city within Idaho to a retired policeman or the unremarried widow of a retired policeman; or 4) retirement benefits paid by the United States to a retired member of the U.S. military service or the unremarried widow of those veterans.

Financial data The amount of retirement or disability benefits may be deducted from taxable state income in Idaho, to a maximum deduction of $41,814 for married couples or $27,876 for single persons.

Duration 1 year; must reapply each year.

Number awarded Varies each year.

Deadline April of each year.

[1104]
IDAHO WAR VETERAN'S EMERGENCY GRANT PROGRAM

Idaho Division of Veterans Services
Attn: Office of Veterans Advocacy
444 Fort Street
Boise, ID 83702
(208) 577-2300   Fax: (208) 577-2333
E-mail: info@veterans.idaho.gov
Web: www.veterans.idaho.gov/Veterans_Advocacy.aspx

Summary To provide emergency assistance to disabled veterans, wartime veterans, and their families in Idaho.

Eligibility Eligible for these grants are veterans who had at least 90 days of honorable wartime military service and entered the military from Idaho or lived within the state for at least 5 years. Veterans with a service-connected disability are eligible with earlier separation. Surviving spouses and dependent children are also eligible. Applicants must be current residents of Idaho in need of assistance because of a major catastrophe (e.g., natural disaster or death of a spouse or child), loss of job because of a disability, or other extreme financial emergency (e.g., cut-off notice from a utility company, eviction notice from a landlord, arrears payment notice from the lien holder of a home).

Financial data   The maximum amount available under this program is $1,000, issued in small incremental grants.

Duration   The limit of $1,000 applies for the lifetime of each veteran or his/her family.

Additional information   This program was established by the Idaho legislature in lieu of granting a wartime bonus to Idaho veterans.

Number awarded   Varies each year.

Deadline   Deadline not specified.

[1105]
ILLINOIS DISABLED VETERANS' HOMESTEAD EXEMPTION

Illinois Department of Revenue
101 West Jefferson Street
P.O. Box 19044
Springfield, IL 62794-9044
(217) 782-3336   Toll Free: (800) 732-8866
TDD: (800) 544-5304
Web: www.revenue.state.il.us

Summary   To exempt a portion of the value of specially adapted housing owned by disabled veterans and their spouses in Illinois for purposes of property taxation.

Eligibility   This exemption applies to housing owned and used by disabled veterans and their unmarried surviving spouses. The housing must have been purchased or constructed with funds provided by the U.S. Department of Veterans Affairs (VA) as part of a program of specially adapted housing for disabled veterans. The exemption is also available to disabled veterans and spouses who live in mobile homes. They may not utilize this exemption and either the Disabled Persons' Homestead Exemption or the Disabled Veterans Standard Homestead Exemption.

Financial data   The exemption provides a reduction of $70,000 in the assessed value of the homestead.

Duration   Veterans must file an annual application to continue to receive this exemption.

Deadline   Deadline not specified.

[1106]
ILLINOIS DISABLED VETERANS' STANDARD HOMESTEAD EXEMPTION

Illinois Department of Revenue
101 West Jefferson Street
P.O. Box 19044
Springfield, IL 62794-9044
(217) 782-3336   Toll Free: (800) 732-8866
TDD: (800) 544-5304
Web: www.revenue.state.il.us

Summary   To reduce the value for property taxation of homesteads owned by disabled veterans in Illinois.

Eligibility   This exemption is available to veterans who own or lease a single-family residence in Illinois and are liable for payment of property taxes. Applicants must have a service-connected disability verified by the U.S. Department of Veterans Affairs of at least 50%. They may not utilize this exemption and either the Disabled Persons' Homestead Exemption or the Disabled Veterans Homestead Exemption.

Financial data   Veterans whose disability is rated as at least 50% but less than 70% receive a $2,500 reduction in the equalized assessed value (EAV) of their property. Veterans whose disability is rated as at least 70% receive a $5,000 reduction in the EAV of their property.

Duration   Veterans must file an annual application to continue to receive this exemption.

Additional information   This program began in 2007.

Deadline   Deadline not specified.

[1107]
ILLINOIS INCOME TAX SUBTRACTION FOR GOVERNMENT RETIREES

Illinois Department of Revenue
101 West Jefferson Street
P.O. Box 19044
Springfield, IL 62794-9044
(217) 782-3336   Toll Free: (800) 732-8866
TDD: (800) 544-5304
Web: www.revenue.state.il.us

Summary   To exempt the retirement and disability income of veterans and other government employees from state taxation in Illinois.

Eligibility   This exemption applies to the income received from government retirement and disability plans, including military plans.

Financial data   All government retirement and disability income of eligible residents is exempt from state income taxation.

Duration   The exemption continues as long as the recipient resides in Illinois.

Deadline   Deadline not specified.

[1108]
ILLINOIS KOREAN, VIETNAM, PERSIAN GULF, AND GLOBAL WAR ON TERRORISM CONFLICT BONUS

Illinois Department of Veterans' Affairs
833 South Spring Street
P.O. Box 19432
Springfield, IL 62794-9432
(217) 782-6641   Toll Free: (800) 437-9824 (within IL)
Fax: (217) 524-0344   TDD: (217) 524-4645
E-mail: webmail@dva.state.il.us
Web: www.veterans.illinois.gov/benefits/bonuspayment.htm

Summary   To provide a bonus to Illinois veterans of the Korean, Vietnam, Persian Gulf, or Iraqi conflicts or their survivors.

Eligibility   Eligible for this bonus are veterans who served in Korea between June 27, 1950 and July 27, 1953, or in Vietnam between January 1, 1961 and March 28, 1973 or on April 29 or 30, 1975, the Persian Gulf between August 2, 1990 and November 30, 1995, or in Operation Enduring Freedom or Operation Iraqi Freedom (the Global War on Terrorism) for at least 30 consecutive or 60 nonconsecutive days foreign or sea service on or after September 11, 2001. They must have received the Korean Service Medal, the Vietnam Service Medal, the Armed Forces Expeditionary Medal Vietnam Era, the Southwest Asia Service Medal, the Global War on Terrorism Expeditionary Medal, or the Global War on Terrorism Service Medal, along with having been honorably discharged and a resident of Illinois for 12 months before entering service. Survivors of deceased veterans are eligible if the veteran's death was service connected and within the specified dates.

Financial data Veterans are entitled to a bonus of $100; survivors are entitled to $1,000.

Duration This is a 1-time payment.

Deadline Deadline not specified.

[1109]
ILLINOIS RETURNING VETERANS' EXEMPTION

Illinois Department of Revenue
101 West Jefferson Street
P.O. Box 19044
Springfield, IL 62794-9044
(217) 782-3336   Toll Free: (800) 732-8866
TDD: (800) 544-5304
Web: www.revenue.state.il.us

Summary To provide an exemption on the value for property taxation of homesteads owned by veterans in Illinois who are returning from conflict.

Eligibility This exemption is available to veterans who own or lease a homestead in Illinois as their primary residence. Applicants must be returning from active duty in an armed conflict involving the armed forces of the United States.

Financial data Qualifying veterans receive a $5,000 reduction in the equalized assessed value (EAV) of their property.

Duration Qualifying veterans may utilize this exemption during each of the first 2 years following their return home.

Additional information This program began in 2007.

Deadline Deadline not specified.

[1110]
INDIANA MILITARY RETIREMENT OR SURVIVOR'S BENEFIT INCOME TAX DEDUCTION

Indiana Department of Revenue
Attn: Taxpayer Services Division
Indiana Government Center North
100 North Senate Avenue
Indianapolis, IN 46204-2253
(317) 232-2240   TDD: (317) 232-4952
E-mail: individualtaxassistance@dor.in.gov
Web: www.in.gov/dor

Summary To exempt a portion of the income of veterans and surviving spouses from state taxation in Indiana.

Eligibility This program is open to Indiana residents who are retired from the military or are the surviving spouse of a person who was in the military. Applicants must be at least 60 years of age and receiving military retirement or survivor's benefits.

Financial data Up to $5,000 of the income from military retirement or survivor's benefits is exempt from state income taxation in Indiana.

Duration The exemption continues as long as the recipient resides in Indiana.

Deadline Deadline not specified.

[1111]
INDIANA PROPERTY TAX DEDUCTIONS FOR DISABLED VETERANS

Department of Local Government Finance
Indiana Government Center North, Room N1058(B)
100 North Senate Avenue
Indianapolis, IN 46201
(317) 232-3777   Fax: (317) 232-8779
E-mail: PropertyTaxInfo@dlgf.in.gov
Web: www.in.gov/dlgf

Summary To exempt disabled Indiana veterans and their spouses from a portion of their property taxes.

Eligibility This program is open to the following categories of veterans who are residents of Indiana: 1) served honorably at least 90 days and are either totally disabled (the disability does not need to be service connected) or are at least 62 years of age and have at least a 10% service-connected disability; 2) served honorably during wartime and have at least a 10% service-connected disability; or 3) served honorably during wartime and either have a 100% service-connected disability or are at least 62 years of age and have at least a 10% service-connected disability. A statutory disability rating for pulmonary tuberculosis does not qualify. A disability incurred during Initial Active Duty for Training (IADT) with the National Guard or Reserves is eligible only if the disability occurred from an event during the period of active duty and that duty was performed during wartime. Surviving spouses of those 3 categories of veterans are also eligible.

Financial data Property tax exemptions are $12,480 for veterans and spouses in the first category (only if the assessed value of the combined real and personal property owned by the veteran or spouse does not exceed $143,160), $24,960 in the second category, or $37,440 in the third category; there is no limit on the value of the property owned by a surviving spouse).

Duration 1 year; may be renewed as long as the eligible veteran or surviving unremarried spouse owns and occupies the primary residence in Indiana.

Number awarded Varies each year.

Deadline Applications must be submitted no later than May of each year.

[1112]
INDIANA VETERANS' BURIAL ALLOWANCE

Indiana Department of Veterans' Affairs
302 West Washington Street, Room E-120
Indianapolis, IN 46204-2738
(317) 232-3910   Toll Free: (800) 400-4520 (within IN)
Fax: (317) 232-7721
Web: www.in.gov/dva/2343.htm

Summary To provide a burial allowance for Indiana veterans and their spouses.

Eligibility This benefit is available to honorably-discharged veterans from Indiana and their spouses. Applications must be filed with the county auditor in the county of residence.

Financial data County auditors are authorized to pay up to $1,000 for burial costs of a veteran or the veteran's spouse and up to $100 for the setting of a federal headstone.

Duration This is a 1-time payment.

Number awarded Varies each year.

Deadline Requests for assistance may be submitted at any time.

[1113]
IOWA INJURED VETERANS GRANT PROGRAM

Iowa Department of Veterans Affairs
Camp Dodge, Building 3663
7105 N.W. 70th Avenue
Johnston, IA 50131-1824
(515) 242-5331   Toll Free: (800) VET-IOWA
Fax: (515) 242-5659   E-mail: idva.info@iowa.gov
Web: va.iowa.gov/benefits/injured_vets_grant.html

Summary To provide assistance to Iowa residents who were injured in combat while serving in the armed forces after September 11, 2001.

Eligibility This assistance is available to members of the armed forces of the United States who are still serving or who have been discharged or released from service under honorable conditions. Applicants must have sustained an injury or illness in a combat zone or hostile fire zone after September 11, 2001. The illness or injury must have been serious enough to require medical evacuation from the combat zone and must be considered by the military to be in the line of duty. The veteran or military servicemember must have been a resident of Iowa at the time of injury.

Financial data Qualified veterans or military servicemembers are entitled to the following assistance: $2,500 when they are medically evacuated from the combat zone; $2,500 30 days after evacuation date if still hospitalized, receiving medical treatment, or receiving rehabilitation services from the military or Veterans Administration; $2,500 60 days after evacuation date if still hospitalized, receiving medical treatment, or receiving rehabilitation services from the military or Veterans Administration; and $2,500 90 days after the evacuation date if still hospitalized, receiving medical treatment, or receiving rehabilitation services from the military or Veterans Administration. The maximum assistance is $10,000.

Duration This is a 1-time bonus.

Additional information This program began in 2007.

Number awarded Varies each year.

Deadline Deadline not specified.

[1114]
IOWA MILITARY SERVICE PROPERTY TAX EXEMPTION

Iowa Department of Revenue
Attn: Property Tax Division
Hoover State Office Building
1305 East Walnut
P.O. Box 10469
Des Moines, IA 50306-0469
(515) 281-4040   Toll Free: (800) 367-3388 (within IA)
Fax: (515) 281-3906   E-mail: idr@iowa.gov
Web: www.iowa.gov/tax/taxlaw/PropertyTaxCredits.html

Summary To exempt veterans, military personnel, and their family members from a portion of property taxes in Iowa.

Eligibility This exemption is available to residents of Iowa who are 1) former members of the U.S. armed forces who performed at least 18 months of military service (or for fewer months because of a service-related injury), regardless of the time period, and who were honorably discharged; 2) former members, and members currently serving of the U.S. Reserves and Iowa National Guard who have served at least 20 years; and 3) current members of the U.S. Reserves and Iowa National Guard who were activated for federal duty for at

least 90 days; 4) former members of the armed forces whose enlistment would have occurred during the Korean Conflict but chose to serve 5 years in the Reserves; and 5) honorably discharged veterans who served in a designated eligible service period. Applicants must own a primary residence in the state. Also eligible for the exemption are the spouses, unremarried widow(er)s, minor children, and widowed parent of qualified veterans.

Financial data The amount of the exemption is currently $1,852.

Duration 1 year; continues until the qualifying veteran or dependent no longer lives in the residence.

Number awarded Varies each year; recently, more than $2.4 million in property was exempt from taxation.

Deadline Application must be made by June of the year for which the exemption is first requested. The exemption is provided annually, from then on, as long as the qualifying veteran or dependent resides in the house.

[1115]
KANSAS INCOME TAX EXEMPTION FOR VETERANS AND OTHER FEDERAL RETIREES

Kansas Department of Revenue
Attn: Taxpayer Assistance Center
Robert B. Docking State Office Building
915 S.W. Harrison Street
Topeka, KS 66612-1712
(785) 368-8222   Toll Free: (877) 526-7738
Fax: (785) 291-3614   TDD: (785) 296-6461
Web: www.ksrevenue.org/perstaxtypesii.html

Summary To exempt the income received by federal retirees, including veterans, from state taxation in Kansas.

Eligibility This exemption applies to all amounts received by residents of Kansas as retirement benefits from employment by the federal government or for service in the U.S. armed forces.

Financial data All federal retirement income, including that for military service, is exempt from state taxation in Kansas.

Duration This benefit continues as long as the recipient remains a resident of Kansas for state income tax purposes.

Number awarded Varies each year.

Deadline Deadline not specified.

[1116]
KENTUCKY PENSION INCOME EXCLUSION

Kentucky Department of Revenue
Attn: Individual Income Tax
501 High Street
P.O. Box 181
Frankfort, KY 40602-0181
(502) 564-4581   Fax: (502) 564-3875
Web: revenue.ky.gov/individual/incometax.htm

Summary To exempt a portion of the income of public retirees (including veterans) in Kentucky from state income taxation.

Eligibility This exemption applies to Kentucky residents who are required to pay state income taxes and who receive retirement income from state and federal systems, including the U.S. military and the Department of Veterans Affairs.

Financial data For veterans and others who retired prior to January 1, 1998, all pension income is exempt from taxation in Kentucky. For those who retired after December 31, 1997 and whose retirement income is less than $41,110, all income is exempt; for those whose retirement income is greater than $41,110, the exemption depends on the proportion of service credit earned after December 31, 1997.

Duration The exemption continues as long as the recipient resides in Kentucky.

Deadline Deadline not specified.

[1117]
LOUISIANA INCOME EXEMPTION FOR FEDERAL RETIREMENT PAY

Louisiana Department of Revenue
Attn: Individual Income Tax
P.O. Box 201
Baton Rouge, LA 70821
(225) 219-0102
Web: www.revenue.louisiana.gov

Summary To exempt the retirement income of all federal employees, including the military and their surviving spouses, from state taxation in Louisiana.

Eligibility This exemption is available to all residents of Louisiana who are receiving retirement benefits from the federal retirement system, including veterans and their surviving spouses.

Financial data All federal retirement income is exempt from state income taxation in Louisiana.

Duration The benefit continues as long as the recipient remains a resident of Louisiana for state income tax purposes.

Number awarded Varies each year.

Deadline Deadline not specified.

[1118]
MAINE PROPERTY TAX EXEMPTIONS FOR VETERANS

Maine Revenue Services
Attn: Property Tax Division
P.O. Box 9106
Augusta, ME 04332-9106
(207) 287-2013   Fax: (207) 287-6396
E-mail: prop.tax@maine.gov
Web: www.maine.gov/revenue/propertytax/homepage.html

Summary To exempt the estates of disabled Maine veterans and selected family members from property taxation.

Eligibility Eligible for this program are veterans who served in wartime during World War I, World War II, the Korean campaign, the Vietnam war, the Persian Gulf war, or other recognized service periods, are legal residents of Maine, and are either older than 62 years of age or are receiving a pension or compensation from the U.S. government for total disability (whether service connected or not). Vietnam veterans must have served 180 days on active duty unless discharged earlier for a service-connected disability. The exemption also includes 1) property held in joint tenancy with the veterans' spouses, and 2) property of unremarried widow(er)s, minor children, and parents of deceased veterans, if those dependents are receiving a pension or compensation from the U.S. government.

Financial data Estates of disabled veterans and eligible dependents, including both real and personal property, are exempt up to $6,000 of just valuation. For veterans and dependents who served in wartime prior to World War II, estates up to $7,000 are exempt.

Duration Veterans, spouses, unremarried widow(er)s, and mothers are eligible for this exemption throughout their lifetimes; minor children of veterans are eligible until they reach the age of 18.

Number awarded Varies each year.

Deadline When an eligible person first submits an application, the proof of entitlement must reach the assessors of the local municipality prior to the end of March. Once eligibility has been established, notification need not be repeated in subsequent years.

[1119]
MAINE TAX EXEMPTION FOR SPECIALLY ADAPTED HOUSING UNITS

Maine Revenue Services
Attn: Property Tax Division
P.O. Box 9106
Augusta, ME 04332-9106
(207) 287-2013   Fax: (207) 287-6396
E-mail: prop.tax@maine.gov
Web: www.maine.gov/revenue/propertytax/homepage.html

Summary To exempt the specially adapted housing units of paraplegic veterans or their surviving spouses from taxation in Maine.

Eligibility Veterans who served in the U.S. armed forces during any federally-recognized war period, are legal residents of Maine, are paraplegic veterans within the meaning of U.S. statutes, and have received a grant from the U.S. government for specially adapted housing are eligible. The exemption also applies to property held in joint tenancy with the veteran's spouse and to the specially adapted housing of unremarried widow(er)s of eligible veterans.

Financial data Estates of paraplegic veterans are exempt up to $50,000 of just valuation for a specially adapted housing unit.

Duration The exemption is valid for the lifetime of the paraplegic veteran or unremarried widow(er).

Number awarded Varies each year.

Deadline When an eligible person first submits an application, the proof of entitlement must reach the assessors of the local municipality prior to the end of March. Once eligibility has been established, notification need not be repeated in subsequent years.

[1120]
MARYLAND INCOME TAX EXEMPTION FOR MILITARY RETIRED PAY

Comptroller of Maryland
Attn: Revenue Administration Division
80 Calvert Street
Annapolis, MD 21411
(410) 260-7980   Toll Free: (800) MD-TAXES (within MD)
Fax: (410) 974-3456   TDD: (410) 260-7157
E-mail: taxhelp@comp.state.md.us
Web: individuals.marylandtaxes.com

Summary To exempt certain portions of military retirement pay from Maryland state income tax.

Eligibility This exemption is available to residents of Maryland who are receiving retirement income as a member of an active or Reserve component of the U.S. armed forces, the

Maryland National Guard, the Public Health Service, the National Oceanic and Atmospheric Administration, or the Coast and Geodetic Survey.

Financial data Up to $5,000 of military retired pay, depending on income, may be excluded from state income taxation.

Duration The exemption is available annually.

Number awarded Varies each year.

Deadline Retired military personnel can claim this exemption when they file their state income tax return, in April of each year.

[1121]
MARYLAND PROPERTY TAX EXEMPTION FOR DISABLED VETERANS AND SURVIVING SPOUSES

Maryland Department of Assessments and Taxation
Attn: Property Taxes
301 West Preston Street
Baltimore, MD 21201-2395
(410) 767-1184   Toll Free: (888) 246-5941
TDD: (800) 735-2258
Web: www.dat.state.md.us/sdatweb/exempt.html

Summary To exempt the homes of disabled veterans and their surviving spouses from property taxation in Maryland.

Eligibility This exemption is available to armed services veterans with a permanent service-connected disability rated 100% by the U.S. Department of Veterans Affairs who own a dwelling house in Maryland. Unremarried surviving spouses are also eligible.

Financial data The dwelling houses of eligible veterans and surviving spouses are exempt from real property taxes.

Duration The exemption is available as long as the veteran or surviving spouse owns the dwelling house in Maryland.

Number awarded Varies each year.

Deadline Applications may be submitted at any time.

[1122]
MASSACHUSETTS INCOME TAX EXEMPTION FOR UNIFORMED SERVICES RETIREMENT PAY

Massachusetts Department of Revenue
Attn: Personal Income Tax
P.O. Box 7010
Boston, MA 02204
(617) 887-MDOR   Toll Free: (800) 392-6089 (within MA)
Fax: (617) 887-1900
Web: www.mass.gov

Summary To exempt the retirement income and survivorship benefits received from the U.S. uniformed services from state income taxation in Massachusetts.

Eligibility Eligible for this exemption are residents of Massachusetts who are receiving noncontributory pension income or survivorship benefits from the U.S. uniformed services (including the Army, Navy, Marine Corps, Air Force, Coast Guard, National Oceanic and Atmospheric Administration, and commissioned corps of the Public Health Service).

Financial data All uniformed services retirement income and survivorship benefits are exempt from state income taxation.

Duration The benefit continues as long as the recipient remains a resident of Massachusetts for state income tax purposes.

Additional information This exemption became effective with income received in 1997.

Number awarded Varies each year.

Deadline Deadline not specified.

[1123]
MASSACHUSETTS PROPERTY TAX EXEMPTION FOR VETERANS AND THEIR FAMILIES

Massachusetts Department of Revenue
Attn: Division of Local Services
100 Cambridge Street
Boston, MA 02114
(617) 626-2386   Fax: (617) 626-2330
Web: www.mass.gov/dor/all-taxes/excise-and-property

Summary To provide a property tax exemption to blind, disabled, and other veterans (and their families) in Massachusetts.

Eligibility This program is open to veterans who are residents of Massachusetts, were residents for at least 6 months prior to entering the service, have been residents for at least 5 consecutive years, and are occupying property as their domicile. Applicants must have an ownership interest in the domicile that ranges from $2,000 to $10,000, depending on the category of exemption. Veterans must have been discharged under conditions other than dishonorable. Several categories of veterans and their families qualify: 1) veterans who have a service-connected disability rating of 10% or more; veterans who have been awarded the Purple Heart; Gold Star mothers and fathers; and surviving spouses of eligible veterans who do not remarry; 2) veterans who suffered, in the line of duty, the loss or permanent loss of use of 1 foot, 1 hand, or 1 eye; veterans who received the Congressional Medal of Honor, Distinguished Service Cross, Navy Cross, or Air Force Cross; and their spouses or surviving spouses; 3) veterans who suffered, in the line of duty, the loss or permanent loss of use of both feet, both hands, or both eyes; and their spouses or surviving spouses; 4) veterans who suffered total disability in the line of duty and received assistance in acquiring specially adapted housing, which they own and occupy as their domicile; and their spouses or surviving spouses; 5) unremarried surviving spouses of military personnel who died due to injury or disease from being in a combat zone, or are missing and presumed dead due to combat; 6) veterans who suffered total disability in the line of duty and are incapable of working; and their spouses or surviving spouses; and 7) veterans who are certified by the Veterans Administration as paraplegic and their surviving spouses.

Financial data Qualified veterans and family members are entitled to an annual exemption from their taxes for the different categories: 1), $400; 2), $750; 3), $1,250; 4), $1,500; 5), total exemption for 5 years after death, and up to $2,500 after 5 years; 6), $1,000; or 7), total.

Duration The exemptions are provided each year that the veteran or unremarried surviving spouse lives in Massachusetts and owns the property as a domicile.

Additional information Applications are available from local assessor's offices.

Number awarded Varies each year.

Deadline Applications must be filed with the local assessor by December of each year.

[1124]
MASSACHUSETTS VETERANS ANNUITY PROGRAM

Department of Veterans' Services
Attn: Annuities
600 Washington Street, Seventh Floor
Boston, MA 02111
(617) 210-5480   Fax: (617) 210-5755
E-mail: mdvs@vet.state.ma.us
Web: www.mass.gov/veterans

Summary To provide an annuity to blind or disabled veterans from Massachusetts and to the parents and spouses of deceased military personnel.

Eligibility This program is open to 1) veterans who are blind, double amputee, paraplegic, or have a 100% service-connected disability; 2) the parents of military personnel who died of service-connected causes; and 3) the unremarried spouses of military personnel who died of service-connected causes. Veterans must have been residents of Massachusetts at the time of entry into military service who served during specified wartime periods and received other than a dishonorable discharge. All applicants must currently be residents of Massachusetts.

Financial data Recipients are entitled to an annuity of $2,000 per year.

Duration The annuity is paid as long as the recipient continues to reside in Massachusetts.

Deadline Deadline not specified.

[1125]
MASSACHUSETTS WELCOME HOME BONUS

Office of the State Treasurer
Attn: Veterans' Bonus Division
One Ashburton Place, 12th Floor
Boston, MA 02108-1608
(617) 367-9333, ext. 859   Fax: (617) 227-1622
E-mail: veteransbonus@tre.state.ma.us
Web: www.mass.gov/treasury/veterans/welc-home-bonus

Summary To provide a bonus to Massachusetts veterans and servicemembers who served after September 11, 2001.

Eligibility The first-time bonus is available to veterans and current servicemembers who had resided in Massachusetts for at least 6 months immediately prior to their enlistment or commission in the armed forces. The subsequent bonus is available to veterans and current servicemembers who had resided in Massachusetts for at least 6 months prior to their most recent tour or deployment. Both categories of applicants must have performed at least 6 months of service on or after September 11, 2001 and/or 1 or more days in Iraq or Afghanistan. They must still be serving or have been honorably discharged.

Financial data The first-time bonus is $1,000 for active service that includes time in Afghanistan or Iraq or $500 for 6 months or more of active service in the United States or overseas; veterans and servicemembers may be eligible for both types of bonuses. Each subsequent bonus is $500 for active service the includes time in Afghanistan or Iraq or $250 for 6 months or more of active service overseas.

Duration Veterans and servicemembers may be eligible for 1 or both of the first-time bonuses and for a subsequent bonus for each subsequent tour or deployment.

Number awarded Varies each year.

Deadline Deadline not specified.

[1126]
MEDAL OF HONOR PENSION

Department of Veterans Affairs
Attn: Veterans Benefits Administration
810 Vermont Avenue, N.W.
Washington, DC 20420
(202) 418-4343   Toll Free: (800) 827-1000
Web: www1.va.gov

Summary To provide a monthly payment to veterans who hold the Medal of Honor.

Eligibility This program is open to veterans who hold the Congressional Medal of Honor and are at least 40 years of age.

Financial data Qualified veterans receive a pension of $1,237 per month.

Number awarded Depends on the number of qualified Medal of Honor holders currently living.

Deadline This is an entitlement program available to all Medal of Honor holders.

[1127]
MICHIGAN HOMESTEAD PROPERTY TAX CREDIT FOR VETERANS AND BLIND PEOPLE

Michigan Department of Treasury
Attn: Homestead Exemption
Treasury Building
430 West Allegan Street
Lansing, MI 48922
(517) 636-4486   TDD: (800) 649-3777
E-mail: treasIndTax@michigan.gov
Web: www.michigan.gov/taxes

Summary To provide an income tax credit to veterans, military personnel, their spouses, blind people, and their surviving spouses in Michigan.

Eligibility Eligible to apply are residents of Michigan who are 1) blind and own their homestead; 2) a veteran with a service-connected disability or his/her surviving spouse; 3) a surviving spouse of a veteran deceased in service; 4) a pensioned veteran, a surviving spouse of those veterans, or an active military member, all of whose household income is less than $7,500; or 5) a surviving spouse of a non-disabled or non-pensioned veteran of the Korean War, World War II, or World War I whose household income is less than $7,500. All applicants must own or rent a home in Michigan, have been a Michigan resident for at least 6 months during the year in which application is made, and fall within qualifying income levels (up to $82,650 in household income).

Financial data The maximum credit, applied to state income taxes, is $1,200. The exact amount varies. For homeowners, the credit depends on the state equalized value of the homestead and on an allowance for filing category. For renters, 20% of the rent is considered property tax eligible for credit.

Duration 1 year; eligibility must be established each year.

Number awarded Varies each year.

Deadline April of each year.

[1128]
MICHIGAN HOMESTEAD PROPERTY TAX EXEMPTION FOR SPECIALLY ADAPTED HOUSING

Michigan Department of Treasury
Attn: Homestead Exemption
Treasury Building
430 West Allegan Street
Lansing, MI 48922
(517) 373-3200   TDD: (800) 649-3777
E-mail: treasPtd2@michigan.gov
Web: www.michigan.gov/taxes

Summary To exempt specially adapted housing occupied as homesteads by disabled veterans and their unremarried spouses from property taxation in Michigan.

Eligibility This exemption is available to Michigan residents who are disabled veterans living in specially adapted housing that they acquired with financial assistance from the U.S. Department of Veterans Affairs (VA). If the veteran has died, the exemption continues for the unremarried surviving spouse.

Financial data All taxes on qualified housing are cancelled.

Duration This exemption continues as long as the disabled veteran or unremarried surviving spouse owns the property in Michigan and, in the case of surviving spouses, remains unmarried.

Number awarded Varies each year.

Deadline Deadline not specified.

[1129]
MICHIGAN INCOME TAX EXEMPTION FOR VETERANS AND MILITARY PERSONNEL

Michigan Department of Treasury
Attn: Income Tax
Treasury Building
430 West Allegan Street
Lansing, MI 48922
(517) 373-3200   TDD: (800) 649-3777
E-mail: treasIndTax@michigan.gov
Web: www.michigan.gov/taxes

Summary To exempt the income of military personnel and veterans in Michigan from state income taxation.

Eligibility Eligible for this exemption are military personnel and veterans considered Michigan residents for purposes of state income taxation.

Financial data All active-duty military and retirement pay from the U.S. armed forces is exempt from state income taxation.

Duration The exemption continues as long as the recipient resides in Michigan.

Deadline Deadline not specified.

[1130]
MICHIGAN VETERANS TRUST FUND EMERGENCY GRANTS

Department of Military and Veterans Affairs
Attn: Michigan Veterans Trust Fund
2500 South Washington Avenue
Lansing, MI 48913-5101
(517) 373-3130   E-mail: dutchera@michigan.gov
Web: www.michigan.gov

Summary To provide temporary financial assistance to disabled and other Michigan veterans and their families, if they are facing personal emergencies.

Eligibility Eligible for this assistance are veterans and their families residing in Michigan who are temporarily unable to provide the basic necessities of life. Support is not provided for long-term problems or chronic financial difficulties. The qualifying veteran must have been discharged under honorable conditions with at least 180 days of active wartime service or have been separated as a result of a physical or mental disability incurred in the line of duty.

Financial data No statutory limit exists on the amount of assistance that may be provided; a local board in each Michigan county determines if the applicant is genuinely needy and the amount of assistance to be awarded.

Duration This assistance is provided to meet temporary needs only.

Number awarded Varies each year.

Deadline Applications may be submitted at any time.

[1131]
MILITARY FAMILY SUPPORT TRUST FINANCIAL ASSISTANCE

Military Family Support Trust
1010 American Eagle Boulevard
P.O. Box 301
Sun City Center, FL 33573
(813) 634-4675   Fax: (813) 633-2412
E-mail: president@mobc-online.org
Web: www.mobc-online.org/financial.html

Summary To provide financial assistance for emergency needs to active-duty, retired, and deceased officers who served in the military or designated public service agencies and to their families.

Eligibility This assistance is available to 1) retired, active-duty, National Guard, or Reserve officers and former officers of the U.S. Army, Navy, Marine Corps, Air Force, Coast Guard, Public Health Service, or National Oceanic and Atmospheric Administration, at the rank of E-5 through E-9; 2) recipients of the Purple Heart, regardless of pay grade or length of service; 3) World War II combat veterans of the Merchant Marine; 4) federal employees at the grade of GS-7 or higher; 5) Foreign Service Officers at the grade of FSO-8 or lower; 6) honorably discharged or retired foreign military officers of friendly nations meeting the service and disability retirement criteria of their respective country and living in the United States; and 7) spouses, surviving spouses, and dependents (including grandchildren) of those categories. Applicants must be in need of financial assistance for personal care, subsistence, housing, all aspects of health care, or other special circumstances.

Financial data Grants depend on the need of the recipient.

Duration Assistance is provided in the form of 1-time grants or monthly payments.

Additional information This foundation began in 1992 as the Military Officers' Benevolent Corporation. It changed its name in 2008.

Number awarded Varies each year.

Deadline Applications may be submitted at any time.

[1132]
MINNESOTA INCOME TAX SUBTRACTION FOR THE ELDERLY OR DISABLED

Minnesota Department of Revenue
Attn: Individual Income Tax Division
600 North Robert Street
Mail Station 5510
St. Paul, MN 55146-5510
(651) 296-3781   Toll Free: (800) 652-9094 (within MN)
E-mail: indinctax@state.mn.us
Web: www.taxes.state.mn.us

Summary To exempt from state taxation a portion of the income received by residents of Minnesota who are disabled or elderly.

Eligibility This exemption is available to residents of Minnesota who are either 65 years of age or older or permanently and totally disabled and receiving disability income from the Social Security Administration or U.S. Department of Veterans Affairs. Their adjusted gross income must be less than $42,000 if married filing a joint return and both spouses qualify, $38,500 if married filing a joint return and 1 spouse qualifies, $21,000 if married filing a separate return, or $33,700 if filing single, head of household, or qualifying widow(er).

Financial data Qualified taxpayers are entitled to subtract from their income for purposes of Minnesota state taxation $18,000 if married filing a joint return and both spouses qualify, $14,500 if married filing a joint return and 1 spouse qualifies, $9,000 if married filing a separate return, or $14,500 if filing single, head of household, or qualifying widow(er).

Duration This exemption is available as long as the taxpayer resides in Minnesota.

Number awarded Varies each year.

Deadline Income tax returns must be submitted by April of each year.

[1133]
MINNESOTA MARKET VALUE EXCLUSION FOR DISABLED VETERANS

Minnesota Department of Revenue
Attn: Property Tax Division
600 North Robert Street
Mail Station 3340
St. Paul, MN 55146-3340
(651) 556-6087
Web: www.taxes.state.mn.us

Summary To exclude from property taxation a portion of the value of homesteads owned by disabled veterans, primary family caregivers, and surviving spouses in Minnesota.

Eligibility This exclusion is available to owners of homesteads in Minnesota who are veterans who have a service-connected disability rated at least at 70% by the U.S. Department of Veterans Affairs. If a disabled veteran has died (or was killed in action without becoming disabled), the surviving spouse is eligible for the exclusion. If a veteran meets the disability qualification but does not own homestead property, the homestead of the veteran's primary family caregiver, if any, is eligible for the exclusion for that veteran.

Financial data For veterans with a service-connected of 70% or more (and their surviving spouses or primary family caregivers), $150,000 of the market value of the homestead is excluded from property taxation. For veterans with a total (100%) and permanent service-connected disability (and

their surviving spouses or primary family caregivers), $300,000 of the market value of the homestead is excluded from property taxation.

Duration This exclusion is available as long as the veteran, surviving spouse, or primary family caregiver owns the homestead and meets the eligibility requirements.

Additional information This exclusion was established by the Minnesota legislature for veterans in 2008 and expanded to included surviving spouses and primary family caregivers in 2011.

Deadline Applications must be submitted by June of each year.

[1134]
MINNESOTA STATE SOLDIERS ASSISTANCE PROGRAM

Minnesota Department of Veterans Affairs
Veterans Service Building
20 West 12th Street, Room 206C
St. Paul, MN 55155-2006
(651) 757-1556   Toll Free: (888) LINK-VET
Fax: (651) 296-3954 E-mail: kathy.schwartz@state.mn.us
Web: www.mdva.state.mn.us/SSAP/index.htm

Summary To provide emergency financial assistance to disabled veterans and their families in Minnesota.

Eligibility This assistance is available to veterans who are unable to work because of a temporary disability (from service-connected or other causes). Their dependents and survivors are also eligible. Applicants must also meet income and asset guidelines and be residents of Minnesota.

Financial data The maximum grant is $1,500. Funds may be used to pay for food and shelter, utility bills, and emergency medical treatment (including optical and dental benefits).

Duration This is a short-term program, with benefits payable up to 6 months only. If the veteran's disability is expected to be long term in nature or permanent, the department may continue to provide assistance while application is made for long-term benefits, such as Social Security disability or retirement benefits.

Number awarded Varies each year. A total of $1.4 million is available for this program annually.

Deadline Applications may be submitted at any time.

[1135]
MISSISSIPPI AD VALOREM TAX EXEMPTION FOR DISABLED VETERANS

Mississippi State Veterans Affairs Board
3466 Highway 80
P.O. Box 5947
Pearl, MS 39288-5947
(601) 576-4850   Toll Free: (877) 203-5632
Fax: (601) 576-4868
Web: www.vab.ms.gov

Summary To exempt the property of disabled veterans from ad valorem taxation in Mississippi.

Eligibility This exemption applies to homesteads owned by American veterans in Mississippi who were honorably discharged. Applicants must have a 100% permanent service-connected disability.

Financial data All qualifying homesteads of $7,500 or less in assessed value are exempt from ad valorem taxation.

Duration This exemption applies as long as the disabled veteran owns the homestead in Mississippi.

Number awarded Varies each year.

Deadline Deadline not specified.

[1136]
MISSOURI INCOME TAX MILITARY PENSION EXEMPTION

Missouri Department of Revenue
Attn: Taxation Division
301 West High Street, Room 330
P.O. Box 2200
Jefferson City, MO 65105-2200
(573) 751-3505   Toll Free: (800) 877-6881
Fax: (573) 751-2195   TDD: (800) 735-2966
E-mail: income@dor.mo.gov
Web: dor.mo.gov/personal

Summary To exempt a portion of the retirement income of federal employees, including veterans, from state taxation in Missouri.

Eligibility This exemption is available to all residents of Missouri who are receiving pension payments from the armed forces. Applicants must have state adjusted gross incomes below $100,000 for married couples or $85,000 for single individuals.

Financial data A specified percentage of pension income is exempt from state income taxation in Missouri; that percentage was 15% for 2010, rising in 15% increments until 2016, when all military pension income will be tax free.

Duration This exemption is available as long as the recipient remains a resident of Missouri for state income tax purposes.

Additional information The current exemption became effective for income earned in 2010.

Number awarded Varies each year.

Deadline Deadline not specified.

[1137]
MONTANA DISABLED AMERICAN VETERAN PROPERTY TAX BENEFIT

Montana Department of Revenue
Attn: Property Tax
125 North Roberts, Third Floor
P.O. Box 5805
Helena, MT 59604-5805
(406) 444-6900   Toll Free: (866) 859-2254
Fax: (406) 444-1505   TDD: (406) 444-2830
Web: mt.gov/revenue

Summary To reduce the property tax rate in Montana for disabled veterans and their surviving spouses.

Eligibility This benefit is available to residents of Montana who own and occupy property in the state. Applicants must have been honorably discharged from active service in the armed forces and be currently rated 100% disabled or compensated at the 100% disabled rate because of a service-connected disability. They must have an adjusted gross income less than $53,867 if married or $46,685 if single. Also eligible are unremarried surviving spouses with an adjusted gross income less than $40,700 whose spouse was a veteran with a 100% service-connected disability or compensation at the 100% disabled rate at the time of death, died while on active duty, or died of a service-connected disability.

Financial data Qualifying veterans and surviving spouses are entitled to a reduction in local property taxes on their residence, 1 attached or detached garage, and up to 1 acre of land. The amount of the reduction depends on the status of the applicant (married, single, or surviving spouse) and adjusted gross income, but ranges from 50% to 100%.

Duration The reduction continues as long as the recipient resides in Montana and owns and occupies property used as a primary residence.

Number awarded Varies each year.

Deadline Applications must be filed with the local Department of Revenue Office by April of each year.

[1138]
NATIONAL ASSOCIATION OF AMERICAN VETERANS EMERGENCY ASSISTANCE

National Association of American Veterans
Attn: Executive Director
P.O. Box 6865
Washington, DC 20020-9994
Web: www.naavets.org/services.html

Summary To provide emergency financial assistance to veterans, military personnel, and their families.

Eligibility This assistance is available to veterans, military service members, and their family members who are experiencing financial hardship. Applicants must be seeking funding for mortgage assistance, rent, home repair or maintenance, vehicle repair or maintenance, medical expenses, or transportation expenses.

Financial data The amount of the grant depends on the need of the recipient.

Duration These are 1-time grants.

Additional information This association began in 2005.

Number awarded Varies each year.

Deadline Applications may be submitted at any time.

[1139]
NAVY-MARINE CORPS RELIEF SOCIETY FINANCIAL ASSISTANCE

Navy-Marine Corps Relief Society
875 North Randolph Street, Suite 225
Arlington, VA 22203-1757
(703) 696-4904   Fax: (703) 696-0144
Web: www.nmcrs.org/intfreeloan.html

Summary To provide emergency assistance, in the form of interest-free loans or grants, to current and former Navy and Marine Corps personnel and their families who need temporary funding.

Eligibility This program is open to active-duty and retired Navy and Marine Corps personnel, their eligible family members, eligible family members of Navy and Marine Corps personnel who died on active duty or in a retired status, Reservists on extended active duty, indigent mothers (65 years of age or older) of deceased servicemembers who have limited resources and no family to provide for their welfare, ex-spouses whose marriage to a servicemember lasted for at least 20 years while the servicemember was on active duty and who have not remarried, and uniformed members of the National Oceanic and Atmospheric Administration (NOAA). Applicants must need emergency funding for funeral expenses, medical or dental bills, food, rent, utilities, emergency transportation, disaster relief, child care expenses, essential vehicle repairs, or other unforeseen family emergencies. Funding is not available to pay bills for non-essentials, finance liberty and vacations, pay fines or legal expenses, pay taxes, finance recreational boats or vehicles or help Navy and Marine Corps families live beyond their means.

Financial data Funds are provided in the form of interest-free loans or grants.

Number awarded Varies each year.

Deadline Applications may be submitted at any time.

[1140]
NEBRASKA HOMESTEAD EXEMPTION

Nebraska Department of Revenue
301 Centennial Mall South
P.O. Box 94818
Lincoln, NE 68509-4818
(402) 471-5729
Toll Free: (800) 742-7474 (within NE and IA)
Web: www.revenue.ne.gov/PAD/homestead.html

Summary To exempt the property of Nebraska residents who are elderly, disabled, or veterans and their widow(er)s from a portion of taxation.

Eligibility This exemption is available to 3 categories of Nebraska residents: the elderly, certain people with disabilities, and certain disabled veterans and their widow(er)s. Elderly people are those 65 years of age or older who own a homestead with a value less than $95,000 or 200% of their county's average assessed value of single family residential property, whichever is greater. Disabled people are those who 1) have a permanent physical disability and have lost all mobility such as to preclude locomotion without the regular use of a mechanical aid or prosthesis; 2) have undergone amputation of both arms above the elbow, or 3) have a permanent partial disability of both arms in excess of 75%. They must own a homestead with a value less than $110,000 or 225% of their county's average assessed value of single family residential property, whichever is greater. Veterans are those who served on active duty in the U.S. armed forces (or a government allied with the United States) during specified periods of war and received an honorable discharge. They must 1) be drawing compensation from the U.S. Department of Veterans Affairs (VA) because of a 100% service-connected disability; 2) be totally disabled by a nonservice-connected illness or accident; or 3) own a home that is substantially contributed to by VA. Also eligible are unremarried widow(er)s of veterans who died because of a service-connected disability, whose death while on active duty was service-connected, who died while on active duty during wartime, or who drew compensation from VA because of a 100% service-connected disability The homestead maximum value is $110,000 or 225% of the county's average assessed value of single family residential property, whichever is greater. Elderly people must have a household income less than $31,801 if single or $37,401 if married. Disabled persons, veterans, and widow(er)s (except veterans and widow(er)s who own a home that is substantially contributed to by the VA) must have a household income less than $34,901 if single or $40,301 if married.

Financial data Exemptions depend on the income of the applicant, ranging from 25% to 100% of the value of the homestead. For the elderly, the maximum exemption is the taxable value of the homestead up to $40,000 or 100% of the county's average assessed value of single family residential property, whichever is greater. For disabled people and veterans, the maximum exemption is the taxable value of the homestead up to $50,000 or 120% of the county's average assessed value of single family residential property, whichever is greater. For veterans and widow(er)s whose home was substantially contributed to by the VA, the homestead is 100% exempt regardless of the value of the homestead or the income of the owner.

Duration The exemption is provided as long as the qualifying homestead owner resides in Nebraska.

Number awarded Varies each year.

Deadline Applications must be filed by June of each year.

[1141]
NEBRASKA VETERANS' AID FUND

Department of Veterans' Affairs
State Office Building
301 Centennial Mall South, Sixth Floor
P.O. Box 95083
Lincoln, NE 68509-5083
(402) 471-2458   Fax: (402) 471-2491
E-mail: john.hilgert@nebraska.gov
Web: www.vets.state.ne.us/benefits.html

Summary To assist veterans, their spouses, and their dependents in Nebraska who have a temporary emergency need.

Eligibility This assistance is available to veterans, their spouses, and their dependent children who are residents of Nebraska. The veteran must have served on active duty in the armed forces of the United States, other than active duty for training, and either 1) was discharged or otherwise separated with a characterization of honorable or general (under honorable conditions), or 2) died while in service or as a direct result of such service.

Financial data The amount of aid awarded varies, depending upon the needs of the recipient. Recently, grants averaged nearly $1,000. Aid can only be used for food, fuel, shelter, wearing apparel, funeral, medical, or surgical items.

Duration The funds are provided for emergency situations only; the program does not assist ongoing financial needs.

Additional information The Nebraska Veterans' Aid Fund was established in 1921 in lieu of a bonus for veterans of wartime service. Applications must be made through the county service officer or post service officer of any recognized veterans' organization in the county nearest the applicant's place of residence and submitted to the Department of Veterans' Affairs.

Number awarded Varies each year. In a recent year, nearly $840,000 in aid was provided to 773 veterans.

Deadline Applications may be submitted at any time.

[1142]
NEVADA DISABLED VETERAN'S TAX EXEMPTION

Nevada Office of Veterans Services
Attn: Executive Director
5460 Reno Corporate Drive
Reno, NV 89511
(775) 688-1653   Toll Free: (866) 630-8387
Fax: (775) 688-1656
Web: veterans.nv.gov/veteran_benefits.html

Summary To exempt from taxation in Nevada a portion of the property owned by disabled veterans or their surviving spouses.

Eligibility This program is open to veterans who are residents of Nevada and have incurred a service-connected disability of 60% or more. Applicants must have received an honorable separation from military service. The widow(er) of a disabled veteran, who was eligible at the time of death, may also be eligible for this benefit.

Financial data Veterans and widow(er)s are entitled to exempt from taxation a portion of their property's assessed value. The amount depends on the extent of the disability and the year filed; it ranges from $6,250 to $20,000 and doubles over a 4-year period.

Duration Disabled veterans and their widow(er)s are entitled to this exemption as long as they live in Nevada.

Additional information Disabled veterans and widow(er)s are able to split their exemption between vehicle taxes and/or property taxes.

Number awarded Varies each year.

Deadline Deadline not specified.

[1143]
NEVADA VETERAN'S TAX EXEMPTION

Nevada Office of Veterans Services
Attn: Executive Director
5460 Reno Corporate Drive
Reno, NV 89511
(775) 688-1653   Toll Free: (866) 630-8387
Fax: (775) 688-1656
Web: veterans.nv.gov/veteran_benefits.html

Summary To exempt from taxation in Nevada a portion of the property owned by wartime veterans.

Eligibility This program is open to veterans who have been residents of Nevada for at least 6 months and have wartime service (including in-theater service during the wars in the Persian Gulf, Afghanistan, and Iraq). Veterans are entitled to an exemption on their vehicle privilege tax or real property tax, but they cannot split the benefit between the 2 taxes.

Financial data The exact amount of the exemption is available from the local county assessor. The value of the exemption doubles over a 4-year period.

Duration Wartime veterans are entitled to this exemption as long as they live in Nevada.

Number awarded Varies each year.

Deadline Deadline not specified.

[1144]
NEW HAMPSHIRE PROPERTY TAX EXEMPTION FOR CERTAIN DISABLED VETERANS

New Hampshire Department of Revenue Administration
109 Pleasant Street
Concord, NH 03301
(603) 271-2191   Fax: (603) 271-6121
TDD: (800) 735-2964
Web: revenue.nh.gov

Summary To exempt from taxation certain property owned by New Hampshire disabled veterans or their surviving spouses.

Eligibility Eligible for this exemption are New Hampshire residents who are honorably discharged veterans with a total

and permanent service-connected disability that involves double amputation of the upper or lower extremities or any combination thereof, paraplegia, or blindness of both eyes with visual acuity of 5/200 or less. Applicants or their surviving spouses must own a specially adapted homestead that has been acquired with the assistance of the U.S. Department of Veterans Affairs.

Financial data Qualifying disabled veterans and surviving spouses are exempt from all taxation on their specially adapted homestead.

Duration 1 year; once the credit has been approved, it is automatically renewed as long as the qualifying person owns the same residence in New Hampshire.

Number awarded Varies each year.

Deadline The original application for a permanent tax credit must be submitted by April.

[1145]
NEW HAMPSHIRE SERVICE-CONNECTED TOTAL AND PERMANENT DISABILITY TAX CREDIT

New Hampshire Department of Revenue Administration
109 Pleasant Street
Concord, NH 03301
(603) 271-2191   Fax: (603) 271-6121
TDD: (800) 735-2964
Web: revenue.nh.gov

Summary To provide property tax credits in New Hampshire to disabled veterans or their surviving spouses.

Eligibility Eligible for this tax credit are honorably discharged veterans residing in New Hampshire who 1) have a total and permanent service-connected disability, or 2) are a double amputee or paraplegic because of a service-connected disability. Unremarried surviving spouses of qualified veterans are also eligible.

Financial data Qualifying disabled veterans and surviving spouses receive an annual credit of $700 for property taxes on residential property. In addition, individual towns in New Hampshire may adopt a local option to increase the dollar amount credited to disabled veterans, to a maximum of $2,000.

Duration 1 year; once the credit has been approved, it is automatically renewed for as long as the qualifying person owns the same residence in New Hampshire.

Number awarded Varies each year.

Deadline The original application for a permanent tax credit must be submitted by April.

[1146]
NEW JERSEY INCOME TAX EXCLUSION FOR MILITARY PENSIONS AND SURVIVOR'S BENEFITS

New Jersey Division of Taxation
Attn: Technical Information Branch
50 Barrack Street
P.O. Box 281
Trenton, NJ 08695-0281
(609) 292-6400
Toll Free: (800) 323-4400 (within NJ, NY, PA, DE, and MD)
TDD: (800) 286-6613 (within NJ, NY, PA, DE, and MD)
E-mail: taxation@tax.state.nj.us
Web: www.state.nj.us/treasury/taxation/prntgit.shtml

Summary To exclude from income taxation in New Jersey military pensions and survivor's benefits.

Eligibility This exclusion is available to residents of New Jersey who are receiving 1) a military pension resulting from service in the Army, Navy, Air Force, Marine Corps, or Coast Guard, or 2) survivor's benefits related to such service. It does not apply to civil service pensions or annuities, even if the pension or annuity is based on credit for military service.

Financial data All military pensions and survivor's benefit payments are excluded from income for state taxation purposes.

Duration The exclusion applies as long as the individual resides in New Jersey.

Additional information This exclusion became effective in 2001.

Number awarded Varies each year.

Deadline Deadline not specified.

[1147]
NEW JERSEY PROPERTY TAX EXEMPTION FOR DISABLED VETERANS OR SURVIVING SPOUSES

New Jersey Division of Taxation
Attn: Technical Information Branch
50 Barrack Street
P.O. Box 281
Trenton, NJ 08695-0281
(609) 292-6400
Toll Free: (800) 323-4400 (within NJ, NY, PA, DE, and MD)
TDD: (800) 286-6613 (within NJ, NY, PA, DE, and MD)
E-mail: taxation@tax.state.nj.us
Web: www.state.nj.us/treasury/taxation/otherptr.shtml

Summary To provide a real estate tax exemption to New Jersey veterans with disabilities and certain surviving widow(er)s.

Eligibility This exemption is available to New Jersey residents who have been honorably discharged with active wartime service in the U.S. armed forces and have been certified by the U.S. Department of Veterans Affairs as totally and permanently disabled as a result of wartime service-connected conditions. Unremarried surviving spouses and civil union partners of eligible disabled veterans or of certain wartime servicepersons who died on active duty are also entitled to this exemption. Applicants must be the full owner of and a permanent resident in the dwelling house for which the exemption is claimed.

Financial data A 100% exemption from locally-levied real estate taxes is provided.

Duration 1 year; the exemption continues as long as the eligible veteran remains a resident of New Jersey.

Additional information This program is administered by the local tax assessor or collector. Veterans who are denied exemptions have the right to appeal the decision to their county and state governments.

Number awarded Varies each year.

Deadline Applications may be submitted at any time.

[1148]
NEW MEXICO DISABLED VETERAN PROPERTY TAX EXEMPTION

New Mexico Department of Veterans' Services
Attn: Benefits Division
407 Galisteo Street, Room 142
P.O. Box 2324
Santa Fe, NM 87504-2324
(505) 827-6374   Toll Free: (866) 433-VETS
Fax: (505) 827-6372   E-mail: alan.martinez@state.nm.us
Web: www.dvs.state.nm.us/benefits.html

Summary To exempt disabled veterans and their spouses from payment of property taxes in New Mexico.

Eligibility This exemption is available to veterans who are rated 100% service-connected disabled by the U.S. Department of Veterans Affairs, are residents of New Mexico, and own a primary residence in the state. Also eligible are qualifying veterans' unremarried surviving spouses, if they are New Mexico residents and continue to own the residence.

Financial data Veterans and surviving spouses are exempt from payment of property taxes in New Mexico.

Duration 1 year; continues until the qualifying veteran or spouse no longer live in the residence.

Number awarded Varies each year.

Deadline Deadline not specified.

[1149]
NEW MEXICO VETERANS PROPERTY TAX EXEMPTION

New Mexico Department of Veterans' Services
Attn: Benefits Division
407 Galisteo Street, Room 142
P.O. Box 2324
Santa Fe, NM 87504-2324
(505) 827-6374   Toll Free: (866) 433-VETS
Fax: (505) 827-6372   E-mail: alan.martinez@state.nm.us
Web: www.dvs.state.nm.us/benefits.html

Summary To exempt veterans and their spouses from a portion of property taxes in New Mexico.

Eligibility This exemption is available to veterans who served honorably for at least 90 days during wartime (World War I, World War II, Korea, Vietnam, Persian Gulf), are residents of New Mexico, and own a primary residence in the state. Also eligible are qualifying veterans' unremarried surviving spouses, if they are New Mexico residents and continue to own the residence.

Financial data Veterans and surviving spouses are entitled to a reduction in the value of their property that is currently $4,000. The exemption is deducted from the taxable value of the property to determine net taxable value. Veterans who are entitled to this exemption and do not have sufficient real or personal property to claim the full exemption may be eligible to claim a one-third reduction in motor vehicle registration fees.

Duration 1 year; continues until the qualifying veteran or spouse no longer lives in the residence.

Number awarded Varies each year.

Deadline Deadline not specified.

[1150]
NEW YORK ALTERNATIVE PROPERTY TAX EXEMPTIONS FOR VETERANS

New York State Department of Taxation and Finance
Attn: Office of Real Property Tax Services
W.A. Harriman Campus
Building 8, Sixth Floor
Albany, NY 12227
(518) 486-4403   Fax: (518) 486-7754
Web: www.orps.state.ny.us

Summary   To provide wartime veterans and their spouses who are residents of New York with a partial exemption from property taxes.

Eligibility   This program is open to veterans who served during specified periods of wartime. Applicants must have been discharged under honorable conditions; additional benefits are available to those who served in a combat zone and to those who have a service-connected disability. The legal title to the property must be in the name of the veteran or the spouse of the veteran or both, or the unremarried surviving spouse of a deceased veteran. The property must be used exclusively for residential purposes. This program is only available in counties, cities, towns, and villages in New York that have opted to participate.

Financial data   This program provides an exemption of 15% of the assessed valuation of the property, to a basic maximum of $12,000 per year; local governments may opt for reduced maximums of $9,000 or $6,000, or for increased maximums of $15,000 to $36,000. For combat-zone veterans, an additional 10% of the assessed valuation is exempt, to a basic maximum of $8,000 per year; local governments may opt for a reduced maximum of $6,000 or $4,000, or for increased maximums of $10,000 to $24,000. For disabled veterans, the exemption is the percentage of assessed value equal to half of the service-connected disability rating, to a basic maximum of $40,000 per year; local governments may opt for a reduced maximum of $30,000 or $20,000, or for increased maximums of $50,000 to $120,000. At its option, New York City and other high appreciation municipalities may use the following increased maximum exemptions: war veteran, $54,000; combat-zone veteran, $36,000; disabled veteran, $180,000.

Duration   This exemption is available annually.

Number awarded   Varies each year.

Deadline   Applications must be filed with the local assessor by "taxable status date;" in most towns, that is the end of February.

[1151]
NEW YORK COLD WAR VETERANS PROPERTY TAX EXEMPTIONS

New York State Department of Taxation and Finance
Attn: Office of Real Property Tax Services
W.A. Harriman Campus
Building 8, Sixth Floor
Albany, NY 12227
(518) 486-4403   Fax: (518) 486-7754
Web: www.orps.state.ny.us

Summary   To provide New York veterans who served during the Cold War and their spouses with a partial exemption from property taxes.

Eligibility   This program is open to veterans who served during the Cold War, defined as September 2, 1945 to December 26, 1991. Applicants must have been discharged under honorable conditions; additional benefits are available to those who have a service-connected disability. The legal title to the property must be in the name of the veteran or the spouse of the veteran or both, or the unremarried surviving spouse of a deceased veteran. The property must be used exclusively for residential purposes. This program is only available in counties, cities, towns, and villages in New York that have opted to participate.

Financial data   Local governments may opt to grant exemptions of 15% or 10%. For the 15% option, the basic maximum exemption is $12,000 per year; local governments may opt for reduced maximums of $9,000 or $6,000, or for increased maximums of $15,000 to $36,000. For the 10% option, the basic maximum exemption is $8,000 per year; local governments may opt for a reduced maximum of $6,000 or $4,000, or for increased maximums of $10,000 to $24,000. For disabled veterans, the exemption is the percentage of assessed value equal to half of the service-connected disability rating, to a basic maximum of $40,000 per year; local governments may opt for a reduced maximum of $30,000 or $20,000, or for increased maximums of $50,000 to $120,000. At its option, New York City and other high appreciation municipalities may use the following increased maximum exemptions: 15% option, $54,000; 10% option, $36,000; disabled veteran, $180,000.

Duration   This exemption is available annually.

Number awarded   Varies each year.

Deadline   Applications must be filed with the local assessor by "taxable status date;" in most towns, that is the end of February.

[1152]
NEW YORK "ELIGIBLE FUNDS" PROPERTY TAX EXEMPTIONS FOR VETERANS

New York State Department of Taxation and Finance
Attn: Office of Real Property Tax Services
W.A. Harriman Campus
Building 8, Sixth Floor
Albany, NY 12227
(518) 486-4403   Fax: (518) 486-7754
Web: www.orps.state.ny.us

Summary   To provide a partial exemption from property taxes to veterans and their surviving spouses who are residents of New York.

Eligibility   This program is open to veterans who have purchased properties in New York with such income as retirement pay, disability compensation, or death gratuities (referred to as "eligible funds"). Specially adapted homes of paraplegics, or the homes of their widowed spouses, are also covered.

Financial data   This exemption reduces the property's assessed value to the extent that "eligible funds" were used in the purchase, generally to a maximum of $5,000. It is applicable to general municipal taxes but not to school taxes or special district levies.

Duration   This exemption is available annually.

Number awarded   Varies each year.

Deadline Applications must be filed with the local assessor by "taxable status date;" in most towns, that is the end of February.

[1153]
NEW YORK STATE BLIND ANNUITY

New York State Division of Veterans' Affairs
5 Empire State Plaza, Suite 2836
Albany, NY 12223-1551
(518) 486-3602   Toll Free: (888) VETS-NYS (within NY)
Fax: (518) 473-0379   E-mail: dvainfo@veterans.ny.gov
Web: veterans.ny.gov/state-benefits.html

Summary To provide an annuity to blind wartime veterans and their surviving spouses in New York.

Eligibility This benefit is available to veterans who served on active duty during specified periods of war. Applicants must 1) meet the New York standards of blindness; 2) have received an honorable or general discharge, or a discharge other than for dishonorable service; and 3) be now, and continue to be, residents of and continuously domiciled in New York. The annuity is also payable to unremarried spouses of deceased veterans who were receiving annuity payments (or were eligible to do so) at the time of their death, and are residents of and continuously domiciled in New York.

Financial data The annuity is currently $1,220.76 per year.

Number awarded Varies each year.

Deadline Deadline not specified.

[1154]
NEW YORK STATE INCOME TAX EXEMPTION FOR RETIRED MILITARY PERSONNEL

New York State Department of Taxation and Finance
W.A. Harriman Campus
Tax and Finance Building
Albany, NY 12227-0001
(518) 438-8581   Toll Free: (800) 225-5829 (within NY)
Web: www.tax.ny.gov/pit/file/military_page.htm

Summary To exempt the pension income of retired New York military personnel from state and designated local income tax.

Eligibility This exemption applies to retired military personnel and their beneficiaries who are residents of New York and receiving a military pension.

Financial data All pension payments are exempt from income taxes of New York State, New York City, and Yonkers.

Duration The exemption is available as long as the recipient resides in New York.

Number awarded Varies each year.

Deadline Deadline not specified.

[1155]
NORTH CAROLINA PROPERTY TAX RELIEF FOR DISABLED VETERANS

North Carolina Department of Revenue
Attn: Property Tax Division
501 North Wilmington Street
P.O. Box 871
Raleigh, NC 27602
(919) 733-7711   Fax: (919) 733-1821
Web: www.dornc.com/taxes/property/index.html

Summary To provide property tax relief to disabled North Carolina veterans.

Eligibility Disabled veterans who are residents of North Carolina are eligible for these programs. They must own 1) a vehicle that is altered with special equipment to accommodate a service-connected disability; or 2) specially adapted housing purchased with the assistance of the U.S. Department of Veterans Affairs.

Financial data Qualifying vehicles are exempt from personal property taxes. Qualifying housing is eligible for an exemption on the first $45,000 in assessed value of the housing and land that is owned and used as a residence by the disabled veteran.

Duration The exemptions continue as long as the eligible veteran is a resident of North Carolina.

Number awarded Varies each year.

Deadline Deadline not specified.

[1156]
NORTH DAKOTA PROPERTY TAX CREDIT FOR DISABLED VETERANS

Office of State Tax Commissioner
State Capitol Building
600 East Boulevard Avenue, Department 127
Bismarck, ND 58505-0599
(701) 328-7088   Toll Free: (877) 328-7088
Fax: (701) 328-3700   TDD: (800) 366-6888
E-mail: taxinfo@state.nd.us
Web: www.nd.gov/tax/property

Summary To provide property tax credits to disabled North Dakota veterans and their surviving spouses.

Eligibility This property tax credit is available to honorably-discharged veterans who have more than a 50% service-connected disability as certified by the U.S. Department of Veterans Affairs. Applicants must own and occupy a homestead according to state law. Unremarried surviving spouses are also eligible. If a disabled veteran co-owns the property with someone other than a spouse, the credit is limited to the disabled veteran's interest in the fixtures, buildings, and improvements of the homestead.

Financial data The credit is applied against the first $120,000 of true and full valuation of the fixtures, buildings, and improvements of the homestead, to a maximum amount calculated by multiplying $120,000 by the percentage of the disabled veteran's disability compensation rating for service-connected disabilities.

Duration 1 year; renewable as long as qualified individuals continue to reside in North Dakota and live in their homes.

Number awarded Varies each year.

Deadline Applications may be submitted to the county auditor at any time.

[1157]
NORTH DAKOTA PROPERTY TAX EXEMPTION FOR VETERANS WHO LIVE IN SPECIALLY ADAPTED HOUSING

Office of State Tax Commissioner
State Capitol Building
600 East Boulevard Avenue, Department 127
Bismarck, ND 58505-0599
(701) 328-7088   Toll Free: (877) 328-7088
Fax: (701) 328-3700   TDD: (800) 366-6888
E-mail: taxinfo@state.nd.us
Web: www.nd.gov/tax/property

Summary To provide property tax exemptions to North Dakota veterans and their surviving spouses who have been awarded specially adapted housing.

Eligibility This exemption is available to paraplegic disabled veterans of the U.S. armed forces or any veteran who has been awarded specially adapted housing by the U.S. Department of Veterans Affairs. The paraplegic disability does not have to be service connected. The unremarried surviving spouses of such deceased veterans are also eligible. Income and assets are not considered in determining eligibility for the exemption.

Financial data The maximum benefit may not exceed $5,400 taxable value, because the exemption is limited to the first $120,000 of true and full value of fixtures, buildings, and improvements.

Duration 1 year; renewable as long as qualified individuals continue to reside in North Dakota and live in their homes.

Number awarded Varies each year.

Deadline Applications may be submitted to the county auditor at any time.

[1158]
OHIO INCOME TAX DEDUCTION FOR MILITARY RETIREMENT INCOME

Ohio Department of Taxation
Attn: Individual Income Tax
30 East Broad Street
P.O. Box 530
Columbus, OH 43216-0530
(614) 433-5817   Toll Free: (800) 282-1780 (within OH)
Fax: (614) 433-7771
Web: tax.ohio.gov

Summary To deduct from state income taxation in Ohio the pay received by retired military personnel and their surviving spouses.

Eligibility This deduction is available to residents of Ohio who are retired from service in the active or reserve components of the U.S. armed forces. Surviving and former spouses of military retirees who are receiving payments under the survivor benefit plan are also eligible.

Financial data All retirement income received by military personnel and their surviving or former spouses is excluded from state income taxation in Ohio.

Duration The exclusion is available as long as the recipient remains an Ohio resident.

Number awarded Varies each year.

Deadline Deadline not specified.

[1159]
OHIO VETERANS BONUS

Ohio Department of Veterans Services
Attn: Veterans Bonus Program
P.O. Box 373
Sandusky, OH 44871
Toll Free: (877) OHIO-VET
Web: veteransbonus.ohio.gov/odvs_web

Summary To provide a bonus to Ohio veterans and active-duty servicemembers who served during the Persian Gulf War, Afghanistan, or Iraq and their family members.

Eligibility This bonus is available to current residents of Ohio who were also residents of the state when they began active-duty military service, including as a member of a Reserve component or the Ohio National Guard. Applicants must have served at least 90 days or be currently serving in the U.S. armed forces during the periods of the Persian Gulf War (August 2, 1990 through March 3, 1991), the war in Afghanistan (October 7, 2001 through the present), or the war in Iraq (March 19, 2003 through the present). If no longer serving, they must have received an honorable discharge. Additional bonuses are available to of 1) veterans who were medically discharged or retired because of combat-related disabilities sustained in the Persian Gulf, Afghanistan, or Iraq; and 2) veterans who were declared Missing in Action (MIA) or Prisoner of War (POW) or (if the veteran is deceased) their family members. Also eligible are family members (in order of preference: spouses, children, parents) 1) veterans who have died but whose death was not a result of injuries or illness sustained in the Persian Gulf, Afghanistan, or Iraq; or 2) veterans who died as a result of injuries or illness sustained in the Persian Gulf, Afghanistan, or Iraq.

Financial data The bonus for veterans and military personnel who served in the Persian Gulf, Afghanistan, or Iraq is $100 per month of service, to a maximum of $1,000; the bonus for veterans and military personnel who served during the specified time periods but elsewhere in the world is $50 per month of service, to a maximum of $500; veterans who were medically discharged or retired because of combat-related disabilities are eligible for an in-theater bonus of $1,000 (regardless of time served in-theater) plus $50 per month for non-theater service time, to a maximum benefit of $1,500; veterans who were declared MIA or POW or family members are eligible for a bonus of $5,000; families of deceased veterans whose death was not a result of injuries or illness are eligible for the same bonus that the veteran would have received if still living, to a maximum of $1,500; families of veterans who died as a result of injuries or illness are eligible for a bonus of $5,000.

Duration These are 1-time bonuses.

Number awarded Varies each year.

Deadline Applications may be submitted at any time. For veterans and current military members who served during the wars in Afghanistan or Iraq, applications must be submitted within 3 years after the President has officially proclaimed the end of those hostilities.

[1160]
OHIO VETERANS' FINANCIAL ASSISTANCE

Ohio Department of Veterans Services
77 South High Street, Seventh Floor
Columbus, OH 43215
(614) 644-0898   Toll Free: (888) DVS-OHIO
Fax: (614) 728-9498   E-mail: ohiovet@dvs.ohio.gov
Web: dvs.ohio.gov

Summary To provide emergency aid to Ohio veterans, military personnel, and their dependents who, because of disability or disaster, are in financial need.

Eligibility This assistance is available to veterans and active-duty members of the U.S. armed forces, as well as their spouses, surviving spouses, dependent parents, minor children, and wards. Applicants must have been residents of the Ohio county in which they are applying for at least 3 months. They must be able to demonstrate need for relief because of sickness, accident, or destitution.

Financial data The amount granted varies, depending on the needs of the recipient.

Duration These are emergency funds only and are not designed to be a recurring source of income.

Additional information These grants are made by the various county veterans services offices in Ohio.

Number awarded Varies each year.

Deadline Applications may be submitted at any time.

[1161]
OKLAHOMA FINANCIAL ASSISTANCE PROGRAM

Oklahoma Department of Veterans Affairs
Veterans Memorial Building
2311 North Central Avenue
P.O. Box 53067
Oklahoma City, OK 73152
(405) 521-3684   Fax: (405) 521-6533
E-mail: mspear@odva.state.ok.us
Web: www.ok.gov

Summary To provide emergency aid to Oklahoma veterans and their families who, because of disability or disaster, are in financial need.

Eligibility This program is open to veterans with at least 90 days of wartime service (unless discharged earlier because of a service-connected disability) and an honorable discharge who are current residents of Oklahoma and have resided in the state for at least 1 year immediately preceding the date of application. Applicants must be seeking assistance because of an interruption or loss of job and income resulting from illness, injury, or disaster (such as loss of home due to fire, floor, or storm). Widow(er)s and minor children may also qualify for the benefit.

Financial data The amount of the grant depends on the need of the recipient.

Duration The grant is available only on a 1-time basis.

Additional information No financial assistance will be granted when regular monetary benefits are being received from other state agencies. The funds cannot be used for old debts, car payments, or medical expenses.

Number awarded Varies each year.

Deadline Applications must be submitted to the local post or chapter of a veterans services organization for initial approval or disapproval. They may be submitted at any time during the year.

[1162]
OKLAHOMA MILITARY RETIREMENT INCOME TAX EXCLUSION

Oklahoma Tax Commission
Attn: Income Tax
2501 North Lincoln Boulevard
Oklahoma City, OK 73194-0009
(405) 521-3160   Toll Free: (800) 522-8165 (within OK)
Fax: (405) 522-0063   E-mail: otcmaster@tax.ok.gov
Web: www.tax.ok.gov/incometax.html

Summary To exclude a portion of the income of military retirees and their spouses from state taxation in Oklahoma.

Eligibility This exclusion is available to residents of Oklahoma and their spouses who are receiving retirement benefits from a component of the U.S. armed forces.

Financial data Military retirees are entitled to exclude 75% of their retirement benefits or $10,000, whichever is greater, from state taxation.

Duration The exclusion is available as long as the recipient resides in Oklahoma.

Deadline Deadline not specified.

[1163]
OKLAHOMA PROPERTY TAX EXEMPTION FOR DISABLED VETERANS

Oklahoma Tax Commission
Attn: Ad Valorem Division
2501 North Lincoln Boulevard
P.O. Box 269060
Oklahoma City, OK 73126-9060
(405) 319-8200   Toll Free: (800) 522-8165 (within OK)
Fax: (405) 522-0166   E-mail: otcmaster@tax.ok.gov
Web: www.tax.ok.gov/adval.html

Summary To exempt the property of disabled veterans and their surviving spouses from taxation in Oklahoma.

Eligibility This program is available to Oklahoma residents who are veterans honorably discharged from a branch of the armed forces or the Oklahoma National Guard. Applicants must have a 100% permanent disability sustained through military action or accident or resulting from a disease contracted while in active service; the disability must be certified by the U.S. Department of Veterans Affairs. They must own property that qualifies for the Oklahoma homestead exemption. Surviving spouses of qualified veterans are also eligible.

Financial data Qualified veterans and surviving spouses are eligible for exemption of the taxes on the full fair cash value of their homestead.

Duration The exemption is available as long as the veteran or surviving spouse resides in Oklahoma and owns a qualifying homestead.

Additional information This exemption was first available in 2006.

Deadline Deadline not specified.

[1164]
OPERATION FAMILY FUND FINANCIAL ASSISTANCE

Operation Family Fund
P.O. Box 837
Ridgecrest, CA 93556
(760) 793-0053   Fax: (888) 851-1456
E-mail: support@operatonfamilyfund.org
Web: operationfamilyfund.org

Summary To provide personal assistance to military and civilian personnel and the families of those personnel who died or were severely disabled as a result of service as a result of the Global War on Terror.

Eligibility This assistance is available to military and civilian personnel and their families who died or were severely disabled as a result of Operations Enduring or Iraqi Freedom, either domestically or abroad. Civilians must have been serving officially as an employee of the U.S. government or contractor to the U.S. government. Applicants must be seeking funding for such short- and long-term living needs as food; rent or utilities; emergency transportation; vehicle repair; funeral expenses; medical and dental expenses; assistance with a home, rental, lease, or purchase; home improvements; or assistance with the purchase, rent, or lease of a vehicle. Grants are approved to applicants in the following priority order: 1) member injured because of a hostile action and have a Department of Veterans Affairs (VA) disability rating of 50% or higher; 2) member injured because of an accident while serving in Iraq or Afghanistan and have a VA disability rating of 50% or higher; 3) member who has post-traumatic stress disorder with a VA disability rating of 50% or higher as a result of serving in Iraq or Afghanistan; 4) member who has other service-connected injuries caused in support of the Global War on Terror and a VA disability rating of 50% or higher; 5) member in any of the prior categories but still in the medical board process with a pending VA disability rating; 6) child (under 22 years of age) and/or spouse of a military member killed in action who did not receive government death benefit or SGLA; and 7) second requests.

Financial data Most grants are at least $1,000 but less than $10,000.

Duration These are 1-time grants; renewals may be approved if funding is available.

Number awarded Varies each year; since this organization was established, it has awarded more than 385 grants.

Deadline Applications may be submitted at any time.

[1165]
OPERATION HOMEFRONT GRANTS

Operation Homefront
8930 Fourwinds Drive, Suite 340
San Antonio, TX 78239
(210) 659-7756   Toll Free: (800) 722-6098
Fax: (210) 566-7544
Web: www.operationhomefront.net

Summary To provide assistance to military families and wounded personnel who face financial difficulties related to service.

Eligibility This program is open to 1) veterans who are disabled as a result of service-connected injuries and their families; and 2) other military families who face financial needs because of the hardships associated with military service.

Examples of financial needs include food assistance, auto repair, moving assistance, transitional family housing, vision care, child and dependent care, critical baby needs, travel and transportation, home repair, and essential home items.

Financial data The amounts of the grants vary, depending on the need of the applicant. Recently, average grants were $100 to families for critical baby items, $161 for food assistance, $300 to assist in paying utilities, or $1,117 to help with rent or mortgage payments.

Duration This are 1-time grants.

Additional information This foundation began in 2002.

Number awarded Varies each year; since the foundation was established, it has awarded approximately $128 million to support more than 400,000 families and personnel.

Deadline Applications may be submitted at any time.

[1166]
OPERATION REBOUND GRANTS

Challenged Athletes Foundation
Attn: Program Manager
9990 Mesa Rim Road
P.O. Box 910769
San Diego, CA 92191
(858) 866-0959   Fax: (858) 866-0958
E-mail: info@challengedathletes.org
Web: www.challengedathletes.org

Summary To provide funding to veterans and September 11 first responders who became disabled as a result of service and wish to participate in athletic activities.

Eligibility This program is open to 1) veterans and service members who suffered a permanent physical disability (such as loss of a limb(s), sight, or spinal cord injury, in the Global War on Terror; and 2) law enforcement personnel, fire fighters, and others who were the first to respond to the September 11, 2001 attacks and became disabled as a result. Applicants must need funding for 1 of 3 categories: 1) equipment, for wheelchairs, prosthetics, or other assistive devices; 2) training, for club or gym dues or membership fees, team or association dues or membership fees, or coaching or training expense; or 3) competition, for travel, entry fees, or other costs to participate in a recognized event. They may apply for only 1 category per year. Along with their application, they must submit a brief autobiography with their personal and athletic goals, a brief summary of their military or law enforcement history, a statement on how they are planning to raise awareness for "Operation Rebound" and the Challenged Athletes Foundation, and documentation of financial need.

Financial data Grant amounts depend on the documented need of the applicant.

Duration These are 1-time grants. Recipients may reapply.

Additional information This program was established for veterans in 2004 and expanded to include first responders in 2008.

Number awarded Varies each year.

Deadline Applications may be submitted at any time, but they must be received at least 90 days prior to the date needed.

[1167]
OPERATION SECOND CHANCE FAMILY ASSISTANCE GRANTS

Operation Second Chance
Attn: President
22708 Birchcrest Lane
P.O. Box 461
Clarksburg, MD 20871
Toll Free: (888) OSC-4VET
E-mail: assistance@operationsecondchance.org
Web: www.operationsecondchance.org

Summary To provide assistance for payment of ordinary living expenses to disabled veterans and military personnel and their families.

Eligibility This assistance is available to disabled veterans and military personnel who are within 18 months of their injury or are currently receiving care at a military health care facility and have an expected or adjudicated disability rating of 70% or higher. Their family members are also eligible. Applicants must be seeking funding for payment of rent or mortgages, utility bills, child care during illness or injury, or housing and/or airfare for a family member to assist an injured or recovering member.

Financial data The amount of the grant depends on the need of the recipient.

Duration These are 1-time grants.

Number awarded Varies each year.

Deadline Applications may be submitted at any time.

[1168]
OREGON PROPERTY TAX EXEMPTION FOR VETERANS WITH DISABILITIES AND THEIR SPOUSES

Oregon Department of Revenue
Attn: Property Tax Division
Revenue Building
955 Center Street, N.E.
Salem, OR 97310-2555
(503) 378-4988   Toll Free: (800) 356-4222 (within OR)
Fax: (503) 945-8738   TDD: (800) 886-7204 (within OR)
Web: www.oregon.gov/DOR/PTD/exemptions.shtml

Summary To exempt disabled Oregon veterans and their spouses from a portion of their property taxes.

Eligibility Qualifying veterans are those who received a discharge or release under honorable conditions after service of either 1) 90 consecutive days during World War I, World War II, or the Korean Conflict; or 2) 210 consecutive days after January 31, 1955. Eligible individuals must meet 1 of these conditions: 1) a war veteran who is officially certified by the U.S. Department of Veterans Affairs (VA) or any branch of the U.S. armed forces as having disabilities of 40% or more; 2) a war veteran who is certified each year by a licensed physician as being 40% or more disabled and has total gross income that is less than 185% of the federal poverty level; or 3) a war veteran's surviving spouse who has not remarried, even if the veteran's spouse was not disabled or did not take advantage of the exemption if disabled. Recipients of this exemption must own and live on a property in Oregon.

Financial data The exemption is $17,911 of the homestead property's real market value.

Duration 1 year; may be renewed as long as the eligible veteran or surviving unremarried spouse owns and occupies the primary residence.

Number awarded Varies each year.

Deadline This exemption is not automatic. Applications must be submitted by March of each year.

[1169]
OREGON PROPERTY TAX EXEMPTION FOR VETERANS WITH SERVICE-CONNECTED DISABILITIES AND THEIR SPOUSES

Oregon Department of Revenue
Attn: Property Tax Division
Revenue Building
955 Center Street, N.E.
Salem, OR 97310-2555
(503) 378-4988   Toll Free: (800) 356-4222 (within OR)
Fax: (503) 945-8738   TDD: (800) 886-7204 (within OR)
Web: www.oregon.gov/DOR/PTD/exemptions.shtml

Summary To exempt Oregon veterans with service-connected disabilities and their spouses from a portion of their property taxes.

Eligibility Qualifying veterans are those who received a discharge or release under honorable conditions after service of either 1) 90 consecutive days during World War I, World War II, or the Korean Conflict; or 2) 210 consecutive days after January 31, 1955. Eligible individuals must meet 1 of these conditions: 1) a war veteran who is certified by the U.S. Department of Veterans Affairs (VA) or any branch of the U.S. armed forces as having service-connected disabilities of 40% or more; or 2) a surviving spouse of a war veteran who died because of service-connected injury or illness or who received at least 1 year of this exemption. Recipients of this exemption must own and live on a property in Oregon.

Financial data The exemption is $21,493 of the homestead property's real market value.

Duration 1 year; may be renewed as long as the eligible veterans or surviving spouse owns and occupies the primary residence.

Number awarded Varies each year.

Deadline This exemption is not automatic. Applications must be submitted by March of each year.

[1170]
OREGON VETERANS' EMERGENCY FINANCIAL ASSISTANCE

Oregon Department of Veterans' Affairs
Attn: Veterans' Services Division
700 Summer Street N.E., Suite 150
Salem, OR 97310-1285
(503) 373-2000   Toll Free: (800) 692-9666 (within OR)
Fax: (503) 373-2362   TDD: (503) 373-2217
Web: www.oregon.gov

Summary To provide emergency financial assistance to Oregon veterans and their families.

Eligibility This assistance is available to Oregon residents who are veterans and their spouses, children, and grandchildren. Applicants must be in need of assistance for emergency or temporary housing and related housing expenses, such as utilities, insurance, house repairs, rent assistance, or food; emergency medical or dental expenses; emergency transportation; expenses related to starting a business, such as business licenses or occupational licenses; temporary income after military discharge; or legal assistance for certain veteran issues.

Financial data   Grants depend on the need of the recipient.

Duration   These are 1-time grants.

Number awarded   Varies each year.

Deadline   Applications may be submitted at any time.

[1171]
PARALYZED VETERANS OF AMERICA DISASTER RELIEF FUND

Paralyzed Veterans of America
Attn: Disaster Relief Fund
801 18th Street, N.W.
Washington, DC 20006-3517
Toll Free: (866) 734-0857   E-mail: info@pva.org
Web: www.pva.org

Summary   To provide emergency assistance to members of Paralyzed Veterans of America (PVA) who have been victimized by natural disasters.

Eligibility   This assistance is available to PVA members whose property has been severely damaged by natural disasters. Applicants may be seeking funding for transportation, temporary shelter, food, home repairs, or modifications that are needed for wheelchair accessibility, medical supplies, or prosthetic appliances.

Financial data   Grants range up to $2,500; more than $100,000 is available for relief each year.

Additional information   Membership in PVA is open to veterans with spinal cord injury or disease.

Number awarded   2 each year.

Deadline   Applications may be submitted at any time.

[1172]
PENNSYLVANIA BLIND VETERANS PENSION

Office of the Deputy Adjutant General for Veterans Affairs
Building S-0-47, FTIG
Annville, PA 17003-5002
(717) 865-8911   Toll Free: (800) 54 PA VET (within PA)
Fax: (717) 861-8589   E-mail: RA-VA-Info@pa.gov
Web: www.dmva.state.pa.us

Summary   To provide financial assistance to blind residents of Pennsylvania who lost their sight while serving in the U.S. armed forces.

Eligibility   Persons who have 3/60 or 10/200 or less normal vision are eligible if they are honorably-discharged veterans and were residents of Pennsylvania when they joined the U.S. armed forces. Their blindness must have resulted from a service-connected injury or disease.

Financial data   The pension is $150 per month.

Duration   The pension is awarded for the life of the veteran.

Number awarded   Varies each year.

Deadline   Applications may be submitted at any time.

[1173]
PENNSYLVANIA DISABLED VETERANS REAL ESTATE TAX EXEMPTION

Office of the Deputy Adjutant General for Veterans Affairs
Building S-0-47, FTIG
Annville, PA 17003-5002
(717) 865-8907   Toll Free: (800) 54 PA VET (within PA)
Fax: (717) 861-8589   E-mail: RA-VA-Info@pa.gov
Web: www.dmva.state.pa.us

Summary   To exempt blind and disabled Pennsylvania veterans and their unremarried surviving spouses from all state real estate taxes.

Eligibility   Eligible to apply for this exemption are honorably-discharged veterans who are residents of Pennsylvania and who are blind, paraplegic, or 100% disabled from a service-connected disability sustained during wartime military service. The dwelling must be owned by the veteran solely or jointly with a spouse, and financial need for the exemption must be determined by the State Veterans' Commission. Veterans whose income is less than $81,340 per year are presumed to have financial need; veterans with income greater than $81,340 must document need. Upon the death of the veteran, the tax exemption passes on to the veteran's unremarried surviving spouse.

Financial data   This program exempts the principal residence (and the land on which it stands) from all real estate taxes.

Duration   The exemption continues as long as the eligible veteran or unremarried widow resides in Pennsylvania.

Number awarded   Varies each year.

Deadline   Deadline not specified.

[1174]
PENNSYLVANIA INCOME TAX EXEMPTION FOR MILITARY PENSION BENEFITS

Pennsylvania Department of Revenue
Attn: Bureau of Individual Taxes
Department 280600
Harrisburg, PA 17128-0600
(717) 787-8201   Toll Free: (888) PA-TAXES
Fax: (717) 787-2391   TDD: (800) 447-3020
E-mail: parev@revenue.state.pa.us
Web: www.revenue.state.pa.us

Summary   To exempt from state taxation the income received by Pennsylvania residents as a military pension.

Eligibility   Eligible are residents of Pennsylvania who are receiving military pension benefits.

Financial data   All military pension benefits are exempt from state taxation in Pennsylvania.

Duration   The exemption continues as long as the recipient resides in Pennsylvania.

Deadline   Deadline not specified.

[1175]
PENNSYLVANIA MILITARY FAMILY RELIEF ASSISTANCE PROGRAM

Pennsylvania Department of Military and Veterans Affairs
Attn: Military Family Relief Assistance Program
Building 0-47
Fort Indiantown Gap
Annville, PA 17003-5002
(717) 861-6500   Toll Free: (866) 292-7201
Fax: (717) 861-2600   E-mail: ra-pa-mfrap@pa.gov
Web: www.portal.state.pa.us

Summary To provide emergency financial assistance to members of the armed forces from Pennsylvania and their families.

Eligibility This assistance is available to residents of Pennsylvania who are 1) serving on 30 or more consecutive days of active duty with the Pennsylvania Army or Air National Guard or Reserve components of the armed forces; 2) serving on 30 or more consecutive days of active duty with the active armed forces; 3) serving on 30 or more consecutive days of state active duty for emergencies or duty under the Emergency Management Assistance Compact in the Pennsylvania National Guard; 4) current members of the Pennsylvania National Guard within 1 year of a qualifying tour of active duty of 30 days or more who can demonstrate a financial need directly related to the active-duty period; 5) former members of the armed forces, Reserve components, or Pennsylvania National Guard within 2 years of a medical discharge for a disability incurred in the line of duty if they can demonstrate a financial need directly related to active duty or medical disability; and 6) eligible relatives (spouses, parents, siblings, or children) of military service members. Applicants must be able to demonstrate a direct and immediate financial need as a result of military service; that financial need may include, but is not limited to, a sudden or unexpected loss of income directly related to military service; emergency need for child care for which the applicant lacks financial resources; natural or man-made disasters resulting in a need for food, shelter, or other necessities; or the death or critical illness of a parent, spouse, sibling, or child resulting in immediate need for travel, lodging, or subsistence for which the applicant lacks financial resources.

Financial data The maximum grant is $3,500.

Duration Only 1 grant will be awarded in each 12-month period.

Additional information This program began in 2005.

Number awarded Varies each year.

Deadline Applications may be submitted at any time.

[1176]
PENNSYLVANIA PARALYZED VETERANS PENSION

Office of the Deputy Adjutant General for Veterans Affairs
Building S-0-47, FTIG
Annville, PA 17003-5002
(717) 865-8911   Toll Free: (800) 54 PA VET (within PA)
Fax: (717) 861-8589   E-mail: RA-VA-Info@pa.gov
Web: www.dmva.state.pa.us

Summary To provide financial assistance to Pennsylvania veterans who became disabled while serving in the U.S. armed forces.

Eligibility Applicants must be current residents of Pennsylvania who suffered an injury or disease resulting in loss or loss of use of 2 or more extremities while serving in the U.S. armed forces during an established period of war or armed conflict or as a result of hostilities during combat-related activities in peacetime. They must be rated by the U.S. Department of Veterans Affairs as 100% permanent and service-connected disabled. At the time of entry into military service, applicants must have been residents of Pennsylvania.

Financial data The pension is $150 per month.

Duration The pension is awarded for the life of the veteran.

Number awarded Varies each year.

Deadline Applications may be submitted at any time.

[1177]
PENNSYLVANIA PERSIAN GULF CONFLICT VETERANS' BENEFIT PROGRAM

Office of the Deputy Adjutant General for Veterans Affairs
Building S-0-47, FTIG
Annville, PA 17003-5002
(717) 865-8911   Toll Free: (800) 54 PA VET (within PA)
Fax: (717) 861-8589   E-mail: RA-VA-Info@pa.gov
Web: www.dmva.state.pa.us

Summary To provide a bonus to veterans from Pennsylvania who served in the Persian Gulf Conflict or to their survivors.

Eligibility Eligible to receive this bonus are veterans who served on active duty in the Persian Gulf Theater of Operations during the period from August 2, 1990 to August 31, 1991 and received the Southwest Asia Service Medal. Applicants must have been a resident of Pennsylvania at the time of military service and must have served under honorable conditions.

Financial data The bonus is $75 per month for each month (or major fraction) of active service in the Gulf, to a maximum of $525. For veterans who died in active service, a bonus of $5,000 is paid to the family. In addition, $5,000 is paid to Persian Gulf Conflict prisoners of war.

Duration This is a 1-time benefit.

Additional information This program was authorized in 2006.

Number awarded Varies each year.

Deadline Applications may be submitted at any time prior to August 31, 2015.

[1178]
RED CROSS EMERGENCY FINANCIAL ASSISTANCE

American Red Cross
Attn: Military Call Center
2025 E Street, N.W.
Washington, DC 20006
(202) 303-4498   Toll Free: (877) 272-7337
Web: www.redcross.org

Summary To provide funding to active and retired military personnel and their families who are in need of emergency financial assistance.

Eligibility This program is open to servicemembers, their families, retired military personnel, and widows of retired military personnel. Members of the National Guard and Reserves are also eligible. Applicants must be in need of such emergency financial assistance as travel that requires the presence of the servicemember or his or her family, burial of a loved one, or other assistance that cannot wait until the next business day (food, temporary lodging, urgent medical needs, or the minimum amount required to avoid eviction or utility shut-off).

Financial data The amount of the assistance depends on the need of the recipient.

Duration These are 1-time grants.

Additional information The Red Cross works with the military aid societies (Army Emergency Relief, Navy-Marine Corps Relief Society, Air Force Aid Society, and Coast Guard Mutual Assistance).

Number awarded Varies each year; recently, more than 5,000 servicemembers and their families received more than $5.8 million in emergency grants.

Deadline Applications may be submitted at any time.

[1179]
SENTINELS OF FREEDOM SCHOLARSHIPS

Sentinels of Freedom
P.O. Box 1316
San Ramon, CA 94583
(925) 380-6342   Fax: (925) 867-1078
E-mail: info@sentinelsoffreedom.org
Web: www.sentinelsoffreedom.org

Summary To provide funding to veterans and current military personnel who became blind or disabled as a result of injuries sustained in the line of duty on or after September 11, 2001.

Eligibility This program is open to members of the U.S. Air Force, Army, Coast Guard, Marines, or Navy who sustained injuries in the line of duty on or after September 11, 2001. Applicants must be rated as 60% or more disabled as a result of 1 or more of the following conditions: amputation, blindness, deafness, paraplegia, severe burns, limited traumatic brain injury (TBI), or limited post-traumatic stress disorder (PTSD); other severe injuries may be considered on a case-by-case basis. They must complete an interview process and demonstrate that they have the skills, experience, and attitude that lead to employment.

Financial data Assistance is available for the following needs: housing (adapted for physical needs if necessary), new furniture and other household supplies, career-placement assistance and training, new adaptive vehicles, educational opportunities in addition to the new GI Bill, or financial and personal mentorship.

Duration Assistance may be provided for up to 4 years.

Additional information The first assistance granted by this program was awarded in 2004.

Number awarded Varies each year. Since the program was established, it has supported 84 current and former service members.

Deadline Applications may be submitted at any time.

[1180]
SOUTH CAROLINA PROPERTY TAX EXEMPTION FOR DISABLED VETERANS, LAW ENFORCEMENT OFFICERS, AND FIREFIGHTERS

South Carolina Department of Revenue
Attn: Property Division
301 Gervais Street
P.O. Box 125
Columbia, SC 29214
(803) 898-5480   Fax: (803) 898-5822
Web: www.sctax.org

Summary To exempt the residence of disabled South Carolina veterans, law enforcement officers, fire fighters, their unremarried widow(er)s, and others from property taxation.

Eligibility This exemption is available to owners of homes in South Carolina who are veterans of the U.S. armed forces, former law enforcement officers, or former fire fighters (including volunteer fire fighters). Applicants must be permanently and totally disabled from service-connected causes. The exemption is also available to qualified surviving spouses (defined to include unremarried spouses of disabled veterans, law enforcement officers, and fire fighters, as well as surviving spouses of servicemembers killed in the line of duty, law enforcement officers who died in the line of duty, and fire fighters who died in the line of duty).

Financial data The exemption applies to all taxes on 1 house and a lot (not to exceed 1 acre).

Duration The exemption extends as long as the veteran, law enforcement officer, or fire fighter resides in the house, or as long as the spouse of a deceased veteran, servicemember, law enforcement officer, or fire fighter remains unremarried and resides in the original house or a single new dwelling.

Number awarded Varies each year.

Deadline Applications may be submitted at any time.

[1181]
SOUTH CAROLINA PROPERTY TAX EXEMPTION FOR MEDAL OF HONOR RECIPIENTS AND PRISONERS OF WAR

South Carolina Department of Revenue
Attn: Property Division
301 Gervais Street
P.O. Box 125
Columbia, SC 29214
(803) 898-5480   Fax: (803) 898-5822
Web: www.sctax.org

Summary To exempt the residence of disabled South Carolina veterans who received a Medal of Honor or who were a prisoner of war from property taxation.

Eligibility This exemption is available to owners of homes in South Carolina who are veterans of the U.S. armed forces and who received a Medal of Honor or were a prisoner of war during World War I, World War II, the Korean Conflict, or the Vietnam Conflict. The exemption is also available to qualified surviving spouses as long as they remain unmarried.

Financial data The exemption applies to all taxes on 1 house and a lot (not to exceed 1 acre).

Duration The exemption extends as long as the veteran or the spouse of a deceased veteran resides in the original house or a single new dwelling.

Number awarded Varies each year.

Deadline Applications may be submitted at any time.

[1182]
SOUTH CAROLINA RETIREMENT INCOME TAX DEDUCTION

South Carolina Department of Revenue
301 Gervais Street
P.O. Box 125
Columbia, SC 29214
(803) 898-5000   Toll Free: (800) 763-1295
Fax: (803) 898-5822
Web: www.sctax.org

Summary To exempt part of the retirement income received by veterans and others from state taxation in South Carolina.

Eligibility This program is open to residents of South Carolina who are receiving public employee retirement income from federal, state, or local government, including individual retirement accounts, Keogh plans, and military retirement (including retirement income paid by the U.S. government for service in the Reserves or National Guard. Spouses are also entitled to the exemption.

Financial data The maximum retirement income deduction is $3,000 for taxpayers under 65 years of age and $10,000 in subsequent years. Taxpayers who wait until they are 65 and older until declaring a retirement exemption are entitled to deduct $15,000 per year. All retirement income paid by the U.S. government for service in the Reserves or National Guard is exempt from taxation in South Carolina.

Duration The exemption continues as long as the eligible veteran or spouse resides in South Carolina and receives the specified income.

Number awarded Varies each year.

Deadline Deadline not specified.

[1183]
SOUTH DAKOTA PROPERTY TAX EXEMPTION FOR PARAPLEGIC VETERANS

South Dakota Department of Revenue and Regulation
Attn: Property Tax Division
445 East Capitol Avenue
Pierre, SD 57501-3185
(605) 773-3311   Toll Free: (800) TAX-9188
Fax: (605) 773-6729   E-mail: PropTaxIn@state.sd.us
Web: www.state.sd.us/drr2/propspectax/property/relief.htm

Summary To exempt from property taxation the homes of paraplegic veterans in South Dakota and their widow(er)s.

Eligibility This benefit is available to residents of South Dakota who are 1) paraplegic veterans, 2) veterans with loss or loss of use of both lower extremities, or 3) unremarried widows or widowers of such veterans. Applicants must own and occupy a dwelling (including the house, garage, and up to 1 acre on which the building is located) that is specifically designed for wheelchair use within the structure. The veteran's injury does not have to be service connected.

Financial data Qualified dwellings are exempt from property taxation in South Dakota.

Duration The exemption applies as long as the dwelling is owned and occupied by the disabled veteran or widow(er).

Number awarded Varies each year.

Deadline Deadline not specified.

[1184]
SOUTH DAKOTA VETERANS BONUS

South Dakota Department of Veterans Affairs
Attn: Veterans Bonus
425 East Capitol Avenue
Pierre, SD 57501
(605) 773-3269   Toll Free: (877) 579-0015 (within SD)
Fax: (605) 773-5380
Web: mva.sd.gov/vet_benefits_sd.html

Summary To provide a bonus to veterans in South Dakota who served after 1990.

Eligibility This bonus is available to veterans who were residents of South Dakota for at least 6 months prior to entering service. They must have served after August 2, 1990. For August 2, 1990 to March 3, 1991, all active service is accepted; for March 4, 1991 to December 31, 1992, only service in a hostile area qualifying for the Southwest Asia Service Medal is accepted; for January 1, 1993 to September 10, 2001, only service in a hostile area qualifying for a United States campaign or service medal awarded for combat operations against hostile forces is accepted; for September 11, 2001 to the present, all active service is accepted. Veterans with qualifying service before December 31, 1992 and after January 1, 1993 are eligible for a double bonus.

Financial data The bonus is $500 or $1,000 for those veterans who qualify for the double bonus.

Duration This is a 1-time bonus.

Number awarded Varies each year.

Deadline Deadline not specified.

[1185]
SPECIAL HOUSING ADAPTATIONS GRANTS

Department of Veterans Affairs
Attn: Specially Adapted Housing
810 Vermont Avenue, N.W.
Washington, DC 20420
(202) 461-9546   Toll Free: (800) 827-1000
Web: www.benefits.va.gov/homeloans/sah_info.asp

Summary To provide grants to certain disabled or blind veterans or servicemembers who wish to make adaptations to their home to meet their needs.

Eligibility These grants are available to veterans and servicemembers who are entitled to compensation for permanent and total service-connected disability due to: 1) blindness in both eyes with 5/200 visual acuity or less; 2) the anatomical loss or loss of use of both hands; or 3) a severe burn injury. Applicants must be planning to 1) adapt a house which they plan to purchase and in which they intend to reside; 2) adapt a house which a member of their family plans to purchase and in which they intend to reside; 3) adapt a house which they already own and in which they intend to reside; 4) adapt a house which is already owned by a member of their family in which they intend to reside; or 5) purchase a house that has already been adapted with special features that are reasonably necessary because of their disability and in which they intend to reside.

Financial data Eligible veterans and servicemembers are entitled to grants up to $12,756 to adapt a house.

Duration Eligible veterans and servicemembers are entitled to up to 3 usages of these grants.

Number awarded Varies each year.

Deadline Applications are accepted at any time.

[1186]
SPECIALLY ADAPTED HOUSING GRANTS

Department of Veterans Affairs
Attn: Specially Adapted Housing
810 Vermont Avenue, N.W.
Washington, DC 20420
(202) 461-9546   Toll Free: (800) 827-1000
Web: www.homeloans.va.gov/sah.htm

Summary   To provide loans, grants, and loan guaranties to blind and disabled veterans and servicemembers for a home specially adapted to their needs.

Eligibility   These grants are available to veterans and servicemembers who are entitled to compensation for permanent and total service-connected disability due to: 1) the loss or loss of use of both lower extremities, such as to preclude locomotion without the aid of braces, crutches, canes, or a wheelchair; or 2) blindness in both eyes, having only light perception, plus loss or loss of use of 1 lower extremity; 3) a loss or loss of use of 1 lower extremity together with residuals of organic disease or injury or the loss or loss of use of 1 upper extremity, such as to preclude locomotion without resort to braces, canes, crutches, or a wheelchair; 4) the loss or loss of use of both upper extremities, so as to preclude use of the arms at or above the elbows; or 5) a severe burn injury. Applicants must be planning to 1) construct a home on land to be acquired for that purpose; 2) build a home on land already owned if it is suitable for specially adapted housing; 3) remodel an existing home if it can be made suitable for specially adapted housing, or 4) apply funds against the unpaid principle mortgage balance of a specially adapted home that has already been acquired.

Financial data   The U.S. Department of Veterans Affairs (VA) may approve a grant of not more than 50% of the cost of building, buying, or remodeling homes for eligible veterans, or paying indebtedness on such homes already acquired, up to a maximum grant of $63,780. Eligible veterans with available loan guarantee entitlements may also obtain a guaranteed loan from the VA to supplement the grant to acquire a specially adapted home. If private financing is not available, the VA may make a direct loan up to $33,000 to cover the difference between the total cost of the home and the grant.

Duration   This is a 1-time grant, guaranteed loan, or direct loan.

Additional information   Veterans who receive a specially adapted housing grant may be eligible for Veterans Mortgage Life Insurance.

Number awarded   Varies each year.

Deadline   Applications are accepted at any time.

[1187]
TENNESSEE PROPERTY TAX RELIEF FOR DISABLED VETERANS AND THEIR SPOUSES

Tennessee Comptroller of the Treasury
Attn: Property Tax Relief Program
James K. Polk State Office Building
505 Deaderick Street, Room 1700
Nashville, TN 37243-1402
(615) 747-8858   Fax: (615) 532-3866
E-mail: kim.darden@cot.tn.gov
Web: www.comptroller1.state.tn.us/pa/patxr.asp

Summary   To provide property tax relief to blind and disabled veterans and their spouses in Tennessee.

Eligibility   This exemption is offered to veterans or their surviving unremarried spouses who are residents of Tennessee and own and live in their home in the state. The veteran must have served in the U.S. armed forces and 1) have acquired, as a result of such service, a disability from paraplegia, permanent paralysis of both legs and lower part of the body resulting from traumatic injury, disease to the spinal cord or brain, legal blindness, or loss or loss of use of both legs or arms from any service-connected cause; 2) have been rated by the U.S. Department of Veterans Affairs (VA) as 100% permanently disabled as a result of service as a prisoner of war for at least 5 months; or 3) have been rated by the VA as 100% permanently and totally disabled from any other service-connected cause. Unremarried spouses of deceased veterans are also eligible if 1) the veteran was receiving tax relief as a disabled veteran before death; 2) death resulted from a service-connected, combat-related cause, or killed in action; or 3) death resulted from being deployed, away from any home base of training, and in support of combat operations.

Financial data   The amount of the relief depends on the property assessment and the tax rate in the city or county where the beneficiary lives. The maximum market value on which tax relief is calculated is $175,000.

Duration   1 year; may be renewed as long as the eligible veteran or surviving unremarried spouse owns and occupies the primary residence.

Number awarded   Varies each year.

Deadline   Deadline not specified.

[1188]
TEXAS PROPERTY TAX EXEMPTION FOR DISABLED VETERANS AND THEIR FAMILIES

Texas Veterans Commission
P.O. Box 12277
Austin, TX 78711-2277
(512) 463-5538   Toll Free: (800) 252-VETS (within TX)
Fax: (512) 475-2395   E-mail: info@tvc.state.tx.us
Web: texas-veterans.com/claims/property-tax-exemption

Summary   To extend property tax exemptions on the appraised value of their property to blind, disabled, and other Texas veterans and their surviving family members.

Eligibility   Eligible veterans must be Texas residents rated at least 10% service-connected disabled. Surviving spouses and children of eligible veterans are also covered by this program.

Financial data   For veterans in Texas whose disability is rated as 10% through 29%, the first $5,000 of the appraised property value is exempt from taxation; veterans rated as 30% through 49% disabled are exempt from the first $7,500 of appraised value; those with a 50% through 69% disability are exempt from the first $10,000 of appraised value; the exemption applies to the first $12,000 of appraised value for veterans with disabilities rated as 70% to 99%; veterans rated as 100% disabled are exempt from 100% of the appraised value of their property. A veteran whose disability is 10% or more and who is 65 years or older is entitled to exemption of the first $12,000 of appraised property value. A veteran whose disability consists of the loss of use of 1 or more limbs, total blindness in 1 or both eyes, or paraplegia is exempt from the first $12,000 of the appraised value. The unremarried surviving spouse of a deceased veteran who died on active duty and who, at the time of death had a compensable disability and was entitled to an exemption, is entitled to the same exemption. The surviving spouse of a person who died on active duty is entitled to exemption of the first $5,000 of appraised value of the spouse's property; they are also eligible for the 100% exemption. A surviving child of a person who dies on active duty is entitled to exemption of the first $5,000 of appraised value of the child's property, as long as the child is unmarried and under 21 years of age.

Duration 1 year; may be renewed as long as the eligible veteran (or unremarried surviving spouse or child) owns and occupies the primary residence in Texas.

Additional information This program is administered at the local level by the various taxing authorities.

Number awarded Varies each year.

Deadline April of each year.

[1189]
THE 9-11 HELPAMERICA FOUNDATION ASSISTANCE

The 9-11 HelpAmerica Foundation
14147 Hawthorne Boulevard
Hawthorne, CA 90250
(310) 355-0266
Web: www.911helpamerica.com

Summary To provide support to veterans wounded in Iraq or Afghanistan and to families of veterans and military personnel wounded or killed in combat.

Eligibility This assistance is available to 1) veterans disabled as a result of service in Operation Iraqi Freedom or Operation Enduring Freedom; and 2) families of veterans and military personnel injured or killed in those operations. Applicants must need general financial assistance to help meet special circumstances, especially those associated with the death or disability of the veteran or military service member.

Financial data The amount of the support depends on the need of the recipient.

Duration Support is provided for up to 18 months.

Additional information This foundation began in October, 2001.

Number awarded Varies; in a recent year, 20 disabled veterans or survivors received support from this foundation.

Deadline Applications may be submitted at any time.

[1190]
TROOPS-TO-TEACHERS PROGRAM

Defense Activity for Non-Traditional Education Support
Attn: Troops to Teachers
6490 Sauffley Field Road
Pensacola, FL 32509-5243
(850) 452-1242   Toll Free: (800) 231-6242
Fax: (850) 452-1096   E-mail: ttt@navy.mil
Web: www.dantes.doded.mil

Summary To provide a bonus to veterans and military personnel interested in a second career as a public school teacher.

Eligibility This program is open to 1) active-duty military personnel who are retired, have an approved date of retirement within 1 year, or separated on or after January 8, 2002 for physical disability; 2) members of a Reserve component who are retired, currently serving in the Selected Reserve with 10 or more years of credible service and commit to serv-

ing an additional 3 years, separated on or after January 8, 2002 due to a physical disability, or transitioned from active duty on or after January 8, 2002 after at least 6 years on active duty and commit to 3 years with a Selected Reserve unit. Applicants must have a baccalaureate or advanced degree, the equivalent of 1 year of college with 6 years of work experience in a vocational or technical field, or meet state requirements for vocational/technical teacher referral. A bonus is available to applicants who are willing to accept employment as a teacher in 1) a school district that has at least 10% of the students from families living below the poverty level, and 2) at a specific school within the district where at least 50% of the students are eligible for the free or reduced cost lunch program or where at least 13.5% of the students have disabilities. A stipend is available to applicants who are willing to accept employment as a teacher at 1) any school within a "high need" district that has at least 20% of the students from families living below the poverty level; or 2) at a specific school where at least 50% of the students are eligible for the free or reduced cost lunch program or at least 13.5% of the students have disabilities, as long as that school is in a district that has between 10% and 20% of students who come from poverty-level families. Preference is given to applicants interested in teaching mathematics, science, or special education.

Financial data A bonus of $10,000 is awarded to recipients who agree to teach for 3 years in a school that serves a high percentage of students from low-income families. A stipend of $5,000 is awarded to recipients who agree to teach for 3 years in a school located in a "high-need" district; stipend funds are intended to help pay for teacher certification costs.

Duration The bonuses are intended as 1-time grants.

Additional information This program was established in 1994 by the Department of Defense (DoD). In 2000, program oversight and funding were transferred to the U.S. Department of Education, but DoD continues to operate the program. The No Child Left Behind Act of 2001 provided for continuation of the program.

Number awarded Varies each year.

Deadline Deadline not specified.

[1191]
UTAH DISABLED VETERAN PROPERTY TAX ABATEMENT

Utah Department of Veteran's Affairs
Attn: Director
550 Foothill Boulevard, Room 202
Salt Lake City, UT 84108
(801) 326-2372   Toll Free: (800) 894-9497 (within UT)
Fax: (801) 326-2369   E-mail: veterans@utah.gov
Web: veterans.utah.gov/homepage/stateBenefits/index.html

Summary To exempt a portion of the property of disabled veterans and their families in Utah from taxation.

Eligibility This program is available to residents of Utah who are disabled veterans or their unremarried widow(er)s or minor orphans. The disability must be at least 10% and incurred as the result of injuries in the line of duty.

Financial data The exemption is based on the disability rating of the veteran, to a maximum of $232,312 for a 100% disability. The exemption for veterans with lesser disabilities is equal to $232,312 times the percentage of their disability.

Duration This benefit is available as long as the disabled veteran or family members reside in Utah.

Deadline Tax exemption applications must be filed with the county government of residence by August of the initial year; once eligibility has been established, reapplication is not required.

[1192]
UTAH VETERAN'S PROPERTY TAX EXEMPTION

Utah State Tax Commission
Attn: Property Tax Division
210 North 1950 West
Salt Lake City, UT 84134
(801) 297-3600   Toll Free: (800) 662-4335, ext. 3600
Fax: (801) 297-7699   TDD: (801) 297-2020
E-mail: propertytax@utah.gov
Web: propertytax.utah.gov

Summary To exempt from taxation a portion of the real and tangible property of disabled veterans and their families in Utah.

Eligibility This exemption is available to property owners in Utah who are veterans with a disability of at least 10% incurred in the line of duty, along with their unremarried surviving spouses or minor orphans. First year applications must be accompanied by proof of military service and proof of disability or death.

Financial data Veterans with a 100% disability are entitled to a full current-year exemption (recently, that was $237,949). Veterans with disabilities rated at a smaller percentage are entitled to that percentage of the current year exemption amount. Survivors are entitled to the same percentage as if the veteran were still living.

Duration The exemption is available each year the beneficiary owns property in Utah.

Number awarded Varies each year.

Deadline Applications must be submitted by August of each year.

[1193]
VERMONT PROPERTY TAX EXEMPTION FOR DISABLED VETERANS

Vermont Department of Taxes
Attn: Property Valuation and Review Division
P.O. Box 1577
Montpelier, VT 05601-1577
(802) 828-2865   Toll Free: (866) 828-2865 (within VT)
Fax: (802) 828-2824
Web: www.state.vt.us/tax/pvrmilitary.shtml

Summary To exempt disabled Vermont veterans and their dependents from the payment of at least a portion of the state's property tax.

Eligibility Entitled to a property tax exemption are veterans of any war (or their spouses, widow(er)s, or children) who are receiving wartime disability compensation for at least a 50% disability, wartime death compensation, wartime dependence and indemnity compensation, or pension for disability paid through any military department or the Department of Veterans Affairs. Unremarried widow(er)s of previously qualified veterans are also entitled to the exemption whether or not they are receiving government compensation or a pension.

Financial data Up to $10,000 of the assessed value of real and personal property belonging to eligible veterans or their

unremarried widow(er)s is exempt from taxation; individual towns may increase the exemption to as much as $40,000.

Duration 1 year; may be renewed as long as the eligible veteran or widow(er) continues to be the owner/occupant of the residence and lives in Vermont.

Additional information Only 1 exemption may be allowed on a property.

Number awarded Varies each year.

Deadline April of each year.

[1194]
VERMONT RECENTLY DEPLOYED VETERAN BUSINESS INCOME TAX EXEMPTION

Vermont Department of Taxes
133 State Street
Montpelier, VT 05633-1401
(802) 828-2865   Toll Free: (866) 828-2865 (within VT)
Fax: (802) 828-2720   E-mail: indincome@tax.state.vt.us
Web: www.state.vt.us/tax/individual.shtml

Summary To exempt from state taxation a portion of the profits of recently deployed veterans in Vermont who have established a business.

Eligibility This exemption is available to residents of Vermont who were mobilized to active, federal military service while a member of the Vermont National Guard or other reserve unit located in Vermont, regardless of the resident's home of record. Applicants must have received an honorable or general discharge from active, federal military service within the past 2 years. They must have established a start-up business in the state in which they have at least a 50% ownership interest and which showed a net profit of at least $3,000 during the past year.

Financial data Eligible veterans are entitled to an exemption of $2,000 from the profits of their business for purposes of income taxation in Vermont.

Duration The exemption is available for the first 2 years of the operation of the business.

Deadline Deadline not specified.

[1195]
VETERANS DISABILITY COMPENSATION

Department of Veterans Affairs
Attn: Veterans Benefits Administration
810 Vermont Avenue, N.W.
Washington, DC 20420
(202) 418-4343   Toll Free: (800) 827-1000
Web: www.vba.va.gov/bin/21/compensation/index.htm

Summary To provide monthly compensation to veterans who have a disability that occurred or was made worse during military service.

Eligibility Disabled persons who are eligible for compensation under this program are those whose disability resulted from injury or disease incurred or aggravated during active service in the U.S. armed forces in the line of duty during wartime or peacetime service. They must have been discharged or separated under other than dishonorable conditions.

Financial data Disabled veterans who are found to be eligible for disability compensation are entitled to monthly payments, depending on the degree of disability as determined by the Department of Veterans Affairs. Recent monthly rates for veterans living alone with no dependents ranged from $127 for 10% disability to $2,769 for 100% disability. Veterans whose service-connected disabilities are rated at 30% or more are entitled to additional allowances for dependent children, spouses, and/or parents. The additional amount is determined according to the number of dependents and the degree of disability. In addition, a veteran whose disability is rated at 30% or more and whose spouse is in need of the aid and attendance of another person may receive an additional amount.

Duration Compensation continues as long as the veteran remains disabled.

Additional information In addition to monthly compensation under this program, disabled veterans may also be entitled to prosthetic appliances if they are receiving treatment in a facility under the direct jurisdiction of the Department of Veterans Affairs (VA), or outpatient care under certain specified conditions. Blind veterans are eligible for various aids and services, including adjustment to blindness training, home improvements and structural alterations, low vision aids and training in their use, guide dogs, and material for the blind from the Library of Congress. Former prisoners of war who were incarcerated for at least 30 days and have at least a 10% disability are entitled to a presumption of service connection. Persian Gulf veterans who suffer from chronic disabilities resulting from undiagnosed illnesses may receive disability compensation.

Number awarded Varies each year.

Deadline Applications are accepted at any time.

[1196]
VETERANS SPECIAL MONTHLY COMPENSATION

Department of Veterans Affairs
Attn: Veterans Benefits Administration
810 Vermont Avenue, N.W.
Washington, DC 20420
(202) 418-4343   Toll Free: (800) 827-1000
Web: www1.va.gov

Summary To provide monthly compensation to veterans who have a disability that exceeds the 100% combined degree compensation or that results from special circumstances.

Eligibility This assistance is available to honorably-discharged veterans who have service-connected disabilities that have resulted in anatomical loss or loss of use of 1 hand, 1 foot, both buttocks, 1 or more creative organs, blindness of 1 eye having only light perception, deafness of both ears, having absence of air and bone conduction, complete organic aphonia with constant inability to communicate by speech, or (in the case of a female veteran) loss of 25% or more of tissue from a single breast or both breasts. Additional assistance is available to veterans who are permanently bedridden or so helpless as to be in need of regular aid and attendance. A special allowance is also available to veterans who have a spouse determined to require regular aid and attendance.

Financial data Disabled veterans who are found to be eligible for special compensation are entitled to monthly payments, depending on the nature of the disability and the type and number of dependents. Recent monthly rates ranged from $3,100 to $7,925 for veterans living alone with no dependents, from $3,255 to $8,080 for a veteran and spouse, from $3,368 to $8,193 for a veteran with spouse and 1 child, from $3,204 to $8,029 for a veteran and 1 child, $77 for each additional child under 18 years of age, and $248 for each

additional child over 18 years of age and enrolled in school. Other rates are available for veterans who live with 1 or more parents. In addition, a veteran whose spouse is in need of the aid and attendance of another person may receive an additional $141.

Duration Compensation continues as long as the veteran remains disabled.

Number awarded Varies each year.

Deadline Applications are accepted at any time.

[1197]
VIRGINIA INCOME TAX SUBTRACTION FOR CONGRESSIONAL MEDAL OF HONOR RECIPIENTS

Virginia Department of Taxation
Attn: Office of Customer Services
1957 Westmoreland Street
P.O. Box 1115
Richmond, VA 23218-1115
(804) 367-8031   Fax: (804) 254-6113
E-mail: TaxIndReturns@tax.virginia.gov
Web: www.tax.virginia.gov/site?alias=MilitaryTaxTips

Summary To subtract the retirement income received by recipients of the Congressional Medal of Honor from state income taxation in Virginia.

Eligibility This subtraction is available to residents of Virginia who received the Congressional Medal of Honor and receive military retirement income subject to federal taxation. The subtraction is not available to benefits received by surviving spouses.

Financial data All military income received by Congressional Medal of Honor recipients is exempt from state taxation in Virginia.

Duration The exemption is available as long as the Medal of Honor recipient remains a resident of Virginia and receives military retirement income.

Number awarded Varies each year.

Deadline The request for an exemption is filed with the state income tax return in April of each year.

[1198]
VOCATIONAL REHABILITATION AND EMPLOYMENT VETSUCCESS PROGRAM

Department of Veterans Affairs
Attn: Veterans Benefits Administration
Vocational Rehabilitation and Employment Service
810 Vermont Avenue, N.W.
Washington, DC 20420
(202) 418-4343   Toll Free: (800) 827-1000
Web: www.vba.va.gov/bin/vre/index.htm

Summary To provide funding to veterans with service-connected disabilities who need assistance to find employment or, if seriously disabled, to live independently.

Eligibility This program is open to veterans who have a service-connected disability of at least 10% or a memorandum rating of 20% or more from the Department of Veterans Affairs (VA). They must qualify for services provided by the VA VetSuccess that include assistance finding and keeping a job, including the use of special employer incentives and job accommodations; on-the-job training, apprenticeships, and non-paid work experiences; postsecondary training at a college, vocational, technical, or business school; supportive rehabilitation services such as case management, counseling, and medical referrals; independent living services for veterans unable to work due to the severity of their disabilities.

Financial data　While in training and for 2 months after, eligible disabled veterans may receive subsistence allowances in addition to their disability compensation or retirement pay. Generally, the current full-time monthly rate is $566.97 with no dependents, $703.28 with 1 dependent, $828.76 with 2 dependents, and $60.41 for each additional dependent; proportional rates apply for less than full-time training.

Duration　Veterans remain eligible for these services up to 12 years from either the date of separation from active military service or the date the veteran was first notified by VA of a service-connected disability rating (whichever came later).

Number awarded　Varies each year.

Deadline　Applications are accepted at any time.

[1199]
WASHINGTON PROPERTY TAX EXEMPTIONS FOR SENIOR CITIZENS AND DISABLED PERSONS

Washington State Department of Revenue
Attn: Property Tax Division
P.O. Box 47471
Olympia, WA 98504-7471
(360) 534-1410　　　　　　　Toll Free: (800) 647-7706
TDD: (360) 705-6718
Web: dor.wa.gov

Summary　To exempt a portion of the property owned by senior citizens and people with disabilities, including their surviving spouses, from taxation in Washington.

Eligibility　This exemption is available to residents of Washington who are 1) unable to work because of a disability, 2) veterans with a 100% service-connected disability, 3) at least 61 years of age, or 4) a surviving spouse at least 57 years of age of a person who was approved for this exemption. Applicants must own property that they use as their principal home for at least 6 months of the year; mobile homes may qualify as a residence even if its owner does not own the land where it is located. Their annual disposable income may not exceed $35,000 per year.

Financial data　Property owners whose annual income is $25,000 or less are exempt from regular property taxes on the first $60,000 or 60% of their home's assessed value, whichever is greater. Property owners whose annual income is between $25,001 and $30,000 are exempt from regular property taxes on $50,000 or 35% of the assessed value, whichever is greater, not to exceed $70,000 or the assessed value. Property owners whose annual income is $35,000 or less are exempt from all levies that have been approved by voters in excess of regular property taxes.

Duration　The exemption is available as long as the property owner meets the eligibility requirements.

Number awarded　Varies each year.

Deadline　Applications for each year are due by December of the preceding year.

[1200]
WEST VIRGINIA HOMESTEAD EXEMPTION

West Virginia State Tax Department
Attn: Property Tax Division
1124 Smith Street
P.O. Box 2389
Charleston, WV 25328-2389
(304) 558-3940　　Toll Free: (800) WVA-TAXS (within WV)
Fax: (304) 558-1843　　　　　　TDD: (800) 282-9833
Web: www.wva.state.wv.us/wvtax/propertyTax/default.aspx

Summary　To provide a partial exemption of property taxes on residences owned by disabled veterans or elderly persons and retired veterans in West Virginia.

Eligibility　Eligible for this exemption are single-family residences owned and occupied by any person who is permanently and totally disabled or at least 65 years old. Applicants must have been West Virginia residents for 2 consecutive calendar years prior to the tax year to which the exemption relates. Members of the U.S. military forces who maintain West Virginia as their state of residence throughout military service and return to the state to purchase a homestead upon retirement or separation from the military because of permanent and total disability are considered to meet the residency requirement and also qualify for this exemption.

Financial data　The exemption applies to the first $20,000 of the total assessed value of eligible property.

Duration　The exemption continues as long as the eligible property is owned and occupied by the qualifying person in West Virginia.

Additional information　Applications for this program are submitted to the office of the county assessor in each West Virginia county.

Number awarded　Varies each year.

Deadline　Individuals with disabilities apply for this exemption during July, August, or September of any year. Once they have filed for the exemption, they do not need to refile in subsequent years if they sign a statement that they will notify the assessor within 30 days if they cease to be eligible for the exemption on the basis of disability.

[1201]
WEST VIRGINIA INCOME TAX EXEMPTION FOR MILITARY RETIREES

West Virginia State Tax Department
Attn: Taxpayer Services Division
P.O. Box 3784
Charleston, WV 25337-3784
(304) 558-3333　　Toll Free: (800) WVA-TAXS (within WV)
Fax: (304) 558-3269　　　　　　TDD: (800) 282-9833
Web: www.wva.state.wv.us/wvtax/default.aspx

Summary　To exempt a portion of the income of military retirees and their spouses in West Virginia from state taxation.

Eligibility　This exemption is available to residents of West Virginia who are receiving retirement benefits from any branch of the military. Surviving spouses of eligible residents are also entitled to the exemptions.

Financial data　Military retirees and their spouses are entitled to exempt the first $20,000 of annual military retirement income, including survivorship annuities. That exemption is in addition to the $2,000 exemption available to all retired public employees in West Virginia.

Duration The exemption continues as long as eligible residents (or their spouses) remain residents of West Virginia.
Deadline Deadline not specified.

[1202]
WEST VIRGINIA VETERANS BONUS

West Virginia Department of Veteran's Assistance
Attn: Bonus Office
1321 Plaza East, Suite 101
Charleston, WV 25301-1400
(304) 558-3661   Toll Free: (888) 838-2332 (within WV)
Fax: (304) 558-3662   E-mail: wvdva@state.wv.us
Web: www.veterans.wv.gov/Pages/VeteransBonus.aspx

Summary To provide a bonus to living veterans in West Virginia who served in Kosovo, Afghanistan, or Iraq and to the families of deceased veterans.

Eligibility This bonus is available to veterans who were residents of West Virginia when they entered into active duty and for at least 6 months previously. Applicants must have been members of the armed forces of the United States or of Reserve components called to active duty. They must have 1) received a campaign badge or expeditionary medal for Kosovo between November 20, 1995 and December 31, 2000; 2) served in Afghanistan between October 7, 2001 and a date to be determined; or 3) served in Iraq between March 19, 2003 and a date to be determined. A bonus is also available to veterans who had active service outside the combat zone during the time periods specified for Afghanistan and Iraq. Surviving family members of a deceased veteran are also eligible if the veteran's death was connected with the service during the specified time periods.

Financial data Bonuses are $600 for veterans who served in the specified combat zone, $400 for veterans who served outside the combat zone but during the specified time periods, or $2,000 for surviving relatives of deceased veterans. The amount of the bonus is not considered income for state taxation purposes in West Virginia.

Duration This is a 1-time bonus.

Number awarded Varies each year.

Deadline Applications may be submitted at any time.

[1203]
WISCONSIN ASSISTANCE TO NEEDY VETERANS AND FAMILY MEMBERS

Wisconsin Department of Veterans Affairs
201 West Washington Avenue
P.O. Box 7843
Madison, WI 53707-7843
(608) 266-1311   Toll Free: (800) WIS-VETS
Fax: (608) 267-0403   E-mail: WDVAInfo@dva.state.wi.us
Web: www.dva.state.wi.us/Ben_emergencygrants.asp

Summary To provide temporary, emergency financial aid to veterans and their families in Wisconsin.

Eligibility This program is open to Wisconsin residents who served either 1) at least 2 years on active duty in the U.S. armed forces; or 2) at least 90 days on active duty during designated periods of wartime (including the Persian Gulf War since August 1, 1990, the Afghanistan War since September 11, 2001, and the Iraq War since March 19, 2003). The unremarried surviving spouse and dependent children of an eligible veteran who died in the line of duty while or active duty or inactive duty for training also qualify. Applicants must have

applied for, and been denied or determined to be ineligible for, all other applicable aid programs (e.g., unemployment insurance, Medicaid, Medicare, BadgerCare, federal Veterans Administration health care). The veteran must be a resident of Wisconsin with an income that does not exceed 130% of the federal poverty guidelines (currently, $14,521 for a family of 1, rising to $50,557 for a family of 8). The family must be facing an economic emergency, such as failure of the sole means of transportation; failure of a stove or refrigerator or of heating, electrical, or plumbing systems; a medical emergency; or severe damage to the primary residence as a result of a natural disaster.

Financial data Grants do not exceed $7,500 in a lifetime.

Duration Grants are awarded as needed.

Number awarded Varies each year.

Deadline Applications may be submitted at any time.

[1204]
WISCONSIN INCOME TAX EXEMPTION FOR MILITARY AND UNIFORMED SERVICES RETIREMENT BENEFITS

Wisconsin Department of Revenue
Attn: Individual Income Tax
2135 Rimrock Road
P.O. Box 59
Madison, WI 53785-0001
(608) 266-2486   Fax: (608) 267-0834
E-mail: income@revenue.wi.gov
Web: www.revenue.wi.gov/individuals/military.html

Summary To exempt from state taxation in Wisconsin retirement income received for service in the military.

Eligibility This exemption is available to residents of Wisconsin who receive income from 1) a U.S. military retirement system, or 2) the U.S. government that relates to service with the Coast Guard, the commissioned corps of the National Oceanic and Atmospheric Administration, or the commissioned corps of the Public Health Service.

Financial data All qualified military or uniformed services retirement pay is exempt from state income taxation in Wisconsin.

Duration The exemption is available as long as the recipient resides in Wisconsin.

Number awarded Varies each year.

Deadline Income tax returns must be filed by April of each year.

[1205]
WISCONSIN VETERANS AND SURVIVING SPOUSES PROPERTY TAX CREDIT

Wisconsin Department of Revenue
Attn: Homestead Credit
2135 Rimrock Road
P.O. Box 34
Madison, WI 53786-0001
(608) 266-8641   Fax: (608) 267-1030
E-mail: homestd@revenue.wi.gov
Web: www.revenue.wi.gov/individuals/military.html

Summary To provide an income tax credit to disabled Wisconsin veterans and their surviving spouses equal to the amount of property taxes they pay.

Eligibility This credit is available to Wisconsin veterans who served on active duty under honorable conditions in the

U.S. armed forces and have resided in Wisconsin for any consecutive 5-year period after entry into active duty. Applicants must have either a service-connected disability rating of 100% or a 100% disability rating based on individual unemployability. Also eligible are unremarried surviving spouses of such disabled veterans and of members of the National Guard or a Reserve component of the U.S. armed forces who were residents of Wisconsin and died in the line of duty while on active or inactive duty for training purposes.

Financial data Eligible veterans and surviving spouses are entitled to an income tax credit equal to the amount of property taxes they pay on their principal residence.

Duration The credit is available as long as the recipient resides in Wisconsin.

Number awarded Varies each year.

Deadline Income tax returns must be filed by April of each year.

[1206]
WISCONSIN VETERANS' SUBSISTENCE AID GRANTS

Wisconsin Department of Veterans Affairs
201 West Washington Avenue
P.O. Box 7843
Madison, WI 53707-7843
(608) 266-1311 Toll Free: (800) WIS-VETS
Fax: (608) 267-0403 E-mail: WDVAInfo@dva.state.wi.us
Web: www.dva.state.wi.us/Ben_emergencygrants.asp

Summary To provide temporary, emergency financial aid to Wisconsin veterans or their dependents.

Eligibility This program is open to current residents of Wisconsin who 1) were residents of the state when they entered or reentered active duty in the U.S. armed forces, or 2) have moved to the state and have been residents for any consecutive 12-month period after entry or reentry into service. Applicants must have served on active duty for at least 2 continuous years or for at least 90 days during specified wartime periods. Also eligible are 1) unremarried surviving spouses and dependent children of eligible veterans who died in the line of duty while on active service or inactive duty for training; and 2) spouses and dependent children of eligible servicemembers who are currently activated or deployed. Applicants must have suffered a loss of income because of illness, injury, or natural disaster and be seeking temporary, emergency financial aid. Their income may not exceed 130% of the federal poverty guidelines (currently, $14,521 for a family of 1, rising to $50,557 for a family of 8).

Financial data Grants do not exceed $3,000 during any consecutive 12-month period or the program limit of $7,500 in a lifetime.

Duration Grants are awarded for subsistence aid for a 30-day period, up to a maximum of 3 months.

Number awarded Varies each year.

Deadline Applications may be submitted at any time.

[1207]
WYOMING VETERANS PROPERTY TAX EXEMPTION

Wyoming Department of Revenue
Attn: Property Tax Relief Program
122 West 25th Street, Second Floor West
Cheyenne, WY 82002-0110
(307) 777-7320 Fax: (307) 777-7527
E-mail: DirectorOfRevenue@wy.gov
Web: revenue.state.wy.us

Summary To provide a partial tax exemption on the property owned by veterans and their surviving spouses in Wyoming.

Eligibility This program is open to honorably-discharged veterans who were Wyoming residents at the time they entered military service and have resided in Wyoming for 3 years prior to applying for this exemption. Applicants must have served during specified periods of wartime or have received an armed forces expeditionary medal or other authorized service or campaign medal for service in an armed conflict in a foreign country. Surviving spouses of qualified veterans are also eligible. The exemption applies to county fees only, not state fees.

Financial data Veterans and spouses may exempt $3,000 in assessed value of property from taxation per year. Disabled veterans are entitled to additional exemptions that depend on the level of their disability, to a maximum of $2,000 for a 100% disability.

Duration Veterans and spouses are entitled to use these exemptions as long as they reside in Wyoming and own the property as their principal residence.

Number awarded Varies each year.

Deadline Applicants must advise their county assessor of their intent to use the exemption by May of each year.

Military Personnel

[1208]
AIR FORCE ACTIVE DUTY HEALTH PROFESSIONS LOAN REPAYMENT PROGRAM

U.S. Air Force
Attn: ADHPLRP Program Manager
AFIT/ENEM
2950 Hobson Way
Wright-Patterson AFB, OH 45433-7765
(937) 255-2259, ext. 3015
Toll Free: (800) 543-3490, ext. 3015
Fax: (937) 255-4712 E-mail: enem.adhplrp@afit.edu
Web: airforcemedicine.afms.mil

Summary To repay the educational loans of Air Force officers serving in the health professions.

Eligibility This program is open to 1) commissioned Air Force officers qualified for or holding a position in a health profession; 2) full-time students enrolled in the final year of a course of study at an accredited educational institution leading to a degree in a health profession other than medicine or osteopathic medicine; and 3) students enrolled in the final year of an approved graduate program leading to specialty qualification in medicine, dentistry, osteopathic medicine, or other health profession. Applicants may not have received full support from the Air Force Health Professions Scholarship Program. They must have incurred government or commercial loans for actual costs paid for tuition, reasonable educational expenses, and reasonable living expenses relating to the attainment of a degree in the designated health care discipline.

Financial data The maximum annual payment is $40,000 per year.

Duration Up to 4 years.

Additional information Participants in this program incur an active-duty obligation of 2 years or 1 year for each annual payment, whichever is greater.

Number awarded Varies each year; recently, the program provided support for 114 nurses, 10 physicians, 32 dentists, 10 psychologists, and 10 public health officers.

Deadline January of each year.

[1209]
AIR FORCE AID SOCIETY EMERGENCY FINANCIAL ASSISTANCE

Air Force Aid Society
Attn: Financial Assistance Department
241 18th Street South, Suite 202
Arlington, VA 22202-3409
(703) 607-3072, ext. 51   Toll Free: (800) 769-8951
Fax: (703) 607-3022
Web: www.afas.org/Assistance/HowWeCanHelp.cfm

Summary To provide loans and grants-in-aid to current and former Air Force personnel and their families who are facing emergency situations.

Eligibility This program is open to active-duty Air Force members and their dependents, retired Air Force personnel and their dependents, Air National Guard and Air Force Reserve personnel on extended duty over 15 days, and spouses and dependent children of deceased Air Force personnel who died on active duty or in retired status. Applicants must be facing problems, usually for relatively short periods, that affect their job or the essential quality and dignity of life the Air Force wants for its people. Examples of such needs include basic living expenses (food, rent, utilities), medical and dental care, funeral expenses, vehicle expenses, emergency travel, moving expenses, or child or respite care. Funding is generally not provided if it merely postpones a long-term inability to exist on present pay and allowances, for non-essentials, for continuing long-term assistance commitments, or to replace funds lost due to garnishment.

Financial data Assistance is provided as an interest-free loan, a grant, or a combination of both.

Number awarded Varies each year.

Deadline Applications may be submitted at any time.

[1210]
AIR FORCE AID SOCIETY RESPITE CARE

Air Force Aid Society
Attn: Financial Assistance Department
241 18th Street South, Suite 202
Arlington, VA 22202-3409
(703) 607-3072, ext. 51   Toll Free: (800) 769-8951
Fax: (703) 607-3022
Web: www.afas.org/Community/RespireCareProgram.cfm

Summary To provide financial assistance to Air Force personnel and their families who have a family member with special needs.

Eligibility This program is open to active-duty Air Force members and their families who are responsible for 24 hour a day care for an ill or disabled family member (child, spouse, or parent) living in the household. Applicants must be referred by the Exceptional Family Member Program (EFMP) or the Family Advocacy Office. Selection is based on need, both financial need and the need of the family for respite time.

Financial data Assistance is provided as a grant that depends on the needs of the family.

Number awarded Varies each year.

Deadline Applications may be submitted at any time.

[1211]
AIR FORCE COLLEGE LOAN REPAYMENT PROGRAM

U.S. Air Force
Attn: Air Force Personnel Center
Headquarters USAF/DPPAT
550 C Street West, Suite 10
Randolph AFB, TX 78150-4712
Fax: (210) 565-2328
Web: www.airforce.com

Summary To provide an opportunity for individuals to repay their federally-insured student loans by serving in the Air Force.

Eligibility This program is open to non-prior service Air Force enlistees who utilized any of the following loans to help pay for their college education: Auxiliary Loan Assistance for Students (ALAS), Parent Loans for Undergraduate Students (PLUS), Supplemental Loans for Students (SLS), Stafford Loans, Perkins Loans, William D. Ford Loans, or Consolidated Loans. Private loans, equity loans, state-funded loans, institution loans, and consolidated loans for someone else do not qualify. Enlistees for the Air National Guard are also eligible if they qualify for specific shortage AFSCs.

Financial data Recipients have their indebtedness reduced by one-third or $1,500, whichever amount is greater, for each year of active-duty service. The maximum amount payable under this program is $10,000 for active-duty enlistees or $20,000 for Air National Guard enlistees who qualify.

Duration To qualify for this program, individuals must enlist for 4 years on active duty or 6 years in the Air National Guard.

Additional information Loans that are in default cannot qualify for this program.

Number awarded Varies each year.

Deadline Deadline not specified.

[1212]
AIR TRAFFIC CONTROL ASSOCIATION FULL-TIME EMPLOYEE SCHOLARSHIP PROGRAM
Air Traffic Control Association
Attn: Scholarship Fund
1101 King Street, Suite 300
Alexandria, VA 22314
(703) 299-2430   Fax: (703) 299-2437
E-mail: info@atca.org
Web: www.atca.org/ATCA-Scholarship

Summary To provide financial assistance to aviation professionals engaged in advanced study.

Eligibility This program is open to full-time employees in an aviation-related field in the federal government, U.S. military service, or industry. Applicants must be engaged in advanced (not necessarily degree) study designed to enhance their skill in an aviation or air traffic control discipline. Along with their application, they must submit an essay, up to 500 words, on how their educational efforts will enhance their potential contribution to aviation. Financial need is considered in the selection process.

Financial data The amount of the stipend depends on the availability of funds.

Duration 1 year; may be renewed.

Number awarded Varies each year; recently, 1 of these scholarships was awarded.

Deadline April of each year.

[1213]
AIR WARRIOR COURAGE FOUNDATION GRANTS
Air Warrior Courage Foundation
P.O. Box 877
Silver Spring, MD 20918
(301) 588-3282   Fax: (540) 636-9776
E-mail: awcf@awcfoundation.com
Web: www.airwarriorcourage.org

Summary To provide emergency assistance to veterans, military personnel, and their families, especially members of the Red River Valley Fighter Pilots Association (RRVA), who are facing unusual situations.

Eligibility These grants are available to active, Guard, Reserve, retired, and former military and Coast Guard personnel and dependent family members. Applicants must be able to demonstrate financial and material needs unmet by insurance programs, community support, or other service agencies. Special consideration is given to applicants eligible for the RRVA scholarship program (spouses and children of servicemembers missing in action or killed in action in armed conflicts by U.S. forces since August 1964, of U.S. military aircrew members killed in a non-combat aircraft accident in which they were performing aircrew duties, and of current members of the association). Assistance includes the following activities: the troop support 9/11 Terrorism Memorial Fund, which provides financial assistance, college savings programs, and/or material support to surviving family members of those lost or injured in the war on terror and military units performing humanitarian activities worldwide; grants for individuals, which provides emergency financial support for utilities, rent, transportation, auto repairs, and medical expenses; the Professional Association for Therapeutic Horsemanship (PATH) grants, which supports horseback riding for children with certain mental, physical, or developmental challenges; and the College Savings Plan (529) program, which opens College Savings Plan (529) accounts for children of aviators killed during the performance of aircrew duties.

Financial data The amount awarded varies. Recent grants included more than $900,000 for the troop support 9/11 Terrorism Memorial Fund, $63,000 in grants to 57 individuals, $88,000 to support 88 children through the PATH program, and the opening of 22 College Savings Plans (529) at $2,000 for combat deaths or $1,000 for training accidents.

Duration These are 1-time grants.

Additional information This foundation began in 1998 as a charitable organization affiliated with the RRVA.

Number awarded Varies each year.

Deadline Applications may be submitted at any time.

[1214]
ALABAMA INCOME TAX EXEMPTION FOR MILITARY COMBAT PAY
Alabama Department of Revenue
Attn: Income Tax Division
Gordon Persons Building
50 North Ripley Street, Room 4212
P.O. Box 327410
Montgomery, AL 36132-7410
(334) 242-1105   Fax: (334) 242-0064
E-mail: erohelpdesk@revenue.state.al.us
Web: www.ador.state.al.us

Summary To exempt portions of the income of military personnel who are residents of Alabama from state taxation.

Eligibility Eligible for these exemptions are residents of Alabama who are in the armed forces. The exemptions apply to 1) compensation for service in a combat zone designated by the president of the United States and 2) military allowances paid to active-duty military, National Guard, and active Reserves for quarters, subsistence, uniforms, and travel.

Financial data Qualified income received by military personnel who are Alabama residents is not subject to state income tax.

Duration These exemptions continue as long as the servicemember remains a resident of Alabama and receives designated income.

Number awarded Varies each year.

Deadline Deadline not specified.

[1215]
ARIZONA INCOME TAX EXEMPTION FOR ACTIVE-DUTY PAY
Arizona Department of Revenue
1600 West Monroe Street
Phoenix, AZ 85007-2650
(602) 542-3572   Toll Free: (800) 352-4090 (within AZ)
TDD: (602) 542-4021
Web: www.azdor.gov

Summary To exempt the pay of military personnel from state income taxes in Arizona.

Eligibility This exemption is available to Arizona residents who serve on active duty in the U.S. armed forces, including members of the Reserves and National Guard called to active duty.

Financial data All active duty pay is exempt from state income taxation.

Duration The exemption continues as long as the recipient resides in Arizona and receives active duty pay.

Deadline Deadline not specified.

[1216]
ARIZONA MILITARY FAMILY RELIEF FUND

Arizona Department of Veterans' Services
Attn: Military Family Relief Fund
3839 North Third Street, Suite 209
Phoenix, AZ 85012
(602) 234-8403   E-mail: mfrf@azdvs.gov
Web: www.azdvs.gov/benefits/relief_fund.aspx

Summary To provide assistance to military service members from Arizona and their families who face financial difficulties that result from the deployment of the military member to a combat zone.

Eligibility This assistance is available to military service members who have been deployed to a combat zone since September 11, 2001, are currently deployed in a combat zone, or became deceased, wounded, or seriously ill after September 11, 2001 due to a deployment. Applicants must be Arizona residents, as evidenced by having been deployed from a military base in the state, entered active military service after September 11, 2001 from the state, claimed the state as home of record, or been a member of the Arizona National Guard at the time of deployment. Military service members who have been discharged must have done so under honorable conditions. Family members (spouses, widows and widowers, dependent children, siblings, and parents) are also eligible. All applicants must be able to demonstrate how deployment affected their financial situation. Family members of those who were killed in action may request up to 6 months' living expenses and other appropriate expenses; family members of those who were wounded in action may request temporary living expenses while care in being delivered to the qualifying military person and other appropriate expenses; families of service members who are experiencing financial hardship may request living or other appropriate expenses to resolve financial hardship caused by deployment and assist with transition to financial stability.

Financial data Grants up to $20,000 are available, of which $3,000 is available for emergency situations.

Duration The maximum grant of $20,000 is a lifetime limit.

Number awarded Varies each year.

Deadline Applications may be submitted at any time.

[1217]
ARIZONA NATIONAL GUARD EMERGENCY RELIEF FUND GRANTS

Arizona National Guard Emergency Relief Fund
Attn: Fund Administrator
P.O. Box 64252
Phoenix, AZ 85082
E-mail: azng.er@gmail.com

Summary To provide emergency assistance to members of the Arizona National Guard and their families.

Eligibility This program is open to members of the Arizona Army and Air National Guard who have not been mobilized under Presidential Order. Surviving spouses, children, and orphans of soldiers who died while on active duty are also eli-

gible. Applicants must be seeking assistance for such emergency needs as delay in receiving pay or reimbursement from the government; temporary shelter, lodging, or rent; emergency utility assistance; emergency transportation and vehicle repair; costs incurred for emergency travel due to death of immediate family member; or any other special circumstance deemed appropriate by the fund's directors. Support is not provided to help pay for nonessentials, finance ordinary leave or vacation, pay fines or legal expenses, assist with home purchase or improvements, cover bad checks, or help purchase, rent, or lease a vehicle.

Financial data Most support is provided in the form of interest-free loans, although outright grants are also available.

Duration These are 1-time grants.

Number awarded Varies each year.

Deadline Applications may be submitted at any time.

[1218]
ARIZONA NATIONAL GUARD FAMILY ASSISTANCE FUND

Arizona National Guard Emergency Relief Fund
Attn: Fund Administrator
P.O. Box 64252
Phoenix, AZ 85082
E-mail: azng.er@gmail.com

Summary To provide emergency assistance to members of the Arizona Reserve Component who have been mobilized and their families.

Eligibility This program is open to members of the Arizona Reserve Component (including the Army and Air National Guard and Reserve units of all 5 branches of service) and their dependents. They must have been mobilized under Presidential Order. Surviving spouses, children, and orphans of soldiers who died while on active duty are also eligible. Applicants must be seeking assistance for such emergency needs as delay in receiving pay or reimbursement from the government; temporary shelter, lodging, or rent; emergency utility assistance; emergency transportation and vehicle repair; costs incurred for emergency travel due to death of immediate family member; or any other special circumstance deemed appropriate by the fund's directors. Support is not provided to help pay for nonessentials, financial ordinary leave or vacation, pay fines or legal expenses, assist with home purchase or improvements, cover bad checks, or help purchase, rent, or lease a vehicle.

Financial data Most support is provided in the form of interest-free loans, although outright grants are also available.

Duration These are awarded on a 1-time basis.

Number awarded Varies each year.

Deadline Applications may be submitted at any time.

[1219]
ARKANSAS INCOME TAX EXEMPTIONS FOR MILITARY COMPENSATION AND DISABILITY PAY

Arkansas Department of Finance and Administration
Attn: Office of Income Tax Administration
Joel Ledbetter Building, Room 2300
1816 West Seventh Street
P.O. Box 3628
Little Rock, AR 72203-3628
(501) 682-1100   Fax: (501) 682-7692
E-mail: individual.income@dfa.arkansas.gov
Web: www.dfa.arkansas.gov

Summary   To exempt a portion of the income of military personnel and disabled veterans from Arkansas state income taxes.

Eligibility   Eligible are residents of Arkansas receiving military compensation or military disability income.

Financial data   The first $9,000 of U.S. military compensation pay or military disability income is exempt from state income taxation.

Duration   The exemptions continue as long as the recipient resides in Arkansas.

Deadline   Deadline not specified.

[1220]
ARMY COLLEGE LOAN REPAYMENT PROGRAM

U.S. Army
Human Resources Command
AHRC-PDP-E
Attn: Education Incentives and Counseling Branch
1500 Spearhead Division Avenue
Fort Knox, KY 40122-5408
Toll Free: (888) ARMY-HRC
E-mail: askhrc@conus.army.mil
Web: www.hrc.army.mil

Summary   To provide an opportunity for individuals to repay their federally-insured student loans by serving in the Army.

Eligibility   This program is open to Army enlistees who utilized any of the following loans to help pay for their college education: Auxiliary Loan Assistance for Students (ALAS), Parent Loans for Undergraduate Students (PLUS), Supplemental Loans for Students (SLS), Stafford Loans, Perkins Loans, William D. Ford Loans, or Consolidated Loans. Private loans, equity loans, state-funded loans, institution loans, and consolidated loans for someone else do not qualify. Applicants must have an Armed Forces Qualification Test score of 50 or higher and must enlist in a critical military occupational specialty.

Financial data   Recipients have their indebtedness reduced by one-third or $1,500, whichever amount is greater, for each year of active-duty service. The maximum amount payable under this program is $65,000 for active-duty personnel or $20,000 for Reservists and National Guard members.

Duration   To qualify for this program, individuals must enlist for 3 years of active duty or 6 years in the Reserves or National Guard.

Additional information   Loans that are in default cannot qualify for this program.

Number awarded   Varies each year.

Deadline   Deadline not specified.

[1221]
ARMY EMERGENCY RELIEF LOANS/GRANTS

Army Emergency Relief
200 Stovall Street
Alexandria, VA 22332-0600
(703) 428-0000   Toll Free: (866) 878-6378
Fax: (703) 325-7183   E-mail: aer@aerhq.org
Web: www.aerhq.org/dnn563/FinancialAssistance.aspx

Summary   To provide loans and grants-in-aid to help with the emergency financial needs of Army veterans, military personnel, and their dependents.

Eligibility   Eligible to apply are active-duty soldiers (single or married) and their dependents, Army National Guard and Army Reserve soldiers on continuous active duty for more than 30 days and their dependents, soldiers retired from active duty for longevity or physical disability and their dependents, Army National Guard and Army Reserve soldiers who retired at age 60 and their dependents, and surviving spouses and orphans of soldiers who died while on active duty or after they retired. Applicants must be seeking assistance for such emergency needs as food, rent, and utilities; emergency transportation and vehicle repair; funeral expenses; medical and dental expenses; or personal needs when pay is delayed or stolen. Support is not available to help pay for nonessentials, finance ordinary leave or vacation, pay fines or legal expenses, help liquidate or consolidate debt, assist with house purchase or home improvements, cover bad checks, pay credit card bills, or acquire a vehicle.

Financial data   Support is provided in the form of loans or grants (or a combination).

Duration   Qualifying individuals can apply whenever they have a valid emergency need.

Additional information   This organization began in 1942.

Number awarded   Varies each year; recently, the organization helped more than 66,000 Army people with more than $70 million, including $60 million to 58,820 active-duty soldiers and their families, $7.3 million to 4,914 retired soldiers and their families, and $2.7 million to 2,304 widow(er)s and orphans of deceased soldiers. Since it was established, the organization has helped more than 3.2 million qualifying individuals with more than $1.2 billion in financial assistance.

Deadline   Applications may be submitted at any time.

[1222]
ARMY HEALTH PROFESSIONS LOAN REPAYMENT PROGRAM

U.S. Army
Human Resources Command, Health Services Division
Attn: AHRC-OPH-AN
1500 Spearhead Division Avenue
Fort Knox, KY 40122-5408
Toll Free: (888) ARMY-HRC
E-mail: askhrc@conus.army.mil
Web: www.goarmy.com

Summary   To repay the educational loans of health professionals who are willing to serve in the Army on active duty or in the Army Reserve.

Eligibility   This program is open to fully-qualified health care professionals, full-time students in the final year of a course of study, and trainees in the final year of an approved graduate program leading to specialty qualification in a designated health care skill. Applicants must have qualified government and commercial loans for actual costs paid for tuition, reasonable educational expenses, and reasonable living expenses relating to the attainment of a degree in the designated health care discipline. Eligible health care professions are determined annually by the Secretary of Defense. U.S. citizenship is required.

Financial data Health care professionals who serve on active duty are entitled to reimbursement of educational loans up to amounts that vary; recently, the maximum was $40,000 per year. Health care professionals who serve in the Army Reserve are entitled to reimbursement of a total of $50,000 in loans, payable at the rate of $20,000 for the first year, $20,000 for the second year, and $10,000 for the third year.

Duration Up to 3 years of active-duty service or 3 years in the Reserves.

Additional information This program began in 1998. Recently, this program was available to physicians, dentists, nurses, veterinarians, and pharmacists serving on active duty and to physicians, dentists (general, comprehensive, prosthodontists, and oral surgeons), nurses (community/public health, critical care, medical-surgical, perioperative, and nurse anesthetists), veterinarians, clinical psychologists, entomologists, microbiologists, clinical laboratory professionals, nuclear medicine specialists, and optometrists serving in the Reserves. Participants incur a service obligation of 1 year for each year of loan reimbursement.

Number awarded Varies each year.

Deadline Applications may be submitted at any time.

[1223]
ARMY NATIONAL GUARD STUDENT LOAN REPAYMENT PROGRAM

U.S. Army National Guard
c/o DANTES
6490 Saufley Field Road
Pensacola, FL 32509-5243
(850) 452-1085   Fax: (850) 452-1161
Web: www.nationalguard.com

Summary To repay the educational loans of members of the Army National Guard in each state.

Eligibility This program is open to current or entering members of the Army National Guard in every state who have existing student loans (Stafford, Ford Direct, or Perkins). Applicants may be 1) non-prior service soldiers who enlist for either 8 years or 6 years plus 2 years in the Individual Ready Reserve (IRR), enlist into a unit eligible for deployment, and qualify as a Category I-IIIA enlistment with a score of 50 or higher on their Armed Forces Qualifying Test; 2) prior-service soldiers or current National Guard soldiers who enlist for 6 years or extend their current contract for 6 years, enlist or are assigned to a unit eligible for deployment, are Duty Military Occupation Specialty Qualified (DMOSQ) for their position, and have not previously received this loan repayment assistance; or 3) entering Officer Candidate School and have at least 90 college credits, agree to a 6-year commitment, and enroll prior to commissioning.

Financial data Loans are repaid at the rate of 15% of the total loan amount (to a maximum of $7,500 per soldier per year) or $500, whichever is greater. The total amount of student loans repaid may not exceed $50,000.

Duration Up to 6 or 8 years, depending on the length of the enlistment or extension.

Number awarded Varies each year.

Deadline Deadline not specified.

[1224]
AUTOMOBILE ALLOWANCE FOR DISABLED VETERANS

Department of Veterans Affairs
Attn: Veterans Benefits Administration
810 Vermont Avenue, N.W.
Washington, DC 20420
(202) 418-4343   Toll Free: (800) 827-1000
Web: www1.va.gov

Summary To provide funding to certain disabled veterans and current service personnel who require specially adapted automobiles.

Eligibility To be eligible for a grant for an automobile, a veteran or current servicemember must have a service-connected loss or permanent loss of use of 1 or both hands or feet or permanent impairment of vision of both eyes to a prescribed degree. For adaptive equipment eligibility only, veterans entitled to compensation for ankylosis of 1 or both knees, or 1 or both hips, also qualify.

Financial data The grant consists of a payment by the Department of Veterans Affairs (VA) of up to $18,900 toward the purchase of an automobile or other conveyance. The VA will also pay for the adaptive equipment, its repair, and the replacement or reinstallation required for the safe operation of the vehicle purchased with VA assistance or for a previously or subsequently acquired vehicle.

Duration This is a 1-time grant.

Number awarded Varies each year.

Deadline Applications may be submitted at any time.

[1225]
COAST GUARD MUTUAL ASSISTANCE GRANTS-IN-AID

Coast Guard Mutual Assistance
4200 Wilson Boulevard, Suite 610
Arlington, VA 20598-7180
(202) 493-6621   Toll Free: (800) 881-2462
Fax: (202) 493-6686   E-mail: ARL-DG-CGMA@uscg.mil
Web: www.cgmahq.org/Assistance/programs.html

Summary To provide funding to members of the Coast Guard Mutual Assistance (CGMA) and their families who need temporary assistance.

Eligibility This program is open to CGMA members who are facing special needs. Categories of aid that are available include emergency assistance (basic living expenses, emergency home repair, emergency travel expenses, fire and other disasters, funeral expenses, loss of funds, temporary living expenses); general assistance (adoption, child support, child care, family in-home day care facility, financial counseling, government travel cards, household furnishings, immigration fees, insurance, loss of income, moving expenses, non-emergency travel, non-support or inadequate support, past due bills and expenses, pay and allotment problems, vehicle repair, vehicle other expenses); housing assistance (payment of settlement charges associated with purchasing a residence, rental assistance, utilities); and medical and dental assistance (provider won't proceed without payment; mental health and family counseling; patient's cost share; durable medical equipment; prosthetic devices; rehabilitation, nursing, home, or respite care; orthodontia; long-term dental care; travel, transportation, and incidental expenses). Applicants must be able to demonstrate a need for assistance.

Financial data The assistance depends on the nature of the need.

Duration These are 1-time grants. A new application must accompany each request for assistance.

Additional information CGMA membership is open to active-duty and retired members of the U.S. Coast Guard, civilian employees of the U.S. Coast Guard, U.S. Coast Guard Reserve members, U.S. Coast Guard Auxiliary members, Public Health Service officers serving with the U.S. Coast Guard, and family members of all of those.

Number awarded Varies each year.

Deadline Deadline not specified.

[1226]
COLORADO MILITARY FAMILY RELIEF FUND

Department of Military and Veterans Affairs
Attn: Military Family Relief
6848 South Revere Parkway
Centennial, CO 80112-6703
(720) 250-1550   Fax: (720) 250-1559
E-mail: tuition@dmva.state.co.us
Web: www.dmva.state.co.us/page/mfr

Summary To provide funding to military personnel (active-duty, National Guard, Reserves) in Colorado who have been deployed overseas and whose families have experienced financial need as a result.

Eligibility This program is open to residents of Colorado who are either 1) members of the Colorado National Guard or Reserve military members who have been on active military duty in a combat zone for at least 30 days; or 2) active-duty military members who are deployed overseas and are in receipt of hostile fire pay or the equivalent. Applicants must be able to show a loss of household income due to the deployment or submit receipts for emergency expenses that occurred during the deployment.

Financial data This program provides assistance to help families defray the costs of food, housing, utilities, medical services, and other expenses that may be difficult to afford when a family member leaves civilian employment for active military duty or is on active military duty in a hostile fire zone.

Duration These are 1-time grants.

Number awarded Varies each year.

Deadline Applicants may be submitted at any time, but they must be received within 6 months after the return of the military member from the overseas assignment.

[1227]
CONNECTICUT NATIONAL GUARD FOUNDATION ASSISTANCE

Connecticut National Guard Foundation, Inc.
Attn: Assistance Committee
360 Broad Street
Hartford, CT 06105-3795
(860) 241-1550   Fax: (860) 293-2929
E-mail: assistance.committee@ctngfoundation.org
Web: www.ctngfoundation.org

Summary To provide emergency and other assistance to members of the Connecticut National Guard and their families.

Eligibility This program is open to members of the Connecticut Army National Guard and Organized Militia, their children under 18 years of age, and their spouses who live with them. Applicants must be in need of assistance for such benefits as clothing, food, medical and surgical aid, and general care and relief. They must be able to demonstrate a need for assistance.

Financial data Grants depend on the need of the recipient.

Duration These are 1-time grants.

Additional information Applications are available at all State Armories and Family Assistance Centers.

Number awarded Varies each year.

Deadline Applications may be submitted at any time.

[1228]
C.W. "BILL" AND BEVERLY YOUNG FINANCIAL ASSISTANCE FUND

Armed Forces Foundation
Attn: Family Assistance Program
16 North Carolina Avenue, N.E.
Washington, DC 20003
(202) 547-4713   Fax: (202) 547-4712
E-mail: info@armedforcesfoundation.org
Web: www.armedforcesfoundation.org

Summary To provide financial assistance to active-duty military personnel and those recently discharged from service who need funds to pay for the needs of their families.

Eligibility This program is open to 1) military personnel currently on active duty and receiving active-duty pay; 2) Reservists or National Guardsmen activated for at least 6 months; and 3) veterans released or discharged from active duty within the last 18 months. Applicants must be able to demonstrate that they need funding to help cover such expenses as utility bills, rent or mortgage payments for civilian housing, car payments, childcare (during illness, surgery or recovery), or car insurance or registration payments.

Financial data The amount of the assistance depends on the nature of the need and the availability of funds.

Duration These are 1-time grants.

Number awarded Varies each year.

Deadline Applications may be submitted at any time.

[1229]
DEPARTMENT OF THE NAVY STUDENT LOAN REPAYMENT PROGRAM

U.S. Navy
Attn: Navy Recruiting Command
5720 Integrity Drive, Building 874
Millington, TN 38054
(901) 874-9345   Toll Free: (877) 747-7657
Fax: (901) 874-9327   E-mail: CNRC_LRP-EB@navy.mil
Web: www.crnc.navy.mil/EIncentives/EB%20_FAQ.htm

Summary To repay the educational loans of college students who enlist in the Navy.

Eligibility This program is open to recent college graduates who have outstanding federally-insured student loans made by education institutions or banks and other private lenders. Applicants must enlist in the active-duty Navy. The loan may not be in default and it must be the applicant's first enlistment.

Financial data Up to $65,000 of qualified loans may be repaid.

Duration This is a 1-time benefit.

Number awarded Varies each year.

Deadline Applications may be submitted at any time.

[1230]
FLORIDA DEPLOYED MILITARY EXEMPTION

Florida Department of Revenue
Attn: Taxpayer Services
5050 West Tennessee Street
Tallahassee, FL 32399-0100
(850) 617-8600   Toll Free: (800) 352-3671
E-mail: EMailDOR@dor.state.fl.us
Web: www.myflorida.com

Summary To provide members of the military who are deployed outside the United States with a partial exemption from taxation on their homesteads in Florida.

Eligibility This exemption is available to Florida residents who have real estate that they own and use as a homestead and for which they are already receiving the standard homestead exemption. Applicants must be members of any branch of the U.S. military or military reserves, the U.S. Coast Guard or its reserves, or the Florida National Guard. They must have been deployed during the preceding calendar year outside the continental United States, Alaska, or Hawaii in support of an operation that is designated annually by the Florida legislature.

Financial data Military personnel are entitled to a percentage exemption on the value of their Florida homestead equal to the percentage of time during the preceding year when they were deployed on a designated operation.

Duration The exemption applies as long as the taxpayer owns the property in Florida and remains deployed outside the United States.

Number awarded Varies each year.

Deadline Applications must be submitted by February of the year for which the exemption is sought.

[1231]
GEORGIA INCOME TAX EXCLUSION FOR COMBAT PAY

Georgia Department of Revenue
Attn: Taxpayer Services Division
1800 Century Boulevard, Room 8300
Atlanta, GA 30345-3205
(404) 417-2400   Toll Free: (877) GADOR-11
Fax: (404) 417-2439   TDD: (404) 417-4302
E-mail: taxpayer.services@dor.ga.gov
Web: etax.dor.ga.gov/IndTax_TSD.aspx

Summary To exclude from state income taxation combat pay received by residents of Georgia.

Eligibility This exclusion is available to residents of Georgia who are members of the National Guard or any Reserve component of the armed services and stationed in a combat zone.

Financial data All combat pay received by National Guard and Reserve servicemembers is not subject to Georgia income tax. The exclusion applies only to military income earned in the combat zone during the period covered by the soldier's military orders.

Duration The exclusion continues as long as the recipient is assigned to a combat zone as a resident of Georgia.

Additional information This exclusion became effective in 2003.

Deadline Deadline not specified.

[1232]
HAWAII INCOME TAX EXEMPTIONS FOR MILITARY RESERVE AND NATIONAL GUARD DUTY PAY

Department of Taxation
Attn: Taxpayer Services Branch
425 Queen Street
P.O. Box 259
Honolulu, HI 96809-0259
(808) 587-4242   Toll Free: (800) 222-3229
Fax: (808) 587-1488   TDD: (808) 587-1418
Web: hawaii.gov/tax

Summary To exempt a portion of the income of members of the Reserves and National Guard from state income taxation in Hawaii.

Eligibility Eligible are members of the Reserve components of the Army, Navy, Air Force, Marine Corps, and Coast Guard, and the Hawaii National Guard who are classified as residents of Hawaii for state income tax purposes.

Financial data The first $5,800 of income from service in the Reserves or the Hawaii National Guard is excluded.

Duration The exemption continues as long as the recipient resides in Hawaii.

Deadline Deadline not specified.

[1233]
HONORABLE LOUIS L. GOLDSTEIN VOLUNTEER POLICE, FIRE, RESCUE AND EMERGENCY MEDICAL SERVICES PERSONNEL SUBTRACTION MODIFICATION PROGRAM

Comptroller of Maryland
Attn: Revenue Administration Division
80 Calvert Street
Annapolis, MD 21411
(410) 260-7980   Toll Free: (800) MD-TAXES (within MD)
Fax: (410) 974-3456   TDD: (410) 260-7157
E-mail: taxhelp@comp.state.md.us
Web: individuals.marylandtaxes.com/incometax/default.asp

Summary To exempt from state income taxation in Maryland a portion of the income of members of the U.S. Coast Guard Auxiliary and other emergency medical services personnel.

Eligibility Eligible are Maryland residents who are members of the U.S. Coast Guard Auxiliary or qualifying volunteers certified by a Maryland fire, police, rescue, or emergency medical services organization.

Financial data Eligible residents may exclude $3,500 of their income from state taxation.

Duration The exclusion continues as long as the recipient resides in Maryland and remains a member of the organization or a qualifying volunteer.

Deadline Deadline not specified.

[1234]
HOPE FOR THE WARRIORS IMMEDIATE NEEDS GRANTS

Hope for the Warriors
Attn: Immediate Needs
1335 Western Boulevard, Suite E
Jacksonville, NC 28546-5539
(910) 938-1817   Toll Free: (877) 246-7349
E-mail: imn@hopeforthewarriors.org
Web: www.hopeforthewarriors.org/immneeds.html

Summary To provide funding for immediate needs to disabled military personnel, veterans, and their families.

Eligibility This assistance is available to wounded service members and their families. Applicants must need assistance to meet such immediate needs as travel to bedside where the government does not provide assistance, rental cars, lodging assistance, groceries, gas, furniture, assistance with child care, emergency assistance with essentials to daily living (e.g., rent and utilities), or items that assist and/or supplement programs at military treatment facilities and Veterans Administration polytrauma units.

Financial data The amount of the grant depends on the need of the recipient. Payment is always made to a third party.

Duration Applicants may apply once a year.

Number awarded Varies each year.

Deadline Applications may be submitted at any time.

[1235]
ILLINOIS INCOME TAX SUBTRACTIONS FOR MILITARY PERSONNEL

Illinois Department of Revenue
101 West Jefferson Street
P.O. Box 19044
Springfield, IL 62794-9044
(217) 782-3336   Toll Free: (800) 732-8866
TDD: (800) 544-5304
Web: www.revenue.state.il.us

Summary To exempt the income of military personnel from state taxation in Illinois.

Eligibility Illinois does not tax the income received for: full-time active duty in the armed forces, including basic training; duty in the Reserves or an Illinois National Guard unit, including ROTC; or full-time duty as a cadet at the U.S. Military, Air Force, or Coast Guard academies or as a midshipman at the U.S. Naval Academy.

Financial data All qualified pay received by military personnel is exempt from state income taxation.

Duration The exemption continues as long as the recipient resides in Illinois.

Additional information Income received under the Voluntary Separation Incentive, from the military as a civilian, as a member of the National Guard of another state, or under the Ready Reserve Mobilization Income Insurance Program, is not subject to this exemption.

Deadline Deadline not specified.

[1236]
INDIANA MILITARY SERVICE INCOME TAX DEDUCTION

Indiana Department of Revenue
Attn: Taxpayer Services Division
Indiana Government Center North
100 North Senate Avenue
Indianapolis, IN 46204-2253
(317) 232-2240   TDD: (317) 232-4952
E-mail: individualtaxassistance@dor.in.gov
Web: www.in.gov/dor

Summary To exempt a portion of the income of military personnel from state taxation in Indiana.

Eligibility Military personnel on active duty or in the Reserves who are classified as Indiana residents for purposes of state income taxation are eligible for this income adjustment.

Financial data Qualified military personnel may deduct up to $5,000 of military pay from state income taxation in Indiana. In addition, they may exclude from taxation all re-enlistment bonuses awarded for serving in a combat zone and all pay received for active service in a combat zone or pay received while hospitalized as a result of service in a combat zone.

Duration The adjustments continue as long as the recipient resides in Indiana.

Deadline Deadline not specified.

[1237]
INDIANA NATIONAL GUARD AND RESERVE COMPONENT MEMBERS INCOME TAX DEDUCTION

Indiana Department of Revenue
Attn: Taxpayer Services Division
Indiana Government Center North
100 North Senate Avenue
Indianapolis, IN 46204-2253
(317) 232-2240   TDD: (317) 232-4952
E-mail: individualtaxassistance@dor.in.gov
Web: www.in.gov/dor

Summary To exempt the income of Indiana National Guard and Reserve members who are called to active duty from state taxation.

Eligibility This exemption is available to members of the Indiana Army National Guard, the Indiana Air National Guard, and Reserve components of all branches of the armed forces. It applies to income received while the National Guard unit was federalized or the Reserve component was deployed or mobilized for involuntary full-time service.

Financial data All qualified income from National Guard or Reserve service is exempt from state income taxation in Indiana.

Duration The exemption continues as long as the recipient receives full-time active-duty income.

Deadline Deadline not specified.

[1238]
INJURED MARINE SEMPER FI GRANTS

Injured Marine Semper Fi Fund
c/o Wounded Warrior Center
Building H49
P.O. Box 555193
Camp Pendleton, CA 92055-5193
(760) 725-3680   Fax: (760) 725-3685
E-mail: info@semperfifund.org
Web: semperfifund.org/assistance

Summary To provide supplemental assistance to Marines injured in combat and their families.

Eligibility This program is open to Marines injured in post-9/11 combat operations or facing a life-threatening illness and their families. Members of the Army, Air Force, Coast Guard, and Navy who served in support of Marine forces are also eligible. Applicants must need financial assistance to deal with such needs as family support (e.g., travel and lodging, costs of hospitalization and rehabilitation, mortgages, car payments, utilities, grocery bills), adaptive housing support, adaptive transportation, or specialized and adaptive equipment.

Financial data Funds are available for such expenses as child care, travel expenses for families, and other necessities. Assistance is also available for the purchase of adaptive transportation, home modifications, and specialized equipment such as wheelchairs, audio/visual equipment for the blind, and software for traumatic brain injuries.

Duration Grants are provided as needed.

Additional information This fund was established in 2004 by a small group of Marine Corps spouses.

Number awarded Varies each year. Since this program was established, it has awarded more than 38,000 grants worth more than $57 million.

Deadline Applications may be submitted at any time.

[1239]
IOWA INCOME TAX EXEMPTION OF ACTIVE-DUTY MILITARY PAY

Iowa Department of Revenue
Attn: Taxpayer Services
Hoover State Office Building
1305 East Walnut
P.O. Box 10457
Des Moines, IA 50306-0457
(515) 281-3114   Toll Free: (800) 367-3388 (within IA)
Fax: (515) 242-6487   E-mail: idr@iowa.gov
Web: www.iowa.gov/tax

Summary To exempt the income earned by military personnel in Iraq from state taxation in Iowa.

Eligibility This exemption applies to the income received as members of the armed forces, armed forces military Reserve, and the National Guard in an active-duty status. Applicants must be residents of Iowa for state income tax purposes.

Financial data All eligible income is exempt for purposes of state income tax purposes.

Duration The exemption continues as long as the military personnel remain assigned to peacekeeping activities in Iraq and residents of Iowa for state income tax purposes.

Number awarded Varies each year.

Deadline Deadline not specified.

[1240]
IOWA INJURED VETERANS GRANT PROGRAM

Iowa Department of Veterans Affairs
Camp Dodge, Building 3663
7105 N.W. 70th Avenue
Johnston, IA 50131-1824
(515) 242-5331   Toll Free: (800) VET-IOWA
Fax: (515) 242-5659   E-mail: idva.info@iowa.gov
Web: va.iowa.gov/benefits/injured_vets_grant.html

Summary To provide assistance to Iowa residents who were injured in combat while serving in the armed forces after September 11, 2001.

Eligibility This assistance is available to members of the armed forces of the United States who are still serving or who have been discharged or released from service under honorable conditions. Applicants must have sustained an injury or illness in a combat zone or hostile fire zone after September 11, 2001. The illness or injury must have been serious enough to require medical evacuation from the combat zone and must be considered by the military to be in the line of duty. The veteran or military servicemember must have been a resident of Iowa at the time of injury.

Financial data Qualified veterans or military servicemembers are entitled to the following assistance: $2,500 when they are medically evacuated from the combat zone; $2,500 30 days after evacuation date if still hospitalized, receiving medical treatment, or receiving rehabilitation services from the military or Veterans Administration; $2,500 60 days after evacuation date if still hospitalized, receiving medical treatment, or receiving rehabilitation services from the military or Veterans Administration; and $2,500 90 days after the evacuation date if still hospitalized, receiving medical treatment, or receiving rehabilitation services from the military or Veterans Administration. The maximum assistance is $10,000.

Duration This is a 1-time bonus.

Additional information This program began in 2007.

Number awarded Varies each year.

Deadline Deadline not specified.

[1241]
IOWA MILITARY SERVICE PROPERTY TAX EXEMPTION

Iowa Department of Revenue
Attn: Property Tax Division
Hoover State Office Building
1305 East Walnut
P.O. Box 10469
Des Moines, IA 50306-0469
(515) 281-4040   Toll Free: (800) 367-3388 (within IA)
Fax: (515) 281-3906   E-mail: idr@iowa.gov
Web: www.iowa.gov/tax/taxlaw/PropertyTaxCredits.html

Summary To exempt veterans, military personnel, and their family members from a portion of property taxes in Iowa.

Eligibility This exemption is available to residents of Iowa who are 1) former members of the U.S. armed forces who performed at least 18 months of military service (or for fewer months because of a service-related injury), regardless of the time period, and who were honorably discharged; 2) former members, and members currently serving of the U.S. Reserves and Iowa National Guard who have served at least 20 years; and 3) current members of the U.S. Reserves and Iowa National Guard who were activated for federal duty for at least 90 days; 4) former members of the armed forces whose enlistment would have occurred during the Korean Conflict but chose to serve 5 years in the Reserves; and 5) honorably discharged veterans who served in a designated eligible service period. Applicants must own a primary residence in the state. Also eligible for the exemption are the spouses, unremarried widow(er)s, minor children, and widowed parent of qualified veterans.

Financial data The amount of the exemption is currently $1,852.

Duration 1 year; continues until the qualifying veteran or dependent no longer lives in the residence.

Number awarded Varies each year; recently, more than $2.4 million in property was exempt from taxation.

Deadline Application must be made by June of the year for which the exemption is first requested. The exemption is provided annually, from then on, as long as the qualifying veteran or dependent resides in the house.

[1242]
KENTUCKY INCOME TAX MILITARY PAY EXCLUSION

Kentucky Department of Revenue
Attn: Individual Income Tax
501 High Street
P.O. Box 181
Frankfort, KY 40602-0181
(502) 564-4581   Fax: (502) 564-3875
Web: revenue.ky.gov/individual/incometax.htm

Summary To exclude the income of military personnel from state taxation in Kentucky.

Eligibility This exclusion applies to all military pay received by Kentucky residents who are active-duty members of the U.S. armed forces, members of Reserve components of the U.S. armed forces, and members of the National Guard. The exclusion applies regardless of where the military person is stationed.

Financial data All income received for military service is excluded from Kentucky state taxation.

Duration The exclusion continues as long as the recipient resides in Kentucky and remains a member of the military.

Additional information This exclusion become effective in 2010.

Deadline Deadline not specified.

[1243]
KENTUCKY MILITARY FAMILY ASSISTANCE TRUST FUND

Kentucky Department of Military Affairs
Attn: State Family Program
Boone National Guard Center
100 Minuteman Parkway
Frankfort, KY 40601-6168
(502) 607-1156   Toll Free: (800) 372-7601
Fax: (502) 607-1394   E-mail: steven.engels@us.army.mil
Web: www.dma.ky.gov

Summary To provide emergency financial assistance to Kentucky residents serving in the armed forces outside of the United States and their spouses.

Eligibility This assistance is available to 1) members of the U.S. armed forces who are deployed outside of the United States and who have a Kentucky home of record; and 2) Ken-

tucky resident spouses of eligible military members. Applicants must be facing expenses that create an undue hardship directly related to deployment outside the country. They may not have reasonable access to any other funding source. There is no limitation on the type of expense for which the assistance is requested, only that it create an undue hardship.

Financial data Grants are limited to $2,500 for a single application or $5,000 per fiscal year.

Duration Assistance is available while the military member is deployed overseas and for 90 days following the end of deployment or deactivation.

Additional information This program began in 2006.

Number awarded Varies each year.

Deadline Applications may be submitted at any time.

[1244]
LOUISIANA MILITARY PAY INCOME TAX EXCLUSION

Louisiana Department of Revenue
Attn: Individual Income Tax
P.O. Box 201
Baton Rouge, LA 70821
(225) 219-0102
Web: www.revenue.louisiana.gov

Summary To exempt specified income of military personnel from state taxation in Louisiana.

Eligibility This exemption is available to residents of Louisiana who are on active full-time duty as a member of the armed forces performing service outside the state. Applicants must have served 120 or more consecutive days on active duty.

Financial data Qualifying armed forces members may exempt up to $30,000 of compensation for service outside the state from income taxation in Louisiana.

Duration The benefit continues as long as the recipient remains a resident of Louisiana and serves outside the state for state income tax purposes.

Number awarded Varies each year.

Deadline Deadline not specified.

[1245]
MAINE MILITARY FAMILY RELIEF FUND

Maine Department of Defense, Veterans and Emergency Management
Attn: Family Program Office
Camp Keyes
Augusta, ME 04333-0033
(207) 626-4271
Web: www.me.ngb.army.mil

Summary To provide emergency relief to members of the National Guard or Reserves in Maine who have been called to active duty and their families.

Eligibility This assistance is available to 1) members of the Maine National Guard; and 2) residents of Maine who are members of the Reserves of the armed forces. Applicants must have been called to active military duty and be facing emergency financial needs as a result. Also eligible are members of their immediate family, defined as spouses, children, parents, grandparents, siblings, stepchildren, or others who have a military identification card identifying the military member as a sponsor.

Financial data The amount of the grant depends on the need of the applicant. Funds are available for such needs as food, rent, utilities, emergency transportation and vehicle repair, funeral expenses, medical and dental expenses, short-term emergency needs if pay is delayed or stolen, emergency home repairs, or other emergency needs approved by the unit of assignment.

Duration These are normally 1-time grants.

Number awarded Varies each year.

Deadline Applications may be submitted at any time.

[1246]
MARINE CORPS LAW SCHOOL EDUCATION DEBT SUBSIDY PROGRAM

U.S. Marine Corps
Attn: Manpower and Reserve Affairs (MPP-30)
3280 Russell Road
Quantico, VA 22134-5103
(703) 784-9364   E-mail: Michael.sandstrom@usmc.mil
Web: www.usmc.mil

Summary To repay the law school debts of attorneys (judge advocates) serving in the U.S. Marine Corps.

Eligibility This program is open to judge advocates who have completed their Initial Active Duty Service Obligation (IADSO), or 42 months, and have not been selected for promotion to Major or have been twice passed for promotion to Major. Officers who accessed into the Marine Corps judge advocate community through such programs as the Marine Corps Funded Law Education Program are not eligible.

Financial data Judge advocates approved for this program receive a payment of $10,000 per year.

Duration Up to 5 years.

Additional information Officers who accept a payment through this program incur an active-duty service obligation of 5 years.

Number awarded Varies each year.

Deadline August of each year.

[1247]
MARYLAND INCOME TAX EXEMPTION FOR MILITARY PERSONNEL

Comptroller of Maryland
Attn: Revenue Administration Division
80 Calvert Street
Annapolis, MD 21411
(410) 260-7980   Toll Free: (800) MD-TAXES (within MD)
Fax: (410) 974-3456   TDD: (410) 260-7157
E-mail: taxhelp@comp.state.md.us
Web: individuals.marylandtaxes.com

Summary To exempt certain portions of military pay from Maryland state income tax.

Eligibility Military personnel who are legal residents of Maryland and have earned overseas pay are eligible for this exemption. Personnel whose total military pay exceeds $30,000 do not qualify for this exemption.

Financial data Military personnel who are legal residents of Maryland must file a resident state income tax return and report all income from all sources. However, if they have earned overseas pay, they may subtract up to $15,000 of that pay (depending upon their total income) from their gross income.

Duration The exemption is available annually.

Number awarded Varies each year.

Deadline Military personnel claim this exemption when they file their state income tax return, in April of each year.

[1248]
MASSACHUSETTS WELCOME HOME BONUS

Office of the State Treasurer
Attn: Veterans' Bonus Division
One Ashburton Place, 12th Floor
Boston, MA 02108-1608
(617) 367-9333, ext. 859   Fax: (617) 227-1622
E-mail: veteransbonus@tre.state.ma.us
Web: www.mass.gov/treasury/veterans/welc-home-bonus

Summary To provide a bonus to Massachusetts veterans and servicemembers who served after September 11, 2001.

Eligibility The first-time bonus is available to veterans and current servicemembers who had resided in Massachusetts for at least 6 months immediately prior to their enlistment or commission in the armed forces. The subsequent bonus is available to veterans and current servicemembers who had resided in Massachusetts for at least 6 months prior to their most recent tour or deployment. Both categories of applicants must have performed at least 6 months of service on or after September 11, 2001 and/or 1 or more days in Iraq or Afghanistan. They must still be serving or have been honorably discharged.

Financial data The first-time bonus is $1,000 for active service that includes time in Afghanistan or Iraq or $500 for 6 months or more of active service in the United States or overseas; veterans and servicemembers may be eligible for both types of bonuses. Each subsequent bonus is $500 for active service the includes time in Afghanistan or Iraq or $250 for 6 months or more of active service overseas.

Duration Veterans and servicemembers may be eligible for 1 or both of the first-time bonuses and for a subsequent bonus for each subsequent tour or deployment.

Number awarded Varies each year.

Deadline Deadline not specified.

[1249]
MCCORMICK GRANTS

Society of the First Infantry Division
Attn: 1st Infantry Division Foundation
1933 Morris Road
Blue Bell, PA 19422-1422
Toll Free: (888) 324-4733   Fax: (215) 661-1934
E-mail: Fdn1ID@aol.com
Web: 1stid.org/foundation/grants.cfm

Summary To provide emergency financial assistance to active First Division soldiers and their families.

Eligibility This assistance is available to soldiers currently serving in the First Infantry Division and their families. Applicants must be facing emergency financial needs that cannot be met through the usual forms of assistance available to them.

Financial data Grant amounts depend on the need of the recipient. Recently, they ranged up to $1,500.

Duration These are 1-time grants.

Additional information This program was established in 2005 with funding from the Robert R. McCormick Tribune Foundation.

Number awarded Varies each year; recently, 3 grants, with a total value of $2,313.49, were awarded.

Deadline Applications may be submitted at any time.

[1250]
MICHIGAN HOMESTEAD PROPERTY TAX CREDIT FOR VETERANS AND BLIND PEOPLE

Michigan Department of Treasury
Attn: Homestead Exemption
Treasury Building
430 West Allegan Street
Lansing, MI 48922
(517) 636-4486   TDD: (800) 649-3777
E-mail: treasIndTax@michigan.gov
Web: www.michigan.gov/taxes

Summary To provide an income tax credit to veterans, military personnel, their spouses, blind people, and their surviving spouses in Michigan.

Eligibility Eligible to apply are residents of Michigan who are 1) blind and own their homestead; 2) a veteran with a service-connected disability or his/her surviving spouse; 3) a surviving spouse of a veteran deceased in service; 4) a pensioned veteran, a surviving spouse of those veterans, or an active military member, all of whose household income is less than $7,500; or 5) a surviving spouse of a non-disabled or non-pensioned veteran of the Korean War, World War II, or World War I whose household income is less than $7,500. All applicants must own or rent a home in Michigan, have been a Michigan resident for at least 6 months during the year in which application is made, and fall within qualifying income levels (up to $82,650 in household income).

Financial data The maximum credit, applied to state income taxes, is $1,200. The exact amount varies. For homeowners, the credit depends on the state equalized value of the homestead and on an allowance for filing category. For renters, 20% of the rent is considered property tax eligible for credit.

Duration 1 year; eligibility must be established each year.

Number awarded Varies each year.

Deadline April of each year.

[1251]
MICHIGAN INCOME TAX EXEMPTION FOR VETERANS AND MILITARY PERSONNEL

Michigan Department of Treasury
Attn: Income Tax
Treasury Building
430 West Allegan Street
Lansing, MI 48922
(517) 373-3200   TDD: (800) 649-3777
E-mail: treasIndTax@michigan.gov
Web: www.michigan.gov/taxes

Summary To exempt the income of military personnel and veterans in Michigan from state income taxation.

Eligibility Eligible for this exemption are military personnel and veterans considered Michigan residents for purposes of state income taxation.

Financial data All active-duty military and retirement pay from the U.S. armed forces is exempt from state income taxation.

Duration The exemption continues as long as the recipient resides in Michigan.

Deadline Deadline not specified.

[1252]
MICHIGAN MILITARY FAMILY RELIEF FUND GRANTS

Department of Military and Veterans Affairs
Attn: Military Family Relief Fund
3423 North Martin Luther King Boulevard
P.O. Box 30261
Lansing, MI 48909-7761
Toll Free: (866) 271-4404   Fax: (517) 481-7644
E-mail: paocmn@michigan.gov
Web: www.michigan.gov

Summary To provide temporary financial support to members of the Michigan National Guard and Reserves who have been called to active duty as part of the national response to the September 11, 2001 terrorist attacks and their families.

Eligibility This assistance is available to members of the Michigan National Guard and Reserves and their families. The military member must have been called to active duty as part of the national response to the events of September 11, 2001 and has served at least 30 days of active duty. Applicants must be able to demonstrate a need for assistance as a result of the military member's service.

Financial data The maximum grant is $2,000.

Duration This assistance is provided to meet temporary needs only.

Additional information The state of Michigan established this program in 2004.

Number awarded Varies each year.

Deadline Applications may be submitted at any time.

[1253]
MINNESOTA INCOME TAX SUBTRACTION FOR ACTIVE MILITARY SERVICE

Minnesota Department of Revenue
Attn: Individual Income Tax Division
600 North Robert Street
Mail Station 5510
St. Paul, MN 55146-5510
(651) 296-3781   Toll Free: (800) 652-9094 (within MN)
E-mail: indinctax@state.mn.us
Web: www.taxes.state.mn.us

Summary To exempt from state taxation the income received by military personnel who are residents of Minnesota.

Eligibility This exemption is available to active-duty military personnel and members of the National Guard and other Reserves who are Minnesota residents serving in active military service in Minnesota. Applicants must have earned income for state active service (for disasters, riots, etc., but not regular drill pay), federally-funded state active service, or federal active service.

Financial data Qualifying income earned by military personnel for active-duty service is exempt from Minnesota state taxation.

Duration This exemption is available as long as the taxpayer earns qualifying income.

Additional information This exemption first applied to income earned in 2005.

Number awarded Varies each year.

Deadline   Income tax returns must be submitted by April of each year.

[1254]
MINUTEMAN EMERGENCY ASSISTANCE FUND

National Guard Association of Washington
Attn: Minuteman Emergency Assistance Fund
P.O. Box 5144
Camp Murray
Tacoma, WA 98430-5144
(253) 584-5411   Toll Free: (800) 588-6420
Fax: (253) 582-9521   E-mail: ngawa@aol.com
Web: www.ngaw.org/minuteman.html

Summary   To provide financial assistance to members of the Washington National Guard who are facing emergency situations.

Eligibility   This program is open to members of the Washington National Guard who are facing financial emergencies.

Financial data   The amount of the grant depends on the need of the applicant and the availability of funds. If possible, payments are made directly to creditors.

Duration   These are 1-time grants.

Additional information   Although these are grants that do not need to be repaid, recipients are encouraged to make a contribution to the fund at a future date.

Number awarded   Varies each year; recently, 47 of these grants, worth nearly $22,000, were awarded.

Deadline   Deadline not specified.

[1255]
MISSISSIPPI INCOME TAX EXCLUSION FOR NATIONAL GUARD AND RESERVE FORCE PAY

Mississippi Department of Revenue
Attn: Individual Income Tax Division
P.O. Box 1033
Jackson, MS 39215-1033
(601) 923-7089   Fax: (601) 923-7039
Web: www.dor.ms.gov/taxareas/individ/main.htm

Summary   To exclude a portion of the income of selected Mississippi military personnel from state income taxation.

Eligibility   This deduction is available to Mississippi residents who are currently members of the National Guard or Reserve Forces in the state. Applicants must have received income for inactive duty training (monthly drills), active-duty training (summer camps and special schools), and state active duty (emergency duty for floods, hurricanes, and disasters). Compensation received for full-time active-duty training and compensation as an employee of the National Guard or Reserve Forces is not subject to the exclusion.

Financial data   Excluded from state income taxation is the lesser of $15,000 or the amount received from the National Guard or Reserve Forces as qualified income.

Duration   The deduction continues as long as the recipient resides in Mississippi and receives eligible compensation from the National Guard or Reserve Forces.

Number awarded   Varies each year.

Deadline   Eligible Guard members or Reservists may claim this deduction when they file their state income tax return, in April of each year.

[1256]
MISSOURI MILITARY FAMILY RELIEF FUND GRANTS

Missouri Military Family Relief Fund
Attn: J1/DPP-F
2302 Militia Drive
Jefferson City, MO 65101-1203
(573) 638-9827   Fax: (573) 638-9548
E-mail: MilitaryRelief@mo.ngb.army.mil
Web: www.mmfrf.mo.gov

Summary   To provide emergency financial assistance to members of the National Guard and Reserves in Missouri or their families who are facing difficulties as a result of deployment after September 11, 2001.

Eligibility   This program is open to 1) members of the Missouri National Guard who have been on Title 10 orders as a result of the September 11, 2001 terrorist attacks for 30 consecutive days or more or have been off Title 10 orders as a result of the September 11, 2001 terrorist attacks for 120 days or less; 2) Reserve component members who are residents of Missouri and have been on Title 32 orders as a result of the September 11, 2001 terrorist attacks for 30 days or more or have been off Title 32 orders as a result of the September 11, 2001 terrorist attacks for 120 days or less; 3) immediate relatives of members of those National Guard or Reserve units. The Guard or Reserve member must have a rank no higher than O-3 or W-2. Applicants must be in need of emergency financial assistance; funding is not provided for nonessentials, to finance leave or vacations, to pay fines or legal expenses, to help liquidate or consolidate debts, to assist with house purchase or home improvements, to cover bad checks, or to pay credit card bills.

Financial data   Grants up to $1,000 are available.

Duration   Grants may be awarded only once in a 12-month period.

Additional information   This program began in 2005.

Number awarded   Varies each year.

Deadline   Applications may be submitted at any time.

[1257]
MONTANA MILITARY SALARY INCOME TAX EXCLUSION

Montana Department of Revenue
Attn: Individual Income Tax
125 North Roberts, Third Floor
P.O. Box 5805
Helena, MT 59604-5805
(406) 444-6900   Toll Free: (866) 859-2254
Fax: (406) 444-6642   TDD: (406) 444-2830
Web: mt.gov/revenue

Summary   To exclude the income of military personnel from state taxation in Montana.

Eligibility   This exclusion is available to residents of Montana for purposes of state income taxation who are 1) serving on active duty as a member of the regular armed forces; 2) a member of a Reserve component of the Army, Navy, Marine Corps, Air Force, or Coast Guard serving on active duty in a "contingent operation;" or 3) a member of the Montana National Guard serving on active duty for a period of more than 30 consecutive days for the purpose of responding to a national emergency.

Financial data All basic, special, and incentive pay for active-duty service is exempt from state income taxation.
Duration The exemption continues as long as the recipient resides in Montana and serves on active duty.
Deadline Deadline not specified.

[1258]
NATIONAL ASSOCIATION OF AMERICAN VETERANS EMERGENCY ASSISTANCE

National Association of American Veterans
Attn: Executive Director
P.O. Box 6865
Washington, DC 20020-9994
Web: www.naavets.org/services.html

Summary To provide emergency financial assistance to veterans, military personnel, and their families.
Eligibility This assistance is available to veterans, military service members, and their family members who are experiencing financial hardship. Applicants must be seeking funding for mortgage assistance, rent, home repair or maintenance, vehicle repair or maintenance, medical expenses, or transportation expenses.
Financial data The amount of the grant depends on the need of the recipient.
Duration These are 1-time grants.
Additional information This association began in 2005.
Number awarded Varies each year.
Deadline Applications may be submitted at any time.

[1259]
NAVY HEALTH PROFESSIONS LOAN REPAYMENT PROGRAM

U.S. Navy
Attn: Navy Medicine Professional Development Center
Code OH
8901 Wisconsin Avenue, Building 1, 13th Floor, Room
  1313<NL>Bethesda, MD 20889-5611
(301) 319-4531   Toll Free: (800) USA-NAVY
Fax: (301) 295-1811   E-mail: oh@med.navy.mil
Web: www.med.navy.mil

Summary To repay the educational loans of health care professionals willing to serve as an active-duty officer in the Navy.
Eligibility This program is open to 1) full-time students enrolled in the final year of a course of study at an accredited educational institution leading to a degree in a health profession other than medicine, dentistry, or osteopathic medicine; and 2) residents enrolled in the final year of specialty training in medicine, dentistry, or osteopathic medicine. Applicants must be serving as, or willing to serve as, active-duty Navy officers in the Medical Corps, Dental Corps, Nurse Corps, or Medical Service Corps. They must have qualified government or commercial loans for actual costs paid for tuition, reasonable educational expenses, and reasonable living expenses relating to the attainment of a degree in allopathic or osteopathic medicine, dentistry, or other health profession.
Financial data This program provides funding for the repayment of educational loans up to $40,000 per year.
Duration 1 year; may be renewed. Each of the 4 Corps (Medical, Dental, Nurse, and Medical Service) determines the total number of years of repayment that may be authorized.

Additional information In additional to applicants in medicine, dentistry, nursing, and osteopathic medicine, this program provides repayment of educational loans in health profession fields designated as necessary to meet identified skill shortages in the Navy; currently, those are clinical psychology, physician assistant, podiatry, pharmacy, social work, entomology, radiation health, microbiology, and physical therapy. Participants incur an active-duty service obligation of 2 years or 1 year for each annual repayment, whichever is greater.
Number awarded Varies each year.
Deadline November of each year.

[1260]
NAVY-MARINE CORPS RELIEF SOCIETY FINANCIAL ASSISTANCE

Navy-Marine Corps Relief Society
875 North Randolph Street, Suite 225
Arlington, VA 22203-1757
(703) 696-4904   Fax: (703) 696-0144
Web: www.nmcrs.org/intfreeloan.html

Summary To provide emergency assistance, in the form of interest-free loans or grants, to current and former Navy and Marine Corps personnel and their families who need temporary funding.
Eligibility This program is open to active-duty and retired Navy and Marine Corps personnel, their eligible family members, eligible family members of Navy and Marine Corps personnel who died on active duty or in a retired status, Reservists on extended active duty, indigent mothers (65 years of age or older) of deceased servicemembers who have limited resources and no family to provide for their welfare, ex-spouses whose marriage to a servicemember lasted for at least 20 years while the servicemember was on active duty and who have not remarried, and uniformed members of the National Oceanic and Atmospheric Administration (NOAA). Applicants must need emergency funding for funeral expenses, medical or dental bills, food, rent, utilities, emergency transportation, disaster relief, child care expenses, essential vehicle repairs, or other unforeseen family emergencies. Funding is not available to pay bills for non-essentials, finance liberty and vacations, pay fines or legal expenses, pay taxes, finance recreational boats or vehicles or help Navy and Marine Corps families live beyond their means.
Financial data Funds are provided in the form of interest-free loans or grants.
Number awarded Varies each year.
Deadline Applications may be submitted at any time.

[1261]
NCOA DISASTER RELIEF FUND

Non Commissioned Officers Association of the United
  States of America
Attn: Benevolent Programs
10635 IH 35 North
P.O. Box 33610
San Antonio, TX 78265-3610
(210) 653-6161   Toll Free: (800) 662-2620
E-mail: membsvc@ncoausa.org
Web: www.ncoausa.org

Summary To provide funding to military members of the Non Commissioned Officers Association (NCOA) and their families who need disaster relief.

Eligibility This program is open to military members of the association and their families who suffer losses as a result of such disasters as acts of God, hurricanes, fires, floods, and earthquakes.

Financial data The amount of the aid depends on the availability of funds and the need of the recipient.

Additional information This program began in 1994.

Number awarded Varies each year.

Deadline Applications may be submitted at any time.

[1262]
NEW MEXICO TAX EXCLUSION FOR MILITARY ACTIVE DUTY PAY

New Mexico Taxation and Revenue Department
Attn: Personal Income Tax Division
1100 South St. Francis Drive
P.O. Box 25122
Santa Fe, NM 87504-5122
(505) 827-0700
Web: www.tax.newmexico.gov

Summary To exclude the income of active-duty military personnel from state income taxation in New Mexico.

Eligibility This exclusion is available to members of the armed forces, including those on active duty, full-time training duty, annual training duty, full-time National Guard duty, and attendance (while in the active service) at a school designated as a service school. Both residents and non-residents of New Mexico are eligible.

Financial data All pay received in New Mexico for qualifying military service is excluded from income for income tax purposes.

Duration The exclusion continues as long as the service member earns income from the military in New Mexico.

Number awarded Varies each year.

Deadline The qualifying service member claims the exclusion on the New Mexico state income tax return, which is due in April.

[1263]
NEW YORK ORGANIZED MILITIA INCOME TAX EXEMPTION

New York State Department of Taxation and Finance
W.A. Harriman Campus
Tax and Finance Building
Albany, NY 12227-0001
(518) 438-8581   Toll Free: (800) 225-5829 (within NY)
Web: www.tax.ny.gov/pit/file/military_page.htm

Summary To exempt the income of members of the New York organized militia from state income tax.

Eligibility This exemption is available to members of the New York organized militia (including the New York Army National Guard, the New York Air National Guard, the New York Naval Militia, and the New York Guard). Applicants must have received income for the performance of active service within New York in accordance with active-duty orders issued by the governor or to federal active Guard duty orders. The exemption does not cover income received for regular duties in the organized militia or active duty in the U.S. armed forces.

Financial data Qualified income is exempt from state income taxation in New York.

Duration The exemption is available whenever the militia member receives qualified income.

Number awarded Varies each year.

Deadline Deadline not specified.

[1264]
NORTH DAKOTA STATE INCOME TAX NATIONAL GUARD OR RESERVE MEMBER EXCLUSION

Office of State Tax Commissioner
State Capitol Building
600 East Boulevard Avenue, Department 127
Bismarck, ND 58505-0599
(701) 328-7088   Toll Free: (877) 328-7088
Fax: (701) 328-3700   TDD: (800) 366-6888
E-mail: taxinfo@state.nd.us
Web: www.nd.gov/tax/indincome

Summary To exempt from state income taxation the income received by members of the National Guard and armed forces Reserves in North Dakota.

Eligibility Eligible for this benefit are North Dakota residents who are members of the North Dakota National Guard or a Reserve unit of the U.S. armed forces. Applicants must have been mobilized for federal active-duty service and received compensation for that service. Compensation received for attending annual training, basic military training, professional military education, or active duty for which they volunteered but did not receive mobilization orders does not qualify.

Financial data All qualified income may be excluded from income for state tax purposes.

Duration The exclusion may be taken as long as the recipient resides in North Dakota and receives qualified pay.

Number awarded Varies each year.

Deadline Deadline not specified.

[1265]
NORTH DAKOTA STATE INCOME TAX SERVICEMEMBER CIVIL RELIEF ACT ADJUSTMENT

Office of State Tax Commissioner
State Capitol Building
600 East Boulevard Avenue, Department 127
Bismarck, ND 58505-0599
(701) 328-7088   Toll Free: (877) 328-7088
Fax: (701) 328-3700   TDD: (800) 366-6888
E-mail: taxinfo@state.nd.us
Web: www.nd.gov/tax/indincome

Summary To exempt from state income taxation the income received by members of the U.S. uniformed services who are nonresidents or part-year residents of North Dakota.

Eligibility Eligible for this benefit are members of the U.S. uniformed services who are nonresidents or part-year residents of North Dakota for state income tax purposes. Applicants must have received compensation in North Dakota for active-duty service in the U.S. armed forces or for active duty in the commissioned corps of the Public Health Service or the National Oceanic and Atmospheric Administration. For part-year residents, only the compensation received for this service while a nonresident of North Dakota qualifies.

Financial data   All qualified income may be excluded from income for state tax purposes.

Duration   The exclusion may be taken as long as the recipient earns qualifying income in North Dakota.

Number awarded   Varies each year.

Deadline   Deadline not specified.

[1266]
OHIO INCOME TAX DEDUCTION FOR MILITARY PAY

Ohio Department of Taxation
Attn: Individual Income Tax
30 East Broad Street
P.O. Box 530
Columbus, OH 43216-0530
(614) 433-5817   Toll Free: (800) 282-1780 (within OH)
Fax: (614) 433-7771
Web: tax.ohio.gov

Summary   To deduct from state income taxation in Ohio the pay received by military personnel who are residents of the state but stationed elsewhere.

Eligibility   This deduction is available to residents of Ohio who are members of an active component of the U.S. armed forces or of a Reserve component or the National Guard under federal mobilization orders. Applicants must be assigned to a permanent duty station outside Ohio.

Financial data   All military pay received by military personnel stationed outside the state is excluded from income for purposes of Ohio state taxation.

Duration   The exclusion is available as long as the recipient remains an Ohio resident but stationed outside the state.

Additional information   This deduction became effective in 2007.

Number awarded   Varies each year.

Deadline   Deadline not specified.

[1267]
OHIO VETERANS BONUS

Ohio Department of Veterans Services
Attn: Veterans Bonus Program
P.O. Box 373
Sandusky, OH 44871
Toll Free: (877) OHIO-VET
Web: veteransbonus.ohio.gov/odvs_web

Summary   To provide a bonus to Ohio veterans and active-duty servicemembers who served during the Persian Gulf War, Afghanistan, or Iraq and their family members.

Eligibility   This bonus is available to current residents of Ohio who were also residents of the state when they began active-duty military service, including as a member of a Reserve component or the Ohio National Guard. Applicants must have served at least 90 days or be currently serving in the U.S. armed forces during the periods of the Persian Gulf War (August 2, 1990 through March 3, 1991), the war in Afghanistan (October 7, 2001 through the present), or the war in Iraq (March 19, 2003 through the present). If no longer serving, they must have received an honorable discharge. Additional bonuses are available to of 1) veterans who were medically discharged or retired because of combat-related disabilities sustained in the Persian Gulf, Afghanistan, or Iraq; and 2) veterans who were declared Missing in Action (MIA) or Prisoner of War (POW) or (if the veteran is deceased) their

family members. Also eligible are family members (in order of preference: spouses, children, parents) 1) veterans who have died but whose death was not a result of injuries or illness sustained in the Persian Gulf, Afghanistan, or Iraq; or 2) veterans who died as a result of injuries or illness sustained in the Persian Gulf, Afghanistan, or Iraq.

Financial data   The bonus for veterans and military personnel who served in the Persian Gulf, Afghanistan, or Iraq is $100 per month of service, to a maximum of $1,000; the bonus for veterans and military personnel who served during the specified time periods but elsewhere in the world is $50 per month of service, to a maximum of $500; veterans who were medically discharged or retired because of combat-related disabilities are eligible for an in-theater bonus of $1,000 (regardless of time served in-theater) plus $50 per month for non-theater service time, to a maximum benefit of $1,500; veterans who were declared MIA or POW or family members are eligible for a bonus of $5,000; families of deceased veterans whose death was not a result of injuries or illness are eligible for the same bonus that the veteran would have received if still living, to a maximum of $1,500; families of veterans who died as a result of injuries or illness are eligible for a bonus of $5,000.

Duration   These are 1-time bonuses.

Number awarded   Varies each year.

Deadline   Applications may be submitted at any time. For veterans and current military members who served during the wars in Afghanistan or Iraq, applications must be submitted within 3 years after the President has officially proclaimed the end of those hostilities.

[1268]
OHIO VETERANS' FINANCIAL ASSISTANCE

Ohio Department of Veterans Services
77 South High Street, Seventh Floor
Columbus, OH 43215
(614) 644-0898   Toll Free: (888) DVS-OHIO
Fax: (614) 728-9498   E-mail: ohiovet@dvs.ohio.gov
Web: dvs.ohio.gov

Summary   To provide emergency aid to Ohio veterans, military personnel, and their dependents who, because of disability or disaster, are in financial need.

Eligibility   This assistance is available to veterans and active-duty members of the U.S. armed forces, as well as their spouses, surviving spouses, dependent parents, minor children, and wards. Applicants must have been residents of the Ohio county in which they are applying for at least 3 months. They must be able to demonstrate need for relief because of sickness, accident, or destitution.

Financial data   The amount granted varies, depending on the needs of the recipient.

Duration   These are emergency funds only and are not designed to be a recurring source of income.

Additional information   These grants are made by the various county veterans services offices in Ohio.

Number awarded   Varies each year.

Deadline   Applications may be submitted at any time.

[1269]
OKLAHOMA MILITARY PAY EXCLUSION

Oklahoma Tax Commission
Attn: Income Tax
2501 North Lincoln Boulevard
Oklahoma City, OK 73194-0009
(405) 521-3160   Toll Free: (800) 522-8165 (within OK)
Fax: (405) 522-0063   E-mail: otcmaster@tax.ok.gov
Web: www.tax.ok.gov/incometax.html

Summary   To exempt the income of military personnel in Oklahoma from state income taxation.

Eligibility   Members of the armed forces who are defined, for state income tax purposes, as residents of Oklahoma are eligible for this exemption. National Guard and Reserve pay also qualifies to the extent that such pay is included in federal adjusted gross income.

Financial data   All salary received for active-duty service in the U.S. armed forces is deducted from taxable income in Oklahoma.

Duration   The exemption is available as long as the recipient resides in Oklahoma and receives salary from the military.

Deadline   Deadline not specified.

[1270]
OPERATION FAMILY FUND FINANCIAL ASSISTANCE

Operation Family Fund
P.O. Box 837
Ridgecrest, CA 93556
(760) 793-0053   Fax: (888) 851-1456
E-mail: support@operatonfamilyfund.org
Web: operationfamilyfund.org

Summary   To provide personal assistance to military and civilian personnel and the families of those personnel who died or were severely disabled as a result of service as a result of the Global War on Terror.

Eligibility   This assistance is available to military and civilian personnel and their families who died or were severely disabled as a result of Operations Enduring or Iraqi Freedom, either domestically or abroad. Civilians must have been serving officially as an employee of the U.S. government or contractor to the U.S. government. Applicants must be seeking funding for such short- and long-term living needs as food; rent or utilities; emergency transportation; vehicle repair; funeral expenses; medical and dental expenses; assistance with a home, rental, lease, or purchase; home improvements; or assistance with the purchase, rent, or lease of a vehicle. Grants are approved to applicants in the following priority order: 1) member injured because of a hostile action and have a Department of Veterans Affairs (VA) disability rating of 50% or higher; 2) member injured because of an accident while serving in Iraq or Afghanistan and have a VA disability rating of 50% or higher; 3) member who has post-traumatic stress disorder with a VA disability rating of 50% or higher as a result of serving in Iraq or Afghanistan; 4) member who has other service-connected injuries caused in support of the Global War on Terror and a VA disability rating of 50% or higher; 5) member in any of the prior categories but still in the medical board process with a pending VA disability rating; 6) child (under 22 years of age) and/or spouse of a military member killed in action who did not receive government death benefit or SGLA; and 7) second requests.

Financial data   Most grants are at least $1,000 but less than $10,000.

Duration   These are 1-time grants; renewals may be approved if funding is available.

Number awarded   Varies each year; since this organization was established, it has awarded more than 385 grants.

Deadline   Applications may be submitted at any time.

[1271]
OPERATION HOMEFRONT GRANTS

Operation Homefront
8930 Fourwinds Drive, Suite 340
San Antonio, TX 78239
(210) 659-7756   Toll Free: (800) 722-6098
Fax: (210) 566-7544
Web: www.operationhomefront.net

Summary   To provide assistance to military families and wounded personnel who face financial difficulties related to service.

Eligibility   This program is open to 1) veterans who are disabled as a result of service-connected injuries and their families; and 2) other military families who face financial needs because of the hardships associated with military service. Examples of financial needs include food assistance, auto repair, moving assistance, transitional family housing, vision care, child and dependent care, critical baby needs, travel and transportation, home repair, and essential home items.

Financial data   The amounts of the grants vary, depending on the need of the applicant. Recently, average grants were $100 to families for critical baby items, $161 for food assistance, $300 to assist in paying utilities, or $1,117 to help with rent or mortgage payments.

Duration   This are 1-time grants.

Additional information   This foundation began in 2002.

Number awarded   Varies each year; since the foundation was established, it has awarded approximately $128 million to support more than 400,000 families and personnel.

Deadline   Applications may be submitted at any time.

[1272]
OPERATION ONCE IN A LIFETIME ASSISTANCE

Operation Once in a Lifetime
P.O. Box 797052
Dallas, TX 75379
E-mail: contact@operationonceinalifetime.com
Web: operationonceinalifetime.com

Summary   To provide assistance for a variety of special needs to military personnel of all ranks and branches of service.

Eligibility   This assistance is available to military personnel, wounded or not, deployed or not, all ranks and branches, during peace time and war time. Applicants must be able to demonstrate a special need. The organization conducts special activities such as operation logistics drop (to deliver used furniture, clothes, toys, or electronics to military families), operation moral support (to provide transportation and admission to a major sporting event or theme park), operation full support (to publicize on the organization's web sites the special needs of individual military personnel and seek donations to assist with that need), operation fly every soldier home (to pay for transportation of military personnel not pro-

vided by the military), and operation day care (to provide child care services at facilities near military bases worldwide).
Financial data The amount of the assistance depends on the need of the recipient.
Duration These are 1-time grants.
Number awarded Varies each year. Since March 2007, this program has assisted 1,200 military personnel.
Deadline Applications may be submitted at any time.

[1273]
OPERATION REBOUND GRANTS
Challenged Athletes Foundation
Attn: Program Manager
9990 Mesa Rim Road
P.O. Box 910769
San Diego, CA 92191
(858) 866-0959   Fax: (858) 866-0958
E-mail: info@challengedathletes.org
Web: www.challengedathletes.org
Summary To provide funding to veterans and September 11 first responders who became disabled as a result of service and wish to participate in athletic activities.
Eligibility This program is open to 1) veterans and service members who suffered a permanent physical disability (such as loss of a limb(s), sight, or spinal cord injury, in the Global War on Terror; and 2) law enforcement personnel, fire fighters, and others who were the first to respond to the September 11, 2001 attacks and became disabled as a result. Applicants must need funding for 1 of 3 categories: 1) equipment, for wheelchairs, prosthetics, or other assistive devices; 2) training, for club or gym dues or membership fees, team or association dues or membership fees, or coaching or training expense; or 3) competition, for travel, entry fees, or other costs to participate in a recognized event. They may apply for only 1 category per year. Along with their application, they must submit a brief autobiography with their personal and athletic goals, a brief summary of their military or law enforcement history, a statement on how they are planning to raise awareness for "Operation Rebound" and the Challenged Athletes Foundation, and documentation of financial need.
Financial data Grant amounts depend on the documented need of the applicant.
Duration These are 1-time grants. Recipients may reapply.
Additional information This program was established for veterans in 2004 and expanded to include first responders in 2008.
Number awarded Varies each year.
Deadline Applications may be submitted at any time, but they must be received at least 90 days prior to the date needed.

[1274]
OPERATION SECOND CHANCE FAMILY ASSISTANCE GRANTS
Operation Second Chance
Attn: President
22708 Birchcrest Lane
P.O. Box 461
Clarksburg, MD 20871
Toll Free: (888) OSC-4VET
E-mail: assistance@operationsecondchance.org
Web: www.operationsecondchance.org

Summary To provide assistance for payment of ordinary living expenses to disabled veterans and military personnel and their families.
Eligibility This assistance is available to disabled veterans and military personnel who are within 18 months of their injury or are currently receiving care at a military health care facility and have an expected or adjudicated disability rating of 70% or higher. Their family members are also eligible. Applicants must be seeking funding for payment of rent or mortgages, utility bills, child care during illness or injury, or housing and/or airfare for a family member to assist an injured or recovering member.
Financial data The amount of the grant depends on the need of the recipient.
Duration These are 1-time grants.
Number awarded Varies each year.
Deadline Applications may be submitted at any time.

[1275]
OREGON INCOME TAX EXEMPTION FOR MILITARY ACTIVE DUTY PAY
Oregon Department of Revenue
Revenue Building
955 Center Street, N.E.
Salem, OR 97310-2555
(503) 378-4988   Toll Free: (800) 356-4222 (within OR)
Fax: (503) 945-8738   TDD: (800) 886-7204 (within OR)
Web: www.oregon.gov/DOR/PERTAX/index.shtml
Summary To exempt a portion of the income of military personnel from state taxation in Oregon.
Eligibility Eligible are military personnel considered Oregon residents for purposes of state income taxation.
Financial data Military pay exempt from state income taxation includes 1) all military active-duty income earned outside Oregon during the year of entry into or discharge from military service; 2) up to $6,000 of active-duty pay earned within Oregon, regardless of other military pay exemptions; and 3) all income earned while serving in a combat zone.
Duration The exemption continues as long as the recipient resides in Oregon.
Deadline Exemptions are filed with state income tax returns in April of each year.

[1276]
OREGON INCOME TAX NATIONAL GUARD ACTIVE DUTY PAY SUBTRACTION
Oregon Department of Revenue
Revenue Building
955 Center Street, N.E.
Salem, OR 97310-2555
(503) 378-4988   Toll Free: (800) 356-4222 (within OR)
Fax: (503) 945-8738   TDD: (800) 886-7204 (within OR)
Web: www.oregon.gov/DOR/PERTAX
Summary To exempt the income of National Guard members called to active duty from state taxation in Oregon.
Eligibility This exemption is available to members of the Oregon National Guard who served on active duty (under U.S. Code Title 32) in Oregon at any time after January 2001. Applicants must have been called to active duty status (under U.S. Code Title 10).

Financial data All pay received by members of the Oregon National Guard while on active-duty status (under U.S. Code Title 10) is exempt from state income taxation in Oregon.

Duration The exemption continues as long as the recipient serves on active duty as a member of the Oregon National Guard.

Deadline Exemptions are filed with state income tax returns in April of each year.

[1277]
OREGON PROPERTY TAX EXEMPTION FOR ACTIVE DUTY MILITARY SERVICE

Oregon Department of Revenue
Attn: Property Tax Division
Revenue Building
955 Center Street, N.E.
Salem, OR 97310-2555
(503) 378-4988   Toll Free: (800) 356-4222 (within OR)
Fax: (503) 945-8738   TDD: (800) 886-7204 (within OR)
Web: www.oregon.gov/DOR/PTD/exemptions.shtml

Summary To exempt members of the Oregon National Guard and military Reserves called to active duty and their survivors from a portion of their property taxes.

Eligibility This exemption is available to members of the Oregon National Guard and Reserves called to federal active duty (U.S. Code Title 10) who serve more than 178 days with that status during the tax year. Applicants must own property that they occupy as their primary residence in Oregon. Occupants of a home owned by a qualified Guard member or Reservist who is killed in action also qualify for this exemption.

Financial data The exemption was set as $60,000 of the homestead property's assessed value as of July 1, 2006. It increases by 3% annually.

Duration 1 year; may be renewed as long as the eligible Guard member or surviving occupant of the home owns and occupies the primary residence.

Additional information This exemption was first available in 2005.

Number awarded Varies each year.

Deadline This exemption is not automatic. Applications must be submitted by July of each year.

[1278]
PENNSYLVANIA INCOME TAX EXEMPTION FOR MILITARY PERSONNEL

Pennsylvania Department of Revenue
Attn: Bureau of Individual Taxes
Department 280600
Harrisburg, PA 17128-0600
(717) 787-8201   Toll Free: (888) PA-TAXES
Fax: (717) 787-2391   TDD: (800) 447-3020
E-mail: parev@revenue.state.pa.us
Web: www.revenue.state.pa.us

Summary To exempt from state taxation the income received by Pennsylvania residents for military service outside the state.

Eligibility Eligible are military personnel considered to be Pennsylvania residents for the purposes of state income taxation. Reservists and National Guard members ordered to active duty for training are also eligible.

Financial data All military pay earned on active duty outside of Pennsylvania or while on federal active duty for training outside of Pennsylvania is not taxable.

Duration The exemption continues as long as the recipient resides in Pennsylvania.

Deadline Deadline not specified.

[1279]
PENNSYLVANIA MILITARY FAMILY RELIEF ASSISTANCE PROGRAM

Pennsylvania Department of Military and Veterans Affairs
Attn: Military Family Relief Assistance Program
Building 0-47
Fort Indiantown Gap
Annville, PA 17003-5002
(717) 861-6500   Toll Free: (866) 292-7201
Fax: (717) 861-2600   E-mail: ra-pa-mfrap@pa.gov
Web: www.portal.state.pa.us

Summary To provide emergency financial assistance to members of the armed forces from Pennsylvania and their families.

Eligibility This assistance is available to residents of Pennsylvania who are 1) serving on 30 or more consecutive days of active duty with the Pennsylvania Army or Air National Guard or Reserve components of the armed forces; 2) serving on 30 or more consecutive days of active duty with the active armed forces; 3) serving on 30 or more consecutive days of state active duty for emergencies or duty under the Emergency Management Assistance Compact in the Pennsylvania National Guard; 4) current members of the Pennsylvania National Guard within 1 year of a qualifying tour of active duty of 30 days or more who can demonstrate a financial need directly related to the active-duty period; 5) former members of the armed forces, Reserve components, or Pennsylvania National Guard within 2 years of a medical discharge for a disability incurred in the line of duty if they can demonstrate a financial need directly related to active duty or medical disability; and 6) eligible relatives (spouses, parents, siblings, or children) of military service members. Applicants must be able to demonstrate a direct and immediate financial need as a result of military service; that financial need may include, but is not limited to, a sudden or unexpected loss of income directly related to military service; emergency need for child care for which the applicant lacks financial resources; natural or man-made disasters resulting in a need for food, shelter, or other necessities; or the death or critical illness of a parent, spouse, sibling, or child resulting in immediate need for travel, lodging, or subsistence for which the applicant lacks financial resources.

Financial data The maximum grant is $3,500.

Duration Only 1 grant will be awarded in each 12-month period.

Additional information This program began in 2005.

Number awarded Varies each year.

Deadline Applications may be submitted at any time.

[1280]
PERKINS LOAN CANCELLATION

Department of Education
Attn: Federal Student Aid Information Center
P.O. Box 84
Washington, DC 20044-0084
(319) 337-5665   Toll Free: (800) 4-FED-AID
TDD: (800) 730-8913
Web: studentaid.ed.gov

Summary To cancel Federal Perkins Loans of borrowers who die, become disabled, or provide specified public service.

Eligibility This loan cancellation is available to college graduates who borrowed money from their institutions through the Perkins Loan Program. Cancellation of 100% of the loan is provided if the borrower becomes totally and permanently disabled, dies, or becomes a provider of public services in 1 of the following capacities: a full-time teacher in a designated elementary or secondary school serving students from low-income families; a full-time special education teacher of infants, toddlers, children, or youth with disabilities in a public or other nonprofit elementary or secondary school; a full-time teacher of designated shortage fields (currently defined as mathematics, science, foreign languages, bilingual education, or other discipline determined by a state education agency to have a shortage of qualified teachers in that state); a teacher in a low-income educational service agency; a full-time staff member in a prekindergarten, childcare or Head Start program; a full-time qualified professional provider of early intervention services for the disabled; a librarian with a master's degree at an eligible elementary or secondary school; a librarian with a master's degree at a public library serving an area containing an eligible elementary or secondary school; a full-time employee of a public or nonprofit child or family service agency providing services to high-risk children and their families from low-income communities; a full-time nurse or medical technician providing health care services directly to patients; a full-time law enforcement officer, corrections officer, prosecuting attorney, or public defender attorney; a full-time fire fighter with a local, state, or federal fire department or district; a full-time faculty member at a Tribal College or University; a full-time speech-language pathologist with a master's degree working exclusively with Title I-eligible schools; or an active-duty member of the U.S. armed forces serving in an area of hostilities or an area of imminent danger. Up to 70% of a loan may be cancelled if the student serves as a VISTA or Peace Corps volunteer.

Financial data For teachers, public servants, and military personnel loans are cancelled at the rate of 15% of the original principal amount for each of the first and second years of service, 20% for each of the third and fourth years of service, and 30% for the fifth year of service. For VISTA and Peace Corps volunteers, 15% of the original principal amount is cancelled for each of the first and second years and 20% for each of the third and fourth years of service.

Duration Complete cancellation of the loan is provided after 5 years of most kinds of service. For VISTA and Peace Corps volunteers, partial cancellation is provided after 4 years.

Number awarded Varies each year.

Deadline Deadline not specified.

[1281]
RED CROSS EMERGENCY FINANCIAL ASSISTANCE

American Red Cross
Attn: Military Call Center
2025 E Street, N.W.
Washington, DC 20006
(202) 303-4498   Toll Free: (877) 272-7337
Web: www.redcross.org

Summary To provide funding to active and retired military personnel and their families who are in need of emergency financial assistance.

Eligibility This program is open to servicemembers, their families, retired military personnel, and widows of retired military personnel. Members of the National Guard and Reserves are also eligible. Applicants must be in need of such emergency financial assistance as travel that requires the presence of the servicemember or his or her family, burial of a loved one, or other assistance that cannot wait until the next business day (food, temporary lodging, urgent medical needs, or the minimum amount required to avoid eviction or utility shut-off).

Financial data The amount of the assistance depends on the need of the recipient.

Duration These are 1-time grants.

Additional information The Red Cross works with the military aid societies (Army Emergency Relief, Navy-Marine Corps Relief Society, Air Force Aid Society, and Coast Guard Mutual Assistance).

Number awarded Varies each year; recently, more than 5,000 servicemembers and their families received more than $5.8 million in emergency grants.

Deadline Applications may be submitted at any time.

[1282]
SENTINELS OF FREEDOM SCHOLARSHIPS

Sentinels of Freedom
P.O. Box 1316
San Ramon, CA 94583
(925) 380-6342   Fax: (925) 867-1078
E-mail: info@sentinelsoffreedom.org
Web: www.sentinelsoffreedom.org

Summary To provide funding to veterans and current military personnel who became blind or disabled as a result of injuries sustained in the line of duty on or after September 11, 2001.

Eligibility This program is open to members of the U.S. Air Force, Army, Coast Guard, Marines, or Navy who sustained injuries in the line of duty on or after September 11, 2001. Applicants must be rated as 60% or more disabled as a result of 1 or more of the following conditions: amputation, blindness, deafness, paraplegia, severe burns, limited traumatic brain injury (TBI), or limited post-traumatic stress disorder (PTSD); other severe injuries may be considered on a case-by-case basis. They must complete an interview process and demonstrate that they have the skills, experience, and attitude that lead to employment.

Financial data Assistance is available for the following needs: housing (adapted for physical needs if necessary), new furniture and other household supplies, career-placement assistance and training, new adaptive vehicles, educational opportunities in addition to the new GI Bill, or financial and personal mentorship.

Duration Assistance may be provided for up to 4 years.

Additional information The first assistance granted by this program was awarded in 2004.

Number awarded Varies each year. Since the program was established, it has supported 84 current and former service members.

Deadline Applications may be submitted at any time.

[1283]
SOUTH CAROLINA MILITARY FAMILY RELIEF FUND

South Carolina Office of Veterans Affairs
Attn: SCMFRF Coordinator
1205 Pendleton Street, Suite 477
Columbia, SC 29201-3789
(803) 734-0200   Fax: (803) 734-0421
E-mail: va@oepp.sc.gov
Web: www.govoepp.state.sc.us/va/benefits.html

Summary To provide emergency assistance to members and families of the National Guard and Reserve forces in South Carolina who have been called to active duty as a result of the September 11, 2001 terrorist attacks.

Eligibility This assistance is available to families of South Carolina National Guard members and South Carolina residents serving in the U.S. armed forces reserve units who were called to active duty as a result of the September 11, 2001 terrorist attacks. Status-based grants are available to National Guard and Reserve members and their family members enrolled in the Defense Enrollment Eligibility Reporting System (DEERS); the servicemember must have been on active duty for at least 30 consecutive days, have a rank no higher than O-3 or W-2, and have orders for Operation Nobel Eagle, Enduring Freedom, Iraqi Freedom, Executive Order 13223, or other approved operation. Need-based grants are available to servicemembers and their families who meet those requirements and who also can demonstrate that the servicemember sustained a 30% or greater decrease in income from his or her civilian salary. Casualty-based grants are available to servicemembers who sustained a service-connected injury or illness and to next of kin of servicemembers killed in action, missing in action, or a prisoner of war. The following servicemembers are ineligible: those who are unmarried or have no family members enrolled in DEERS; personnel serving in active Guard, Reserve, or similar full-time unit support programs but not called to Title 10 service; and members who receive a discharge under other than honorable conditions.

Financial data Status grants are $500; need-based grants range up to $2,000; casualty-based grants are $1,000.

Duration Status grants are available only once in each fiscal year and only 1 time for each active-duty order; need-based grants may be renewed after 180 days have elapsed; casualty-based grants may be awarded only 1 time for each active-duty order.

Additional information This program, which began in 2005, is funded by a voluntary check-off on South Carolina individual income tax forms and by other grants and donations.

Number awarded Varies each year.

Deadline Applications may be submitted at any time.

[1284]
SOUTH CAROLINA NATIONAL GUARD AND RESERVE ANNUAL TRAINING AND DRILL PAY EXEMPTION

South Carolina Department of Revenue
301 Gervais Street
P.O. Box 125
Columbia, SC 29214
(803) 898-5000   Toll Free: (800) 763-1295
Fax: (803) 898-5822
Web: www.sctax.org

Summary To exempt the pay received by military Reserve and National Guard members from state taxation in South Carolina.

Eligibility This exemption is available to members of the military Reserves and National Guard in South Carolina who receive income for weekend drills and customary training (normally 1 weekend per month and 2 weeks per year). The exemption may include all inactive duty pay received from the United States or any state for weekend drills and other inactive duty training actually attended, up to 15 days of customary annual training pay (also referred to as active duty training or ADT), up to 14 days of ADT pay plus up to 2 days of travel time listed on official orders, or up to 15 days of annual training plus up to 24 days of weekend drills.

Financial data Qualified Reserve and Guard income is exempt from state income taxation in South Carolina.

Duration The exemption continues as long as the eligible Reserve or Guard member resides in South Carolina and receives the specified income.

Number awarded Varies each year.

Deadline Deadline not specified.

[1285]
SPECIAL HOUSING ADAPTATIONS GRANTS

Department of Veterans Affairs
Attn: Specially Adapted Housing
810 Vermont Avenue, N.W.
Washington, DC 20420
(202) 461-9546   Toll Free: (800) 827-1000
Web: www.benefits.va.gov/homeloans/sah_info.asp

Summary To provide grants to certain disabled or blind veterans or servicemembers who wish to make adaptations to their home to meet their needs.

Eligibility These grants are available to veterans and servicemembers who are entitled to compensation for permanent and total service-connected disability due to: 1) blindness in both eyes with 5/200 visual acuity or less; 2) the anatomical loss or loss of use of both hands; or 3) a severe burn injury. Applicants must be planning to 1) adapt a house which they plan to purchase and in which they intend to reside; 2) adapt a house which a member of their family plans to purchase and in which they intend to reside; 3) adapt a house which they already own and in which they intend to reside; 4) adapt a house which is already owned by a member of their family in which they intend to reside; or 5) purchase a house that has already been adapted with special features that are reasonably necessary because of their disability and in which they intend to reside.

Financial data Eligible veterans and servicemembers are entitled to grants up to $12,756 to adapt a house.

Duration Eligible veterans and servicemembers are entitled to up to 3 usages of these grants.

Number awarded Varies each year.

Deadline Applications are accepted at any time.

[1286]
SPECIALLY ADAPTED HOUSING GRANTS

Department of Veterans Affairs
Attn: Specially Adapted Housing
810 Vermont Avenue, N.W.
Washington, DC 20420
(202) 461-9546   Toll Free: (800) 827-1000
Web: www.homeloans.va.gov/sah.htm

Summary To provide loans, grants, and loan guaranties to blind and disabled veterans and servicemembers for a home specially adapted to their needs.

Eligibility These grants are available to veterans and servicemembers who are entitled to compensation for permanent and total service-connected disability due to: 1) the loss or loss of use of both lower extremities, such as to preclude locomotion without the aid of braces, crutches, canes, or a wheelchair; or 2) blindness in both eyes, having only light perception, plus loss or loss of use of 1 lower extremity; 3) a loss or loss of use of 1 lower extremity together with residuals of organic disease or injury or the loss or loss of use of 1 upper extremity, such as to preclude locomotion without resort to braces, canes, crutches, or a wheelchair; 4) the loss or loss of use of both upper extremities, so as to preclude use of the arms at or above the elbows; or 5) a severe burn injury. Applicants must be planning to 1) construct a home on land to be acquired for that purpose; 2) build a home on land already owned if it is suitable for specially adapted housing; 3) remodel an existing home if it can be made suitable for specially adapted housing, or 4) apply funds against the unpaid principle mortgage balance of a specially adapted home that has already been acquired.

Financial data The U.S. Department of Veterans Affairs (VA) may approve a grant of not more than 50% of the cost of building, buying, or remodeling homes for eligible veterans, or paying indebtedness on such homes already acquired, up to a maximum grant of $63,780. Eligible veterans with available loan guarantee entitlements may also obtain a guaranteed loan from the VA to supplement the grant to acquire a specially adapted home. If private financing is not available, the VA may make a direct loan up to $33,000 to cover the difference between the total cost of the home and the grant.

Duration This is a 1-time grant, guaranteed loan, or direct loan.

Additional information Veterans who receive a specially adapted housing grant may be eligible for Veterans Mortgage Life Insurance.

Number awarded Varies each year.

Deadline Applications are accepted at any time.

[1287]
TROOPS-TO-TEACHERS PROGRAM

Defense Activity for Non-Traditional Education Support
Attn: Troops to Teachers
6490 Sauffley Field Road
Pensacola, FL 32509-5243
(850) 452-1242   Toll Free: (800) 231-6242
Fax: (850) 452-1096   E-mail: ttt@navy.mil
Web: www.dantes.doded.mil

Summary To provide a bonus to veterans and military personnel interested in a second career as a public school teacher.

Eligibility This program is open to 1) active-duty military personnel who are retired, have an approved date of retirement within 1 year, or separated on or after January 8, 2002 for physical disability; 2) members of a Reserve component who are retired, currently serving in the Selected Reserve with 10 or more years of credible service and commit to serving an additional 3 years, separated on or after January 8, 2002 due to a physical disability, or transitioned from active duty on or after January 8, 2002 after at least 6 years on active duty and commit to 3 years with a Selected Reserve unit. Applicants must have a baccalaureate or advanced degree, the equivalent of 1 year of college with 6 years of work experience in a vocational or technical field, or meet state requirements for vocational/technical teacher referral. A bonus is available to applicants who are willing to accept employment as a teacher in 1) a school district that has at least 10% of the students from families living below the poverty level, and 2) at a specific school within the district where at least 50% of the students are eligible for the free or reduced cost lunch program or where at least 13.5% of the students have disabilities. A stipend is available to applicants who are willing to accept employment as a teacher at 1) any school within a "high need" district that has at least 20% of the students from families living below the poverty level; or 2) at a specific school where at least 50% of the students are eligible for the free or reduced cost lunch program or at least 13.5% of the students have disabilities, as long as that school is in a district that has between 10% and 20% of students who come from poverty-level families. Preference is given to applicants interested in teaching mathematics, science, or special education.

Financial data A bonus of $10,000 is awarded to recipients who agree to teach for 3 years in a school that serves a high percentage of students from low-income families. A stipend of $5,000 is awarded to recipients who agree to teach for 3 years in a school located in a "high-need" district; stipend funds are intended to help pay for teacher certification costs.

Duration The bonuses are intended as 1-time grants.

Additional information This program was established in 1994 by the Department of Defense (DoD). In 2000, program oversight and funding were transferred to the U.S. Department of Education, but DoD continues to operate the program. The No Child Left Behind Act of 2001 provided for continuation of the program.

Number awarded Varies each year.

Deadline Deadline not specified.

[1288]
UNMET NEEDS PROGRAM GRANTS

Veterans of Foreign Wars of the United States
Attn: VFW Foundation
Unmet Needs Program
406 West 34th Street, Suite 216
Kansas City, MO 64111
(816) 968-2779   Toll Free: (866) 789-NEED
Fax: (816) 968-1128   E-mail: unmetneeds@vfw.org
Web: www.unmetneeds.com

Summary To provide assistance to military personnel and their families who are facing special circumstances.

Eligibility This assistance is available to members of the 5 branches of service (Army, Navy, Air Force, Marines, and Coast Guard) as well as members of the Reserves and National Guard. Applicants must have served on active duty within the past 3 years. They must be able to demonstrate need for assistance because of deployment, military pay issue, military illness or injury, or natural disaster. Examples of needs that may be met include medical bills, prescriptions, and eyeglasses; housing expenses (mortgage, rent, repairs, insurance); appliance repair; vehicle expenses (payments, insurance, repairs); utilities; food and clothing; or children's clothing, diapers, formula, or school or childcare expenses. Dependents who are listed with the Defense Enrollment Eligibility Reporting System (DEERS) are also eligible.

Financial data Grants range up to $2,500.

Duration These are 1-time grants.

Additional information This program was established in 2004 with support from Vermont American Power Tools Accessories.

Number awarded Varies each year. Since this program was established, it has awarded 1,146 grants with a value of $1,640,308.

Deadline Applications may be submitted at any time.

[1289]
VERMONT INCOME TAX EXEMPTION FOR MILITARY PERSONNEL

Vermont Department of Taxes
133 State Street
Montpelier, VT 05633-1401
(802) 828-2865   Toll Free: (866) 828-2865 (within VT)
Fax: (802) 828-2720   E-mail: indincome@tax.state.vt.us
Web: www.state.vt.us/tax/individual.shtml

Summary To exempt from state taxation the income of military personnel in Vermont.

Eligibility Eligible are military personnel considered Vermont residents for purposes of state income taxation.

Financial data All full-time, active-duty military pay earned outside of Vermont is exempt from state income taxation.

Duration The exemption continues as long as the recipient resides in Vermont.

Deadline Deadline not specified.

[1290]
VERMONT MILITARY FAMILY ASSISTANCE FUND GRANTS

Vermont Military Family Assistance Fund
P.O. Box 26
Essex Junction, VT 05453-0026

Summary To provide emergency assistance to military personnel in Vermont and their families.

Eligibility This assistance is available to active-duty service members and their families if they live within the geographical boundaries of the state of Vermont or live outside the state but belong to a Vermont unit. They must be facing emergency financial difficulties. Along with their application, they must submit an explanation of the need and amount of each bill for which they are requesting assistance.

Financial data Support is provided in the form of grants that do not need to be repaid.

Duration These are 1-time grants.

Additional information This program was originally established in 1991 to assist mobilized active-duty members during Desert Storm and revived in 2003.

Number awarded Varies each year.

Deadline Applications may be submitted at any time.

[1291]
VERMONT NATIONAL GUARD INCOME TAX EXEMPTION

Vermont Department of Taxes
133 State Street
Montpelier, VT 05633-1401
(802) 828-2865   Toll Free: (866) 828-2865 (within VT)
Fax: (802) 828-2720   E-mail: indincome@tax.state.vt.us
Web: www.state.vt.us/tax/individual.shtml

Summary To exempt from state taxation a portion of the income of members of the Vermont National Guard and Reserve units of the armed forces.

Eligibility This exemption is available to National Guard and armed forces Reserve personnel in Vermont who 1) were enlisted for the full calendar year, 2) attended all training assemblies for their unit during the training year, and 3) had a federal adjusted gross income of less than $50,000 in the prior tax year.

Financial data The first $2,000 of military pay for training assemblies is exempt from state income taxation.

Duration The exemption continues as long as the recipient resides in Vermont.

Deadline Deadline not specified.

[1292]
VIRGINIA BASIC MILITARY PAY INCOME TAX EXEMPTION

Virginia Department of Taxation
Attn: Office of Customer Services
1957 Westmoreland Street
P.O. Box 1115
Richmond, VA 23218-1115
(804) 367-8031   Fax: (804) 254-6113
E-mail: TaxIndReturns@tax.virginia.gov
Web: www.tax.virginia.gov/site?alias=MilitaryTaxTips

Summary To subtract a portion of the income received by military personnel from state income taxation in Virginia.

Eligibility This subtraction is available to residents of Virginia (as defined by federal income tax law) who receive basic military pay. Applicants must have served on active duty for 90 days or more during the year. They may be stationed inside or outside of Virginia.

Financial data   Up to $15,000 of basic military pay may be exempted from Virginia income tax. The exemption is reduced when military pay exceeds $15,000 and is fully phased out when pay reaches $30,000.

Duration   The exemption is available as long as the tax-payer remains a resident of Virginia and receives military pay.

Number awarded   Varies each year.

Deadline   The request for an exemption is filed with the state income tax return in April of each year.

[1293]
VIRGINIA NATIONAL GUARD INCOME TAX SUBTRACTION

Virginia Department of Taxation
Attn: Office of Customer Services
1957 Westmoreland Street
P.O. Box 1115
Richmond, VA 23218-1115
(804) 367-8031   Fax: (804) 254-6113
E-mail: TaxIndReturns@tax.virginia.gov
Web: www.tax.virginia.gov/site?alias=MilitaryTaxTips

Summary   To subtract a portion of the income received by members of the income received by members of the Virginia National Guard from state income taxation.

Eligibility   This subtraction is available to members of the Virginia National Guard at the military rank of O3 (captain) or below. Applicants must have received income for active or inactive service in the Guard.

Financial data   Eligible members of the Guard are allowed to subtract income received for up to 39 days of service or $3,000, whichever is less, from their income for purposes of state taxation in Virginia.

Duration   The subtraction is available as long as the Guard member receives income for service in Virginia.

Number awarded   Varies each year.

Deadline   The request for an exemption is filed with the state income tax return in April of each year.

[1294]
WEST VIRGINIA INCOME TAX EXEMPTION FOR ACTIVE DUTY MILITARY PAY

West Virginia State Tax Department
Attn: Taxpayer Services Division
P.O. Box 3784
Charleston, WV 25337-3784
(304) 558-3333   Toll Free: (800) WVA-TAXS (within WV)
Fax: (304) 558-3269   TDD: (800) 282-9833
Web: www.wva.state.wv.us/wvtax/default.aspx

Summary   To exempt the income received by members of the National Guard or armed forces Reserves in West Virginia serving on active duty from state taxation.

Eligibility   This exemption is available to residents of West Virginia who are Members of the National Guard or armed forces Reserves called to active duty pursuant to an Executive Order of the President of the United States.

Financial data   Qualifying income is not subject to taxation in West Virginia.

Duration   The exemption continues as long as the Guard or Reserves members remain on active duty.

Deadline   Deadline not specified.

[1295]
WISCONSIN INCOME TAX EXEMPTION FOR NATIONAL GUARD AND RESERVE PAY

Wisconsin Department of Revenue
Attn: Individual Income Tax
2135 Rimrock Road
P.O. Box 59
Madison, WI 53785-0001
(608) 266-2486   Fax: (608) 267-0834
E-mail: income@revenue.wi.gov
Web: www.revenue.wi.gov/individuals/military.html

Summary   To exempt from state taxation the income received by members of the National Guard and Reserves in Wisconsin who are serving on active duty.

Eligibility   This exemption is available to residents of Wisconsin who are serving in the National Guard or Reserves. Applicants must have been called into active federal service or special state service.

Financial data   All pay received for active service in the National Guard or Reserves is exempt from state income taxation in Wisconsin.

Duration   The exemption is available for all active-duty pay received by residents of Wisconsin.

Additional information   This exemption was first available in 2004. The exemption does not apply to pay received for weekend or 2-week annual training.

Number awarded   Varies each year.

Deadline   Income tax returns must be filed by April of each year.

[1296]
WYOMING MILITARY ASSISTANCE TRUST FUND GRANTS

Wyoming Military Department
Attn: State Family Program Coordinator
5500 Bishop Boulevard
Cheyenne, WY 82009
(307) 772-5208   Fax: (307) 772-5330
Web: sites.google.com

Summary   To provide emergency assistance to residents of Wyoming who are facing financial difficulties because a family member has been deployed to active military service.

Eligibility   This assistance is available to 1) members of the Wyoming National Guard or Reserve units based in Wyoming who have been called to active duty or active state service; 2) Wyoming residents who are members of a military Reserve unit not based in Wyoming, if the member has been called to active service; 3) other Wyoming residents performing service in the uniformed forces for any branch of the military of the United States; and 4) members of the immediate family (spouses, children, and dependent parents, grandparents, siblings, stepchildren, and adult children) of those military personnel. Applicants must be facing financial hardship resulting from the military member's active-duty status.

Financial data   The amount of the grant depends on the need of the recipient.

Duration   These are 1-time grants.

Additional information   The Wyoming Legislature created this fund in 2004. These funds may not be used to replace other funds available from public or private sources.

Number awarded Varies each year; since this program was established, it has awarded more than $1.18 million in grants.

Deadline Applications may be submitted at any time.

Family Members

[1297]
AIR FORCE AID SOCIETY EMERGENCY FINANCIAL ASSISTANCE

Air Force Aid Society
Attn: Financial Assistance Department
241 18th Street South, Suite 202
Arlington, VA 22202-3409
(703) 607-3072, ext. 51   Toll Free: (800) 769-8951
Fax: (703) 607-3022
Web: www.afas.org/Assistance/HowWeCanHelp.cfm

Summary To provide loans and grants-in-aid to current and former Air Force personnel and their families who are facing emergency situations.

Eligibility This program is open to active-duty Air Force members and their dependents, retired Air Force personnel and their dependents, Air National Guard and Air Force Reserve personnel on extended duty over 15 days, and spouses and dependent children of deceased Air Force personnel who died on active duty or in retired status. Applicants must be facing problems, usually for relatively short periods, that affect their job or the essential quality and dignity of life the Air Force wants for its people. Examples of such needs include basic living expenses (food, rent, utilities), medical and dental care, funeral expenses, vehicle expenses, emergency travel, moving expenses, or child or respite care. Funding is generally not provided if it merely postpones a long-term inability to exist on present pay and allowances, for nonessentials, for continuing long-term assistance commitments, or to replace funds lost due to garnishment.

Financial data Assistance is provided as an interest-free loan, a grant, or a combination of both.

Number awarded Varies each year.

Deadline Applications may be submitted at any time.

[1298]
AIR FORCE AID SOCIETY RESPITE CARE

Air Force Aid Society
Attn: Financial Assistance Department
241 18th Street South, Suite 202
Arlington, VA 22202-3409
(703) 607-3072, ext. 51   Toll Free: (800) 769-8951
Fax: (703) 607-3022
Web: www.afas.org/Community/RespireCareProgram.cfm

Summary To provide financial assistance to Air Force personnel and their families who have a family member with special needs.

Eligibility This program is open to active-duty Air Force members and their families who are responsible for 24 hour a day care for an ill or disabled family member (child, spouse, or parent) living in the household. Applicants must be referred by the Exceptional Family Member Program (EFMP) or the Family Advocacy Office. Selection is based on need, both financial need and the need of the family for respite time.

Financial data Assistance is provided as a grant that depends on the needs of the family.

Number awarded Varies each year.

Deadline Applications may be submitted at any time.

[1299]
AIR WARRIOR COURAGE FOUNDATION GRANTS

Air Warrior Courage Foundation
P.O. Box 877
Silver Spring, MD 20918
(301) 588-3282   Fax: (540) 636-9776
E-mail: awcf@awcfoundation.com
Web: www.airwarriorcourage.org

Summary To provide emergency assistance to veterans, military personnel, and their families, especially members of the Red River Valley Fighter Pilots Association (RRVA), who are facing unusual situations.

Eligibility These grants are available to active, Guard, Reserve, retired, and former military and Coast Guard personnel and dependent family members. Applicants must be able to demonstrate financial and material needs unmet by insurance programs, community support, or other service agencies. Special consideration is given to applicants eligible for the RRVA scholarship program (spouses and children of servicemembers missing in action or killed in action in armed conflicts by U.S. forces since August 1964, of U.S. military aircrew members killed in a non-combat aircraft accident in which they were performing aircrew duties, and of current members of the association). Assistance includes the following activities: the troop support 9/11 Terrorism Memorial Fund, which provides financial assistance, college savings programs, and/or material support to surviving family members of those lost or injured in the war on terror and military units performing humanitarian activities worldwide; grants for individuals, which provides emergency financial support for utilities, rent, transportation, auto repairs, and medical expenses; the Professional Association for Therapeutic Horsemanship (PATH) grants, which supports horseback riding for children with certain mental, physical, or developmental challenges; and the College Savings Plan (529) program, which opens College Savings Plan (529) accounts for children of aviators killed during the performance of aircrew duties.

Financial data The amount awarded varies. Recent grants included more than $900,000 for the troop support 9/11 Terrorism Memorial Fund, $63,000 in grants to 57 individuals, $88,000 to support 88 children through the PATH program, and the opening of 22 College Savings Plans (529) at $2,000 for combat deaths or $1,000 for training accidents.

Duration These are 1-time grants.

Additional information This foundation began in 1998 as a charitable organization affiliated with the RRVA.

Number awarded Varies each year.

Deadline Applications may be submitted at any time.

[1300]
ALABAMA AD VALOREM TAX EXEMPTION FOR SPECIALLY ADAPTED HOUSES

Alabama Department of Revenue
Attn: Property Tax Division
Gordon Persons Building
50 North Ripley Street, Room 4126
P.O. Box 327210
Montgomery, AL 36132-7210
(334) 242-1525
Web: www.ador.state.al.us

Summary To provide a property tax exemption to the owners of specially adapted housing (housing adapted for disabled veterans) in Alabama.

Eligibility The home of any veteran which is or was acquired pursuant to the provisions of Public Law 702, 80th Congress (specially adapted housing grants for veterans) as amended (38 USC) will be exempted from ad valorem taxation if the house is owned and occupied by the veteran or the veteran's unremarried widow(er).

Financial data Qualifying houses are exempt from all ad valorem taxation.

Duration This exemption continues as long as the veteran or the unremarried widow(er) resides in the house.

Number awarded Varies each year.

Deadline Deadline not specified.

[1301]
ALABAMA MILITARY RETIREE INCOME TAX EXEMPTION

Alabama Department of Revenue
Attn: Income Tax Division
Gordon Persons Building
50 North Ripley Street, Room 4212
P.O. Box 327410
Montgomery, AL 36132-7410
(334) 242-1105   Fax: (334) 242-0064
E-mail: erohelpdesk@revenue.state.al.us
Web: www.ador.state.al.us

Summary To exempt a portion of the income of veterans and their survivors from taxation in Alabama.

Eligibility Eligible are Alabama recipients of regular military retired pay or military survivors benefits. Recipients of benefits paid by the U.S. Department of Veterans Affairs (including disability retirement payments) are also eligible for this exemption.

Financial data All income received as military retired pay, veterans' disability payment, or military survivors benefits is exempt from state, county, or municipal income taxation.

Duration The exemption continues as long as the recipient resides in Alabama.

Deadline Deadline not specified.

[1302]
AMERICAN LEGION AUXILIARY EMERGENCY FUND

American Legion Auxiliary
Attn: AEF Program Case Manager
8945 North Meridian Street
Indianapolis, IN 46260
(317) 569-4544   Fax: (317) 569-4502
E-mail: aef@alaforveterans.org
Web: www.alaforveterans.org

Summary To provide funding to members of the American Legion Auxiliary who are facing temporary emergency needs.

Eligibility This program is open to members of the American Legion Auxiliary who have maintained their membership for the immediate past 2 consecutive years and have paid their dues for the current year. Applicants must need emergency assistance for the following purposes: 1) food, shelter, and utilities during a time of financial crisis; 2) food and shelter because of weather-related emergencies and natural disasters; or 3) educational training for eligible members who lack the necessary skills for employment or to upgrade competitive work force skills. They must have exhausted all other sources of financial assistance, including funds and/or services available through the local Post and/or Unit, appropriate community welfare agencies, or state and federal financial aid for education. Grants are not available to settle already existing or accumulated debts, handle catastrophic illness, resettle disaster victims, or other similar problems.

Financial data The maximum grant is $2,400. Payments may be made directly to the member or to the mortgage company or utility. Educational grants may be paid directly to the educational institution.

Duration Grants are expended over no more than 3 months.

Additional information This program began in 1969. In 1981, it was expanded to include the Displaced Homemaker Fund (although that title is no longer used).

Number awarded Varies each year.

Deadline Applications may be submitted at any time.

[1303]
ARIZONA MILITARY FAMILY RELIEF FUND

Arizona Department of Veterans' Services
Attn: Military Family Relief Fund
3839 North Third Street, Suite 209
Phoenix, AZ 85012
(602) 234-8403   E-mail: mfrf@azdvs.gov
Web: www.azdvs.gov/benefits/relief_fund.aspx

Summary To provide assistance to military service members from Arizona and their families who face financial difficulties that result from the deployment of the military member to a combat zone.

Eligibility This assistance is available to military service members who have been deployed to a combat zone since September 11, 2001, are currently deployed in a combat zone, or became deceased, wounded, or seriously ill after September 11, 2001 due to a deployment. Applicants must be Arizona residents, as evidenced by having been deployed from a military base in the state, entered active military service after September 11, 2001 from the state, claimed the state as home of record, or been a member of the Arizona National Guard at the time of deployment. Military service members who have been discharged must have done so under honorable conditions. Family members (spouses, widows and widowers, dependent children, siblings, and parents) are also eligible. All applicants must be able to demonstrate how deployment affected their financial situation. Family members of those who were killed in action may request up to 6 months' living expenses and other appropriate expenses; family members of those who were wounded in action may request temporary living expenses while care in being delivered to the qualifying military person and other appropriate expenses; families of service members who are experiencing financial hardship may request living or other appropriate expenses to resolve financial hardship caused by deployment and assist with transition to financial stability.

Financial data Grants up to $20,000 are available, of which $3,000 is available for emergency situations.

Duration The maximum grant of $20,000 is a lifetime limit.

Number awarded Varies each year.

Deadline Applications may be submitted at any time.

[1304]
ARIZONA NATIONAL GUARD EMERGENCY RELIEF FUND GRANTS

Arizona National Guard Emergency Relief Fund
Attn: Fund Administrator
P.O. Box 64252
Phoenix, AZ 85082
E-mail: azng.er@gmail.com

Summary To provide emergency assistance to members of the Arizona National Guard and their families.

Eligibility This program is open to members of the Arizona Army and Air National Guard who have not been mobilized under Presidential Order. Surviving spouses, children, and orphans of soldiers who died while on active duty are also eligible. Applicants must be seeking assistance for such emergency needs as delay in receiving pay or reimbursement from the government; temporary shelter, lodging, or rent; emergency utility assistance; emergency transportation and vehicle repair; costs incurred for emergency travel due to death of immediate family member; or any other special circumstance deemed appropriate by the fund's directors. Support is not provided to help pay for nonessentials, finance ordinary leave or vacation, pay fines or legal expenses, assist with home purchase or improvements, cover bad checks, or help purchase, rent, or lease a vehicle.

Financial data Most support is provided in the form of interest-free loans, although outright grants are also available.

Duration These are 1-time grants.

Number awarded Varies each year.

Deadline Applications may be submitted at any time.

[1305]
ARIZONA NATIONAL GUARD FAMILY ASSISTANCE FUND

Arizona National Guard Emergency Relief Fund
Attn: Fund Administrator
P.O. Box 64252
Phoenix, AZ 85082
E-mail: azng.er@gmail.com

Summary To provide emergency assistance to members of the Arizona Reserve Component who have been mobilized and their families.

Eligibility This program is open to members of the Arizona Reserve Component (including the Army and Air National Guard and Reserve units of all 5 branches of service) and their dependents. They must have been mobilized under Presidential Order. Surviving spouses, children, and orphans of soldiers who died while on active duty are also eligible. Applicants must be seeking assistance for such emergency needs as delay in receiving pay or reimbursement from the government; temporary shelter, lodging, or rent; emergency utility assistance; emergency transportation and vehicle repair; costs incurred for emergency travel due to death of immediate family member; or any other special circumstance deemed appropriate by the fund's directors. Support is not provided to help pay for nonessentials, financial ordinary leave or vacation, pay fines or legal expenses, assist with home purchase or improvements, cover bad checks, or help purchase, rent, or lease a vehicle.

Financial data Most support is provided in the form of interest-free loans, although outright grants are also available.

Duration These are awarded on a 1-time basis.

Number awarded Varies each year.

Deadline Applications may be submitted at any time.

[1306]
ARKANSAS DISABLED VETERANS PROPERTY TAX EXEMPTION

Arkansas Assessment Coordination Department
1614 West Third Street
Little Rock, AR 72201-1815
(501) 324-9240   Fax: (501) 324-9242
E-mail: dasbury@acd.state.ar.us
Web: www.arkansas.gov/acd

Summary To exempt from taxation the property owned by blind or disabled veterans, surviving spouses, and minor dependent children in Arkansas.

Eligibility This program is open to disabled veterans in Arkansas who have been awarded special monthly compensation by the U.S. Department of Veterans Affairs and who have 1) the loss of or the loss of use of 1 or more limbs, 2) total blindness in 1 or both eyes, or 3) total and permanent disability. The benefit also extends to veterans' unremarried surviving spouses and their minor children.

Financial data Qualifying veterans (or their unremarried widows or dependent children) are exempt from payment of all state taxes on their homestead and personal property.

Duration This exemption continues as long as the qualifying veteran (or dependent) resides in Arkansas.

Number awarded Varies each year.

Deadline Applications may be submitted at any time.

[1307]
ARMY EMERGENCY RELIEF LOANS/GRANTS

Army Emergency Relief
200 Stovall Street
Alexandria, VA 22332-0600
(703) 428-0000   Toll Free: (866) 878-6378
Fax: (703) 325-7183   E-mail: aer@aerhq.org
Web: www.aerhq.org/dnn563/FinancialAssistance.aspx

Summary To provide loans and grants-in-aid to help with the emergency financial needs of Army veterans, military personnel, and their dependents.

Eligibility Eligible to apply are active-duty soldiers (single or married) and their dependents, Army National Guard and Army Reserve soldiers on continuous active duty for more than 30 days and their dependents, soldiers retired from active duty for longevity or physical disability and their dependents, Army National Guard and Army Reserve soldiers who retired at age 60 and their dependents, and surviving spouses and orphans of soldiers who died while on active duty or after they retired. Applicants must be seeking assistance for such emergency needs as food, rent, and utilities; emergency transportation and vehicle repair; funeral expenses; medical and dental expenses; or personal needs when pay is delayed or stolen. Support is not available to help pay for nonessentials, finance ordinary leave or vacation, pay fines or legal expenses, help liquidate or consolidate debt, assist with house purchase or home improvements, cover bad checks, pay credit card bills, or acquire a vehicle.

Financial data Support is provided in the form of loans or grants (or a combination).

Duration Qualifying individuals can apply whenever they have a valid emergency need.

Additional information This organization began in 1942.

Number awarded Varies each year; recently, the organization helped more than 66,000 Army people with more than $70 million, including $60 million to 58,820 active-duty soldiers and their families, $7.3 million to 4,914 retired soldiers and their families, and $2.7 million to 2,304 widow(er)s and orphans of deceased soldiers. Since it was established, the organization has helped more than 3.2 million qualifying individuals with more than $1.2 billion in financial assistance.

Deadline Applications may be submitted at any time.

[1308]
CALIFORNIA DISABLED VETERAN EXEMPTION FROM THE IN LIEU TAX FEE FOR A MANUFACTURED HOME OR MOBILEHOME

Department of Housing and Community Development
Attn: Registration and Titling
1800 Third Street
P.O. Box 2111
Sacramento, CA 95812-2111
(916) 323-9224   Toll Free: (800) 952-8356
Web: www.hcd.ca.gov

Summary To provide a special property tax exemption to blind or disabled California veterans and/or their spouses who own and occupy a mobile home.

Eligibility This program is open to disabled veterans and/or their spouses in California who have a manufactured home or mobile home as their principal place of residence. Veterans must be disabled as a result of injury or disease incurred in military service and have been a resident of California 1) at the time of entry into the service and be blind, or have lost the use of 1 or more limbs, or be totally disabled; 2) on November 7, 1972 and be blind in both eyes, or have lost the use of 2 or more limbs; or 3) on January 1, 1975 and be totally disabled. The spouses and unremarried surviving spouses of those disabled veterans are also eligible.

Financial data The exemption applies to the first $20,000 of the assessed market value of the manufactured home or

mobile home. Veterans and/or spouses whose income falls below a specified level are entitled to an additional $10,000 exemption. The amount of the exemption is 100% if the home is owned by a veteran only, a veteran and spouse, or a spouse only; 50% if owned by a veteran and another person other than a spouse or by a spouse and another person other than the veteran; 67% if owned by a veteran, the spouse, and another person; 34% if owned by a veteran and 2 other people other than a spouse or by a spouse and 2 other people; 50% if owned by a veteran, the spouse, and 2 other people; or 25% if owned by a veteran and 3 other people or by a spouse and 3 other people.

Duration The exemption is available annually as long as the applicant meets all requirements.

Number awarded Varies each year.

Deadline Deadline not specified.

[1309]
CALIFORNIA PROPERTY TAX EXEMPTIONS FOR VETERANS

California Department of Veterans Affairs
Attn: Division of Veterans Services
1227 O Street, Room 101
P.O. Box 942895
Sacramento, CA 94295
(916) 653-2573   Toll Free: (877) 741-8532
Fax: (916) 653-2563   TDD: (800) 324-5966
Web: www.cdva.ca.gov/VetServices/Benefits.aspx

Summary To exempt a portion of the property of blind or disabled veterans in California and their spouses from taxation.

Eligibility This exemption is available to homeowners in California who are wartime veterans in receipt of service-connected disability compensation that is 1) at the totally disabled rate, 2) for loss or loss of use of 2 or more limbs, or 3) for blindness. Unremarried surviving spouses, including registered domestic partners, of veterans who are in receipt of service-connected death benefits are also eligible.

Financial data For veterans and spouses whose total household income from all sources is greater than $51,669 per year, up to $115,060 of the assessed value of a home is exempt from taxation. For veterans and spouses whose total household income from all sources is less than $51,669 per year, up to $172,592 of the assessed value of a home is exempt from taxation.

Duration The exemption is available as long as the veteran or spouse owns a home in California.

Additional information Information is available from the local county assessor's office in each California county.

Number awarded Varies each year.

Deadline Applications may be submitted at any time.

[1310]
CHILDREN OF FALLEN SOLDIERS RELIEF FUND FINANCIAL ASSISTANCE GRANTS

Children of Fallen Soldiers Relief Fund
P.O. Box 3968
Gaithersburg, MD 20885-3968
(301) 685-3421   Toll Free: (866) 96-CFSRF
Fax: (301) 630-0592   E-mail: grants@cfsrf.org
Web: www.cfsrf.org

Summary To provide personal financial assistance to veterans severely disabled during service in Iraq or Afghanistan and to the families of military personnel killed or severely disabled in those countries.

Eligibility This program is open to 1) veterans severely disabled as a result of service in Operation Iraqi Freedom or Operation Enduring Freedom; and 2) the spouses and children of military personnel killed or severely disabled during that service. Applicants must submit a 1-page statement describing their reason for requesting funds, the amount requested, the intended use of the funds, a list of monthly income and expenses, 2 recent months of bank statements, and overdue bills.

Financial data Grants have ranged from $1,650 to $16,916, depending on the need of the recipient.

Duration These are 1-time grants.

Additional information This organization was founded in 2003.

Number awarded Varies each year; since the organization was founded, it has awarded 18 of these financial assistance grants.

Deadline Applications may be submitted at any time.

[1311]
CHILDREN OF WOMEN VIETNAM VETERANS ALLOWANCE

Department of Veterans Affairs
Attn: Veterans Benefits Administration
810 Vermont Avenue, N.W.
Washington, DC 20420
(202) 418-4343   Toll Free: (888) 820-1756
Web: www1.va.gov

Summary To provide support to children of female Vietnam veterans who have birth defects.

Eligibility This program is open to biological children of female veterans who served in the Republic of Vietnam and were conceived after the date the veteran first served, which must have been between February 28, 1961 and May 7, 1975. Applicants must have certain birth defects identified as resulting in permanent physical or mental disability. Conditions that are a family disorder, a birth-related injury, or a fetal or neonatal infirmity with well-established causes are not included.

Financial data Support depends on the degree of disability. The monthly rate for children at the first level is $136, at the second level $297, at the third level $1,020, or at the fourth level $1,739.

Additional information Applications are available from the nearest VA medical center. Recipients are also entitled to vocational training and medical treatment.

Number awarded Varies each year.

Deadline Applications are accepted at any time.

[1312]
COAST GUARD MUTUAL ASSISTANCE GRANTS-IN-AID

Coast Guard Mutual Assistance
4200 Wilson Boulevard, Suite 610
Arlington, VA 20598-7180
(202) 493-6621   Toll Free: (800) 881-2462
Fax: (202) 493-6686   E-mail: ARL-DG-CGMA@uscg.mil
Web: www.cgmahq.org/Assistance/programs.html

Summary To provide funding to members of the Coast Guard Mutual Assistance (CGMA) and their families who need temporary assistance.

Eligibility This program is open to CGMA members who are facing special needs. Categories of aid that are available include emergency assistance (basic living expenses, emergency home repair, emergency travel expenses, fire and other disasters, funeral expenses, loss of funds, temporary living expenses); general assistance (adoption, child support, child care, family in-home day care facility, financial counseling, government travel cards, household furnishings, immigration fees, insurance, loss of income, moving expenses, non-emergency travel, non-support or inadequate support, past due bills and expenses, pay and allotment problems, vehicle repair, vehicle other expenses); housing assistance (payment of settlement charges associated with purchasing a residence, rental assistance, utilities); and medical and dental assistance (provider won't proceed without payment; mental health and family counseling; patient's cost share; durable medical equipment; prosthetic devices; rehabilitation, nursing, home, or respite care; orthodontia; long-term dental care; travel, transportation, and incidental expenses). Applicants must be able to demonstrate a need for assistance.

Financial data The assistance depends on the nature of the need.

Duration These are 1-time grants. A new application must accompany each request for assistance.

Additional information CGMA membership is open to active-duty and retired members of the U.S. Coast Guard, civilian employees of the U.S. Coast Guard, U.S. Coast Guard Reserve members, U.S. Coast Guard Auxiliary members, Public Health Service officers serving with the U.S. Coast Guard, and family members of all of those.

Number awarded Varies each year.

Deadline Deadline not specified.

[1313]
COLORADO PROPERTY TAX EXEMPTION FOR DISABLED VETERANS

Division of Veterans Affairs
1355 South Colorado Boulevard, Building C, Suite 113
Denver, CO 80220
(303) 343-1268   Fax: (303) 343-7238
Web: www.dmva.state.co.us/page/va/prop_tax

Summary To provide a partial exemption of taxes on property owned by disabled veterans or their spouses in Colorado.

Eligibility This exemption is open to veterans who reside in Colorado and have been rated 100% permanent and total service-connected disabled by the U.S. Department of Veterans Affairs. Applicants must have been honorably discharged and must own property in Colorado which they use as their primary residence. The exemption also applies to members of the National Guard or Reserves who sustained their injury during a period in which they were called to active duty, property owned by a veteran's spouse if both occupy the property as their primary residence, and property owned by a trust or other legal entity if the veteran or spouse is a major of the trust or other legal entity, the property was transferred solely for estate planning purposes, and the veteran or spouse would otherwise be the owner of record.

Financial data For qualifying veterans, 50% of the first $200,000 of actual value of the primary residence is exempted from taxes.

Duration The exemption continues as long as the veteran resides in the property.

Additional information This program was approved by Colorado voters in 2006.

Number awarded Varies each year.

Deadline Applications must be submitted by June of the year for which the exemption is requested.

[1314]
CONNECTICUT NATIONAL GUARD FOUNDATION ASSISTANCE

Connecticut National Guard Foundation, Inc.
Attn: Assistance Committee
360 Broad Street
Hartford, CT 06105-3795
(860) 241-1550   Fax: (860) 293-2929
E-mail: assistance.committee@ctngfoundation.org
Web: www.ctngfoundation.org

Summary To provide emergency and other assistance to members of the Connecticut National Guard and their families.

Eligibility This program is open to members of the Connecticut Army National Guard and Organized Militia, their children under 18 years of age, and their spouses who live with them. Applicants must be in need of assistance for such benefits as clothing, food, medical and surgical aid, and general care and relief. They must be able to demonstrate a need for assistance.

Financial data Grants depend on the need of the recipient.

Duration These are 1-time grants.

Additional information Applications are available at all State Armories and Family Assistance Centers.

Number awarded Varies each year.

Deadline Applications may be submitted at any time.

[1315]
CONNECTICUT PERSONAL PROPERTY TAX EXEMPTION FOR WARTIME VETERANS

Office of Policy and Management
Attn: Intergovernmental Policy Division
450 Capitol Avenue
Hartford, CT 06106-1308
(860) 418-6278   Toll Free: (800) 286-2214 (within CT)
Fax: (860) 418-6493   TDD: (860) 418-6456
E-mail: leeann.graham@ct.gov
Web: www.ct.gov/opm/cwp/view.asp?a=2985&Q=383132

Summary To exempt wartime veterans and their family members from a portion of their personal property taxes if they are Connecticut residents.

Eligibility Eligible to apply for this exemption are veterans with 90 days of wartime service who are residents of Connecticut. Spouses, minor children, and parents of deceased veterans may also be eligible. An additional exemption may be available to veterans and spouses whose total adjusted gross income is less than $32,300 if unmarried or $39,500 if married. If the veteran is rated as 100% disabled by the U.S. Department of Veterans Affairs (VA), the maximum income levels are $18,000 if unmarried or $21,000 if married.

Financial data Property to the amount of $1,000 belonging to, or held in trust for, an eligible veteran is exempt from taxation. The same exemption is available to the surviving unremarried spouse, minor children, and (if there is no surviving unremarried spouse) parent of a deceased veteran. If the death was service-connected and occurred while on active duty, the exemption for a surviving unremarried spouse or minor child is $3,000. Municipalities may provide veterans and spouses with an additional exemption up to $2,000 of the assessed value of the property, provided their income is less than the qualifying level. The additional municipality exemption for spouses and children of veterans who died on active duty of service-connected causes is $6,000. The additional municipality exemptions for veterans and family members who do not meet the income requirements are $500 and $1,500, respectively.

Duration 1 year; exemptions continue as long as the eligible resident lives in Connecticut.

Number awarded Varies each year; recently, a total of 19,669 veterans received property tax exemptions through this and other programs in Connecticut.

Deadline Applications for the additional municipality exemption must be submitted to the assessor's office of the town of residence by September of every other year.

[1316]
CONNECTICUT REAL ESTATE TAX EXEMPTION FOR DISABLED VETERANS

Office of Policy and Management
Attn: Intergovernmental Policy Division
450 Capitol Avenue
Hartford, CT 06106-1308
(860) 418-6278   Toll Free: (800) 286-2214 (within CT)
Fax: (860) 418-6493   TDD: (860) 418-6456
E-mail: leeann.graham@ct.gov
Web: www.ct.gov/opm/cwp/view.asp?a=2985&Q=383132

Summary To exempt disabled or blind Connecticut veterans and their surviving spouses from the payment of a portion of their local property taxes.

Eligibility There are 2 categories of Connecticut veterans who qualify for exemptions from their dwelling house and the lot on which it is located: 1) those with major service-connected disabilities (paraplegia or osteochondritis resulting in permanent loss of the use of both legs or permanent paralysis of both legs and lower parts of the body; hemiplegia with permanent paralysis of 1 leg and 1 arm or either side of the body resulting from injury to the spinal cord, skeletal structure, or brain, or from disease of the spinal cord not resulting from syphilis; total blindness; amputation of both arms, both legs, both hands or both feet, or the combination of a hand and a foot; sustained through enemy action or resulting from an accident occurring or disease contracted in such active service) and 2) those with less severe disabilities (loss of use of 1 arm or 1 leg because of service-connected injuries). Surviving unremarried spouses of eligible deceased veterans are entitled to the same exemption as would have been granted to the veteran, as long as they continue to be the legal owner/occupier of the exempted residence. An additional exemption is available to veterans and spouses whose total adjusted gross income is less than $32,300 if unmarried or $39,500 if married. If the veteran is rated as 100% disabled by the U.S. Department of Veterans Affairs (VA), the maximum income levels are $18,000 if unmarried or $21,000 if married.

Financial data Veterans in the first category receive an exemption from local property taxation of $10,000 of assessed valuation. Veterans in the second category receive exemptions of $5,000 of assessed valuation. For veterans whose income is less than the specified levels, additional exemptions of $20,000 for the first category or $10,000 for the second category are available from municipalities that choose to participate. For veterans whose income exceeds the specified levels, the additional exemption from participating municipalities is $5,000 for the first category or $2,500 for the second category. Connecticut municipalities may also elect to exempt from taxation specially adapted housing acquired or modified by a veteran under the provisions of Section 801 of Title 38 of the United States Code.

Duration 1 year; exemptions continue as long as the eligible resident (or surviving spouse) owns/occupies the primary residence and lives in Connecticut.

Number awarded Varies each year; recently, a total of 19,669 veterans received property tax exemptions through this and other programs in Connecticut.

Deadline Applications for the additional municipality exemption must be submitted to the assessor's office of the town or residence by September of every other year.

[1317]
CONNECTICUT VETERANS' ADDITIONAL EXEMPTION TAX RELIEF PROGRAM

Office of Policy and Management
Attn: Intergovernmental Policy Division
450 Capitol Avenue
Hartford, CT 06106-1308
(860) 418-6278   Toll Free: (800) 286-2214 (within CT)
Fax: (860) 418-6493   TDD: (860) 418-6456
E-mail: leeann.graham@ct.gov
Web: www.ct.gov/opm/cwp/view.asp?a=2985&Q=383132

Summary To exempt disabled veterans and their surviving spouses who are residents of Connecticut from a portion of their personal property taxes.

Eligibility Eligible to apply for this exemption are Connecticut veterans who are rated as disabled by the U.S. Department of Veterans Affairs (VA). Unremarried surviving spouses of qualified veterans are also eligible. An additional exemption may be available to veterans and spouses whose total adjusted gross income is less than $32,300 if unmarried or $39,500 if married. If the veteran is rated as 100% disabled by the U.S. Department of Veterans Affairs (VA), the maximum income levels are $18,000 if unmarried or $21,000 if married.

Financial data The amount of the exemption depends on the level of the VA disability rating: for 10% to 25%, it is $1,500; for more than 25% to 50%, $2,000; for more than 50% to 75%, $2,500; for more than 75% and for veterans older than 65 years of age with any level of disability, $3,000. Municipalities may elect to provide an additional exemption, equal to twice the amount provided, to veterans and spouses whose income is less than the qualifying level. For veterans and spouses who do not meet the income requirement, the additional exemption from participating municipalities is equal to 50% of the basic state exemption.

Duration 1 year; exemptions continue as long as the eligible resident lives in Connecticut.

Number awarded Varies each year; recently, a total of 19,669 veterans received property tax exemptions through this and other programs in Connecticut.

Deadline Applications for the additional municipality exemption must be submitted to the assessor's office of the town of residence by September of every other year.

[1318]
DEATH GRATUITY FOR MILITARY PERSONNEL

Department of Veterans Affairs
Attn: Veterans Benefits Administration
810 Vermont Avenue, N.W.
Washington, DC 20420
(202) 418-4343   Toll Free: (800) 827-1000
Web: www1.va.gov

Summary To provide a death gratuity for the surviving spouses and dependents of veterans or military personnel.

Eligibility Dependents of military personnel who die of any cause in active service or within 120 days after leaving active duty from specified causes related to service are entitled to this benefit. Payment will be made to the spouse, children, or, if designated by the deceased, parents, brothers, or sisters.

Financial data This benefit is $100,000.

Duration This is a 1-time payment.

Additional information The last military command of the deceased pays this benefit. If funds are not received within a reasonable time, application should be made to the service concerned.

Deadline Applications may be submitted at any time.

[1319]
DEATH PENSION FOR SURVIVORS OF VETERANS

Department of Veterans Affairs
Attn: Veterans Benefits Administration
810 Vermont Avenue, N.W.
Washington, DC 20420
(202) 418-4343   Toll Free: (800) 827-1000
Web: www.vba.va.gov/bln/21/pension/spousepen.htm

Summary To provide pensions to disabled and other spouses and children of deceased veterans with wartime service.

Eligibility This program is open to surviving spouses and unmarried children of deceased veterans who were discharged under conditions other than dishonorable and who had at least 90 days of active military service, at least 1 day of which was during a period of war. Veterans who enlisted after September 7, 1980 generally had to have served at least 24 months or the full period for which they were called to active duty. The countable income of spouses and children must be below specified limits.

Financial data Currently, the maximum annual pension rate is $8,219 for a surviving spouse without dependent children or $10,759 for a surviving spouse with 1 dependent child. Other rates apply to surviving spouses in need of regular aid and attendance, surviving spouses permanently housebound without dependent children, and surviving children who are living alone.

Duration For surviving spouse: until remarriage. For surviving unmarried child: until the age of 18, or 23 if attending a VA-approved school. For surviving child with disability: as long as the condition exists or until marriage.

Number awarded Varies each year.

Deadline Applications may be submitted at any time.

[1320]
DEPENDENCY AND INDEMNITY COMPENSATION (DIC)

Department of Veterans Affairs
Attn: Veterans Benefits Administration
810 Vermont Avenue, N.W.
Washington, DC 20420
(202) 418-4343   Toll Free: (800) 827-1000
Web: www.vba.va.gov/bln/dependents/index.htm

Summary To provide financial support to the spouses and children of servicemembers and veterans who died of disabilities or other causes.

Eligibility This program is open to dependents (surviving spouses, unmarried children under 18, helpless children, and those between 18 and 23 if attending a VA-approved school) of servicemembers who died while on active duty and veterans whose death resulted from a service-related disease or injury. Also eligible are spouses and children of veterans whose death resulted from a nonservice-related injury or disease and who was receiving, or was entitled to receive, compensation from the U.S. Department of Veterans Affairs for a service-connected disability that was rated as totally disabling for at least 10 years immediately preceding death, or since the veteran's release from active duty and for at least 5 years immediately preceding death, or for at least 1 year before death if the veteran was a former prisoner of war who died after September 30, 1999.

Financial data Surviving spouses of veterans who died after January 1, 1993 receive a flat rate of $1,195 per month, regardless of pay grade. For veterans who died before January 1, 1993, the monthly amount of DIC is based on the deceased veteran's highest military pay grade. Monthly payments range from $1,195 for E-1 to $1,470 for E-9, from $1,262 for W-1 to $1,429 for W-4, and from $1,262 for O-1 to $2,738 for O-10. Additional payments include the following: $254 per month if the veteran had been receiving compensation for a service-connected disability for at least 8 years prior to death and the survivor had been married to the veteran for those 8 years; $296 per month if the recipient requires the aid and attendance of another person; $139 per month if the recipient is housebound; and $296 for each child under 18 years of age.

Duration Monthly payments continue for the life of the surviving spouse and until unmarried children reach the age of 18 (or 23 if disabled or attending a VA-approved school).

Number awarded Varies each year.

Deadline Applications are accepted at any time.

[1321]
FALLEN PATRIOT FUND GRANTS

Fallen Patriot Fund
c/o Bank of America Private Bank
TX1-492-19-09
P.O. Box 832409
Dallas, TX 75283-2409
(214) 658-7125   Fax: (214) 696-6310
E-mail: info@fallenpatriotfund.org
Web: www.fallenpatriotfund.org

Summary To provide personal financial assistance to veterans disabled as a result of combat in Iraq and to spouses and children of military personnel injured or killed in action in Iraq.

Eligibility This program is open to 1) veterans who were wounded in combat in support of Operation Iraqi Free, have been medically discharged from military service, received a disability rating from the U.S. Department of Veterans Affairs of 75% or greater, and can demonstrate dire financial hardship; 2) spouses of military personnel injured or killed in action in support of Operation Iraqi Freedom who can demonstrate dire financial hardship; and 3) children under 18 years of age of military personnel injured or killed in action in support of Operation Iraqi Freedom. Applicants who are currently enrolled as full-time undergraduate or vocational school students must demonstrate that all funds will be used to meet basic living expenses, not educational expenses. Graduate students, spouses who have received SGLI life insurance benefits, parents of military personnel injured or killed in action in support of Operation Iraqi Freedom, children over 18 years of age, and children or spouses of deceased military personnel whose death was a result of suicide are all ineligible. All applicants must state the nature of their financial hardship and how the money will be spent if a grant is provided.

Financial data The maximum grant is $3,000.

Duration Each disabled veteran or surviving spouse is limited to a total of 3 separate grants.

Additional information This program was established by the Mark Cuban Foundation.

Number awarded Varies each year; since the program was established, it has awarded more than $4.8 million in grants.

Deadline Applications may be submitted at any time.

[1322]
FINANCIAL AND MEDICAL ASSISTANCE FOR MASSACHUSETTS VETERANS

Department of Veterans' Services
600 Washington Street, Seventh Floor
Boston, MA 02111
(617) 210-5927   Fax: (617) 210-5755
E-mail: mdvs@vet.state.ma.us
Web: www.mass.gov

Summary To provide financial and medical assistance to indigent veterans and their dependents in Massachusetts.

Eligibility This assistance is open to veterans who are residents of Massachusetts and served in the U.S. armed services on active duty either for 90 days during specified periods of wartime or for 180 days during peacetime. Members of the National Guard and Reserves are also eligible if they have been called to regular active duty. Also eligible are spouses of the veteran, widows or widowers of the veteran, dependent parents of the veteran, any person who acted as a parent to the veteran for 5 years immediately prior to entering wartime service, children of the veteran under 19 years of age, children of the veteran between 19 and 23 years of age who are attending high school or an institution of higher education, children of the veteran 19 years of age or older who are mentally or physically unable to support themselves and were affected by the disability prior to their 18th birthday, and legally adopted children of the veteran. Applicants must be able to demonstrate a need for assistance for food, shelter, clothing, housing supplies, and medical care.

Financial data Grants depend on the need of the recipient.

Duration These are 1-time grants.

Number awarded Varies each year.

Deadline Applications may be submitted at any time.

[1323]
FLORIDA SERVICE-CONNECTED TOTAL AND PERMANENT DISABILITY PROPERTY TAX EXEMPTION

Florida Department of Revenue
Attn: Taxpayer Services
5050 West Tennessee Street
Tallahassee, FL 32399-0100
(850) 617-8600   Toll Free: (800) 352-3671
E-mail: EMailDOR@dor.state.fl.us
Web: www.myflorida.com

Summary To exempt from property taxation real estate owned by disabled veterans and their surviving spouses.

Eligibility This exemption is available to Florida residents who have real estate that they own and use as a homestead. Applicants must be honorably-discharged veterans who have a total and permanent disability or require a wheelchair for mobility as a result of their military service. Under certain circumstances, the benefit of this exemption can carry over to a surviving spouse.

Financial data All real estate used and owned as a homestead, less any portion used for commercial purposes, is exempt from taxation.

Duration The exemption applies as long as the taxpayer owns the property in Florida.

Additional information Initial applications should be made in person at the appropriate county property appraiser's office.

Number awarded Varies each year.

Deadline Applications must be submitted by February of the year for which the exemption is sought.

[1324]
GEORGIA HOMESTEAD TAX EXEMPTION FOR DISABLED VETERANS

Georgia Department of Revenue
Attn: Property Tax Division
4245 International Parkway, Suite A
Hapeville, GA 30354-3918
(404) 968-0707   Fax: (404) 968-0778
E-mail: Local.Government.Services@dor.ga.gov
Web: etax.dor.ga.gov

Summary To exempt from property taxation a portion of the value of homesteads owned by disabled veterans in Georgia and their families.

Eligibility This program is open to residents of Georgia who qualify as a 100% disabled veteran under any of several provisions of state law. Surviving spouses and minor children are also eligible. Applicants must actually occupy a homestead and use it as their legal residence for all purposes.

Financial data The first $50,000 of assessed valuation of the homestead owned by disabled veterans or their family members is exempt from property taxes for state, county, municipal, and school purposes.

Duration The exemption remains in effect as long as the veteran or family member owns and resides in the homestead.

Number awarded Varies each year.

Deadline Applications must be filed with local tax officials by February of each year.

[1325]
GEORGIA HOMESTEAD TAX EXEMPTION FOR SURVIVING SPOUSES OF U.S. SERVICE MEMBERS

Georgia Department of Revenue
Attn: Property Tax Division
4245 International Parkway, Suite A
Hapeville, GA 30354-3918
(404) 968-0707   Fax: (404) 968-0778
E-mail: Local.Government.Services@dor.ga.gov
Web: etax.dor.ga.gov

Summary To exempt from property taxation a portion of the value of homesteads in Georgia owned by surviving spouses of deceased U.S. servicemembers.

Eligibility This program is open to residents of Georgia who are the unremarried spouse of a U.S. servicemember who was killed in action or died as a result of any war or armed conflict.

Financial data The first $50,000 of assessed valuation of the homestead owned by qualifying spouses is exempt from property taxes for state, county, municipal, and school purposes.

Duration The exemption remains in effect as long as the spouse owns and resides in the homestead and remains unmarried.

Number awarded Varies each year.

Deadline Applications must be filed with local tax officials by February of each year.

[1326]
HAWAII PROPERTY TAX EXEMPTIONS FOR DISABLED VETERANS

Office of Veterans Services
Attn: Veterans Services Coordinator
459 Patterson Road
E-Wing, Room 1-A103
Honolulu, HI 96819-1522
(808) 433-0420   Fax: (808) 433-0385
E-mail: ovs@ovs.hawaii.gov
Web: hawaii.gov/dod/ovs/benefits/state-provided-benefits

Summary To exempt the homes of disabled veterans and surviving spouses in Hawaii from real estate taxation.

Eligibility This program is open to totally disabled veterans in Hawaii and their surviving spouses.

Financial data The real property owned and occupied as a home is exempt from taxation.

Duration The exemption applies as long as the disabled veteran or his/her widow(er) resides in Hawaii.

Deadline Deadline not specified.

[1327]
HOPE FOR THE WARRIORS IMMEDIATE NEEDS GRANTS

Hope for the Warriors
Attn: Immediate Needs
1335 Western Boulevard, Suite E
Jacksonville, NC 28546-5539
(910) 938-1817   Toll Free: (877) 246-7349
E-mail: imn@hopeforthewarriors.org
Web: www.hopeforthewarriors.org/immneeds.html

Summary To provide funding for immediate needs to disabled military personnel, veterans, and their families.

Eligibility This assistance is available to wounded service members and their families. Applicants must need assistance to meet such immediate needs as travel to bedside where the government does not provide assistance, rental cars, lodging assistance, groceries, gas, furniture, assistance with child care, emergency assistance with essentials to daily living (e.g., rent and utilities), or items that assist and/or supplement programs at military treatment facilities and Veterans Administration polytrauma units.

Financial data The amount of the grant depends on the need of the recipient. Payment is always made to a third party.

Duration Applicants may apply once a year.

Number awarded Varies each year.

Deadline Applications may be submitted at any time.

[1328]
IDAHO RETIREMENT BENEFITS DEDUCTION

Idaho State Tax Commission
Attn: Public Information Office
800 Park Boulevard, Plaza IV
P.O. Box 36
Boise, ID 83722-0410
(208) 334-7660   Toll Free: (800) 972-7660
TDD: (800) 377-3529
Web: tax.idaho.gov/i-1039.cfm

Summary To deduct the retirement and disability income of certain residents from state income tax in Idaho.

Eligibility Eligible for this deduction are full-year residents of Idaho who are age 65 or older, or disabled and age 62 and older, and who are receiving the following annuities and benefits: 1) retirement annuities paid by the United States to a retired civil service employee or the unremarried widow of the employee; 2) retirement benefits paid from the firemen's retirement fund of the state of Idaho to a retired fireman or the unremarried widow of a retired fireman; 3) retirement benefits paid from the policeman's retirement fund of a city within Idaho to a retired policeman or the unremarried widow of a retired policeman; or 4) retirement benefits paid by the United States to a retired member of the U.S. military service or the unremarried widow of those veterans.

Financial data The amount of retirement or disability benefits may be deducted from taxable state income in Idaho, to a maximum deduction of $41,814 for married couples or $27,876 for single persons.

Duration 1 year; must reapply each year.

Number awarded Varies each year.

Deadline April of each year.

[1329]
IDAHO WAR VETERAN'S EMERGENCY GRANT PROGRAM

Idaho Division of Veterans Services
Attn: Office of Veterans Advocacy
444 Fort Street
Boise, ID 83702
(208) 577-2300   Fax: (208) 577-2333
E-mail: info@veterans.idaho.gov
Web: www.veterans.idaho.gov/Veterans_Advocacy.aspx

Summary To provide emergency assistance to disabled veterans, wartime veterans, and their families in Idaho.

Eligibility Eligible for these grants are veterans who had at least 90 days of honorable wartime military service and entered the military from Idaho or lived within the state for at least 5 years. Veterans with a service-connected disability are eligible with earlier separation. Surviving spouses and dependent children are also eligible. Applicants must be current residents of Idaho in need of assistance because of a major catastrophe (e.g., natural disaster or death of a spouse or child), loss of job because of a disability, or other extreme financial emergency (e.g., cut-off notice from a utility company, eviction notice from a landlord, arrears payment notice from the lien holder of a home).

Financial data The maximum amount available under this program is $1,000, issued in small incremental grants.

Duration The limit of $1,000 applies for the lifetime of each veteran or his/her family.

Additional information This program was established by the Idaho legislature in lieu of granting a wartime bonus to Idaho veterans.

Number awarded Varies each year.

Deadline Deadline not specified.

[1330]
ILLINOIS DISABLED VETERANS' HOMESTEAD EXEMPTION

Illinois Department of Revenue
101 West Jefferson Street
P.O. Box 19044
Springfield, IL 62794-9044
(217) 782-3336   Toll Free: (800) 732-8866
TDD: (800) 544-5304
Web: www.revenue.state.il.us

Summary To exempt a portion of the value of specially adapted housing owned by disabled veterans and their spouses in Illinois for purposes of property taxation.

Eligibility This exemption applies to housing owned and used by disabled veterans and their unmarried surviving spouses. The housing must have been purchased or constructed with funds provided by the U.S. Department of Veterans Affairs (VA) as part of a program of specially adapted housing for disabled veterans. The exemption is also available to disabled veterans and spouses who live in mobile homes. They may not utilize this exemption and either the Disabled Persons' Homestead Exemption or the Disabled Veterans Standard Homestead Exemption.

Financial data The exemption provides a reduction of $70,000 in the assessed value of the homestead.

Duration Veterans must file an annual application to continue to receive this exemption.

Deadline Deadline not specified.

[1331]
ILLINOIS GLOBAL WAR ON TERRORISM SURVIVORS' COMPENSATION

Illinois Department of Veterans' Affairs
833 South Spring Street
P.O. Box 19432
Springfield, IL 62794-9432
(217) 782-6641   Toll Free: (800) 437-9824 (within IL)
Fax: (217) 524-0344   TDD: (217) 524-4645
E-mail: webmail@dva.state.il.us
Web: www2.illinois.gov

Summary To pay a bonus to survivors of Illinois veterans killed by terrorist acts or hostile activities.

Eligibility Eligible to receive this bonus are survivors of persons who had been Illinois residents for 1 year prior to entering military service and who were killed by terrorist acts or hostile activities during performance of military service in periods not recognized as wartime or by U.S. campaign or service medals.

Financial data The bonus is $3,000.

Duration This is a 1-time payment.

Deadline Deadline not specified.

[1332]
ILLINOIS KOREAN, VIETNAM, PERSIAN GULF, AND GLOBAL WAR ON TERRORISM CONFLICT BONUS

Illinois Department of Veterans' Affairs
833 South Spring Street
P.O. Box 19432
Springfield, IL 62794-9432
(217) 782-6641   Toll Free: (800) 437-9824 (within IL)
Fax: (217) 524-0344   TDD: (217) 524-4645
E-mail: webmail@dva.state.il.us
Web: www.veterans.illinois.gov/benefits/bonuspayment.htm

Summary To provide a bonus to Illinois veterans of the Korean, Vietnam, Persian Gulf, or Iraqi conflicts or their survivors.

Eligibility Eligible for this bonus are veterans who served in Korea between June 27, 1950 and July 27, 1953, or in Vietnam between January 1, 1961 and March 28, 1973 or on April 29 or 30, 1975, the Persian Gulf between August 2, 1990 and November 30, 1995, or in Operation Enduring Freedom or Operation Iraqi Freedom (the Global War on Terrorism) for at least 30 consecutive or 60 nonconsecutive days foreign or sea service on or after September 11, 2001. They must have received the Korean Service Medal, the Vietnam Service Medal, the Armed Forces Expeditionary Medal Vietnam Era, the Southwest Asia Service Medal, the Global War on Terrorism Expeditionary Medal, or the Global War on Terrorism Service Medal, along with having been honorably discharged and a resident of Illinois for 12 months before entering service. Survivors of deceased veterans are eligible if the veteran's death was service connected and within the specified dates.

Financial data Veterans are entitled to a bonus of $100; survivors are entitled to $1,000.

Duration This is a 1-time payment.

Deadline Deadline not specified.

[1333]
ILLINOIS VIETNAM VETERAN SURVIVORS COMPENSATION

Illinois Department of Veterans' Affairs
833 South Spring Street
P.O. Box 19432
Springfield, IL 62794-9432
(217) 782-6641   Toll Free: (800) 437-9824 (within IL)
Fax: (217) 524-0344   TDD: (217) 524-4645
E-mail: webmail@dva.state.il.us
Web: www2.illinois.gov

Summary To pay a bonus to survivors of Illinois veterans who served in Vietnam.

Eligibility Eligible to receive this bonus are survivors of persons who had been Illinois residents for 1 year prior to entering military service and who served in Vietnam between January 1, 1961 and March 28, 1973 or on April 29 or 30, 1975. The veteran's death must have been service connected or the direct result of service-connected disabilities incurred during the specified time period.

Financial data The bonus is $1,000.

Duration This is a 1-time payment.

Deadline Deadline not specified.

[1334]
INDIANA MILITARY RETIREMENT OR SURVIVOR'S BENEFIT INCOME TAX DEDUCTION

Indiana Department of Revenue
Attn: Taxpayer Services Division
Indiana Government Center North
100 North Senate Avenue
Indianapolis, IN 46204-2253
(317) 232-2240   TDD: (317) 232-4952
E-mail: individualtaxassistance@dor.in.gov
Web: www.in.gov/dor

Summary To exempt a portion of the income of veterans and surviving spouses from state taxation in Indiana.

Eligibility This program is open to Indiana residents who are retired from the military or are the surviving spouse of a person who was in the military. Applicants must be at least 60 years of age and receiving military retirement or survivor's benefits.

Financial data Up to $5,000 of the income from military retirement or survivor's benefits is exempt from state income taxation in Indiana.

Duration The exemption continues as long as the recipient resides in Indiana.

Deadline Deadline not specified.

[1335]
INDIANA PROPERTY TAX DEDUCTIONS FOR DISABLED VETERANS

Department of Local Government Finance
Indiana Government Center North, Room N1058(B)
100 North Senate Avenue
Indianapolis, IN 46201
(317) 232-3777   Fax: (317) 232-8779
E-mail: PropertyTaxInfo@dlgf.in.gov
Web: www.in.gov/dlgf

Summary To exempt disabled Indiana veterans and their spouses from a portion of their property taxes.

Eligibility This program is open to the following categories of veterans who are residents of Indiana: 1) served honorably at least 90 days and are either totally disabled (the disability does not need to be service connected) or are at least 62 years of age and have at least a 10% service-connected disability; 2) served honorably during wartime and have at least a 10% service-connected disability; or 3) served honorably during wartime and either have a 100% service-connected disability or are at least 62 years of age and have at least a 10% service-connected disability. A statutory disability rating for pulmonary tuberculosis does not qualify. A disability incurred during Initial Active Duty for Training (IADT) with the National Guard or Reserves is eligible only if the disability occurred from an event during the period of active duty and that duty was performed during wartime. Surviving spouses of those 3 categories of veterans are also eligible.

Financial data Property tax exemptions are $12,480 for veterans and spouses in the first category (only if the assessed value of the combined real and personal property owned by the veteran or spouse does not exceed $143,160), $24,960 in the second category, or $37,440 in the third category; there is no limit on the value of the property owned by a surviving spouse).

Duration 1 year; may be renewed as long as the eligible veteran or surviving unremarried spouse owns and occupies the primary residence in Indiana.

Number awarded Varies each year.

Deadline Applications must be submitted no later than May of each year.

[1336]
INDIANA VETERANS' BURIAL ALLOWANCE

Indiana Department of Veterans' Affairs
302 West Washington Street, Room E-120
Indianapolis, IN 46204-2738
(317) 232-3910   Toll Free: (800) 400-4520 (within IN)
Fax: (317) 232-7721
Web: www.in.gov/dva/2343.htm

Summary To provide a burial allowance for Indiana veterans and their spouses.

Eligibility This benefit is available to honorably-discharged veterans from Indiana and their spouses. Applications must be filed with the county auditor in the county of residence.

Financial data County auditors are authorized to pay up to $1,000 for burial costs of a veteran or the veteran's spouse and up to $100 for the setting of a federal headstone.

Duration This is a 1-time payment.

Number awarded Varies each year.

Deadline Requests for assistance may be submitted at any time.

[1337]
INJURED MARINE SEMPER FI GRANTS

Injured Marine Semper Fi Fund
c/o Wounded Warrior Center
Building H49
P.O. Box 555193
Camp Pendleton, CA 92055-5193
(760) 725-3680   Fax: (760) 725-3685
E-mail: info@semperfifund.org
Web: semperfifund.org/assistance

Summary To provide supplemental assistance to Marines injured in combat and their families.

Eligibility This program is open to Marines injured in post-9/11 combat operations or facing a life-threatening illness and their families. Members of the Army, Air Force, Coast Guard, and Navy who served in support of Marine forces are also eligible. Applicants must need financial assistance to deal with such needs as family support (e.g., travel and lodging, costs of hospitalization and rehabilitation, mortgages, car payments, utilities, grocery bills), adaptive housing support, adaptive transportation, or specialized and adaptive equipment.

Financial data Funds are available for such expenses as child care, travel expenses for families, and other necessities. Assistance is also available for the purchase of adaptive transportation, home modifications, and specialized equipment such as wheelchairs, audio/visual equipment for the blind, and software for traumatic brain injuries.

Duration Grants are provided as needed.

Additional information This fund was established in 2004 by a small group of Marine Corps spouses.

Number awarded Varies each year. Since this program was established, it has awarded more than 38,000 grants worth more than $57 million.

Deadline Applications may be submitted at any time.

[1338]
IOWA MILITARY SERVICE PROPERTY TAX EXEMPTION

Iowa Department of Revenue
Attn: Property Tax Division
Hoover State Office Building
1305 East Walnut
P.O. Box 10469
Des Moines, IA 50306-0469
(515) 281-4040   Toll Free: (800) 367-3388 (within IA)
Fax: (515) 281-3906   E-mail: idr@iowa.gov
Web: www.iowa.gov/tax/taxlaw/PropertyTaxCredits.html

Summary To exempt veterans, military personnel, and their family members from a portion of property taxes in Iowa.

Eligibility This exemption is available to residents of Iowa who are 1) former members of the U.S. armed forces who performed at least 18 months of military service (or for fewer months because of a service-related injury), regardless of the time period, and who were honorably discharged; 2) former members, and members currently serving of the U.S. Reserves and Iowa National Guard who have served at least 20 years; and 3) current members of the U.S. Reserves and Iowa National Guard who were activated for federal duty for at least 90 days; 4) former members of the armed forces whose enlistment would have occurred during the Korean Conflict but chose to serve 5 years in the Reserves; and 5) honorably discharged veterans who served in a designated eligible service period. Applicants must own a primary residence in the state. Also eligible for the exemption are the spouses, unremarried widow(er)s, minor children, and widowed parent of qualified veterans.

Financial data The amount of the exemption is currently $1,852.

Duration 1 year; continues until the qualifying veteran or dependent no longer lives in the residence.

Number awarded Varies each year; recently, more than $2.4 million in property was exempt from taxation.

Deadline Application must be made by June of the year for which the exemption is first requested. The exemption is provided annually, from then on, as long as the qualifying veteran or dependent resides in the house.

[1339]
KENTUCKY MILITARY FAMILY ASSISTANCE TRUST FUND

Kentucky Department of Military Affairs
Attn: State Family Program
Boone National Guard Center
100 Minuteman Parkway
Frankfort, KY 40601-6168
(502) 607-1156   Toll Free: (800) 372-7601
Fax: (502) 607-1394   E-mail: steven.engels@us.army.mil
Web: www.dma.ky.gov

Summary To provide emergency financial assistance to Kentucky residents serving in the armed forces outside of the United States and their spouses.

Eligibility This assistance is available to 1) members of the U.S. armed forces who are deployed outside of the United States and who have a Kentucky home of record; and 2) Kentucky resident spouses of eligible military members. Applicants must be facing expenses that create an undue hardship directly related to deployment outside the country. They may not have reasonable access to any other funding source. There is no limitation on the type of expense for which the assistance is requested, only that it create an undue hardship.

Financial data Grants are limited to $2,500 for a single application or $5,000 per fiscal year.

Duration Assistance is available while the military member is deployed overseas and for 90 days following the end of deployment or deactivation.

Additional information This program began in 2006.

Number awarded Varies each year.

Deadline Applications may be submitted at any time.

[1340]
LOUISIANA INCOME EXEMPTION FOR FEDERAL RETIREMENT PAY

Louisiana Department of Revenue
Attn: Individual Income Tax
P.O. Box 201
Baton Rouge, LA 70821
(225) 219-0102
Web: www.revenue.louisiana.gov

Summary To exempt the retirement income of all federal employees, including the military and their surviving spouses, from state taxation in Louisiana.

Eligibility This exemption is available to all residents of Louisiana who are receiving retirement benefits from the federal retirement system, including veterans and their surviving spouses.

Financial data All federal retirement income is exempt from state income taxation in Louisiana.

Duration The benefit continues as long as the recipient remains a resident of Louisiana for state income tax purposes.

Number awarded Varies each year.

Deadline Deadline not specified.

[1341]
MAINE MILITARY FAMILY RELIEF FUND

Maine Department of Defense, Veterans and Emergency Management
Attn: Family Program Office
Camp Keyes
Augusta, ME 04333-0033
(207) 626-4271
Web: www.me.ngb.army.mil

Summary To provide emergency relief to members of the National Guard or Reserves in Maine who have been called to active duty and their families.

Eligibility This assistance is available to 1) members of the Maine National Guard; and 2) residents of Maine who are members of the Reserves of the armed forces. Applicants must have been called to active military duty and be facing emergency financial needs as a result. Also eligible are members of their immediate family, defined as spouses, children, parents, grandparents, siblings, stepchildren, or others who have a military identification card identifying the military member as a sponsor.

Financial data The amount of the grant depends on the need of the applicant. Funds are available for such needs as food, rent, utilities, emergency transportation and vehicle repair, funeral expenses, medical and dental expenses, short-term emergency needs if pay is delayed or stolen, emergency home repairs, or other emergency needs approved by the unit of assignment.

Duration These are normally 1-time grants.

Number awarded Varies each year.

Deadline Applications may be submitted at any time.

[1342]
MAINE PROPERTY TAX EXEMPTIONS FOR VETERANS

Maine Revenue Services
Attn: Property Tax Division
P.O. Box 9106
Augusta, ME 04332-9106
(207) 287-2013   Fax: (207) 287-6396
E-mail: prop.tax@maine.gov
Web: www.maine.gov/revenue/propertytax/homepage.html

Summary To exempt the estates of disabled Maine veterans and selected family members from property taxation.

Eligibility Eligible for this program are veterans who served in wartime during World War I, World War II, the Korean campaign, the Vietnam war, the Persian Gulf war, or other recognized service periods, are legal residents of Maine, and are either older than 62 years of age or are receiving a pension or compensation from the U.S. government for total disability (whether service connected or not). Vietnam veterans must have served 180 days on active duty unless discharged earlier for a service-connected disability. The exemption also includes 1) property held in joint tenancy with the veterans' spouses, and 2) property of unremarried widow(er)s, minor children, and parents of deceased veterans, if those dependents are receiving a pension or compensation from the U.S. government.

Financial data Estates of disabled veterans and eligible dependents, including both real and personal property, are exempt up to $6,000 of just valuation. For veterans and dependents who served in wartime prior to World War II, estates up to $7,000 are exempt.

Duration Veterans, spouses, unremarried widow(er)s, and mothers are eligible for this exemption throughout their lifetimes; minor children of veterans are eligible until they reach the age of 18.

Number awarded Varies each year.

Deadline When an eligible person first submits an application, the proof of entitlement must reach the assessors of the local municipality prior to the end of March. Once eligibility has been established, notification need not be repeated in subsequent years.

[1343]
MAINE TAX EXEMPTION FOR SPECIALLY ADAPTED HOUSING UNITS

Maine Revenue Services
Attn: Property Tax Division
P.O. Box 9106
Augusta, ME 04332-9106
(207) 287-2013   Fax: (207) 287-6396
E-mail: prop.tax@maine.gov
Web: www.maine.gov/revenue/propertytax/homepage.html

Summary To exempt the specially adapted housing units of paraplegic veterans or their surviving spouses from taxation in Maine.

Eligibility Veterans who served in the U.S. armed forces during any federally-recognized war period, are legal residents of Maine, are paraplegic veterans within the meaning of U.S. statutes, and have received a grant from the U.S. government for specially adapted housing are eligible. The exemption also applies to property held in joint tenancy with the veteran's spouse and to the specially adapted housing of unremarried widow(er)s of eligible veterans.

Financial data Estates of paraplegic veterans are exempt up to $50,000 of just valuation for a specially adapted housing unit.

Duration The exemption is valid for the lifetime of the paraplegic veteran or unremarried widow(er).

Number awarded Varies each year.

Deadline When an eligible person first submits an application, the proof of entitlement must reach the assessors of the local municipality prior to the end of March. Once eligibility has been established, notification need not be repeated in subsequent years.

[1344]
MARYLAND DEATH BENEFIT PROGRAM

Maryland Department of Veterans Affairs
Attn: Veterans Service and Benefits Program
Federal Building, Room 3020
31 Hopkins Plaza
Baltimore, MD 21201
(410) 230-4444   Toll Free: (800) 446-4926, ext. 6450
Fax: (410) 230-4445
E-mail: mdveteransinfo@mdva.state.md.us
Web: www.mdva.state.md.us/state/survivorBenefits.html

Summary To provide a death benefit to surviving family members of Maryland residents killed as military personnel in Iraq or Afghanistan.

Eligibility This benefit is available to survivors of Maryland residents who have been killed or died as a result of injuries sustained in combat in Afghanistan or Iraq. The benefit is payable to survivors in the following priority: 1) to the surviving spouse; 2) if there is no surviving spouse, to the surviving child or children; 3) if there is no surviving spouse or child, to surviving dependent parents; or 4) if there is no surviving spouse, child, or dependent parent, to the estate of the decedent.

Financial data This benefit is $125,000.

Duration This is a 1-time benefit.

Additional information This program began in 2006.

Number awarded Varies each year.

Deadline Deadline not specified.

[1345]
MARYLAND PROPERTY TAX EXEMPTION FOR DISABLED VETERANS AND SURVIVING SPOUSES

Maryland Department of Assessments and Taxation
Attn: Property Taxes
301 West Preston Street
Baltimore, MD 21201-2395
(410) 767-1184   Toll Free: (888) 246-5941
TDD: (800) 735-2258
Web: www.dat.state.md.us/sdatweb/exempt.html

Summary To exempt the homes of disabled veterans and their surviving spouses from property taxation in Maryland.

Eligibility This exemption is available to armed services veterans with a permanent service-connected disability rated 100% by the U.S. Department of Veterans Affairs who own a dwelling house in Maryland. Unremarried surviving spouses are also eligible.

Financial data The dwelling houses of eligible veterans and surviving spouses are exempt from real property taxes.

Duration The exemption is available as long as the veteran or surviving spouse owns the dwelling house in Maryland.

Number awarded Varies each year.

Deadline Applications may be submitted at any time.

[1346]
MARYLAND PROPERTY TAX EXEMPTION FOR SURVIVING SPOUSES OF DECEASED VETERANS

Maryland Department of Assessments and Taxation
Attn: Property Taxes
301 West Preston Street
Baltimore, MD 21201-2395
(410) 767-1184   Toll Free: (888) 246-5941
TDD: (800) 735-2258
Web: www.dat.state.md.us/sdatweb/exempt.html

Summary To exempt the homes of surviving spouses of deceased military personnel from property taxation in Maryland.

Eligibility This exemption is available to surviving spouses of active military personnel who died in the line of duty. Applicants must own a dwelling house in Maryland.

Financial data The dwelling houses of eligible surviving spouses is exempt from real property taxes.

Duration The exemption is available as long as the surviving spouse owns the dwelling house in Maryland.

Number awarded Varies each year.

Deadline Applications may be submitted at any time.

[1347]
MASSACHUSETTS INCOME TAX EXEMPTION FOR UNIFORMED SERVICES RETIREMENT PAY

Massachusetts Department of Revenue
Attn: Personal Income Tax
P.O. Box 7010
Boston, MA 02204
(617) 887-MDOR   Toll Free: (800) 392-6089 (within MA)
Fax: (617) 887-1900
Web: www.mass.gov

Summary To exempt the retirement income and survivorship benefits received from the U.S. uniformed services from state income taxation in Massachusetts.

Eligibility Eligible for this exemption are residents of Massachusetts who are receiving noncontributory pension income or survivorship benefits from the U.S. uniformed services (including the Army, Navy, Marine Corps, Air Force, Coast Guard, National Oceanic and Atmospheric Administration, and commissioned corps of the Public Health Service).

Financial data All uniformed services retirement income and survivorship benefits are exempt from state income taxation.

Duration The benefit continues as long as the recipient remains a resident of Massachusetts for state income tax purposes.

Additional information This exemption became effective with income received in 1997.

Number awarded Varies each year.

Deadline Deadline not specified.

[1348]
MASSACHUSETTS PROPERTY TAX EXEMPTION FOR VETERANS AND THEIR FAMILIES

Massachusetts Department of Revenue
Attn: Division of Local Services
100 Cambridge Street
Boston, MA 02114
(617) 626-2386   Fax: (617) 626-2330
Web: www.mass.gov/dor/all-taxes/excise-and-property

Summary To provide a property tax exemption to blind, disabled, and other veterans (and their families) in Massachusetts.

Eligibility This program is open to veterans who are residents of Massachusetts, were residents for at least 6 months prior to entering the service, have been residents for at least 5 consecutive years, and are occupying property as their domicile. Applicants must have an ownership interest in the domicile that ranges from $2,000 to $10,000, depending on the category of exemption. Veterans must have been discharged under conditions other than dishonorable. Several categories of veterans and their families qualify: 1) veterans who have a service-connected disability rating of 10% or more; veterans who have been awarded the Purple Heart; Gold Star mothers and fathers; and surviving spouses of eligible veterans who do not remarry; 2) veterans who suffered, in the line of duty, the loss or permanent loss of use of 1 foot, 1 hand, or 1 eye; veterans who received the Congressional Medal of Honor, Distinguished Service Cross, Navy Cross, or Air Force Cross; and their spouses or surviving spouses; 3) veterans who suffered, in the line of duty, the loss or permanent loss of use of both feet, both hands, or both eyes; and their spouses or surviving spouses; 4) veterans who suffered total disability in the line of duty and received assistance in acquiring specially adapted housing, which they own and occupy as their domicile; and their spouses or surviving spouses; 5) unremarried surviving spouses of military personnel who died due to injury or disease from being in a combat zone, or are missing and presumed dead due to combat; 6) veterans who suffered total disability in the line of duty and are incapable of working; and their spouses or surviving spouses; and 7) veterans who are certified by the Veterans Administration as paraplegic and their surviving spouses.

Financial data Qualified veterans and family members are entitled to an annual exemption from their taxes for the different categories: 1), $400; 2), $750; 3), $1,250; 4), $1,500; 5), total exemption for 5 years after death, and up to $2,500 after 5 years; 6), $1,000; or 7), total.

Duration The exemptions are provided each year that the veteran or unremarried surviving spouse lives in Massachusetts and owns the property as a domicile.

Additional information Applications are available from local assessor's offices.

Number awarded Varies each year.

Deadline Applications must be filed with the local assessor by December of each year.

[1349]
MASSACHUSETTS SOLDIERS LEGACY FUND PRE-COLLEGE EDUCATION GRANTS

Massachusetts Soldiers Legacy Fund
P.O. Box 962061
Milk Street Post Office
Boston, MA 02196
Toll Free: (866) 856-5533   E-mail: info@mslfund.org
Web: www.mslfund.org

Summary To provide funding for educational activities to the minor children of service members from Massachusetts who were killed in Afghanistan or Iraq.

Eligibility This program is open to children younger than 18 years of age of members of the U.S. armed forces who died while deployed on operations Enduring Freedom or Iraqi Freedom. The parent's home of record must have been Massachusetts. Applicants must be seeking funding for such activities as pre-school education and day care, private school tuition and related expenses (e.g., general or SAT tutoring), educational computer software and equipment, or special needs programs. All qualified children receive this assistance; there is no selection process.

Financial data The amount of the grant depends on the need of the child.

Duration Grants are renewed as necessary.

Additional information This program began in 2004.

Number awarded Varies each year.

Deadline Deadline not specified.

[1350]
MASSACHUSETTS VETERANS ANNUITY PROGRAM

Department of Veterans' Services
Attn: Annuities
600 Washington Street, Seventh Floor
Boston, MA 02111
(617) 210-5480   Fax: (617) 210-5755
E-mail: mdvs@vet.state.ma.us
Web: www.mass.gov/veterans

Summary   To provide an annuity to blind or disabled veterans from Massachusetts and to the parents and spouses of deceased military personnel.

Eligibility   This program is open to 1) veterans who are blind, double amputee, paraplegic, or have a 100% service-connected disability; 2) the parents of military personnel who died of service-connected causes; and 3) the unremarried spouses of military personnel who died of service-connected causes. Veterans must have been residents of Massachusetts at the time of entry into military service who served during specified wartime periods and received other than a dishonorable discharge. All applicants must currently be residents of Massachusetts.

Financial data   Recipients are entitled to an annuity of $2,000 per year.

Duration   The annuity is paid as long as the recipient continues to reside in Massachusetts.

Deadline   Deadline not specified.

[1351]
MCCORMICK GRANTS

Society of the First Infantry Division
Attn: 1st Infantry Division Foundation
1933 Morris Road
Blue Bell, PA 19422-1422
Toll Free: (888) 324-4733   Fax: (215) 661-1934
E-mail: Fdn1ID@aol.com
Web: 1stid.org.org/foundation/grants.cfm

Summary   To provide emergency financial assistance to active First Division soldiers and their families.

Eligibility   This assistance is available to soldiers currently serving in the First Infantry Division and their families. Applicants must be facing emergency financial needs that cannot be met through the usual forms of assistance available to them.

Financial data   Grant amounts depend on the need of the recipient. Recently, they ranged up to $1,500.

Duration   These are 1-time grants.

Additional information   This program was established in 2005 with funding from the Robert R. McCormick Tribune Foundation.

Number awarded   Varies each year; recently, 3 grants, with a total value of $2,313.49, were awarded.

Deadline   Applications may be submitted at any time.

[1352]
MICHIGAN HOMESTEAD PROPERTY TAX CREDIT FOR VETERANS AND BLIND PEOPLE

Michigan Department of Treasury
Attn: Homestead Exemption
Treasury Building
430 West Allegan Street
Lansing, MI 48922
(517) 636-4486   TDD: (800) 649-3777
E-mail: treasIndTax@michigan.gov
Web: www.michigan.gov/taxes

Summary   To provide an income tax credit to veterans, military personnel, their spouses, blind people, and their surviving spouses in Michigan.

Eligibility   Eligible to apply are residents of Michigan who are 1) blind and own their homestead; 2) a veteran with a service-connected disability or his/her surviving spouse; 3) a surviving spouse of a veteran deceased in service; 4) a pensioned veteran, a surviving spouse of those veterans, or an active military member, all of whose household income is less than $7,500; or 5) a surviving spouse of a non-disabled or non-pensioned veteran of the Korean War, World War II, or World War I whose household income is less than $7,500. All applicants must own or rent a home in Michigan, have been a Michigan resident for at least 6 months during the year in which application is made, and fall within qualifying income levels (up to $82,650 in household income).

Financial data   The maximum credit, applied to state income taxes, is $1,200. The exact amount varies. For homeowners, the credit depends on the state equalized value of the homestead and on an allowance for filing category. For renters, 20% of the rent is considered property tax eligible for credit.

Duration   1 year; eligibility must be established each year.

Number awarded   Varies each year.

Deadline   April of each year.

[1353]
MICHIGAN HOMESTEAD PROPERTY TAX EXEMPTION FOR SPECIALLY ADAPTED HOUSING

Michigan Department of Treasury
Attn: Homestead Exemption
Treasury Building
430 West Allegan Street
Lansing, MI 48922
(517) 373-3200   TDD: (800) 649-3777
E-mail: treasPtd2@michigan.gov
Web: www.michigan.gov/taxes

Summary   To exempt specially adapted housing occupied as homesteads by disabled veterans and their unremarried spouses from property taxation in Michigan.

Eligibility   This exemption is available to Michigan residents who are disabled veterans living in specially adapted housing that they acquired with financial assistance from the U.S. Department of Veterans Affairs (VA). If the veteran has died, the exemption continues for the unremarried surviving spouse.

Financial data   All taxes on qualified housing are cancelled.

Duration   This exemption continues as long as the disabled veteran or unremarried surviving spouse owns the property in

Michigan and, in the case of surviving spouses, remains unmarried.

Number awarded Varies each year.

Deadline Deadline not specified.

[1354]
MICHIGAN MILITARY FAMILY RELIEF FUND GRANTS

Department of Military and Veterans Affairs
Attn: Military Family Relief Fund
3423 North Martin Luther King Boulevard
P.O. Box 30261
Lansing, MI 48909-7761
Toll Free: (866) 271-4404   Fax: (517) 481-7644
E-mail: paocmn@michigan.gov
Web: www.michigan.gov

Summary To provide temporary financial support to members of the Michigan National Guard and Reserves who have been called to active duty as part of the national response to the September 11, 2001 terrorist attacks and their families.

Eligibility This assistance is available to members of the Michigan National Guard and Reserves and their families. The military member must have been called to active duty as part of the national response to the events of September 11, 2001 and has served at least 30 days of active duty. Applicants must be able to demonstrate a need for assistance as a result of the military member's service.

Financial data The maximum grant is $2,000.

Duration This assistance is provided to meet temporary needs only.

Additional information The state of Michigan established this program in 2004.

Number awarded Varies each year.

Deadline Applications may be submitted at any time.

[1355]
MICHIGAN VETERANS TRUST FUND EMERGENCY GRANTS

Department of Military and Veterans Affairs
Attn: Michigan Veterans Trust Fund
2500 South Washington Avenue
Lansing, MI 48913-5101
(517) 373-3130   E-mail: dutchera@michigan.gov
Web: www.michigan.gov

Summary To provide temporary financial assistance to disabled and other Michigan veterans and their families, if they are facing personal emergencies.

Eligibility Eligible for this assistance are veterans and their families residing in Michigan who are temporarily unable to provide the basic necessities of life. Support is not provided for long-term problems or chronic financial difficulties. The qualifying veteran must have been discharged under honorable conditions with at least 180 days of active wartime service or have been separated as a result of a physical or mental disability incurred in the line of duty.

Financial data No statutory limit exists on the amount of assistance that may be provided; a local board in each Michigan county determines if the applicant is genuinely needy and the amount of assistance to be awarded.

Duration This assistance is provided to meet temporary needs only.

Number awarded Varies each year.

Deadline Applications may be submitted at any time.

[1356]
MILITARY FAMILY SUPPORT TRUST FINANCIAL ASSISTANCE

Military Family Support Trust
1010 American Eagle Boulevard
P.O. Box 301
Sun City Center, FL 33573
(813) 634-4675   Fax: (813) 633-2412
E-mail: president@mobc-online.org
Web: www.mobc-online.org/financial.html

Summary To provide financial assistance for emergency needs to active-duty, retired, and deceased officers who served in the military or designated public service agencies and to their families.

Eligibility This assistance is available to 1) retired, active-duty, National Guard, or Reserve officers and former officers of the U.S. Army, Navy, Marine Corps, Air Force, Coast Guard, Public Health Service, or National Oceanic and Atmospheric Administration, at the rank of E-5 through E-9; 2) recipients of the Purple Heart, regardless of pay grade or length of service; 3) World War II combat veterans of the Merchant Marine; 4) federal employees at the grade of GS-7 or higher; 5) Foreign Service Officers at the grade of FSO-8 or lower; 6) honorably discharged or retired foreign military officers of friendly nations meeting the service and disability retirement criteria of their respective country and living in the United States; and 7) spouses, surviving spouses, and dependents (including grandchildren) of those categories. Applicants must be in need of financial assistance for personal care, subsistence, housing, all aspects of health care, or other special circumstances.

Financial data Grants depend on the need of the recipient.

Duration Assistance is provided in the form of 1-time grants or monthly payments.

Additional information This foundation began in 1992 as the Military Officers' Benevolent Corporation. It changed its name in 2008.

Number awarded Varies each year.

Deadline Applications may be submitted at any time.

[1357]
MINNESOTA MARKET VALUE EXCLUSION FOR DISABLED VETERANS

Minnesota Department of Revenue
Attn: Property Tax Division
600 North Robert Street
Mail Station 3340
St. Paul, MN 55146-3340
(651) 556-6087
Web: www.taxes.state.mn.us

Summary To exclude from property taxation a portion of the value of homesteads owned by disabled veterans, primary family caregivers, and surviving spouses in Minnesota.

Eligibility This exclusion is available to owners of homesteads in Minnesota who are veterans who have a service-connected disability rated at least at 70% by the U.S. Department of Veterans Affairs. If a disabled veteran has died (or was killed in action without becoming disabled), the surviving spouse is eligible for the exclusion. If a veteran meets the disability qualification but does not own homestead property, the homestead of the veteran's primary family caregiver, if any, is eligible for the exclusion for that veteran.

Financial data For veterans with a service-connected of 70% or more (and their surviving spouses or primary family caregivers), $150,000 of the market value of the homestead is excluded from property taxation. For veterans with a total (100%) and permanent service-connected disability (and their surviving spouses or primary family caregivers), $300,000 of the market value of the homestead is excluded from property taxation.

Duration This exclusion is available as long as the veteran, surviving spouse, or primary family caregiver owns the homestead and meets the eligibility requirements.

Additional information This exclusion was established by the Minnesota legislature for veterans in 2008 and expanded to included surviving spouses and primary family caregivers in 2011.

Deadline Applications must be submitted by June of each year.

[1358]
MINNESOTA STATE SOLDIERS ASSISTANCE PROGRAM

Minnesota Department of Veterans Affairs
Veterans Service Building
20 West 12th Street, Room 206C
St. Paul, MN 55155-2006
(651) 757-1556   Toll Free: (888) LINK-VET
Fax: (651) 296-3954 E-mail: kathy.schwartz@state.mn.us
Web: www.mdva.state.mn.us/SSAP/index.htm

Summary To provide emergency financial assistance to disabled veterans and their families in Minnesota.

Eligibility This assistance is available to veterans who are unable to work because of a temporary disability (from service-connected or other causes). Their dependents and survivors are also eligible. Applicants must also meet income and asset guidelines and be residents of Minnesota.

Financial data The maximum grant is $1,500. Funds may be used to pay for food and shelter, utility bills, and emergency medical treatment (including optical and dental benefits).

Duration This is a short-term program, with benefits payable up to 6 months only. If the veteran's disability is expected to be long term in nature or permanent, the department may continue to provide assistance while application is made for long-term benefits, such as Social Security disability or retirement benefits.

Number awarded Varies each year. A total of $1.4 million is available for this program annually.

Deadline Applications may be submitted at any time.

[1359]
MISSOURI MILITARY FAMILY RELIEF FUND GRANTS

Missouri Military Family Relief Fund
Attn: J1/DPP-F
2302 Militia Drive
Jefferson City, MO 65101-1203
(573) 638-9827   Fax: (573) 638-9548
E-mail: MilitaryRelief@mo.ngb.army.mil
Web: www.mmfrf.mo.gov

Summary To provide emergency financial assistance to members of the National Guard and Reserves in Missouri or their families who are facing difficulties as a result of deployment after September 11, 2001.

Eligibility This program is open to 1) members of the Missouri National Guard who have been on Title 10 orders as a result of the September 11, 2001 terrorist attacks for 30 consecutive days or more or have been off Title 10 orders as a result of the September 11, 2001 terrorist attacks for 120 days or less; 2) Reserve component members who are residents of Missouri and have been on Title 32 orders as a result of the September 11, 2001 terrorist attacks for 30 days or more or have been off Title 32 orders as a result of the September 11, 2001 terrorist attacks for 120 days or less; 3) immediate relatives of members of those National Guard or Reserve units. The Guard or Reserve member must have a rank no higher than O-3 or W-2. Applicants must be in need of emergency financial assistance; funding is not provided for nonessentials, to finance leave or vacations, to pay fines or legal expenses, to help liquidate or consolidate debts, to assist with house purchase or home improvements, to cover bad checks, or to pay credit card bills.

Financial data Grants up to $1,000 are available.

Duration Grants may be awarded only once in a 12-month period.

Additional information This program began in 2005.

Number awarded Varies each year.

Deadline Applications may be submitted at any time.

[1360]
MONTANA DISABLED AMERICAN VETERAN PROPERTY TAX BENEFIT

Montana Department of Revenue
Attn: Property Tax
125 North Roberts, Third Floor
P.O. Box 5805
Helena, MT 59604-5805
(406) 444-6900   Toll Free: (866) 859-2254
Fax: (406) 444-1505   TDD: (406) 444-2830
Web: mt.gov/revenue

Summary To reduce the property tax rate in Montana for disabled veterans and their surviving spouses.

Eligibility This benefit is available to residents of Montana who own and occupy property in the state. Applicants must have been honorably discharged from active service in the armed forces and be currently rated 100% disabled or compensated at the 100% disabled rate because of a service-connected disability. They must have an adjusted gross income less than $53,867 if married or $46,685 if single. Also eligible are unremarried surviving spouses with an adjusted gross income less than $40,700 whose spouse was a veteran with a 100% service-connected disability or compensation at the 100% disabled rate at the time of death, died while on active duty, or died of a service-connected disability.

Financial data Qualifying veterans and surviving spouses are entitled to a reduction in local property taxes on their residence, 1 attached or detached garage, and up to 1 acre of land. The amount of the reduction depends on the status of the applicant (married, single, or surviving spouse) and adjusted gross income, but ranges from 50% to 100%.

Duration The reduction continues as long as the recipient resides in Montana and owns and occupies property used as a primary residence.

Number awarded Varies each year.

Deadline Applications must be filed with the local Department of Revenue Office by April of each year.

[1361]
MONTGOMERY GI BILL (ACTIVE DUTY) DEATH BENEFIT

Department of Veterans Affairs
Attn: Veterans Benefits Administration
810 Vermont Avenue, N.W.
Washington, DC 20420
(202) 418-4343   Toll Free: (800) 827-1000
Web: www1.va.gov

Summary To provide a death benefit to a designated survivor of a serviceperson who was participating in the Montgomery GI Bill at the time of death.

Eligibility This benefit goes to the designated survivor of a serviceperson participating in the Montgomery GI Bill at the time of death, if the serviceperson's death occurred in service or within 1 year after discharge or release and was service connected. The benefit also will be paid if the serviceperson would have been eligible to participate but for the high school diploma requirement or the length-of-service requirement.

Financial data The amount paid is equal to the participant's actual military pay reduction less any education benefits paid.

Duration This is a 1-time disbursement.

Number awarded Varies each year.

Deadline Deadline not specified.

[1362]
NATIONAL ASSOCIATION OF AMERICAN VETERANS EMERGENCY ASSISTANCE

National Association of American Veterans
Attn: Executive Director
P.O. Box 6865
Washington, DC 20020-9994
Web: www.naavets.org/services.html

Summary To provide emergency financial assistance to veterans, military personnel, and their families.

Eligibility This assistance is available to veterans, military service members, and their family members who are experiencing financial hardship. Applicants must be seeking funding for mortgage assistance, rent, home repair or maintenance, vehicle repair or maintenance, medical expenses, or transportation expenses.

Financial data The amount of the grant depends on the need of the recipient.

Duration These are 1-time grants.

Additional information This association began in 2005.

Number awarded Varies each year.

Deadline Applications may be submitted at any time.

[1363]
NAVY-MARINE CORPS RELIEF SOCIETY FINANCIAL ASSISTANCE

Navy-Marine Corps Relief Society
875 North Randolph Street, Suite 225
Arlington, VA 22203-1757
(703) 696-4904   Fax: (703) 696-0144
Web: www.nmcrs.org/intfreeloan.html

Summary To provide emergency assistance, in the form of interest-free loans or grants, to current and former Navy and Marine Corps personnel and their families who need temporary funding.

Eligibility This program is open to active-duty and retired Navy and Marine Corps personnel, their eligible family members, eligible family members of Navy and Marine Corps personnel who died on active duty or in a retired status, Reservists on extended active duty, indigent mothers (65 years of age or older) of deceased servicemembers who have limited resources and no family to provide for their welfare, ex-spouses whose marriage to a servicemember lasted for at least 20 years while the servicemember was on active duty and who have not remarried, and uniformed members of the National Oceanic and Atmospheric Administration (NOAA). Applicants must need emergency funding for funeral expenses, medical or dental bills, food, rent, utilities, emergency transportation, disaster relief, child care expenses, essential vehicle repairs, or other unforeseen family emergencies. Funding is not available to pay bills for non-essentials, finance liberty and vacations, pay fines or legal expenses, pay taxes, finance recreational boats or vehicles or help Navy and Marine Corps families live beyond their means.

Financial data Funds are provided in the form of interest-free loans or grants.

Number awarded Varies each year.

Deadline Applications may be submitted at any time.

[1364]
NCOA DISASTER RELIEF FUND

Non Commissioned Officers Association of the United States of America
Attn: Benevolent Programs
10635 IH 35 North
P.O. Box 33610
San Antonio, TX 78265-3610
(210) 653-6161   Toll Free: (800) 662-2620
E-mail: membsvc@ncoausa.org
Web: www.ncoausa.org

Summary To provide funding to military members of the Non Commissioned Officers Association (NCOA) and their families who need disaster relief.

Eligibility This program is open to military members of the association and their families who suffer losses as a result of such disasters as acts of God, hurricanes, fires, floods, and earthquakes.

Financial data The amount of the aid depends on the availability of funds and the need of the recipient.

Additional information This program began in 1994.

Number awarded Varies each year.

Deadline   Applications may be submitted at any time.

[1365]
NEBRASKA HOMESTEAD EXEMPTION

Nebraska Department of Revenue
301 Centennial Mall South
P.O. Box 94818
Lincoln, NE 68509-4818
(402) 471-5729
Toll Free: (800) 742-7474 (within NE and IA)
Web: www.revenue.ne.gov/PAD/homestead.html

Summary   To exempt the property of Nebraska residents who are elderly, disabled, or veterans and their widow(er)s from a portion of taxation.

Eligibility   This exemption is available to 3 categories of Nebraska residents: the elderly, certain people with disabilities, and certain disabled veterans and their widow(er)s. Elderly people are those 65 years of age or older who own a homestead with a value less than $95,000 or 200% of their county's average assessed value of single family residential property, whichever is greater. Disabled people are those who 1) have a permanent physical disability and have lost all mobility such as to preclude locomotion without the regular use of a mechanical aid or prosthesis; 2) have undergone amputation of both arms above the elbow, or 3) have a permanent partial disability of both arms in excess of 75%. They must own a homestead with a value less than $110,000 or 225% of their county's average assessed value of single family residential property, whichever is greater. Veterans are those who served on active duty in the U.S. armed forces (or a government allied with the United States) during specified periods of war and received an honorable discharge. They must 1) be drawing compensation from the U.S. Department of Veterans Affairs (VA) because of a 100% service-connected disability; 2) be totally disabled by a nonservice-connected illness or accident; or 3) own a home that is substantially contributed to by VA. Also eligible are unremarried widow(er)s of veterans who died because of a service-connected disability, whose death while on active duty was service-connected, who died while on active duty during wartime, or who drew compensation from VA because of a 100% service-connected disability The homestead maximum value is $110,000 or 225% of the county's average assessed value of single family residential property, whichever is greater. Elderly people must have a household income less than $31,801 if single or $37,401 if married. Disabled persons, veterans, and widow(er)s (except veterans and widow(er)s who own a home that is substantially contributed to by the VA) must have a household income less than $34,901 if single or $40,301 if married.

Financial data   Exemptions depend on the income of the applicant, ranging from 25% to 100% of the value of the homestead. For the elderly, the maximum exemption is the taxable value of the homestead up to $40,000 or 100% of the county's average assessed value of single family residential property, whichever is greater. For disabled people and veterans, the maximum exemption is the taxable value of the homestead up to $50,000 or 120% of the county's average assessed value of single family residential property, whichever is greater. For veterans and widow(er)s whose home was substantially contributed to by the VA, the homestead is 100% exempt regardless of the value of the homestead or the income of the owner.

Duration   The exemption is provided as long as the qualifying homestead owner resides in Nebraska.

Number awarded   Varies each year.

Deadline   Applications must be filed by June of each year.

[1366]
NEBRASKA VETERANS' AID FUND

Department of Veterans' Affairs
State Office Building
301 Centennial Mall South, Sixth Floor
P.O. Box 95083
Lincoln, NE 68509-5083
(402) 471-2458   Fax: (402) 471-2491
E-mail: john.hilgert@nebraska.gov
Web: www.vets.state.ne.us/benefits.html

Summary   To assist veterans, their spouses, and their dependents in Nebraska who have a temporary emergency need.

Eligibility   This assistance is available to veterans, their spouses, and their dependent children who are residents of Nebraska. The veteran must have served on active duty in the armed forces of the United States, other than active duty for training, and either 1) was discharged or otherwise separated with a characterization of honorable or general (under honorable conditions), or 2) died while in service or as a direct result of such service.

Financial data   The amount of aid awarded varies, depending upon the needs of the recipient. Recently, grants averaged nearly $1,000. Aid can only be used for food, fuel, shelter, wearing apparel, funeral, medical, or surgical items.

Duration   The funds are provided for emergency situations only; the program does not assist ongoing financial needs.

Additional information   The Nebraska Veterans' Aid Fund was established in 1921 in lieu of a bonus for veterans of wartime service. Applications must be made through the county service officer or post service officer of any recognized veterans' organization in the county nearest the applicant's place of residence and submitted to the Department of Veterans' Affairs.

Number awarded   Varies each year. In a recent year, nearly $840,000 in aid was provided to 773 veterans.

Deadline   Applications may be submitted at any time.

[1367]
NEVADA DISABLED VETERAN'S TAX EXEMPTION

Nevada Office of Veterans Services
Attn: Executive Director
5460 Reno Corporate Drive
Reno, NV 89511
(775) 688-1653   Toll Free: (866) 630-8387
Fax: (775) 688-1656
Web: veterans.nv.gov/veteran_benefits.html

Summary   To exempt from taxation in Nevada a portion of the property owned by disabled veterans or their surviving spouses.

Eligibility   This program is open to veterans who are residents of Nevada and have incurred a service-connected disability of 60% or more. Applicants must have received an honorable separation from military service. The widow(er) of a disabled veteran, who was eligible at the time of death, may also be eligible for this benefit.

Financial data Veterans and widow(er)s are entitled to exempt from taxation a portion of their property's assessed value. The amount depends on the extent of the disability and the year filed; it ranges from $6,250 to $20,000 and doubles over a 4-year period.

Duration Disabled veterans and their widow(er)s are entitled to this exemption as long as they live in Nevada.

Additional information Disabled veterans and widow(er)s are able to split their exemption between vehicle taxes and/or property taxes.

Number awarded Varies each year.

Deadline Deadline not specified.

[1368]
NEW HAMPSHIRE PROPERTY TAX EXEMPTION FOR CERTAIN DISABLED VETERANS

New Hampshire Department of Revenue Administration
109 Pleasant Street
Concord, NH 03301
(603) 271-2191   Fax: (603) 271-6121
TDD: (800) 735-2964
Web: revenue.nh.gov

Summary To exempt from taxation certain property owned by New Hampshire disabled veterans or their surviving spouses.

Eligibility Eligible for this exemption are New Hampshire residents who are honorably discharged veterans with a total and permanent service-connected disability that involves double amputation of the upper or lower extremities or any combination thereof, paraplegia, or blindness of both eyes with visual acuity of 5/200 or less. Applicants or their surviving spouses must own a specially adapted homestead that has been acquired with the assistance of the U.S. Department of Veterans Affairs.

Financial data Qualifying disabled veterans and surviving spouses are exempt from all taxation on their specially adapted homestead.

Duration 1 year; once the credit has been approved, it is automatically renewed as long as the qualifying person owns the same residence in New Hampshire.

Number awarded Varies each year.

Deadline The original application for a permanent tax credit must be submitted by April.

[1369]
NEW HAMPSHIRE SERVICE-CONNECTED TOTAL AND PERMANENT DISABILITY TAX CREDIT

New Hampshire Department of Revenue Administration
109 Pleasant Street
Concord, NH 03301
(603) 271-2191   Fax: (603) 271-6121
TDD: (800) 735-2964
Web: revenue.nh.gov

Summary To provide property tax credits in New Hampshire to disabled veterans or their surviving spouses.

Eligibility Eligible for this tax credit are honorably discharged veterans residing in New Hampshire who 1) have a total and permanent service-connected disability, or 2) are a double amputee or paraplegic because of a service-connected disability. Unremarried surviving spouses of qualified veterans are also eligible.

Financial data Qualifying disabled veterans and surviving spouses receive an annual credit of $700 for property taxes on residential property. In addition, individual towns in New Hampshire may adopt a local option to increase the dollar amount credited to disabled veterans, to a maximum of $2,000.

Duration 1 year; once the credit has been approved, it is automatically renewed for as long as the qualifying person owns the same residence in New Hampshire.

Number awarded Varies each year.

Deadline The original application for a permanent tax credit must be submitted by April.

[1370]
NEW HAMPSHIRE SURVIVING SPOUSE TAX CREDIT

New Hampshire Department of Revenue Administration
109 Pleasant Street
Concord, NH 03301
(603) 271-2191   Fax: (603) 271-6121
TDD: (800) 735-2964
Web: revenue.nh.gov

Summary To provide property tax credits in New Hampshire to surviving spouses of servicemembers who died while on active duty.

Eligibility Eligible for this tax credit are New Hampshire residents who are the unremarried surviving spouses of persons who were killed or died while on active duty in the armed forces.

Financial data Qualifying spouses receive an annual credit of $700 for property taxes on residential property. In addition, individual towns in New Hampshire may adopt a local option to increase the dollar amount credited to surviving spouses of deceased veterans, to a maximum of $2,000.

Duration 1 year; once the credit has been approved, it is automatically renewed as long as the qualifying person owns the same residence in New Hampshire.

Number awarded Varies each year.

Deadline The original application for a permanent tax credit must be submitted by April.

[1371]
NEW JERSEY INCOME TAX EXCLUSION FOR MILITARY PENSIONS AND SURVIVOR'S BENEFITS

New Jersey Division of Taxation
Attn: Technical Information Branch
50 Barrack Street
P.O. Box 281
Trenton, NJ 08695-0281
(609) 292-6400
Toll Free: (800) 323-4400 (within NJ, NY, PA, DE, and MD)
TDD: (800) 286-6613 (within NJ, NY, PA, DE, and MD)
E-mail: taxation@tax.state.nj.us
Web: www.state.nj.us/treasury/taxation/prntgit.shtml

Summary To exclude from income taxation in New Jersey military pensions and survivor's benefits.

Eligibility This exclusion is available to residents of New Jersey who are receiving 1) a military pension resulting from service in the Army, Navy, Air Force, Marine Corps, or Coast Guard, or 2) survivor's benefits related to such service. It does not apply to civil service pensions or annuities, even if the pension or annuity is based on credit for military service.

Financial data All military pensions and survivor's benefit payments are excluded from income for state taxation purposes.

Duration The exclusion applies as long as the individual resides in New Jersey.

Additional information This exclusion became effective in 2001.

Number awarded Varies each year.

Deadline Deadline not specified.

[1372]
NEW JERSEY PROPERTY TAX EXEMPTION FOR DISABLED VETERANS OR SURVIVING SPOUSES

New Jersey Division of Taxation
Attn: Technical Information Branch
50 Barrack Street
P.O. Box 281
Trenton, NJ 08695-0281
(609) 292-6400
Toll Free: (800) 323-4400 (within NJ, NY, PA, DE, and MD)
TDD: (800) 286-6613 (within NJ, NY, PA, DE, and MD)
E-mail: taxation@tax.state.nj.us
Web: www.state.nj.us/treasury/taxation/otherptr.shtml

Summary To provide a real estate tax exemption to New Jersey veterans with disabilities and certain surviving widow(er)s.

Eligibility This exemption is available to New Jersey residents who have been honorably discharged with active wartime service in the U.S. armed forces and have been certified by the U.S. Department of Veterans Affairs as totally and permanently disabled as a result of wartime service-connected conditions. Unremarried surviving spouses and civil union partners of eligible disabled veterans or of certain wartime servicepersons who died on active duty are also entitled to this exemption. Applicants must be the full owner of and a permanent resident in the dwelling house for which the exemption is claimed.

Financial data A 100% exemption from locally-levied real estate taxes is provided.

Duration 1 year; the exemption continues as long as the eligible veteran remains a resident of New Jersey.

Additional information This program is administered by the local tax assessor or collector. Veterans who are denied exemptions have the right to appeal the decision to their county and state governments.

Number awarded Varies each year.

Deadline Applications may be submitted at any time.

[1373]
NEW MEXICO DISABLED VETERAN PROPERTY TAX EXEMPTION

New Mexico Department of Veterans' Services
Attn: Benefits Division
407 Galisteo Street, Room 142
P.O. Box 2324
Santa Fe, NM 87504-2324
(505) 827-6374   Toll Free: (866) 433-VETS
Fax: (505) 827-6372   E-mail: alan.martinez@state.nm.us
Web: www.dvs.state.nm.us/benefits.html

Summary To exempt disabled veterans and their spouses from payment of property taxes in New Mexico.

Eligibility This exemption is available to veterans who are rated 100% service-connected disabled by the U.S. Department of Veterans Affairs, are residents of New Mexico, and own a primary residence in the state. Also eligible are qualifying veterans' unremarried surviving spouses, if they are New Mexico residents and continue to own the residence.

Financial data Veterans and surviving spouses are exempt from payment of property taxes in New Mexico.

Duration 1 year; continues until the qualifying veteran or spouse no longer live in the residence.

Number awarded Varies each year.

Deadline Deadline not specified.

[1374]
NEW MEXICO VETERANS PROPERTY TAX EXEMPTION

New Mexico Department of Veterans' Services
Attn: Benefits Division
407 Galisteo Street, Room 142
P.O. Box 2324
Santa Fe, NM 87504-2324
(505) 827-6374   Toll Free: (866) 433-VETS
Fax: (505) 827-6372   E-mail: alan.martinez@state.nm.us
Web: www.dvs.state.nm.us/benefits.html

Summary To exempt veterans and their spouses from a portion of property taxes in New Mexico.

Eligibility This exemption is available to veterans who served honorably for at least 90 days during wartime (World War I, World War II, Korea, Vietnam, Persian Gulf), are residents of New Mexico, and own a primary residence in the state. Also eligible are qualifying veterans' unremarried surviving spouses, if they are New Mexico residents and continue to own the residence.

Financial data Veterans and surviving spouses are entitled to a reduction in the value of their property that is currently $4,000. The exemption is deducted from the taxable value of the property to determine net taxable value. Veterans who are entitled to this exemption and do not have sufficient real or personal property to claim the full exemption may be eligible to claim a one-third reduction in motor vehicle registration fees.

Duration 1 year; continues until the qualifying veteran or spouse no longer lives in the residence.

Number awarded Varies each year.

Deadline Deadline not specified.

[1375]
NEW YORK ALTERNATIVE PROPERTY TAX EXEMPTIONS FOR VETERANS

New York State Department of Taxation and Finance
Attn: Office of Real Property Tax Services
W.A. Harriman Campus
Building 8, Sixth Floor
Albany, NY 12227
(518) 486-4403   Fax: (518) 486-7754
Web: www.orps.state.ny.us

Summary To provide wartime veterans and their spouses who are residents of New York with a partial exemption from property taxes.

Eligibility This program is open to veterans who served during specified periods of wartime. Applicants must have been discharged under honorable conditions; additional benefits are available to those who served in a combat zone and to those who have a service-connected disability. The legal title to the property must be in the name of the veteran or the spouse of the veteran or both, or the unremarried surviving spouse of a deceased veteran. The property must be used exclusively for residential purposes. This program is only available in counties, cities, towns, and villages in New York that have opted to participate.

Financial data This program provides an exemption of 15% of the assessed valuation of the property, to a basic maximum of $12,000 per year; local governments may opt for reduced maximums of $9,000 or $6,000, or for increased maximums of $15,000 to $36,000. For combat-zone veterans, an additional 10% of the assessed valuation is exempt, to a basic maximum of $8,000 per year; local governments may opt for a reduced maximum of $6,000 or $4,000, or for increased maximums of $10,000 to $24,000. For disabled veterans, the exemption is the percentage of assessed value equal to half of the service-connected disability rating, to a basic maximum of $40,000 per year; local governments may opt for a reduced maximum of $30,000 or $20,000, or for increased maximums of $50,000 to $120,000. At its option, New York City and other high appreciation municipalities may use the following increased maximum exemptions: war veteran, $54,000; combat-zone veteran, $36,000; disabled veteran, $180,000.

Duration This exemption is available annually.

Number awarded Varies each year.

Deadline Applications must be filed with the local assessor by "taxable status date;" in most towns, that is the end of February.

[1376]
NEW YORK COLD WAR VETERANS PROPERTY TAX EXEMPTIONS

New York State Department of Taxation and Finance
Attn: Office of Real Property Tax Services
W.A. Harriman Campus
Building 8, Sixth Floor
Albany, NY 12227
(518) 486-4403   Fax: (518) 486-7754
Web: www.orps.state.ny.us

Summary To provide New York veterans who served during the Cold War and their spouses with a partial exemption from property taxes.

Eligibility This program is open to veterans who served during the Cold War, defined as September 2, 1945 to December 26, 1991. Applicants must have been discharged under honorable conditions; additional benefits are available to those who have a service-connected disability. The legal title to the property must be in the name of the veteran or the spouse of the veteran or both, or the unremarried surviving spouse of a deceased veteran. The property must be used exclusively for residential purposes. This program is only available in counties, cities, towns, and villages in New York that have opted to participate.

Financial data Local governments may opt to grant exemptions of 15% or 10%. For the 15% option, the basic maximum exemption is $12,000 per year; local governments may opt for reduced maximums of $9,000 or $6,000, or for increased maximums of $15,000 to $36,000. For the 10% option, the basic maximum exemption is $8,000 per year;

local governments may opt for a reduced maximum of $6,000 or $4,000, or for increased maximums of $10,000 to $24,000. For disabled veterans, the exemption is the percentage of assessed value equal to half of the service-connected disability rating, to a basic maximum of $40,000 per year; local governments may opt for a reduced maximum of $30,000 or $20,000, or for increased maximums of $50,000 to $120,000. At its option, New York City and other high appreciation municipalities may use the following increased maximum exemptions: 15% option, $54,000; 10% option, $36,000; disabled veteran, $180,000.

Duration This exemption is available annually.

Number awarded Varies each year.

Deadline Applications must be filed with the local assessor by "taxable status date;" in most towns, that is the end of February.

[1377]
NEW YORK "ELIGIBLE FUNDS" PROPERTY TAX EXEMPTIONS FOR VETERANS

New York State Department of Taxation and Finance
Attn: Office of Real Property Tax Services
W.A. Harriman Campus
Building 8, Sixth Floor
Albany, NY 12227
(518) 486-4403   Fax: (518) 486-7754
Web: www.orps.state.ny.us

Summary To provide a partial exemption from property taxes to veterans and their surviving spouses who are residents of New York.

Eligibility This program is open to veterans who have purchased properties in New York with such income as retirement pay, disability compensation, or death gratuities (referred to as "eligible funds"). Specially adapted homes of paraplegics, or the homes of their widowed spouses, are also covered.

Financial data This exemption reduces the property's assessed value to the extent that "eligible funds" were used in the purchase, generally to a maximum of $5,000. It is applicable to general municipal taxes but not to school taxes or special district levies.

Duration This exemption is available annually.

Number awarded Varies each year.

Deadline Applications must be filed with the local assessor by "taxable status date;" in most towns, that is the end of February.

[1378]
NEW YORK STATE BLIND ANNUITY

New York State Division of Veterans' Affairs
5 Empire State Plaza, Suite 2836
Albany, NY 12223-1551
(518) 486-3602   Toll Free: (888) VETS-NYS (within NY)
Fax: (518) 473-0379   E-mail: dvainfo@veterans.ny.gov
Web: veterans.ny.gov/state-benefits.html

Summary To provide an annuity to blind wartime veterans and their surviving spouses in New York.

Eligibility This benefit is available to veterans who served on active duty during specified periods of war. Applicants must 1) meet the New York standards of blindness; 2) have received an honorable or general discharge, or a discharge other than for dishonorable service; and 3) be now, and continue to be, residents of and continuously domiciled in New York. The annuity is also payable to unremarried spouses of deceased veterans who were receiving annuity payments (or were eligible to do so) at the time of their death, and are residents of and continuously domiciled in New York.

Financial data The annuity is currently $1,220.76 per year.

Number awarded Varies each year.

Deadline Deadline not specified.

[1379]
NEW YORK STATE INCOME TAX EXEMPTION FOR RETIRED MILITARY PERSONNEL

New York State Department of Taxation and Finance
W.A. Harriman Campus
Tax and Finance Building
Albany, NY 12227-0001
(518) 438-8581   Toll Free: (800) 225-5829 (within NY)
Web: www.tax.ny.gov/pit/file/military_page.htm

Summary To exempt the pension income of retired New York military personnel from state and designated local income tax.

Eligibility This exemption applies to retired military personnel and their beneficiaries who are residents of New York and receiving a military pension.

Financial data All pension payments are exempt from income taxes of New York State, New York City, and Yonkers.

Duration The exemption is available as long as the recipient resides in New York.

Number awarded Varies each year.

Deadline Deadline not specified.

[1380]
NEW YORK VETERANS SUPPLEMENTAL BURIAL ALLOWANCE

New York State Division of Veterans' Affairs
5 Empire State Plaza, Suite 2836
Albany, NY 12223-1551
(518) 474-6114   Toll Free: (888) VETS-NYS (within NY)
Fax: (518) 473-0379   E-mail: dvainfo@veterans.ny.gov
Web: veterans.ny.gov/state-benefits.html

Summary To provide a burial allowance for New York veterans killed in combat.

Eligibility This benefit is available to the families of New York military personnel killed in combat or while on active duty in hostile or imminent danger locations on or after September 29, 2003.

Financial data This program provides a supplemental burial allowance of up to $6,000. Funds are paid to the family member responsible for funeral and burial expenses.

Number awarded Varies each year.

Deadline Applications may be submitted at any time, but they must be received within 2 years of permanent burial or cremation of the body.

[1381]
NORTH DAKOTA PROPERTY TAX CREDIT FOR DISABLED VETERANS

Office of State Tax Commissioner
State Capitol Building
600 East Boulevard Avenue, Department 127
Bismarck, ND 58505-0599
(701) 328-7088   Toll Free: (877) 328-7088
Fax: (701) 328-3700   TDD: (800) 366-6888
E-mail: taxinfo@state.nd.us
Web: www.nd.gov/tax/property

Summary To provide property tax credits to disabled North Dakota veterans and their surviving spouses.

Eligibility This property tax credit is available to honorably-discharged veterans who have more than a 50% service-connected disability as certified by the U.S. Department of Veterans Affairs. Applicants must own and occupy a homestead according to state law. Unremarried surviving spouses are also eligible. If a disabled veteran co-owns the property with someone other than a spouse, the credit is limited to the disabled veteran's interest in the fixtures, buildings, and improvements of the homestead.

Financial data The credit is applied against the first $120,000 of true and full valuation of the fixtures, buildings, and improvements of the homestead, to a maximum amount calculated by multiplying $120,000 by the percentage of the disabled veteran's disability compensation rating for service-connected disabilities.

Duration 1 year; renewable as long as qualified individuals continue to reside in North Dakota and live in their homes.

Number awarded Varies each year.

Deadline Applications may be submitted to the county auditor at any time.

[1382]
NORTH DAKOTA PROPERTY TAX EXEMPTION FOR VETERANS WHO LIVE IN SPECIALLY ADAPTED HOUSING

Office of State Tax Commissioner
State Capitol Building
600 East Boulevard Avenue, Department 127
Bismarck, ND 58505-0599
(701) 328-7088   Toll Free: (877) 328-7088
Fax: (701) 328-3700   TDD: (800) 366-6888
E-mail: taxinfo@state.nd.us
Web: www.nd.gov/tax/property

Summary To provide property tax exemptions to North Dakota veterans and their surviving spouses who have been awarded specially adapted housing.

Eligibility This exemption is available to paraplegic disabled veterans of the U.S. armed forces or any veteran who has been awarded specially adapted housing by the U.S. Department of Veterans Affairs. The paraplegic disability does not have to be service connected. The unremarried surviving spouses of such deceased veterans are also eligible. Income and assets are not considered in determining eligibility for the exemption.

Financial data The maximum benefit may not exceed $5,400 taxable value, because the exemption is limited to the first $120,000 of true and full value of fixtures, buildings, and improvements.

Duration 1 year; renewable as long as qualified individuals continue to reside in North Dakota and live in their homes.

Number awarded Varies each year.

Deadline Applications may be submitted to the county auditor at any time.

[1383]
OHIO BURIAL ALLOWANCE FOR INDIGENT VETERANS

Ohio Department of Veterans Services
77 South High Street, Seventh Floor
Columbus, OH 43215
(614) 644-0898   Toll Free: (888) DVS-OHIO
Fax: (614) 728-9498   E-mail: ohiovet@dvs.ohio.gov
Web: dvs.ohio.gov

Summary To provide an allowance for the burial of indigent Ohio veterans and certain of their dependents.

Eligibility Eligible to receive this allowance are the survivors of Ohio veterans, their spouses, widow(er)s, or mothers.

Financial data This allowance is $1,000.

Additional information These grants are made by the various county veterans services offices in Ohio.

Number awarded Varies each year.

Deadline Applications may be submitted at any time.

[1384]
OHIO INCOME TAX DEDUCTION FOR MILITARY RETIREMENT INCOME

Ohio Department of Taxation
Attn: Individual Income Tax
30 East Broad Street
P.O. Box 530
Columbus, OH 43216-0530
(614) 433-5817   Toll Free: (800) 282-1780 (within OH)
Fax: (614) 433-7771
Web: tax.ohio.gov

Summary To deduct from state income taxation in Ohio the pay received by retired military personnel and their surviving spouses.

Eligibility This deduction is available to residents of Ohio who are retired from service in the active or reserve components of the U.S. armed forces. Surviving and former spouses of military retirees who are receiving payments under the survivor benefit plan are also eligible.

Financial data All retirement income received by military personnel and their surviving or former spouses is excluded from state income taxation in Ohio.

Duration The exclusion is available as long as the recipient remains an Ohio resident.

Number awarded Varies each year.

Deadline Deadline not specified.

[1385]
OHIO VETERANS BONUS

Ohio Department of Veterans Services
Attn: Veterans Bonus Program
P.O. Box 373
Sandusky, OH 44871
Toll Free: (877) OHIO-VET
Web: veteransbonus.ohio.gov/odvs_web

Summary To provide a bonus to Ohio veterans and active-duty servicemembers who served during the Persian Gulf War, Afghanistan, or Iraq and their family members.

Eligibility This bonus is available to current residents of Ohio who were also residents of the state when they began active-duty military service, including as a member of a Reserve component or the Ohio National Guard. Applicants must have served at least 90 days or be currently serving in the U.S. armed forces during the periods of the Persian Gulf War (August 2, 1990 through March 3, 1991), the war in Afghanistan (October 7, 2001 through the present), or the war in Iraq (March 19, 2003 through the present). If no longer serving, they must have received an honorable discharge. Additional bonuses are available to of 1) veterans who were medically discharged or retired because of combat-related disabilities sustained in the Persian Gulf, Afghanistan, or Iraq; and 2) veterans who were declared Missing in Action (MIA) or Prisoner of War (POW) or (if the veteran is deceased) their family members. Also eligible are family members (in order of preference: spouses, children, parents) 1) veterans who have died but whose death was not a result of injuries or illness sustained in the Persian Gulf, Afghanistan, or Iraq; or 2) veterans who died as a result of injuries or illness sustained in the Persian Gulf, Afghanistan, or Iraq.

Financial data The bonus for veterans and military personnel who served in the Persian Gulf, Afghanistan, or Iraq is $100 per month of service, to a maximum of $1,000; the bonus for veterans and military personnel who served during the specified time periods but elsewhere in the world is $50 per month of service, to a maximum of $500; veterans who were medically discharged or retired because of combat-related disabilities are eligible for an in-theater bonus of $1,000 (regardless of time served in-theater) plus $50 per month for non-theater service time, to a maximum benefit of $1,500; veterans who were declared MIA or POW or family members are eligible for a bonus of $5,000; families of deceased veterans whose death was not a result of injuries or illness are eligible for the same bonus that the veteran would have received if still living, to a maximum of $1,500; families of veterans who died as a result of injuries or illness are eligible for a bonus of $5,000.

Duration These are 1-time bonuses.

Number awarded Varies each year.

Deadline Applications may be submitted at any time. For veterans and current military members who served during the wars in Afghanistan or Iraq, applications must be submitted within 3 years after the President has officially proclaimed the end of those hostilities.

[1386]
OHIO VETERANS' FINANCIAL ASSISTANCE

Ohio Department of Veterans Services
77 South High Street, Seventh Floor
Columbus, OH 43215
(614) 644-0898   Toll Free: (888) DVS-OHIO
Fax: (614) 728-9498   E-mail: ohiovet@dvs.ohio.gov
Web: dvs.ohio.gov

Summary To provide emergency aid to Ohio veterans, military personnel, and their dependents who, because of disability or disaster, are in financial need.

Eligibility This assistance is available to veterans and active-duty members of the U.S. armed forces, as well as their spouses, surviving spouses, dependent parents, minor children, and wards. Applicants must have been residents of the Ohio county in which they are applying for at least 3 months. They must be able to demonstrate need for relief because of sickness, accident, or destitution.

Financial data The amount granted varies, depending on the needs of the recipient.

Duration These are emergency funds only and are not designed to be a recurring source of income.

Additional information These grants are made by the various county veterans services offices in Ohio.

Number awarded Varies each year.

Deadline Applications may be submitted at any time.

[1387]
OKLAHOMA FINANCIAL ASSISTANCE PROGRAM

Oklahoma Department of Veterans Affairs
Veterans Memorial Building
2311 North Central Avenue
P.O. Box 53067
Oklahoma City, OK 73152
(405) 521-3684   Fax: (405) 521-6533
E-mail: mspear@odva.state.ok.us
Web: www.ok.gov

Summary To provide emergency aid to Oklahoma veterans and their families who, because of disability or disaster, are in financial need.

Eligibility This program is open to veterans with at least 90 days of wartime service (unless discharged earlier because of a service-connected disability) and an honorable discharge who are current residents of Oklahoma and have resided in the state for at least 1 year immediately preceding the date of application. Applicants must be seeking assistance because of an interruption or loss of job and income resulting from illness, injury, or disaster (such as loss of home due to fire, floor, or storm). Widow(er)s and minor children may also qualify for the benefit.

Financial data The amount of the grant depends on the need of the recipient.

Duration The grant is available only on a 1-time basis.

Additional information No financial assistance will be granted when regular monetary benefits are being received from other state agencies. The funds cannot be used for old debts, car payments, or medical expenses.

Number awarded Varies each year.

Deadline Applications must be submitted to the local post or chapter of a veterans services organization for initial approval or disapproval. They may be submitted at any time during the year.

[1388]
OKLAHOMA MILITARY RETIREMENT INCOME TAX EXCLUSION

Oklahoma Tax Commission
Attn: Income Tax
2501 North Lincoln Boulevard
Oklahoma City, OK 73194-0009
(405) 521-3160   Toll Free: (800) 522-8165 (within OK)
Fax: (405) 522-0063   E-mail: otcmaster@tax.ok.gov
Web: www.tax.ok.gov/incometax.html

Summary To exclude a portion of the income of military retirees and their spouses from state taxation in Oklahoma.

Eligibility This exclusion is available to residents of Oklahoma and their spouses who are receiving retirement benefits from a component of the U.S. armed forces.

Financial data Military retirees are entitled to exclude 75% of their retirement benefits or $10,000, whichever is greater, from state taxation.

Duration The exclusion is available as long as the recipient resides in Oklahoma.

Deadline Deadline not specified.

[1389]
OKLAHOMA PROPERTY TAX EXEMPTION FOR DISABLED VETERANS

Oklahoma Tax Commission
Attn: Ad Valorem Division
2501 North Lincoln Boulevard
P.O. Box 269060
Oklahoma City, OK 73126-9060
(405) 319-8200   Toll Free: (800) 522-8165 (within OK)
Fax: (405) 522-0166   E-mail: otcmaster@tax.ok.gov
Web: www.tax.ok.gov/adval.html

Summary To exempt the property of disabled veterans and their surviving spouses from taxation in Oklahoma.

Eligibility This program is available to Oklahoma residents who are veterans honorably discharged from a branch of the armed forces or the Oklahoma National Guard. Applicants must have a 100% permanent disability sustained through military action or accident or resulting from a disease contracted while in active service; the disability must be certified by the U.S. Department of Veterans Affairs. They must own property that qualifies for the Oklahoma homestead exemption. Surviving spouses of qualified veterans are also eligible.

Financial data Qualified veterans and surviving spouses are eligible for exemption of the taxes on the full fair cash value of their homestead.

Duration The exemption is available as long as the veteran or surviving spouse resides in Oklahoma and owns a qualifying homestead.

Additional information This exemption was first available in 2006.

Deadline Deadline not specified.

[1390]
OPERATION FAMILY FUND FINANCIAL ASSISTANCE

Operation Family Fund
P.O. Box 837
Ridgecrest, CA 93556
(760) 793-0053   Fax: (888) 851-1456
E-mail: support@operatonfamilyfund.org
Web: operationfamilyfund.org

Summary To provide personal assistance to military and civilian personnel and the families of those personnel who died or were severely disabled as a result of service as a result of the Global War on Terror.

Eligibility This assistance is available to military and civilian personnel and their families who died or were severely disabled as a result of Operations Enduring or Iraqi Freedom, either domestically or abroad. Civilians must have been serving officially as an employee of the U.S. government or contractor to the U.S. government. Applicants must be seeking funding for such short- and long-term living needs as food;

rent or utilities; emergency transportation; vehicle repair; funeral expenses; medical and dental expenses; assistance with a home, rental, lease, or purchase; home improvements; or assistance with the purchase, rent, or lease of a vehicle. Grants are approved to applicants in the following priority order: 1) member injured because of a hostile action and have a Department of Veterans Affairs (VA) disability rating of 50% or higher; 2) member injured because of an accident while serving in Iraq or Afghanistan and have a VA disability rating of 50% or higher; 3) member who has post-traumatic stress disorder with a VA disability rating of 50% or higher as a result of serving in Iraq or Afghanistan; 4) member who has other service-connected injuries caused in support of the Global War on Terror and a VA disability rating of 50% or higher; 5) member in any of the prior categories but still in the medical board process with a pending VA disability rating; 6) child (under 22 years of age) and/or spouse of a military member killed in action who did not receive government death benefit or SGLA; and 7) second requests.

Financial data Most grants are at least $1,000 but less than $10,000.

Duration These are 1-time grants; renewals may be approved if funding is available.

Number awarded Varies each year; since this organization was established, it has awarded more than 385 grants.

Deadline Applications may be submitted at any time.

[1391]
OPERATION HOMEFRONT GRANTS

Operation Homefront
8930 Fourwinds Drive, Suite 340
San Antonio, TX 78239
(210) 659-7756   Toll Free: (800) 722-6098
Fax: (210) 566-7544
Web: www.operationhomefront.net

Summary To provide assistance to military families and wounded personnel who face financial difficulties related to service.

Eligibility This program is open to 1) veterans who are disabled as a result of service-connected injuries and their families; and 2) other military families who face financial needs because of the hardships associated with military service. Examples of financial needs include food assistance, auto repair, moving assistance, transitional family housing, vision care, child and dependent care, critical baby needs, travel and transportation, home repair, and essential home items.

Financial data The amounts of the grants vary, depending on the need of the applicant. Recently, average grants were $100 to families for critical baby items, $161 for food assistance, $300 to assist in paying utilities, or $1,117 to help with rent or mortgage payments.

Duration This are 1-time grants.

Additional information This foundation began in 2002.

Number awarded Varies each year; since the foundation was established, it has awarded approximately $128 million to support more than 400,000 families and personnel.

Deadline Applications may be submitted at any time.

[1392]
OPERATION SECOND CHANCE FAMILY ASSISTANCE GRANTS

Operation Second Chance
Attn: President
22708 Birchcrest Lane
P.O. Box 461
Clarksburg, MD 20871
Toll Free: (888) OSC-4VET
E-mail: assistance@operationsecondchance.org
Web: www.operationsecondchance.org

Summary To provide assistance for payment of ordinary living expenses to disabled veterans and military personnel and their families.

Eligibility This assistance is available to disabled veterans and military personnel who are within 18 months of their injury or are currently receiving care at a military health care facility and have an expected or adjudicated disability rating of 70% or higher. Their family members are also eligible. Applicants must be seeking funding for payment of rent or mortgages, utility bills, child care during illness or injury, or housing and/or airfare for a family member to assist an injured or recovering member.

Financial data The amount of the grant depends on the need of the recipient.

Duration These are 1-time grants.

Number awarded Varies each year.

Deadline Applications may be submitted at any time.

[1393]
OREGON PROPERTY TAX EXEMPTION FOR ACTIVE DUTY MILITARY SERVICE

Oregon Department of Revenue
Attn: Property Tax Division
Revenue Building
955 Center Street, N.E.
Salem, OR 97310-2555
(503) 378-4988   Toll Free: (800) 356-4222 (within OR)
Fax: (503) 945-8738   TDD: (800) 886-7204 (within OR)
Web: www.oregon.gov/DOR/PTD/exemptions.shtml

Summary To exempt members of the Oregon National Guard and military Reserves called to active duty and their survivors from a portion of their property taxes.

Eligibility This exemption is available to members of the Oregon National Guard and Reserves called to federal active duty (U.S. Code Title 10) who serve more than 178 days with that status during the tax year. Applicants must own property that they occupy as their primary residence in Oregon. Occupants of a home owned by a qualified Guard member or Reservist who is killed in action also qualify for this exemption.

Financial data The exemption was set as $60,000 of the homestead property's assessed value as of July 1, 2006. It increases by 3% annually.

Duration 1 year; may be renewed as long as the eligible Guard member or surviving occupant of the home owns and occupies the primary residence.

Additional information This exemption was first available in 2005.

Number awarded Varies each year.

Deadline This exemption is not automatic. Applications must be submitted by July of each year.

[1394]
OREGON PROPERTY TAX EXEMPTION FOR VETERANS WITH DISABILITIES AND THEIR SPOUSES

Oregon Department of Revenue
Attn: Property Tax Division
Revenue Building
955 Center Street, N.E.
Salem, OR 97310-2555
(503) 378-4988   Toll Free: (800) 356-4222 (within OR)
Fax: (503) 945-8738   TDD: (800) 886-7204 (within OR)
Web: www.oregon.gov/DOR/PTD/exemptions.shtml

Summary To exempt disabled Oregon veterans and their spouses from a portion of their property taxes.

Eligibility Qualifying veterans are those who received a discharge or release under honorable conditions after service of either 1) 90 consecutive days during World War I, World War II, or the Korean Conflict; or 2) 210 consecutive days after January 31, 1955. Eligible individuals must meet 1 of these conditions: 1) a war veteran who is officially certified by the U.S. Department of Veterans Affairs (VA) or any branch of the U.S. armed forces as having disabilities of 40% or more; 2) a war veteran who is certified each year by a licensed physician as being 40% or more disabled and has total gross income that is less than 185% of the federal poverty level; or 3) a war veteran's surviving spouse who has not remarried, even if the veteran's spouse was not disabled or did not take advantage of the exemption if disabled. Recipients of this exemption must own and live on a property in Oregon.

Financial data The exemption is $17,911 of the homestead property's real market value.

Duration 1 year; may be renewed as long as the eligible veteran or surviving unremarried spouse owns and occupies the primary residence.

Number awarded Varies each year.

Deadline This exemption is not automatic. Applications must be submitted by March of each year.

[1395]
OREGON PROPERTY TAX EXEMPTION FOR VETERANS WITH SERVICE-CONNECTED DISABILITIES AND THEIR SPOUSES

Oregon Department of Revenue
Attn: Property Tax Division
Revenue Building
955 Center Street, N.E.
Salem, OR 97310-2555
(503) 378-4988   Toll Free: (800) 356-4222 (within OR)
Fax: (503) 945-8738   TDD: (800) 886-7204 (within OR)
Web: www.oregon.gov/DOR/PTD/exemptions.shtml

Summary To exempt Oregon veterans with service-connected disabilities and their spouses from a portion of their property taxes.

Eligibility Qualifying veterans are those who received a discharge or release under honorable conditions after service of either 1) 90 consecutive days during World War I, World War II, or the Korean Conflict; or 2) 210 consecutive days after January 31, 1955. Eligible individuals must meet 1 of these conditions: 1) a war veteran who is certified by the U.S. Department of Veterans Affairs (VA) or any branch of the U.S. armed forces as having service-connected disabilities of 40% or more; or 2) a surviving spouse of a war veteran who died

because of service-connected injury or illness or who received at least 1 year of this exemption. Recipients of this exemption must own and live on a property in Oregon.

Financial data The exemption is $21,493 of the homestead property's real market value.

Duration 1 year; may be renewed as long as the eligible veterans or surviving spouse owns and occupies the primary residence.

Number awarded Varies each year.

Deadline This exemption is not automatic. Applications must be submitted by March of each year.

[1396]
OREGON VETERANS' EMERGENCY FINANCIAL ASSISTANCE

Oregon Department of Veterans' Affairs
Attn: Veterans' Services Division
700 Summer Street N.E., Suite 150
Salem, OR 97310-1285
(503) 373-2000   Toll Free: (800) 692-9666 (within OR)
Fax: (503) 373-2362   TDD: (503) 373-2217
Web: www.oregon.gov

Summary To provide emergency financial assistance to Oregon veterans and their families.

Eligibility This assistance is available to Oregon residents who are veterans and their spouses, children, and grandchildren. Applicants must be in need of assistance for emergency or temporary housing and related housing expenses, such as utilities, insurance, house repairs, rent assistance, or food; emergency medical or dental expenses; emergency transportation; expenses related to starting a business, such as business licenses or occupational licenses; temporary income after military discharge; or legal assistance for certain veteran issues.

Financial data Grants depend on the need of the recipient.

Duration These are 1-time grants.

Number awarded Varies each year.

Deadline Applications may be submitted at any time.

[1397]
PARENTS' DEPENDENCY AND INDEMNITY COMPENSATION (DIC)

Department of Veterans Affairs
Attn: Veterans Benefits Administration
810 Vermont Avenue, N.W.
Washington, DC 20420
(202) 418-4343   Toll Free: (800) 827-1000
Web: www.vba.va.gov/bln/dependents/index.htm

Summary To provide financial support to the parents of servicemembers and veterans who died of disabilities or other causes.

Eligibility This program is open to parents (biological, adoptive, and foster) of servicemembers and veterans who died from a disease or injury aggravated while on active duty or active duty for training, an injury incurred or aggravated in the line of duty while on inactive duty for training, or a service-connected disability. If the parent is the sole surviving parent or 1 of 2 parents not living with a spouse, their countable income may not exceed $13,941 per year; if the parent is the sole surviving parent living with a spouse, or 1 of 2 parents living with a spouse, their countable income may not exceed $18,739 per year.

Financial data Benefits depend on the income and current marital status of parents. For sole surviving parents unremarried or remarried and living with a spouse, the maximum benefit is $590 per month. For 1 of 2 parents not living with a spouse, the maximum benefit is $427 per month. For 1 of 2 parents living with a spouse, the maximum benefit is $401 per month. All categories of parents are entitled to an additional payment of $320 per month if they are receiving aid and assistance.

Duration Monthly payments continue for the life of the parent.

Number awarded Varies each year.

Deadline Applications are accepted at any time.

[1398]
PENNSYLVANIA DISABLED VETERANS REAL ESTATE TAX EXEMPTION

Office of the Deputy Adjutant General for Veterans Affairs
Building S-0-47, FTIG
Annville, PA 17003-5002
(717) 865-8907   Toll Free: (800) 54 PA VET (within PA)
Fax: (717) 861-8589   E-mail: RA-VA-Info@pa.gov
Web: www.dmva.state.pa.us

Summary To exempt blind and disabled Pennsylvania veterans and their unremarried surviving spouses from all state real estate taxes.

Eligibility Eligible to apply for this exemption are honorably-discharged veterans who are residents of Pennsylvania and who are blind, paraplegic, or 100% disabled from a service-connected disability sustained during wartime military service. The dwelling must be owned by the veteran solely or jointly with a spouse, and financial need for the exemption must be determined by the State Veterans' Commission. Veterans whose income is less than $81,340 per year are presumed to have financial need; veterans with income greater than $81,340 must document need. Upon the death of the veteran, the tax exemption passes on to the veteran's unremarried surviving spouse.

Financial data This program exempts the principal residence (and the land on which it stands) from all real estate taxes.

Duration The exemption continues as long as the eligible veteran or unremarried widow resides in Pennsylvania.

Number awarded Varies each year.

Deadline Deadline not specified.

[1399]
PENNSYLVANIA MILITARY FAMILY RELIEF ASSISTANCE PROGRAM

Pennsylvania Department of Military and Veterans Affairs
Attn: Military Family Relief Assistance Program
Building 0-47
Fort Indiantown Gap
Annville, PA 17003-5002
(717) 861-6500   Toll Free: (866) 292-7201
Fax: (717) 861-2600   E-mail: ra-pa-mfrap@pa.gov
Web: www.portal.state.pa.us

Summary To provide emergency financial assistance to members of the armed forces from Pennsylvania and their families.

Eligibility This assistance is available to residents of Pennsylvania who are 1) serving on 30 or more consecutive days of active duty with the Pennsylvania Army or Air National Guard or Reserve components of the armed forces; 2) serving on 30 or more consecutive days of active duty with the active armed forces; 3) serving on 30 or more consecutive days of state active duty for emergencies or duty under the Emergency Management Assistance Compact in the Pennsylvania National Guard; 4) current members of the Pennsylvania National Guard within 1 year of a qualifying tour of active duty of 30 days or more who can demonstrate a financial need directly related to the active-duty period; 5) former members of the armed forces, Reserve components, or Pennsylvania National Guard within 2 years of a medical discharge for a disability incurred in the line of duty if they can demonstrate a financial need directly related to active duty or medical disability; and 6) eligible relatives (spouses, parents, siblings, or children) of military service members. Applicants must be able to demonstrate a direct and immediate financial need as a result of military service; that financial need may include, but is not limited to, a sudden or unexpected loss of income directly related to military service; emergency need for child care for which the applicant lacks financial resources; natural or man-made disasters resulting in a need for food, shelter, or other necessities; or the death or critical illness of a parent, spouse, sibling, or child resulting in immediate need for travel, lodging, or subsistence for which the applicant lacks financial resources.

Financial data The maximum grant is $3,500.

Duration Only 1 grant will be awarded in each 12-month period.

Additional information This program began in 2005.

Number awarded Varies each year.

Deadline Applications may be submitted at any time.

[1400]
PENNSYLVANIA PERSIAN GULF CONFLICT VETERANS' BENEFIT PROGRAM

Office of the Deputy Adjutant General for Veterans Affairs
Building S-0-47, FTIG
Annville, PA 17003-5002
(717) 865-8911   Toll Free: (800) 54 PA VET (within PA)
Fax: (717) 861-8589   E-mail: RA-VA-Info@pa.gov
Web: www.dmva.state.pa.us

Summary To provide a bonus to veterans from Pennsylvania who served in the Persian Gulf Conflict or to their survivors.

Eligibility Eligible to receive this bonus are veterans who served on active duty in the Persian Gulf Theater of Operations during the period from August 2, 1990 to August 31, 1991 and received the Southwest Asia Service Medal. Applicants must have been a resident of Pennsylvania at the time of military service and must have served under honorable conditions.

Financial data The bonus is $75 per month for each month (or major fraction) of active service in the Gulf, to a maximum of $525. For veterans who died in active service, a bonus of $5,000 is paid to the family. In addition, $5,000 is paid to Persian Gulf Conflict prisoners of war.

Duration This is a 1-time benefit.

Additional information This program was authorized in 2006.

Number awarded   Varies each year.

Deadline   Applications may be submitted at any time prior to August 31, 2015.

[1401]
RED CROSS EMERGENCY FINANCIAL ASSISTANCE

American Red Cross
Attn: Military Call Center
2025 E Street, N.W.
Washington, DC 20006
(202) 303-4498   Toll Free: (877) 272-7337
Web: www.redcross.org

Summary   To provide funding to active and retired military personnel and their families who are in need of emergency financial assistance.

Eligibility   This program is open to servicemembers, their families, retired military personnel, and widows of retired military personnel. Members of the National Guard and Reserves are also eligible. Applicants must be in need of such emergency financial assistance as travel that requires the presence of the servicemember or his or her family, burial of a loved one, or other assistance that cannot wait until the next business day (food, temporary lodging, urgent medical needs, or the minimum amount required to avoid eviction or utility shut-off).

Financial data   The amount of the assistance depends on the need of the recipient.

Duration   These are 1-time grants.

Additional information   The Red Cross works with the military aid societies (Army Emergency Relief, Navy-Marine Corps Relief Society, Air Force Aid Society, and Coast Guard Mutual Assistance).

Number awarded   Varies each year; recently, more than 5,000 servicemembers and their families received more than $5.8 million in emergency grants.

Deadline   Applications may be submitted at any time.

[1402]
REIMBURSEMENT OF BURIAL EXPENSES

Department of Veterans Affairs
Attn: Veterans Benefits Administration
810 Vermont Avenue, N.W.
Washington, DC 20420
(202) 418-4343   Toll Free: (800) 827-1000
Web: www1.va.gov

Summary   To provide reimbursement of burial expenses for wartime and certain peacetime veterans.

Eligibility   Survivors are eligible for reimbursement if the veteran, at the time of death, was entitled to receive a pension or compensation or would have been entitled to compensation but for receipt of military pay. Eligibility is also established if the veteran died while hospitalized or domiciled in a U.S. Department of Veterans Affairs (VA) facility or other facility at VA expense. The veteran must have been discharged under conditions other than dishonorable.

Financial data   Up to $300 is provided for the veteran's burial expenses. The costs of transporting the remains may be allowed if the veteran died while hospitalized or domiciled in a VA hospital or domiciliary or at VA's expense or died in transit at VA's expense to or from a medical facility. Up to $300 is also paid as a plot or interment allowance (in addition to the $300 basic burial allowance) when the veteran is not buried in a national cemetery or other cemetery under the jurisdiction of the U.S. government. For veterans who died of service-connected causes, the payment is $2,000.

Duration   For service-connected deaths, the claim may be filed at any time. For other deaths, the claim must be filed within 2 years after permanent burial or cremation.

Number awarded   Varies each year.

Deadline   Applications may be submitted at any time.

[1403]
RESTORED ENTITLEMENT PROGRAM FOR SURVIVORS (REPS)

Department of Veterans Affairs
Attn: Veterans Benefits Administration
810 Vermont Avenue, N.W.
Washington, DC 20420
(202) 418-4343   Toll Free: (800) 827-1000
Web: www1.va.gov

Summary   To provide benefits to survivors of certain deceased veterans.

Eligibility   Survivors of deceased veterans who died of service-connected causes incurred or aggravated prior to August 13, 1981 are eligible for these benefits.

Financial data   The benefits are similar to the benefits for students and surviving spouses with children between the ages of 16 and 18 that were eliminated from the Social Security Act. The exact amount of the benefits is based on information provided by the Social Security Administration.

Additional information   The benefits are payable in addition to any other benefits to which the family may be entitled.

Number awarded   Varies each year.

Deadline   Applications may be submitted at any time.

[1404]
SOUTH CAROLINA MILITARY FAMILY RELIEF FUND

South Carolina Office of Veterans Affairs
Attn: SCMFRF Coordinator
1205 Pendleton Street, Suite 477
Columbia, SC 29201-3789
(803) 734-0200   Fax: (803) 734-0421
E-mail: va@oepp.sc.gov
Web: www.govoepp.state.sc.us/va/benefits.html

Summary   To provide emergency assistance to members and families of the National Guard and Reserve forces in South Carolina who have been called to active duty as a result of the September 11, 2001 terrorist attacks.

Eligibility   This assistance is available to families of South Carolina National Guard members and South Carolina residents serving in the U.S. armed forces reserve units who were called to active duty as a result of the September 11, 2001 terrorist attacks. Status-based grants are available to National Guard and Reserve members and their family members enrolled in the Defense Enrollment Eligibility Reporting System (DEERS); the servicemember must have been on active duty for at least 30 consecutive days, have a rank no higher than O-3 or W-2, and have orders for Operation Nobel Eagle, Enduring Freedom, Iraqi Freedom, Executive Order 13223, or other approved operation. Need-based grants are available to servicemembers and their families who meet those requirements and who also can demonstrate that the servicemember sustained a 30% or greater decrease in income from his or her civilian salary. Casualty-based grants are available to servicemembers who sustained a service-connected injury or illness and to next of kin of servicemembers killed in action, missing in action, or a prisoner of war. The following servicemembers are ineligible: those who are unmarried or have no family members enrolled in DEERS; personnel serving in active Guard, Reserve, or similar full-time unit support programs but not called to Title 10 service; and members who receive a discharge under other than honorable conditions.

Financial data Status grants are $500; need-based grants range up to $2,000; casualty-based grants are $1,000.

Duration Status grants are available only once in each fiscal year and only 1 time for each active-duty order; need-based grants may be renewed after 180 days have elapsed; casualty-based grants may be awarded only 1 time for each active-duty order.

Additional information This program, which began in 2005, is funded by a voluntary check-off on South Carolina individual income tax forms and by other grants and donations.

Number awarded Varies each year.

Deadline Applications may be submitted at any time.

[1405]
SOUTH CAROLINA PROPERTY TAX EXEMPTION FOR DISABLED VETERANS, LAW ENFORCEMENT OFFICERS, AND FIREFIGHTERS

South Carolina Department of Revenue
Attn: Property Division
301 Gervais Street
P.O. Box 125
Columbia, SC 29214
(803) 898-5480   Fax: (803) 898-5822
Web: www.sctax.org

Summary To exempt the residence of disabled South Carolina veterans, law enforcement officers, fire fighters, their unremarried widow(er)s, and others from property taxation.

Eligibility This exemption is available to owners of homes in South Carolina who are veterans of the U.S. armed forces, former law enforcement officers, or former fire fighters (including volunteer fire fighters). Applicants must be permanently and totally disabled from service-connected causes. The exemption is also available to qualified surviving spouses (defined to include unremarried spouses of disabled veterans, law enforcement officers, and fire fighters, as well as surviving spouses of servicemembers killed in the line of duty, law enforcement officers who died in the line of duty, and fire fighters who died in the line of duty).

Financial data The exemption applies to all taxes on 1 house and a lot (not to exceed 1 acre).

Duration The exemption extends as long as the veteran, law enforcement officer, or fire fighter resides in the house, or as long as the spouse of a deceased veteran, servicemember, law enforcement officer, or fire fighter remains unremarried and resides in the original house or a single new dwelling.

Number awarded Varies each year.

Deadline Applications may be submitted at any time.

[1406]
SOUTH CAROLINA PROPERTY TAX EXEMPTION FOR MEDAL OF HONOR RECIPIENTS AND PRISONERS OF WAR

South Carolina Department of Revenue
Attn: Property Division
301 Gervais Street
P.O. Box 125
Columbia, SC 29214
(803) 898-5480   Fax: (803) 898-5822
Web: www.sctax.org

Summary To exempt the residence of disabled South Carolina veterans who received a Medal of Honor or who were a prisoner of war from property taxation.

Eligibility This exemption is available to owners of homes in South Carolina who are veterans of the U.S. armed forces and who received a Medal of Honor or were a prisoner of war during World War I, World War II, the Korean Conflict, or the Vietnam Conflict. The exemption is also available to qualified surviving spouses as long as they remain unmarried.

Financial data The exemption applies to all taxes on 1 house and a lot (not to exceed 1 acre).

Duration The exemption extends as long as the veteran or the spouse of a deceased veteran resides in the original house or a single new dwelling.

Number awarded Varies each year.

Deadline Applications may be submitted at any time.

[1407]
SOUTH CAROLINA RETIREMENT INCOME TAX DEDUCTION

South Carolina Department of Revenue
301 Gervais Street
P.O. Box 125
Columbia, SC 29214
(803) 898-5000   Toll Free: (800) 763-1295
Fax: (803) 898-5822
Web: www.sctax.org

Summary To exempt part of the retirement income received by veterans and others from state taxation in South Carolina.

Eligibility This program is open to residents of South Carolina who are receiving public employee retirement income from federal, state, or local government, including individual retirement accounts, Keogh plans, and military retirement (including retirement income paid by the U.S. government for service in the Reserves or National Guard. Spouses are also entitled to the exemption.

Financial data The maximum retirement income deduction is $3,000 for taxpayers under 65 years of age and $10,000 in subsequent years. Taxpayers who wait until they are 65 and older until declaring a retirement exemption are entitled to deduct $15,000 per year. All retirement income paid by the U.S. government for service in the Reserves or National Guard is exempt from taxation in South Carolina.

Duration The exemption continues as long as the eligible veteran or spouse resides in South Carolina and receives the specified income.

Number awarded Varies each year.

Deadline Deadline not specified.

[1408]
SOUTH DAKOTA PROPERTY TAX EXEMPTION FOR PARAPLEGIC VETERANS

South Dakota Department of Revenue and Regulation
Attn: Property Tax Division
445 East Capitol Avenue
Pierre, SD 57501-3185
(605) 773-3311   Toll Free: (800) TAX-9188
Fax: (605) 773-6729   E-mail: PropTaxIn@state.sd.us
Web: www.state.sd.us/drr2/propspectax/property/relief.htm

Summary To exempt from property taxation the homes of paraplegic veterans in South Dakota and their widow(er)s.

Eligibility This benefit is available to residents of South Dakota who are 1) paraplegic veterans, 2) veterans with loss or loss of use of both lower extremities, or 3) unremarried widows or widowers of such veterans. Applicants must own and occupy a dwelling (including the house, garage, and up to 1 acre on which the building is located) that is specifically designed for wheelchair use within the structure. The veteran's injury does not have to be service connected.

Financial data Qualified dwellings are exempt from property taxation in South Dakota.

Duration The exemption applies as long as the dwelling is owned and occupied by the disabled veteran or widow(er).

Number awarded Varies each year.

Deadline Deadline not specified.

[1409]
SPINA BIFIDA PROGRAM FOR CHILDREN OF VETERANS

Department of Veterans Affairs
Attn: Veterans Benefits Administration
810 Vermont Avenue, N.W.
Washington, DC 20420
(202) 418-4343   Toll Free: (888) 820-1756
Web: www.va.gov/hac/forbeneficiaries/spina/spina.asp

Summary To provide support to children of certain veterans who have spina bifida.

Eligibility This program is open to spina bifida patients whose veteran parent performed active military, naval, or air service 1) in the Republic of Vietnam during the period from January 9, 1962 through May 7, 1975; or 2) in or near the Korean demilitarized zone during the period from September 1, 1967 through August 31, 1971. Children may be of any age or marital status, but they must have been conceived after the date on which the veteran first served in Vietnam or Korea. The monthly allowance is set at 3 levels, depending upon the degree of disability suffered by the child. The levels are based on neurological manifestations that define the severity of disability: impairment of the functioning of the extremities, impairment of bowel or bladder function, and impairment of intellectual functioning.

Financial data Support depends on the degree of disability. The monthly rate for children at the first level is $297, the second level $1,020, or at the third level $1,739.

Additional information Applications are available from the nearest VA medical center. Recipients are also entitled to vocational training and medical treatment.

Number awarded Varies each year; currently, approximately 1,100 children of veterans qualify for this program.

Deadline Applications are accepted at any time.

[1410]
TENNESSEE PROPERTY TAX RELIEF FOR DISABLED VETERANS AND THEIR SPOUSES

Tennessee Comptroller of the Treasury
Attn: Property Tax Relief Program
James K. Polk State Office Building
505 Deaderick Street, Room 1700
Nashville, TN 37243-1402
(615) 747-8858   Fax: (615) 532-3866
E-mail: kim.darden@cot.tn.gov
Web: www.comptroller1.state.tn.us/pa/patxr.asp

Summary To provide property tax relief to blind and disabled veterans and their spouses in Tennessee.

Eligibility This exemption is offered to veterans or their surviving unremarried spouses who are residents of Tennessee and own and live in their home in the state. The veteran must have served in the U.S. armed forces and 1) have acquired, as a result of such service, a disability from paraplegia, permanent paralysis of both legs and lower part of the body resulting from traumatic injury, disease to the spinal cord or brain, legal blindness, or loss or loss of use of both legs or arms from any service-connected cause; 2) have been rated by the U.S. Department of Veterans Affairs (VA) as 100% permanently disabled as a result of service as a prisoner of war for at least 5 months; or 3) have been rated by the VA as 100% permanently and totally disabled from any other service-connected cause. Unremarried spouses of deceased veterans are also eligible if 1) the veteran was receiving tax relief as a disabled veteran before death; 2) death resulted from a service-connected, combat-related cause, or killed in action; or 3) death resulted from being deployed, away from any home base of training, and in support of combat operations.

Financial data The amount of the relief depends on the property assessment and the tax rate in the city or county where the beneficiary lives. The maximum market value on which tax relief is calculated is $175,000.

Duration 1 year; may be renewed as long as the eligible veteran or surviving unremarried spouse owns and occupies the primary residence.

Number awarded Varies each year.

Deadline Deadline not specified.

[1411]
TEXAS PROPERTY TAX EXEMPTION FOR DISABLED VETERANS AND THEIR FAMILIES

Texas Veterans Commission
P.O. Box 12277
Austin, TX 78711-2277
(512) 463-5538   Toll Free: (800) 252-VETS (within TX)
Fax: (512) 475-2395   E-mail: info@tvc.state.tx.us
Web: texas-veterans.com/claims/property-tax-exemption

Summary To extend property tax exemptions on the appraised value of their property to blind, disabled, and other Texas veterans and their surviving family members.

Eligibility Eligible veterans must be Texas residents rated at least 10% service-connected disabled. Surviving spouses and children of eligible veterans are also covered by this program.

Financial data For veterans in Texas whose disability is rated as 10% through 29%, the first $5,000 of the appraised property value is exempt from taxation; veterans rated as

30% through 49% disabled are exempt from the first $7,500 of appraised value; those with a 50% through 69% disability are exempt from the first $10,000 of appraised value; the exemption applies to the first $12,000 of appraised value for veterans with disabilities rated as 70% to 99%; veterans rated as 100% disabled are exempt from 100% of the appraised value of their property. A veteran whose disability is 10% or more and who is 65 years or older is entitled to exemption of the first $12,000 of appraised property value. A veteran whose disability consists of the loss of use of 1 or more limbs, total blindness in 1 or both eyes, or paraplegia is exempt from the first $12,000 of the appraised value. The unremarried surviving spouse of a deceased veteran who died on active duty and who, at the time of death had a compensable disability and was entitled to an exemption, is entitled to the same exemption. The surviving spouse of a person who died on active duty is entitled to exemption of the first $5,000 of appraised value of the spouse's property; they are also eligible for the 100% exemption. A surviving child of a person who dies on active duty is entitled to exemption of the first $5,000 of appraised value of the child's property, as long as the child is unmarried and under 21 years of age.

Duration 1 year; may be renewed as long as the eligible veteran (or unremarried surviving spouse or child) owns and occupies the primary residence in Texas.

Additional information This program is administered at the local level by the various taxing authorities.

Number awarded Varies each year.

Deadline April of each year.

[1412]
THE 9-11 HELPAMERICA FOUNDATION ASSISTANCE

The 9-11 HelpAmerica Foundation
14147 Hawthorne Boulevard
Hawthorne, CA 90250
(310) 355-0266
Web: www.911helpamerica.com

Summary To provide support to veterans wounded in Iraq or Afghanistan and to families of veterans and military personnel wounded or killed in combat.

Eligibility This assistance is available to 1) veterans disabled as a result of service in Operation Iraqi Freedom or Operation Enduring Freedom; and 2) families of veterans and military personnel injured or killed in those operations. Applicants must need general financial assistance to help meet special circumstances, especially those associated with the death or disability of the veteran or military service member.

Financial data The amount of the support depends on the need of the recipient.

Duration Support is provided for up to 18 months.

Additional information This foundation began in October, 2001.

Number awarded Varies; in a recent year, 20 disabled veterans or survivors received support from this foundation.

Deadline Applications may be submitted at any time.

[1413]
UNMET NEEDS PROGRAM GRANTS

Veterans of Foreign Wars of the United States
Attn: VFW Foundation
Unmet Needs Program
406 West 34th Street, Suite 216
Kansas City, MO 64111
(816) 968-2779   Toll Free: (866) 789-NEED
Fax: (816) 968-1128   E-mail: unmetneeds@vfw.org
Web: www.unmetneeds.com

Summary To provide assistance to military personnel and their families who are facing special circumstances.

Eligibility This assistance is available to members of the 5 branches of service (Army, Navy, Air Force, Marines, and Coast Guard) as well as members of the Reserves and National Guard. Applicants must have served on active duty within the past 3 years. They must be able to demonstrate need for assistance because of deployment, military pay issue, military illness or injury, or natural disaster. Examples of needs that may be met include medical bills, prescriptions, and eyeglasses; housing expenses (mortgage, rent, repairs, insurance); appliance repair; vehicle expenses (payments, insurance, repairs); utilities; food and clothing; or children's clothing, diapers, formula, or school or childcare expenses. Dependents who are listed with the Defense Enrollment Eligibility Reporting System (DEERS) are also eligible.

Financial data Grants range up to $2,500.

Duration These are 1-time grants.

Additional information This program was established in 2004 with support from Vermont American Power Tools Accessories.

Number awarded Varies each year. Since this program was established, it has awarded 1,146 grants with a value of $1,640,308.

Deadline Applications may be submitted at any time.

[1414]
UTAH DISABLED VETERAN PROPERTY TAX ABATEMENT

Utah Department of Veteran's Affairs
Attn: Director
550 Foothill Boulevard, Room 202
Salt Lake City, UT 84108
(801) 326-2372   Toll Free: (800) 894-9497 (within UT)
Fax: (801) 326-2369   E-mail: veterans@utah.gov
Web: veterans.utah.gov/homepage/stateBenefits/index.html

Summary To exempt a portion of the property of disabled veterans and their families in Utah from taxation.

Eligibility This program is available to residents of Utah who are disabled veterans or their unremarried widow(er)s or minor orphans. The disability must be at least 10% and incurred as the result of injuries in the line of duty.

Financial data The exemption is based on the disability rating of the veteran, to a maximum of $232,312 for a 100% disability. The exemption for veterans with lesser disabilities is equal to $232,312 times the percentage of their disability.

Duration This benefit is available as long as the disabled veteran or family members reside in Utah.

Deadline Tax exemption applications must be filed with the county government of residence by August of the initial year; once eligibility has been established, reapplication is not required.

[1415]
UTAH VETERAN'S PROPERTY TAX EXEMPTION

Utah State Tax Commission
Attn: Property Tax Division
210 North 1950 West
Salt Lake City, UT 84134
(801) 297-3600   Toll Free: (800) 662-4335, ext. 3600
Fax: (801) 297-7699   TDD: (801) 297-2020
E-mail: propertytax@utah.gov
Web: propertytax.utah.gov

Summary To exempt from taxation a portion of the real and tangible property of disabled veterans and their families in Utah.

Eligibility This exemption is available to property owners in Utah who are veterans with a disability of at least 10% incurred in the line of duty, along with their unremarried surviving spouses or minor orphans. First year applications must be accompanied by proof of military service and proof of disability or death.

Financial data Veterans with a 100% disability are entitled to a full current-year exemption (recently, that was $237,949). Veterans with disabilities rated at a smaller percentage are entitled to that percentage of the current year exemption amount. Survivors are entitled to the same percentage as if the veteran were still living.

Duration The exemption is available each year the beneficiary owns property in Utah.

Number awarded Varies each year.

Deadline Applications must be submitted by August of each year.

[1416]
VERMONT MILITARY FAMILY ASSISTANCE FUND GRANTS

Vermont Military Family Assistance Fund
P.O. Box 26
Essex Junction, VT 05453-0026

Summary To provide emergency assistance to military personnel in Vermont and their families.

Eligibility This assistance is available to active-duty service members and their families if they live within the geographical boundaries of the state of Vermont or live outside the state but belong to a Vermont unit. They must be facing emergency financial difficulties. Along with their application, they must submit an explanation of the need and amount of each bill for which they are requesting assistance.

Financial data Support is provided in the form of grants that do not need to be repaid.

Duration These are 1-time grants.

Additional information This program was originally established in 1991 to assist mobilized active-duty members during Desert Storm and revived in 2003.

Number awarded Varies each year.

Deadline Applications may be submitted at any time.

[1417]
VERMONT PROPERTY TAX EXEMPTION FOR DISABLED VETERANS

Vermont Department of Taxes
Attn: Property Valuation and Review Division
P.O. Box 1577
Montpelier, VT 05601-1577
(802) 828-2865   Toll Free: (866) 828-2865 (within VT)
Fax: (802) 828-2824
Web: www.state.vt.us/tax/pvrmilitary.shtml

Summary To exempt disabled Vermont veterans and their dependents from the payment of at least a portion of the state's property tax.

Eligibility Entitled to a property tax exemption are veterans of any war (or their spouses, widow(er)s, or children) who are receiving wartime disability compensation for at least a 50% disability, wartime death compensation, wartime dependence and indemnity compensation, or pension for disability paid through any military department or the Department of Veterans Affairs. Unremarried widow(er)s of previously qualified veterans are also entitled to the exemption whether or not they are receiving government compensation or a pension.

Financial data Up to $10,000 of the assessed value of real and personal property belonging to eligible veterans or their unremarried widow(er)s is exempt from taxation; individual towns may increase the exemption to as much as $40,000.

Duration 1 year; may be renewed as long as the eligible veteran or widow(er) continues to be the owner/occupant of the residence and lives in Vermont.

Additional information Only 1 exemption may be allowed on a property.

Number awarded Varies each year.

Deadline April of each year.

[1418]
VIRGINIA INCOME TAX SUBTRACTION FOR MILITARY COMBAT PAY

Virginia Department of Taxation
Attn: Office of Customer Services
1957 Westmoreland Street
P.O. Box 1115
Richmond, VA 23218-1115
(804) 367-8031   Fax: (804) 254-6113
E-mail: TaxIndReturns@tax.virginia.gov
Web: www.tax.virginia.gov/site?alias=MilitaryTaxTips

Summary To subtract military combat pay from state income taxation in Virginia.

Eligibility This subtraction is available to residents of Virginia who earned military pay or allowances while serving by the order of the President with the consent of Congress in a combat zone or qualified hazardous duty area.

Financial data Income received as military combat pay is exempt from state taxation in Virginia, to the extent that it has not been otherwise subtracted, deducted, or exempted from federal adjusted gross income.

Duration The exemption is available in each year that a Virginia resident receives military combat pay.

Number awarded Varies each year.

Deadline The request for an exemption is filed with the state income tax return in April of each year.

[1419]
VIRGINIA INCOME TAX SUBTRACTION FOR MILITARY DEATH GRATUITY PAYMENTS

Virginia Department of Taxation
Attn: Office of Customer Services
1957 Westmoreland Street
P.O. Box 1115
Richmond, VA 23218-1115
(804) 367-8031   Fax: (804) 254-6113
E-mail: TaxIndReturns@tax.virginia.gov
Web: www.tax.virginia.gov/site?alias=MilitaryTaxTips

Summary To subtract military death gratuity payments from state income taxation in Virginia.

Eligibility This subtraction is available to residents of Virginia who received military death gratuity payments after September 11, 2001 that were included as income subject to federal taxation.

Financial data Income received as military death gratuity payments is exempt from state taxation in Virginia.

Duration The exemption is retroactive to taxable year 2001.

Number awarded Varies each year.

Deadline The request for an exemption is filed with the state income tax return in April of each year.

[1420]
WASHINGTON PROPERTY TAX ASSISTANCE PROGRAM FOR WIDOWS OR WIDOWERS OF VETERANS

Washington State Department of Revenue
Attn: Property Tax Division
P.O. Box 47471
Olympia, WA 98504-7471
(360) 534-1410   Toll Free: (800) 647-7706
TDD: (360) 705-6718
Web: dor.wa.gov

Summary To exempt from taxation in Washington a portion of the assessed valuation of property owned by senior citizens and veterans with disabilities who are widows or widowers of veterans.

Eligibility This exemption is available to residents of Washington who are either 62 years of age or older or who have a disability that prevents them from being gainfully employed and is expected to last for at least 12 months. Applicants must be the unmarried widow or widower of a veteran who 1) died as a result of a service-connected disability; 2) was 100% disabled for 10 years prior to his or her death; 3) was a former prisoner of war and rated as 100% disabled for at least 1 year prior to death; or 4) died in active duty or in active training status. They must own property that they use as their principal home for at least 6 months of the year; mobile homes may qualify as a residence even if its owner does not own the land where it is located. Their annual disposable income may not exceed $40,000 per year.

Financial data The exemption is $100,000 of the home's assessed value if disposable income is $30,000 or less, $75,000 if disposable income is $30,001 to $35,000, or $50,000 if disposable income is $35,001 to $40,000.

Duration The exemption is available as long as the widow or widower meets the eligibility requirements.

Additional information This program offered assistance beginning with the 2006 tax year.

Number awarded Varies each year.

Deadline Applications are due 30 days before taxes are due.

[1421]
WEST VIRGINIA INCOME TAX EXEMPTION FOR MILITARY RETIREES

West Virginia State Tax Department
Attn: Taxpayer Services Division
P.O. Box 3784
Charleston, WV 25337-3784
(304) 558-3333   Toll Free: (800) WVA-TAXS (within WV)
Fax: (304) 558-3269   TDD: (800) 282-9833
Web: www.wva.state.wv.us/wvtax/default.aspx

Summary To exempt a portion of the income of military retirees and their spouses in West Virginia from state taxation.

Eligibility This exemption is available to residents of West Virginia who are receiving retirement benefits from any branch of the military. Surviving spouses of eligible residents are also entitled to the exemptions.

Financial data Military retirees and their spouses are entitled to exempt the first $20,000 of annual military retirement income, including survivorship annuities. That exemption is in addition to the $2,000 exemption available to all retired public employees in West Virginia.

Duration The exemption continues as long as eligible residents (or their spouses) remain residents of West Virginia.

Deadline Deadline not specified.

[1422]
WEST VIRGINIA VETERANS BONUS

West Virginia Department of Veteran's Assistance
Attn: Bonus Office
1321 Plaza East, Suite 101
Charleston, WV 25301-1400
(304) 558-3661   Toll Free: (888) 838-2332 (within WV)
Fax: (304) 558-3662   E-mail: wvdva@state.wv.us
Web: www.veterans.wv.gov/Pages/VeteransBonus.aspx

Summary To provide a bonus to living veterans in West Virginia who served in Kosovo, Afghanistan, or Iraq and to the families of deceased veterans.

Eligibility This bonus is available to veterans who were residents of West Virginia when they entered into active duty and for at least 6 months previously. Applicants must have been members of the armed forces of the United States or of Reserve components called to active duty. They must have 1) received a campaign badge or expeditionary medal for Kosovo between November 20, 1995 and December 31, 2000; 2) served in Afghanistan between October 7, 2001 and a date to be determined; or 3) served in Iraq between March 19, 2003 and a date to be determined. A bonus is also available to veterans who had active service outside the combat zone during the time periods specified for Afghanistan and Iraq. Surviving family members of a deceased veteran are also eligible if the veteran's death was connected with the service during the specified time periods.

Financial data Bonuses are $600 for veterans who served in the specified combat zone, $400 for veterans who served outside the combat zone but during the specified time periods, or $2,000 for surviving relatives of deceased veterans.

The amount of the bonus is not considered income for state taxation purposes in West Virginia.

Duration This is a 1-time bonus.

Number awarded Varies each year.

Deadline Applications may be submitted at any time.

[1423]
WISCONSIN AID TO MILITARY FAMILIES

Wisconsin Department of Veterans Affairs
201 West Washington Avenue
P.O. Box 7843
Madison, WI 53707-7843
(608) 266-1311 Toll Free: (800) WIS-VETS
Fax: (608) 267-0403 E-mail: WDVAInfo@dva.state.wi.us
Web: www.dva.state.wi.us/Ben_emergencygrants.asp

Summary To provide temporary, emergency financial aid to families of activated or deployed servicemembers in Wisconsin.

Eligibility This program is open to spouses and dependent children of activated or deployed military servicemembers of the U.S. armed forces or of the Wisconsin National Guard. Applicants must have suffered, or be suffering, a loss of income because of the activation or deployment, although there is no maximum income limitation. The servicemember must be a resident of Wisconsin. The family must be facing an economic emergency, such as failure of the sole means of transportation; failure of a stove or refrigerator or of heating, electrical, or plumbing systems; a medical emergency; or severe damage to the primary residence as a result of a natural disaster.

Financial data Grants do not exceed $7,500 in a lifetime.

Duration Grants are awarded as needed.

Number awarded Varies each year.

Deadline Applications may be submitted at any time.

[1424]
WISCONSIN ASSISTANCE TO NEEDY VETERANS AND FAMILY MEMBERS

Wisconsin Department of Veterans Affairs
201 West Washington Avenue
P.O. Box 7843
Madison, WI 53707-7843
(608) 266-1311 Toll Free: (800) WIS-VETS
Fax: (608) 267-0403 E-mail: WDVAInfo@dva.state.wi.us
Web: www.dva.state.wi.us/Ben_emergencygrants.asp

Summary To provide temporary, emergency financial aid to veterans and their families in Wisconsin.

Eligibility This program is open to Wisconsin residents who served either 1) at least 2 years on active duty in the U.S. armed forces; or 2) at least 90 days on active duty during designated periods of wartime (including the Persian Gulf War since August 1, 1990, the Afghanistan War since September 11, 2001, and the Iraq War since March 19, 2003). The unremarried surviving spouse and dependent children of an eligible veteran who died in the line of duty while or active duty or inactive duty for training also qualify. Applicants must have applied for, and been denied or determined to be ineligible for, all other applicable aid programs (e.g., unemployment insurance, Medicaid, Medicare, BadgerCare, federal Veterans Administration health care). The veteran must be a resident of Wisconsin with an income that does not exceed 130% of the federal poverty guidelines (currently, $14,521 for a family

of 1, rising to $50,557 for a family of 8). The family must be facing an economic emergency, such as failure of the sole means of transportation; failure of a stove or refrigerator or of heating, electrical, or plumbing systems; a medical emergency; or severe damage to the primary residence as a result of a natural disaster.

Financial data Grants do not exceed $7,500 in a lifetime.

Duration Grants are awarded as needed.

Number awarded Varies each year.

Deadline Applications may be submitted at any time.

[1425]
WISCONSIN VETERANS AND SURVIVING SPOUSES PROPERTY TAX CREDIT

Wisconsin Department of Revenue
Attn: Homestead Credit
2135 Rimrock Road
P.O. Box 34
Madison, WI 53786-0001
(608) 266-8641 Fax: (608) 267-1030
E-mail: homestd@revenue.wi.gov
Web: www.revenue.wi.gov/individuals/military.html

Summary To provide an income tax credit to disabled Wisconsin veterans and their surviving spouses equal to the amount of property taxes they pay.

Eligibility This credit is available to Wisconsin veterans who served on active duty under honorable conditions in the U.S. armed forces and have resided in Wisconsin for any consecutive 5-year period after entry into active duty. Applicants must have either a service-connected disability rating of 100% or a 100% disability rating based on individual unemployability. Also eligible are unremarried surviving spouses of such disabled veterans and of members of the National Guard or a Reserve component of the U.S. armed forces who were residents of Wisconsin and died in the line of duty while on active or inactive duty for training purposes.

Financial data Eligible veterans and surviving spouses are entitled to an income tax credit equal to the amount of property taxes they pay on their principal residence.

Duration The credit is available as long as the recipient resides in Wisconsin.

Number awarded Varies each year.

Deadline Income tax returns must be filed by April of each year.

[1426]
WISCONSIN VETERANS' SUBSISTENCE AID GRANTS

Wisconsin Department of Veterans Affairs
201 West Washington Avenue
P.O. Box 7843
Madison, WI 53707-7843
(608) 266-1311 Toll Free: (800) WIS-VETS
Fax: (608) 267-0403 E-mail: WDVAInfo@dva.state.wi.us
Web: www.dva.state.wi.us/Ben_emergencygrants.asp

Summary To provide temporary, emergency financial aid to Wisconsin veterans or their dependents.

Eligibility This program is open to current residents of Wisconsin who 1) were residents of the state when they entered or reentered active duty in the U.S. armed forces, or 2) have moved to the state and have been residents for any consecutive 12-month period after entry or reentry into service. Applicants must have served on active duty for at least 2 continuous years or for at least 90 days during specified wartime periods. Also eligible are 1) unremarried surviving spouses and dependent children of eligible veterans who died in the line of duty while on active service or inactive duty for training; and 2) spouses and dependent children of eligible servicemembers who are currently activated or deployed. Applicants must have suffered a loss of income because of illness, injury, or natural disaster and be seeking temporary, emergency financial aid. Their income may not exceed 130% of the federal poverty guidelines (currently, $14,521 for a family of 1, rising to $50,557 for a family of 8).

Financial data Grants do not exceed $3,000 during any consecutive 12-month period or the program limit of $7,500 in a lifetime.

Duration Grants are awarded for subsistence aid for a 30-day period, up to a maximum of 3 months.

Number awarded Varies each year.

Deadline Applications may be submitted at any time.

[1427]
WYOMING MILITARY ASSISTANCE TRUST FUND GRANTS

Wyoming Military Department
Attn: State Family Program Coordinator
5500 Bishop Boulevard
Cheyenne, WY 82009
(307) 772-5208   Fax: (307) 772-5330
Web: sites.google.com

Summary To provide emergency assistance to residents of Wyoming who are facing financial difficulties because a family member has been deployed to active military service.

Eligibility This assistance is available to 1) members of the Wyoming National Guard or Reserve units based in Wyoming who have been called to active duty or active state service; 2) Wyoming residents who are members of a military Reserve unit not based in Wyoming, if the member has been called to active service; 3) other Wyoming residents performing service in the uniformed forces for any branch of the military of the United States; and 4) members of the immediate family (spouses, children, and dependent parents, grandparents, siblings, stepchildren, and adult children) of those military personnel. Applicants must be facing financial hardship resulting from the military member's active-duty status.

Financial data The amount of the grant depends on the need of the recipient.

Duration These are 1-time grants.

Additional information The Wyoming Legislature created this fund in 2004. These funds may not be used to replace other funds available from public or private sources.

Number awarded Varies each year; since this program was established, it has awarded more than $1.18 million in grants.

Deadline Applications may be submitted at any time.

[1428]
WYOMING VETERANS PROPERTY TAX EXEMPTION

Wyoming Department of Revenue
Attn: Property Tax Relief Program
122 West 25th Street, Second Floor West
Cheyenne, WY 82002-0110
(307) 777-7320   Fax: (307) 777-7527
E-mail: DirectorOfRevenue@wy.gov
Web: revenue.state.wy.us

Summary To provide a partial tax exemption on the property owned by veterans and their surviving spouses in Wyoming.

Eligibility This program is open to honorably-discharged veterans who were Wyoming residents at the time they entered military service and have resided in Wyoming for 3 years prior to applying for this exemption. Applicants must have served during specified periods of wartime or have received an armed forces expeditionary medal or other authorized service or campaign medal for service in an armed conflict in a foreign country. Surviving spouses of qualified veterans are also eligible. The exemption applies to county fees only, not state fees.

Financial data Veterans and spouses may exempt $3,000 in assessed value of property from taxation per year. Disabled veterans are entitled to additional exemptions that depend on the level of their disability, to a maximum of $2,000 for a 100% disability.

Duration Veterans and spouses are entitled to use these exemptions as long as they reside in Wyoming and own the property as their principal residence.

Number awarded Varies each year.

Deadline Applicants must advise their county assessor of their intent to use the exemption by May of each year.

Indexes

Program Title Index

If you know the name of a particular funding program and want to find out where it is covered in the directory, use the Program Title Index. Here, program titles are arranged alphabetically, word by word. To assist you in your search, every program is listed by all its known names or abbreviations. In addition, we've used a two-character alphabetical code (within parentheses) to help you determine if the program falls within your scope of interest. The first character (capitalized) in the code identifies program type: S = Scholarships; F = Fellowships; G = Grants-in-Aid. The second character (lower cased) identifies eligible groups: v = Veterans; m = Military Personnel; f = Family Members. Here's how the code works: if a program is followed by (S–v) 241, the program is described in the Scholarships section under Veterans, in entry 241. If the same program title is followed by another entry number—for example, (G–m) 1250— the program is also described in the Grants-in-Aid section, under Military Personnel, in entry 1250. Remember: the numbers cited here refer to program entry numbers, not to page numbers in the book.

S—Scholarships
v—Veterans

F—Fellowships
m—Military Personnel

G—Grants-in-Aid
f—Family Members

433

S—Scholarships
v—Veterans

F—Fellowships
m—Military Personnel

G—Grants-in-Aid
f—Family Members

S—Scholarships
v—Veterans

F—Fellowships
m—Military Personnel

G—Grants-in-Aid
f—Family Members

S—Scholarships
v—Veterans

F—Fellowships
m—Military Personnel

G—Grants-in-Aid
f—Family Members

Eleanor Colona Scholarship Grant. *See* Art and Eleanor Colona Scholarship Grant, entry (S—f) 423

Eleanor Smith Scholarship. *See* Wisconsin Legion Auxiliary Merit and Memorial Scholarships, entry (S—f) 820

Elkey Award. *See* CSM Robert W. Elkey Award, entries (S—m) 191, (F—m) 922

Ellen Willis Martin Scholarships. *See* Chappie Hall Memorial Scholarship Program, entry (S—f) 446

Ellinwood Scholarship. *See* Joseph H. Ellinwood Scholarship, entry (S—f) 591

Emanuel American Legion Scholarships. *See* Schneider-Emanuel American Legion Scholarships, entries (S—v) 113, (S—f) 757

Emmett Paige Scholarships. *See* General Emmett Paige Scholarships, entries (S—v) 41, (S—m) 212, (S—f) 528

English Memorial Scholarship Award. *See* John Cornelius/Max English Memorial Scholarship Award, entries (S—m) 231, (S—f) 586, (F—m) 936, (F—f) 1028

Enlisted Association of the National Guard of Georgia Scholarship. *See* EANGGA Scholarship, entries (S—m) 200, (S—f) 497

Enlisted Association of the National Guard of Tennessee Scholarship Programs. *See* EANGTN Scholarship Program, entries (S—m) 201, (S—f) 498

Enlisted Association of the National Guard of the United States Auxiliary Scholarship Program. *See* EANGUS Auxiliary Scholarship Program, entry (S—f) 499

Enlisted Association of the National Guard of Utah Scholarship. *See* EANGUT Scholarship, entries (S—m) 202, (S—f) 500

Enlisted National Guard Association of Florida Scholarship Program. *See* National Guard Association of Florida and Enlisted National Guard Association of Florida Scholarship Program, entries (S—m) 275, (S—f) 665

Essay Competition for Children of Public Employees, (S—f) 505

Ethyl and Armin Wiebke Memorial Scholarship. *See* Women Marines Association Scholarship Program, entries (S—v) 139, (S—m) 376, (S—f) 825, (F—v) 886, (F—m) 991, (F—f) 1065

Eugene C. Renzi, USA (Ret.)/ManTech International Corporation Teacher's Scholarship. *See* MG Eugene C. Renzi, USA (Ret.)/ManTech International Corporation Teacher's Scholarship, entries (S—v) 73, (F—v) 861

Eugenia Bradford Roberts Memorial Fund. *See* Society of Daughters of the United States Army Scholarships, entry (S—f) 768

Evelyn Bukovac Hamilton Health Care Scholarship. *See* Marines' Memorial Association Scholarship Fund, entries (S—v) 69, (S—m) 247, (S—f) 623

Exemption for Dependents of Texas Veterans, (S—f) 506

Exemption for Orphans of Texas Members of the U.S. Armed Forces or National Guard, (S—f) 507

Exemption for Texas Veterans, (S—v) 36, (F—v) 847

Exemption from Tuition Fees for Dependents of Kentucky Veterans, (S—f) 508, (F—f) 1016

Explosive Ordnance Disposal Memorial Scholarships, (S—f) 509

Explosive Ordnance Disposal Option of the Seaman to Admiral-21 Program, (S—m) 204

F

Fallen Patriot Fund Grants, (G—v) 1093, (G—f) 1321

FCDA Scholarships, (S—m) 205, (S—f) 510

Feldman Scholarships. *See* Renee Feldman Scholarships, entry (S—f) 747

Felix M. DelGreco, Jr. Scholarship Fund. *See* Sergeant Felix M. DelGreco, Jr. Scholarship Fund, entry (S—f) 765

Ferretti Scholarship. *See* Lt. Col. Romeo and Josephine Bass Ferretti Scholarship, entry (S—f) 611

Fifth Marine Division Association Scholarship, (S—f) 511

Financial and Medical Assistance for Massachusetts Veterans, (G—v) 1094, (G—f) 1322

First Cavalry Division Association Scholarships. *See* FCDA Scholarships, entries (S—m) 205, (S—f) 510

First Lieutenant Michael L. Lewis, Jr. Memorial Fund Scholarship, (S—f) 512

First Lieutenant Scott McClean Love Memorial Scholarship, (S—f) 513

First Marine Division Association Scholarship, (S—f) 514

First Sergeant Douglas and Charlotte DeHorse Scholarship, (S—v) 37, (S—m) 206, (F—v) 848, (F—m) 926

Fitzgerald Memorial Scholarship. *See* Ruth Lang Fitzgerald Memorial Scholarship, entries (F—v) 876, (F—m) 981

Fleet Reserve Association Non-Member Scholarships. *See* FRA Non-Member Scholarships, entries (S—v) 39, (S—m) 209, (S—f) 523, (F—v) 849, (F—m) 928, (F—f) 1018

Fleet Reserve Association Scholarships. *See* FRA Scholarships, entries (S—v) 40, (S—m) 210, (S—f) 524, (F—v) 850, (F—m) 929, (F—f) 1019

Florida American Legion General Scholarships, (S—f) 515

Florida Boys State Scholarship, (S—f) 516

Florida Deployed Military Exemption, (G—m) 1230

Florida Disabled Veterans' Property Tax Discount on Homestead Property, (G—v) 1095

Florida Legion Auxiliary Department Scholarship, (S—f) 517

Florida Legion Auxiliary Master's Program Grant, (F—f) 1017

Florida Legion Auxiliary Memorial Scholarship, (S—f) 518

Florida National Guard Educational Dollars for Duty (EDD) Program, (S—m) 207, (F—m) 927

Florida Property Tax Disability Exemption for Ex-Service Members, (G—v) 1096

Florida Scholarships for Children and Spouses of Deceased or Disabled Veterans, (S—f) 519

Florida Service-Connected Total and Permanent Disability Property Tax Exemption, (G—v) 1097, (G—f) 1323

Folds of Honor Scholarships, (S—f) 520

Force Recon Association Scholarships, (S—v) 38, (S—m) 208, (S—f) 521

Ford Scholarships. *See* Lillie Lois Ford Scholarships, entry (S—f) 608

Foronda Memorial Scholarship. *See* California Legion Auxiliary Scholarships for Continuing and/or Reentry Students, entries (S—v) 23, (S—m) 178, (S—f) 441

Fourth Marine Division Association of WWII Scholarship, (S—f) 522

FRA Non-Member Scholarships, (S—v) 39, (S—m) 209, (S—f) 523, (F—v) 849, (F—m) 928, (F—f) 1018

FRA Scholarships, (S—v) 40, (S—m) 210, (S—f) 524, (F—v) 850, (F—m) 929, (F—f) 1019

Frances Booth Medical Scholarship. *See* Past National President Frances Booth Medical Scholarship, entry (S—f) 732

Francis P. Matthews and John E. Swift Educational Trust Scholarships, (S—f) 525

Frank R. Kelley Scholarship. *See* Massachusetts Legion Department General Scholarships, entry (S—f) 632

Frederick C. Branch Marine Corps Leadership Scholarships, (S—m) 211

Freedom Alliance Scholarships, (S—f) 526

Fry Scholarship. *See* Marine Gunnery Sergeant John David Fry Scholarship, entry (S—f) 622

S—Scholarships
v—Veterans
F—Fellowships
m—Military Personnel
G—Grants-in-Aid
f—Family Members

New Mexico Veterans Property Tax Exemption, (G—v) 1149, (G—f) 1374

New Mexico Vietnam Veteran Scholarships, (S—v) 91, (F—v) 869

New York Alternative Property Tax Exemptions for Veterans, (G—v) 1150, (G—f) 1375

New York American Legion Press Association Scholarship. *See* NYALPA Scholarship, entry (S—f) 718

New York Cold War Veterans Property Tax Exemptions, (G—v) 1151, (G—f) 1376

New York "Eligible Funds" Property Tax Exemptions for Veterans, (G—v) 1152, (G—f) 1377

New York Legion Auxiliary Department Scholarship, (S—f) 706

New York Legion Auxiliary District Scholarships, (S—f) 707

New York Legion Auxiliary Past Presidents Parley Student Scholarship in Medical Field, (S—f) 708

New York Organized Militia Income Tax Exemption, (G—m) 1263

New York Recruitment Incentive and Retention Program, (S—m) 309

New York State Blind Annuity, (G—v) 1153, (G—f) 1378

New York State Income Tax Exemption for Retired Military Personnel, (G—v) 1154, (G—f) 1379

New York State Military Service Recognition Scholarships, (S—v) 92, (S—f) 709

New York Veterans Supplemental Burial Allowance, (G—f) 1380

New York Veterans Tuition Awards, (S—v) 93, (F—v) 870

NHA Active Duty Scholarships, (S—v) 94, (S—m) 310, (F—v) 871, (F—m) 968

Niles Memorial Scholarship. *See* PNGAS Scholarship Fund, entries (S—m) 329, (S—f) 739

Nolan Scholarship. *See* Robert W. Nolan Scholarship, entries (F—v) 875, (F—m) 980, (F—f) 1054

Non Commissioned Officers Association Disaster Relief Fund. *See* NCOA Disaster Relief Fund, entries (G—m) 1261, (G—f) 1364

Non Commissioned Officers Association Scholarship Fund, (S—f) 710

Nonresident Tuition Waivers for Veterans and Their Dependents Who Move to Texas, (S—v) 95, (S—f) 711

Norfleet Scholarship. *See* Nannie W. Norfleet Scholarship, entry (S—f) 660

North Carolina National Guard Association Academic Excellence/Leadership Award. *See* North Carolina National Guard Association Scholarships, entries (S—v) 96, (S—m) 311, (S—f) 712

North Carolina National Guard Association Scholarships, (S—v) 96, (S—m) 311, (S—f) 712

North Carolina National Guard Association Special Population Scholarship. *See* North Carolina National Guard Association Scholarships, entries (S—v) 96, (S—m) 311, (S—f) 712

North Carolina National Guard Tuition Assistance Program, (S—m) 312, (F—m) 969

North Carolina Property Tax Relief for Disabled Veterans, (G—v) 1155

North Carolina Scholarships for Children of War Veterans, (S—f) 713

North Carolina Vietnam Veterans Scholarship Program, (S—v) 97, (S—f) 714

North Dakota Educational Assistance for Dependents of Veterans, (S—f) 715

North Dakota National Guard Enlisted Association Scholarships, (S—m) 313, (S—f) 716

North Dakota National Guard Fee Waiver, (S—m) 314

North Dakota National Guard Tuition Assistance Program, (S—m) 315, (F—m) 970

North Dakota Property Tax Credit for Disabled Veterans, (G—v) 1156, (G—f) 1381

North Dakota Property Tax Exemption for Veterans Who Live in Specially Adapted Housing, (G—v) 1157, (G—f) 1382

North Dakota State Income Tax National Guard or Reserve Member Exclusion, (G—m) 1264

North Dakota State Income Tax Servicemember Civil Relief Act Adjustment, (G—m) 1265

North Dakota Veterans Dependents Fee Waiver, (S—f) 717

Nuclear Propulsion Officer Candidate (NUPOC) Program, (S—m) 316

Nuclear (Submarine and Surface) Option of the Seaman to Admiral-21 Program, (S—m) 317

NUPOC Program. *See* Nuclear Propulsion Officer Candidate (NUPOC) Program, entry (S—m) 316

Nurse Corps Option of the Seaman to Admiral-21 Program, (S—m) 318

NYALPA Scholarship, (S—f) 718

O

Oceanography Option of the Seaman to Admiral-21 Program, (S—m) 319

O'Connell Memorial Veterans Rehabilitation Scholarship. *See* William P. O'Connell Memorial Veterans Rehabilitation Scholarship, entry (S—f) 814

Oden Memorial Scholarship. *See* Allie Mae Oden Memorial Scholarship, entry (S—f) 399

Odom Memorial Scholarship. *See* Army Scholarship Foundation Scholarships, entry (S—f) 421

Ohio Burial Allowance for Indigent Veterans, (G—f) 1383

Ohio Income Tax Deduction for Military Pay, (G—m) 1266

Ohio Income Tax Deduction for Military Retirement Income, (G—v) 1158, (G—f) 1384

Ohio Legion Auxiliary Department President's Scholarship, (S—v) 98, (S—f) 719

Ohio Legion Scholarships, (S—v) 99, (S—f) 720

Ohio National Guard Association Leadership Grants, (S—m) 320, (S—f) 721

Ohio National Guard Enlisted Association Scholarship Program. *See* ONGEA Scholarship Program, entries (S—v) 101, (S—m) 323, (S—f) 726

Ohio National Guard Scholarship Program, (S—m) 321

Ohio Safety Officers College Memorial Fund, (S—f) 722

Ohio Veterans Bonus, (G—v) 1159, (G—m) 1267, (G—f) 1385

Ohio Veterans' Financial Assistance, (G—v) 1160, (G—m) 1268, (G—f) 1386

Ohio War Orphans Scholarship, (S—f) 723

Oklahoma Financial Assistance Program, (G—v) 1161, (G—f) 1387

Oklahoma Military Pay Exclusion, (G—m) 1269

Oklahoma Military Retirement Income Tax Exclusion, (G—v) 1162, (G—f) 1388

Oklahoma National Guard Tuition Waiver Program, (S—m) 322

Oklahoma Property Tax Exemption for Disabled Veterans, (G—v) 1163, (G—f) 1389

Oklahoma Tuition Waiver for Prisoners of War, Persons Missing in Action, and Dependents, (S—v) 100, (S—f) 724

Oliphant Memorial Scholarship. *See* Claire Oliphant Memorial Scholarship, entry (S—f) 453

Olson Memorial Scholarship. *See* Roy C. and Dorothy Jean Olson Memorial Scholarship, entry (S—f) 750

Pyle Scholarship. *See* Schuyler S. Pyle Scholarship, entries (S—v) 114, (S—m) 341, (S—f) 760, (F—v) 877, (F—m) 983, (F—f) 1055

R

RADM William A. Sullivan, USN (Ret.) Scholarship, (S—f) 742

Ranger Memorial Scholarships, (S—v) 107, (S—m) 331, (S—f) 743

Ratay Educational Fund Grants. *See* General John Paul Ratay Educational Fund Grants, entry (S—f) 530

Raymond A. Matera Scholarship. *See* Wisconsin National Guard Enlisted Association College Grant Program, entries (S—m) 374, (S—f) 823, (F—m) 990, (F—f) 1064

Raymond T. Wellington, Jr. Memorial Scholarship, (S—f) 744

Ream Memorial Scholarship. *See* Naval Helicopter Association Undergraduate Scholarships, entry (S—f) 685

Red Cross Emergency Financial Assistance, (G—v) 1178, (G—m) 1281, (G—f) 1401

Red River Valley Fighter Pilots Association Scholarship Grant Program, (S—f) 745, (F—f) 1053

Redden Scholarship. *See* Massachusetts Legion Department General Scholarships, entry (S—f) 632

Reduced Tuition for Children and Spouses of South Dakota National Guardsmen Disabled or Deceased in the Line of Duty, (S—f) 746

Reduced Tuition for South Dakota National Guard Members, (S—m) 332, (F—m) 975

Reilly Memorial Graduate Scholarship. *See* Henry J. Reilly Memorial Graduate Scholarship, entries (F—v) 853, (F—m) 931

Reilly Memorial Scholarship for College Sophomores and Juniors. *See* Henry J. Reilly Memorial Scholarship for College Sophomores and Juniors, entries (S—v) 45, (S—m) 219, (S—f) 543

Reilly Memorial Scholarship for Freshmen in College. *See* Henry J. Reilly Memorial Scholarship for Freshmen in College, entry (S—f) 544

Reilly Memorial Scholarship for Graduating High School Seniors. *See* Henry J. Reilly Memorial Scholarship for Graduating High School Seniors, entry (S—f) 545

Reimbursement of Burial Expenses, (G—f) 1402

Renee Feldman Scholarships, (S—f) 747

Renzi, USA (Ret.)/ManTech International Corporation Teacher's Scholarship. *See* MG Eugene C. Renzi, USA (Ret.)/ManTech International Corporation Teacher's Scholarship, entries (S—v) 73, (F—v) 861

REPS. *See* Restored Entitlement Program for Survivors (REPS), entry (G—f) 1403

Reserve Educational Assistance Program, (S—m) 333, (F—m) 976

Restored Entitlement Program for Survivors (REPS), (G—f) 1403

The Retired Enlisted Association National Scholarships. *See* TREA National Scholarships, entry (S—f) 788

Rhode Island Educational Benefits for Disabled American Veterans, (S—v) 108

Rhode Island National Guard State Tuition Assistance Program, (S—m) 334, (F—m) 977

Rhode Island National Guard State Tuition Exemption Program, (S—m) 335, (F—m) 978

Richard D. Kisling Scholarship. *See* Chief Master Sergeants of the Air Force Scholarships, entry (S—f) 449

Richard E. Thorn Memorial Scholarship. *See* PNGAS Scholarship Fund, entries (S—m) 329, (S—f) 739

Richard Hallock Scholarship. *See* Marines' Memorial Association Scholarship Fund, entries (S—v) 69, (S—m) 247, (S—f) 623

Richards UDT-SEAL Memorial Scholarship. *See* Had Richards UDT-SEAL Memorial Scholarship, entry (S—f) 539

Ridgeway Scholarship. *See* 82nd Airborne Division Association Awards, entries (S—v) 3, (S—f) 384

Robert H. Connal Education Awards, (S—m) 336, (S—f) 748

Robert L. Walters Scholarship. *See* VADM Robert L. Walters Scholarship, entries (S—f) 801, (F—f) 1059

Robert (Sam) Murphy Scholarship. *See* Massachusetts Legion Department General Scholarships, entry (S—f) 632

Robert W. Brunsman Memorial Scholarship, (S—m) 337, (F—m) 979

Robert W. Elkey Award. *See* CSM Robert W. Elkey Award, entries (S—m) 191, (F—m) 922

Robert W. Nolan Scholarship, (F—v) 875, (F—m) 980, (F—f) 1054

Roberts Memorial Fund. *See* Society of Daughters of the United States Army Scholarships, entry (S—f) 768

Robin Kelleher-New Beginnings Award. *See* Hope for the Warriors Spouse/Caregiver Scholarships, entries (S—f) 552, (F—f) 1023

The ROCKS Washington D.C. Chapter Scholarships, (S—m) 358

Romeo and Josephine Bass Ferretti Scholarship. *See* Lt. Col. Romeo and Josephine Bass Ferretti Scholarship, entry (S—f) 611

Ronald J. Cantin Scholarship. *See* Commander Ronald J. Cantin Scholarship, entry (S—f) 469, 812

Ronald Lessing Memorial Scholarship. *See* Scholarships for USPHS Commissioned Corps Dependents, entry (S—f) 759

Rosamond P. Haeberle Memorial Scholarship, (S—v) 109, (S—m) 338

Roscoe C. Cartwright Awards. *See* Brigadier General Roscoe C. Cartwright Awards, entry (S—m) 175

Rose Memorial Scholarship. *See* Sam Rose Memorial Scholarship, entry (S—f) 755

Rose Scholarship. *See* Marines' Memorial Association Scholarship Fund, entries (S—v) 69, (S—m) 247, (S—f) 623

Rosedale Post 346 Scholarship Fund, (S—f) 749

Ross Scholarship. *See* Colonel Jerry W. Ross Scholarship, entries (F—m) 918, (F—f) 1007

Rotberg Memorial Scholarship. *See* Jewish War Veterans National Educational Grants, entry (S—f) 583

Roy C. and Dorothy Jean Olson Memorial Scholarship, (S—f) 750

RSF Memorial Scholarship, (S—v) 110, (S—m) 339

Ruby Lorraine Paul Scholarship Fund, (S—v) 111, (S—f) 751

Ruby Paul Campaign Fund Scholarship, (S—v) 112, (S—f) 752

Ruth Lang Fitzgerald Memorial Scholarship, (F—v) 876, (F—m) 981

S

Saban Military Wife Educational Scholarships, (S—f) 753

Sad Sacks Nursing Scholarship, (S—f) 754

Sam Murphy Scholarship. *See* Massachusetts Legion Department General Scholarships, entry (S—f) 632

Sam Rose Memorial Scholarship, (S—f) 755

Samsung American Legion Scholarships, (S—f) 756

Samuel Eliot Morison Naval History Scholarship, (F—m) 982

Samuel L. Gravely, Jr., USN (Ret.) Memorial Scholarships. *See* VADM Samuel L. Gravely, Jr., USN (Ret.) Memorial Scholarships, entries (S—v) 128, (S—m) 367

Schmidt Leadership Scholarship. *See* 11th Armored Cavalry Veterans of Vietnam and Cambodia Scholarship, entries (S—v) 2, (S—f) 383

Schneider-Emanuel American Legion Scholarships, (S—v) 113, (S—f) 757

Schober Memorial Scholarship. *See* Louis J. Schober Memorial Scholarship, entries (S—m) 241, (S—f) 609

S—Scholarships
v—Veterans

F—Fellowships
m—Military Personnel

G—Grants-in-Aid
f—Family Members

S—Scholarships   F—Fellowships   G—Grants-in-Aid
v—Veterans   m—Military Personnel   f—Family Members

Sponsoring Organization Index

The Sponsoring Organization Index makes it easy to identify agencies that offer financial aid to veterans, military personnel, or members of their families. In this index, sponsoring organizations are listed alphabetically, word by word. In addition, we've used a two-character alphabetical code (within parentheses) to help you identify which programs sponsored by these organizations fall within your scope of interest. The first character (capitalized) in the code identifies program type: S = Scholarships; F = Fellowships; G = Grants-in-Aid. The second character (lower cased) identifies eligible groups: v = Veterans; m = Military Personnel; f = Family Members. For example, if the name of a sponsoring organization is followed by (S–v) 241, a program sponsored by that organization is described in the Scholarship section under Veterans, in entry 241. If that sponsoring organization's name is followed by another entry number—for example, (G–m) 1250—the same or a different program sponsored by that organization is described in the Grants-in-Aid section, under Military Personnel, in entry 1250. Remember: the numbers cited here refer to program entry numbers, not to page numbers in the book.

S—Scholarships
v—Veterans

F—Fellowships
m—Military Personnel

G—Grants-in-Aid
f—Family Members

455

American Legion. Massachusetts Department, (S—f) 591, 632

American Legion. Michigan Auxiliary, (S—f) 639

American Legion. Minnesota Auxiliary, (S—f) 650-651

American Legion. Missouri Department, (S—v) 78, (S—f) 608

American Legion. Nebraska Auxiliary, (S—v) 111-112, (S—f) 751-752

American Legion. New Hampshire Auxiliary, (S—v) 5, (S—f) 624

American Legion. New Hampshire Department, (S—f) 397, 585

American Legion. New Jersey Auxiliary, (S—f) 444, 453, 490, 701

American Legion. New Jersey Department, (S—f) 699

American Legion. New Mexico Auxiliary, (S—f) 705

American Legion. New York Auxiliary, (S—f) 512, 542, 628, 706-708, 744

American Legion. New York Department, (S—f) 491

American Legion. North Carolina Auxiliary, (S—f) 660

American Legion. North Dakota Department, (S—f) 541

American Legion. Ohio Auxiliary, (S—v) 98, (S—f) 719

American Legion. Ohio Department, (S—v) 99, (S—f) 720

American Legion. Oregon Auxiliary, (S—f) 728-729

American Legion. Pennsylvania Department, (S—f) 592

American Legion. Texas Auxiliary, (S—f) 781

American Legion. Utah Auxiliary, (S—f) 798

American Legion. Virginia Auxiliary, (S—f) 412, 492, 804

American Legion. Washington Department, (S—f) 810

American Legion. Wisconsin Auxiliary, (S—f) 485, 554, 819-822, (F—f) 1024, 1063

American Legion. Wisconsin Department, (S—v) 113, (S—f) 757

American Legion. Wyoming Department, (S—f) 495

American Logistics Association. New York Chapter, (S—f) 643

American Military Retirees Association, Inc., (S—v) 116, (S—f) 766

American Pharmacists Association, (F—m) 918, (F—f) 1007

American Red Cross, (G—v) 1178, (G—m) 1281, (G—f) 1401

American Society of Military Comptrollers, (S—m) 170, (F—m) 912

American Society of Military Comptrollers. National Guard Chapter, (S—f) 678

American Society of Safety Engineers, (S—v) 16, (F—v) 839

American Society of Safety Engineers. Craters of the Moon Chapter, (S—v) 115, (S—m) 342, (F—v) 878, (F—m) 984

American Systems, (S—v) 10, 128, (S—m) 158, 367

AMVETS. Department of Illinois, (S—f) 560-562, 754

AMVETS National Headquarters, (S—v) 11, 32, (S—m) 198, (S—f) 408, 681, (F—v) 836

AMVETS National Ladies Auxiliary, (S—f) 409

Anchor Scholarship Foundation, (S—f) 411

Andrew J. Zabierek Foundation, (S—v) 13

Arizona Army National Guard, (S—m) 160

Arizona Department of Revenue, (G—v) 1072, (G—m) 1215

Arizona Department of Veterans' Services, (G—v) 1073, (G—m) 1216, (G—f) 1303

Arizona National Guard Emergency Relief Fund, (G—m) 1217-1218, (G—f) 1304-1305

Arkansas Assessment Coordination Department, (G—v) 1074, (G—f) 1306

Arkansas Community Foundation, (S—f) 416

Arkansas Department of Finance and Administration, (G—v) 1075, (G—m) 1219

Arkansas Department of Higher Education, (S—f) 415

Arkansas National Guard, (S—m) 161

Armed Forces Benefit Association, (S—m) 193, (S—f) 447, 479

Armed Forces Communications and Electronics Association, (S—v) 6, 10, 41, 73, 128, 130, (S—m) 144-145, 158, 199, 212, 255, 367-368, (S—f) 528, (F—v) 861, (F—m) 921

Armed Forces Communications and Electronics Association. Northern Virginia Chapter, (S—v) 130, (S—m) 368

Armed Forces Communications and Electronics Association. Tidewater Chapter, (S—m) 359

Armed Forces Foundation, (G—v) 1089, (G—m) 1228

Armed Forces Insurance Company, (S—m) 193, (S—f) 479

Army Aviation Association of America Scholarship Foundation, (S—v) 15, (S—m) 162, (S—f) 418, (F—v) 838, (F—m) 903, (F—f) 1000

Army Emergency Relief, (S—f) 636, 776, (G—v) 1076, (G—m) 1221, (G—f) 1307

Army Engineer Association, (S—m) 187, 191, 258, (S—f) 459-460, 462, 472, (F—m) 922, 949, (F—f) 1004-1005

Army Engineer Spouses' Club, (S—f) 419, 535

Army Nurse Corps Association, (S—v) 12, (S—m) 159, (S—f) 410, (F—v) 837, (F—m) 900, (F—f) 999

Army Officers' Wives' Club of the Greater Washington Area, (S—f) 420

Army Scholarship Foundation, (S—f) 421, 513, 764

Associates of Vietnam Veterans of America, (S—v) 18, (S—f) 427

Association of Former Intelligence Officers, (F—m) 897, 939, (F—f) 997, 1031

Association of Graduates, (S—f) 424

Association of Old Crows, (S—m) 171

Association of the United States Army, (S—v) 17, (S—m) 172, 239

Association of the United States Navy, (S—f) 425

Aviation Boatswain's Mates Association, (S—f) 576

B

Belvoir Officers' Spouses' Club, (S—f) 426

Blackhorse Association, (S—f) 429

Blinded Veterans Association, (S—f) 597, (F—f) 1030

Blinded Veterans Association Auxiliary, (S—f) 747

C

California. Department of Housing and Community Development, (G—v) 1078, (G—f) 1308

California Department of Veterans Affairs, (S—v) 21, (S—f) 434-437, (G—v) 1079, (G—f) 1309

California Enlisted Association of the National Guard of the United States, (S—m) 176

California. Office of the Adjutant General, (S—m) 179, (F—m) 914

California Student Aid Commission, (S—m) 179, (F—m) 914

Career College Association, (S—v) 25, 61, (S—m) 181, 240

Catching the Dream, (S—v) 37, (S—m) 206, (F—v) 848, (F—m) 926

Challenged Athletes Foundation, (G—v) 1166, (G—m) 1273

Chase Bank, (S—m) 152, (S—f) 388, (F—m) 895, (F—f) 994

Chief Warrant and Warrant Officers Association, (S—f) 423

Children of Fallen Patriots Foundation, (S—f) 450

Children of Fallen Soldiers Relief Fund, (S—f) 451, (G—v) 1080, (G—f) 1310

Civil Service Employees Insurance Group, (S—f) 505

Club 100 Veterans, (S—f) 725

Coast Guard Foundation, (S—f) 457

Coast Guard Mutual Assistance, (G—v) 1081, (G—m) 1225, (G—f) 1312

Coca-Cola Company, (S—m) 152, (S—f) 388, (F—m) 895, (F—f) 994

Colorado Commission on Higher Education, (S—f) 464

Colorado. Department of Military and Veterans Affairs, (S—m) 186, (F—m) 919, (G—m) 1226

Colorado Department of Revenue, (G—v) 1082

Colorado. Division of Veterans Affairs, (G—v) 1083, (G—f) 1313

Commander William S. Stuhr Scholarship Fund, (S—f) 470

Commissioned Officers Association of the USPHS Inc., (S—f) 759

Community Foundation of the Ozarks, (F—v) 844

Comptroller of Maryland, (G—v) 1120, (G—m) 1233, 1247

Congressional Medal of Honor Foundation, (S—m) 255

Congressional Medal of Honor Society, (S—f) 471

Connecticut Community Foundation, (S—f) 765

Connecticut Department of Veterans' Affairs, (G—v) 1087

Connecticut National Guard, (S—m) 188

Connecticut National Guard Foundation, Inc., (S—m) 189, (S—f) 473, 765, (G—m) 1227, (G—f) 1314

Connecticut Office of Financial and Academic Affairs for Higher Education, (S—v) 27, (S—m) 190, (S—f) 474, (F—v) 841, (F—m) 920, (F—f) 1008

Connecticut. Office of Policy and Management, (G—v) 1085-1086, 1088, (G—f) 1315-1317

Council of College and Military Educators, (S—m) 229, (S—f) 445

CSC Defense Group, (F—m) 921

D

Daedalian Foundation, (S—m) 214, 230, 253, (S—f) 480, (F—f) 1010

Datatel Scholars Foundation, (S—v) 30, (S—f) 482, (F—v) 843, (F—f) 1011

Daughters of the American Revolution. Michigan State Society, (S—v) 109, (S—m) 338

Daughters of the American Revolution. National Society, (S—f) 614

Daughters of the Cincinnati, (S—f) 483

Defense Activity for Non-Traditional Education Support, (G—v) 1190, (G—m) 1287

Delaware Commission of Veterans Affairs, (G—v) 1090

Delaware Department of Education, (S—f) 484

Delaware National Guard, (S—m) 195

Department of Defense, (G—v) 1084

Disabled American Veterans Auxiliary, (S—f) 486, (F—f) 1012

Distinguished Flying Cross Society, (S—f) 487

District of Columbia National Guard, (S—m) 196, (F—m) 924

DKF Veterans Assistance Foundation, (S—v) 31, (S—f) 488

Dolphin Scholarship Foundation, (S—f) 489

D.P. Associates Inc., (S—f) 685

DRS Technologies, Inc., (S—f) 494

E

E.E. Mixon Second Dragoon Foundation, (S—v) 35, (S—f) 503

Enlisted Association National Guard of New Jersey, (S—m) 192, 270, (S—f) 478

Enlisted Association of the National Guard of Georgia, (S—m) 200, (S—f) 497

Enlisted Association of the National Guard of Iowa, (S—v) 46, (S—m) 223, (S—f) 553

Enlisted Association of the National Guard of Tennessee, (S—m) 201, (S—f) 498

Enlisted Association of the National Guard of the United States, (S—m) 193, (S—f) 479, 499

Enlisted Association of the National Guard of Utah, (S—m) 202, (S—f) 500

Enlisted Association of the New York National Guard, Inc., (S—m) 336, (S—f) 748

Enlisted National Guard Association of Florida, (S—m) 275, (S—f) 443, 665

Explosive Ordnance Disposal Memorial Foundation, (S—f) 509

F

Fifth Marine Division Association Scholarship Fund, (S—f) 511

First Cavalry Division Association, (S—m) 205, (S—f) 510, 555

First Cleveland Cavalry Association, (S—v) 101, (S—m) 323, (S—f) 726

First Command Educational Foundation, (S—f) 420

First Marine Division Association, (S—f) 514

Fisher House Foundation, (S—f) 546, 758

Fleet Reserve Association, (S—v) 39-40, 114, (S—m) 209-210, 341, (S—f) 463, 523-524, 760, 777, (F—v) 849-851, 856, 875, 877, (F—m) 928-930, 937, 980, 983, (F—f) 1018-1020, 1029, 1054-1056

Fleet Reserve Association. Past Regional Presidents Club, (S—m) 371, (S—f) 809

Florida Department of Education, (S—f) 519

Florida. Department of Military Affairs, (S—m) 207, (F—m) 927

Florida Department of Revenue, (G—v) 1095-1097, (G—m) 1230, (G—f) 1323

Folds of Honor Foundation, (S—f) 520

Force Recon Association, (S—v) 38, (S—m) 208, (S—f) 521

Fourth Marine Division Association of WWII, (S—f) 522

Fraternal Order of Eagles, (S—f) 496

Freedom Alliance, (S—f) 526

G

Gamewardens Association, Vietnam to Present, (S—f) 527

GEICO Insurance, (S—m) 193, (S—f) 479

General Motors Foundation, (S—v) 20, (S—f) 433

Georgia Department of Revenue, (G—v) 1098, (G—m) 1231, (G—f) 1324-1325

Georgia Guard Insurance Trust, (S—m) 287-288, (S—f) 679-680

Georgia Student Finance Commission, (S—m) 213, (S—f) 534

Go For Broke Memorial Education Center, (S—f) 504, (F—f) 1015

Google Inc., (S—v) 43, (F—v) 852

H

Hanscom Spouses' Club, (S—f) 386

Hawai'i Community Foundation, (S—f) 380, 430, (F—f) 993

Hawaii. Department of Taxation, (G—m) 1232

Hawaii National Guard Enlisted Association, (S—m) 221, (S—f) 550

Hawaii. Office of Veterans Services, (G—v) 1099-1100, (G—f) 1326

Hickam Officers' Spouses' Club, (S—f) 548, (F—f) 1021

Hoehl Family Foundation, (S—f) 727

Homefront America, (S—f) 406

Hope for the Warriors, (S—f) 552, (F—f) 1023, (G—v) 1101, (G—m) 1234, (G—f) 1327

I

Idaho Division of Veterans Services, (G—v) 1104, (G—f) 1329

Idaho Enlisted Association of the National Guard of the United States, (S—m) 379, (S—f) 833

Idaho State Board of Education, (S—f) 556

Idaho State Tax Commission, (G—v) 1102-1103, (G—f) 1328

Illinois Association of Realtors, (S—v) 42

S—Scholarships
v—Veterans

F—Fellowships
m—Military Personnel

G—Grants-in-Aid
f—Family Members

S—Scholarships	F—Fellowships	G—Grants-in-Aid
v—Veterans	m—Military Personnel	f—Family Members

Residency Index

Some programs listed in this book are restricted to residents of a particular state or region. Others are open to applicants wherever they may live. The Residency Index will help you pinpoint programs available only to residents in your area as well as programs that have no residency restrictions at all (these are listed under the term "United States"). To use this index, look up the geographic areas that apply to you (always check the listings under "United States"), jot down the entry numbers listed after the program types and recipient groups that apply to you, and use those numbers to find the program descriptions in the directory. To help you in your search, we've provided some "see also" references in the index entries. Remember: the numbers cited here refer to program entry numbers, not to page numbers in the book.

A

Alabama
  Scholarships: **Military Personnel,** 155; **Family Members,** 392
  Fellowships: **Military Personnel,** 898; **Family Members,** 998
  Grants-in-Aid: **Veterans,** 1069-1070; **Military Personnel,** 1214; **Family Members,** 1300-1301
  See also United States

Alaska
  Scholarships: **Veterans,** 7; **Military Personnel,** 156, 173; **Family Members,** 393-395, 428
  Fellowships: **Veterans,** 835; **Military Personnel,** 899, 913; **Family Members,** 1001
  Grants-in-Aid: **Veterans,** 1071
  See also United States

Alexandria, Virginia
  Scholarships: **Family Members,** 420
  See also Virginia

Arizona
  Scholarships: **Veterans,** 115, 135; **Military Personnel,** 160, 272, 342; **Family Members,** 505, 662, 815
  Fellowships: **Veterans,** 878; **Military Personnel,** 984
  Grants-in-Aid: **Veterans,** 1072-1073; **Military Personnel,** 1215-1218; **Family Members,** 1303-1305
  See also United States

Arkansas
  Scholarships: **Military Personnel,** 161; **Family Members,** 414-416, 476
  Grants-in-Aid: **Veterans,** 1074-1075; **Military Personnel,** 1219; **Family Members,** 1306
  See also United States

Arlington County, Virginia
  Scholarships: **Family Members,** 420, 686
  See also Virginia

C

California
  Scholarships: **Veterans,** 21-23, 31, 83; **Military Personnel,** 176-179, 273; **Family Members,** 398, 434-441, 488, 505, 663
  Fellowships: **Military Personnel,** 914
  Grants-in-Aid: **Veterans,** 1078-1079; **Family Members,** 1308-1309
  See also United States

Calvert County, Maryland
  Scholarships: **Family Members,** 420, 686
  See also Maryland

Canada
  Scholarships: **Family Members,** 496
  See also Foreign countries

Charles County, Maryland
  Scholarships: **Family Members,** 420, 686
  See also Maryland

Chatham County, North Carolina
  Scholarships: **Veterans,** 97; **Family Members,** 714
  See also North Carolina

Colorado
  Scholarships: **Veterans,** 26, 33, 56, 115; **Military Personnel,** 186, 203, 342; **Family Members,** 464-467, 501
  Fellowships: **Veterans,** 845, 857, 878; **Military Personnel,** 919, 925, 984; **Family Members,** 1013
  Grants-in-Aid: **Veterans,** 1082-1083; **Military Personnel,** 1226; **Family Members,** 1313
  See also United States

Connecticut
  Scholarships: **Veterans,** 27, 82; **Military Personnel,** 188-190, 271, 274; **Family Members,** 473-474, 661, 664, 765
  Fellowships: **Veterans,** 841; **Military Personnel,** 920; **Family Members,** 1008
  Grants-in-Aid: **Veterans,** 1085-1088; **Military Personnel,** 1227; **Family Members,** 1314-1317
  See also New England states; United States

Tenability Index

Some programs listed in this book can be used only in specific cities, counties, states, or regions. Others may be used anywhere in the United States (or even abroad). The Tenability Index will help you locate funding that is restricted to a specific area as well as funding that has no tenability restrictions (these are listed under the term "United States"). To use this index, look up the geographic areas where you'd like to go (always check the listings under "United States"), jot down the entry numbers listed after the program types and recipient groups that apply to you, and use those numbers to find the program descriptions in the directory. To help you in your search, we've provided some "see also" references in the index entries. Remember: the numbers cited here refer to program entry numbers, not to page numbers in the book.

A

Alabama
Scholarships: **Military Personnel,** 155; **Family Members,** 392
Fellowships: **Military Personnel,** 898; **Family Members,** 998
Grants-in-Aid: **Veterans,** 1069-1070; **Military Personnel,** 1214; **Family Members,** 1300-1301
See also United States

Alaska
Scholarships: **Veterans,** 7; **Military Personnel,** 156, 173; **Family Members,** 393, 428
Fellowships: **Veterans,** 835; **Military Personnel,** 899, 913; **Family Members,** 1001
Grants-in-Aid: **Veterans,** 1071
See also United States

Albuquerque, New Mexico
Scholarships: **Military Personnel,** 317
See also New Mexico

Arizona
Scholarships: **Veterans,** 135; **Military Personnel,** 160, 272; **Family Members,** 662, 815
Grants-in-Aid: **Veterans,** 1072-1073; **Military Personnel,** 1215-1218; **Family Members,** 1303-1305
See also United States

Arkansas
Scholarships: **Military Personnel,** 161; **Family Members,** 415-416, 476
Grants-in-Aid: **Veterans,** 1074-1075; **Military Personnel,** 1219; **Family Members,** 1306
See also United States

Atlanta, Georgia
Scholarships: **Military Personnel,** 211, 220
See also Georgia

Auburn, Alabama
Scholarships: **Military Personnel,** 317
See also Alabama

Austin, Texas
Scholarships: **Military Personnel,** 211, 220, 317
See also Texas

B

Baton Rouge, Louisiana
Scholarships: **Military Personnel,** 211, 220, 317
See also Louisiana

C

California
Scholarships: **Veterans,** 21-23; **Military Personnel,** 176-179; **Family Members,** 434-441
Fellowships: **Military Personnel,** 914
Grants-in-Aid: **Veterans,** 1078-1079; **Family Members,** 1308-1309
See also United States

Canada
Scholarships: **Family Members,** 496, 786
See also Foreign countries

Cape Girardeau, Missouri
Scholarships: **Veterans,** 110; **Military Personnel,** 339
See also Missouri

Champaign, Illinois
Scholarships: **Military Personnel,** 317
See also Illinois

Charleston, South Carolina
Scholarships: **Military Personnel,** 317
See also South Carolina

Colorado
Scholarships: **Veterans,** 26, 56; **Military Personnel,** 186; **Family Members,** 464-467
Fellowships: **Veterans,** 857; **Military Personnel,** 919
Grants-in-Aid: **Veterans,** 1082-1083; **Military Personnel,** 1226; **Family Members,** 1313
See also United States

Columbia, Missouri
Scholarships: **Veterans,** 110; **Military Personnel,** 339
See also Missouri

Columbia, South Carolina
Scholarships: **Military Personnel,** 211, 220, 317
See also South Carolina

Subject Index

There are more than 250 different subject areas indexed in this directory. Use the Subject Index when you want to identify the subject focus of available funding programs. To help you pinpoint your search, we've also included hundreds of "see" and "see also" references. In addition to looking for terms that represent your specific subject interest, be sure to check the "General programs" entry; hundreds of programs are listed there that can be used to support study, research, or other activities in *any* subject area (although the programs may be restricted in other ways). Remember: the numbers cited in this index refer to program entry numbers, not to page numbers in the book.

A

Accounting
    Scholarships: **Veterans,** 20; **Military Personnel,** 170, 363; **Family Members,** 433, 678
    Fellowships: **Military Personnel,** 912, 985
    See also Finance; General programs

Administration. *See* Business administration; Education, administration; Management; Personnel administration; Public administration

Aeronautical engineering. *See* Engineering, aeronautical

Aeronautics
    Scholarships: **Family Members,** 480
    Fellowships: **Family Members,** 1010
    See also Aviation; Engineering, aeronautical; General programs; Physical sciences

Aerospace engineering. *See* Engineering, aerospace

Aerospace sciences. *See* Space sciences

American history. *See* History, American

Anesthetic nurses and nursing. *See* Nurses and nursing, anesthesiology

Aquaculture
    Scholarships: **Veterans,** 55; **Military Personnel,** 232; **Family Members,** 590
    See also General programs

Aquatic sciences. *See* Oceanography

Architectural engineering. *See* Engineering, architectural

Architecture
    Scholarships: **Veterans,** 19, 82; **Military Personnel,** 146, 149, 154, 173-174, 182, 222, 271, 363; **Family Members,** 428, 443, 551, 661
    Fellowships: **Military Personnel,** 913, 932, 985; **Family Members,** 1001, 1022
    See also Fine arts; General programs

Arithmetic. *See* Mathematics

Armed services. *See* Military affairs

Art
    Scholarships: **Family Members,** 629
    See also Fine arts; General programs; names of specific art forms

Astronautics
    Scholarships: **Family Members,** 480
    Fellowships: **Family Members,** 1010
    See also General programs; Space sciences

Athletic training
    Scholarships: **Veterans,** 56
    Fellowships: **Veterans,** 857
    See also General programs

Atmospheric sciences
    Scholarships: **Military Personnel,** 146, 154
    See also General programs; Physical sciences

Attorneys. *See* Law, general

Audiology
    Scholarships: **Veterans,** 56
    Fellowships: **Veterans,** 857
    See also General programs; Health and health care; Medical sciences

Automation. *See* Computer sciences; Technology

Aviation
    Scholarships: **Veterans,** 8; **Military Personnel,** 214, 230, 253, 371; **Family Members,** 480, 745, 809
    Fellowships: **Family Members,** 1010, 1053
    Grants-in-Aid: **Military Personnel,** 1212
    See also General programs; Space sciences

B

Behavioral sciences
    Fellowships: **Veterans,** 880
    See also General programs; Social sciences; names of special behavioral sciences

Biomedical sciences
    Fellowships: **Veterans,** 880
    See also General programs; Medical sciences

Biotechnology
    Scholarships: **Veterans,** 17; **Military Personnel,** 172
    See also General programs; Technology

Systems engineering. *See* Engineering, systems

T

Tagalog language. *See* Language, Tagalog

Teaching. *See* Education

Technology
    Scholarships: **Veterans,** 6, 41, 130; **Military Personnel,** 144-145, 212, 292, 317, 368; **Family Members,** 528, 611
    Fellowships: **Veterans,** 867; **Military Personnel,** 958
    See also Computer sciences; General programs; Sciences

Telecommunications
    Scholarships: **Military Personnel,** 359
    See also Communications; General programs

Theology. *See* Religion and religious activities

Trade unions. *See* Labor unions and members

Turkish language. *See* Language, Turkish

U

Unions and unionization. *See* Industrial relations; Labor unions and members

Unrestricted programs. *See* General programs

V

Veteran law. *See* Military law

Veterans. *See* Military affairs

Veterinary sciences
    Fellowships: **Military Personnel,** 904
    Grants-in-Aid: **Military Personnel,** 1222
    See also General programs; Sciences

Vietnamese language. *See* Language, Vietnamese

Voice
    Scholarships: **Family Members,** 386
    See also General programs; Music

W

Welfare. *See* Social services

Work. *See* Employment

Calendar Index

Since most financial aid programs have specific deadline dates, some may have already closed by the time you begin to look for funding. You can use the Calendar Index to identify which programs are still open. To do that, go to the recipient category and program type that applies to you, think about when you'll be able to complete your application forms, go to the appropriate months, jot down the entry numbers listed there, and use those numbers to find the program descriptions in the directory. Keep in mind that the numbers cited here refer to program entry numbers, not to page numbers in the book.

Veterans

Military Personnel

Family Members